CALCULUS

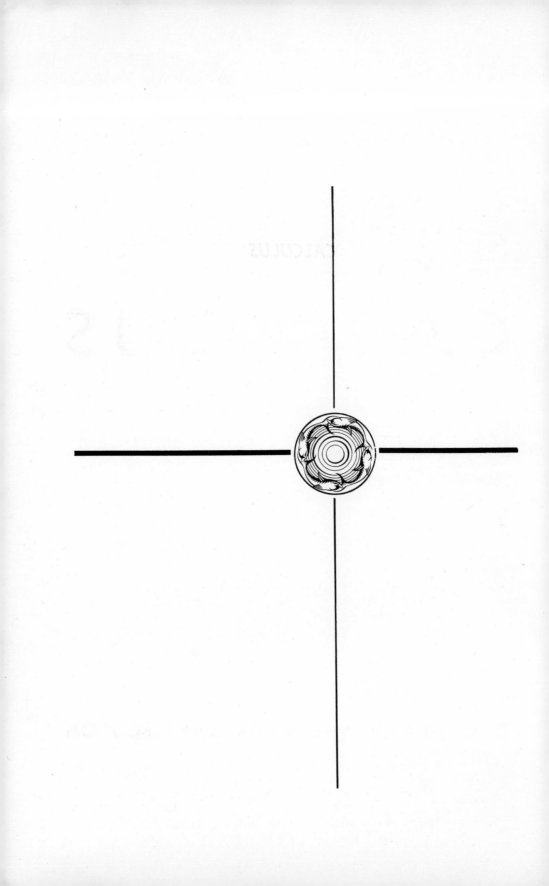

CALCULUS

William L. Hart

Professor of Mathematics
University of Minnesota

D. C. HEATH AND COMPANY   BOSTON

PREFACE

This text provides a basis for a first course in calculus for students having a foundation in analytic geometry. The complete book is designed for a substantial course taught five hours per week for two semesters. However, various features facilitate the organization of less complete courses, taught three hours per week for just two semesters, or five hours per week for two quarters. The text encourages relatively early treatment of multiple integrals and some partial differentiation in any complete course, and definite inclusion of these topics in any briefer course, by inserting this content with other sequential topics in the first two thirds of the book. It should be noticed that the text supplies complete chapters on solid analytic geometry and differential equations. Also, the book includes substantial review of various prerequisite topics which might not be well recalled by the student.

Theoretical tone. The basic theory is presented in a sound, yet simple, fashion definitely within the range of appreciation of the normal student, and will give him very little to unlearn if he proceeds to more advanced courses. This feature is particularly evident in the systematic consistency and the nature of the analytic definitions of definite integrals in one, two, and three dimensions, and in the foundations for length of arc. Also, the book is completely frank in admitting the impossibility of proof when even an intuitional argument is beyond the level of the course. However, there is no hesitation at mentioning unproved advanced results when they are useful, or when they will interest the superior student. In a few instances, proofs above the natural level of the text are inserted in the Appendix, as supplementary content. The literary style takes full advantage of the general maturity of the college student, within the limitations of good pedagogy as dictated by his powers of mathematical appreciation. The mathematical level naturally rises throughout the book. For instance, increasing sophistication in appreciation of the function concept and the limit notion is encouraged. In particular, this specific aim is exploited with a simplifying effect when approximating sums for an integral are earmarked as many-valued functions of the norm of the partition, and prolific intuitional use is made of formal limits as the norm approaches zero.

Attitude concerning applications. With a subject such as calculus, whose basic concepts arose first in geometric and physical applications, a text on the subject would present a sterile and unnatural picture if applications and numerical aspects of the content were not emphasized. This book endeavors to make it evident that the content is essential for achieving important objectives in diverse fields, including economics and statistics as well as the physical sciences and technology. The text aims at applications as varied as possible within the normal limits of student experience. Of course, the interesting applications of calculus in purely mathematical situations receive their deserved emphasis. Specific planning for utility in applied mathematics is evident at many points, such as in the emphasis on differentials; the use of right-handed coordinate systems in space; features of the notation, and the applications of partial differentiation; the heavy attack on directional derivatives. On the whole, the text aims to show the student a true picture of the range of calculus applications, and also to give him confidence in his own power to use calculus later.

The skills of calculus. Even after just a brief course, the student should have automatic proficiency in routine differentiation and integration, and in setting up definite integrals on the basis of reasoning about elements of approximating sums. These skills can be gained only as a result of a large amount of text illustration and student practice. Hence, this book emphasizes illustrative examples, and graphical aids (330 figures, with a reference table of curves). Also, the text develops differentiation and integration very systematically, and contains quantities of associated routine examples. In addition, there are generous lists of miscellaneous problems, problems of special difficulty,* and many review exercises. Answers for odd-numbered problems are included in the text, and the answers for even-numbered problems are available in a separate pamphlet.

Special Features

1. An intuitional introduction to derivatives, with typical applications, before the formal discussion of limits.

2. Separation of the introduction to limits into two parts, with the second part delayed until it is needed.

3. A very early location for multiple integrals.

4. Separation of the work on partial differentiation into two parts.

5. Key role for parametric form in the content involving arc length.

6. Frequent emphasis on the function concept, with illustrations of possible peculiarities as well as commonplace features.

7. Definition of a definite integral analytically, apart from its applications, before the concept of an indefinite integral is introduced.

8. Brief early consideration of differentials as a background for introduction of the quotient notation dy/dx.

9. Repeated appearances of content relating to differentials.

10. Treatment of each situation of the Duhamel type in integration by simple but heuristically sound reasoning relating to continuity.

11. Use of rectangular meshes in the definitions of multiple integrals, not only for simplicity, but also to establish a logical order for introduction of the concepts of area in a plane, and volume in space.

---

* Problems and sections are marked with a black star when the content is particularly difficult or is definitely nonessential in a typical course.

12. Natural approach to Taylor's formula through integration by parts, leading first to an integral form for the remainder.

13. Prominent place given to applications of Taylor's formula, and operations on power series.

14. Considerable use of direction cosines in a plane as well as in space.

15. Early introduction of a minimum of standard terminology about differential equations, and their solution in simple cases. A full chapter on differential equations is given at the end of the book.

Attention is called to the care exercised by the publishers in the arrangement of the format and preparation of the figures. The author thanks the staff of D. C. Heath and Company for its cooperation in carrying out all of the details of publication.

When a member of a lively department of mathematics writes a text on calculus, it is obvious that credit for any commendable features of the book should go jointly to all members of the department. In the present instance, the author wishes to acknowledge his debt to practically all of his colleagues for innumerable informal discussions of the content of calculus and its pedagogy. He is particularly appreciative of his contacts during the last few years with members of the department who were co-workers with him in courses in calculus.

WILLIAM L. HART
University of Minnesota

CONTENTS

ix

CALCULUS

C H A P T E R

1

RATES OF CHANGE

1. Introduction

Calculus is a field of mathematics whose basic notions arose through the study of various problems of physics and geometry. The subject matter of calculus is concerned mainly with the theory and applications of two major concepts, the notions of a *derivative* and an *integral*, whose definitions involve the idea of a *limit* as a basic feature. A derivative is a *rate of change* in value, illustrated in physics by the instantaneous velocity of a moving body. An integral is *the limit of a set of finite sums* and, in the most simple setting, can be identified with the value of a certain area. The first use of integration is credited to the Greek mathematician ARCHIMEDES (287–212 B.C.) in his computation of lengths of curves, areas, volumes, and centroids. His work had little influence until late in the 16th Century. The first clear recognition of the connection between differentiation and integration is credited to the English mathematician ISAAC BARROW (1630–1677), who was the principal mathematical teacher of Sir ISAAC NEWTON (1642–1727). In the late 17th Century, Newton and GOTTFRIED WILHELM LEIBNIZ (1646–1716) independently formulated the fundamental concepts of calculus as an effective discipline, and hence usually are referred to as the founders of calculus.*

2. Absolute value

In this text, imaginary numbers will occur rarely. Hence, when we mention a *number*, we shall mean a *real number*, unless otherwise specified. Any single letter introduced without previous description will represent a number. Real numbers are classed as positive, negative, or zero. Zero is not said to be either positive or negative. To say that a number is *nonnegative* means that it is positive or zero.

The *absolute value* of a number b is defined as b itself if b is nonnegative, and as $-b$ if b is negative. The absolute value of b is represented by the

---

* For interesting historical facts, see *The History of Calculus*, by *Arthur Rosenthal;* American Mathematical Monthly, Volume 58 (1951), pages 75–86.

symbol $|b|$. Sometimes, $|b|$ is called the *numerical value* of b. We say that two numbers b and c are *numerically equal* if $|b| = |c|$; then, b and c differ at most in sign. We observe that

$$|bc| = |b| \cdot |c|; \quad \left|\frac{b}{c}\right| = \frac{|b|}{|c|}, \text{ if } c \neq 0.$$

ILLUSTRATION 1. $|5| = |-5| = 5$; 5 and -5 are numerically equal.

3. Geometrical language concerning numbers

Consider the directed line OX in Figure 1, where O is a fixed point, and the positive direction is to the right. If P is any point on OX, the *directed distance* * OP is *positive* or *negative* according as P is to the *right* or the *left* of O, and $OP = 0$ if P is O itself. If x is any real number, we associate it with that point P for which $x = OP$. Then, we refer to OX as a number scale, with O as the origin, and call x the coordinate of P. We may call the scale an x-axis. If the coordinates of P_1 and P_2 on the scale are x_1 and x_2, respectively, the directed distance P_1P_2 is given by

$$P_1P_2 = x_2 - x_1, \tag{1}$$

and the *length* of P_1P_2 is $|x_2 - x_1|$. Thus, the distance between x_1 and x_2 on the scale is the absolute value of their difference.

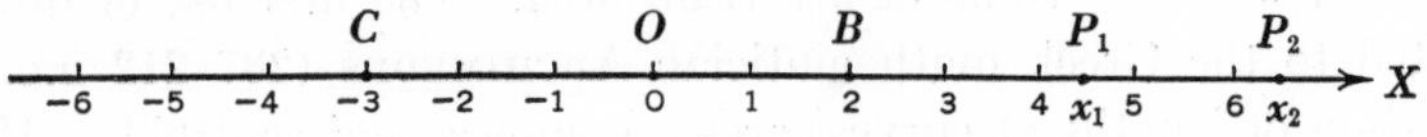

Fig. 1

ILLUSTRATION 1. In Figure 1, the coordinates of B and C are 2 and -3, respectively. From (1), $BC = -3 - 2 = -5$; the distance between 2 and -3 is $|BC| = |-3 - 2| = 5$.

We use the number scale as a background for geometrical language where each *number* may be talked of as a *point*. Thus, to remark that b is *close* to c will mean that the distance $|b - c|$ is small.

4. Inequalities

If b and c are real numbers, we say that b is *less than* c, or c is *greater than* b, if b is to the *left* of c on the number scale. We use the inequality sign " $<$ " to abbreviate "*less than*," and " $>$ " for "*greater than*." If $b < c$, as in Figure 2, the directed segment from b to c on the number scale has the value $(c - b)$, which is *positive* because b is to the *left* of c. Hence,

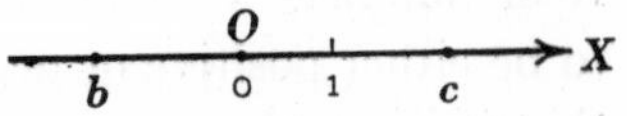

Fig. 2

$$\text{"} b < c \text{" means that } (c - b) \text{ is positive.} \tag{1}$$

---

* The word *length* or the unqualified word *distance* will refer to a *positive number* or *zero* which is the measure of some distance in terms of a given unit.

ILLUSTRATION 1. $-5 < 2$ because -5 is to the left of 2 on the number scale, and also because $2 - (-5) = 7$, which is positive.

ILLUSTRATION 2. To indicate that x is positive, we write $x > 0$. The inequality $|x| < c$ means that $-c < x < c$. To state that x lies *between* b *and* c, where $b < c$, we write $b < x < c$.

If b and c are distinct numbers, then all numbers x from b to c, with one, both, or neither of the end-points b and c included, is called an *interval* of numbers. If b and c *are not included*, the interval is said to be *open*. If b and c *are included*, the interval is said to be *closed*. If just b or c is included, the interval is said to be *half-open*, or *half-closed*. If a set of numbers is called merely an *interval of numbers*, this will indicate that it is immaterial whether or not the end-points are included. In referring to an interval of numbers, we may think geometrically of the corresponding segment of a number scale.

ILLUSTRATION 3. The numbers x satisfying $-3 < x < 5$ form an open interval. The interval defined by $-3 \leqq x \leqq 5$ is a closed interval.

5. Agreements about coordinate systems

In referring to a system of *rectangular coordinates* in a plane, we shall assume that a *single unit* is used for measuring *all distances* in the plane, unless we specify otherwise. In an *xy*-plane, we shall use $P:(x, y)$ to mean *point P with coordinates* (x, y), where x is the *abscissa* and y is the *ordinate*. We read "$P:(x, y)$" simply as "P, x, y."

6. Variables, constants, functions

A *variable* is a symbol, such as x, or y, etc., which may represent any particular thing which we choose to designate from a specified set of things. Then, this set of things is called the **range** of the variable.

ILLUSTRATION 1. We may use x to represent any person in the population of the United States. Then, this population is the range for the variable x. In particular, x might represent the author of this text.

Hereafter, in this book, the range for any variable will be a corresponding set of *numbers*, unless otherwise specified. If x is a variable whose range is S, then x may take on as its value any one of the numbers in S.

In a given discussion, a *constant* is a number symbol having a fixed value. A constant may be an explicit number, such as 3, $-\frac{5}{2}$, etc.; or, a constant may be a symbol such as b, c, etc., with a fixed value, which may or may not be known explicitly. If desired, a constant may be thought of as a variable whose range consists of just one number.

ILLUSTRATION 2. In the formula $A = \pi r^2$ for the area of a circle, if all circles are considered, π is a constant while A and r are variables.

Note 1. Whenever we introduce a number symbol for a concrete quantity, we shall understand that the symbol represents the *measure* of the quantity in terms of an appropriate unit. Thus, in Illustration 2, when we refer to *r* simply as *the radius*, and to *A* as *the area*, we mean that *r* is *the measure of the radius* in terms of some linear unit and *A* is *the measure of the area* in a corresponding area unit.

Related variables enter frequently in mathematics. Thus, let *x* be a variable with a given range *S*. Suppose that, for each value of *x*, some law or rule specifies one or more corresponding numbers, and let *T* represent the set of *all these numbers*, for *all values of x*. Let *y* be a variable whose range is *T*. Then, we introduce the following terminology.

DEFINITION I. *If two variables x and y are so related that, whenever a value is assigned to x, one or more corresponding values of y are determined, then* **this law of correspondence is called a function** *and y is said to be a* **function of x.**

In Definition I, the range *S* for *x* is called the **domain** of the function. Each value of *y* is called a *value of the function;* the set *T* of all these values of *y* is called the **range** of the function. Thus, a function is *a rule of correspondence between its domain and its range.*

ILLUSTRATION 3. Let *S* be the set of numbers *x* from 1 to 3 inclusive on *OX*, in Figure 3. For each value of *x*, let $y = 2x + 3$. If $x = 1$, then $y = 5$; if $x = 2$, then $y = 7$; etc. Then, with *x* in *S*, the values of *y* make up the closed interval *T* from 5 to 9 on *OY*, in Figure 3, where the correspondence between *x* and *y* is shown by representative arrows. The correspondence between *S* and *T* is a *function* whose *range* is the closed interval from 5 to 9 and whose *domain* is the closed interval from 1 to 3.

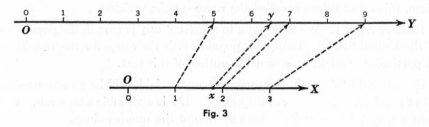

Fig. 3

If *y* is a function of *x*, we refer to *x* as the **independent variable** and to *y* as the **dependent variable**. If just *one* value of *y* corresponds to each value of *x*, we call *y* a *single-valued* function of *x*. If just *two* values of *y* correspond to each value of *x*, we call *y* a *double-valued* function. In general, we speak of *many-valued* functions. Any formula for *y* in terms of *x* defines *y* as a function of *x*. However, useful functions arise for which no formulas are available, even when the word formula is interpreted liberally.

If a function is defined by a formula, the function frequently is named on the basis of the nature of its formula. Thus, in previous mathematics, we have met algebraic, trigonometric, logarithmic, and exponential functions. These types are called the *elementary functions* of mathematical analysis.

If y is a function of x, it is possible to refer to x as a function of y. Also, as a rule, *any equation in two variables defines either variable as a function of the other variable.*

ILLUSTRATION 4. The equation $y = x^2$ defines y as a single-valued function of x. On solving for x, we obtain $x = \pm \sqrt{y}$, so that x is a double-valued function of y; each of the equations $x = \sqrt{y}$ and $x = -\sqrt{y}$ is said to define a single-valued *branch* of the double-valued function.

ILLUSTRATION 5. If $y = \arcsin x$, infinitely many values of y correspond to each value of x on the interval $-1 \leqq x \leqq 1$. Thus, if $x = 0$, we find * $y = 0, \pm \pi, \pm 2\pi, \cdots$.

A variable z is said to be a function of two independent variables x and y if one or more values of z can be determined corresponding to each pair of values of x and y. Also, we may speak of a function of three or more variables.

ILLUSTRATION 6. If x and y are variables, and $z = 3x^2 + 5y$, then z is an algebraic function of x and y.

Hereafter, any function to which we refer will be *single-valued* unless otherwise implied. Frequently, in later discussions, many-valued functions will be covered implicitly, as combinations of single-valued functions.

7. Functional notation

We sometimes represent functions by symbols like $f(x)$, $H(z)$, etc., where the letter in parentheses is the independent variable. We read "$f(x)$" as "*f of x*," or "*f at x*." If a is any value of x, then

$$f(a) \text{ represents the value of } f(x) \text{ at } x = a. \tag{1}$$

A notation $f(x)$ for a function may be thought of as a symbol for the *whole correspondence* set up between the domain and the range of the function. However, we also use $f(x)$ for the *value* of the function corresponding to any particular value of x. Whenever ambiguity might arise about the meaning of the symbol $f(x)$, and the *complete function* is in mind, we shall write "*the function* $f(x)$" instead of merely "$f(x)$." Or, we may refer simply to "*the function f.*"

ILLUSTRATION 1. If $g(x) = 3x^2 - 5 - x$, then

$$g(-3) = 3(-3)^2 - 5 + 3 = 25;$$

$$g(x + h) = 3(x + h)^2 - 5 - (x + h) = 3x^2 + (6h - 1)x - 5 - h + 3h^2.$$

* In this reference, *radian measure* is used. See page 123.

Similarly, $f(x, y)$ represents a function of x and y, and $g(x, y, z)$ represents a function of x, y, and z.

ILLUSTRATION 2.   If $F(x, y) = 3x^2 - 2xy$, then

$$F(2, -5) = 3(4) - 2(2)(-5) = 32.$$

If a function $f(x)$ is defined by a formula, we shall infer that x does not assume any value for which the formula is meaningless.   Also, in this text, we shall exclude any value of x for which the formula would give an imaginary value, because, with minor exceptions, we shall deal only with real values for all variables.   Unless otherwise stated, we shall assume that the range for x, or the domain of the function, consists of *all values of x for which the given formula has meaning.*

ILLUSTRATION 3.   If $f(x) = \dfrac{\sqrt{4-x}}{x+2}$, then $f(x)$ is not defined when $x + 2 = 0$, or $x = -2$, because *division by zero is not an operation of algebra.*   Also, $f(x)$ is not defined when $4 - x < 0$, or $4 < x$, because then $\sqrt{4-x}$ is imaginary. Thus, $f(x)$ is defined when $x \leqq 4$, excluding $x = -2$;   these values of x constitute the domain of $f(x)$.

8. Graph of an equation and of a function

A **solution** of an equation in the variables x and y is a *pair of values* of the variables which satisfy the equation.   The graph of an equation in x and y is the set of all points in an xy-plane whose co-ordinates * (x, y) form solutions of the equation.

ILLUSTRATION 1.   To graph $4x^2 + 9y^2 = 36$, we compute representative solutions (x, y), plot the corresponding points, and connect them by a smooth curve.   Thus, if $x = 0$ we find $y = \pm 2$; if $y = 0$ then $x = \pm 3$;   etc.   The graph, in Figure 4, is an ellipse.

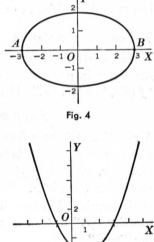

Fig. 4

If y is a function of x, each pair of corresponding values (x, y) gives a point in an xy-plane. Then, the resulting set of points is called *the graph of the function.*   This is equivalent to stating that *the graph of a function $f(x)$ is the graph of the equation $y = f(x)$.*

ILLUSTRATION 2.   The graph of the function $x^2 - 2x - 3$ is the graph of the corresponding equation $y = x^2 - 2x - 3$, as in Figure 5.   The graph is a parabola.

Fig. 5

---

* Unless otherwise indicated, when a pair of values of two variables, say (x, y), is interpreted as coordinates, *rectangular* coordinates will be involved.

REVIEW EXERCISE 1

1. Insert the proper sign, $<$ or $>$, between 5 and -3; -8 and -2.

Express the facts by use of inequalities without absolute value symbols.

2. x lies to the right of 5.   **3.** x lies to the left of -4.

4. x is negative.   **5.** x lies between 3 and 7.

6. x lies between -2 and -7.   **7.** x lies between 5 and -8.

8. $|x| < 3$.   **9.** $|x| > a$.   **10.** $|x - 2| \leqq 3$.

11. Write inequalities defining the open interval of numbers between -3 and 9; the half-open interval from -3 to 9, including 9 but not -3.

12. If $G(z) = 2z - 3z^2$, find $G(-3)$; $G(5)$; $G(b)$; $G(b+1)$.

13. If $f(x) = x^2 - x + 3$, find $f(-2)$; $f\left(\dfrac{c}{d}\right)$; $f(x+2)$.

14. If $F(w) = \dfrac{3w + 2}{w}$, find $3F(5)$; $[F(2)]^3$; $\dfrac{F(2)}{F(3)}$.

If $f(x) = x^2 + 2x$, find the specified quantity.

15. $f(2 + a)$.   **16.** $f(-1 + d)$.   **17.** $f(3 + h)$.   **18.** $f(x + h)$.

19. If $f(x) = 3x^2 + 2$ and $g(x) = \sin(x - 1)$, find $f[g(x)]$.

Find expressions for the function y of the variable x, and for the function x of the variable y, which are defined by the equation.

20. $4x + 3y = 12$.   **21.** $4x^2 - 3y = 7$.   **22.** $3xy - 2x + 3y = 5$.

Graph the equation.

23. $9y^2 - 4x^2 = 36$.   **24.** $xy = -4$.   **25.** $25x^2 + 9y^2 = 225$.

Graph the function.

26. $3x - 4$.   **27.** $x^2 - 2x + 5$.   **28.** $x^3 - 3x + 1$.

If $f(x, y) = 3x^2 - x + y^2$, compute the specified quantity.

29. $f(-2, 3)$.   **30.** $f(2, -4)$.   **31.** $f(a, -b)$.   **32.** $f(-x, -y)$.

9. Slope and inclination for a line

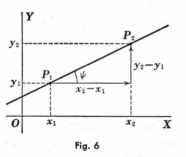

Fig. 6

If l is a nonvertical line in an xy-plane, the **slope** of l is defined * as *the ratio of the change in the ordinate to the change in the abscissa* as we move from any point on l to any second point on l. Or, *the slope is the rate of change of y with respect to x if we move on l.* If $x_1 \neq x_2$ and m is the slope of the line l through $P_1:(x_1, y_1)$ and $P_2:(x_2, y_2)$, as in Figure 6, then

$$m = \frac{y_2 - y_1}{x_2 - x_1}. \qquad (1)$$

* The units on the x-axis and y-axis *need not be equal,* with this definition.

Suppose that the units on the coordinate axes are equal. Let l be a non-horizontal line in the xy-plane, as in Figure 6. Then, the **inclination** of l is defined as the angle ψ less than $180°$ through which the x-axis must be rotated counterclockwise about its intersection with l in order to coincide with l. If l is horizontal, its inclination is defined as $\psi = 0°$. Thus, in any case, we have

$$0° \leq \psi < 180°. \tag{2}$$

If l is not vertical, its slope m and inclination ψ are related by the equation $m = \tan \psi$. If $\psi = 90°$, then $\tan 90°$ is undefined; in this case, the slope also is undefined. Moreover, if a line l varies so that ψ approaches $90°$, then $|\tan \psi|$ grows *large without bound*. For this reason, sometimes it is said that a vertical line has *infinite slope*.

From analytic geometry, we recall that the line in the xy-plane with slope m and y-intercept b has the equation

$$y = mx + b. \tag{3}$$

The line with slope m through the point (x_1, y_1) has the equation (in the so-called *point-slope form*)

$$y - y_1 = m(x - x_1). \tag{4}$$

If $x_1 \neq x_2$, by use of m from (1), the line through $P_1:(x_1, y_1)$ and $P_2:(x_2, y_2)$ has the equation

$$y - y_1 = \frac{y_2 - y_1}{x_2 - x_1}(x - x_1). \tag{5}$$

REVIEW EXERCISE 2

Find the slope of the line through the points.

1. $(3, 5)$; $(2, -3)$.　　　　　　**2.** $(-1, 2)$; $(4, -3)$.
3. $(-2, 4)$; $(-5, -3)$.　　　　　**4.** $(0, -3)$; $(5, -7)$.

Write an equation for the line with given slope m and y-intercept b, or through the given point with slope m, or through the given points.

5. $m = 3$, $b = -2$.　　　　　　**6.** $m = -2$, $b = 3$.
7. $m = 2$; through $(-3, 2)$.　　　**8.** $m = -1$; through $(4, -3)$.
9. $m = 0$; through $(5, 2)$.　　　　**10.** $m = 0$; through $(-3, 4)$.
11. Through $(1, 3)$ and $(2, 5)$
12. Through $(0, -4)$ and $(2, -3)$.

10. Notation for limits

The student has met the concept of a *limit* at least informally in various places in previous mathematics. Wherever we refer to a limit, it will be *the limit of some dependent variable as a corresponding independent variable behaves in a certain way.*

ILLUSTRATION 1. The sum T of the endless geometric progression

$$1 + \frac{1}{2} + \frac{1}{4} + \cdots$$

is defined in algebra as *the limit of the sum of the first n terms, S(n), as n becomes infinite.* By use of (5), page 435,

$$S(n) = 1 + \frac{1}{2} + \frac{1}{4} + \cdots + \frac{1}{2^{n-1}} = 2 - \frac{1}{2^{n-1}}.$$

Then, $$T = \lim_{n \to \infty} S(n) = 2 - 0 = 2,$$

where we read "*T is equal to the limit of S(n) as n becomes infinite.*" In this case, the values of the independent variable n form a *sequence* $1, 2, 3, \cdots$, and the values of $S(n)$ form a *corresponding sequence.* Thus, the illustration talks of *the limit of a sequence.* Limits of this nature will be studied later.

ILLUSTRATION 2. Let $P(n)$ be the perimeter of a regular polygon of n sides inscribed in a circle, with $n > 2$. Then, the circumference C of the circle is defined as the limit of $P(n)$ as n becomes infinite.

Let a function $f(x)$ be defined at all values of x on some interval, except perhaps at $x = c$ on this interval. Then, we shall deal with statements such as

the limit of f(x) is L as x approaches c,   (1)

which is abbreviated by writing

$$\lim_{x \to c} f(x) = L, \tag{2}$$

where "$\to$" is used as an abbreviation for the word "*approaches.*" In place of (1), we may say that "$f(x)$ *approaches L as x approaches c,*" and write "$f(x) \to L$ *as* $x \to c$." Terminology for limits will be formalized in Chapter 2. At present, the terminology will be used on an intuitional basis.

ILLUSTRATION 3. If $f(h) = 3h^2 + 2h + 5$, then

$$\lim_{h \to 0} f(h) = \lim_{h \to 0} 3h^2 + \lim_{h \to 0} 2h + \lim_{h \to 0} 5 = 0 + 0 + 5;$$

or, $f(h) \to 5$ as $h \to 0$.

11. Corresponding increments of related variables

Suppose that $y = f(x)$. Let the independent variable x be assigned the value $x = x_0$. If we add a number Δx, read "*delta x,*" we obtain $x = x_0 + \Delta x$, and say that an *increment* Δx has been given to the value $x = x_0$. Let $y = y_0$ when $x = x_0$, and $y = y_0 + \Delta y$ when $x = x_0 + \Delta x$. Then, we refer to Δy as the increment in the value of y *corresponding to the increment* Δx. We have

$$y_0 = f(x_0) \quad and \quad y_0 + \Delta y = f(x_0 + \Delta x); \tag{1}$$

$$\Delta y = f(x_0 + \Delta x) - f(x_0). \tag{2}$$

In Figure 7, $P:(x_0, y_0)$ and $Q:(x_0 + \Delta x, y_0 + \Delta y)$ are indicated on the graph of $y = f(x)$. The increments Δx and Δy are the differences of corresponding coordinates of P and Q.

ILLUSTRATION 1. Let $y = x^2$. If $x = 3$ then $y = 9$. If we give the increment $\Delta x = .2$ to $x = 3$, we obtain $x = 3.2$. Then,

$$y = (3.2)^2 = 10.24 \quad and \quad \Delta y = 10.24 - 9 = 1.24.$$

Or, immediately from (2),

$$\Delta y = (3.2)^2 - 3^2 = 10.24 - 9 = 1.24.$$

12. Average and instantaneous rates of change

Consider a function * $y = f(x)$, where $y = y_0$ when $x = x_0$; $y = y_0 + \Delta y$ when $x = x_0 + \Delta x$. Then, *the average rate of change of y with respect to x over the interval from x_0 to $(x_0 + \Delta x)$ is defined as the ratio of the change in y to the change in x*, or

$$\left\{ \begin{array}{c} the\ average\ rate\ of\ change \\ of\ y\ with\ respect\ to\ x \end{array} \right\} = \frac{\Delta y}{\Delta x}. \tag{1}$$

Observe that the average rate in (1) is equal to the slope of the secant through $P:(x_0, y_0)$ and $Q:(x_0 + \Delta x, y_0 + \Delta y)$ on the graph of $y = f(x)$, as in Figure 7. If the graph of $y = f(x)$ is a line, that is, if $f(x)$ is of the form $(mx + b)$, then the average rate is a constant for all values of x_0 and Δx, and the rate is equal to *the slope m of the line $y = mx + b$* which is involved. The important situation occurs when the graph of $y = f(x)$ is *not* a line, and the average rate in (1) is *not* a constant. This possibility leads us to introduce the following terminology.

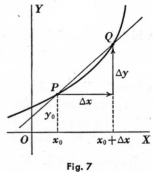

Fig. 7

DEFINITION II. *The **instantaneous rate of change** of a function $y = f(x)$ with respect to x, at an assigned point $x = x_0$, is the limit of the average rate of change of y over the interval from x_0 to $(x_0 + \Delta x)$ as Δx approaches zero, if the limit exists. That is,*

$$\left\{ \begin{array}{c} the\ instantaneous\ rate\ of \\ change\ of\ y\ with\ respect\ to\ x \end{array} \right\} = \lim_{\Delta x \to 0} \frac{\Delta y}{\Delta x}. \tag{2}$$

EXAMPLE 1. At $x = 3$, find the instantaneous rate of change of y with respect to x if

$$y = x^2 - 4x + 7. \tag{3}$$

---

* A reference to "*a function $y = f(x)$*" should be thought of as abbreviating "*a function $f(x)$ which we shall represent also by the single letter y.*"

Solution.   1. When $x = 3$, $y = 9 - 12 + 7 = 4$.   Let $y = 4 + \Delta y$ when $x = 3 + \Delta x$.   Then, from (3),

$$4 + \Delta y = (3 + \Delta x)^2 - 4(3 + \Delta x) + 7, \text{ or}$$

$$\Delta y = 2\Delta x + (\Delta x)^2.$$

Hence, over the interval from $x = 3$ to $x = 3 + \Delta x$,

$$\left\{ \begin{array}{c} \text{the average rate of change} \\ \text{of } y \text{ with respect to } x \end{array} \right\} = \frac{\Delta y}{\Delta x} = 2 + \Delta x. \qquad (4)$$

By use of (4), we compute the following values.

$\Delta x =$	$-.5$	$-.1$	$-.01$	$(As\ \Delta x \to 0)$	$.01$	$.1$	$.5$
$\left\{ \begin{array}{l} \text{AVER. RATE} \\ \text{OF CHANGE} \end{array} \right\} = \frac{\Delta y}{\Delta x} =$	1.5	1.9	1.99	LIMIT *is* 2	2.01	2.1	2.5

2. The preceding table checks the following result, from (4):

$$\lim_{\Delta x \to 0} \frac{\Delta y}{\Delta x} = \lim_{\Delta x \to 0} (2 + \Delta x) = 2 + 0 = 2. \qquad (5)$$

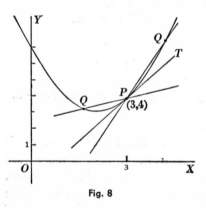

Fig. 8

That is, from (2) and (5), the instantaneous rate of change of y with respect to x at $x = 3$ is 2.

Comment.   Each value of $\Delta y/\Delta x$ in the preceding table is the slope of a corresponding secant PQ for the graph of $y = f(x)$ in Figure 8:

$$m = (\textit{slope of } PQ) = \frac{\Delta y}{\Delta x}. \qquad (6)$$

From (5) and (6), $m \to 2$ as $Q \to P$ on the graph.   Hence, if PT is the line through P with slope 2, the angle between PQ and PT aproaches zero as $\Delta x \to 0$.   We then say that PT is the *limiting position* of PQ as $Q \to P$, and define PT as the *tangent* to the graph of (3) at P.   Thus, we meet a special case of the following result, which will be discussed later.

The instantaneous rate of change of y with respect to x at $x = x_0$ is the slope of the tangent to the graph of $y = f(x)$ at $P:(x_0, y_0)$.

Hence, the tangent PT in Figure 8 is the line with slope 2 through $P:(3, 4)$; by use of the point-slope form, the equation of PT is

$$y - 4 = 2(x - 3), \quad \text{or} \quad y = 2x - 2.$$

Instantaneous rates of change are of fundamental importance.   Later, any instantaneous rate of change will be called a **derivative**.

SUMMARY.   *To find the instantaneous rate of change of a function $y = f(x)$ with respect to x at a particular point $x = x_0$.*

1. *Compute $y_0 = f(x_0)$, and insert $(x = x_0 + \Delta x,\ y = y_0 + \Delta y)$ in $y = f(x)$, to obtain Δy in terms of Δx:*

$$y_0 + \Delta y = f(x_0 + \Delta x), \quad or \quad \Delta y = f(x_0 + \Delta x) - f(x_0). \tag{7}$$

2. *Divide by Δx to find the average rate of change $\Delta y / \Delta x$.*

3. *Compute the instantaneous rate of change, $\lim_{\Delta x \to 0} (\Delta y / \Delta x)$.*

EXERCISE 3

1. If $y = x^2 - 6x + 4$, (a) find the average rates of change of y with respect to x over the interval from $x = 4$ to $x = 4 + \Delta x$ if Δx is $\pm .5$; $\pm .2$; $\pm .1$; $\pm .01$. (b) Obtain the instantaneous rate of change of y with respect to x at $x = 4$. (c) Graph the given equation. (d) Write the equation of the tangent to the graph where $x = 4$, by use of the slope found in (b), and draw this tangent.

2. Repeat Problem 1 if $y = 6 - x^2 - 4x$, from $x = -5$ to $x = -5 + \Delta x$.

Find the instantaneous rate of change of y with respect to x.

3. $y = x^3$, at $x = 2$.   4. $y = 3x - 2x^2$, at $x = 3$.

HINT.   By the binomial expansion for $(a + b)^n$, page 561,

$$(2 + \Delta x)^3 = 2^3 + 3(2^2)\Delta x + 3(2)(\Delta x)^2 + (\Delta x)^3.$$

5. $y = 7 - 3x - 5x^2$, at $x = -2$.   6. $y = 2x^3 - x$, at $x = 2$.
7. $y = 2x^2 - x^3 + x - 5$, at $x = 3$.   8. $y = 3 - x - 3x^2 + x^3$, at $x = -2$.

13. Average and instantaneous velocity

Consider the motion of an object on a straight line, labeled as an s-axis in Figure 9, where the object is idealized as a point P. Motion of this nature is referred to as *rectilinear motion*. The object will be referred to as a *particle*. Let s be the measure, in a given unit, of the directed distance of the particle from the origin of the s-axis. Let any instant be designated as t units of time from some fixed instant where $t = 0$, with $t > 0$ after $t = 0$ and $t < 0$ before $t = 0$. We assume that s is specified as a function of the time, $s = f(t)$. Then, we shall define the notion of *velocity* for the particle. Let Δt be a variable increment, not zero, with $s = s_0$ and $s = s_0 + \Delta s$ corresponding, respectively, to $t = t_0$ and $t = t_0 + \Delta t$, as indicated in Figure 9.

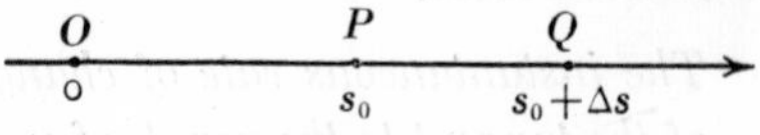

Fig. 9

DEFINITION III.   *In the rectilinear motion of a particle, its average velocity over the time interval from t_0 to $(t_0 + \Delta t)$ is the average rate of change of the distance s with respect to the time t:*

$$\textbf{(average velocity)} = \frac{\Delta s}{\Delta t}. \tag{1}$$

If the average velocity is a constant for all time intervals, this means that equal distances, in the same direction, are passed over by the particle in equal intervals of time. Then, it is said that the object is moving with *uniform velocity*, and the motion is referred to as *uniform motion*. The *velocity* in this case is defined as the constant *average velocity*.

ILLUSTRATION 1. If the uniform velocity is 3′ per second, (1) becomes

$$\frac{\Delta s}{\Delta t} = 3 \quad or \quad \Delta s = 3\Delta t.$$

Thus, the object travels 3 linear units in the positive direction on the *s*-axis in each unit of time.

When the average velocity is *not* a constant, we are led to the following terminology.

DEFINITION IV. *The* **instantaneous velocity,** *v, or simply the* **velocity** *of the moving particle, at any instant* t_0*, is the limit of the average velocity* $\Delta s/\Delta t$ *when* $\Delta t \to 0$*. That is,*

$$v = \lim_{\Delta t \to 0} \frac{\Delta s}{\Delta t}. \tag{2}$$

From Definition II on page 12, the velocity *v* is simply *the instantaneous rate of change of the distance s with respect to the time t.*

Note 1. Let $s = f(t)$, with $s = s_1$ at $t = t_1$ and $s = s_2$ at $t = t_2$, where $t_1 \neq t_2$. Let $\Delta s = s_2 - s_1$ and $\Delta t = t_2 - t_1$. Then, over the interval from t_1 to t_2,

$$(average\ velocity) = \frac{s_2 - s_1}{t_2 - t_1}. \tag{3}$$

EXAMPLE 1. Suppose that a projectile is shot vertically upward from the earth, with an initial velocity of v_0 feet per second. Then, if air resistance and other complications are neglected, the projectile's height *s* in feet above the ground *t* seconds later is given by

$$s = -\tfrac{1}{2}gt^2 + v_0 t, \tag{4}$$

where $g = 32$, approximately. If $v_0 = 96$, (*a*) find the projectile's average velocity over the interval from $t = 1$ to $t = 3$. (*b*) Compute the average velocity over the interval from $t = 2$ to $t = 2 + \Delta t$ for various values of Δt. (*c*) Find the instantaneous velocity at $t = 2$.

SOLUTION. 1. From (4) with $v_0 = 96$ and $g = 32$,

$$s = -16t^2 + 96t. \tag{5}$$

2. From (5) at $t = 1$, $s = 80$; at $t = 3$, $s = 144$. Hence, from (3), over the interval from $t = 1$ to $t = 3$,

$$(the\ average\ velocity) = \frac{144 - 80}{3 - 1} = 32'\ per\ sec.$$

3. For Parts (b) and (c), use the Summary on page 14. If $t = 2$ in (5), we obtain $s = 128$. Then, let $s = 128 + \Delta s$ when $t = 2 + \Delta t$, and use these values in (5):

$$128 + \Delta s = -16(2 + \Delta t)^2 + 96(2 + \Delta t);$$

$$128 + \Delta s = -64 - 64\Delta t - 16(\Delta t)^2 + 192 + 96\Delta t, \text{ or}$$

$$\Delta s = 32\Delta t - 16(\Delta t)^2.$$

Hence, $\left\{ \begin{array}{c} \textit{the average velocity} \\ \textit{from } t = 2 \textit{ to } t = 2 + \Delta t \end{array} \right\} = \dfrac{\Delta s}{\Delta t} = 32 - 16\Delta t.$ (6)

In (6), with Δt having the values 1, .5, .3, .2, .1, .01, and .001, we obtain the following corresponding average velocities, in feet per second: 16, 24, 27.2, 28.8, 30.4, 31.84, and 31.984, which seem to indicate a limit equal to 32. This fact is verified by use of (2) and (6):

$$v = \lim_{\Delta t \to 0} \frac{\Delta s}{\Delta t} = \lim_{\Delta t \to 0} (32 - 16\Delta t) = 32 - 0 = 32.$$

Or, the instantaneous velocity at $t = 2$ is $v = 32'$ per second.

In a later chapter, the velocity v in (2) will be recognized as the *derivative* of the distance s with respect to the time t.

EXERCISE 4

1. For the projectile * involved in (4) on page 15, let $v_0 = 128$. (a) Compute the average velocity by use of (3), page 15, over the interval from $t = 0$ to $t = 2$; from $t = 1$ to $t = 2$; from $t = 2$ to $t = 4$. (b) By the method of the Summary on page 14, compute the average velocities over the intervals from $t = 2$ to $t = 2 + \Delta t$, if Δt has the values ± 1, $\pm .5$, $\pm .2$, $\pm .1$, $\pm .01$. (c) Find the instantaneous velocity at $t = 2$.

2. For an object moving in a vertical line, the height s above sea level at any time t is given by $s = -16t^2 + 96t + 48$. (a) Find the average velocity over the interval from $t = \frac{1}{2}$ to $t = 1$. (b) Find the instantaneous velocity at $t = 4$. (c) Find the average velocity over the interval from $t = 4$ to $t = 4 + \Delta t$, if $\Delta t = 1$; $\Delta t = .1$; $\Delta t = .01$.

The equation specifies the position at any time t for an object on an s-axis. Find the instantaneous velocity at each given value of t.

3. $s = 3t^2 + 5t - 6$; at $t = 3$; at $t = 2$.
4. $s = t^3 - 3t - 4$; at $t = 2$; at $t = 1$.
5. $s = 2t + t^3 - 7$; at $t = 1$; at $t = 2$.

* Unless otherwise specified, in motion problems in this book, the units will be one foot for distance and one second for time.

2

LIMITS

14. Limits for functions of a continuous variable

In the following definition, we consider a function $f(x)$, defined at all values of x on some interval, except perhaps at $x = c$ on the interval. In such a case we call x a *continuous variable*. Any value of x referred to is on the specified interval, and $x = c$ may be one of its end-points.

DEFINITION I. *We say that a number L is the limit of $f(x)$ as $x \to c$, or*

> **the limit of $f(x)$ as x approaches c is L,** (1)

if, for $x \neq c$,* $f(x)$ is as near L as we please at all values of x sufficiently near c.

Thus, (1) means that, if $x \neq c$, then $\mid f(x) - L \mid$ is as small as we please when $\mid x - c \mid$ is sufficiently small. Instead of (1), we may say that "$f(x)$ approaches L as x approaches c," abbreviated by "$f(x) \to L$ as $x \to c$." We abbreviate (1) by writing

$$\lim_{x \to c} f(x) = L \quad or \quad \lim_{x \to c} f(x) = L. \tag{2}$$

ILLUSTRATION 1. Consider the function

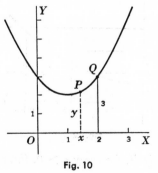

Fig. 10

$$f(x) = (x - 2)^2 + 2(x - 2) + 3.$$

If $x \to 2$, then $(x - 2) \to 0$, $(x - 2)^2 \to 0$, and $f(x)$ will be as near 3 as we please if x is sufficiently near 2. Hence, $\lim_{x \to 2} f(x) = 3$. We observe that $f(2) = 3$, so that

$$\lim_{x \to 2} f(x) = f(2). \tag{3}$$

Thus, if $P:(x, y)$ is on the graph of $y = f(x)$, in Figure 10, and if $x \to 2$, the ordinate y of P approaches $f(2)$, which is the ordinate of $Q:(2, 3)$.

---

* Thus, even if $f(c)$ exists, it is not involved in the definition. Redundantly, for contrast with so-called *infinite limits* later, we emphasize that L is finite.

ILLUSTRATION 2. Let $f(x)$ be the cost in cents of mailing a letter of weight
x ounces at 3 cents per ounce or fraction thereof. For instance, $f(1) = 3$;
$f(1.01) = 6$; etc. The graph of the function $f(x)$, in Figure 11, has breaks
at $x = 0, 1, 2, \cdots$. In particular, there is no number L such that $f(x)$ is as
near L as we please at all values of x sufficiently near 2, with *both sides*,
$x > 2$ and $x < 2$, considered. The circle at C in Figure 11 indicates that

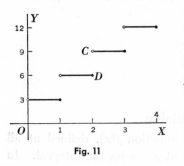

Fig. 11

C is not on the graph. When $x = 2$, we obtain D on the graph. Thus, $\lim_{x \to 2} f(x)$ does
not exist. However, $f(x) \to 6$ as "*x approaches*
2 *from the left*," abbreviated "$x \to 2-$," and
$f(x) \to 9$ as "*x approaches* 2 *from the right*,"
abbreviated "$x \to 2+$." We then say that,
at $x = 2$, the **left-hand limit** of $f(x)$ is 6,
and the **right-hand limit** is 9, and write

$$\lim_{x \to 2-} f(x) = 6; \quad \lim_{x \to 2+} f(x) = 9. \qquad (4)$$

In contrast to *one-sided limits*, such as (4), we may refer to $\lim_{x \to c} f(x)$ as the
unrestricted limit as $x \to c$, to emphasize that values on *both sides*, $x < c$ and
$x > c$, are in mind in Definition I.

We call attention to the useful fact that

$$\lim_{x \to c} f(x) = L \quad \textit{is equivalent to} \quad \lim_{x \to c} [f(x) - L] = 0. \qquad (5)$$

Also, if $f(x) = x$, we observe that $\lim_{x \to c} f(x) = c$; or, $\lim_{x \to c} x = c$.

ILLUSTRATION 3. If k is a constant and $f(x) = k$ for all values of x, then
$f(x) \to k$ when $x \to c$, for any value of c.

★*Note 1. The (ϵ, δ)-definition of a limit.* Suppose that $\lim_{x \to c} f(x) = L$, and
consider the graph of $y = f(x)$ in Figure 12. Assign any number $\epsilon > 0$ as a
measure of closeness to L. Then, Definition I states that, if $x \neq c$, the graph
of $y = f(x)$ is between the lines $y = L - \epsilon$ and $y = L + \epsilon$ at all values of x
sufficiently near $x = c$, say between $x = c - \delta$
and $x = c + \delta$, where δ is sufficiently small.
We leave a hole at $Q:(c, L)$ in Figure 12
because the definition of "$\lim_{x \to c} f(x) = L$"
includes no stipulation about $f(x)$ when
$x = c$. The preceding remarks are true for
any $\epsilon > 0$, but are of greatest interest if ϵ is
thought of as arbitrarily small. In terms
of ϵ and δ, Definition I can be restated as
follows:

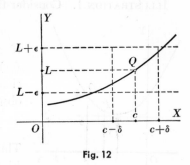

Fig. 12

The limit of $f(x)$ as x approaches c is L if and only if, for every $\epsilon > 0$, there
exists a corresponding $\delta > 0$, such that

$$\textit{when} \quad 0 < |x - c| < \delta \quad \textit{then} \quad |f(x) - L| < \epsilon. \qquad (6)$$

15. Theorems on limits

The following theorems are concerned with functions $f(x)$ and $g(x)$ having limits L and M, respectively, as $x \to c$. We omit the corresponding proofs.

THEOREM I.   *The limit of a sum of two (or more) functions is equal to the sum of their limits. That is,*

$$\lim_{x \to c} [f(x) + g(x)] = L + M.$$

THEOREM II.   *The limit of a constant k times a function $f(x)$ is equal to the constant times the limit of the function. That is,*

$$\lim_{x \to c} kf(x) = kL.$$

THEOREM III.   *The limit of the product of two (or more) functions is the product of their limits. That is,*

$$\lim_{x \to c} f(x)g(x) = LM.$$

THEOREM IV.   *The limit of a quotient of two functions is the quotient of their limits, provided that the limit of the divisor is different from zero. That is,*

$$\lim_{x \to c} \frac{f(x)}{g(x)} = \frac{L}{M} \quad if \quad M \neq 0.$$

We observe that Theorem II is the special case of Theorem III where one function is a constant.

By use of Theorem I, and then Theorem II with $k = -1$, we prove that *the limit of a difference is equal to the difference of the limits:*

$$\lim_{x \to c} [f(x) - g(x)] = \lim_{x \to c} f(x) + \lim_{x \to c} [-g(x)]$$
$$= \lim_{x \to c} f(x) - \lim_{x \to c} g(x) = L - M.$$

ILLUSTRATION 1.   From Theorems II and III, since $\lim_{x \to c} x = c$,

$$\lim_{x \to c} 5x^3 = 5 \left[\lim_{x \to c} (x \cdot x \cdot x) \right] = 5c \cdot c \cdot c = 5c^3.$$

Similarly, if k is a constant, and m is a positive integer,

$$\lim_{x \to c} kx^m = kc^m. \tag{1}$$

ILLUSTRATION 2.   By use of Theorem IV, and then Theorems I and II,

$$\lim_{x \to 3} \frac{2x^2 + x - 5}{3x - 7} = \frac{\lim_{x \to 3} (2x^2 + x - 5)}{\lim_{x \to 3} (3x - 7)}$$

$$= \frac{2 \left(\lim_{x \to 3} x^2 \right) + \lim_{x \to 3} x - \lim_{x \to 3} 5}{3 \lim_{x \to 3} x - \lim_{x \to 3} 7} = \frac{18 + 3 - 5}{9 - 7} = \frac{16}{2} = 8.$$

If n is a positive integer and $\lim_{x \to c} f(x) = L$, we accept the fact that

$$\lim_{x \to c} \sqrt[n]{f(x)} = \sqrt[n]{L}. \tag{2}$$

ILLUSTRATION 3. $\lim_{x \to 4} \sqrt[3]{3 + 6x} = \sqrt[3]{3 + \lim_{x \to 4} 6x} = \sqrt[3]{27} = 3.$

THEOREM V. *If a fraction $N(x)/D(x)$ has a limit as $x \to c$, and if $D(x) \to 0$ as $x \to c$, then $N(x) \to 0$ as $x \to c$.*

Proof. Let $f(x) = N(x)/D(x)$, and let $\lim_{x \to c} f(x) = L$. If $x \neq c$, then $N(x) = f(x)D(x)$ and

$$\lim_{x \to c} N(x) = \left[\lim_{x \to c} f(x)\right]\left[\lim_{x \to c} D(x)\right] = L \cdot 0 = 0.$$

A fraction of the type met in Theorem V tends to the meaningless form, or so-called *indeterminate form,* $0/0$ as $x \to c$. This form is important in the development of calculus. To evaluate the limit of a particular fraction $N(x)/D(x)$ of this nature, first try to alter it in order to avoid the form $0/0$.

EXAMPLE 1. Investigate $\lim_{x \to 2} \dfrac{2x^2 + x - 10}{3x - 6}.$ (3)

SOLUTION. Let $f(x)$ represent the fraction in (3). As $x \to 2$, $f(x)$ tends to the form $0/0$. In fact, at $x = 2$, both numerator and denominator are zero. Thus, by the Factor Theorem * of algebra, both numerator and denominator have the factor $(x - 2)$, which we divide out:

$$\lim_{x \to 2} f(x) = \lim_{x \to 2} \frac{(x - 2)(2x + 5)}{3(x - 2)} = \lim_{x \to 2} \frac{2x + 5}{3} = 3. \tag{4}$$

EXERCISE 5

Evaluate the limit by use of theorems on limits.

1. $\lim_{x \to 3} [(x - 3)^2 + 4].$ **2.** $\lim_{h \to -2} (2h^2 - 3h).$ **3.** $\lim_{x \to 3} \sqrt[3]{2x + 2}.$

4. $\lim_{x \to 4} \dfrac{x^2 - 6x + 9}{x^2 + 3x}.$ **5.** $\lim_{x \to 2} \dfrac{2x^2 - x - 6}{4x + 8}.$

6. $\lim_{x \to 3} \dfrac{2x^2 - 7x + 3}{2x - 6}.$ **7.** $\lim_{x \to -2} \dfrac{3x^2 + x - 10}{x^2 - 4}.$

8. $\lim_{x \to -3} \dfrac{x^3 + 27}{2x + 6}.$ **9.** $\lim_{h \to 0} \dfrac{4h^2 + 3h + 6}{2h + 1}.$

10. $\lim_{x \to 0} \dfrac{5x^2 + 6x}{3x^2 + 5x}.$ **11.** $\lim_{h \to 0} \dfrac{3h^3 + 2h^2 + 5h}{3h^2 + 2h}.$

12. Suppose that $f(x) \to L_1$ and $f(x) \to L_2$ as $x \to c$. Prove that $L_1 = L_2$. Thus, *if $f(x)$ has a limit as $x \to c$, then this limit is unique.*

HINT. $L_1 - L_2 = [L_1 - f(x)] + [f(x) - L_2].$

* If a polynomial $f(x)$ is zero when $x = r$, then $(x - r)$ is a factor of $f(x)$.

13. Graph the function $f(x)$ which is defined on the interval from $x = 0$ to $x = 4$ by the equations

$$f(x) = 2x \text{ when } 0 \leq x \leq 2, \quad and \quad f(x) = 9 - 2x \text{ when } 2 < x \leq 4.$$

What can be said about $\lim_{x \to 2} f(x)$; $\lim_{x \to 2-} f(x)$; $\lim_{x \to 2+} f(x)$?

Evaluate the limit.

14. $\lim\limits_{x \to 4} \dfrac{3\sqrt{x} - 6}{x - 4}$.

15. $\lim\limits_{x \to 3} \dfrac{\sqrt{3 + 2x} - 3}{x - 3}$.

HINT for Problem 14. Avoid $0/0$ by multiplying both numerator and denominator by $(3\sqrt{x} + 6)$, and simplifying.

★16. Let $f(x) = \sin(1/x)$. Is $f(x)$ defined at $x = 0$? If x is on the interval $.01 \leq x \leq .1$, between what values does $f(x)$ vary? Draw curves showing, roughly, the nature of the graph of $f(x)$ for positive values, and for negative values of x near $x = 0$. What can be said about

$$\lim\nolimits_{x \to 0} f(x); \quad \lim\nolimits_{x \to 0-} f(x); \quad \lim\nolimits_{x \to 0+} f(x)?$$

16. Continuity

In the following statements, $f(x)$ is defined at all points x on some interval including $x = c$, except possibly at $x = c$.

DEFINITION II. *A function $f(x)$ is said to be* **continuous** *at $x = c$ if $f(c)$ exists, $f(x)$ has a limit as $x \to c$, and*

$$\lim_{x \to c} f(x) = f(c). \tag{1}$$

DEFINITION III. *If a function $f(x)$ is not continuous at $x = c$, then $f(x)$ is said to be* **discontinuous** *at $x = c$.*

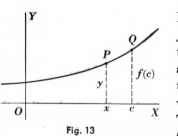

Fig. 13

Let the graph of $y = f(x)$ be the curve in Figure 13. Then, (1) states that the ordinate $f(x)$ at a variable point $P:(x, y)$ approaches the ordinate $f(c)$ at the fixed point $Q:[c, f(c)]$ as $x \to c$. In (1), let the fixed value of x be taken simply as x instead of c, and the variable value as $(x + \Delta x)$, with $y + \Delta y = f(x + \Delta x)$. Then, at any point x where $f(x)$ is defined, the function is said to be continuous if and only if

$$\lim_{\Delta x \to 0} f(x + \Delta x) = f(x), \text{ or} \tag{2}$$

$$\lim_{\Delta x \to 0} [f(x + \Delta x) - f(x)] = 0, \quad or \quad \lim_{\Delta x \to 0} \Delta y = 0. \tag{3}$$

If $f(x)$ is continuous at all values of x on some interval, we say that $f(x)$ is *continuous on the interval*. If we state simply that a function $f(x)$ is *continuous*, we shall mean that it is continuous at all values of x involved.

ILLUSTRATION 1. If $f(x) = 3x^2 + x - 4$, then $f(2) = 10$, and

$$\lim_{x \to 2} f(x) = 3 \lim_{x \to 2} x^2 + \lim_{x \to 2} x - \lim_{x \to 2} 4 = 10.$$

Or, $\lim_{x \to 2} f(x) = f(2)$. Thus, by (1), $f(x)$ is continuous at $x = 2$.

ILLUSTRATION 2. Let $$f(x) = \frac{x^2 - x - 6}{x - 3}. \tag{4}$$

Then $f(x)$ is undefined when $x = 3$, and hence is discontinuous at $x = 3$.

$$\lim_{x \to 3} f(x) = \lim_{x \to 3} \frac{(x - 3)(x + 2)}{x - 3} = \lim_{x \to 3} (x + 2) = 5. \tag{5}$$

The graph of $y = f(x)$, in Figure 14, is line AB with a hole at P, because $f(x)$ is not defined at $x = 3$. The line AB, with the hole filled, is the graph of the continuous function $y = x + 2$, which has the same values as $f(x)$ when $x \neq 3$. The hole in the graph of $f(x)$ would be filled if we should define $f(x)$ by (4) when $x \neq 3$ and, separately, define $f(3) = 5$. Hence, we say that $f(x)$ has a *removable discontinuity* at $x = 3$.

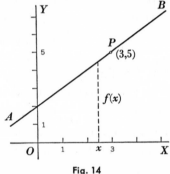

Fig. 14

ILLUSTRATION 3. In Illustration 2, page 18, $f(x)$ is discontinuous at all positive integral values of x. There is a finite jump of three units at each discontinuity, as shown in Figure 11, page 18.

As a special case of a later definition, the graph of a continuous function $y = f(x)$ is said to be a *continuous curve*. At present, intuitively, we take this to mean that *the graph has no breaks*. Suppose that, for any particular function $y = f(x)$, we are convinced geometrically that its graph is a curve without breaks if x lies on a certain interval of values. Then, without analytical proof based on Definition II, we permit the inference that $f(x)$ is a continuous function at these values of x.

Each part of the following theorem can be proved by use of a corresponding theorem on limits from Section 15.

THEOREM VI. *A sum, a difference, or a product of continuous functions is continuous, and a quotient of two continuous functions is continuous wherever the divisor is not zero.*

Proof (for a quotient). Let the functions $f(x)$ and $h(x)$ be continuous at $x = c$, where $h(c) \neq 0$. Then, by Definition I, $f(x) \to f(c)$ and $h(x) \to h(c)$ when $x \to c$. Let $g(x) = f(x)/h(x)$. Hence, by Theorem IV on page 19,

$$\lim_{x \to c} g(x) = \frac{\lim_{x \to c} f(x)}{\lim_{x \to c} h(x)} = \frac{f(c)}{h(c)}.$$

Or, $g(x) \to g(c)$ as $x \to c$. Thus, $g(x)$ is continuous at $x = c$.

17. Integral rational functions

A term is said to be *integral and rational* in certain variables, or to be an *integral rational term* in the variables, if and only if the term is the product of a constant and powers of the variables, where the exponents are nonnegative integers. The sum of the exponents, for any set of the variables, is called the *degree* of the term in these variables.

ILLUSTRATION 1. $8x^2y^3$ is an integral rational term of degree 5 in x and y.

By definition, an *integral rational function* of certain variables, or simply a *polynomial* in the variables, is a function which is a sum of terms which are integral and rational in the variables. The *degree of the polynomial* in any variable, or in any set of the variables, is defined as the corresponding degree of that term which has the highest degree of the specified type.

ILLUSTRATION 2. If $f(x, y) = 3x^2y^3 + xy^2 + 7xy$, then $f(x, y)$ is of degree 2 in x, degree 3 in y, and degree 5 in x and y.

ILLUSTRATION 3. Any polynomial of the nth degree in x is of the form

$$P(x) = a_0x^n + a_1x^{n-1} + a_2x^{n-2} + \cdots + a_{n-1}x + a_n, \tag{1}$$

where a_0, a_1, a_2, $\cdots$ are constants and $a_0 \neq 0$.

A function $R(x)$ is said to be a **rational function** of x if and only if there exist polynomials $P(x)$ and $Q(x)$ such that $R(x) = P(x)/Q(x)$. In such a form, we shall assume that $P(x)$ and $Q(x)$ have no common polynomial factor except for constants, so that there is no value $x = c$ where $Q(c) = 0$ and $P(c) = 0$. Then, $R(x)$ is defined at all values of x where $Q(x) \neq 0$, and $R(x)$ is not defined where $Q(x) = 0$.

ILLUSTRATION 4. $(3x^2 + 5)/(x - 2)$ is not defined when $x = 2$.

THEOREM VII. *If k is a constant, and m is a nonnegative integer, then the integral rational term kx^m is a continuous function of x.*

Proof. Let $f(x) = kx^m$. At any point $x = c$, from (1) on page 19,

$$\lim_{x \to c} f(x) = kc^m = f(c).$$

Hence, $f(x)$ is continuous at $x = c$.

THEOREM VIII. *A polynomial $P(x)$ is continuous at all values of x.*

Proof. By Theorem VII, each term of $P(x)$ in (1) is continuous. Thus, $P(x)$ is a sum of continuous functions, and hence is continuous.

THEOREM IX. *A rational function $P(x)/Q(x)$, where $P(x)$ and $Q(x)$ are polynomials, is continuous at all values of x where $Q(x) \neq 0$.*

Proof. By Theorem VIII, $P(x)$ and $Q(x)$ are continuous functions. Hence, by Theorem VI of page 22, $P(x)/Q(x)$ is continuous where $Q(x) \neq 0$.

Note 1. If $P(x, y)$ and $Q(x, y)$ are polynomials in x and y, then the function $P(x, y)/Q(x, y)$ is called a **rational function** of x and y. Rational functions of any number of variables are defined similarly.

18. Evaluation of limits by continuity

If a function $f(x)$ is continuous at $x = c$, then $f(x) \to f(c)$ as $x \to c$. This permits the following method for evaluating certain limits.

SUMMARY. *If $f(x)$ is continuous at $x = c$, we may compute $\lim_{x \to c} f(x)$ by substituting $x = c$ in $f(x)$, to find $f(c)$.*

ILLUSTRATION 1. The following fraction is continuous at $x = 3$, where the denominator is not zero. Hence, substitute $x = 3$ to evaluate the limit:

$$\lim_{x \to 3} \frac{2x^2 - 5x}{x^3 - 2} = \frac{2(3^2) - 5(3)}{3^3 - 2} = \frac{3}{25}.$$

Whenever common knowledge of the graph of a function $y = f(x)$ shows that $f(x)$ is continuous at a value $x = c$, we shall permit use of the preceding summary without demanding analytic proof of the continuity of $f(x)$.

EXERCISE 6

Evaluate the limit, by use of continuity in the final stage.

1. $\lim\limits_{x \to 3} \dfrac{x^2 + 5}{3x + x^3}$.

2. $\lim\limits_{x \to \frac{1}{2}\pi} \dfrac{\cos x + \sin x}{3 + \csc^2 x}$.

3. $\lim\limits_{x \to \frac{3}{4}\pi} \dfrac{\tan^2 x - \sin x}{\cos x}$.

4. $\lim\limits_{x \to 2} \dfrac{3x + 5}{2x + 7}$.

5. $\lim\limits_{x \to -4} \dfrac{x^2 + 2x - 8}{2x + 8}$.

6. $\lim\limits_{h \to 0} \dfrac{\sqrt{3 + h} - \sqrt{3}}{h}$.

7. In Problem 5, let $f(x)$ represent the fraction. Observe that $f(x)$ is not defined if $x = -4$, and $f(x) = \frac{1}{2}(x - 2)$ when $x \neq -4$. Graph the function $f(x)$, showing a hole. Where is $f(x)$ discontinuous?

8. Graph the function $f(x)$ if

$$f(x) = 3 \text{ when } x \leqq 2 \quad and \quad f(x) = x + 2 \text{ when } x > 2.$$

Where is $f(x)$ discontinuous? What can be said about

$$\lim_{x \to 2+} f(x); \quad \lim_{x \to 2-} f(x); \quad \lim_{x \to 2} f(x)?$$

9. Let $f(x)$ be defined as the greatest integer less than or equal to x. Graph $y = f(x)$. Investigate the limits of $f(x)$ as $x \to 2-$, $x \to 2+$, and $x \to 2$. Where is $f(x)$ discontinuous? Why?

10. Let $f(x) = x/|x|$, and graph $f(x)$. Investigate the limits of $f(x)$ as $x \to 0-$, $x \to 0+$, and $x \to 0$. Where is $f(x)$ discontinuous? Why?

★11. Prove those parts of Theorem VI on page 22 referring to a sum, a difference, and a product.

3

THE DERIVATIVE

19. Definition of a derivative

On page 12, we defined the average rate of change of a function $y = f(x)$, over an interval from $x = x_0$ to $x = x_0 + \Delta x$, as the change in the value of the function divided by the change in x. That is, this average rate is equal to the *difference quotient*

$$\frac{f(x_0 + \Delta x) - f(x_0)}{(x_0 + \Delta x) - x_0}, \quad or \quad \frac{\Delta y}{\Delta x}. \tag{1}$$

The related instantaneous rate of change now will be called a *derivative*. In its definition, which follows, we assume that $\Delta x \neq 0$.

DEFINITION I. *At a given point $x = x_0$, if the ratio of the increment of the function $f(x)$ to the corresponding increment Δx approaches a limit as $\Delta x \to 0$, this limit is called the derivative of $f(x)$ with respect to x at $x = x_0$. Or,*

$$\left\{ \begin{array}{l} \textit{the } \textbf{derivative } \textit{of } f(x) \textit{ at } x = x_0 \textit{ is the instantaneous} \\ \textit{rate of change of } f(x) \textit{ with respect * to } x \textit{ at } x = x_0. \end{array} \right\} \tag{2}$$

If $f(x)$ has a derivative at $x = x_0$, then $f(x)$ is said *to be differentiable* at $x = x_0$. To state merely that a function $f(x)$ is *differentiable* will mean that the derivative exists at all values of x where $f(x)$ is defined.

ILLUSTRATION 1. Let $f(x) = x^2 - 4x + 7$. In Example 1 on page 12, the work shows that the derivative of $f(x)$ is 2 at $x = 3$.

By Definition I, at each point $x = x_0$ where the stipulated limit exists, there is specified a corresponding value called the *derivative* at $x = x_0$. This correspondence between values of x and values of the derivative defines a *function* which is called the *derivative function* of the function $f(x)$, and is denoted frequently by $f'(x)$, read "*f prime at x*." From (1) and Definition I, at any point $x = x_0$ where $f'(x)$ exists,

* We omit the phrase "*with respect to x*" when no ambiguity results.

$$f'(x_0) = \lim_{\Delta x \to 0} \frac{f(x_0 + \Delta x) - f(x_0)}{\Delta x}. \tag{3}$$

Hereafter, when we refer to the *derivative* of a function $f(x)$, we shall mean the *derivative function* $f'(x)$, or an expression for its value at an arbitrary value of x, except where our remarks are limited to particular values of x. The process of finding $f'(x)$ is spoken of as *differentiating* $f(x)$. If $y = f(x)$, the derivative $f'(x)$ is represented also by $D_x y$, or by y', either of which may be read "*the derivative of y with respect to x*." Or, we read "y'" simply as "y *prime*." The derivative at any point $x = x_0$ is denoted by $f'(x_0)$, or by $D_x y \mid_{x=x_0}$ which is read "*the derivative of y with respect to x at $x = x_0$.*"

Suppose that $y = f(x)$, with $y + \Delta y = f(x + \Delta x)$. Then, from (3), at any point x where $f(x)$ has a derivative, its definition is summarized as follows:

$$f'(x) = \lim_{\Delta x \to 0} \frac{f(x + \Delta x) - f(x)}{\Delta x}, \quad or \quad D_x y = \lim_{\Delta x \to 0} \frac{\Delta y}{\Delta x}. \tag{4}$$

EXAMPLE 1. If $f(x) = x^2 - 4x + 7$, find $f'(x)$.

SOLUTION. 1. Let $y = x^2 - 4x + 7$, and let $x = x_0$ be any fixed value. Then, with $(x = x_0, y = y_0)$ and $(x = x_0 + \Delta x, y = y_0 + \Delta y)$, in turn,

$$y_0 = x_0^2 - 4x_0 + 7; \tag{5}$$

$$y_0 + \Delta y = (x_0 + \Delta x)^2 - 4(x_0 + \Delta x) + 7. \tag{6}$$

Subtract, in the order (5) from (6):

$$\Delta y = 2x_0 \Delta x + (\Delta x)^2 - 4\Delta x. \tag{7}$$

Divide by Δx:
$$\frac{\Delta y}{\Delta x} = 2x_0 + \Delta x - 4. \tag{8}$$

Hence,
$$D_x y \mid_{x=x_0} = \lim_{\Delta x \to 0} (2x_0 + \Delta x - 4) = 2x_0 - 4. \tag{9}$$

2. From (9) with $x_0 = 3$, we obtain $f'(3) = 6 - 4 = 2$, which checks the result in Example 1 on page 12. Finally, consider x_0 as arbitrary, and replace x_0 by x, to obtain an expression for the derivative at any value x. Thus, $f'(x) = 2x - 4$, or $D_x y = 2x - 4$.

EXAMPLE 2. Differentiate
$$f(x) = \frac{3x}{2x + 5}. \tag{10}$$

SOLUTION. Let x temporarily denote a fixed value, where $x \neq -\frac{5}{2}$. Then, with x replaced by $(x + \Delta x)$ in (10),

$$f(x + \Delta x) = \frac{3(x + \Delta x)}{2(x + \Delta x) + 5}.$$

$$\Delta f(x) = f(x + \Delta x) - f(x) = \frac{3x + 3\Delta x}{2x + 2\Delta x + 5} - \frac{3x}{2x + 5},$$

$$= \frac{(3x + 3\Delta x)(2x + 5) - 3x(2x + 2\Delta x + 5)}{(2x + 5)(2x + 2\Delta x + 5)}; \tag{11}$$

$$\frac{f(x + \Delta x) - f(x)}{\Delta x} = \frac{3(\Delta x)(2x + 5) - 6x\Delta x}{\Delta x(2x + 5)(2x + 2\Delta x + 5)}. \tag{12}$$

From (4), $\qquad f'(x) = \lim_{\Delta x \to 0} \frac{3(2x + 5) - 6x}{(2x + 5)(2x + 2\Delta x + 5)}$, or $\qquad$ (13)

$$f'(x) = \frac{15}{(2x + 5)(2x + 0 + 5)} = \frac{15}{(2x + 5)^2}, \tag{14}$$

where, finally, x may have any value $x \neq -\frac{5}{2}$.

Derivatives can be obtained in simple cases by direct use of Definition I, as expressed in (3) and (4). This method will be called the Δ-*process*, read "*delta-process*," and it was used in Examples 1 and 2. The process is equivalent to the method on page 14 for finding an instantaneous rate of change. Later, with emphasis on the Δ-process, we shall derive formulas which will eliminate the necessity of using the Δ-process itself in obtaining derivatives of particular functions.

SUMMARY. *The Δ-process for differentiating a function $f(x)$.*

1. *Let* $\qquad\qquad\qquad\qquad y = f(x)$, $\qquad\qquad\qquad\qquad$ (15)

and temporarily consider x as a particular fixed value.

2. *Replace x by $(x + \Delta x)$ and y by $(y + \Delta y)$ in* (15):

$$y + \Delta y = f(x + \Delta x). \tag{16}$$

3. *Subtract corresponding sides, in the order* (15) *from* (16):

$$\Delta y = f(x + \Delta x) - f(x). \tag{17}$$

4. *Divide by Δx in* (17) *and simplify on the right:*

$$\frac{\Delta y}{\Delta x} = \frac{f(x + \Delta x) - f(x)}{\Delta x}. \tag{18}$$

5. *Obtain $f'(x)$ by evaluating the limit of $\Delta y / \Delta x$ as $\Delta x \to 0$.*

EXERCISE 7

Solve each problem by the Δ-process.

1. If $y = 3x^2 + 4x - 5$, find the derivative of y with respect to x. Then, obtain $D_x y \big|_{x=3}$ and $D_x y \big|_{x=-2}$.
2. Find y' if $y = 3x - x^2$. Then, obtain the instantaneous * rate of change of y with respect to x at $x = -4$. At what value of x is $y' = 0$?
3. If $f(x) = x^2 - x + 2$, obtain $f'(x)$, and then compute $f'(3)$. At what value of x is $f'(x) = 2$?
4. If $y = 5z^2$, obtain $D_z y$. Also, compute $D_z y \big|_{z=-1}$.
5. If $z = w^3$, obtain the instantaneous rate of change of z with respect to w at $w = 2$.

---

* Frequently hereafter, the word *instantaneous* will be omitted, and "*rate of change*" will mean "*instantaneous rate of change*."

Differentiate the function of x, y, or z.

6. $f(x) = x - 4x^2 - 5.$ **7.** $f(x) = 7 - 2x + 3x^2.$

8. $f(x) = x^3.$ **9.** $g(z) = z^4.$ **10.** $f(x) = x^3 - 2x.$

11. $f(z) = 3z^3 - 3z + 4.$ **12.** $g(y) = y - y^2 + 2y^3.$

13. $g(z) = \dfrac{3}{z}.$ **14.** $f(x) = \dfrac{2}{x^2}.$ **15.** $f(y) = \dfrac{2}{2y+3}.$

Find $D_x y$.

16. $y = \dfrac{2x-1}{3x+1}.$ **17.** $y = \dfrac{x^2}{2x+1}.$ **18.** $y = \dfrac{x^2-1}{2x+1}.$

19. $y = \sqrt{2x}.$ **20.** $y = \sqrt{3x-1}.$ **21.** $y = 1/\sqrt{3x}.$

HINT for Problem 19. $\Delta y = \sqrt{2x + 2\Delta x} - \sqrt{2x}.$ In $\Delta y / \Delta x$, rationalize the *numerator* by using $(\sqrt{2x + 2\Delta x} + \sqrt{2x})$ as a factor in both numerator and denominator, before evaluating the limit as $\Delta x \to 0$.

22. Show that the rate of change of the area of a square with respect to the length of a side is equal to one-half of the perimeter of the square.

HINT. Let x be the length of a side. A derivative is involved.

23. Show that the rate of change of the volume of a cube with respect to the length of an edge is equal to one-half of the surface area.

24. Show that the rate of change of the volume of a sphere with respect to its radius is equal to the surface area.

20. Relationship between continuity and differentiability

The following theorem shows that continuity is a *necessary* condition for differentiability.

THEOREM I. *If a function $f(x)$ has a derivative at $x = x_0$, then $f(x)$ is continuous at $x = x_0$.*

Proof. Let $y = f(x)$. Then, if $y_0 = f(x_0)$ and $y_0 + \Delta y = f(x_0 + \Delta x)$,

$$\lim_{\Delta x \to 0} \frac{\Delta y}{\Delta x} = f'(x_0). \tag{1}$$

We may write
$$\Delta y = \frac{\Delta y}{\Delta x} \cdot \Delta x. \tag{2}$$

Hence, $$\lim_{\Delta x \to 0} \Delta y = \left(\lim_{\Delta x \to 0} \frac{\Delta y}{\Delta x} \right) \left(\lim_{\Delta x \to 0} \Delta x \right) = f'(x_0) \cdot 0 = 0.$$

Therefore, by (3) on page 21, $f(x)$ is continuous at $x = x_0$.

An example on page 31 will show that *a function may be continuous at $x = x_0$ and yet have no derivative at $x = x_0$.*

Note 1. On account of Theorem I, $\Delta y / \Delta x$ tends to the form $0/0$ as $\Delta x \to 0$, wherever the function $y = f(x)$ has a derivative, unless the form of $\Delta y / \Delta x$ is altered before the limit is taken.

21. Tangent line to a curve

Let P be a fixed point and let Q be a second point on a continuous * curve C in an xy-plane. If Q moves on C, secant PQ revolves about P, as indicated by sample positions for PQ in Figure 15. Then, a line PT through P is defined as the **limiting position** of PQ as † $Q \rightarrow P$ if and only if *the smallest nonnegative angle θ formed by PQ and PT approaches zero as $Q \rightarrow P$.* The preceding remarks lead to the following terminology.

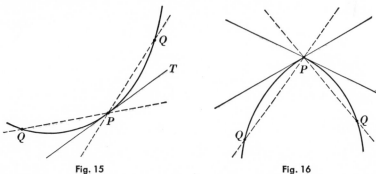

Fig. 15   Fig. 16

DEFINITION II. *The tangent PT to a curve C at P is the limiting position, if it exists, of secant PQ as $Q \rightarrow P$ along C.*

ILLUSTRATION 1. If C is the curve QPQ in Figure 16, no limiting position exists for secant PQ as $Q \rightarrow P$ without restriction, and thus there is no tangent at P. However, at P, so-called *right-hand* and *left-hand* tangents exist, which are obtained as the limiting positions of PQ as $Q \rightarrow P$ from the right and from the left, respectively. In Figure 16, we call P a *corner point* of the curve.

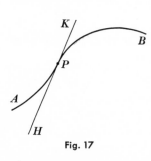

Fig. 17

ILLUSTRATION 2. In Figure 17, the line PK satisfies Definition II as the tangent to curve APB at P. The curve crosses its tangent at P. We call P an **inflection point** of curve APB. Inflection points will be discussed in Chapter 6.

22. The derivative as the slope of a tangent

If $P:(x_0, y_0)$ and $Q:(x_0 + \Delta x, y_0 + \Delta y)$ are distinct points on the graph of a function $y = f(x)$, as in Figure 18 on page 30, we have

$$(slope\ of\ PQ) = \frac{\Delta y}{\Delta x}. \tag{1}$$

---

* At present, this will mean that C is the graph of a continuous function $y = f(x)$, for values of x on some interval.
† To say that $Q \rightarrow P$ means that the distance $PQ \rightarrow 0$.

THEOREM II. *If the function $f(x)$ has a derivative at $x = x_0$, then the graph of $y = f(x)$ has a nonvertical tangent at $P:(x_0, y_0)$, where*

$$f'(x_0) = D_x y\,|_{x=x_0} = [\textbf{slope of tangent at } P\!:\!(x_0, y_0)].\qquad(2)$$

Proof. Assume that $f'(x_0)$ exists. Then, y is a continuous function at $x = x_0$, so that $\Delta y \to 0$ as $\Delta x \to 0$. Thus, if $\Delta x \to 0$ then $Q \to P$ in Figure 18. Therefore, from (1) and the definition of a derivative,

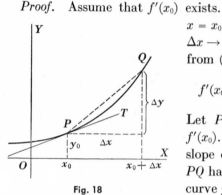

Fig. 18

$$f'(x_0) = \lim_{\Delta x \to 0} \frac{\Delta y}{\Delta x} = \lim_{\Delta x \to 0} (slope\ of\ PQ).\quad(3)$$

Let PT be the line through P with slope $f'(x_0)$. Then, as $Q \to P$, (3) shows that the slope of PQ approaches the slope of PT, or PQ has PT as a *limiting position.* Hence, the curve $y = f(x)$ has PT as the tangent at P.

THEOREM III. *If the function $y = f(x)$ is continuous at $x = x_0$, and if the graph of $y = f(x)$ has a nonvertical tangent PT at $P:(x_0, y_0)$ with slope m, then $f(x)$ has a derivative at $x = x_0$, with $f'(x_0) = m$.*

Proof. By hypothesis, the limit on the right in (3) exists and is equal to m. Hence, $m = \lim_{\Delta x \to 0} (\Delta y / \Delta x)$, which proves the theorem.

We use (2) to obtain the equation of the tangent. In particular, the slope of the graph is *zero,* or *the tangent to the graph is horizontal,* if and only if x satisfies $f'(x) = 0$.

EXAMPLE 1. Differentiate with respect to x, and graph the following equation. Also, find the tangent to the graph where $x = 1$.

$$y = 2x^3 - 3x^2 - 12x + 6.\qquad(4)$$

SOLUTION. 1. By use of the Δ-process, we find

$$\frac{\Delta y}{\Delta x} = 6x^2 - 6x - 12 + 6x(\Delta x) - 3\Delta x + 2(\Delta x)^2;$$

$$D_x y = \lim_{\Delta x \to 0} \frac{\Delta y}{\Delta x} = 6x^2 - 6x - 12 = 6(x - 2)(x + 1).\qquad(5)$$

2. $D_x y = 0$ when $(x - 2)(x + 1) = 0$. Hence, the tangent to the graph of (4) is horizontal if and only if $x = 2$ or $x = -1$.

3. The slope, m, of the tangent to the graph of (4) at $x = 1$ is

$$D_x y\,|_{x=1} = 6(-1)(2) = -12, \quad and \quad y = -7 \quad at \quad x = 1.$$

The tangent at $(1, -7)$ is

$$y + 7 = -12(x - 1), \quad or \quad y + 12x = 5.$$

4. The graph of (4) in Figure 19 was obtained by use of the following table of values, where we particularly use $x = 2$ and $x = -1$.

x	-2	-1	0	1	2	3
y	2	13	6	-7	-14	-3

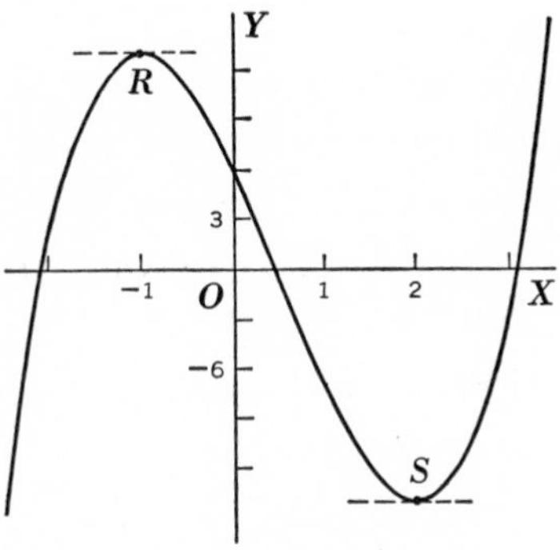

If a curve has a tangent at a point P, the *slope of the tangent* is called the *slope of the curve at P.* If the tangent is *vertical,* and hence has no slope, we say that the slope of the curve is *infinite* at P. We shall consider cases of this nature later.

In the following illustration, a function $f(x)$ is exhibited which is continuous at a certain point but does not possess a derivative there. Thus, this example proves that *continuity* at a point $x = x_0$ is *not a sufficient condition* to imply differentiability at $x = x_0$.

Fig. 19

ILLUSTRATION 1. Let $f(x)$ be defined as follows:

$$f(x) = x \text{ if } x \leqq 2 \quad and \quad f(x) = 4 - x \text{ if } x > 2. \tag{6}$$

The graph of $y = f(x)$ is the ridge OPB in Figure 20, where OP has the equation $y = x$ and PB the equation $y = 4 - x$. If $x = 2$ then $y = 2$, which gives $P:(2, 2)$ in Figure 20. We see that $f(x)$ is continuous at all values of x. Let the point $Q:(2 + \Delta x, 2 + \Delta y)$ be on the graph. If $\Delta x > 0$, then Q is on PB and $\Delta y/\Delta x$ is equal to -1, the slope of PB. If $\Delta x < 0$, then Q is on OP and $\Delta y/\Delta x$ is equal to $+1$. Hence,

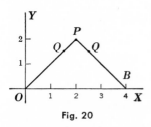

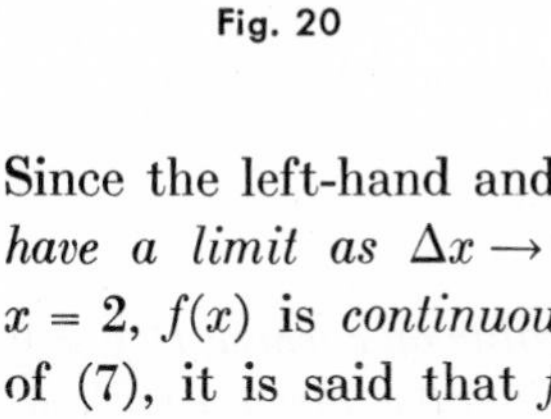

Fig. 20

$$\lim_{\Delta x \to 0-} \frac{\Delta y}{\Delta x} = 1; \quad \lim_{\Delta x \to 0+} \frac{\Delta y}{\Delta x} = -1. \tag{7}$$

Since the left-hand and right-hand limits in (7) are *unequal,* $\Delta y/\Delta x$ *fails to have a limit as $\Delta x \to 0$* without restriction, from either side. Thus, at $x = 2$, $f(x)$ is *continuous* but *does not have a derivative.* However, because of (7), it is said that $f(x)$ has a *left-hand derivative,* $+1$, and a *right-hand derivative,* -1, at $x = 2$. Also, at P, *the graph of $y = f(x)$ is said to have a left-hand tangent, OP, and a right-hand tangent, PB,* but the curve OPB has *no tangent* at the **corner point** P.

23. Interpretation of the sign of the derivative

Consider a function $y = f(x)$, and let its graph be the curve in Figure 21. To say that $f(x)$ is **increasing** at $x = x_0$ will mean that, if Δx is sufficiently near zero, then Δx and Δy *have the* **same sign;** or, a small increase in x

causes an increase in y, and a small decrease in x causes a decrease in y, as at P in Figure 21. Similarly, to say that $f(x)$ is **decreasing** at $x = x_0$ will mean that, if Δx is sufficiently near zero, then Δx and Δy are of **opposite signs,** as at Q in Figure 21. To say that $f(x)$ is increasing, or decreasing, on an interval of values of x, means that the specified property holds at each point on the interval.

THEOREM IV. *Suppose that $f(x)$ has a derivative $f'(x_0) \neq 0$ at $x = x_0$. Then, at $x = x_0$, $f(x)$ is an increasing function if $f'(x_0) > 0$, and is a decreasing function if $f'(x_0) < 0$.*

Proof. 1. Let $y = f(x)$. Then, we have

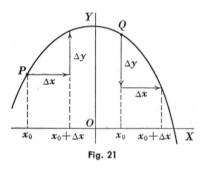

Fig. 21

$$f'(x_0) = \lim_{\Delta x \to 0} \frac{\Delta y}{\Delta x}. \qquad (1)$$

2. Assume that $f'(x_0) > 0$. Then, by (1), if Δx is sufficiently near zero, $\Delta y/\Delta x$ will be so near $f'(x_0)$ that $\Delta y/\Delta x$ as well as $f'(x_0)$ will be *positive*, and hence Δy and Δx will have the *same sign*. Thus, $f(x)$ is increasing at $x = x_0$.

3. Similarly, if $f'(x_0) < 0$, then Δy and Δx are of *opposite signs* if Δx is sufficiently near zero, and hence $f(x)$ is a decreasing function at $x = x_0$.

Note 1. We observe that, on an interval of values of x where $f'(x) > 0$, $f(x)$ increases as x increases, that is, if $x_1 < x_2$, then $f(x_1) < f(x_2)$; the graph of $y = f(x)$ rises as x increases; the slope of the graph is positive. The student should state corresponding facts with $f'(x) < 0$.

A function $y = f(x)$ is said to be **stationary** at $x = x_0$ if and only if $f'(x_0) = 0$. The corresponding point on the graph of $y = f(x)$ is called a *stationary point* of the graph; at such a point, the slope is zero, or the tangent is horizontal, as at R and S in Figure 19 on page 31.

EXERCISE 8

(a) *Use the Δ-process to obtain $D_x y$.* (b) *Find each value of x where $D_x y = 0$ and use the corresponding stationary point in graphing the given equation.* (c) *Obtain the equations of the tangents to the graph where x has the indicated values, and graph these tangents.* (d) *By inspection of the graph, specify the values of x for which y is an increasing function, or a decreasing function.*

1. $y = x^2 - 6x + 3$; find the tangents where $x = 2$ and $x = 4$.

2. $y = -x^2 - 4x + 5$; find the tangents where $x = -3$ and $x = 0$. Also, find the value of x where the slope of the graph is equal to 2.

3. $y = -2x^2 + 4x - 3$; find the tangents where $x = 1$ and $x = 4$. At what value of x is the slope of the graph equal to 5?

4. $y = 2x^2 - 8x + 3$; find the tangents where $x = 2$ and $x = 5$.

5. $y = x^3 - 3x + 2$; find the tangents where $x = 2$ and $x = 0$.

6. $y = -x^3 - 3x^2 + 5$; find the tangents where $x = 2$ and $x = -1$.

★**7.** Give formulas defining a function $f(x)$ on some interval where $f(x)$ is continuous but where there is at least one point where $f(x)$ does not possess a derivative.

24. Velocity as a derivative

Consider the motion of an object in a straight line, labeled as an s-axis in Figure 22, where the object is idealized as a *particle* located at point P. Let the coordinate s of the particle at any time t be specified as a function of t, for instance, $s = f(t)$. From page 15, we recall that the velocity of the particle at any instant $t = t_0$ is defined as *the instantaneous rate of change of the distance s with respect to the time t.* Let v be the velocity at any instant t. Then, v is a function of t and, by the definition of a derivative as an instantaneous rate of change,

$$v = D_t s, \quad or \quad v = f'(t). \tag{1}$$

Thus, in rectilinear motion, *the velocity is the derivative of the distance with respect to the time.* Over any time interval where v, or $D_t s$, is positive, the distance s is an increasing function of t, and the object moves in the positive direction on the s-axis. If $v < 0$, the object is moving in the negative direction. Thus, the sign of v shows the direction of the motion. At any instant when $v = 0$, we say that the object is *instantaneously at rest.* *The absolute value of the velocity is called the* **speed.**

Fig. 22

EXAMPLE 1. For the projectile involved in (4) on page 15, suppose that $v_0 = 96$. (a) Find the average velocity from $t = 2$ to $t = 2.5$. (b) Find the velocity at any instant t. (c) Compute the velocities at $t = 2$ and $t = 2.5$. (d) Investigate the motion of the projectile. (e) Find the speed at $t = 5$.

SOLUTION. 1. From (4) on page 15, $\qquad s = -16t^2 + 96t.$ (2)

2. By use of (2), $s = 128$ if $t = 2$; $s = 140$ if $t = 2.5$. Hence, by use of (3), on page 15, over the interval from $t = 2$ to $t = 2.5$.

$$(the\ average\ velocity) = \frac{140 - 128}{2.5 - 2} = 24' \ per\ sec. \tag{3}$$

3. To obtain v at any instant t, we find $D_t s$ by the Δ-process:

$$D_t s = \lim_{\Delta t \to 0} \frac{\Delta s}{\Delta t} = \lim_{\Delta t \to 0} (-32t + 96 - 16\Delta t) = -32t + 96; \ or$$

$$v = -32t + 96. \tag{4}$$

If $t = 2$, then $v = 32'$ per sec. If $t = 2.5$, then $v = 16'$ per sec.

4. Consider the graph of (2) in Figure 23. For any value of t, at the corresponding point of the graph, the slope is $D_t s$, or v. At the stationary point of the graph, where s will have its maximum value, the slope is zero or

$$v = 0, \quad or \quad -32t + 96 = 0, \quad or \quad t = 3. \tag{5}$$

If $t = 3$ in (2), then $s = 144$. The graph was drawn by use of the stationary point R:(3, 144), and other points. From the graph, we see that s is an *increasing* function, and the projectile *rises*, from $t = 0$ to $t = 3$, when the projectile comes to rest with $v = 0$ at the highest point in the motion. The projectile is at ground level when $s = 0$, or

$$-16t^2 + 96t = 0, \quad or \quad t = 0 \quad and \quad t = 6.$$

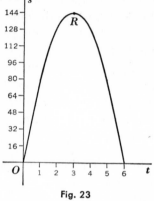

Hence, if $t > 3$, the projectile is falling, and hits the ground at $t = 6$.

5. At $t = 5$, from (4) we have $v = -64'$ per second. Hence, the speed is 64' per second.

Comment. From (4), $v = 32(3 - t)$. Then, $v = 0$ at $t = 3$; $v < 0$ when $3 - t < 0$ or $t > 3$; $v > 0$ when $3 - t > 0$ or $t < 3$. Thus, without Figure 23, we conclude that s is increasing for $t < 3$, stationary at $t = 3$, etc.

Fig. 23

EXERCISE 9

Any desired derivative should be computed by the Δ-process.

1. For the projectile in (4) on page 15, let $v_0 = 64$. (a) Find the velocity at any time t. (b) Compute v when $t = 1$ and $t = 3$. (c) Find the speed when $t = 3$. (d) Graph s as a function of t. (e) For what values of t is $v > 0$; $v = 0$; $v < 0$? (f) When is the speed 32' per second? (g) Describe the motion of the projectile.

2. Repeat Problem 1 if $v_0 = 80$.

3. For a certain object moving in a vertical line, the height s above the earth at time t is given by $s = -16t^2 + 32t + 48$. (a) Find the velocity v at any instant t, and at some point where the object is rising; is falling. (b) Graph s as a function of t and describe the motion.

4. Repeat Problem 3 with $s = -16t^2 + 64t - 80$.

5. An object is sliding down an inclined plane. The distance s of the object from the top t seconds after starting is given by the equation $s = 8t^2 + 4t$. (a) Find v at any instant t and also when $t = 3$. (b) Find the initial velocity, that is, the velocity at $t = 0$.

6. Repeat Problem 5 with $s = 4t^2 + 10t$.

7. In the motion of a particle on an s-axis, the distance s is given by $s = t^3 + t$. (a) Find the velocity at any time t, and then at $t = 3$. (b) Find the average velocity from $t = 2$ to $t = 4$. (c) Find the velocity at $t = 2$ and at $t = 4$. (d) Compare (b) with (a), and with the average of the velocities in (c).

25. A quotient form for the derivative

Consider a differentiable function $y = f(x)$. Then, at any point $P:(x, y)$ on the graph of $y = f(x)$, there is a tangent PT with

$$(slope\ of\ PT) = f'(x). \tag{1}$$

For present purposes, we choose to use "dx" instead of "Δx" to represent an *increment in the value of* x. Then, if an arbitrary increment $dx \neq 0$ is given to the value of x, let dy, or $df(x)$, represent the corresponding *increment of the ordinate of the tangent* PT, and let Δy be the increment of the function $y = f(x)$, as in Figure 24. We have $Q:(x + dx, y + \Delta y)$ on the graph of $y = f(x)$ and $R:(x + dx, y + dy)$ on PT. From (1) on page 9, the slope of PR, or PT, is dy/dx. Hence, from (1),

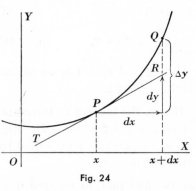

Fig. 24

$$\frac{dy}{dx} = f'(x) \quad or \quad \frac{df(x)}{dx} = f'(x). \tag{2}$$

From Figure 24, we notice that, in general, $\Delta y \neq dy$. We refer to dx, dy, and $df(x)$ as **differentials**. We may read dx as "*differential x*," or simply "*d, x*," and read dy and $df(x)$ similarly. On multiplying both sides of either equation in (2) by dx, we observe that, without reference to Figure 24, we may introduce dy, or $df(x)$, as follows.

DEFINITION III. *Suppose that the function* $y = f(x)$ *is differentiable. Then, at any value of* x, *and at any value of the variable* $dx \neq 0$, *the* **differential** dy, *or* $df(x)$, *of the function is defined by the equation*

$$dy = f'(x)dx, \quad or \quad df(x) = f'(x)dx. \tag{3}$$

ILLUSTRATION 1. At P in Figure 24, suppose that $f'(x) = \frac{1}{2}$. Then, at any value of dx, from (3) we obtain $dy = \frac{1}{2}dx$. Thus, if $dx = .6$ then $dy = .3$.

In (3), dy is described as a function of *two variables x and dx*, where $dx \neq 0$. From (2) or (3), we are led to use the left-hand sides of the equations in (2) as new notations for the derivative of the function $y = f(x)$. Thus, $D_x y$ may be written as *a quotient of corresponding differentials, dy/dx*. We read "dy/dx" as "*the derivative of y with respect to x*," or simply "*dy over dx*." In place of dy/dx or $df(x)/dx$, we sometimes write

$$\frac{d}{dx}y \quad and \quad \frac{d}{dx}f(x),$$

where $\frac{d}{dx}$ abbreviates "*the derivative with respect to x of*," and may be thought of as replacing "D_x" in the symbol $D_x y$. In using dy/dx for a derivative, it is not necessary to think of any particular value of dx, because the ratio dy/dx does not depend on the value of dx. We may treat dy/dx as a *whole*, just as we have done with the symbol $D_x y$. Or, when desired, we may use dy/dx as a *fraction*, with $dx \neq 0$. From (4) on page 26,

$$\frac{dy}{dx} = \lim_{\Delta x \to 0} \frac{\Delta y}{\Delta x}. \tag{4}$$

We now have the following symbols for the derivative of a function $y = f(x)$:

$$y', \quad f'(x), \quad \frac{dy}{dx}, \quad \frac{df(x)}{dx}, \quad D_x y, \quad D_x f(x), \quad \frac{d}{dx} y, \quad \frac{d}{dx} f(x).$$

EXAMPLE 1. If $y = x^2 - 2x + 2$, obtain y'; also find dy at $x = 2$ if $dx = 1.5$.

SOLUTION. 1. From $y + \Delta y = (x + \Delta x)^2 - 2(x + \Delta x) + 2$,

$$\Delta y = \Delta x(2x - 2) + (\Delta x)^2; \tag{5}$$

$$\frac{\Delta y}{\Delta x} = 2x - 2 + \Delta x; \quad \frac{dy}{dx} = \lim_{\Delta x \to 0} \frac{\Delta y}{\Delta x} = 2x - 2. \tag{6}$$

Hence, from (3), $dy = (2x - 2)dx$. Then, if $x = 2$ and $dx = 1.5$, we obtain $dy = 3$. From (5) with $\Delta x = dx = 1.5$, we find $\Delta y = 5.25$.

2. If $x = 2$ then $y = 2$; from (6), $y' = 2$. Hence, the tangent to the graph of $y = x^2 - 2x + 2$ at $(x = 2, y = 2)$ has the equation $y - 2 = 2(x - 2)$. Figure 25 shows a graph of $y = x^2 - 2x + 2$, with dx, dy, and Δy represented by directed line segments, where $x = 2$, $\Delta y = MQ$, and $dx = 1.5$.

Note 1. In Chapter 7, we shall emphasize the fact that, as inferred from Figure 24, dy may be a useful approximation for Δy if dx is *small*. At present, our main interest in differentials is that they justify the quotient form dy/dx for a derivative. The notation dy/dx was introduced by LEIBNIZ.

If $f(x) = x$, then $f'(x) = 1$ and (3) gives

$$df(x) = 1 \cdot dx, \quad or \quad d(x) = dx.$$

That is, at any value of x, *the differential of the function "x" is the same as dx*. Thus, although $d(x)$ and dx are distinct conceptually, they have the same value for any values of x and dx.

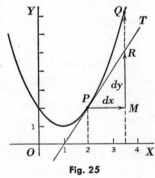

Fig. 25

EXERCISE 10

Compute the derivative of the function by the Δ-process, making use of the Leibniz notation in (4) on this page. Then, write the differential of the function for arbitrary values of x and dx. Also, compute dy when $x = -2$, if $dx = .3$ and also if $dx = 6$.

1. $y = 2x + 5$.   2. $y = 3x^2 - x$.   3. $y = x^3 - 2x$.   4. $y = 3 - x^{-2}$.

4

DIFFERENTIATION OF ALGEBRAIC FUNCTIONS

26. Algebraic functions

A *polynomial* in variables x and y, or an *integral rational function* of x and y, is a sum of terms of the type $Ax^h y^k$, where A is a constant and h and k are nonnegative integers. An *integral rational equation* in x and y is an equation of the form $f(x, y) = g(x, y)$, where f and g are polynomials. The degree of the equation in x, in y, or in x and y is the corresponding degree of the polynomial $[f(x, y) - g(x, y)]$.

ILLUSTRATION 1. The integral rational equation

$$xy^2 + y(x^4 - 3) - 5 = 0 \tag{1}$$

is of degree 2 in y, degree 4 in x, and degree 5 in x and y. Equation (1) defines either x or y as a function of the other variable. Thus, by use of the

quadratic formula, $$y = \frac{3 - x^4 \pm \sqrt{x^8 - 6x^4 + 20x + 9}}{2x}. \tag{2}$$

No convenient formula exists giving the solution of (1) for x in terms of y.

DEFINITION I. *To say that a variable y is an* **algebraic function** (*perhaps many-valued*) *of a variable x means that y can be defined as a function of x by an equation of the form $f(x, y) = 0$, where $f(x, y)$ is a polynomial in x and y.*

ILLUSTRATION 2. Equation (1) defines y as a double-valued algebraic function of x, as shown in (2).

ILLUSTRATION 3. Consider any rational function, $P(x)/Q(x)$, and let $y = P(x)/Q(x)$. Then, $yQ(x) - P(x) = 0$, which is an integral rational equation in x and y, defining y as the function $P(x)/Q(x)$. Hence, any rational function of x is an algebraic function of x.

ILLUSTRATION 4. Let $g(x)$ represent any formula involving only a finite number of the operations of algebra as applied to explicit numbers and the value which may be assigned to x. Then, if we let $y = g(x)$, it can be shown (by a discussion beyond the purposes of this text) that y can be defined as a function of x by a corresponding integral rational equation $f(x, y) = 0$. In particular, if we should start with (2), and rationalize, we would arrive at (1).

Suppose that y is an algebraic function of x defined by an equation $f(x, y) = 0$ of degree n in y. If $n = 1$ or $n = 2$, we can solve for y to obtain $y = g(x)$, where $g(x)$ is an explicit algebraic function, as in Illustration 1. If $n = 3$ or $n = 4$, formulas exist which, theoretically, would give an explicit result $y = g(x)$ for any particular equation $f(x, y) = 0$. However, these formulas are so complicated that, practically, the explicit solution would be useful only rarely. If $n > 5$, in general it is impossible to solve $f(x, y) = 0$ to obtain $y = g(x)$ where $g(x)$ is an explicit algebraic function.

DEFINITION II. *If y is an algebraic function of x, and y is not a rational function of x, then y is called an* **irrational function** *of x.*

By Definition II, all algebraic functions of x are divided into two classes, *rational functions* and *irrational functions* of x. In (2), y is an irrational function of x.

Note 1. The preceding terminology extends to functions of two or more variables. Thus, z is an algebraic function of x and y if and only if z can be defined in terms of x and y by an integral rational equation $f(x, y, z) = 0$.

27. Formulas for differentiation

Eventually, we shall establish results which will permit us to differentiate any elementary function of x without direct use of the definition of a derivative, as met in the Δ-process. The following formulas, which we shall prove in later sections, constitute the first stage in our program. By means of these results, we shall be able to differentiate any algebraic function of x. In the formulas, k is any constant and u, v, w, y represent functions of x possessing derivatives at all values of x which are involved.

$$\frac{d}{dx}(k) = 0. \tag{I}$$

$$\frac{d}{dx}(ku) = k\frac{du}{dx}. \tag{II}$$

The power formula. *If n is any rational number,*

$(u \neq 0 \text{ if } n \leq 1)$ $\qquad\qquad \dfrac{d}{dx}(u^n) = nu^{n-1}\dfrac{du}{dx};$ $\tag{III}$

$(x \neq 0 \text{ if } n \leq 1)$ $\qquad\qquad \dfrac{d}{dx}(x^n) = nx^{n-1}.$ $\tag{III}_a$

$$\frac{d}{dx}(u + v + w) = \frac{du}{dx} + \frac{dv}{dx} + \frac{dw}{dx}. \tag{IV}$$

$$\frac{d}{dx}(uv) = u\frac{dv}{dx} + v\frac{du}{dx}. \tag{V}$$

$$\frac{d}{dx}\left(\frac{u}{v}\right) = \frac{v\frac{du}{dx} - u\frac{dv}{dx}}{v^2}. \tag{VI}$$

$$\frac{d}{dx}\left(\frac{1}{v}\right) = -\frac{1}{v^2} \cdot \frac{dv}{dx}. \tag{VI$_a$}$$

If y is a function of u, where u is a function of x, then

$$\frac{dy}{dx} = \frac{dy}{du} \cdot \frac{du}{dx}. \tag{VII}$$

$$\frac{dy}{dx} = \frac{1}{\dfrac{dx}{dy}}. \tag{VIII}$$

28. Differentiation of polynomials

In the following discussion, u, v, w, y are functions of x. At any value of x, the corresponding values of the functions are u, v, w, y. If an increment Δx is given to x, to yield $(x + \Delta x)$, then corresponding increments Δu, Δv, Δw, Δy are given to the functions, to yield

$$(u + \Delta u), \quad (v + \Delta v), \quad (w + \Delta w), \quad (y + \Delta y). \tag{1}$$

We employ the Δ-process in the following proofs.

The derivative of a constant is zero: $\qquad \dfrac{d}{dx}(k) = 0. \tag{I}$

Proof. Let $y = k$. Then, corresponding to x and $x + \Delta x$, we obtain

$$y = k, \quad y + \Delta y = k, \quad \text{and hence} \quad \Delta y = 0.$$

Thus, for all values of $\Delta x \neq 0$, we have $\Delta y / \Delta x = 0$. Therefore,

$$\frac{dy}{dx} = \lim_{\Delta x \to 0} \frac{\Delta y}{\Delta x} = \lim_{\Delta x \to 0} (0) = 0.$$

We may interpret (I) geometrically: the graph of $y = k$ in an xy-plane is a line parallel to the horizontal axis, and hence has slope 0 everywhere.

The derivative of a constant times a function is equal to the constant times the derivative of the function:

$$\frac{d}{dx}(ku) = k\frac{du}{dx}. \tag{II}$$

Proof. Let $y = ku$. Then, corresponding to x and $x + \Delta x$,

$$y = ku \quad \text{and} \quad y + \Delta y = k(u + \Delta u). \tag{2}$$

Hence, $\qquad\qquad \Delta y = k\Delta u; \quad \dfrac{\Delta y}{\Delta x} = k\dfrac{\Delta u}{\Delta x}. \tag{3}$

From (3), $\qquad \dfrac{dy}{dx} = \lim_{\Delta x \to 0} \dfrac{\Delta y}{\Delta x} = k\left(\lim_{\Delta x \to 0} \dfrac{\Delta u}{\Delta x}\right) = k\dfrac{du}{dx}. \tag{4}$

ILLUSTRATION 1. $\dfrac{d}{dx}(6u) = 6\dfrac{du}{dx}.$

$$\frac{d}{dx}(-v) = \frac{d}{dx}[(-1)\cdot v] = -\frac{dv}{dx}. \tag{5}$$

*If n is a positive integer,** $\dfrac{d}{dx}(x^n) = nx^{n-1}.$ (III)$_a$

Proof. Let $y = x^n$. Then, $y + \Delta y = (x + \Delta x)^n$. Expand by use of the binomial theorem, (1) on page 561:

$$y + \Delta y = x^n + nx^{n-1}(\Delta x) + \frac{n(n-1)}{2}\,x^{n-2}(\Delta x)^2 + \cdots + (\Delta x)^n. \tag{6}$$

Subtract the sides of $y = x^n$ from the corresponding sides in (6):

$$\Delta y = nx^{n-1}(\Delta x) + \frac{n(n-1)}{2}\,x^{n-2}(\Delta x)^2 + \cdots + (\Delta x)^n; \tag{7}$$

$$\frac{\Delta y}{\Delta x} = nx^{n-1} + \frac{n(n-1)}{2}\,x^{n-2}(\Delta x) + \cdots + (\Delta x)^{n-1}. \tag{8}$$

In (8), hold x fixed and let $\Delta x \to 0$. Then, the first term on the right is a constant; each term after the first has Δx as a factor, and hence approaches zero as $\Delta x \to 0$. Thus, from (8), we obtain (III)$_a$:

$$\frac{dy}{dx} = \lim_{\Delta x \to 0} \frac{\Delta y}{\Delta x} = nx^{n-1} + 0 + 0 + \cdots + 0. \tag{9}$$

ILLUSTRATION 2. From (III)$_a$, if $f(x) = x^5$ then $f'(x) = 5x^4.$

From (II) and (III)$_a$, $\dfrac{d}{dx}(7x^4) = 7\dfrac{d}{dx}(x^4) = 7\cdot(4x^3) = 28x^3.$

The derivative of a sum of functions is the sum of their derivatives:

$$\frac{d}{dx}(u + v + w) = \frac{du}{dx} + \frac{dv}{dx} + \frac{dw}{dx}. \tag{IV}$$

Proof. Let $y = u + v + w$. Then, corresponding to x and $x + \Delta x$,

$$y = u + v + w \quad \text{and} \quad y + \Delta y = (u + \Delta u) + (v + \Delta v) + (w + \Delta w);$$

$$\Delta y = \Delta u + \Delta v + \Delta w; \quad \frac{\Delta y}{\Delta x} = \frac{\Delta u}{\Delta x} + \frac{\Delta v}{\Delta x} + \frac{\Delta w}{\Delta x}. \tag{10}$$

Hence, $\displaystyle\lim_{\Delta x \to 0} \frac{\Delta y}{\Delta x} = \lim_{\Delta x \to 0} \frac{\Delta u}{\Delta x} + \lim_{\Delta x \to 0} \frac{\Delta v}{\Delta x} + \lim_{\Delta x \to 0} \frac{\Delta w}{\Delta x},$ or

$$\frac{dy}{dx} = \frac{du}{dx} + \frac{dv}{dx} + \frac{dw}{dx}.$$

If any term on the left in (IV) is given a minus sign, this is duplicated on the right. Thus, by use of (5),

* With $x \neq 0$ if $n = 1$. This exception will be mentioned later.

$$\frac{d}{dx}(u-v) = \frac{d}{dx}[u + (-v)] = \frac{du}{dx} + \frac{d}{dx}(-v) = \frac{du}{dx} - \frac{dv}{dx}.$$

Any polynomial can be differentiated by use of (I)–(IV).

EXAMPLE 1. Find the stationary points of the function

$$y = 2x^3 - 3x^2 - 12x + 4, \tag{11}$$

and the equation of the tangent to its graph at $x = 3$.

SOLUTION. 1.

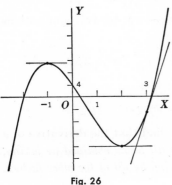

Fig. 26

$$\frac{dy}{dx} = \frac{d}{dx}(2x^3) - \frac{d}{dx}(3x^2) - \frac{d}{dx}(12x) + 0, \text{ or}$$

$$y' = 6x^2 - 6x - 12, \text{ or}$$

$$y' = 6(x-2)(x+1). \tag{12}$$

2. *The stationary points.* Solve $y' = 0$, or $6x^2 - 6x - 12 = 0$, which gives $x = 2$ and $x = -1$. From (11), if $x = 2$ then $y = -16$; if $x = -1$ then $y = 11$. Hence, the stationary points are $(2, -16)$ and $(-1, 11)$.

3. If $x = 3$ then $y = -5$ and $y' = 24$; the tangent at $(3, -5)$ on the graph of (11) in Figure 26 has the equation $y + 5 = 24(x-3)$.

29. Derivative of a product

The derivative of a product uv with respect to x is equal to u times the derivative of v plus v times the derivative of u:

$$\frac{d}{dx}(uv) = u\frac{dv}{dx} + v\frac{du}{dx}. \tag{V}$$

Proof. 1. Let $y = uv$. Then, corresponding to $x = x_0$, we have u_0, v_0, y_0 where $y_0 = u_0 v_0$; corresponding to $x = x_0 + \Delta x$ we obtain

$$y_0 + \Delta y = (u_0 + \Delta u)(v_0 + \Delta v), \text{ or} \tag{1}$$

$$y_0 + \Delta y = u_0 v_0 + u_0 \Delta v + v_0 \Delta u + \Delta u \Delta v. \tag{2}$$

Subtract the sides of $y_0 = u_0 v_0$ from the sides in (2); divide by Δx:

$$\frac{\Delta y}{\Delta x} = u_0 \frac{\Delta v}{\Delta x} + v_0 \frac{\Delta u}{\Delta x} + \frac{\Delta u}{\Delta x} \cdot \Delta v. \tag{3}$$

2. From Theorem I, page 28, since v has a derivative then v is continuous at $x = x_0$. Hence, by (3) on page 21, $\Delta v \to 0$ as $\Delta x \to 0$. Then,

$$\lim_{\Delta x \to 0} \frac{\Delta y}{\Delta x} = u_0 \left(\lim_{\Delta x \to 0} \frac{\Delta v}{\Delta x} \right) + v_0 \left(\lim_{\Delta x \to 0} \frac{\Delta u}{\Delta x} \right) + \left(\lim_{\Delta x \to 0} \frac{\Delta u}{\Delta x} \right) \left(\lim_{\Delta x \to 0} \Delta v \right).$$

The quotients $\Delta y/\Delta x$, $\Delta v/\Delta x$, etc. approach derivatives as limits when $\Delta x \to 0$. Hence, at any point $x = x_0$,

$$\frac{dy}{dx} = u_0 \frac{dv}{dx} + v_0 \frac{du}{dx} + \frac{du}{dx} \cdot 0 = u_0 \frac{dv}{dx} + v_0 \frac{du}{dx}, \tag{4}$$

where all derivatives are evaluated at $x = x_0$. On replacing y by uv in (4), and using simply x, u, v instead of x_0, u_0, v_0, we obtain (V).

ILLUSTRATION 1. From (V), $\quad \frac{d}{dx}[(3x^2 + 7)(2x^3 - 3x)] =$

$$(3x^2 + 7) \frac{d}{dx}(2x^3 - 3x) + (2x^3 - 3x) \frac{d}{dx}(3x^2 + 7) =$$

$$(3x^2 + 7)(6x^2 - 3) + (2x^3 - 3x)(6x) = 30x^4 + 15x^2 - 21.$$

ILLUSTRATION 2. If $f(x) = (x^2 - 3)(2x + x^3)(x + x^4)$, by two applications of (V) we obtain

$$f'(x) = [(x^2 - 3)(2x + x^3)] \cdot \frac{d}{dx}(x + x^4) + (x + x^4) \frac{d}{dx}[(x^2 - 3)(2x + x^3)]$$

$$= (x^2 - 3)(2x + x^3)(1 + 4x^3) +$$

$$(x + x^4)[(x^2 - 3)(2 + 3x^2) + (2x + x^3)(2x)] = etc.$$

Note 1. By use of (V) as in Illustration 2, we find that the derivative of a product of any number of factors is *the sum of all terms obtained by taking, in turn, the derivative of each factor and multiplying by all of the other factors.*

EXERCISE 11

Find dy/dx, or the derivative of the given function of x, t, or z. Early letters of the alphabet are constants. Do not use the Δ-process.

1. $3x^2 + 5x^3$.

2. $6t^3 - 4t^5$.

3. $3z + z^5 - z^8$.

4. $2 + 3x - 5x^2 - 11x^3$.

5. $6 - 3x - \frac{5}{2}x^2 + \frac{7}{6}x^3 - \frac{1}{8}x^4$.

6. $3x^4 - \frac{5}{6}x^3 - \frac{1}{4}x^2 + 17$.

7. $7z^4 - 3z^3 + \frac{1}{2}z^2 - 8$.

8. $3t^5 - 2t^2 - 5t + 16$.

9. $\frac{4}{3}t^3 - \frac{2}{3}t^2 + 6t - 3$.

10. $2z^6 - 3z^4 + \frac{5}{3}z^3 - \frac{9}{2}z^2$.

11. $21 - 5x - \frac{3}{8}x^2 + x^9$.

12. $y = (x + 2)(3x - 2)$.

13. $y = (x^2 + 3)(2x + 3)$.

14. $y = (x^2 + x)(x^4 - 3x^2)$.

15. $y = (x - 4x^2)(x^3 + 2x)$.

16. $f(x) = (3x + 1)(2x^2 + 7)$.

17. $f(z) = (z^3 - 3z)(1 - 4z)$.

18. $(x + 2)(x - 3)(x^2 + 5)$.

19. $(t^2 - 3t)(t - 1)(2t + 5)$.

20. $(ax + b)(cx + d)(gx + h)$.

21. $(3t - 1)(2t + 1)(t^2 - 6)$.

Find the equation of the tangent to the graph of the function at the given point.

22. $y = 3x^2 - 2x + 7$; at $x = 3$.

23. $y = -2x^2 + x - 5$; at $x = -2$.

24. $y = x^3 - 3x^2 + 5$; at $x = 2$.

25. $y = \frac{2}{3}x^3 - 3x + 6$; at $x = -1$.

Locate the stationary points of the function by use of its derivative; then, use this information in graphing the function.

26. $y = 3x^2 + 12x + 6$.

27. $y = 2x^2 + 4x - 5$.

28. $y = \frac{1}{3}x^3 - \frac{1}{2}x^2 - 2x + 7$.

29. $y = x^3 - 6x^2 + 12x - 3$.

30. The motion of a particle on an s-axis is specified by $s = 6 + 6t - t^2$, where t is the time. (a) Find the velocity at $t = 0$. (b) Find the speed at $t = 4$. (c) When is the velocity zero? (d) Graph s as a function of t and describe the motion for $t \geq 0$; that is, specify where the particle starts; how long it moves to the right or the left; where it stops instantaneously, and where it moves thereafter.

31. Repeat (d) of Problem 30 with $s = t^2 - 5t - 6$.

32. Repeat (d) of Problem 30 with $s = t^3 - 9t^2 + 24t - 15$.

33. A projectile is fired upward, and its distance s in feet above sea level t seconds later is given by $s = -16t^2 + 64t + 80$. Repeat (a)–(d) of Problem 30, with appropriate alterations for directions.

34. When an electric current flows through a resistance, the number of heat units developed is given by $h = .2389I^2Rt$, where h represents the number of gram-calories, I the current in amperes, R the resistance in ohms, and t the time in seconds for which the current flows. If $R = 500$ ohms, and $t = 10$ seconds, find the rate of change of the developed heat units with respect to change in the current, when $I = 30$ amperes.

*Note 1. Terminology from economics.** Let x be the number of units of a certain commodity which can be sold when the price per unit is p units of money. Let the *total cost* of producing the x units be C; the *average cost* of production per unit be A, when x units are produced; the *revenue* obtained by their sale be R. Then p and C are considered as functions of x, say $p = f(x)$ and $C = g(x)$. Also, $R = px$ or $R = xf(x)$, and $A = C/x$ or $A = x^{-1}g(x)$. At any fixed value of x, the *marginal cost* is defined as the limit of the increment in cost, ΔC, divided by the increment in output, Δx, as $\Delta x \to 0$. That is,

$$\textbf{(marginal cost)} = \frac{dC}{dx} = C'. \tag{1}$$

Similarly, by definition $\qquad \textbf{(marginal revenue)} = \dfrac{dR}{dx} = R'. \tag{2}$

35. For a firm making steel drums, the demand function is $p = 300 - 9x - x^2$, where the units are \$1 for p and a certain trade unit for x. Find the marginal revenue when $x = 4$.

36. The demand curve for a certain commodity in the United States is estimated to be $p = 250 - 40x$. Find the marginal revenue when $x = 2$. (When no units are described, it is to be assumed that p and x are measured in trade units which will not be discussed.)

37. Let the total-cost function for a manufacturer be $C = 8500 + 6x - .0002x^2$. Find the marginal cost when $x = 12,000$.

38. Suppose that $C = 5000 + 20x - .0004x^2$ for a factory producing leather gloves. Find the marginal cost when $x = 5000$.

---

* For an extensive background, with numerous associated problems, see *Mathematics and Statistics for Economists* by *Gerhard Tintner;* Rinehart & Co., Inc., publishers.

30. Derivative of a quotient

The derivative of a fraction u/v is equal to the denominator times the derivative of the numerator minus the numerator times the derivative of the denominator, divided by the square of the denominator:

$$\frac{d}{dx}\left(\frac{u}{v}\right) = \frac{v\dfrac{du}{dx} - u\dfrac{dv}{dx}}{v^2}. \qquad \text{(VI)}$$

In particular,
$$\frac{d}{dx}\left(\frac{1}{v}\right) = -\frac{1}{v^2}\frac{dv}{dx}. \qquad \text{(VI)}_a$$

Proof of (VI). Let $y = u/v$. Then, for $x = x_0$ and $x = x_0 + \Delta x$,

$$y_0 = \frac{u_0}{v_0} \quad and \quad y_0 + \Delta y = \frac{u_0 + \Delta u}{v_0 + \Delta v}, \qquad (1)$$

where we assume that $v_0 \neq 0$. On subtracting each side of $y_0 = u_0/v_0$ from the corresponding side of the second equation in (1), we obtain

$$\Delta y = \frac{(u_0 + \Delta u)(v_0) - u_0(v_0 + \Delta v)}{v_0(v_0 + \Delta v)} = \frac{v_0\Delta u - u_0\Delta v}{v_0(v_0 + \Delta v)}; \qquad (2)$$

$$\frac{\Delta y}{\Delta x} = \frac{v_0\dfrac{\Delta u}{\Delta x} - u_0\dfrac{\Delta v}{\Delta x}}{v_0(v_0 + \Delta v)}; \qquad (3)$$

$$\frac{dy}{dx} = \lim_{\Delta x \to 0}\frac{\Delta y}{\Delta x} = \frac{v_0\left(\lim\limits_{\Delta x \to 0}\dfrac{\Delta u}{\Delta x}\right) - u_0\left(\lim\limits_{\Delta x \to 0}\dfrac{\Delta v}{\Delta x}\right)}{\lim\limits_{\Delta x \to 0}v_0(v_0 + \Delta v)}. \qquad (4)$$

Since v has a derivative at $x = x_0$, then v is continuous at $x = x_0$, and hence $\Delta v \to 0$ as $\Delta x \to 0$. Thus, the denominator in (4) has the limit $v_0(v_0 + 0)$ or v_0^2. Hence, at any point $x = x_0$, where $v_0 \neq 0$,

$$\frac{dy}{dx} = \frac{v_0\dfrac{du}{dx} - u_0\dfrac{dv}{dx}}{v_0^2}. \qquad (5)$$

On replacing y by u/v, and on using simply x, u, v instead of x_0, u_0, v_0 for fixed values, from (5) we obtain (VI).

ILLUSTRATION 1. From (VI) with $u = 3x^2 + 2x$ and $v = 2x^3 - 7$,

$$\frac{d}{dx}\left(\frac{3x^2 + 2x}{2x^3 - 7}\right) = \frac{(2x^3 - 7)\dfrac{d}{dx}(3x^2 + 2x) - (3x^2 + 2x)\dfrac{d}{dx}(2x^3 - 7)}{(2x^3 - 7)^2}$$

$$= \frac{(2x^3 - 7)(6x + 2) - (3x^2 + 2x)(6x^2)}{(2x^3 - 7)^2} = -\frac{6x^4 + 8x^3 + 42x + 14}{(2x^3 - 7)^2}.$$

It would be clumsy to use (VI) in differentiating a fraction u/k, where k is a constant. Instead, we write u/k as $(1/k)\cdot u$.

ILLUSTRATION 2. $\dfrac{d}{dx}\left(\dfrac{3x+x^4}{8}\right) = \dfrac{1}{8}\dfrac{d}{dx}(3x+x^4) = \dfrac{3+4x^3}{8}.$

Proof of (VI)$_a$. From (VI) with $u = 1$, and hence $du/dx = 0$,

$$\frac{d}{dx}\left(\frac{1}{v}\right) = \frac{v\dfrac{d}{dx}(1) - 1\cdot\dfrac{dv}{dx}}{v^2} = -\frac{1}{v^2}\cdot\frac{dv}{dx}.$$

ILLUSTRATION 3. By use of (VI)$_a$,

$$\frac{d}{dx}\left(\frac{10}{3x^2+5}\right) = 10\frac{d}{dx}\left(\frac{1}{3x^2+5}\right) = -\frac{10\cdot 6x}{(3x^2+5)^2}.$$

31. Review of definitions for exponents and radicals

If x is any real number and n is a positive integer, then x^n is defined as the product of n factors x. If $n = 0$ and $x \neq 0$, we define x^n to be 1. However, **0^0 is not defined,** for reasons which will become clear later in this text.

If x is any number and q is a positive integer, we call R a qth **root** of x in case $R^q = x$. If $x = 0$, then $R = 0$ is the only qth root of x. If $x \neq 0$, in algebra it is shown that x has just q qth roots, some or all of which may be imaginary numbers. We recall the following facts:

If $x > 0$ and q is even, then x has just two real qth roots, of opposite signs and equal absolute values.

If $x < 0$ and q is even, then all qth roots of x are imaginary.

If q is odd and $x \neq 0$, then x has just one real qth root, which is of the same sign as x.

If $x \neq 0$, we let $\sqrt[q]{x}$ represent just *that qth root of x which is real and has the same sign as x*, when such a root exists. If $x = 0$, we let $\sqrt[q]{x} = 0$. In any of these cases, we read " $\sqrt[q]{x}$ " as "*the qth root of x*," and call $\sqrt[q]{x}$ the **principal qth root** of x. If $x < 0$ and q is even, so that all qth roots are imaginary, we may use the symbol $\sqrt[q]{x}$ for a qth root, but then we merely say that it is an imaginary number, and do not earmark it as any particular root.

ILLUSTRATION 1. $\sqrt[3]{0} = 0.$ $\sqrt[5]{32} = 2.$ $\sqrt[5]{-32} = -2.$ $\sqrt[4]{16} = 2.$
$\sqrt[4]{-8}$ is an imaginary number. The real 4th roots of 16 are $\pm\sqrt[4]{16}$ or ± 2.

A **rational number** is a real number which can be expressed as the quotient of two integers, p/q. If a real number is not rational, it is said to be **irrational.** If a rational number enters as an exponent, we agree to write it in a form p/q where p and q have *no common integer factor except* ± 1. Then, if x is any real number, $p > 0$, and $q > 0$, where q *is not even when* $x < 0$, we define $x^{\frac{p}{q}}$ as $\sqrt[q]{x^p}$, *the (real) principal root of x^p*. If $x^{\frac{p}{q}}$ ever enters discussion when $x < 0$ and q is even, we shall say merely that $x^{\frac{p}{q}}$ is imaginary. In algebra it is verified that $x^{\frac{p}{q}}$ can be written in either of two forms:

$$x^{\frac{p}{q}} = \sqrt[q]{x^p} \quad and \quad x^{\frac{p}{q}} = (\sqrt[q]{x})^p.$$

ILLUSTRATION 2. $4^{\frac{3}{2}} = \sqrt{4^3} = 64 = 8$; or, $4^{\frac{3}{2}} = (\sqrt{4})^3 = 2^3 = 8$.

Finally, if $- p/q$ is any *negative* rational number, where $p > 0$ and $q > 0$, and x is any real number except zero, we define $x^{-\frac{p}{q}} = 1/x^{\frac{p}{q}}$, and *we do not define* $x^{-\frac{p}{q}}$ when $x = 0$.

ILLUSTRATION 3. $x^{-3} = \dfrac{1}{x^3}.$ $125^{-\frac{2}{3}} = \dfrac{1}{125^{\frac{2}{3}}} = \dfrac{1}{25}.$

Note 1. In this text, in any formula involving powers, it is understood that *the formula is not available for values of the literal numbers which would create an undefined symbol 0^n, where n is a rational number and $n \leqq 0$, or a symbol $x^{\frac{p}{q}}$ which could have only imaginary values.*

32. Derivative of a function of a function

If y is a function of u, where u is a function of x, then y is a function of x. Then, we sometimes say that y is a **composite function.**

ILLUSTRATION 1.   If $y = 3u^3 + 5u^2$, and $u = 3x - 2$, then y is a function of x. On eliminating u by substituting $(3x - 2)$, we obtain

$$y = 3(3x - 2)^3 + 5(3x - 2)^2. \tag{1}$$

In considering a composite function, it is not always convenient or possible to eliminate the intermediate variable, as in (1). On this account, and for other reasons, the following result is of importance.

THEOREM I.   *If y is a differentiable function of u, and u is a differentiable function of x, then y is a differentiable function of x, and*

$$\frac{dy}{dx} = \frac{dy}{du} \cdot \frac{du}{dx}. \tag{VII}$$

Proof. 1. If a fixed value x is given an increment Δx, then an increment Δu is given to u, and Δy to y. Let us assume that * $\Delta u \neq 0$ if $|\Delta x|$ is sufficiently small and not zero. With Δx limited to be of this size, multiply numerator and denominator of $\Delta y/\Delta x$ by Δu:

$$\frac{\Delta y}{\Delta x} = \frac{\Delta y}{\Delta u} \cdot \frac{\Delta u}{\Delta x}. \tag{2}$$

2. Since u possesses a derivative, then u is a continuous function of x, and hence $\Delta u \to 0$ if $\Delta x \to 0$. Thus, from (2), we obtain (VII):

$$\frac{dy}{dx} = \lim_{\Delta x \to 0} \frac{\Delta y}{\Delta x} = \left(\lim_{\Delta x \to 0} \frac{\Delta y}{\Delta u}\right) \cdot \left(\lim_{\Delta x \to 0} \frac{\Delta u}{\Delta x}\right) = \left(\lim_{\Delta u \to 0} \frac{\Delta y}{\Delta u}\right) \cdot \frac{du}{dx} = \frac{dy}{du} \cdot \frac{du}{dx}.$$

* For a proof without this assumption, see page 565 in the Appendix.

ILLUSTRATION 2. If $y = (3x^2 + x)^9$, let $u = 3x^2 + x$. Then, $y = u^9$. From $(III)_a$ and (VII),

$$\frac{dy}{dx} = \frac{d}{du}(u^9) \cdot \frac{du}{dx} = 9u^8(6x + 1) = 9(3x^2 + x)^8(6x + 1). \tag{3}$$

By use of (VII), we may prove (III) of page 38 if n is any integer:

$(u \neq 0 \text{ if } n \leq 1)$ $\qquad\qquad \dfrac{du^n}{dx} = nu^{n-1}\dfrac{du}{dx};$ $\qquad\qquad\qquad$ (III)

$[\textit{with } u = x \text{ in (III)}]$ $\qquad\qquad \dfrac{dx^n}{dx} = nx^{n-1}.$ $\qquad\qquad\qquad$ $(III)_a$

Proof. 1. Suppose that n is a *positive* integer. Then, $(III)_a$ already has been proved. From $(III)_a$ with x replaced by u,

$$\frac{du^n}{du} = nu^{n-1}.$$

Hence, by use of (VII), we obtain (III) with n a positive integer:

$$\frac{du^n}{dx} = \frac{du^n}{du} \cdot \frac{du}{dx} = nu^{n-1}\frac{du}{dx}.$$

2. If $n = 0$ and $u \neq 0$, then (III) is true because $u^n = 1$ and each side of (III) is equal to zero.

3. Suppose that n is a *negative* integer, say $n = -m$ where $m > 0$. We recall that $u^{-m} = 1/u^m$. Then, by use of (III) for the exponent m, and $(VI)_a$ of page 39, we obtain (III) for the exponent $n = -m$:

$$\frac{du^{-m}}{dx} = \frac{d}{dx}\left(\frac{1}{u^m}\right) = -\frac{1}{(u^m)^2} \cdot \frac{du^m}{dx} = \frac{(-m)u^{m-1}}{u^{2m}} \cdot \frac{du}{dx}$$

$$= (-m)u^{m-1-2m}\frac{du}{dx} = nu^{-m-1}\frac{du}{dx} = nu^{n-1}\frac{du}{dx}.$$

Hence, (III) is true if n is any integer.

ILLUSTRATION 3. By use of (III) with $u = 3x^2 + x$, we obtain (3):

$$\frac{d}{dx}(3x^2 + x)^9 = 9(3x^2 + x)^8(6x + 1).$$

ILLUSTRATION 4. $\qquad \dfrac{d}{dx}\left(\dfrac{1}{3x^5}\right) = \dfrac{1}{3} \cdot \dfrac{dx^{-5}}{dx} = -\dfrac{5}{3}x^{-6} = -\dfrac{5}{3x^6}.$

ILLUSTRATION 5. $\quad \dfrac{d}{dx}\left[\dfrac{7}{(3x + 4)^4}\right] = 7(-4)(3x + 4)^{-5}(3) = -84(3x + 4)^{-5}.$

$$\frac{d}{dx}\left(\frac{5x^2 + 1}{2x - 4}\right)^3 = 3\left(\frac{5x^2 + 1}{2x - 4}\right)^2 \frac{d}{dx}\left(\frac{5x^2 + 1}{2x - 4}\right) \qquad\qquad \left[u = \frac{5x^2 + 1}{2x - 4} \text{ in (III)}\right]$$

$$= 3\left(\frac{5x^2 + 1}{2x - 4}\right)^2 \cdot \frac{2(5x^2 - 20x - 1)}{(2x - 4)^2} = \frac{6(5x^2 + 1)^2(5x^2 - 20x - 1)}{(2x - 4)^4}.$$

EXERCISE 12

Find y', or differentiate the given function of x, t, s, y, or z. Avoid expanding. Early letters of the alphabet represent constants.

1. $y = \dfrac{3x + 3}{2x + 5}.$

2. $y = \dfrac{3x}{2x^2 + 4}.$

3. $y = \dfrac{2 - 3x^2}{5x - 7}.$

4. $g(z) = \dfrac{2z - 3z^2}{z^3 - 1}.$

5. $h(s) = \dfrac{3}{2s + 4}.$

6. $\dfrac{3x^2 - 5}{2x + 3x^2}.$

7. $y = 7x^{-3}.$

8. $y = 4x^{-5}.$

9. $y = 3x^{-8}.$

10. $y = \dfrac{3}{x^2}.$

11. $y = \dfrac{8}{3x^3}.$

12. $y = \dfrac{a}{bx^6}.$

13. $y = (3x^2 + 2x)^{12}.$

14. $y = (4x - 5x^3)^7.$

15. $y = (3x - 2x^{-4})^5.$

16. $(2z^3 - z^{-2})^4.$

17. $(t^{-1} - 2t^4)^3.$

18. $(2y^{-2} - 3y^{-1})^6.$

19. $(x^2 + 3x)^3 (x - x^3)^4.$

20. $(2t^3 - t^4)^5 (t^2 + 5t)^3.$

HINT. Use (V) and (III).

21. $(s^2 - 2s^{-3})^3 (s - 5s^4)^2.$

22. $(z - z^{-2})^4 (z^{-1} - 2z^{-3})^5.$

23. $(x + 2x^2)^{-1}(2 - 3x)^{-2}.$

24. $(t^{-1} + t^2)^{-1}(2t - t^2)^{-3}.$

HINT. Retain negative exponents and differentiate as a product.

25. $\left(\dfrac{x + 3}{4x^2 + 5}\right)^4.$

26. $\left(\dfrac{2z - 3}{z^2 + z}\right)^3.$

27. $\left(\dfrac{y^4 - 2y^2}{5 - y^3}\right)^2.$

33. Power formula for rational exponents

If u represents any differentiable function of x, we have proved the following result if n is any integer:

$$(u \neq 0 \text{ if } n \leq 1) \qquad \frac{du^n}{dx} = nu^{n-1}\frac{du}{dx}. \qquad (III)$$

We proceed to establish (III) if n is any rational number, not zero.

Proof. 1. Let $n = p/q$, where p and q are integers, $q > 0$, and p/q is in lowest terms. Let $y = u^{p/q}$. Then,

$$y^q = u^p, \qquad (1)$$

where the two sides represent *identical functions of x*. Hence, we may differentiate each side of (1) with respect to x, by use of (III) for integral exponents, and equate the results:

$$\frac{d}{dx}(y^q) = \frac{d}{dx}(u^p), \quad \text{or} \quad qy^{q-1}\frac{dy}{dx} = pu^{p-1}\frac{du}{dx}. \qquad (2)$$

2. Divide both sides of (2) by qy^{q-1}:

$$\frac{dy}{dx} = \frac{p}{q} \cdot \frac{u^{p-1}}{y^{q-1}} \cdot \frac{du}{dx} = \frac{p}{q} \cdot \frac{yu^{p-1}}{y^{q-1}y} \cdot \frac{du}{dx} = \frac{p}{q} \cdot u^{\frac{p}{q}-1}\frac{du}{dx}, \qquad (3)$$

because

$$\frac{yu^{p-1}}{y^q} = yu^{p-1}y^{-q} = u^{\frac{p}{q}}u^{p-1}u^{-p} = u^{\frac{p}{q}-1}.$$

In (3), we have established (III), and its special case (III)$_a$ of page 38, with n as any rational number. To differentiate any radical, we first express it as a fractional power, and then use (III), or (III)$_a$.

ILLUSTRATION 1. By (III)$_a$, $\dfrac{d}{dx} \sqrt[5]{x^3} = \dfrac{d}{dx} x^{\frac{3}{5}} = \dfrac{3}{5} x^{-\frac{2}{5}}.$

ILLUSTRATION 2. $\dfrac{d}{dx} \dfrac{1}{5\sqrt[3]{x}} = \dfrac{d}{dx} \dfrac{1}{5} x^{-\frac{1}{3}} = -\dfrac{1}{15} x^{-\frac{4}{3}}.$

$\dfrac{d}{dx} \sqrt[3]{7x^2} = \sqrt[3]{7} \dfrac{d}{dx} x^{\frac{2}{3}} = \dfrac{2}{3} \sqrt[3]{7} x^{-\frac{1}{3}}.$

With $u = x^2 + 3x$ in (III), $\dfrac{d}{dx} \sqrt[4]{(x^2 + 3x)^3} = \dfrac{3}{4}(x^2 + 3x)^{-\frac{1}{4}}(2x + 3).$

$\dfrac{d}{dx}\sqrt{\dfrac{2+x}{3-x}} = \dfrac{d}{dx}\left(\dfrac{2+x}{3-x}\right)^{\frac{1}{2}} = \dfrac{1}{2}\left(\dfrac{2+x}{3-x}\right)^{-\frac{1}{2}} \dfrac{d}{dx}\left(\dfrac{2+x}{3-x}\right) = \dfrac{5}{2}(3-x)^{-\frac{3}{2}}(2+x)^{-\frac{1}{2}}.$

EXERCISE 13

Find y', or w', or differentiate the given function. Early letters of the alphabet represent constants.

1. $2x^{\frac{4}{3}}.$ **2.** $5\sqrt[4]{z^3}.$ **3.** $\sqrt[3]{4y}.$ **4.** $3x^{-\frac{3}{2}}.$ **5.** $7t^{-\frac{2}{3}}.$

6. $\dfrac{3}{7x^{\frac{1}{2}}}.$ **7.** $\dfrac{2}{5\sqrt{x}}.$ **8.** $\dfrac{5}{2t^{\frac{2}{3}}}.$ **9.** $\dfrac{a}{b\sqrt[3]{x}}.$ **10.** $\dfrac{c}{a\sqrt{z^3}}.$

11. $(2x^2 + 1)^{\frac{5}{4}}.$ **12.** $(3s + s^3)^{\frac{7}{2}}.$ **13.** $(u + 3u^2)^{\frac{8}{3}}.$

14. $y = \sqrt{16 - x^2}.$ **15.** $y = \sqrt{3s^2 + 5}.$ **16.** $y = \sqrt[3]{x^2 - 4x}.$

17. $y = \sqrt{3s^2 - 2s + 5}.$ **18.** $w = \sqrt[3]{2 - 5z + 6z^2}.$

19. $\dfrac{3}{(2x + 5)^{\frac{3}{2}}}.$ **20.** $\dfrac{7}{\sqrt{x^2 + 1}}.$ **21.** $\dfrac{1}{\sqrt[3]{3t + 5}}.$

22. $y = \sqrt{\dfrac{2x}{x - 3}}.$ **23.** $y = \sqrt{\dfrac{3z + 1}{z - 1}}.$ **24.** $y = \dfrac{t + t^2}{\sqrt{2t + 5}}.$

25. $(s^{\frac{1}{2}} - a^{\frac{1}{2}})^{\frac{1}{3}}.$ **26.** $(5x^{-1.352} + 6)^3.$ **27.** $(a^{\frac{2}{3}} - x^{\frac{2}{3}})^{\frac{3}{2}}.$

28. $\dfrac{t^2}{\sqrt{16 + t^2}}.$ **29.** $\dfrac{z^2}{\sqrt{a^2 - z^2}}.$ **30.** $\dfrac{x^2}{\sqrt{a^2 + 2ax}}.$

31. $\sqrt{x^3 - 2x}\sqrt{4 - x^2}.$ **32.** $\sqrt{2t^2 + 3t}\sqrt{3t + 1}.$

33. $\dfrac{1}{x + \sqrt{x^2 - 1}}.$ **34.** $\dfrac{x}{\sqrt{1 - x^2} - x}.$

35. $\dfrac{(2x - 3x^2)^3}{5 - 4x}.$ **36.** $\dfrac{2z - 4z^3}{(5z - 2)^4}.$ **37.** $\dfrac{(2y + 3)^5}{(4y^2 - y)^3}.$

38. The weight w, in pounds of steam per second which will flow through a hole whose cross-section area is A square inches, if the steam approaches the hole under a pressure of P pounds per square inch, is approximated by $w = .0165\, AP^{.97}$ (Grashof's formula). Find the rate of change of w with respect to P when $P = 80$, if $A = 8$.

34. Implicit functions

Let x and y be independent variables; that is, assume that they may be assigned values *independently* on their respective ranges. Consider a function $f(x, y)$, and now restrict the values of x and y to satisfy the equation $f(x, y) = 0$. Then, x and y no longer are both independent, because assignment of a value to *either variable* in general determines a value, or values, of the *other variable*, to satisfy the equation. Hence, as a rule, *an equation $f(x, y) = 0$ determines either variable as a function of the other*, and we shall proceed under the assumption that this is the case. If x is designated as the independent variable, we say that the equation $f(x, y) = 0$ defines y *implicitly* as a function of x, or we refer to y as an *implicit function* of x. If it is possible to solve $f(x, y) = 0$ for y in terms of x, and thus obtain a result $y = G(x)$, this solved form is the *explicit* representation of y as a function of x. Later, we shall be concerned largely with the important case where it is either impossible or inconvenient to solve for y explicitly in terms of x.

ILLUSTRATION 1. Suppose that x and y satisfy

$$y^2 + 2xy - x - 5 = 0. \tag{1}$$

By use of the quadratic formula, $\qquad y = -x \pm \sqrt{x^2 + x + 5}.$ \hfill (2)

Or, (1) defines y implicitly as a *two-valued* function of x. The values of this function consist of the values of two single-valued functions of x,

$$y = -x + \sqrt{x^2 + x + 5} \quad and \quad y = -x - \sqrt{x^2 + x + 5}. \tag{3}$$

ILLUSTRATION 2. With all variables restricted to real values, an equation $f(x, y) = 0$ may have no solutions, and thus may not define either variable as a function of the other variable. In particular, the equation $x^2 + y^2 = -4$ is of this character.

In any reference to implicit functions defined by an equation of the form $f(x, y) = 0$, we shall assume that, if (x_0, y_0) is any particular solution of the equation, then the following condition is satisfied.

$$\left\{ \begin{array}{l} \textit{There exists a function}^* \ y = g(x) \ \textit{which satisfies} \ f(x, y) = 0, \\ \textit{where } g(x) \textit{ is defined, single-valued, and continuous at all values} \\ \textit{of } x \textit{ on some interval including } x = x_0, \textit{ and where } y_0 = g(x_0). \end{array} \right\} \tag{4}$$

A function such as $y = g(x)$ in (4) will be called a *single-valued* **branch** at (x_0, y_0) of the complete function of x which is defined implicitly by $f(x, y) = 0$. Hereafter, as a rule, when we mention an *implicit function*, we shall mean a *single-valued branch of some complete implicit function*. Geometrically, (4) states that, in the xy-plane, through each solution point (x_0, y_0) of $f(x, y) = 0$, there passes a continuous arc of the graph of the equation, where this arc has the equation $y = g(x)$.

* Or, $x = h(y)$, when y is taken as the independent variable.

ILLUSTRATION 3. Each equation in (3) defines a single-valued branch of the function of x determined by (1).

ILLUSTRATION 4. The graph of $x^2 + y^2 = 25$ is the circle in Figure 27. We obtain

$$y = \pm \sqrt{25 - x^2}.$$

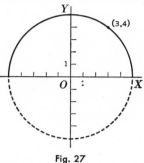

The single-valued branch through (3, 4) is

$$y = + \sqrt{25 - x^2},$$

whose graph is the upper semi-circle in Figure 27. The graph of $x^2 + y^2 = 25$ can be described as the graph of the two-valued function $y = \pm \sqrt{25 - x^2}$,

Fig. 27

and consists of the graphs of the two single-valued branches.

35. Differentiation of implicit functions

Let y be defined implicitly as a function of x by an equation in x and y, and assume that y possesses a derivative with respect to x. Then, in the equation, wherever y occurs it is thought of as an abbreviation for the corresponding function of x. Hence, the two sides of the equation represent identical functions of x, and thus the derivatives of the two sides are equal. These remarks justify the following method for obtaining dy/dx in terms of x and y, *without any necessity for solving the given equation for y in terms of x.*

SUMMARY. *To obtain dy/dx when y is defined implicitly as a function of x by an equation in x and y, differentiate with respect to x on both sides, and solve for dy/dx in terms of x and y.*

ILLUSTRATION 1. If y is a function of x, from (V) and (III),

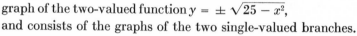

$$\frac{d}{dx}(x^3 y^2) = 3x^2 y^2 + x^3 \frac{d}{dx}(y^2) = 3x^2 y^2 + 2x^3 y \frac{dy}{dx};$$

$$\frac{d}{dx}(3x + y^2)^{\frac{1}{3}} = \tfrac{1}{3}(3x + y^2)^{-\frac{2}{3}} \cdot \frac{d}{dx}(3x + y^2) = \tfrac{1}{3}(3x + y^2)^{-\frac{2}{3}}(3 + 2yy').$$

EXAMPLE 1. Obtain the equations of the tangents to the graph of the following equation at the points where $x = -1$:

$$8x^2 + 4xy + 5y^2 + 28x = 2y - 20. \tag{1}$$

SOLUTION. 1. Equation (1) defines y implicitly as a function of x. Then, the two sides of (1) are identical functions of x. Thus, to find y', we differentiate the sides in (1) and equate the results, which gives

$$16x + 4(y + xy') + 10yy' + 28 = 2y'; \quad or, \tag{2}$$

$$y'(4x + 10y - 2) = -16x - 4y - 28; \quad or, \tag{3}$$

$$y' = \frac{8x + 2y + 14}{1 - 2x - 5y}. \tag{4}$$

2. If $x = -1$ in (1), then $5y^2 - 6y = 0$, or $y = 0$ and $y = \tfrac{6}{5}$. The points

on the graph of (1) are P:$(-1, 0)$ and R:$(-1, \frac{6}{5})$. From (4), we obtain the slopes of the tangents at P and R:

$$\frac{dy}{dx}\Big|_{(x=-1, y=0)} = 2; \quad \frac{dy}{dx}\Big|_{(x=-1, y=\frac{6}{5})} = -\frac{14}{5}. \tag{5}$$

The tangents at P and R are, respectively, $y = 2x + 2$ and $5y = -14x - 8$.

Note 1. If $f(x, y) = 0$, and if dy/dx is requested, this specifies x as the independent variable. A request for dx/dy specifies y as the independent variable. To obtain dx/dy, apply the Summary with x and y interchanged.

EXERCISE 14

If y is an unknown function of x, write an expression for the derivative of the expression with respect to x.

1. x^3y.   **2.** $2x^2y$.   **3.** xy^3.   **4.** x/y.   **5.** $1/(xy)$.
6. $(3x + 2y)^5$.   **7.** $\sqrt{x - y^2}$.   **8.** $x/(x^2 + y^2)$.

Find dy/dx in terms of x and y, without solving for y in terms of x.
9. $x^3 + y^3 = 1$.   **10.** $x^2 + y^2 = 16$.   **11.** $x + xy = 8$.
12. $xy = 10$.   **13.** $4x^2 - 9y^2 = 36$.   **14.** $x^2 + 5y^2 = 16$.
15. $x^2 + 2xy - y^2 = 5$.   **16.** $x^3 - xy^2 - 7y = 4x - 2$.
17. $x^2y + y^3 = 6$.   **18.** $x^3 + y^3 - 6xy = 0$.
19. $x^2y^2 = 4(x^2 + y^2)$.   **20.** $(x + 3y)^2 = 2x - 3y + 5$.
21. $2\sqrt{x} + 3\sqrt{y} = 8$.   **22.** $x + a\sqrt{xy} - y^2 = b$.
23. Find dr/dt if $r^2 + 3r^3t^2 = 5t - 2$.   **24.** Find ds/dy if $y^2 + 3sy - s^3 = 8$.
25–28. Find dx/dy in Problems 13–16, respectively, without use of dy/dx.

Find the equation of the tangent to the curve at the given point. Use implicit function differentiation to obtain dy/dx.
29. $x^2 + y^2 = 34$; at $(3, -5)$.   **30.** $3x^2 + 2y^2 = 14$; at $(-2, 1)$.
31. $y^3 = 2x^2$; at $(2, 2)$.   **32.** $3x^2 - y^2 = 23$; at $(3, -2)$.

Find the slope of the curve where x has the given value.
33. $2x^2 - 3xy + 5y^2 - 6x = 2y + 12$; where $x = -1$.
34. $2x^3 - y^2 + 3xy = x + 7$; where $x = 2$.
35. Find dy/dx if $2(x + 3y^2)^2 - (2x + 5y)^3 = 1$.
36. Find dy/dv if $\sqrt{v - y} + \sqrt{v + y} = 4$.

36. Inverse functions

Consider any function $f(x)$, perhaps not single-valued. As a rule, the equation $y = f(x)$ defines x implicitly as a function of y, say $g(y)$, which may be many-valued even when $f(x)$ is single-valued. The equations

$$y = f(x) \quad and \quad x = g(y) \tag{1}$$

are *equivalent*, or are satisfied by the same pairs of values (x, y), and *hence have the same graph*. In (1), we call $f(x)$ and $g(y)$ *inverse functions*, where each is called *the inverse* of the other. If we refer to $g(y)$ as the inverse of $f(x)$, then we may call $f(x)$ the *direct function*.

ILLUSTRATION 1. Suppose that $y = x^2$. The inverse is $x = \pm \sqrt{y}$. Each of the equations $x = \sqrt{y}$ and $x = -\sqrt{y}$ defines a single-valued branch of the two-valued inverse function.

ILLUSTRATION 2. From trigonometry, if $y = \sin x$, then $x = \arcsin y$. Thus, the sine function and the arcsine function are inverse functions.

ILLUSTRATION 3. If $y = 10^x$ then $x = \log_{10} y$, the *logarithm of y to the base* 10, where x may have any real value. Thus, the *exponential function* 10^x and the *logarithm function* $\log_{10} y$ are inverse functions. The graph of $y = 10^x$, or of $x = \log_{10} y$, is the curve in Figure 28. Each of these functions is single-valued, which corresponds to the property that a perpendicular to either coordinate axis, on the range for x or for y, meets the graph in just one point.

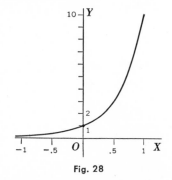

Fig. 28

Hereafter, when we refer to the inverse, $x = g(y)$, of a continuous function $y = f(x)$, usually we shall mean just a single-valued, continuous branch of the function of y defined implicitly by $y = f(x)$. For instance, suppose that the following condition is satisfied at a point (x_0, y_0):

$$\left\{ \begin{array}{l} at\ all\ values\ of\ x\ sufficiently\ near\ x_0,\ f(x) \\ is\ an\ increasing\ (or,\ a\ decreasing)\ function. \end{array} \right\} \tag{2}$$

If (2) is true, any perpendicular to the y-axis on the y-range meets the graph of $y = f(x)$ in just one point; or, for each value of y there is just one value of x, as in Figure 28. This correspondence defines a single-valued, continuous function $x = g(y)$ as the inverse of the function $y = f(x)$. In particular, (2) is satisfied if $f'(x)$ is continuous, with $f'(x_0) \neq 0$. In such a case, $f(x)$ is an increasing or a decreasing function near $x = x_0$ according as $f'(x_0) > 0$ or $f'(x_0) < 0$. Hereafter, if we refer to a pair of *inverse functions* $y = f(x)$ and $x = g(y)$ at any point (x, y), we shall assume that (2) is satisfied at this point.

Note 1. By restating Theorem III of page 30 with the roles of x and y interchanged, we obtain the following result: *If the graph of a function $x = g(y)$ has a nonhorizontal tangent at $P:(x_0, y_0)$, then $g(y)$ has a derivative, $g'(y_0)$, at $y = y_0$.*

THEOREM II. *Suppose that $y = f(x)$ and $x = g(y)$ are inverse functions, and that one of the derivatives, $f'(x)$ or $g'(y)$, exists and is not zero at a point $P:(x_0, y_0)$. Then, both derivatives exist at P, and*

$$f'(x_0) = \frac{1}{g'(y_0)}. \tag{3}$$

Proof. 1. Assume that $f'(x_0)$ exists and $f'(x_0) \neq 0$. Then, at P, the arc which is the graph of both $y = f(x)$ and $x = g(y)$ has a tangent PT, which is not horizontal because $f'(x_0) \neq 0$. Hence, by Note 1, $g'(x_0)$ exists.

2. Let $Q:(x_0 + dx, y_0 + dy)$ be any particular point other than P on PT,

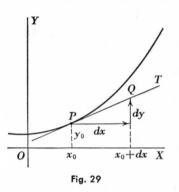

Fig. 29

as in Figure 29. Both $dx \neq 0$ and $dy \neq 0$, because PT is not vertical, since $f'(x_0)$ exists, and is not horizontal. With these particular numbers dx and dy, the definition of differentials on page 35 shows that

$$f'(x_0) = \frac{dy}{dx} \quad and \quad g'(y_0) = \frac{dx}{dy}. \qquad (4)$$

Since the fractions in (4) are *actual quotients*, and are *reciprocals*, we have proved (3). A similar proof applies if we assume that $g'(x_0)$ exists and is not zero.

When (3) is restated for an arbitrary point (x, y), with the general quotients dy/dx and dx/dy used for the derivatives, we obtain

$$\frac{dy}{dx} = \frac{1}{\dfrac{dx}{dy}}. \qquad (VIII)$$

Note 2. We can remember (VIII) as a consequence of taking the reciprocal of the fraction dx/dy on the right, which occurred in the proof of Theorem II.

ILLUSTRATION 1. If $y = x^3$, the inverse is $x = y^{\frac{1}{3}}$. Then, if $x \neq 0$,

$$\frac{dy}{dx} = 3x^2; \quad \frac{dx}{dy} = \frac{1}{3} y^{-\frac{2}{3}} = \frac{1}{3y^{\frac{2}{3}}} = \frac{1}{3x^2} = \frac{1}{\dfrac{dy}{dx}}, \text{ checking (VIII)}.$$

Suppose that an equation $f(x, y) = 0$ defines y implicitly as a function of x, and also x as a function of y. Then, for these inverse functions, (3) is available at any point (x, y) which is a solution of $f(x, y) = 0$. For any equation $f(x, y) = 0$ to be met in this text, we shall assume that (3) can be used, except perhaps at isolated points.

EXAMPLE 1. Find $\dfrac{dy}{dx}$ and $\dfrac{dx}{dy}$ if x and y satisfy

$$3x^2 - 2xy + 7y^2 = 240. \qquad (5)$$

SOLUTION. 1. On differentiating with respect to x in (5) we obtain

$$6x - 2y - 2x\frac{dy}{dx} + 14y\frac{dy}{dx} = 0, \quad or \quad \frac{dy}{dx} = \frac{y - 3x}{7y - x}. \qquad (6)$$

2. By use of (6) and (VIII), $\dfrac{dx}{dy} = \dfrac{7y - x}{y - 3x}. \qquad (7)$

Comment. We justified (VIII) only when $D_x y \neq 0$ and $D_y x \neq 0$. How-ever, in any problem in this text where we shall obtain dx/dy by use of (VIII), the result as in (7) will be correct even when $dx/dy = 0$.

EXERCISE 15

(a) *Find the inverse of the function of x, or of y.* (b) *Obtain dy/dx and dx/dy, without* (VIII), *and check by use of* (VIII).

1. $y = x^5$.   2. $x = y^2$.   3. $x = 4 - y^2$.   4. $x = 9 + y^2$.

Obtain just one of dy/dx and dx/dy by differentiation, and find the other derivative by use of the reciprocal relation.

5. $3x^2 - xy + y^3 = 3$.   6. $2x - 3xy + y^2 = 2y - 5$.

7. $2xy - 3x - 2y = y^2 - 5$.   8. $4x^2 - 5x - 7y = 3y^2 - 7$.

9. $9x^2 = 8y^3$.   10. $27x^3 = 4y^2$.   11. $x^2 + 4y^2 = 16$.

12. $b^2x^2 + a^2y^2 = a^2b^2$.   13. $x^{\frac{1}{2}} + y^{\frac{1}{2}} = a^{\frac{1}{2}}$.

14. $x^{\frac{2}{3}} + y^{\frac{2}{3}} = a^{\frac{2}{3}}$.   15. $x^3 - 2xy^2 + y^3 = 5$.

37. Derivatives of higher order

If a function $f(x)$ has a derivative at each value of x on a specified interval, then the derivative function $f'(x)$ is defined on the interval. If $f'(x)$ has a derivative at a point $x = x_0$, the result is called the **second derivative** of $f(x)$ at x_0. If we refer merely to the *second derivative*, we shall mean the *derivative function* of $f'(x)$. The second derivative of a function $y = f(x)$ is denoted by any one of the symbols

$$f''(x), \quad \frac{d^2y}{dx^2}, \quad y'', \quad D_x^2 y, \quad D_x^2 f(x), \tag{1}$$

each of which can be read "*the second derivative of f(x), or of y, with respect to x.*" We may read $f''(x)$ simply as "*f-second of x,*" and y'' as "*y-second.*" By definition,

$$f''(x) = \frac{d}{dx} f'(x), \quad or \quad \frac{d^2y}{dx^2} = \frac{d}{dx}\left(\frac{dy}{dx}\right). \tag{2}$$

Similarly, the derivative (if it exists) of the second derivative is called the *third derivative*, etc., for the *fourth, fifth,* $\cdots$, *n*th *derivatives,* where n is any positive integer.

ILLUSTRATION 1. We represent the 3d, 4th, $\cdots$, nth derivatives of a function $y = f(x)$ by $f'''(x), f^{(IV)}(x), \cdots, f^{(n)}(x)$, or by

$$\frac{d^3y}{dx^3}, \quad \frac{d^4y}{dx^4}, \quad \cdots, \quad \frac{d^ny}{dx^n}. \tag{3}$$

Or, we use $D_x^{(n)}f(x)$, or $y^{(n)}(x)$, instead of $f^{(n)}(x)$. We may read $f^{(n)}(x)$ as "*f upper n of x,*" or "*the nth derivative of f(x)*"; $y^{(n)}(x)$ may be read "*y upper n of x.*" A symbol $f^{(n)}(x)$ is called a derivative of the nth *order.* By definition,

$$\frac{d^4y}{dx^4} = \frac{d}{dx}\left(\frac{d^3y}{dx^3}\right); \quad \frac{d^ky}{dx^k} = \frac{d}{dx}\left(\frac{d^{k-1}y}{dx^{k-1}}\right).$$

Note 1. Sometimes, we call $f'(x)$ the *first derived function* for $f(x)$, $f''(x)$ the *second derived function*, etc. To say that $f(x)$ is *differentiable twice*, will mean that $f(x)$ possesses a *second derivative*, $f''(x)$, which implies that $f'(x)$ also exists and is continuous. Similar meaning is attached to a statement that $f(x)$ is *differentiable k times*, where k is any positive integer.

ILLUSTRATION 2. If $f(x) = 5x^4 + 3x^3 + 2x - 9$, then

$$f'(x) = 20x^3 + 9x^2 + 2; \quad f''(x) = D_x f'(x) = 60x^2 + 18x;$$

$$f'''(x) = 120x + 18; \quad f^{(IV)}(x) = 120; \quad f^{(V)}(x) = 0.$$

ILLUSTRATION 3. If $y = x^{\frac{5}{3}} - 2x^7 - 7$, then

$$y' = \tfrac{5}{3}x^{\frac{2}{3}} - 14x^6; \quad y'' = D_x y' = \tfrac{2}{3} \cdot \tfrac{5}{3} x^{-\frac{1}{3}} - 84x^5.$$

EXAMPLE 1. Obtain y'' if $\qquad\qquad 4x^2 - 9y^2 = 36.$ $\qquad\qquad$ (4)

SOLUTION. 1. In (4), consider y as an implicit function of x and differentiate with respect to x on both sides:

$$8x - 18yy' = 0, \quad or \quad y' = \frac{4x}{9y}. \tag{5}$$

2. Since $y'' = D_x y'$, differentiate the result in (5) by use of the quotient formula, remembering that $D_x y = y'$:

$$y'' = \frac{d}{dx}\left(\frac{4x}{9y}\right) = \frac{4}{9} \cdot \frac{y - xy'}{y^2}.$$

From (5), $\qquad\qquad y'' = \frac{4}{9} \cdot \dfrac{y - x\dfrac{4x}{9y}}{y^2} = \frac{4(9y^2 - 4x^2)}{81y^3}.$ $\qquad\qquad$ (6)

3. We may simplify (6) by using relation (4) between x and y:

$$y'' = \frac{4(-36)}{81y^3}, \quad or \quad y'' = -\frac{16}{9y^3}.$$

If desired, we could express (6) in terms of x, on replacing y by its value in terms of x, from (4).

Comment. If an equation $f(x, y) = 0$ is not extremely simple, we must expect y'' to be a relatively complicated function of x and y.

Note 2. If we refer merely to *the derivative* of a function $y = f(x)$, we shall mean the *first derivative* $f'(x)$.

Formula (IV) of page 38 extends to derivatives of any order. That is, *the nth derivative of a sum of functions of x is the sum of their nth derivatives.*

ILLUSTRATION 4. $\dfrac{d^2}{dx^2}(u + v) = \dfrac{d}{dx}D_x(u + v) = \dfrac{d}{dx}\left(\dfrac{du}{dx} + \dfrac{dv}{dx}\right) = \dfrac{d^2u}{dx^2} + \dfrac{d^2v}{dx^2}.$

Note 3. If $n \geq 2$, we shall *not* consider $\dfrac{d^n y}{dx^n}$ as a quotient of separately defined quantities $d^n y$ and dx^n.* However,

$$\frac{d^2 y}{dx^2} = \frac{d}{dx}\left(\frac{dy}{dx}\right) = \frac{dy'}{dx},$$

which can be taken as an actual quotient, where dy' is the differential of the first derivative, y', and similarly for derivatives of higher orders.

EXERCISE 16

Find the 2d, 3d, *and* 4th *derivatives of the function of x.*

1. $3x^5 - 2x^3 + 7.$ **2.** $4x^3 - 2x^2 - 6.$ **3.** $x^6 - x^4 - x^3.$

Find the 2d *derivative of the given function of x, s, or t.*

4. $y = \dfrac{2x}{3 + x}.$ **5.** $y = \dfrac{2s^2 - 3s}{s - 1}.$ **6.** $f(x) = x^{-4} - \dfrac{3}{x}.$

7. $g(t) = 2t^{\frac{5}{2}} - 3t^{\frac{1}{3}}.$ **8.** $h(s) = 5s^4 - s^{-3}.$ **9.** $y = 4t^{-5} - 3t^{-2}.$

10. $f(x) = (3x + 7)^{14}.$ **11.** $g(t) = (2t - 3)^7.$ **12.** $h(x) = \sqrt{2x + 3}.$

13. $\sqrt[3]{2s^2 + 5}.$ **14.** $x\sqrt{2x - 3}.$ **15.** $t(6t - 3)^4.$

16. $y = \dfrac{5}{\sqrt[3]{3 - 2x}}.$ **17.** $y = \dfrac{\sqrt{t - 3}}{2t}.$ **18.** $f(t) = \dfrac{3}{\sqrt{t^2 - 1}}.$

Find y″ without solving for y. Letters a, b, c represent constants. Simplify, if possible, by use of the given equation.

19. $x^2 + y^2 = a^2.$ **20.** $y^2 = 8x^3.$ **21.** $x^2 - y^2 = a^2.$

22. $y^2 = 2px.$ **23.** $2x^2 + 5y^2 = 3.$ **24.** $x^3 + y^3 = 8.$

25. $b^2 x^2 + a^2 y^2 = a^2 b^2.$ **26.** $b^2 x^2 - a^2 y^2 = a^2 b^2.$

27. $x^{\frac{1}{2}} + y^{\frac{1}{2}} = a^{\frac{1}{2}}.$ **28.** $3x^2 - 2xy + y^2 = 5.$

29. $x^3 + x + y = y^3.$ **30.** $x^{\frac{2}{3}} + y^{\frac{2}{3}} = a^{\frac{2}{3}}.$

31. Find y' and y'' where $x = 2$ on the graph of $3x^2 - 2xy + 7y^2 = 15.$

32. Find y' and y'' where $y = 3$ on the graph of $2x^2 - 2xy + y^2 = 5.$

33. Find y'' if $x^2 = (2a - x)y^2.$ **34.** Find y'' if $x^3 + y^3 - 3axy = 0.$

35–41. Find $D_y^2 x$ in Problems 19–25, inclusive.

42. Prove that $D_x^n x^n = n!$, where $n! = 1 \cdot 2 \cdot 3 \cdots n$, called **n-factorial.**

In Problems 43–44, u and v are functions of x with all necessary derivatives.

43. Prove that $\dfrac{d^2(uv)}{dx^2} = u''v + 2u'v' + uv''.$

★44. By mathematical induction prove that, if n is a positive integer, then

$$\frac{d^n(uv)}{dx^n} = u^{(n)}v + {}_nC_1 u^{(n-1)}v' + \cdots + {}_nC_k u^{(n-k)}v^{(k)} + \cdots + {}_nC_n uv^{(n)},$$

where ${}_nC_k = n!/k!(n - k)!$, the kth *binomial coefficient*, and $0! = 1.$

---

* We could define $d^2 f(x)$ as $d^2 f(x) = f''(x)(dx)^2$. Then, we obtain $f''(x) = [d^2 f(x)] \div (dx)^2$. We shall not use $d^2 f(x)$.

5

ROLE OF INFINITY IN LIMITS

38. Limit terminology involving infinity

Frequently, a limit of some sort is involved when the term infinite, or infinity, is used mathematically.

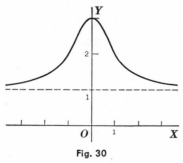

Fig. 30

ILLUSTRATION 1. Consider the function

$$f(x) = \frac{3 + x^2}{1 + x^2} = 1 + \frac{2}{1 + x^2}, \qquad (1)$$

and the graph of $y = f(x)$ in Figure 30. If x increases without bound, or if x decreases without bound, then $2/(1 + x^2)$ approaches zero, and $f(x) \to 1$. Hence, we say that *the limit of $f(x)$ is 1, or $f(x) \to 1$, as "x becomes positively infinite"* $(x \to +\infty)$,* and also as "*x becomes negatively infinite*" $(x \to -\infty)$; we write, respectively,

$$\lim_{x \to +\infty} f(x) = 1 \quad and \quad \lim_{x \to -\infty} f(x) = 1. \qquad (2)$$

The geometrical significance of (2) is that the line $y = 1$ is an asymptote of the graph of $y = f(x)$. Both results in (2) are included in the statement that $f(x) \to 1$ as "*the absolute value of x becomes infinite*," written "$|x| \to \infty$," where plain "∞" has the force of "$+\infty$" because $|x|$ is never negative. Notations such as (2) are defined formally as follows.

DEFINITION I. *To say that the limit of $f(x)$ is L, as x becomes positively infinite, means that $f(x)$ is as near L as we please at all values of x which are sufficiently large. Then, we write*

$$\lim_{x \to +\infty} f(x) = L. \qquad (3)$$

Instead of (3), we may write "$f(x) \to L$ as $x \to +\infty$," which we read "$f(x)$ approaches L as x becomes positively infinite."

* Sometimes read "*x approaches plus infinity.*"

Similarly, we introduce the symbolism "$f(x) \rightarrow L$ as $x \rightarrow -\infty$," whose definition, as above, would conclude with the phrase "*at all values of x where $-x$ is sufficiently large.*"

ILLUSTRATION 2. Sin x varies from -1 to $+1$ at values of x on any interval of length 2π. Hence, sin x has no limit as $x \rightarrow +\infty$, or as $x \rightarrow -\infty$.

DEFINITION II. *To say that "$f(x)$ becomes positively infinite as $x \rightarrow c$" means that, when $x \neq c$, $f(x)$ is as large as we please at all values of x sufficiently near c. Then, we write*

$$\lim_{x \to c} f(x) = +\infty, \quad or \quad f(x) \rightarrow +\infty \ as \ x \rightarrow c. \tag{4}$$

We define similarly "$f(x) \rightarrow -\infty$ as $x \rightarrow c$," and "$|f(x)| \rightarrow \infty$ as $x \rightarrow c$." In (4), we refer to $+\infty$ as an **infinite limit**. For contrast, an ordinary limit then is called a **finite limit**. Hereafter, any limit is understood to be a *finite* limit unless otherwise stated.

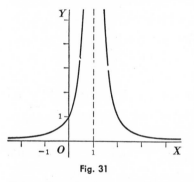

Fig. 31

ILLUSTRATION 3. A graph of the function

$$f(x) = \frac{1}{(x-1)^2} \tag{5}$$

is given in Figure 31. In (5), $(x-1) \rightarrow 0$ as $x \rightarrow 1$; then $f(x) \rightarrow +\infty$ as $x \rightarrow 1$, which corresponds to the fact that the line $x = 1$ is an asymptote of the graph. We say that $f(x)$ has an *infinite discontinuity* at $x = 1$, where $f(x)$ is undefined. Also, in (5),

$f(x) \rightarrow 0$ as $|x| \rightarrow \infty$; the graph of (5) has the corresponding asymptote $y = 0$.

ILLUSTRATION 4. Let $f(x) = 6/x$. In Figure 32, the hyperbola is the graph of $y = f(x)$, or $xy = 6$. If $x > 0$ then $f(x) > 0$, and hence $f(x) \rightarrow +\infty$ if $x \rightarrow 0+$ (from the right). Similarly, $f(x) \rightarrow -\infty$ if $x \rightarrow 0-$. Since these *one-sided* infinite limits are *not identical*, $f(x)$ does not have an infinite limit as $x \rightarrow 0$ without restriction. However, $|f(x)| \rightarrow \infty$ as $x \rightarrow 0$. Thus, we have

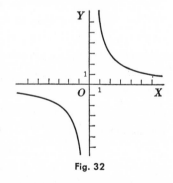

Fig. 32

$$\lim_{x \to 0-} \frac{6}{x} = -\infty; \quad \lim_{x \to 0+} \frac{6}{x} = +\infty; \quad \lim_{x \to 0} \left|\frac{6}{x}\right| = \infty. \tag{6}$$

Because of (6), the graph in Figure 32 has the line $x = 0$ as an asymptote, approached downward ($y \rightarrow -\infty$) as $x \rightarrow 0-$, and upward as $x \rightarrow 0+$.

We may meet infinite limits as the absolute value of the independent variable becomes infinite. Thus, we may have $\lim_{x \to -\infty} f(x) = +\infty$.

ILLUSTRATION 5. $\lim\limits_{x \to +\infty} \dfrac{5 - 3x}{2} = -\infty$,   because $-3x$ becomes negatively

infinite as $x \to +\infty$.

The verbal forms of the theorems on limits in Section 15, on page 19, apply to *finite* limits such as (3), or similar limits involving $-\infty$. When infinite limits are involved, modifications of the theorems can be established. However, at this stage, any related expression involving one or more infinite limits had best be treated as a special example, without use of general theorems about limits.

Let $R(x) = P(x)/Q(x)$, where $P(x)$ and $Q(x)$ are polynomials. Then, to obtain $\lim_{|x| \to \infty} R(x)$, it is convenient to *divide the numerator and denominator of $R(x)$ by the highest power of x found in $Q(x)$.*

ILLUSTRATION 6.   In evaluating the following limit, we divide by x^2, and use Theorems I and IV, page 19:

$$\lim_{|x| \to \infty} \frac{3x^2 + 2}{5x^2 - x} = \lim_{|x| \to \infty} \frac{3 + \dfrac{2}{x^2}}{5 - \dfrac{1}{x}} = \frac{3 + 0}{5 - 0} = \frac{3}{5}.$$

In dealing with a function $f(x)$ whose behavior is well appreciated as $|x|$ grows large, we agree to accept simple facts about corresponding limits without formal proof.

ILLUSTRATION 7.   After thinking of cases like 3^{50} and $3^{-50} = 1/3^{50}$, etc., we accept the facts that $\lim\limits_{x \to +\infty} 3^x = +\infty$; $\lim\limits_{x \to -\infty} 3^x = 0$.

Care must be taken to avoid acting recklessly as if $+\infty$ and $-\infty$ are numbers, although some of the language of limits places $+\infty$ and $-\infty$ in roles also occupied by numbers.

★*Note 1.*   In this text, the symbol "∞" always will be *signed*, $(+)$ or $(-)$, with plain ∞ meaning "$+\infty$." Outside of this book, it sometimes proves convenient to introduce not only $+\infty$ and $-\infty$ but also ∞ without any implied sign. Then, "$v \to \infty$" means "$|v| \to +\infty$" in the sense of this text.

EXERCISE 17

State the value of each specified limit, or decide that the limit does not exist. Then, graph $f(x)$ by use of the corresponding asymptotes and very few computed points.

1. $f(x) = 1/x^2$; limits as $|x| \to \infty$ and as $x \to 0$.

2. $f(x) = 1/x^3$; limits as $|x| \to \infty$, $x \to 0+$, and $x \to 0$.

3. $f(x) = 3/(x - 2)$; limits as $|x| \to \infty$, $x \to 2+$, and $x \to 2-$.

4. $f(x) = 3/(x - 2)^2$; limits as $|x| \to \infty$, $x \to 2+$, $x \to 2-$, and $x \to 2$.

Evaluate each limit, or reach a conclusion that it does not exist.

5. $\lim\limits_{|x|\to\infty} \dfrac{4x^3 + 2x^2}{5x^3 - 3}.$ **6.** $\lim\limits_{|x|\to\infty} \dfrac{2 - 4x}{3 + 5x}.$ **7.** $\lim\limits_{|x|\to\infty} \dfrac{5x - 2x^4}{3x + 4x^4}.$

8. $\lim\limits_{|x|\to\infty} \dfrac{2x^3 - 3x^2 - 5}{5x^3 + x - 4}.$ **9.** $\lim\limits_{x\to+\infty} \dfrac{3x - 2x^2 - x^3}{5x^2 + 3x}.$

10. $\lim\limits_{x\to-\infty} \dfrac{2x^4 - 3x^2 - 5}{5x^3 - x + 2}.$ **11.** $\lim\limits_{x\to-\infty} \dfrac{2x^2 + 3x}{5x^3 + 2x - 4}.$

12. $\lim\limits_{x\to0} \dfrac{1}{\sin^2 x}.$ **13.** $\lim\limits_{x\to0+} \dfrac{1}{\sin x}.$ **14.** $\lim\limits_{x\to0-} \dfrac{1}{\sin x}.$

15. Observe the graph of $y = \tan x$ on page 591. State conclusions about

    (*a*) $\lim\limits_{x\to\frac{1}{2}\pi+} \tan x$;   (*b*) $\lim\limits_{x\to\frac{1}{2}\pi-} \tan x$;   (*c*) $\lim\limits_{x\to\frac{1}{2}\pi} \tan x$.

16. Recall the graph of $y = \csc x$. State conclusions about

    (*a*) $\lim\limits_{x\to\pi+} \csc x$;   (*b*) $\lim\limits_{x\to\pi-} \csc x$;   (*c*) $\lim\limits_{x\to\pi} \csc x$;   (*d*) $\lim\limits_{x\to\pi} |\csc x|$.

17. State conclusions about $\lim_{x\to+\infty} \cos x$ and $\lim_{x\to-\infty} \cos x$.

18. If $\lim_{x\to c} f(x) = 0$, what is true about $\lim_{x\to c} 1/|f(x)|$?

19. If $\lim_{x\to c} |f(x)| = \infty$, what is true about $\lim_{x\to c} 1/f(x)$?

    ★*Evaluate the limit.*

20. $\lim\limits_{x\to\infty} \dfrac{\sin x}{x}.$ **21.** $\lim\limits_{x\to0-} \dfrac{\sqrt{5 + x^2}}{x}.$ **22.** $\lim\limits_{x\to0+} \dfrac{\sqrt{5 + x^2}}{x}.$

★**23.** Definition I, page 58, translates into the following form: *The limit of* $f(x)$ *is* L *as* $x \to +\infty$ *if and only if, for every* $\epsilon > 0$, *there exists a corresponding number* K, *sufficiently large, so that*

$$|f(x) - L| < \epsilon \quad if \quad x > K. \tag{1}$$

Interpret (1) with respect to the graph of $y = f(x)$.

★**24.** Write the analytical forms, like that in Problem 23, for the definitions of $\lim_{x\to-\infty} f(x) = L$, and $\lim_{x\to c} f(x) = +\infty$.

39. Sequences

Let n be a variable whose range is all positive integers, or perhaps just those less than some fixed number. Corresponding to each value of n, let a number S_n be specified. Then, the set

$$S_1, S_2, \cdots, S_n, \cdots, \tag{1}$$

consisting of all values of S_n, is called a *sequence*. If the range of n is just the integers from 1 to k inclusive, where k is fixed, we call (1) a *finite sequence*. If the range of n is *all* positive integers, we call (1) an *infinite sequence*. Unless otherwise specified, any sequence to which we refer will be an infinite sequence. In (1), we call S_1 the 1st term, S_2 the 2d term, $\cdots$, S_n the nth term or the *general term*. Instead of S_n, we could use $S(n)$. This emphasizes the fact that the symbol S_n is a special case of functional notation, where the range of n is the set of positive integers. In such a case, we sometimes call

n a *discrete variable* because its range consists of isolated numbers, rather than intervals of numbers.

ILLUSTRATION 1. If $S_n = 3 + 2n$, the corresponding sequence is

$$S_1 = 3 + 2 = 5, \quad S_2 = 3 + 4 = 7, \quad S_3 = 9, \cdots.$$

ILLUSTRATION 2. An arithmetic progression, with first term a and common difference d, is a sequence with the nth term $S_n = a + (n - 1)d$.

ILLUSTRATION 3. A geometric progression is a sequence where the 1st term is a specified number a, and where each later term is obtained by multiplying the preceding term by a fixed constant r, called the common ratio of the progression. Then, the nth term is $S_n = ar^{n-1}$.

Note 1. Recall that the symbol $n!$, where n is a positive integer, is read "*n factorial*," and $n! = 1 \cdot 2 \cdot 3 \cdots n$. Separately, we define $0! = 1$.

ILLUSTRATION 4. In the sequence $\dfrac{2}{1!}, -\dfrac{4}{3!}, +\dfrac{6}{5!}, \cdots$, we infer that the nth term is

$$S_n = \frac{(-1)^{n+1}(2n)}{(2n - 1)!}.$$

As a check, we place $n = 1, 2, 3$ in S_n to obtain the given terms.

Note 2. Hereafter, a notation such as $n = 1, 2, \cdots$ will mean that the range of n is all positive integers. As a rule, any letter in a subscript, such as n on S_n, will be a variable whose range is all positive integers. A sequence with the general term S_n may be abbreviated by writing "*sequence* $\{S_n\}$."

40. Limit of a sequence

We obtain the following definition for the limit of a sequence $\{S_n\}$ by merely restating Definition I of page 58, with n replacing x. Also, we remember that n has only positive integral values.

DEFINITION III. *To say that "the limit of S_n as n becomes infinite is L" means that the absolute value of $(S_n - L)$ is as small as we please for all values of n which are sufficiently large. Then we write*

$$\lim_{n \to \infty} S_n = L, \quad or \quad S_n \to L \text{ as } n \to \infty. \tag{1}$$

To say that "$S_n \to L$ as $n \to \infty$" is equivalent to saying that "$|S_n - L| \to 0$ as $n \to \infty$." If (1) is true, we say that the sequence $\{S_n\}$ **converges,** or *has the limit L,* or *converges to L.* Also, we introduce infinite limits, and may have $S_n \to +\infty$ or $S_n \to -\infty$ as $n \to \infty$, with meanings like those for $x \to \infty$ on page 60. If S_n has no finite limit as $n \to \infty$, it is said that the sequence $\{S_n\}$ is **divergent,** or that it *diverges.* As a rule, any reference to the *limit* of a sequence will mean a *finite limit.*

ILLUSTRATION 1. Let $$S_n = 2 + \frac{(-1)^n}{2^n}.$$

Observe that $2^n \to +\infty$ as $n \to \infty$, and hence

$$\lim_{n\to\infty} S_n = 2 + 0 = 2.$$

We verify that $S_1 = \frac{3}{2}$, $S_2 = \frac{9}{4}$, $S_3 = \frac{15}{8}$, $S_4 = \frac{33}{16}$, $\cdots$. In Figure 33, the values of S_n are represented by points on the scale. As $n \to \infty$, the point S_n approaches 2 on the scale, or $|S_n - 2| \to 0$.

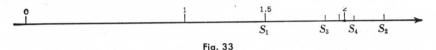

Fig. 33

ILLUSTRATION 2. Let $S_n = (-1)^n$. Then, $S_1 = -1$, $S_2 = 1$, $\cdots$, with -1 and $+1$ occurring alternately. Hence, there is no number L such that S_n will be as close to L as we please for all values of n which are sufficiently large. That is, S_n does not have a limit as $n \to \infty$, or the sequence $\{S_n\}$ is divergent.

Theorems I, II, III, and IV about limits on page 19 apply when interpreted for sequences, that is, for functions of n as $n \to \infty$.

EXAMPLE 1. If $S_n = \dfrac{3n^2 + 2n - 3}{7n^2 + 5n - 4}$, obtain $\lim\limits_{n\to\infty} S_n$.

SOLUTION. (Recall Illustration 6 on page 60.) Divide the numerator and denominator in S_n by *the highest power of n in the denominator:*

$$\lim_{n\to\infty} S_n = \lim_{n\to\infty} \frac{3 + \dfrac{2}{n} - \dfrac{3}{n^2}}{7 + \dfrac{5}{n} - \dfrac{4}{n^2}} = \frac{3 + 0 + 0}{7 + 0 - 0} = \frac{3}{7}.$$

ILLUSTRATION 3. If $S_n = \dfrac{(2n)!}{(4n + 5)[(2n - 1)!]}$, then

$$\lim_{n\to\infty} S_n = \lim_{n\to\infty} \frac{1 \cdot 2 \cdots (2n - 1)(2n)}{1 \cdot 2 \cdots (2n - 1)(4n + 5)} = \lim_{n\to\infty} \frac{2n}{4n + 5} = \frac{1}{2}.$$

★*Note 1.* Definition III may be restated as follows: $S_n \to L$ as $n \to \infty$ *if and only if, for every positive number ϵ, however small, there exists a corresponding integer N such that*

$$|S_n - L| < \epsilon \quad when \quad n > N.$$

That is, if n is sufficiently large $(n > N)$, then S_n will fall between $(L - \epsilon)$ and $(L + \epsilon)$ on the scale in Figure 34.

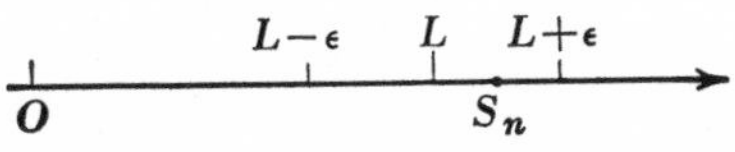

Fig. 34

★Note 2. Intimate connections can be established between the two concepts of a limit as defined for a sequence S_n as $n \to \infty$, and for a function $f(x)$ of a continuous variable x as $x \to c$. Thus, it can be proved that, if $\lim_{x \to c} f(x) = L$, and if $\{x_n\}$ is any sequence (with $x_n \neq c$) such that $x_n \to c$ as $n \to \infty$, then the sequence of functional values $\{f(x_n)\}$ converges to L. Also, if $f(x_n) \to L$ for *every* sequence $\{x_n\}$ as just described, then $\lim_{x \to c} f(x) = L$.

EXERCISE 18

Write a formula for the nth term of the given arithmetic or geometric progression, and also find the 4th and 5th terms.

1. 2, 6, 10, $\cdots$.

2. 17, 15, 13, $\cdots$.

3. 3, $-$ 6, 12, $\cdots$.

4. 4, $-$ .4, .04, $\cdots$.

Write the first four terms of the sequence $\{S_n\}$, $\{T_n\}$, or $\{W_n\}$.

5. $S_n = 3n + 2$.　　　**6.** $T_n = (-1)^n(n!)$.　　　**7.** $W_n = (-1)^{n+1}(2n+1)3^n$.

Write a formula for the nth term of the sequence, consistent with the given terms.

8. 3, 5, 7, $\cdots$.

9. 2!, 4!, 6! $\cdots$.

10. 2, $-$ 4, 6, $\cdots$.

11. $\frac{2}{1}$, $-\frac{4}{3}$, $\frac{8}{5}$, $\cdots$.

Evaluate the limit, if it exists.

12. $\lim_{n \to \infty} \dfrac{3n + 2}{5 - 4n}$.

13. $\lim_{n \to \infty} \dfrac{2n + n^2}{n + 3n^2}$.

14. $\lim_{n \to \infty} \dfrac{n + 5n^2}{6 + 2n^3}$.

15. $\lim_{n \to \infty} \dfrac{6 - 3n + 4n^3}{2n + n^2 - 6n^3}$.

16. $\lim_{n \to \infty} \dfrac{2 + 5n - n^2}{3 + 4n}$.

17. $\lim_{n \to \infty} \dfrac{3 - 4n + 2n^2}{2 + 3n}$.

18. $\lim_{n \to \infty} \dfrac{(2n + 1)(n!)}{(n + 1)!}$.

19. $\lim_{n \to \infty} \dfrac{(3n + 2)(2n - 1)!}{(2n)!}$.

20. $\lim_{n \to \infty} [3 + (-1)^n]$.

6

APPLICATIONS OF DERIVATIVES

41. Angle between two lines

Hereafter, in any discussion involving an angle between two lines in an xy-coordinate plane, it will be assumed that the units of length on the axes are the same. Then, for every line in the plane, we have defined an inclination, α. Any nonvertical line has a slope, m, where $m = \tan \alpha$. We shall use the following results from analytic geometry.

THEOREM I. *If two lines l_1 and l_2 have the slopes m_1 and m_2, respectively, and if θ is the smallest nonnegative angle formed by l_1 and l_2 (thus, $0° \leqq \theta \leqq 90°$), then*

$$\theta = 90° \quad \text{if and only if} \quad m_1 m_2 = -1; \tag{1}$$

$$\text{if } \theta \neq 90°, \qquad \tan \theta = \left| \frac{m_1 - m_2}{1 + m_1 m_2} \right|. \tag{2}$$

Note 1. If we refer to the angle *formed by*, or *between* two lines l_1 and l_2, we shall mean the smallest nonnegative angle θ of Theorem I, as in Figure 35.

42. Tangent and normal

On the graph of an equation $h(x, y) = 0$, at any point $P:(x_0, y_0)$ where dy/dx or dx/dy exists, the graph has a tangent PT, as in Figure 36, page 66. The line PN perpendicular to PT at P is called the **normal**

Fig. 35

to the graph at P. If PT is not horizontal or vertical, both PT and PN have slopes. Then, the slope of PN is the negative reciprocal of the slope of PT, whose slope is known to be the value of dy/dx at (x_0, y_0):

slope of tangent at $P:(x_0, y_0)$: $\qquad \left. \dfrac{dy}{dx} \right|_{(x_0, y_0)};$ $\qquad$ (1)

slope of normal at $P:(x_0, y_0)$: $\qquad -\dfrac{1}{\left. \dfrac{dy}{dx} \right|_{(x_0, y_0)}}$ $\quad,\quad$ or $\quad -\left. \dfrac{dx}{dy} \right|_{(x_0, y_0)}.$ $\qquad$ (2)

65

Suppose that two curves, $h(x, y) = 0$ and $k(x, y) = 0$, intersect at $P:(x_0, y_0)$ where each curve has a tangent. Then, we define *the angle of intersection* of the curves at P as the smallest nonnegative angle θ formed by their tangents at P. The value of dy/dx at P for each curve gives the slope of its tangent, if it is not vertical. Then, formula (2) on page 65 determines $\tan \theta$. If $\theta = 90°$, we say that the curves intersect **orthogonally** at P. This fact can be recognized by use of (1) in Section 41.

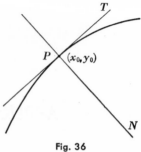

Fig. 36

EXAMPLE 1. Find the equations of the tangent and normal where $x = 2$ on the graph of the function $y = 3x^2 - 2x + 5$.

SOLUTION. 1. $y' = 6x - 2$; at $x = 2$, we find $y' = 10$, the slope of the tangent. When $x = 2$, we obtain $y = 13$. Hence, the equation of the tangent at $(2, 13)$ is $y - 13 = 10(x - 2)$, or $10x - y = 7$.

2. Since the tangent has slope 10, the slope of the normal is $-\frac{1}{10}$. The equation of the normal at $(2, 13)$ is

$$y - 13 = -\tfrac{1}{10}(x - 2), \quad or \quad x + 10y = 132.$$

EXAMPLE 2. Find the angle, θ, at which the curves

$$y = 3x^2 - 5x + 3 \quad and \quad y = x^3 - 2x^2 + 5 \tag{3}$$

intersect at the point where $x = 2$ and $y = 5$.

SOLUTION. From (3), $\qquad y' = 6x - 5 \quad and \quad y' = 3x^2 - 4x. \tag{4}$

Hence, with $x = 2$ in (4), the tangents to the curves have the slopes $m_1 = 7$ and $m_2 = 4$. From (2) on page 65,

$$\tan \theta = \left| \frac{7 - 4}{1 + 28} \right| = .103; \quad \theta = 5.9°. \tag{Table IV}$$

EXAMPLE 3. Find the equation of the tangent at (x_1, y_1) on the ellipse

$$b^2x^2 + a^2y^2 = a^2b^2. \tag{5}$$

SOLUTION. 1. Differentiate with respect to x in (5):

$$2b^2x + 2a^2yy' = 0, \quad or \quad y' = -\frac{b^2x}{a^2y}. \tag{6}$$

2. At (x_1, y_1), the slope, m, of the tangent is $m = -b^2x_1/a^2y_1$. Then, the tangent at (x_1, y_1) is

$$y - y_1 = -\frac{b^2x_1}{a^2y_1}(x - x_1), \quad or \quad b^2x_1x + a^2y_1y = b^2x_1^2 + a^2y_1^2. \tag{7}$$

Since (x_1, y_1) satisfies (5), we have $b^2x_1^2 + a^2y_1^2 = a^2b^2$, and (7) gives

$$b^2xx_1 + a^2yy_1 = a^2b^2. \tag{8}$$

EXERCISE 19

Find the equations of the tangent and normal at the indicated point or points on the curve with the given equation. In Problems 1–6, graph the equation and draw the tangent and normal.

1. $y = x^2 - 4x + 6$; where $x = 3$.   **2.** $y = 6x - x^2 - 5$; where $x = 0$.

3. $x = y^2 + 6y - 4$; where $y = 1$.   **4.** $x = 3y^2 - 6y + 10$; where $y = -2$.

   HINT. Find dx/dy first.

5. $x^2 + 4y^2 = 8$; where $x = 2$.   **6.** $x^2 - 9y^2 = 27$; where $x = -6$.

7. $y = \dfrac{2x + 3}{x^2 + 4}$; where $x = -1$.   **8.** $x^{\frac{1}{2}} + y^{\frac{1}{2}} = 2$; where $x = 1$.

9. $x^2 = 64y^3$; where $x = 8$.   **10.** $x^3 + xy^2 - 4y^2 = 0$; where $x = 2$.

Find the angle of intersection of the curves at the indicated point. In Problems 11–13, also draw a graph showing the tangents at P.

11. $y = x^2$ and $y = \sqrt{x}$, where they intersect.

12. $y = x^2 + 2x - 5$ and $x = 2y - 4$, where $x = 2$.

13. $y = x^2 - 4x + 1$ and $x = 7 - y^2$, where $x = 3$.

14. $y = 3x^2 - 4x + 3$ and $y = x^3 - 2x^2 + 7$, where $x = 2$.

15. $y = 2x^3 - x^2 + 16$ and $y = x^2 - 2x - 12$, where $x = -2$.

Prove that the curves intersect orthogonally at the given point.

16. $3x^2 - 3xy + y^3 = 17$ and $x^2 - 2xy + x = 10y - y^2 - 12$, at $(-1, 2)$.

17. $y^2 = 4x + 4$ and $y^2 = 4 - 4x$, wherever they intersect.

18. Prove that the circle $x^2 - 4x + y^2 - 18y + 60 = 0$ is tangent to the circle $x^2 - 22x + y^2 + 6y + 30 = 0$ at the point $(5, 5)$.

Find the equation of the tangent at any point (x_1, y_1) on the curve.

19. $b^2x^2 - a^2y^2 = a^2b^2$.   **20.** $y^2 = 2px$.

21. $ax^2 + b y^2 + 2dx + 2ey + f = 0$.

22. $ax^2 + 2bxy + cy^2 + 2dx + 2ey + f = 0$.

★*Find each angle of intersection of the curves. Check graphically.*

23. $\begin{cases} y + 2x = 10, \\ y = x^2 - 4x + 7. \end{cases}$ **24.** $\begin{cases} y = 2x^2 - 3, \\ y = x^2 + 2x + 5. \end{cases}$ **25.** $\begin{cases} y = 2x^2, \\ y = x^3 - 3x. \end{cases}$

★**26.** Obtain the tangent at an extremity of the latus rectum of the parabola $y^2 = 2px$, and show that the tangent meets the parabola's axis at the directrix, $x = -\frac{1}{2}p$. [The latus rectum goes through the focus $(\frac{1}{2}p, 0)$.]

★**27.** By finding tangents of two angles, prove that the tangent at any point (x_1, y_1) on the ellipse $b^2x^2 + a^2y^2 = a^2b^2$ makes equal angles with the focal radii of (x_1, y_1). [With $0 < b < a$, the radii are the lines from (x_1, y_1) to the foci, $(\pm ae, 0)$ where $e = \sqrt{a^2 - b^2}/a$.]

★**28.** Prove that the area of the triangle formed by a tangent to the curve $xy = a^2$ and the coordinate axes is a constant.

43. Maxima and minima

DEFINITION I. *If a function f(x) has a largest value,*
it is called the **absolute maximum** *of the func-*
tion. If f(x) has a smallest value, it is called the
absolute minimum *of the function.*

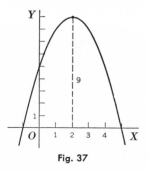

ILLUSTRATION 1. A graph of the function
$f(x) = 4x + 5 - x^2$ is given in Figure 37. The
function has no least value, and has the absolute
maximum 9, attained at $x = 2$; $f(2) = 9$ and $f(x) \leqq 9$
at all values of x.

Fig. 37

DEFINITION II. *To say that a function f(x) has a* **relative maximum** *at*
$x = x_0$ *means that* $f(x) \leqq f(x_0)$ *at all values of x* **sufficiently near** x_0 *on*
the range for x. To say that f(x) has a **relative minimum** *at* $x = x_0$ *means*
that $f(x_0) \leqq f(x)$ *at all values of x* **sufficiently near** x_0.

Thus, to say that $f(x)$ has (or, *attains*) a *relative maximum* at $x = x_0$ means
that, on the graph of $y = f(x)$, the point (x_0, y_0) is *at least as high* as any
neighboring point. The student should rewrite
the preceding sentence for the case of a relative
minimum.

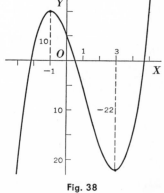

ILLUSTRATION 2. Let $f(x) = x^3 - 3x^2 - 9x + 5$.
A graph of $y = f(x)$ in Figure 38 shows that
$f(x)$ has a relative maximum, 10, attained at
$x = -1$, and a relative minimum, -22, attained at $x = 3$. Suppose that x is restricted
to the range $-4 \leqq x \leqq 6$. Then, the nature of
the graph convinces us that the *absolute* maximum of $f(x)$ is $f(6)$, which we find to be 59; the
student should specify the absolute minimum.

Fig. 38

ILLUSTRATION 3. If a function $f(x)$ has an *absolute* maximum (or, minimum) at a point $x = x_0$, then $f(x_0)$ is also a *relative* maximum (or, minimum).
This remark is illustrated at $x = 2$ for the function whose graph is in Figure 37.

Hereafter, the word **extremum** * (plural, *extrema*) will refer to either a
maximum or a *minimum* when there is no necessity to be more explicit.
Also, in this text, the unqualified word *maximum* (or, *minimum*) will mean
a *relative maximum* (or, *minimum*), unless otherwise indicated. If a function
$y = f(x)$ attains a maximum or a minimum at $x = x_0$, the *point* (x_0, y_0) on
the graph of $y = f(x)$ is called a maximum or a minimum, respectively, or
an *extreme point* of the graph.

* Sometimes written *extreme* (plural, *extremes*).

THEOREM II. *If a function f(x) has a relative extremum at an* **interior point** *
x = x_0 of the range for x, and if the derivative f′(x_0) exists, it is zero. That is,
a* **necessary condition** *for an extremum at x = x_0 is that f′(x_0) = 0.*

Proof. 1. Suppose, for instance, that $f(x)$ has a maximum at $x = x_0$, as
illustrated at $x = -1$ in Figure 38.

2. If $f′(x_0) > 0$, then $f(x)$ is *increasing* at $x = x_0$, so that

$$f(x) < f(x_0) \text{ if } x < x_0, \quad \text{and} \quad f(x_0) < f(x) \text{ if } x > x_0, \tag{1}$$

when x is sufficiently near x_0. But, since $f(x)$ has a *maximum* at x_0, we *must
have* $f(x) \leqq f(x_0)$ when x is *on either side* of x_0, and sufficiently near x_0. Thus,
(1) is impossible, and hence we *cannot* have $f′(x_0) > 0$. Similarly, we *cannot
have* $f′(x_0) < 0$. Therefore, $f′(x_0) = 0$.

ILLUSTRATION 4. In Illustration 2, $y′ = 3(x^2 - 2x - 3)$. We find that
$y′ = 0$ at $x = 3$ and $x = -1$, where the graph in Figure 38 shows extrema.

Note 1. To state that a function $g(x)$ "**changes sign,** *from negative to
positive, at x = x_0,*" will mean that, if x is sufficiently near x_0, then $g(x) < 0$
at $x < x_0$ and $g(x) > 0$ at $x > x_0$. Similarly, we speak of $g(x)$ changing
sign from positive to negative.

THEOREM III. *Suppose that f(x) is continuous at x = x_0, and has a derivative
if x is near x_0, except that f′(x_0) may not exist. Then,* **if f′(x) changes
sign at x = x_0, the function f(x) has an extremum at x = x_0.** *If f′(x)
has the same sign when x < x_0 as when x > x_0, then f(x) does not have an
extremum at x = x_0.*

Proof. 1. Assume that, if x is sufficiently near x_0, then $f′(x) > 0$ if $x < x_0$
and $f′(x) < 0$ if $x > x_0$, as illustrated by a graph of $y = f(x)$ in (α) of Fig-
ure 39. Then, $f(x)$ *increases to* $f(x_0)$ as x increases to x_0, and *decreases from
$f(x_0)$* as x increases from x_0. Hence, $f(x_0) \geqq f(x)$ if x is sufficiently near $x = x_0$,
and thus $f(x_0)$ is a relative maximum for $f(x)$. Similarly, $f(x)$ has a relative
minimum at $x = x_0$ if $f′(x)$ changes from negative to positive at $x = x_0$, as
illustrated by diagram (β) in Figure 39.

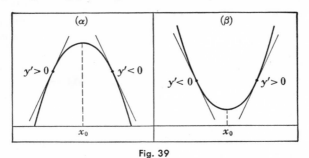

Fig. 39

* Not an end-point of an interval of the range.

2. Now, suppose that, if x is near x_0, $f'(x)$ has the *same sign* when $x < x_0$ as when $x > x_0$, say $f'(x) > 0$. Then, $f(x)$ increases *to* $f(x_0)$ as x increases to x_0, and continues to increase *from* $f(x_0)$ as x increases from x_0, as illustrated at $x = 2$ in Figure 40. Thus, we do *not* have $f(x) \leq f(x_0)$, or $f(x_0) \geq f(x)$, for x on *both* sides of x_0. Hence, $f(x_0)$ is *not* a maximum or a minimum.

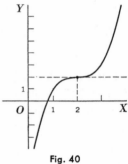

Fig. 40

Note 2. Hereafter, except when otherwise stated, we shall not consider any extremum at an end-point of an interval of the range for x.

From Theorems II and III, we obtain the following **sufficient conditions** for a maximum or a minimum of a function $f(x)$ at a point $x = x_0$ where $f'(x)$ exists. The conditions were illustrated in Figure 39.

Maximum: $f'(x_0) = 0$; $f'(x)$ *changes* **from** $(+)$ *to* $(-)$ *at* $x = x_0$.   (2)

Minimum: $f'(x_0) = 0$; $f'(x)$ *changes* **from** $(-)$ *to* $(+)$ *at* $x = x_0$.   (3)

SUMMARY. *To find extrema for a function $f(x)$ where $f'(x)$ exists:*

1. *Obtain the* **critical values** *of x for extrema by solving $f'(x) = 0$.*

2. *Test each critical value x_0 by finding the sign of $f'(x)$ when $x < x_0$ and when $x > x_0$, for x near x_0, and using* (2) *and* (3).

3. *By use of Theorem III, reject any critical value x_0 where $f'(x)$ has the same sign when $x < x_0$ as when $x > x_0$.*

Before testing a critical value x_0, try to exhibit a linear factor $(x - x_0)$ of $f'(x)$ corresponding to each value x_0 where $f'(x) = 0$.

EXAMPLE 1. Test for extrema: $y = x^3 - 3x^2 - 9x + 5$.   (4)

SOLUTION. 1. From (4), $y' = 3(x - 3)[x - (- 1)]$.   (5)

2. The solutions of $y' = 0$ are $x = 3$ and $x = - 1$.

3. *Test of $x = 3$.* Let x be near 3, on either side; for instance, think of $x = 3.1$ and $x = 2.9$, where any values greater than $- 1$ are satisfactory. Then, $[x - (- 1)]$ is near $+ 4$, while * $x - 3 < 0$ if $x < 3$, and $x - 3 > 0$ if $x > 3$. Similarly, consider x near $- 1$, where $(x - 3)$ remains negative. In the table, we indicate merely signs for factors in (5):

NEAR $x = - 1$	NEAR $x = 3$
$x < - 1$, $y' = (+)(-)(-) = (+)$	$x < 3$, $y' = (+)(-)(+) = (-)$
$x > - 1$, $y' = (+)(-)(+) = (-)$	$x > 3$, $y' = (+)(+)(+) = (+)$
Maximum, *with $y = 10$*	**Minimum,** *with $y = - 22$*

* If $x < a$, then $x - a < 0$; if $x > a$, then $x - a > 0$.

4. The graph of (4) in Figure 38, page 68, was drawn through the extremes $(3, -22)$ and $(-1, 10)$, and a few other solutions of (4).

EXAMPLE 2.   Test for extrema: $y = x^3 - 6x^2 + 12x - 6.$ (6)

SOLUTION.   1. $y' = 3x^2 - 12x + 12;$ or $y' = 3(x - 2)^2.$ (7)

2. If $y' = 0$ then $x = 2$. The exponent of $(x - 2)$ is *even* in (7); hence, $y' > 0$ if $x \neq 2$, and y' *does not change sign* at $x = 2$. Thus, by Theorem III, y does *not* have an extremum at $x = 2$. At $x = 2$, y has a stationary point because $y' = 0$, as shown by the horizontal tangent to the graph of (6) in Figure 40.

From Theorem II, a *necessary condition* for an extremum at an *interior* point $x = x_0$ of an interval where $f(x)$ is defined, and differentiable, is that $f(x)$ be *stationary* at $x = x_0$, or $f'(x_0) = 0$. Example 2 shows that this *necessary condition* is *not a sufficient condition* for an extremum.

EXAMPLE 3.   Determine the extrema, and then graph

$$y = (x - 2)^3(x + 1)^2.$$ (8)

SOLUTION.   1.   From (8), $y' = 3(x - 2)^2(x + 1)^2 + 2(x - 2)^3(x + 1)$

$= (x - 2)^2(x + 1)(5x - 1),$ *or*

$y' = 5(x + 1)(x - \frac{1}{5})(x - 2)^2.$

2. The critical values of x for extrema are $-1, \frac{1}{5}$, and 2. On testing, we find that there is a maximum at $x = -1$, and a minimum at $x = \frac{1}{5}$. Since $(x - 2)^2 > 0$ if $x \neq 2$, then y' does not change sign at $x = 2$, and $y' > 0$ near $x = 2$, when $x \neq 2$. That is, y is an *increasing* function near $x = 2$. A graph of (8) is shown in Figure 41.

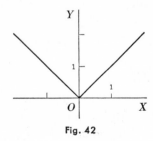

Fig. 41

A continuous function $f(x)$ may have an extremum where $f'(x)$ does not exist.

ILLUSTRATION 5.   A graph of the function $y = |x|$ is shown in Figure 42. We notice that $f(x)$ has a relative minimum, which also is the absolute minimum, at $x = 0$ where $f'(x)$ does not exist, and there is a corner point.

Suppose that $f'(x)$ is continuous. Then, as x increases, if $f'(x)$ changes from $(-)$ to $(+)$ at a point $x = x_0$, the next change will be from $(+)$ to $(-)$, if a change occurs. Thus, from (2) and (3), it follows that any *minimum* is followed by a *maximum*, etc., *maxima and minima alternate as x increases*. This fact can be used to check results in testing for extrema.

Fig. 42

★*Note 3.* If there exists a number U such that $f(x) \leq U$ at all values of x, we call U an **upper bound** for the function $f(x)$, and say that $f(x)$ is bounded above. If U is an upper bound, then any number greater than U also is an upper bound. Similarly, if $L \leq f(x)$ at all values of x, then L is called a **lower bound** of $f(x)$. To say that $f(x)$ is *bounded* means that it has a lower bound and an upper bound; otherwise, $f(x)$ is said to be *unbounded*. If a function has an absolute maximum and an absolute minimum, then the function is *bounded*. But, a bounded function does not necessarily have an absolute maximum or an absolute minimum. Thus, on the half-open interval $0 < x \leq 1$, the function $e^{-1/x}$ is bounded, with 0 as its greatest lower bound; but, $e^{-1/x}$ has no absolute minimum, since $e^{-1/x} \neq 0$ at any value of x. We shall use the following result, which is proved in more advanced courses:

$$\left\{ \begin{array}{l} \textit{If } f(x) \textit{ is continuous on a } \textbf{closed} \textit{ interval } a \leq x \leq b, \textit{ then } f(x) \textit{ has an abso-} \\ \textit{lute maximum, } M, \textit{ and an absolute minimum, } m, \textit{ on the interval. Also, if} \\ m \leq \gamma \leq M, \textit{ then } f(x) \textit{ attains the value } \gamma \textit{ at least once on the interval.} \end{array} \right\} \quad (9)$$

EXERCISE 20

Find any maximum or minimum value of the function, and justify the result by a proper test. Then graph the function.

1. x^2.
2. $-x^4$.
3. x^3.
4. x^5.
5. $x^2 - 6x + 4$. ✓
6. $4x - 2 - x^2$.
7. $2x^3 - 9x^2 + 12x + 12$.
8. $-2x^3 - 3x^2 + 12x + 5$.
9. $x^3 - 3x^2 + 3x - 5$.
10. $x^3 + 6x^2 + 12x - 4$.
11. $y = x^2(x - 1)$.
12. $y = x^2(x - 1)^3$.
13. $y = (x + 1)^2(x - 2)^2$.
14. $y = x^3(x - 2)^3$.

Find the absolute maximum and the absolute minimum of the function.

15. $y = x^2 - 6x + 3$, with $-1 \leq x \leq 4$.

HINT. Investigate *interior* points of the interval; find y at its end-points.

16. $y = \frac{1}{3}x^3 - x^2 - 8x + 5$, with $-3 \leq x \leq 5$.
17. $y = \frac{1}{3}x^3 + x^2 - 15x - 7$, with $-6 \leq x \leq 9$.

Find each extreme value of the function of x without a graph.

18. $f(x) = x^4 - 8x^3$.
19. $f(x) = x^5 + 5x^4$.
20. $f(x) = (x - 1)^3(x + 2)^2$.
21. $f(x) = (x + 1)^4(x - 3)^4$.

Find the maximum or minimum value of the slope on the graph of the given function of x, without drawing a graph.

22. $y = x^3 - 3x^2 + 12x + 3$.
23. $y = 6x^2 - 6x - x^3 + 7$.

24. Let a function $f(x)$ be defined as follows:

$$f(x) = x^2 + 4, \text{ if } x \leq 0; \quad f(x) = 3x + 4 \text{ if } x > 0.$$

By reference to a graph of the function, state where $f(x)$ has a relative minimum. Does $f'(x) = 0$ at the minimum point?

44. Symmetrical results for horizontal and vertical tangents

Let C represent an arc of the graph of an equation $h(x, y) = 0$, as in Figure 43, with C having the equation $y = f(x)$ or $x = g(y)$, where $f(x)$ and $g(y)$ are single-valued inverse functions defined implicitly by $h(x, y) = 0$. In particular, the equation $h(x, y) = 0$ might be given in the form $y - f(x) = 0$, or $y = f(x)$. Suppose that the arc C has a tangent at each point, with dy/dx and dx/dy continuous wherever they exist. Let $P:(x_0, y_0)$ be any point on C. We shall assume that, if $dy/dx = 0$ at P, then $dy/dx \neq 0$ if x is sufficiently near x_0; if $dx/dy = 0$ at P, then $dx/dy \neq 0$ if y is sufficiently near y_0. Under the preceding conditions, the tangent at P is vertical if and only if $dx/dy = 0$ and dy/dx does not exist at P, as in Figure 43. Then, from (VIII) on page 39,

$$\lim_{x \to x_0} \left| \frac{dy}{dx} \right| = \lim_{y \to y_0} \left| \frac{1}{\frac{dx}{dy}} \right| = \infty, \tag{1}$$

because $D_y x \to 0$ as $y \to y_0$. Similarly, the tangent at P is horizontal if and only if $dy/dx = 0$ and $|D_y x| \to \infty$ as $y \to y_0$. The preceding remarks are summarized as follows:

Horizontal tangent: $\left. \dfrac{dy}{dx} \right|_{(x=x_0, \, y=y_0)} = 0; \quad \lim_{y \to y_0} \left| \dfrac{dx}{dy} \right| = \infty. \tag{2}$

Vertical tangent: $\left. \dfrac{dx}{dy} \right|_{(x=x_0, \, y=y_0)} = 0; \quad \lim_{x \to x_0} \left| \dfrac{dy}{dx} \right| = \infty. \tag{3}$

ILLUSTRATION 1.   If $y = x^{\frac{1}{3}}$, the inverse function is $x = y^3$. We find

$$\frac{dy}{dx} = \frac{1}{3} x^{-\frac{2}{3}} = \frac{1}{3x^{\frac{2}{3}}} \quad and \quad \frac{dx}{dy} = 3y^2. \tag{4}$$

Since $dy/dx \neq 0$ at any value of x, there is no point on the graph of $y = x^{\frac{1}{3}}$ where the tangent is horizontal. From (4), we have

$$\frac{dx}{dy} = 0 \ at \ y = 0.$$

When $y = 0$ we find that $x = 0$. Then, from (4),

$$\lim_{x \to 0} \frac{dy}{dx} = +\infty, \tag{5}$$

which illustrates (3). Thus, the tangent to the graph of $y = x^{\frac{1}{3}}$ is vertical at $(0, 0)$, as shown in Figure 44. A point such as $(0, 0)$ on the graph is called an *inflection point*, as defined on page 77.

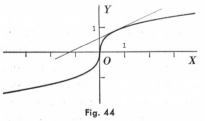

Fig. 44

EXAMPLE 1.   Graph the following equation

$$3x^2 - 2xy + 7y^2 = 240. \tag{6}$$

SOLUTION.   1. By implicit function differentiation,

$$\frac{dy}{dx} = \frac{y - 3x}{7y - x} \quad and \quad \frac{dx}{dy} = \frac{7y - x}{y - 3x}. \tag{7}$$

2. The tangent to the graph is horizontal where $dy/dx = 0$, that is, where $y - 3x = 0$. Hence, the coordinates of the corresponding points on the graph satisfy the system

$$y - 3x = 0 \quad and \quad 3x^2 - 2xy + 7y^2 = 240. \tag{8}$$

With $y = 3x$ in the right-hand equation, we find $60x^2 = 240$, or $x = \pm 2$; then, $y = \pm 6$. The points are $(2, 6)$ and $(- 2, - 6)$.

3. The tangent is vertical where $dx/dy = 0$, or where $7y - x = 0$. On solving this equation and (6) simultaneously, the points where the tangent is vertical are found to be $(2\sqrt{21}, \frac{2}{7}\sqrt{21})$ and $(- 2\sqrt{21}, - \frac{2}{7}\sqrt{21})$, or $(9.2, 1.3)$ and $(- 9.2, - 1.3)$.

4. Since (6) is of the second degree, the locus of (6) is a conic. From (12) on page 564, the discriminant of (6) is $4 - 4(21)$, or $- 80$; hence, the graph is an ellipse. The graph of (6) in Figure 45 was drawn through the points from Steps 2 and 3, with attention to the corresponding tangents. Also, a few other points on the graph were found by substitution in (6).

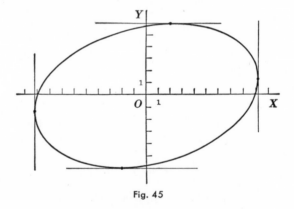

Fig. 45

45. Extrema where the derivative does not exist

A function $f(x)$ may have an extremum at a point $x = x_0$ where $f(x)$ is continuous but $f'(x)$ does not exist. In such a case, we shall assume that $f'(x)$ exists otherwise if x is near $x = x_0$. Then, in most of our examples, the graph of $y = f(x)$ will have a vertical tangent at $x = x_0$. Hereafter, the critical values of x for extrema will be understood to consist of not only the solutions of $f'(x) = 0$, but also of all values of x where $f'(x)$ does not exist. From Theorem III, page 69, sufficient conditions for an extremum at $x = x_0$ where $f'(x)$ does not exist are that $f'(x)$ *should change in sign at* x_0.

EXAMPLE 1. Test for extrema: $y = 2(x - 3)^{\frac{2}{3}}.$ (1)

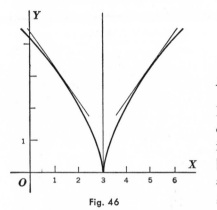

Fig. 46

SOLUTION. 1. From (1),

$$\frac{dy}{dx} = \frac{4}{3}(x - 3)^{-\frac{1}{3}} = \frac{4}{3\sqrt[3]{x - 3}}.$$ (2)

Also, $\frac{dx}{dy} = \frac{3}{4}\sqrt[3]{x - 3}.$

In (2), $D_x y \neq 0$ at any value of x; the only critical value is $x = 3$, where $D_x y$ is not defined, but y is continuous. Also, $|y'| \to \infty$ as $x \to 3$. Since $dx/dy = 0$ at $x = 3$, the graph of (1) has a vertical tangent at $x = 3$.

2. *Test for an extremum.* Suppose that x is near 3.

If $x < 3$, then $x - 3 < 0$, $\sqrt[3]{x - 3} < 0$, *and* $\frac{dy}{dx} < 0.$ (3)

If $x > 3$, then $x - 3 > 0$, $\sqrt[3]{x - 3} > 0$, *and* $\frac{dy}{dx} > 0.$ (4)

Hence, y has a minimum at $x = 3$; the minimum value is $y = 0$. In Figure 46, the minimum point $(3, 0)$ on the graph of (1) is called a **cusp.**

EXERCISE 21

Recall Section 36 on page 52, and find dy/dx and dx/dy. Locate each point on the graph of the equation where the tangent is horizontal or vertical. Then, use this information to obtain the graph.

1. $y = \frac{1}{8}x^3.$ 2. $y = 9 - x^2.$ 3. $x = 4 - y^2.$ 4. $x = y^4.$
5. $x = 3y^2 - 12y + 7.$ 6. $x^2 + y^2 = 9.$
7. $x^2 + y^2 - 4x + 6y = 3.$ 8. $y^2 = x^2 - 2x - 3.$

Find any relative extremum of the function of x by use of the proper test. Then, graph the function, with each horizontal or vertical tangent shown.

9. $y = x^{\frac{2}{3}}.$ 10. $y = (x - 2)^{\frac{1}{3}}.$ 11. $y = x^{\frac{4}{3}}.$ 12. $y = x^{\frac{5}{3}}.$
13. $y = (x + 2)^{\frac{2}{3}}.$ 14. $y = (x + 3)^{\frac{1}{3}}.$ 15. $y = -(x - 1)^{\frac{2}{3}}.$

Graph the equation, with dy/dx and dx/dy used to locate the points where the tangent to the graph is horizontal or vertical.

16. $x^{\frac{1}{2}} + y^{\frac{1}{2}} = 4.$ 17. $x^{\frac{2}{3}} + y^{\frac{2}{3}} = a^{\frac{2}{3}}, (a > 0).$

Note 1. The curve in Problem 17 is called the **hypocycloid** with four cusps.

18. $2x^2 - 2xy + y^2 = 8.$ 19. $3x^2 - 2xy + y^2 = 108.$
20. $x^2 - 2xy + 3y^2 - 2x + 2y = 17.$

★21. Test the function $f(x)$ for extrema, if it is defined as follows:

$$f(x) = -x \text{ if } x \leq 0; \quad f(x) = \sqrt{x} \text{ if } x > 0.$$

46. Concavity of a graph

Consider the graph, C, of a function $y = f(x)$ in Figure 47. If a point $P:(x, y)$ moves to the right on C, the tangent to C at P rotates *counterclockwise*, and C remains *above* the tangent. In such a case, it is said that C is *concave upward*, or *convex downward*. In Figure 48, the tangent rotates *clockwise* as P moves to the right, and C is *below* the tangent. In this case, it is said that C is *concave downward*, or *convex upward*. To state that the tangent rotates *counterclockwise*, as in Figure 47, means that the corresponding slope $f'(x)$ is an *increasing* function. To state that the rotation is *clockwise*, as in Figure 48, means that $f'(x)$ is a *decreasing* function. These remarks are formalized as follows, under the assumption that $f'(x)$ exists.

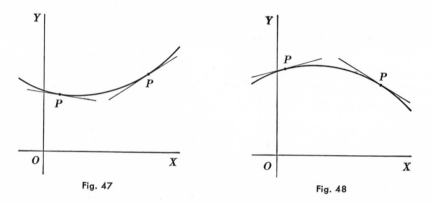

Fig. 47   Fig. 48

DEFINITION III. *To state that the graph of a function* $y = f(x)$ *is* **concave upward** *at* $x = x_0$ *means that, if* x *is near* x_0, *then* $f'(x)$ *is an increasing function. To say that the graph is* **concave downward** *means that* $f'(x)$ *is a decreasing function if* x *is near* x_0.

Note 1. To say that a graph is concave in some *sense*, upward or downward, on an interval of values of x, will mean that the property holds at every value of x on the interval.

Suppose that $f(x)$ has a second derivative, $f''(x)$, and hence also a first derivative, $f'(x)$. Since $f''(x)$ is the rate of change of $f'(x)$, then $f'(x)$ is an *increasing* or a *decreasing* function at any value of x according as $f''(x) > 0$ or $f''(x) < 0$. This leads to tests for concavity.

Suppose that $f''(x)$ *is continuous at* $x = x_0$. *Then, at* $x = x_0$, *the graph of* $y = f(x)$ *is*

$$\text{concave upward if} \quad \frac{d^2y}{dx^2}\bigg|_{x=x_0} > 0; \tag{1}$$

$$\text{concave downward if} \quad \frac{d^2y}{dx^2}\bigg|_{x=x_0} < 0. \tag{2}$$

Proof of (1). Since $f''(x_0) > 0$ and $f''(x)$ is continuous at $x = x_0$, then, if x is sufficiently near x_0, it follows that $f''(x) > 0$ and $f'(x)$ is an *increasing* function. Hence, by Definition III, the graph of $y = f(x)$ is concave upward at $x = x_0$.

ILLUSTRATION 1. If $f(x) = x^3 - 3x^2 - 5x + 2$, then

$$f'(x) = 3x^2 - 6x - 5 \quad and \quad f''(x) = 6x - 6.$$

Since $f''(3) = 12$, the graph of $y = f(x)$ is concave upward at $x = 3$.

A graph of a function $y = f(x)$ is exhibited in Figure 49. Notice that, if we move to the right, the curve changes from concave downward to concave upward at P. There is a tangent to the graph at P, and the curve crosses this tangent at P. According to the following terminology, we then refer to P as an *inflection point* of the graph; the tangent PT is called the *inflection tangent* at P.

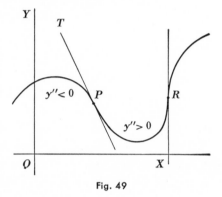

Fig. 49

DEFINITION IV. *Suppose that the graph of $y = f(x)$ has a tangent at $x = x_0$. Then, to say that the graph has an **inflection point** at $x = x_0$ means that, if x is sufficiently near x_0, the graph is concave in one sense if $x < x_0$, and in the opposite sense if $x > x_0$.*

ILLUSTRATION 2. In Figure 49, R is an inflection point at which the tangent is vertical, and hence $f'(x)$ and $f''(x)$ do not exist at R.

Assume that the graph of $y = f(x)$ has an inflection point with a nonvertical tangent at $x = x_0$, as at P in Figure 50, where the broken-line curve is the graph of $y' = f'(x)$. Then, $f'(x_0)$ exists; also, $f'(x)$ is an *increasing function on one side of x_0,* and a *decreasing function on the other side.* These facts demonstrate the following result.

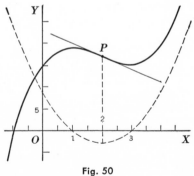

Fig. 50

$$\left\{ \begin{array}{l} \textit{If the graph of } y = f(x) \textit{ has an inflection point with a non-} \\ \textit{vertical tangent at } x = x_0, \textit{ then the function } y' = f'(x) \textit{ has} \\ \textit{either a relative maximum or a relative minimum at } x = x_0. \end{array} \right\} \quad (3)$$

The following result states a *necessary* condition for an inflection point where $f''(x)$ exists.

THEOREM IV. *Assume that the function $y = f(x)$ has a second derivative, $f''(x)$, at $x = x_0$ and that the graph of $y = f(x)$ has an inflection point at $x = x_0$. Then, $f''(x_0) = 0$.*

Proof. By (3), the function $y' = f'(x)$ has an extremum at $x = x_0$. Hence, the derivative of $f'(x)$ is zero at $x = x_0$, or $f''(x_0) = 0$.

On the graph of $y = f(x)$, where $f''(x)$ is continuous, a change in *the sign of $f''(x)$* as x increases through a value x_0 is equivalent to a change in *the sense of concavity*, because of (1) and (2). Hence, from Definition IV, we obtain the following test, illustrated at P in Figure 50 on page 77. The test applies even at a point $x = x_0$ where the inflection tangent is vertical, so that $f'(x_0)$ and $f''(x_0)$ do not exist.

$$\left\{ \begin{array}{l} \textbf{The graph of } y = f(x) \textbf{ has an inflection point at} \\ x = x_0 \textbf{ if and only if } f''(x) \textbf{ changes sign at } x = x_0. \end{array} \right\} \qquad (4)$$

47. Tests for extrema by use of the second derivative

In discussing a procedure for graphing a function $y = f(x)$, any use of $f'(x)$ or $f''(x)$ at a point $x = x_0$ will imply that $f'(x)$ and $f''(x)$ are continuous at $x = x_0$. By use of results concerning concavity, we can supplement earlier tests for extrema.

Suppose that, at $x = x_0$, the graph of $y = f(x)$ has a horizontal tangent and that $f''(x_0) > 0$. Then, the graph is concave upward at $x = x_0$ and has the appearance illustrated in (β) of Figure 51; thus, $f(x)$ has a minimum at $x = x_0$. Similarly, if $f'(x_0) = 0$ and $f''(x_0) < 0$, then the graph is concave downward and $f(x)$ has a maximum at $x = x_0$, as in (α) of Figure 51. These remarks prove the following sufficient conditions for extrema.

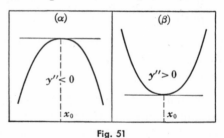

Fig. 51

$$\left\{ \begin{array}{l} \textbf{2d Deriv.} \\ \textbf{Test} \end{array} \right\} \quad \begin{array}{l} \textit{for a minimum,} \quad f'(x_0) = 0 \textit{ and } f''(x_0) > 0; \qquad (1) \\ \textit{for a maximum,} \quad f'(x_0) = 0 \textit{ and } f''(x_0) < 0. \qquad (2) \end{array}$$

ILLUSTRATION 1. If $\qquad\qquad y = x^3 - 3x^2 - 9x + 5, \qquad\qquad (3)$

then $\qquad\qquad y' = 3(x - 3)(x + 1) \quad and \quad y'' = 6(x - 1). \qquad (4)$

We find $y' = 0$ at $x = 3$ and $x = -1$, the critical values for extrema. We test by use of (1) and (2):

$$\text{if } x = 3 \text{ then } y'' = 12; \quad \text{if } x = -1 \text{ then } y'' = -12.$$

Hence, y has a maximum at $x = -1$ and a minimum at $x = 3$. From (3), the corresponding maximum and minimum values of y are 10 and -22. A graph of (3) is observed in Figure 38 on page 68.

SUMMARY. *To locate extrema and inflection points for the graph of $y = f(x)$, at points where $f'(x)$ and $f''(x)$ are continuous.*

1. *Solve $f'(x) = 0$ to obtain critical values of x for extrema. Test each critical value $x = x_0$ by computing $f''(x_0)$. If this test fails, use the test of page 70.*

2. *Solve $f''(x) = 0$ to obtain critical values of x for inflection points with nonvertical tangents; test by use of* (4) *on page 78.*

EXAMPLE 1.   Graph $$y = x^3 - 6x^2 + 9x + 15. \tag{5}$$

SOLUTION.   1. From (5), $$y' = 3(x - 3)(x - 1); \tag{6}$$

$$y'' = 6(x - 2). \tag{7}$$

2. The solutions of $y' = 0$ are $x = 1$ and $x = 3$.

Test for extrema: at $x = 1$, $y'' = -6$;   at $x = 3$, $y'' = +6$.

Hence, there is a maximum at $x = 1$ and a minimum at $x = 3$.

3. If $y'' = 0$ then $x = 2$. We find $y'' < 0$ when $x < 2$, and $y'' > 0$ when $x > 2$. Hence, by (4) on page 78, there is an inflection point at $x = 2$, where the curve changes from concave *downward* to concave *upward*. If $x = 2$ then $y = 17$ and $y' = -3$. Thus, the inflection tangent is $y + 3x = 23$.

4. The maximum, minimum, inflection point, and other solutions of (5) were plotted to give the graph of (5) in Figure 50, page 77.

Comment. With the vertical axis renamed as the y'-axis, the broken-line curve in Figure 50 is the graph of (6), and illustrates (3) on page 77. Essential details of the solution are given in the following table.

x	1	3	2	$x < 2$	$x > 2$
y	19	15	17		
y'	0	0	-3		
y''	-6	$+6$	0	< 0	> 0
CONCLUSION	MAX.	MIN.	INFL. PT.		

EXAMPLE 2.   Graph the function $$y = (x - 2)^3 + 2. \tag{8}$$

SOLUTION.   1. $$y' = 3(x - 2)^2 \quad and \quad y'' = 6(x - 2).$$

2. $y' = 0$ when $x = 2$. If $x = 2$, then $y'' = 0$, and the test $[(1), (2)]$ for an extremum fails. Since $y' > 0$ if $x \neq 2$, then y' *does not change sign at $x = 2$*; hence there is no extremum at $x = 2$.

3. $y'' = 0$ if $x = 2$. We apply test (4) of page 78:

$$y'' < 0 \text{ if } x < 2; \quad y'' > 0 \text{ if } x > 2.$$

Hence, there is an inflection point at $x = 2$. Since $y' = 0$ at $x = 2$, the inflection tangent is horizontal. A graph of (8) is in Figure 40, page 70.

Note 1. The Summary for graphing a function $y = f(x)$ does not apply at a value $x = x_0$ as described below. In such a case, we may use the following routine in testing for an extremum or inflection point. This method, with respect to extrema, was met on page 75.

1. *Locate each point $x = x_0$ where $f(x)$ is continuous but $f'(x_0)$ does not exist, or where $f'(x_0)$ exists and $f''(x_0)$ does not exist.*

2. *Test $x = x_0$ for an extremum by Theorem III on page 69; if no extremum is shown, test for an inflection point by (4), page 78.*

ILLUSTRATION 2.   To graph $$y = (x - 3)^{\frac{1}{3}}, \qquad (9)$$

we obtain $$\frac{dy}{dx} = \frac{1}{3(x - 3)^{\frac{2}{3}}}; \quad \frac{d^2y}{dx^2} = -\frac{2}{9(x - 3)^{\frac{5}{3}}}; \quad \frac{dx}{dy} = 3(x - 3)^{\frac{2}{3}}. \qquad (10)$$

Hence, y' and y'' are not defined at $x = 3$, and $dx/dy = 0$ at $x = 3$. Thus, the graph has a vertical tangent at $x = 3$. Also, $y' > 0$ if $x \neq 3$, and hence y' does not change sign at $x = 3$, so that there is *no extremum at $x = 3$.* However, $y'' > 0$ if $x < 3$ and $y'' < 0$ if $x > 3$. Hence, y'' changes sign at $x = 3$; thus, there is an inflection point at $x = 3$. A graph of (9) is in Figure 52.

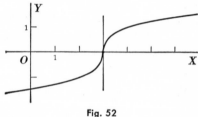

Fig. 52

EXERCISE 22

Graph the equation. Locate each extremum by use of a test involving a second derivative, if possible. Find each inflection point and inflection tangent where convenient. Consider using dx/dy as well as dy/dx.

1. $y = \frac{1}{3}x^3 - \frac{1}{2}x^2 - 6x + 2$.   　　2. $y = -x^3 + 3x^2 + 24x + 7$.

3. $y = x^3 + 9x^2 + 27x - 5$.   　　4. $y = x^3 - 3x^2 + 3x - 4$.

5. $y = -x^3 - 3x^2 - 6x + 2$.   　　6. $y = 2x^3 + 6x^2 + 24x - 5$.

7. $y = (x - 2)^4$.   　　8. $y = (x + 3)^2$.   　　9. $y = (x + 1)^3$.

10. $y = (2 - x)^5$.   　　11. $y = x^4 - 2x^3$.   　　12. $y = x^5 - x^4$.

13. $y = 3x^4 - 8x^3 + 6x^2 - 5$.   　　14. $y = x^4 - 6x^2 - 8x - 5$.

15. $y = (x - 1)(x + 2)^3$.   　　16. $y = x^2(x - 1)^3$.

17. $y^3 = x + 3y$.   　　18. $x = 2y^3 - 3y^2 - 12y + 7$.

HINT.   Interchange the roles of x and y in the Summary, page 79.

19. $x = 2y^3 - 9y^2 + 12y + 12$.   　　20. $x = y^2(y - 2)^2$.

21. $y = (2x - 1)^{\frac{1}{3}}$.   　　22. $y = (x - 3)^{\frac{2}{3}}$.   　　23. $y = x(x - 2)^{\frac{1}{3}}$.

Find each extremum of the function of x without drawing a graph. For each critical value of x, use whichever test is the more convenient.

24. $y = (x - a)^4(x - b)^3$, with $b < a$.

25. $y = (x - a)^n$, where n is an even positive integer.

26. $y = (x - a)^n$, where n is an odd positive integer.

27. $y = (x - a)^n(x - b)^m$, where n and m are positive integers, with n even and m odd, and $a < b$.

Graph by use of just the first derivatives, dy/dx and dx/dy.

28. $y = (x - 2)^{\frac{2}{3}}(x + 1)^{\frac{1}{3}}$.   **29.** $y = (x - 1)^{\frac{5}{3}}(x - 3)^{\frac{2}{3}}$.

★**30.** If k is any positive constant, find each maximum or minimum of the function $y = (k + 2x)^{\frac{2}{3}}(k - x)^{\frac{1}{3}}$.

48. Graphing of rational functions

Any rational function of x can be written in the form $y = P(x)/Q(x)$ where $P(x)$ and $Q(x)$ are polynomials with no common polynomial factor except for constants. Hence, $P(x)$ and $Q(x)$ are not zero simultaneously for any value of x. If $x = c$ is a real root of $Q(x) = 0$, then y is not defined at $x = c$. Also, y is defined and continuous at all values of x where $Q(x) \neq 0$. As a characteristic feature, the graph of $y = P(x)/Q(x)$ has an *asymptote* perpendicular to the x-axis corresponding to each real root $x = c$ of the equation $Q(x) = 0$. That is, $|y| \to \infty$ as $x \to c$; we then say that y has a **pole** at $x = c$. Also, $y = 0$ if and only if $P(x) = 0$. Hence, the **zeros** * of the function $P(x)/Q(x)$ are the *zeros of the numerator $P(x)$*; the *poles* of the function are the *zeros of the denominator $Q(x)$*. We shall observe later that the graph of a rational function of x also may have a horizontal asymptote. To graph a rational function which is not merely a polynomial, as in previous sections, it is useful to refer to the following routine.

SUMMARY. *To graph a rational function $y = P(x)/Q(x)$.*

1. Horizontal asymptote. *Evaluate $\lim_{|x| \to \infty} P(x)/Q(x)$. If this limit is finite, L, then the line $y = L$ is a horizontal asymptote of the graph. If the limit is infinite, no horizontal asymptote exists.*

2. Poles. *Solve $Q(x) = 0$; if $x = c$ is any real root, then the line $x = c$ is a vertical asymptote.*

3. Zeros. *Solve $P(x) = 0$ to obtain the x-intercepts.*

4. Derivatives. *Calculate y', and also y'' if it is simple.*

5. Extrema. *Solve $y' = 0$ to find the critical values of x for extrema; †
test by use of y'' or the method of page 70.*

6. Inflection points. *Test by use of y'', if it is convenient.*

7. *Draw the graph by use of the asymptotes, x-intercepts, extrema, inflection points, and other computed points.*

---

* A *zero* of a function $f(x)$ is a value of x where $f(x) = 0$.
† y' exists except where $Q(x) = 0$, and hence where y is not defined; thus, there are no extrema where y' does not exist.

EXAMPLE 1.   Graph $$y = \frac{2(x^2 - 4x)}{x^2 - 4x - 5}.\tag{1}$$

SOLUTION.   1. $$\lim_{|x|\to\infty} y = \lim_{|x|\to\infty} \frac{2(x^2 - 4x)}{x^2 - 4x - 5} = \lim_{|x|\to\infty} \frac{2\left(1 - \dfrac{4}{x}\right)}{1 - \dfrac{4}{x} - \dfrac{5}{x^2}} = 2.\tag{2}$$

Hence, the line $y = 2$ is an asymptote.

2. *Poles.* $x^2 - 4x - 5 = 0$ if $x = 5$ or $x = -1$.   Then $|y| \to \infty$ as $x \to 5$ and as $x \to -1$, or the lines $x = 5$ and $x = -1$ are asymptotes of the graph. There is no value of y when $x = 5$ and when $x = -1$.

3. *Zeros.*   From $x^2 - 4x = 0$, the x-intercepts are $x = 0$ and $x = 4$.

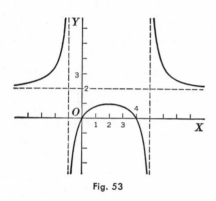

Fig. 53

4. From (1),

$$y' = \frac{20(2 - x)}{(x^2 - 4x - 5)^2}.\tag{3}$$

Since y'' is complicated, we shall not test for inflection points.

5. *Extrema.*   The only solution of $y' = 0$ is $x = 2$.   If $x < 2$, then $y' > 0$; if $x > 2$, then $y' < 0$.   Hence, there is a maximum at $x = 2$; from (1), the maximum value of y is $y = \frac{8}{9}$.   The graph is in Figure 53.

49. General curve tracing

In graphing an equation $f(x, y) = 0$, we consider those parts of the following routine which are applicable conveniently.

I. *Solve for one variable (or, for each variable) in terms of the other variable. Use the result to find the ranges for x and y.*

II. *Find the x-intercepts and y-intercepts.*

III. *Test for asymptotes. (Does either variable become infinite as the other variable approaches some value?   What is the limit of y, or x, as the other variable becomes infinite?)*

IV. *Notice any symmetry:*

        symmetric to y-axis if $f(-x, y) = f(x, y)$;   (1)

        symmetric to x-axis if $f(x, -y) = f(x, y)$;   (2)

        symmetric to origin if $f(-x, -y) = f(x, y)$.   (3)

V. *Calculate dy/dx and dx/dy; locate horizontal or vertical tangents.*

VI. *When second derivatives are convenient, locate inflection points.*

EXAMPLE 1. If $a > 0$, graph $\qquad\qquad\qquad x^3 + xy^2 = 2ay^2.$ $\qquad\qquad$ (4)

SOLUTION. 1. Solve for y: $\qquad y^2 = \dfrac{x^3}{2a - x};\quad y = \pm \sqrt{\dfrac{x^3}{2a - x}}.$ $\qquad$ (5)

The fraction in (5) is negative if $x < 0$, or $x > 2a$. Hence, since $y^2 \geq 0$, we must have $0 \leq x < 2a$. Then, y assumes all real values.

2. y is not defined at $x = 2a$, and $|y| \to \infty$ as $x \to 2a-$ (from the left). Hence, the line $x = 2a$ is a vertical asymptote.

3. Substitution of $-y$ for y leaves (4) unaltered. Hence, the graph is symmetric to the x-axis.

4. Calculate dy/dx by differentiation in (5):

$$2yy' = \frac{3x^2(2a - x) + x^3}{(2a - x)^2}, \quad or \quad y' = \frac{x^2(3a - x)}{y(2a - x)^2}.$$

By use of (5), $\qquad\qquad y' = \pm \dfrac{(3a - x)\sqrt{x}}{\sqrt{(2a - x)^3}}.$ $\qquad\qquad\qquad$ (6)

In (6), the fraction is equal to zero at $x = 3a$ and $x = 0$. Since $x = 3a$ is outside the range for x (found above), the only horizontal tangent occurs when $x = 0$; then $y = 0$. The graph is on page 594, and has a cusp at the origin. The curve is called the **cissoid** of DIOCLES.

EXERCISE 23

Graph the function, or equation.

1. $y = \dfrac{1}{(x + 3)^2}.$

2. $y = \dfrac{1}{x(x + 1)}.$

3. $y = \dfrac{8 - 4x}{x + 2}.$

4. $y = \dfrac{3}{x^2 + 4}.$

5. $x = \dfrac{6y}{y^2 + 4}.$

6. $\dfrac{2x + 2}{x - 3}.$

7. $\dfrac{2(x^2 - 4)}{x^2 - 9}.$

8. $\dfrac{x - 2}{x^2 + 4}.$

9. $x = \dfrac{y - 3}{y^2 + 9}.$

10. $\dfrac{3x^2 + x - 2}{x^2 + x - 6}.$

11. $\dfrac{x^3}{x + 2}.$

12. $x = \dfrac{3y^2 + 6y}{y^2 + 2y - 8}.$

Graph the equation. Any constant (a, b, k) is considered positive. Carry out the discussion without using a particular value for any constant. Then, in graphing, use a particular value for each constant.

13. $2xy + 2 = x + 5y.$

14. $xy^2 - 2x = 2y^2 - xy.$

15. The **semicubical parabola**: $y^2 = kx^3.$

16. $x^2y^2 - 4y^2 = x + 3.$

17. $y^2 = (x - 2)(x - 4).$

HINT for Problem 17. First graph $z = (x - 2)(x - 4)$ roughly, and by inspection specify the range for x to make y real.

18. $y^2 = x(x - 1)(x - 4).$

19. $y^2 = (x + 2)(x - 2)(x - 4).$

20. The **witch** of AGNESI: $x^2y = 4k^2(2k - y).$

21. The **cruciform curve:** $x^2y^2 = k^2(x^2 + y^2)$.

22. The **bipartite cubic:** $y^2 = x(x-a)(x-b)$; $0 < a < b$.

23. The **serpentine:** $y = \dfrac{k^2x}{x^2 + a^2}$.   **24.** The **strophoid:** $y^2 = x^2\left(\dfrac{k+x}{k-x}\right)$.

25. The **trisectrix** of MACLAURIN: $y^2 = \dfrac{3ax^2 - x^3}{x+a}$.

50. Applications of maxima and minima

In a verbal problem involving determination of a maximum or a minimum for a quantity, the following procedure frequently is convenient.

I. *Introduce natural auxiliary variables, and express the fundamental quantity, W, as a function of these variables.*

II. *If two * auxiliary variables were used, search for an equation involving them. Then, use this relation to eliminate one variable. Thus, W is expressed as a function of just one independent variable.*

III. *Maximize or minimize W, and test for the extremum.*

EXAMPLE 1. Find the altitude of the right circular cone † of maximum volume which can be inscribed in a sphere of radius r.

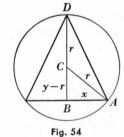
Fig. 54

SOLUTION. 1. Figure 54 shows a cross section of the sphere through its center, with the cross section of an inscribed cone. Let x be the base radius, y be the altitude, and V be the volume of the cone. Then, $V = \frac{1}{3}\pi x^2 y$. We desire to maximize V.

2. From Figure 54, $\overline{AB}^2 + \overline{BC}^2 = r^2$ and $BD = y$. Hence,

$$x^2 + (y-r)^2 = r^2, \quad or \quad x^2 = 2ry - y^2. \tag{1}$$

Thus, $$V = \tfrac{1}{3}\pi y(2ry - y^2). \tag{2}$$

Let $W = 3V/\pi$. Then, $$W = y(2ry - y^2). \tag{3}$$

Since V and W attain any maximum at the same value of y, we choose to investigate extrema for the simpler function W.

3. From (3), $$\frac{dW}{dy} = 4ry - 3y^2 = y(4r - 3y). \tag{4}$$

Thus, $W' = 0$ at $y = 0$ and $y = \frac{4}{3}r$.

4. *Test of the critical value.* The range for y is $0 < y < 2r$. If $y \to 0$ or $y \to 2r$, then $V \to 0$. Hence, V has a maximum at some value of y. Since only $y = \frac{4}{3}r$ is possible, the maximum volume occurs at $y = \frac{4}{3}r$.

---

* If k variables are used, search for $(k-1)$ relations between them.
† Hereafter, in this chapter, "*cone*" and "*cylinder*" will mean "*right circular cone*" and "*right circular cylinder*," respectively.

Comment 1. Notice that, as in (3), we may replace any *function* by a *constant times the function*, in determination of the value of an independent variable which gives an extremum. Also, we illustrated how *verbal* reasoning sometimes may replace the usual analytical test of a critical value. The second derivative test would have applied conveniently.

Comment 2. Example 1 demands an *absolute* maximum. Since $0 < y < 2r$, any absolute maximum of V is attained at an *interior* point on the range for y, and also is a *relative* maximum. Hence, the single *relative* maximum obtained at $y = \frac{4}{3}r$ also is the *absolute* maximum.

EXAMPLE 2. A rectangular field along a river with a straight bank is to have an area of 800 square yards, and is to be fenced along the sides not on the bank. Find the dimensions to minimize the fencing.

SOLUTION. 1. Let y yards be the length along the bank, and x yards be the other dimension, as in Figure 55. Let P be the length in yards of the required fence. Then,

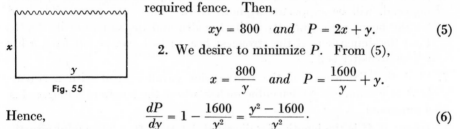

$$xy = 800 \quad and \quad P = 2x + y. \tag{5}$$

2. We desire to minimize P. From (5),

$$x = \frac{800}{y} \quad and \quad P = \frac{1600}{y} + y.$$

Fig. 55

Hence,

$$\frac{dP}{dy} = 1 - \frac{1600}{y^2} = \frac{y^2 - 1600}{y^2}. \tag{6}$$

Thus, $P' = 0$ if $y = \pm 40$, where only $y = 40$ is pertinent.

3. *Test of the critical value.* From (6), $P'' = 3200/y^3$, which is *positive* at $y = 40$. Hence, P has a minimum at $y = 40$. Then, from $x = 800/y$, we obtain $x = 20$. The desired dimensions are 20×40, in yards.

EXAMPLE 3. In an isosceles triangle, the base is $10'$ and the altitude is $20'$. A rectangle has its base on the base of the triangle, and two vertices on its equal sides, as in the figure. Find the dimensions of the rectangle, to give its maximum area.

SOLUTION. 1. For the rectangle, let the length of the base be $2x$ feet, the altitude be y feet, and the area be W square feet. Then, $W = 2xy$.

2. In Figure 56, △'s ABC and DBE are similar, with $AB = 5 - x$. Hence, from ratios of corresponding sides,

$$\frac{5 - x}{y} = \frac{5}{20}, \quad or \quad y = 20 - 4x.$$

Therefore, $W = 2x(20 - 4x)$. Then, we desire to maximize the function W. The student may verify that the maximum occurs when $x = \frac{5}{2}$.

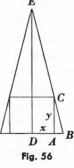

Fig. 56

EXERCISE 24

1. A rectangular field is to be surrounded by a fence, and also will have a similar fence, parallel to one side, dividing the field into two equal parts. Find the dimensions of the field to minimize the cost of fencing, if the area is to be 3750 square yards.

2. A piece of wire 40″ long is bent to form a rectangle. Find its dimensions, to give maximum area.

3. A box with open top will be made by cutting equal squares from the corners of a 10″ × 20″ piece of copper, and folding up the sides. Find the size of the square to give maximum capacity for the box.

4. Find the dimensions of a rectangular parallelepiped with square base, open top, volume of 256 cubic inches, and minimum surface area.

5. Find an equation for the line through the point (3, 2) making with the coordinate axes a triangle of minimum area, in the first quadrant.

6. A wooden beam of rectangular cross section, given length, and specified material, will be supported at both ends. Then, the permissible load for the beam varies directly as its breadth and the square of its depth. Find the dimensions of the strongest beam which can be cut from a log whose diameter is 2′.

7. Find the dimensions of the rectangular parallelepiped with a square base and volume of 64,000 cubic inches, where the length of a diagonal is a minimum.

   HINT. If H is the length of a diagonal, let $W = H^2$. Then minimize W, instead of working with H, *in order to avoid radicals.*

8. A closed box is to be a rectangular parallelepiped with a square base and a capacity of 1125 cubic feet. The cost of the material for the box per square foot is 5¢ for the base and top, and 15¢ for the sides. Find the dimensions of the box to minimize the cost of the material.

9. A farmer buys cattle weighing 500 pounds each, at 25¢ per pound, to fatten for the market. He estimates that each animal will gain ¾ pound per day, at a cost of 9¢ per pound for feed and care. The selling price, starting at 25¢ per pound, can be expected to decrease by .02¢ per day over the next 6 months. When should he plan to sell the cattle to realize maximum profit?

10. Find the point on the curve $y^2 = 4x$ which is nearest to (2, 1).

11. Find the dimensions of the rectangle of maximum area which can be inscribed in a circle whose radius is 8′.

12. A restaurant chain, in planning a new cafeteria, is aware that, with a capacity of 50 to 100 chairs, the monthly profit per chair will be $24. Within reasonable limits on size, if the capacity grows beyond 100 chairs, the monthly profit per chair, for the whole cafeteria, decreases by 10¢ on account of each added chair. What seating capacity would give the maximum profit?

13. Find the dimensions of a rectangle with assigned perimeter, h, and minimum length for the diagonal.

14. Find the dimensions of the rectangular box with square base and open top, of maximum capacity, to be made with 48 square feet of material.

15. Find the altitude of the cone of maximum volume which can be obtained by rotating a right triangle about one leg, if the hypotenuse is $3'$ long.

16. Find the base and altitude of the isosceles triangle of maximum area which can be inscribed in a circle of radius $8''$. (Square the area.)

17. A parabolic segment is bounded on the left by the parabola $y^2 = 8x$ and on the right by the line $x = 8$. A rectangle will have two vertices on the line $x = 8$ and the other two vertices on the parabola. Find the dimensions of the rectangle to maximize its area.

18. A fence, $16'$ high, is $2'$ from a high wall. Find the length of the shortest ladder which will reach over the fence to the wall.

19. A closed rectangular parallelepiped will have a square base, and a volume of 16,000 cubic inches. The base and top will be made of material twice as expensive as that for the sides. Find the dimensions to minimize the cost of the material.

20. A U-shaped gutter will have a cross section consisting of a semicircle at the bottom, with vertical sides of equal length. Find the radius of the semicircle and the length of a side, to give maximum capacity, if the length of a cross section is $10''$.

21. Find the dimensions of the cylinder of maximum curved surface which can be inscribed in a sphere of radius r.

22. A gutter will have a horizontal plane bottom and equally inclined sides, where the bottom and each side is $5''$ wide. Find the width of the gutter across the top, to create maximum capacity.

23. A rectangle is placed inside a triangle with two vertices of the rectangle on the base of the triangle, and one vertex on each of the other sides of the triangle. If the lengths of the base and corresponding altitude of the triangle are $20'$ and $8'$, respectively, find the dimensions of the rectangle to maximize its area.

24. A messenger is in a motorboat 24 miles from a straight shore. He wishes to reach a point P which is 150 miles along the shore from the point on it nearest the boat. His boat can travel 20 miles per hour and then, on reaching land, he will travel by auto at 60 miles per hour. At what point on the shore should he direct his boat, to meet the automobile, in order to reach P in minimum time?

25. Let p be the unknown probability of success for a certain event at any trial. In n trials, suppose that h successes have been observed. Then, in mathematical statistics, the *maximum likelihood estimator* for p is defined as that value $p = \hat{p}$ which maximizes the likelihood function $L(p) = p^h(1 - p)^{n-h}$. Find $\hat{p}$.

26. An experimenter obtains $x_1, x_2, \cdots, x_n$ as n measurements of the value of a quantity whose true value Z is unknown. As an approximation to Z, he decides to take that number Z for which

$$(x_1 - Z)^2 + (x_2 - Z)^2 + \cdots + (x_n - Z)^2$$

is a minimum. Prove that $Z = (x_1 + x_2 + \cdots + x_n)/n$, which is called the **arithmetic mean** of the x's.

27. Find the dimensions of the cone of minimum volume which can be circumscribed about a sphere of radius r.

28. Find the dimensions of the rectangular parallelepiped with a square base and maximum volume which can be inscribed in a given sphere.

29. A certain manufacturing process is maintained by use of a machine whose original cost is C. Suppose that the expense of taxes and interest per year is rC, where r is a fixed rate; the amount which would be spent on repairs in x years is * bx^2; if the machine is to be used just x years before replacement, the annual depreciation charge is C/x, and the average annual cost of operation is A. Then,*

$$A = rC + \frac{C}{x} + \frac{bx^2}{x}, \quad \text{or} \quad A = rC + \frac{C}{x} + bx.$$

Find the value of x which gives A its minimum value.

30. Alter Problem 29 by assuming that the amount which would be spent on repairs in x years is kx^3. Then,

$$A = rC + \frac{C}{x} + \frac{kx^3}{x}, \quad \text{or} \quad A = rC + \frac{C}{x} + kx^2.$$

Show that it is uneconomical to spend more than $\frac{1}{2}C$ on total repair costs.

In the remaining problems, refer to Note 1 on page 43.

With the given total-cost function, find the production, x, for which the average cost, A, is a minimum. Also, draw graphs of A and the marginal cost C' on the same coordinate system, to verify that the curves intersect where A has its minimum.

31. $C = x^3 - 6x^2 + 15x.$ **32.** $C = 2x^3 - 9x^2 + 10x.$

33. Let the total cost and demand curves be $C = x^3 - 15x^2 + 76x + 25$ and $p = 55 - 3x$. Find the number of units of production for which the total profit will be a maximum.

34. Prove that, if the profit assumes a maximum value at an output $x = x_0$ inside the possible range for x, then the marginal cost is equal to the marginal revenue at $x = x_0$. Verify this fact in Problem 33.

35. Let the demand and total cost curves for a manufacturer of a certain article be $p = 75 - 2x$ and $C = 350 + 12x + \frac{1}{4}x^2$, with $1000 as the money unit. Find the price at which the total profit is a maximum. Also, if the government imposes a tax of $\$\tau$ per article, find the increase in the consumer price (including tax) at which the total profit is a maximum.

* See page 312, *Plant Production Control*, by *Charles A. Koepke;* John Wiley & Sons. We obtain bx^2 by taking the *time-rate of increase* in repair cost as kx, where k is a constant.

51. An implicit function method in finding extrema

Suppose that just two auxiliary variables, say x and y, are introduced in a problem of the type just met in Section 50. Then, the analytical basis for the solution is as follows:

$$\left\{ \begin{array}{l} \textit{relation between } x \textit{ and } y, \\ \textit{based on problem constants} \end{array} \right\} \qquad g(x, y) = 0; \qquad (1)$$

$$\left\{ \begin{array}{l} \textit{function, } U, \textit{ to be} \\ \textit{given an extremum} \end{array} \right\} \qquad U = f(x, y). \qquad (2)$$

Instead of using (1) to eliminate one variable, say y, as in Section 50, sometimes it is convenient to consider (1) as defining y implicitly as a function of x, and to *retain both x and y until a final stage.* The routine is as follows.

I. *Select one variable, say x, to be the independent variable. Then, differentiate in (1) and (2) with respect to x; y' will arise from (1) and (2).*

II. *Solve for y' as given by differentiation in (1), and substitute the result in dU/dx as obtained from (2). Then, use $dU/dx = 0$ to obtain a necessary condition on x and y for an extremum of U.*

EXAMPLE 1. Find the shape of a solid cylinder of given volume with minimum surface area.

SOLUTION. 1. Let x, y, V, and S be the radius, altitude, volume, and surface area, respectively, for the cylinder, whose cross-section is seen in Figure 57. Then,

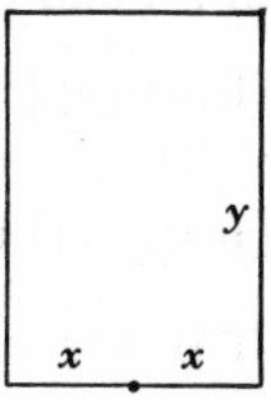

Fig. 57

$$\left\{ \begin{array}{l} \textit{relation between} \\ \textit{auxiliary variables} \end{array} \right\} \qquad V = \pi x^2 y, \quad \textit{or} \quad x^2 y = \frac{V}{\pi}; \qquad (3)$$

(function to minimize) $\qquad\qquad S = 2\pi xy + 2\pi x^2.$ $\qquad\qquad (4)$

Let $W = S/2\pi$. Then, we shall minimize W: $\qquad W = xy + x^2.$ $\qquad (5)$

2. Let x be the independent variable; (3) determines y as a function of x. Differentiate with respect to x; V is a constant:

[from (3)] $\qquad\qquad 2xy + x^2 y' = 0, \quad \textit{or} \quad y' = -\frac{2y}{x};$ $\qquad (6)$

[from (5) and (6)] $\qquad\qquad \dfrac{dW}{dx} = y + xy' + 2x = 2x - y.$ $\qquad (7)$

If W has an extremum, $\qquad\qquad 2x - y = 0.$ $\qquad\qquad (8)$

3. In the problem, $0 < x < \infty$. If $x \to \infty$, from (4) we see that $S \to \infty$. Suppose that $x \to 0$; since $V = \pi x(xy)$, and V is a constant, we see that $xy \to \infty$ and again $S \to \infty$. Hence, S has an absolute minimum for *at least one value* of x where $0 < x < \infty$. Since (8) can lead to just *one* extremum, then $y = 2x$ must give the minimum. That is, for minimum surface, the altitude y is equal to the diameter of the base.

EXAMPLE 2. A closed box will be a rectangular parallelepiped with a square base, as in Figure 58. The material for the sides will cost twice as much per square foot as the material for the top and bottom. Find the relative dimensions of the box, to minimize the expense of the material, for given capacity. (Disregard the thickness of the material in such a problem.)

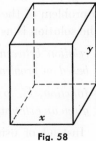

Fig. 58

SOLUTION. 1. Let x, y, V, k, and E represent a side of the base, the altitude, the volume, the cost per square unit of the sides, and the cost of the material, respectively, where V is a constant. Then,

(relation between variables) $\qquad\qquad V = x^2y;$ $\qquad\qquad\qquad$ (9)

(function to minimize) $\qquad\qquad E = 4kxy + kx^2.$ $\qquad\qquad$ (10)

Let $W = E/k$; we shall minimize W: $\qquad\quad W = 4xy + x^2.$ $\qquad\quad$ (11)

2. Let x be the independent variable, and differentiate with respect to x in (9) and (11), recalling that V is a constant:

[from (9)] $\qquad\qquad\qquad 2xy + x^2y' = 0, \quad or \quad y' = -\dfrac{2y}{x};$ $\qquad\quad$ (12)

[from (11) and (12)] $\qquad\qquad \dfrac{dW}{dx} = 4y + 4xy' + 2x = 2x - 4y.$ $\qquad$ (13)

If W has an extremum, then $2x - 4y = 0$ or $\qquad\qquad x = 2y.$ $\qquad\qquad$ (14)

3. In the problem, $0 < x < \infty$. If $x \to 0$ or if $x \to \infty$, the surface area of the box becomes infinite and thus E becomes infinite. Hence, E has a minimum. Since (14) leads to just one extremum, it must be the minimum. That is, for minimum cost, the length of a side of the base is twice the altitude.

EXERCISE 25

It is recommended that each problem be solved by the method involving use of an implicit function.

1. Find the dimensions of the rectangle of maximum area situated with two vertices on the diameter of a semicircle of radius r, and the other two vertices on the semicircle.

2. Find the dimensions of the rectangle of maximum perimeter which can be inscribed in a circle of radius r.

3. Find the relative dimensions * of a closed rectangular parallelepiped with a square base, a specified volume, and minimum surface area.

4. Find the relative dimensions of a solid cylinder with given volume and minimum surface area.

5. Find the shape of a rectangle with an assigned area and (*a*) minimum perimeter; (*b*) minimum length for a diagonal.

* That is, find a simple relation between the dimensions.

6. Find an equation for the line through point (a, b), where $a > 0$ and $b > 0$, making a triangle of minimum area with the coordinate axes in the first quadrant.

7. To reduce friction for water flowing in a channel with rectangular cross section, it is desired to minimize the surface area in contact with the water. Find the ratio of the depth to the breadth, to obtain the desired result, for a channel with specified capacity (that is, specified cross-section area).

8. Find the relative dimensions of the cylinder of maximum curved surface which can be inscribed in a given sphere.

9. A closed rectangular box with a square base is to be made from a given amount of material. Find the relative dimensions for maximum volume.

10. To construct a cylindrical container, we shall use material for the base and top which is twice as expensive, per square foot, as the material for the curved part of the surface. Find the ratio of the radius to the altitude, for minimum cost of material, with a given volume.

11. A cylinder is inscribed in a given cone, with the base of the cylinder on the base of the cone. Find the ratio of the base radius of the cylinder to its altitude, to maximize the cylinder's volume.

12. Find the relative dimensions of a solid cylinder with given surface area and maximum volume.

13. Find the relative dimensions of the cone of maximum volume which can be inscribed in a given sphere.

14. A perfume bottle is to be a rectangular parallelepiped, and will be placed inside a box which is an elliptic cylinder, where the cross section is an ellipse with major axis $4''$ and minor axis $2''$. Find the dimensions of the base of the bottle, to give maximum volume for a given height.

15. An observatory building will consist of a cylinder capped by a hemisphere. Find a relation between the base radius and the altitude of the cylinder to give a specified volume for the building, with minimum area for the floor and exterior surface, combined.

16. Find the ratio of the radius of the base to the altitude, for a conical tent of given capacity which will require the least material.

17. A vat with open top is to form a cylinder. Find the ratio of its base radius to the altitude, to yield a given volume with minimum surface.

18. Find the relative dimensions of a rectangular parallelepiped with a square base (a) if the length of a diagonal is assigned, and the volume is a maximum; (b) if the volume is assigned, and the length of a diagonal is a minimum.

19. A window will consist of a rectangle capped by a semicircle. The window frame will consist of the four sides of the rectangle and the semicircle. With an assigned length for the frame, find the ratio of the base to the altitude for the rectangle, in order to maximize the area for glass.

20. At what point on the ellipse $b^2x^2 + a^2y^2 = a^2b^2$, in the first quadrant, should a tangent be drawn in order that the triangle formed with the coordinate axes will have minimum area?

21. A cone is inscribed in a given cone, with the cones having the same axis, and the vertex of the inscribed cone at the center of the base of the given cone. Find the altitude of the inscribed cone, to maximize its volume.

22. Prove that, if $P:(x_0, y_0)$ is a point on the curve $y = f(x)$ at which $f'(x)$ exists, and if P is a point on the curve at minimum distance from the point (α, β), then (α, β) is on the normal to the curve at P.

23. A pyramid with a square base and maximum volume is inscribed in a sphere of radius r. Find the ratio of a side of the base to the altitude, for the pyramid.

52. Related rates

Suppose that two or more variables are related by a given equation, and that each variable is a function * of a certain independent variable, t. Then, on differentiating both sides of the equation with respect to t, we obtain a relation between the derivatives of the dependent variables with respect to t. If t is a measure of the time, we thus obtain a relation between the time-rates of change of the dependent variables.

EXAMPLE 1. A particle P is moving in an xy-plane. At any instant, the abscissa of P is increasing at the rate of .2 units per second and the ordinate is decreasing at the rate of .3 units per second. At what time-rate is the distance from the origin to P changing when P is at $(5, 12)$?

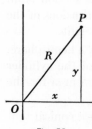

Fig. 59

SOLUTION. 1. In Figure 59, let $R = OP$. Let t be the time in seconds measured from any convenient instant. Then,

$$R^2 = x^2 + y^2, \tag{1}$$

where R, x, and y are functions of t, with $dx/dt = .2$ and $dy/dt = -.3$.

2. In (1), differentiate on both sides with respect to t, by use of the power formula (III) on page 38:

$$2R \frac{dR}{dt} = 2x \frac{dx}{dt} + 2y \frac{dy}{dt}, \quad or \quad \frac{dR}{dt} = \frac{xx' + yy'}{R}. \tag{2}$$

From (1), when $x = 5$ and $y = 12$ we find $R = 13$. Then, with $x' = .2$, $y' = -.3$, $x = 5$, $y = 12$, and $R = 13$, from (2) we obtain $dR/dt = -.2$. Or, R is decreasing at the rate of .2 units per second.

* All functions will be differentiable in our discussion.

Comment. Notice that we avoided radicals by *not solving* (1) *for R.*

EXAMPLE 2. A ladder is 50′ long and reaches from horizontal ground to a vertical wall. The lower end of the ladder is pulled from the wall at the rate of 5′ per second. How fast is the upper end of the ladder descending when the upper end is 48′ from the ground?

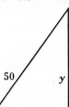

Fig. 60

SOLUTION. 1. At t seconds, measured from some instant, let the distance in feet of the ladder's lower end from the wall, and of the upper end from the ground, be x and y, respectively. Figure 60 shows the situation **at an arbitrary value of** t. Then,

$$x^2 + y^2 = 2500. \tag{3}$$

2. Each side of (3) is a function of t. On equating the derivatives of the two sides with respect to t, we find

$$2x\frac{dx}{dt} + 2y\frac{dy}{dt} = 0. \tag{4}$$

3. From (3), if $y = 48$ then $x = 14$. With $x = 14$, $y = 48$, and $dx/dt = 5$, from (4) we obtain

$$14(5) + 48\left(\frac{dy}{dt}\right) = 0, \quad or \quad \frac{dy}{dt} = -\frac{35}{24} \text{ ft. per sec.,}$$

where the result is *negative* because y is *decreasing*. That is, y is decreasing at the rate of $\frac{35}{24}$ ft. per sec.

EXAMPLE 3. A reservoir is in the shape of an inverted cone, with altitude 24′ and base radius 18′. Water is flowing in at the rate of 60π cubic feet per minute. How fast is the surface of the water rising when it is 12′ above the vertex of the cone?

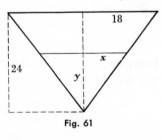

Fig. 61

SOLUTION. 1. At t minutes after the start, in Figure 61 let x feet be the radius, y feet be the altitude, and V cubic feet be the volume of the cone formed by the water. From similar triangles in Figure 61, $x = \frac{3}{4}y$ and hence

$$V = \frac{\pi x^2 y}{3}, \quad or \quad V = \frac{3\pi y^3}{16}; \quad \frac{dV}{dt} = \frac{9\pi y^2}{16}\frac{dy}{dt}. \tag{5}$$

2. From the data, $dV/dt = 60\pi$. Hence, with $y = 12$ in (5),

$$60\pi = \frac{9\pi(144)}{16}\frac{dy}{dt}, \quad or \quad \frac{dy}{dt} = \frac{20}{27}.$$

The water is rising at the rate of $\frac{20}{27}$ ft. per minute when $y = 12$.

Note 1. Suppose that s is a function of t **where $s = 0$ at $t = 0$.** Then, if k is a constant and $ds/dt = k$ at all values of t, it follows that the expression for s as a function of t is simply $s = kt$. If we interpret s as distance traveled in a path, and t as the time, then $s = kt$ is merely the familiar elementary result "*distance is equal to the rate times the time,*" for uniform motion.

EXAMPLE 4. A ship S_1 is sailing north at the rate of 20 miles per hour, and a ship S_2 is sailing west at the rate of 10 miles per hour. At noon, S_1 is 220 miles south of S_2. When will S_1 be closest to S_2?

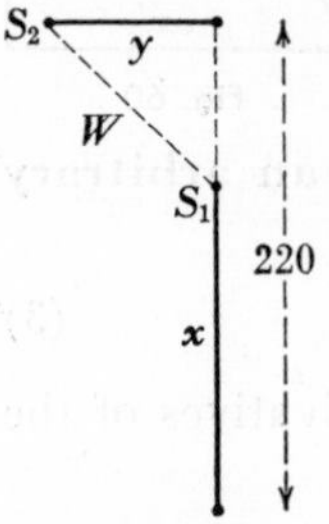

SOLUTION. 1. Let t represent the time in hours after noon; let x and y be the distances in miles traveled by S_1 and S_2, respectively, in t hours, and let W be the distance between S_1 and S_2 at time t. Then, from Note 1 and Figure 62,

$$x = 20t, \quad y = 10t, \quad W^2 = (220 - x)^2 + y^2; \quad or \qquad (6)$$

$$W^2 = (220 - 20t)^2 + 100t^2, \ or$$

$$W^2 = 500t^2 - 8800t + (220)^2. \qquad (7)$$

Fig. 62

2. Let $U = W^2$. Then, U and W attain any minimum at the same value of t. We choose to minimize U:

$$U = 500t^2 - 8800t + (220)^2; \quad \frac{dU}{dt} = 1000t - 8800. \qquad (8)$$

Hence, $dU/dt = 0$ when $1000t - 8800 = 0$, or $t = 8\frac{4}{5}$. Since $U'' = 1000 > 0$, then $t = 8\frac{4}{5}$ gives W its minimum value, for locations of S_1 south * of S_2. The corresponding time is 8:48 P.M.

EXAMPLE 5. If $u = \sqrt[3]{x^2 + xy}$, where $x = t + t^3$ and $y = t^2 - 4$, find du/dt at $t = 2$, without preliminary elimination of x and y.

SOLUTION. Let $v = x^2 + xy$. Then $u = v^{\frac{1}{3}}$ and

$$\frac{du}{dt} = \frac{1}{3} v^{-\frac{2}{3}} \frac{dv}{dt}. \qquad (9)$$

From $v = x^2 + xy$, $x = t + t^3$, and $y = t^2 - 4$, on differentiating with respect to t, we obtain

$$\frac{dv}{dt} = 2x \frac{dx}{dt} + y \frac{dx}{dt} + x \frac{dy}{dt}; \quad \frac{dx}{dt} = 1 + 3t^2; \quad \frac{dy}{dt} = 2t;$$

$$\frac{dv}{dt} = (1 + 3t^2)(2x + y) + 2tx.$$

From (9), $\qquad \dfrac{du}{dt} = \dfrac{1}{3} (x^2 + xy)^{-\frac{2}{3}}(2x + 6t^2x + 2tx + y + 3t^2y).$

If $t = 2$ then $x = 10$ and $y = 0$. Hence, $\dfrac{du}{dt} = \sqrt[3]{100}$.

* Figure 62 shows that W increases when S_1 moves north of S_2.

EXERCISE 26

1. If $u = xy^2$, where x and y are functions of t with $dx/dt = 3$ and $dy/dt = -2$, find du/dt at $(x = 4, y = 8)$.

2. If $u = x^2 + y^3$, where x and y are functions of t with $dx/dt = -3$ and $dy/dt = 4$, find du/dt at $(x = 1, y = 2)$.

3. If $u^2 = xy + x^2$, where x and y are functions of t with $dx/dt = -2$ and $dy/dt = \frac{1}{2}$, find du/dt at $x = 4$ and $y = \frac{9}{4}$.

Avoid introducing radicals when possible in the following problems.

4. A metal cylinder is shrinking in cooling, with the radius decreasing $.001''$ per minute, and the altitude decreasing $.01''$ per minute. At the instant when the altitude is $100''$ and the radius is $5''$, find the rate of decrease of (a) the curved surface; (b) the volume.

5. A man $6'$ tall is walking horizontally, at the rate of $75'$ per minute, directly toward a light which is $20'$ above the ground. At what rate is the length of his shadow changing?

6. A boat is being pulled to a wharf by a rope attached to the boat's deck. If the rope is being hauled in at the rate of $12'$ per minute from a point $10'$ above the deck, how fast is the boat approaching the wharf when it is $24'$ away?

7. A hostile warship is traveling 25 miles per hour on a path 6 miles out from a straight shore and parallel to it. At what rate is the warship approaching a defense battery on the shore when 10 miles from the battery?

8. A boy $5'$ tall is walking at $80'$ per minute on a horizontal path directly toward a building. When he is $20'$ from it, at what rate is the top of his head approaching the lens of a camera located in a window $55'$ above the point where the path meets the building?

9. A man on a dock throws a life preserver to a swimmer and then pulls him in by a rope attached to the preserver. If the man's hands, holding the rope, are $12'$ above the water, and if the rope is being hauled in at the rate of $1.5'$ per second, how fast is the swimmer approaching the dock, when there are $20'$ of rope out between him and the dock?

10. The time T in seconds for one oscillation of a simple pendulum whose length is l centimeters is given by $T = \pi\sqrt{\dfrac{l}{g}}$, where $g = 980$ and $\pi = 3.1416$. If l is increasing at the rate of $.2$ centimeters per second, find the rate of change of T, at an instant when $l = 81$.

11. A vat is in the form of a rectangular parallelepiped, with a horizontal base $4' \times 6'$. Water is flowing in at the rate of 30 cubic feet per second. How fast is the water level rising?

12. An airplane is flying horizontally at a speed of $500'$ per second, at an elevation of $8000'$, toward a ground observer. When the line-of-sight distance from the observer to the airplane is $10,000'$, at what rate is the distance decreasing?

13. At 6 P.M., a ship S_1 is 80 miles north of a ship S_2. If S_1 is traveling south at 20 miles per hour, and S_2 is traveling east at 10 miles per hour, (a) at what rate will the distance between S_1 and S_2 be changing 3 hours later; (b) when will S_1 and S_2 be closest?

14. A horizontal V-shaped oil reservoir is 100′ long, and its cross section is an isosceles right triangle with the hypotenuse horizontal, and each perpendicular side 30′ long. Oil flows in at the rate of 750 cubic feet per minute. How fast is the surface of the oil rising when it is 10 feet deep?

15. An escaped convict is running 520′ per minute on a horizontal road directly away from a tower, where a guard is 100′ above the road. How fast is the distance between the convict and the guard changing when the convict is 250′ from the tower? (Disregard the heights of the men, and consider them as points.)

16. The dimensions of a rectangular parallelepiped are decreasing by .2′, .3′, and .1′ per minute. When the corresponding dimensions are 6′, 9′, and 2′, find the rate of change of (a) the volume; (b) the length of a diagonal.

17. A conical reservoir, with a horizontal top 60′ in diameter, is 25′ deep and is filled with water to a level of 20′. (a) At this instant, how fast is the level falling if water is leaking out at the rate of 80 cubic feet per minute? (b) If the level is falling .4′ per minute, how fast is water leaking from the reservoir?

18. Jones and Smith are walking at rates of 300′ per minute and 200′ per minute, respectively, on perpendicular roads toward their intersection. At noon, the distances of Jones and Smith from the intersection are 2200′ and 3400′, respectively. At what rate is the distance between the men changing 5 minutes later?

19. The electromotive force E in volts which is necessary to produce a current of I amperes in a certain circuit with wire of diameter d inches is given by $E = .1137I/d^2$. At an instant when $E = 300$, it is found that E is decreasing at the rate of 5 volts per second. Find the corresponding rate of change in I, if $d = .05$.

20. A spherical snowball is melting away at the rate of 200 cubic inches per minute. At what rate is the radius of the snowball changing when the radius is 20″?

21. The pressure, p, and volume, v, of a given quantity of a gas at a constant temperature satisfy the relation $pv = c$, where c is a constant. At an instant when the pressure is 5 pounds per square inch and the volume is 100 cubic feet, the volume is decreasing by 2 cubic feet per minute. Find the rate of change of p at this instant.

22. Wheat is being poured on the ground in such a way that the wheat on the ground continually forms a cone, with its altitude twice the radius of the base. If the wheat is being poured at the rate of 12 cubic feet per second, find the rate at which the altitude of the pile is increasing when the altitude is 8′.

23. In manufacturing a certain article, a corporation finds that the proper selling price, H, in dollars per article to assure a required margin of profit is given by $H = 3x^2 + 2x + 7$, where x is a cost index number associated with the business. Find the rate of change of H at an instant when $x = 4$, and x is increasing at the rate of \$.15 per month.

24. In a triangle, a first side is increasing by .2″ per minute, a second side is decreasing by .4″ per minute, and their included angle is constantly 150°. At what rate is the area of the triangle changing when the first side is 15″, and the second side is 20″?

25. A balloon is maintaining spherical shape as gas is inserted. At the instant when the radius of the balloon is 15′, the rate of increase of the volume is 100 cubic feet per second. Find the rate of change of the radius at this instant.

26. A reservoir is 85′ long and its cross section is a trapezoid with the parallel sides horizontal, and sides of lengths 17′, 10′, 5′, and 10′, as shown in Figure 63. At an instant when the water is 5′ deep in the reservoir, find the rate at which water is leaking out if the water level is falling by .2′ per hour.

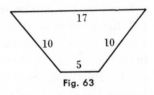

Fig. 63

27. An observer is in a horizontal plane 20 miles north of the take-off point of an airplane, flying upward to the south at the rate of 240 miles per hour, on a path inclined 60° from the horizontal. Two minutes after the take-off, find the rate at which the line-of-sight distance from the observer to the airplane is increasing. (Use the law of cosines for a triangle, from page 563.)

28. An automobile is traveling east at 60 miles per hour, and an airplane is flying south at an elevation of 1 mile, at 300 miles per hour. At a certain instant, the airplane is directly above the automobile. At what rate are they separating 10 minutes later?

Find du/dt without eliminating x, y, or z.

29. $u^2 = x^2 + y^2 + z^2$, when $x = \sqrt{t}$, $y = t^2 + 3$, and $z = 2t + 5$.

30. $u = x^2 + 5xy - y^4$, when $x = t^3 + 2$ and $y = t + t^2$.

31. $u = (2x^2 - 4y)^7$, when $dx/dt = 3$ and $dy/dt = 2$; evaluate at the point $(x = 2, y = 1)$.

32. $u = \sqrt{x + 4y^2}$, when $x = 3t + 6$ and $y = 3t^2 - t^3$; evaluate at $t = 1$.

33. The combined electrical resistance R resulting from two resistances R_1 and R_2, connected in parallel, satisfies the equation

$$\frac{1}{R} = \frac{1}{R_1} + \frac{1}{R_2}.$$

If R_1 and R_2 are increasing at the rates of .5 ohms and .4 ohms per second, respectively, at what rate is R changing when $R_1 = 100$ ohms and $R_2 = 200$ ohms?

34. A point $P:(x, y, z)$ in an xyz-system of rectangular coordinates is moving so that the rates of change for the x, y, and z coordinates are, respectively, 2 units, 3 units, and 1 unit per second. At what rate is the distance OP from the origin changing when $x = 2$, $y = -2$, and $z = 1$?

35. For a perfect gas, the volume v, pressure p, and absolute temperature T, are connected by the relation $pv = RT$, where R is a constant. It is found that $p = 20$ pounds per square inch, and $v = 200$ cubic inches when $T = 400°$. Find T and its time-rate of change at an instant when $p = 15$ pounds per square inch and $v = 300$ cubic inches, if the pressure is decreasing at the rate of .4 pounds per second, while the volume is increasing at the rate of .3 cubic inches per second.

53. Acceleration in rectilinear motion

Consider the motion of a particle on a straight line, labeled as an s-axis. Let the motion be defined by specifying s as a function of t, say $s = f(t)$, where s is the coordinate of the particle at the instant of time t. Hereafter, in such a setting, we shall suppose that $f(t)$ has a continuous second derivative, $f''(t)$. Previously, we have defined the velocity, v, of the particle at any instant t as the *instantaneous rate of change of s with respect to t*, or

$$v = \frac{ds}{dt}, \quad or \quad v = f'(t). \tag{1}$$

We note that dv/dt is the second derivative of s with respect to t. Then, we introduce the following terminology.

DEFINITION V. *In the* **rectilinear motion** *of a particle on an s-axis, the* **acceleration,** *a, of the particle at any instant of time, t, is defined as the corresponding* **instantaneous rate of change of the velocity,** *v, with respect to the time. That is,*

$$a = \frac{dv}{dt}, \quad or \quad a = \frac{d^2s}{dt^2}. \tag{2}$$

EXAMPLE 1. An object is shot vertically upward, with an initial velocity $v_0 = 128'$ per second at $t = 0$. Study the motion.

SOLUTION. 1. Let the distance s, in feet, be measured positive upward, with the object on the s-axis. Then, the motion is defined by *

$$s = v_0 t - \tfrac{1}{2}gt^2, \tag{3}$$

with $v_0 = 128$ and $g = 32$, or $\qquad s = 128t - 16t^2. \tag{4}$

From (1) and (2), as used in (4),

$$v = 128 - 32t; \quad a = -32. \tag{5}$$

---

* In problems relating to projectiles or falling bodies in the earth's atmosphere, we neglect air resistance and other complicating features.

2. From (5), $v = 0$ and thus s attains its maximum at $t = 4$, where $s = 256$. A graph of (4) is given in Figure 64. Since $a = -32$, then v is a *decreasing* function for all values of t. Thus, v starts with the value $v = 128$ at $t = 0$; decreases to $v = 0$ at $t = 4$; then becomes negative and steadily decreases, or v is negative and its absolute value increases, as the object falls from its maximum elevation, $s = 256$, to $s = 0$ at $t = 8$.

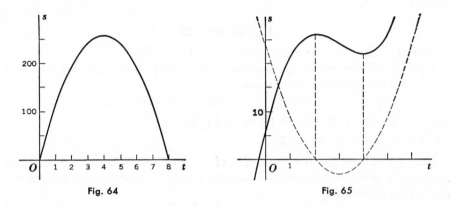

Fig. 64   Fig. 65

Comment. In physics, we learn that "*force equals mass times acceleration,*" or $F = ma$, where the force F acts on an object with mass m, and imparts the acceleration a. In (5), the result $a = -32$, a constant, is a consequence of the fact that the object considered is acted on only by the constant force of gravity.

EXAMPLE 2. For $t \geq 0$, describe the motion of a particle as governed by the equation

$$s = t^3 - 9t^2 + 24t + 6. \tag{6}$$

SOLUTION. 1. From (6),

$$v = \frac{ds}{dt} = 3t^2 - 18t + 24 = 3(t-4)(t-2); \quad a = \frac{d^2s}{dt^2} = 6(t-3). \tag{7}$$

Hence, $v = 0$ at $t = 2$ and $t = 4$, while $a = 0$ at $t = 3$. These results were used to obtain the graph of (6) in Figure 65 with a maximum $s = 26$ at $t = 2$, a minimum $s = 22$ at $t = 4$, and an inflection point (where $a = 0$) at $t = 3$. Also, a graph of v as a function of t is shown by the broken line parabola in Figure 65.

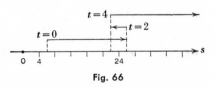

Fig. 66

2. Let the s-axis be considered horizontal, as in Figure 66. From Figure 65 and (6), the particle starts at $s = 6$ when $t = 0$, with $v > 0$, and moves to the right, to $s = 26$ at $t = 2$, where instantaneously the particle is at rest.

Meanwhile, with $a < 0$ at $t = 0$, the velocity decreases until $t = 3$ (corresponding to the inflection point in Figure 65) where $a = 0$; then v increases for all future values of t. From $t = 2$ to $t = 4$, $v < 0$ and the particle moves to the left, to $s = 22$. For $t > 4$ the particle moves continually to the right, with v steadily increasing because $a > 0$ if $t > 4$. Thus, as $t \to \infty$, we have $v \to \infty$, $s \to \infty$, and $a \to \infty$. The arrows in Figure 66 show how the particle moves.

EXERCISE 27

The units are 1 foot for distance and 1 second for time.

Find the velocity and the acceleration of the particle at the specified value of t, for the motion defined by the equation.

1. $s = 5t^3 + 3t - 2$; at $t = 3$.   **2.** $s = 5t^3 + 2t^2$; at $t = 2$.

3. $s = 3t^3 - 2t^2 + 2t - 5$; at $t = 0$; at $t = 3$.

4. $s = 2t^3 + 3t - 7$; at $t = 2$.

With s measured positive upward, and $s = 0$ at the surface of the earth, the motion of a particle shot vertically from the point $s = s_0$, with the velocity $v = v_0$ at $t = 0$, is described by

$$s = s_0 + v_0 t - \tfrac{1}{2}gt^2, \tag{1}$$

where $g = 32$ approximately. For the specified data, (a) find when s attains its maximum; (b) the range of values of t for which $v > 0$, and for which $v < 0$; (c) the acceleration; (d) the velocity when the particle hits the earth. Also, graph s as a function of t, for $t \geq 0$.

5. $s_0 = 0$; $v_0 = 256$.   **6.** $s_0 = 0$; $v_0 = 144$.   **7.** $s_0 = 1600$; $v_0 = 0$.

8. $s_0 = 240$; $v_0 = 160$.   **9.** $s_0 = 153$; $v_0 = 192$.   **10.** $s_0 = 272$; $v_0 = -4$.

A particle has its motion on an s-axis defined by the given equation. Graph s and v as functions of t, with $t \geq 0$. Then, describe how the particle moves on the s-axis, with remarks about the variation of the velocity and the acceleration.

11. $s = t^3 - 3t + 5$.   **12.** $s = 2t^3 - 3t^2 - 12t + 5$.

13. $s = t^3 - 6t^2 + 9t + 12$.   **14.** $s = t^3 - 3t^2 + 3t - 9$.

7

DIFFERENTIALS AND PARAMETRIC FORM

54. Calculation of differentials by formulas

Consider a differentiable function $y = f(x)$. Let dx (instead of Δx) represent an arbitrary increment, not zero, to be assigned to any specified value of x, and let Δy be the corresponding increment for y. Then,

$$\Delta y = f(x + dx) - f(x). \tag{1}$$

On page 35, we defined the differential dy, or $df(x)$, as a function of the independent variables x and dx, by the equation

$$dy = f'(x)dx, \quad or \quad df(x) = f'(x)dx. \tag{2}$$

EXAMPLE 1. If $y = x^2 + 2x$, graph the function and exhibit dx, dy, and Δy at the point where $x = 1$, if $dx = 1.5$.

SOLUTION. 1. $y' = 2x + 2$; $dy = (2x + 2)dx$. If $x = 1$ and $dx = 1.5$, then $dy = 6$.

2. If $x = 1$, then $y = 3$ and $y' = 4$. Hence, the tangent at $(1, 3)$ is $y = 4x - 1$.

3. If (x, y) and $(x + dx, y + \Delta y)$ are pairs of corresponding values of x and y, then

$$y = x^2 + 2x \quad and$$

$$y + \Delta y = (x + dx)^2 + 2(x + dx).$$

Hence, $\Delta y = (2x + 2)dx + (dx)^2$.

If $x = 1$ and $dx = 1.5$, then $\Delta y = 8.25$. Figure 67 exhibits a graph of $y = x^2 + 2x$, with dx, dy, and Δy represented by directed line segments, at $x = 1$ when $dx = 1.5$.

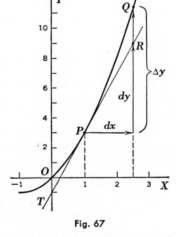

Fig. 67

Let $P:(x, y)$ be any point on the graph of $y = f(x)$, with PT tangent to the graph at P. From page 35, we recall that, for any value of dx, the point

101

$R:(x + dx, y + dy)$ is on PT, whereas $Q:(x + dx, y + \Delta y)$ is on the graph of $y = f(x)$, as illustrated in Figure 67 on page 101.

Since the *differential* of a function $y = f(x)$ is simply *its derivative multiplied by dx*, we obtain standard forms for differentials on multiplying by dx on both sides of formulas (I)–(VII) on pages 38–39. Thus, if u and v are functions of x, we obtain the following formulas, where du and dv are implicitly functions of x and dx:

$$d(k) = 0. \qquad (I)_d \qquad \qquad d(ku) = k\ du \qquad (II)_d$$

$$du^n = nu^{n-1}\ du. \qquad (III)_d \qquad d(u + v) = du + dv. \qquad (IV)_d$$

$$d(uv) = v\ du + u\ dv. \qquad (V)_d \qquad d\left(\frac{u}{v}\right) = \frac{v\ du - u\ dv}{v^2}. \qquad (VI)_d$$

If $y = f(u)$, then dy is given by the formula

$$dy = f'(u)du, \qquad (VII)_d$$

not only when u is the independent variable, but also when u is a differentiable function of the independent variable x, and thus du is implicitly a function of x and dx.

ILLUSTRATION 1. From (III) on page 38,

$$\frac{du^n}{dx} = nu^{n-1}\frac{du}{dx}. \qquad (3)$$

On multiplying by dx on both sides in (3), we obtain $(III)_d$.

ILLUSTRATION 2. From $(VI)_d$,

$$d\left(\frac{3x + 2}{5x^2 + 7}\right) = \frac{(5x^2 + 7)d(3x + 2) - (3x + 2)d(5x^2 + 7)}{(5x^2 + 7)^2}$$

$$= \frac{3(5x^2 + 7) - 10x(3x + 2)}{(5x^2 + 7)^2}\ dx = \frac{21 - 20x - 15x^2}{(5x^2 + 7)^2}\ dx,$$

because $d(3x + 2) = 3\ dx$ and $d(5x^2 + 7) = 10x\ dx$.

ILLUSTRATION 3. From $(III)_d$, with $u = 4x^2 + 2$,

$$d(4x^2 + 2)^8 = 8(4x^2 + 2)^7 d(4x^2 + 2) = 64x(4x^2 + 2)^7 dx.$$

Formula $(VII)_d$ deserves special attention. If $y = f(u)$, and u is the *independent variable*, then $(VII)_d$ is true simply *by the definition of $df(u)$.* Suppose, now, that $y = f(u)$ where $u = \phi(x)$, and that x is the independent variable. Then, from (VII) on page 39,

$$\frac{dy}{dx} = \frac{dy}{du} \cdot \frac{du}{dx}. \qquad (4)$$

On multiplying both sides of (4) by dx, we obtain

$$dy = \frac{dy}{du}\ du = f'(u)du, \text{ as in } (VII)_d,$$

where $du = \phi'(x)dx$. Formula (III)$_d$ is a special case of (VII)$_d$; if $y = u^n$,

$$dy = \frac{dy}{du} du = nu^{n-1} du.$$

Similarly, (VII)$_d$ *will produce a differential formula from each standard form for differentiation which we shall present in a later chapter.*

ILLUSTRATION 4. By use of (III)$_d$, with $u = 4x + 5$,

$$d\sqrt[3]{4x + 5} = d(4x + 5)^{\frac{1}{3}} = \tfrac{1}{3}(4x + 5)^{-\frac{2}{3}}d(4x + 5) = \tfrac{4}{3}(4x + 5)^{-\frac{2}{3}} dx.$$

EXAMPLE 2. Find dy in terms of x, y, and dx, if y is defined implicitly as a function of x by the following equation. Finally, obtain dy/dx.

$$x^2 + 2xy - 3y^2 = 5x - 7. \tag{5}$$

SOLUTION. With y representing a function of x, the two sides of (5) are identical functions of x, and thus have equal differentials. Hence, we take the differential of each side and equate the results:

$$2x\, dx + 2(y\, dx + x\, dy) - 6y\, dy = 5\, dx;$$

$$(2x - 6y)dy = (5 - 2x - 2y)dx, \quad or \quad dy = \frac{5 - 2x - 2y}{2x - 6y}\, dx. \tag{6}$$

Then, from (6),
$$\frac{dy}{dx} = \frac{5 - 2x - 2y}{2x - 6y}.$$

Usually, there is no particular merit in obtaining dy/dx by the preceding method, as compared with the method of page 51. However, the method of Example 2 is worthy of recognition.

Note 1. From the nature of differentials, if one term in an equation involves a differential as a factor, then each term involves a differential factor. This fact is useful in checking equations to prevent careless errors.

ILLUSTRATION 5. By use of (III)$_d$ with $n = -1$ and $u = 3 + x^3$,

$$d\left(\frac{5}{3 + x^3}\right) = d[5(3 + x^3)^{-1}] = -5(3 + x^3)^{-2}(3x^2\, dx) = -15(3 + x^3)^{-2}x^2\, dx.$$

EXERCISE 28

1. Graph the function $y = \tfrac{1}{2}x^2$. Compute dy at $x = 2$, with $dx = .5$, and Δy by use of (1) on page 101. Find the slope and draw the tangent at $x = 2$. Then, exhibit line segments representing Δy, dy, and dx.
2. If $y = 5x^2 + 3x$, compute dy when (a) $x = 3$ and $dx = 2$; (b) $x = 4$ and $dx = -.3$.

Find the differential of the function of x, without expanding integral powers unnecessarily.

3. $2x^3 + 5x^2$.
4. $(2x^2 + x)^5$.
5. $(3 - 5x)^4$.
6. $\sqrt{2x + 3}$.
7. $\sqrt{x^2 + x}$.
8. $\sqrt[3]{2x + 3}$.

9. $(3x + 2)^2(5x - 3)$.   **10.** $(2x - 1)^3(4x + x^2)^4$.

11. $\sqrt{3x}$.   **12.** x^{-2}.   **13.** $5(2x + 3)^{-1}$.   **14.** $\sqrt[3]{x - x^2}$.

15. $\dfrac{\sqrt[3]{2x + 4}}{7}$.   **16.** $\dfrac{2x - 5}{3x + 1}$.   **17.** $\dfrac{(2x - 1)^2}{4x + 3}$.

18. $\dfrac{2x + 1}{(1 - 3x)^2}$.   **19.** $\dfrac{3}{4x^2 + 7}$.   **20.** $\dfrac{2}{5 + 7x}$.

21. $\dfrac{6}{\sqrt[3]{2x + 5}}$.   **22.** $\dfrac{(1 + 2x)^2}{3x}$.   **23.** $\dfrac{\sqrt{2x - 1}}{x}$.

Find dy in terms of x, y, and dx from the given equation, and obtain dy/dx from the preceding result.

24. $2x^3 + 3xy - y = x^2$.   **25.** $2x^{\frac{3}{2}} + y^2 + xy = 3x$.

26. $x^2 + 2y^2 + y = 3x$.   **27.** $(3x + 2y)^4 + y^3 = x^2$.

28. $a^2x^2 + b^2y^2 = a^2b^2$.   **29.** $x^{\frac{2}{3}} + y^{\frac{2}{3}} = a^{\frac{2}{3}}$.

55. Differentials as approximations to increments

From Figure 67 on page 101, we suspect that dy will be a close approximation to Δy if dx is small. The following theorem states the sense in which the preceding statement is true.

THEOREM I. *Assume that the function $y = f(x)$ is differentiable. Then, at any point (x, y),*

$$\lim_{dx \to 0} \frac{\Delta y - dy}{dx} = 0. \tag{1}$$

Proof of (1). For association with formulas about derivatives, temporarily let Δx represent dx. Then, $\Delta y = f(x + \Delta x) - f(x)$. By definition,

$$dy = f'(x)\Delta x. \tag{2}$$

Hence, $$\lim_{\Delta x \to 0} \frac{\Delta y - dy}{\Delta x} = \lim_{\Delta x \to 0} \left[\frac{\Delta y}{\Delta x} - f'(x)\right] = 0,$$

because $f'(x) = \lim_{\Delta x \to 0} (\Delta y/\Delta x)$. Thus, (1) is true.

In (1), $|\Delta y - dy|$ is the *error* of dy as an approximation to Δy. Then, with the fraction in (1) thought of in percent form,* (1) states that the error $|\Delta y - dy|$ will be as small a percentage of $|dx|$ as we please, if dx is sufficiently small. From Figure 67 on page 101, it is seen that, when we take dy as an approximation to Δy, for given values of x and dx, we act as if the graph of $y = f(x)$ is identical with the tangent at (x, y) on the range from x to $(x + dx)$. Hereafter, if $y = f(x)$, when it is requested that an increment Δy be computed approximately by differentials, it is implied that we take

dy as an approximation to Δy.   (3)

---

* To give a measure of the size of one number M as compared to another number N, we may describe the ratio M/N in percent form. Thus, 6 is 3% of 200 because $6/200 = .03$.

EXAMPLE 1. The interior of a box is a cube, with a 10″ edge, and the walls of the box are $\frac{1}{8}$″ thick. Find the volume of the walls approximately by use of differentials.

SOLUTION. 1. Let x be the length in inches of an edge of a variable cube, with volume V. Then, $V = x^3$ and hence $dV = 3x^2\, dx$.

2. The volume of the walls is the increment ΔV due to a change from $x = 10$ to $x = 10\frac{1}{4}$, and is *approximately dV*, with $x = 10$ and $dx = \frac{1}{4}$:

$$\Delta V \approx dV = 3(10^2)(\tfrac{1}{4}) = 75 \text{ cu. in.,} \tag{4}$$

where we use "$\approx$" for "*is approximately equal to.*"

EXAMPLE 2. Compute $\sqrt{38}$ approximately by use of differentials.

SOLUTION. 1. We introduce the function $y = \sqrt{x}$, whose value is known at $x = 36$. Then, $\sqrt{38} = \sqrt{36} + \Delta y$, where Δy is the increment of y due to assigning an increment $dx = 2$ to $x = 36$. We shall *approximate Δy by dy.*

2. We have $y = x^{\frac{1}{2}}$; $dy = \frac{1}{2}x^{-\frac{1}{2}}\, dx$. Hence, with $x = 36$ and $dx = 2$,

$$\sqrt{38} = \sqrt{36} + \Delta y \approx 6 + dy = 6 + \tfrac{1}{2}(36)^{-\frac{1}{2}}(2) = 6 + \tfrac{2}{12} = 6\tfrac{1}{6}.$$

Thus, $\sqrt{38} \approx 6.17$. (From Table I, we find $\sqrt{38} = 6.164$.)

Note 1. If A is the *true value* of a quantity, and B is an *approximation to A*, hereafter we shall allow ourselves the latitude of referring to either $(A - B)$, or $(B - A)$, or $|A - B|$ as the *error of B*. Any reference to a *maximum* or a *minimum error* will imply use of the *nonnegative error formula* $|A - B|$.

Suppose that $y = f(x)$, where x is a variable whose value will be determined experimentally as a basis for computing y. Let (x_0, y_0) be the true values of the variables, with $x = x_0 + dx$ as the measured value of x, for which $f(x_0 + dx) = y_0 + \Delta y$. Then, we define the **relative error** in y as the error Δy divided by the true value y_0. Or,

$$\left\{ \begin{array}{l} \textbf{relative error } in \ y \\ due \ to \ error \ dx \ in \ x \end{array} \right\} = \frac{\Delta y}{y_0} \approx \frac{dy}{y}, \tag{5}$$

where we take y as y_0 and $dy = f'(x_0)dx$ when (x_0, y_0) are *known*, and we take $dy = f'(x)dx$ and $y = f(x)$, with x as the *observed value*, when (x_0, y_0) are *unknown*. In (5), when $(dy)/y$ is expressed in percent form, we refer to it as the **percentage error.**

EXAMPLE 3. For a cone of altitude 24″, the radius of the base was measured as 4″, with at most a 2% error. For the computed volume, find approximately (a) the maximum possible error; (b) the maximum possible percentage error.

SOLUTION. 1. With a variable cone of altitude 24″ and base radius r, the volume is $V = 8\pi r^2$. Then, $dV = 16\pi r\, dr$.

2. *Maximum error.* With $r = 4$ and an error dr,

$$(error\ in\ V\ due\ to\ error\ dr) = \Delta V \approx dV = 16\pi(4)dr = 64\pi\ dr.$$

Since $|dr| \leq 4(.02) = .08$, $\qquad\qquad |dV| \leq 64\pi(.08) = 16.1\ cu.\ in.$

Or, the error in the volume will not exceed 16.1 cu. in., approximately.

3. *Percentage error.* From (5), for any error dr,

$$\left\{\begin{array}{l} relative\ error\ in\ V \\ due\ to\ error\ dr\ in\ r \end{array}\right\} \approx \frac{dV}{V} = \frac{16\pi r\ dr}{8\pi r^2} = 2\frac{dr}{r}. \tag{6}$$

Since the approximate relative error in r is dr/r, from the data we have

$$\left|\frac{dr}{r}\right| \leq .02, \quad and\ thus \quad \left|\frac{dV}{V}\right| = 2\left|\frac{dr}{r}\right| \leq 2(.02) = .04. \tag{7}$$

Hence, the maximum percentage error in V is 4%, approximately.

EXERCISE 29

Solve by use of differentials.

1. An ivory ball is 3″ in diameter, and will be turned down to a diameter of 2.8″. Find approximately the volume of ivory which is taken off.

2. A cylindrical wooden rod is 3 feet long and 4.4″ in diameter. The rod will be turned down to a diameter of 4″. (*a*) Find approximately the volume of wood taken off. (*b*) Compute the exact volume taken off.

HINT. Let $f(x)$ be the volume when the radius is x inches. Then, compute $df(x)$ at $x = 2$, with $dx = .2$. The problem statement also would permit computation of $df(x)$ at $x = 2.2$, with $dx = -.2$. Both results would be approximations to the true value. In any problem of this nature, use the most convenient value for the variable.

3. Find approximately the volume of a cylindrical shell, with altitude 20″, outer radius 5″, and shell thickness .3″.

4. A sphere 40″ in diameter will be covered with a layer of paint .05″ thick. Find approximately the volume of the paint.

5. A particle moves with the equation of motion $s = 25t^2 - 20t + 5$, where s is in feet and the time t is in seconds. If t is measured as 20.4 seconds, with accuracy to one decimal place, find approximately the largest possible error in (*a*) the computed position coordinate, s, on the s-axis; (*b*) the computed velocity, v.

6. With a certain amount of a gas at constant temperature, the pressure p and volume v satisfy the relation $pv = k$, where k is a constant. If $p = 20$ pounds per square inch when $v = 60$ cubic inches, find approximately the change in v if p increases by .4 pounds.

7. The side of a square is measured as 10″, with an error of at most .3″, and then the area, A, is computed. Find approximately the maximum possible error, and percentage error in A.

8. A uniform cylindrical steel bearing, 30″ long, has worn down symmetrically by 2% from a diameter of 3″. Find approximately the percentage change in the weight of the bearing.

9. Assume that the time t in seconds for one oscillation of a simple pendulum of length l feet is given by $t = \pi\sqrt{l/32}$. If l is measured with an error of at most 4%, find approximately the maximum possible percentage error in the computed value of t.

10. With what largest percentage error, approximately, is it satisfactory to measure the radius of a sphere in order to compute its surface area with less than 4% error?

11. A cone has the altitude 30″. The radius of the base is measured as 5″ and the volume is computed. Find approximately the maximum allowable error in the radius if the volume is desired with an error of at most 5 cubic inches.

12. A cylinder is known to have the altitude 75″, and the radius of the base is known to be less than 5″. The radius will be measured and then the volume will be computed. To obtain the volume accurate to the nearest cubic inch, what accuracy in the measured radius would be satisfactory?

Compute the specified quantity approximately by use of differentials.

13. $\sqrt{50}$.   14. $\sqrt{66}$.   15. $\sqrt[3]{130}$.   16. $\sqrt[3]{68}$.

17. The exact side of a square is x inches, and the side is measured as $(x + dx)$ inches, where the error is $dx > 0$. Draw a sketch showing the exact error in the computed area, and its differential approximation.

18. Find an approximate formula for the area of a circular ring, with outer radius r, and a small width dr.

19. The horsepower which a rotating shaft can transmit safely varies as the cube of its diameter and the angular speed of rotation of the shaft. With a given speed of rotation, find approximately the percentage change in the possible horsepower due to an increase of 2% in the diameter.

20. The lifting force exerted by the atmosphere on the wings of an airplane in flight is proportional to the square of the plane's airspeed. Find approximately the percentage change in the lifting force due to an increase of 5% in the airspeed.

21. The electrical resistance of a wire is proportional to its length and inversely proportional to the square of its diameter. For a wire of given length, the diameter is measured with an error of at most 3% and the resistance is computed. Find approximately the maximum possible percentage error in the resistance.

22. Find approximately the change in the reciprocal of a number $x \neq 0$, due to a small change dx in the number.

23. Find an approximate expression for the volume of the walls in a spherical shell of outer radius r, and thickness dr. Show that the result is the product of dr and the surface area of the shell.

24. In order to compute the volume of a cubical box with an error of at most 2%, with what relative accuracy should the edge of the box be measured?

If | y | is small, find an approximate expression for the function.

25. $\sqrt{1+y}$.   **26.** $\sqrt[3]{1+y}$.   **27.** $(1+y)^{-1}$.   **28.** $1/\sqrt{1+y}$.

HINT for Problem 25. Consider the function $\sqrt{x}$, and use $y = dx$.

29. A 12-pound spherical shot for a championship track meet will be made of metal weighing 490 pounds per cubic foot, and the weight must be accurate to the nearest ounce. Find approximately the maximum allowable error in the radius.

56. Parametric equations for a curve

Let the variable t have as its range either a finite interval, or an infinite interval of values. Let $\phi(t)$ and $\psi(t)$ be single-valued continuous functions on the specified t-range. Then, at each value of t, the equations

$$x = \phi(t) \quad and \quad y = \psi(t) \tag{1}$$

give a point $P{:}(x, y)$ in the xy-plane. The locus C of all points $P{:}(x, y)$ thus obtained is called a *continuous curve*, and we refer to (1) as *parametric equations* for C in terms of the *parameter t*. If the range for t consists of two or more disconnected intervals, then C may consist of corresponding disconnected arcs, but for convenience may be referred to simply as one curve. Sometimes, it may be possible to eliminate t between equations as in (1), and thus obtain a single equation in x and y defining the locus of (1). Frequently, the parametric form (1) is more convenient than the xy-equation.

ILLUSTRATION 1. The following parametric equations define a curve:

$$x = 2 + 3t \quad and \quad y = 4 - 2t. \tag{2}$$

From the left-hand equation, $t = \frac{1}{3}(x - 2)$; on using this in $y = 4 - 2t$, we obtain $3y + 2x = 16$. Hence, equations (2) define a line.

EXAMPLE 1. Obtain the xy-equation of the curve defined by

(t as parameter) $x = 2 \cos t \quad and \quad y = 3 \sin t. \tag{3}$

SOLUTION. From (3), $\cos t = \frac{1}{2}x$, $\sin t = \frac{1}{3}y$, and hence

$$\tfrac{1}{4}x^2 + \tfrac{1}{9}y^2 = \sin^2 t + \cos^2 t = 1, \; or \tag{4}$$

$$9x^2 + 4y^2 = 36, \tag{5}$$

which represents an ellipse. Equations (3) are more convenient than (5) in computing points on the ellipse. Thus, if $t = 10°$, from (3) we obtain $x = 2 \cos 10° = 1.97$; $y = 3 \sin 10° = .52$.

THEOREM II. *With t as a parameter, parametric equations for the line through $P_1{:}(x_1, y_1)$ and $P_2{:}(x_2, y_2)$ in an xy-plane are*

$$x = x_1 + t(x_2 - x_1) \quad and \quad y = y_1 + t(y_2 - y_1). \tag{6}$$

Proof. Let L be the line through P_1 and P_2. Let $P:(x, y)$ be any point on L, and construct perpendiculars from P, P_1, and P_2 to the axes, as in Figure 68. Then, from the similar triangles P_1NP and P_1MP_2,

$$P_1N : NP = P_1M : MP_2, \text{ or } *$$

$$(x - x_1):(y - y_1) = (x_2 - x_1):(y_2 - y_1).$$

Hence, for any point $P:(x, y)$, there exists a value of t such that

$$x - x_1 = t(x_2 - x_1) \quad and \quad y - y_1 = t(y_2 - y_1), \tag{7}$$

which are parametric equations for the line L, and agree with (6).

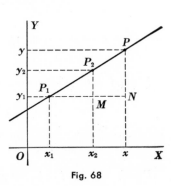

Fig. 68

Note 1. Consider the preceding line L as a *directed* line. Then,

$$\frac{P_1P}{P_1P_2} = \frac{x - x_1}{x_2 - x_1} = t, \text{ or } P_1P = t(P_1P_2).$$

Thus, (6) gives the coordinates of the point $P:(x, y)$ on L such that $P_1P = t(P_1P_2)$, where P is in the direction from P_1 to P_2 when $t > 0$, and in the opposite direction when $t < 0$.

ILLUSTRATION 2. From (6), parametric equations for the line through $(2, 3)$ and $(-4, 1)$ are $x = 2 + t(-4 - 2)$ and $y = 3 + t(1 - 3)$, or

$$x = 2 - 6t \quad and \quad y = 3 - 2t. \tag{8}$$

We could use (8) for computing coordinates of points on the line.

EXAMPLE 2. Obtain parametric equations for the strophoid (page 596):

$$x^3 + xy^2 + ax^2 - ay^2 = 0. \tag{9}$$

SOLUTION. The curve passes through the origin, $(x = 0, y = 0)$. Let $y = tx$ be any particular line through the origin. Then, this line intersects the strophoid at $(0, 0)$ and also at any point (x, y) satisfying (9), with $y = tx$. On placing $y = tx$ in (9), we obtain $x^3 + t^2x^3 + ax^2 - at^2x^2 = 0$, or

$$x^2(x + t^2x + a - at^2) = 0. \tag{10}$$

Hence, aside from $x = 0$, the value of x at any intersection of $y = tx$ and (9) satisfies

$$x + t^2x + a - at^2 = 0, \quad or \quad x = \frac{a(t^2 - 1)}{t^2 + 1}. \tag{11}$$

Then, $y = tx$ or

$$y = \frac{at(t^2 - 1)}{t^2 + 1}. \tag{12}$$

With t as a variable, $[(11), (12)]$ are parametric equations for (9).

* We say that a *and* b *are proportional to* c *and* d, and write $a : b = c : d$, in case there exists a constant $t \neq 0$ such that $a = tc$ and $b = td$.

57. Derivatives from parametric form

Suppose that x and y are functions of a third variable t,

$$x = \phi(t) \quad and \quad y = \psi(t), \tag{1}$$

where $\phi(t)$ and $\psi(t)$ have continuous derivatives. Then, under proper conditions, we may calculate dy/dx or dx/dy without eliminating t.

THEOREM III. *In the neighborhood of any value of t where $\phi'(t) \neq 0$, equations*
(1) *define y as a differentiable function of x, and*

$$\frac{dy}{dx} = \frac{\dfrac{dy}{dt}}{\dfrac{dx}{dt}}, \quad or \quad \frac{dy}{dx} = \frac{\psi'(t)}{\phi'(t)}. \tag{2}$$

If $\psi'(t) \neq 0$, (1) defines x as a function of y, and

$$\frac{dx}{dy} = \frac{\dfrac{dx}{dt}}{\dfrac{dy}{dt}}, \quad or \quad \frac{dx}{dy} = \frac{\phi'(t)}{\psi'(t)}. \tag{3}$$

Proof. 1. At $t = t_0$, where $x = x_0$ and $y = y_0$, suppose that $\phi'(t_0) \neq 0$. Then, from page 53, if t is near t_0, $x = \phi(t)$ defines t as a differentiable function of x, and hence $y = \psi(t)$ defines y as a differentiable function of x.

2. At the point $x = x_0$, assign any increment $dx \neq 0$, with dt and dy as the corresponding differentials of t and y, which are functions of x. Then, by use of $(VII)_d$ on page 102, we obtain

$$dx = \phi'(t_0)dt \quad and \quad dy = \psi'(t_0)dt. \tag{4}$$

Hence,

$$\frac{dy}{dx} = \frac{\psi'(t_0)dt}{\phi'(t_0)dt} = \frac{\psi'(t_0)}{\phi'(t_0)}, \tag{5}$$

which proves (2) when $\phi'(t) \neq 0$. Similar remarks prove (3).

Note 1. If $\phi'(t_0) = \psi'(t_0) = 0$, then neither (2) nor (3) is available at $t = t_0$. However, we shall meet examples where dy/dx, or dx/dy, exists under such circumstances.

Instead of memorizing (2) and (3) mechanically, remember the procedure which led from (4) to (5). That is, calculate dy and dx from (1) in terms of t and dt, and divide, dy/dx or dx/dy, to obtain either derivative. At any value of t where $\phi'(t) \neq 0$ and $\psi'(t) \neq 0$, we have the usual reciprocal relation between dy/dx and dx/dy.

ILLUSTRATION 1. From the equations

$$x = 3t^2 + 2t \quad and \quad y = 2t^2 - 5,$$

we obtain

$$dx = (6t + 2)dt \quad and \quad dy = 4t\, dt;$$

$$\frac{dy}{dx} = \frac{4t\,dt}{(6t+2)dt} = \frac{2t}{3t+1}; \quad \frac{dx}{dy} = \frac{3t+1}{2t}.$$

Let $y' = dy/dx$, where y' is given as a function of t in (2). Then, we apply Theorem III to the variables x and y' to obtain

$$y'' = \frac{d^2y}{dx^2} = \frac{dy'}{dx}. \tag{6}$$

ILLUSTRATION 2. To obtain y'' in Illustration 1, calculate

$$dx = (6t+2)dt; \quad dy' = d\left(\frac{2t}{3t+1}\right) = \frac{2\,dt}{(3t+1)^2}.$$

Hence,
$$\frac{d^2y}{dx^2} = \frac{dy'}{dx} = \frac{2}{(3t+1)^2(6t+2)} = \frac{1}{(3t+1)^3}.$$

Let a curve C in the xy-plane be defined by (1). Then

$$\frac{dx}{dt} = \phi'(t); \quad \frac{dy}{dt} = \psi'(t). \tag{7}$$

To obtain important points on C, find corresponding values of t as follows.

I. *Find x- and y-intercepts by solving $\phi(t) = 0$ and $\psi(t) = 0$.*

II. *Find where x has an extremum by testing the values of t where $\phi'(t) = 0$, and similarly with respect to y, by solving $\psi'(t) = 0$.*

III. *Horizontal and vertical tangents. If $\psi'(t) = 0$ at $t = t_0$, and $\phi'(t_0) \neq 0$, from (2) we find $dy/dx = 0$ at $t = t_0$, so that C has a horizontal tangent when $t = t_0$. If $\phi'(t_0) = 0$ and $\psi'(t_0) \neq 0$, then $dx/dy = 0$ and C has a vertical tangent at $t = t_0$.*

IV. *If both $\phi'(t) = 0$ and $\psi'(t) = 0$ at $t = t_0$, investigate dy/dx or dx/dy as $t \to t_0$, to decide about a possible tangent at $t = t_0$.*

EXAMPLE 1. Graph the curve C defined parametrically by

$$x = 6t - \tfrac{1}{2}t^3 \quad and \quad y = \tfrac{1}{2}t^2 - 6. \tag{8}$$

SOLUTION. 1.
$$\frac{dx}{dt} = (6 - \tfrac{3}{2}t^2); \quad \frac{dy}{dt} = t. \tag{9}$$

Hence,
$$\frac{dy}{dx} = \frac{2t}{3(4 - t^2)}; \quad \frac{dx}{dy} = \frac{3(4 - t^2)}{2t}. \tag{10}$$

2. Since $D_t y = 0$ at $t = 0$, and $D_t^2 y = 1 > 0$, hence y has a minimum at $t = 0$. Since $D_t x \neq 0$ at $t = 0$, in (10) we find $dy/dx = 0$ at $t = 0$, and thus C has a horizontal tangent when $t = 0$.

3. The solutions of $D_t x = 0$ are $t = \pm 2$. Since $D_t^2 x = -3t$, we have $D_t^2 x > 0$ at $t = -2$ and $D_t^2 x < 0$ at $t = 2$. Hence, x has a minimum at $t = -2$ and a maximum at $t = 2$. When $t = \pm 2$, we find $D_t y \neq 0$, and hence, in (10), $dx/dy = 0$, so that C has a vertical tangent

4. *Intercepts.* From (8), $x = 0$ when $t = 0$ and $t = \pm 2\sqrt{3}$, and $y = 0$ when $t = \pm 2\sqrt{3}$. Thus, C goes through the origin when $t = \pm 2\sqrt{3}$. From (10), the slopes of C at $(0, 0)$ are $y' = \pm .3$.

5. Coordinates were computed from (8) for all values of t met in preceding details, and for other values, as a basis for the graph of C in Figure 69. Arc $ABOH$ on C is traced as t ranges from 0 to $+\infty$, and arc $ADOE$ as t ranges from 0 to $-\infty$.

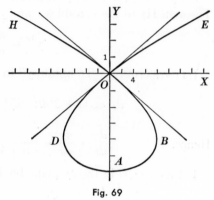

Fig. 69

t	0	± 2	$\pm 2\sqrt{3}$	± 4
x	0	± 8	0	∓ 8
y	-6	-4	0	2

Note 2. From (8), $x = -ty$ or $t = -x/y$. With $t = -x/y$ in $y = \frac{1}{2}t^2 - 6$, we obtain $x^2 = 2y^2(y + 6)$ as the xy-equation for (8).

EXERCISE 30

Write parametric equations for the line through the points; from these equations, compute coordinates for a third point and plot the line.

1. $(2, 5)$; $(-1, 3)$.   **2.** $(-2, 4)$; $(-3, 5)$.   **3.** $(-2, -4)$; $(1, 5)$.

Find $D_x y$ and $D_x^2 y$ if x and y are related through the given equations.

4. $x = 2t - t^2$, $y = 3 - t^2$.

5. $x = t^2 + 4$, $y = t - t^2$.

6. $x = \frac{1}{4}t^2$, $y = \frac{1}{3}t^3$.

7. $x = t + 3t^3$, $y = t^2 + t$.

8. $x = 2t^2 + 5$, $y = \dfrac{2}{1 + t}$.

9. $x = \dfrac{3}{2 - t}$, $y = \dfrac{2}{3 - t}$.

10. $x = 4t + \frac{1}{2}t^3$, $y = \frac{1}{2}t^2 + 4$.

11. $x = \dfrac{3t}{1 + t^3}$, $y = \dfrac{3t^2}{1 + t^3}$.

Find the equation of the tangent to the curve at the given value of t.

12. $x = t^2(3 + 2t)$, $y = t^3(3 + 2t)$; where $t = 2$.

13. $x = \dfrac{5t - 1}{t^3}$, $y = \dfrac{5t - 1}{t^2}$; where $t = -1$.

14. Suppose that a projectile is shot from the earth at an angle of elevation α, with initial speed v_0 feet per second, and that the time t, in seconds, is measured from the instant of firing. Then, under idealized conditions, parametric equations for the projectile's trajectory in a vertical plane, with the x-axis horizontal, are

$$x = v_0 t \cos \alpha \quad and \quad y = -\tfrac{1}{2}gt^2 + v_0 t \sin \alpha.$$

(a) Find the slope of the trajectory at any instant t. (b) Find y at the point of maximum elevation.

Without eliminating t, plot the curve given in parametric form. Locate all points where the tangent is horizontal or vertical.

15. $x = 4t^2 + 4$, $y = 4t^3 + 4t$; also, find the xy-equation.

16. $x = \frac{8}{9}t^3$, $y = \frac{8}{9}t^2$; also, find the xy-equation.

17. $x = 2t^{-\frac{1}{2}}$, $y = 2\sqrt{t}$; also, find the xy-equation.

18. $x = 12 - t^2$, $y = 12t - t^3$; also, find the xy-equation.

19. $x = 16t - t^3$, $y = 16 - t^2$; find the tangents at $(0, 0)$.

20. $x = \dfrac{2}{1 + t^2}$, $y = \dfrac{2t}{1 + t^2}$; also, find the xy-equation.

HINT. When x and y have finite limits x_0 and y_0 as $|t| \to \infty$, include the point (x_0, y_0), to obtain an unbroken curve.

21. $x = \dfrac{36 + 27t^2}{4 + 9t^2}$, $y = \dfrac{24t}{4 + 9t^2}$. (An ellipse.)

22. $x = \dfrac{2at^2}{1 + t^2}$, $y = \dfrac{2at^3}{1 + t^2}$; $a > 0$. (The *cissoid* of DIOCLES.)

★23. $x = \dfrac{a(3 - t^2)}{1 + t^2}$, $y = \dfrac{at(3 - t^2)}{1 + t^2}$; $a > 0$. (The *trisectrix* of MACLAURIN.)

HINT. If $|t| \to \infty$, $x \to -a$ and $|y| \to \infty$; $x = -a$ is an asymptote.

★24. $x = \dfrac{a(t^2 - 1)}{t^2 + 1}$, $y = \dfrac{a(t^3 - t)}{t^2 + 1}$; $a > 0$. (The *strophoid*.)

★25. $x = \dfrac{at}{1 + t^3}$, $y = \dfrac{at^2}{1 + t^3}$. (The *folium* of DESCARTES.)

★26. If a, b, c, and d are constants, where $ab \neq 0$, and t is a parameter, prove that the locus of $[x = at + c, y = bt + d]$ is a line.

58. Vectors

A directed line segment or arrow, such as $\overrightarrow{OR}$ in Figure 70 on page 114, may be called a **stroke**. The measure of the length of $\overrightarrow{OR}$ in some linear unit is called the *magnitude* of $\overrightarrow{OR}$ and is denoted sometimes by $|\overrightarrow{OR}|$. Thus, a stroke $\overrightarrow{OR}$ has a *direction*, a *magnitude*, an *initial point* O, and a *terminal point* R. Now, consider a given set of strokes, all in a certain plane, or perhaps in space of three dimensions. Then, the strokes are called **vectors** if they combine in accordance with certain agreements, where the rules essential for our purposes are met in the following discussion. At present, any vectors which we consider simultaneously will be in the same plane (*coplanar* vectors).

Two vectors are said to be *equal* if they have the same direction and magnitude, regardless of their locations. Thus, *if a vector is moved without altering its direction and magnitude, the vector is considered unaltered.* The *zero vector* is defined as one having the magnitude zero and any direction.

Let two vectors $\overrightarrow{OF}$ and $\overrightarrow{OP}$ be given, and let them be drawn with a common initial point O, as in Figure 70. Then, we define the *sum*,* or the **resultant,** of $\overrightarrow{OP}$ and $\overrightarrow{OF}$ as a vector $\overrightarrow{OR}$ where R is located as follows: *place the initial point, O, of $\overrightarrow{OF}$ on the terminal point, P, of $\overrightarrow{OP}$, giving PR.* When OP and OF do not have the same or opposite directions, the preceding construction is equivalent to the following description: *The resultant of $\overrightarrow{OP}$ and $\overrightarrow{OF}$ is the vector $\overrightarrow{OR}$ which is the diagonal of the parallelogram having $\overrightarrow{OP}$ and $\overrightarrow{OF}$ as adjacent sides.* This definition is referred to as the *parallelogram law for the addition of vectors.* We call $\overrightarrow{OP}$ and $\overrightarrow{OF}$ the *components of $\overrightarrow{OR}$* along the lines of the corresponding sides of the parallelogram. The sum of two vectors of the same magnitude but opposite directions is seen to be the zero vector.

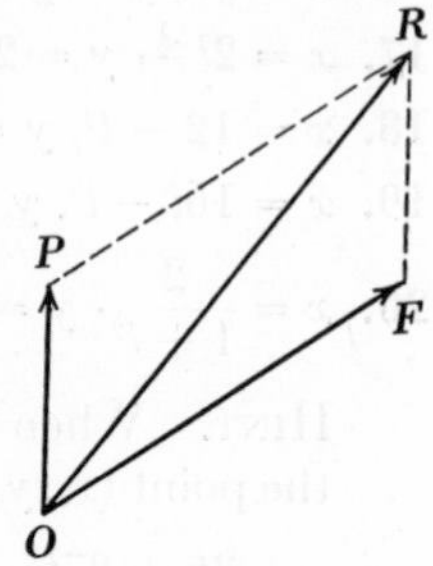

Fig. 70

ILLUSTRATION 1. Any force, velocity, or acceleration, as defined in physics, possesses a direction and a magnitude, and hence can be represented geometrically by a properly directed stroke, with the measure of its length in some linear unit equal to the measure of the physical quantity in some physical unit. In Figure 70, let $\overrightarrow{OF}$ and $\overrightarrow{OP}$ represent any two forces pulling (or *acting*) simultaneously on an object at O. Then, in physics it is found that the combined effect of forces $\overrightarrow{OF}$ and $\overrightarrow{OP}$ is the same as the effect of the single **resultant force** represented by the *resultant vector $\overrightarrow{OR}$.* This fact is referred to as the *parallelogram law for the composition of forces.* If $\overrightarrow{OF}$ and $\overrightarrow{OP}$ represent velocities simultaneously imposed on an object at O, the resultant velocity is represented by $\overrightarrow{OR}$. Thus, velocities and, similarly, accelerations also obey the parallelogram law in composition. Hence, we are justified in representing sets of forces, or velocities, or accelerations as vectors.

Any physical quantity with the property just mentioned for forces, velocities, and accelerations is referred to as a **vector quantity.** In contrast, if a symbol or quantity merely has a *value* (with no direction characteristic), we sometimes call it a **scalar.**

The components of a vector $\overrightarrow{OR}$ along two perpendicular lines ON and OE are the vectors obtained by projecting $\overrightarrow{OR}$ on ON and OE. In Figure 71, the magnitudes of the components are

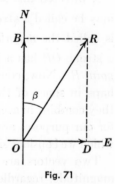

Fig. 71

$$\overline{OB} = \overline{OR} \cos \beta; \quad \overline{OD} = \overline{OR} \sin \beta.$$

The given vector $\overrightarrow{OR}$ is the resultant of its components $\overrightarrow{OB}$ and $\overrightarrow{OD}$. In

---

* In vector analysis, the operation of subtraction, and various notions of products are defined for vectors. Also, the concepts of calculus are extended to vectors.

finding $\overrightarrow{OB}$ and $\overrightarrow{OD}$ in Figure 71, we say that we have *resolved* the given vector into *components*.

ILLUSTRATION 2.   In Figure 71, let $\overrightarrow{OR}$ represent a force of 150 pounds acting in the direction $N\ 31°\ E$; the acute bearing angle is $\beta = 31°$.

$$OB = 150 \cos 31° = 129; \quad OD = 150 \sin 31° = 77.$$

The north component is 129 pounds; the east component is 77 pounds.

59. Velocity in curvilinear motion

In discussing *rectilinear* motion for a particle, we conceived of the motion occurring on a number scale, and then defined *velocity* and *acceleration* as *signed numbers*.   It was mentioned that our setting made the velocity, or acceleration, a *directed* quantity, with its sign showing the direction.   This use of signs avoided the introduction of vectors in the study of rectilinear motion.   In the discussion of curvilinear motion, we shall find it essential to define velocity and acceleration as *vectors*.

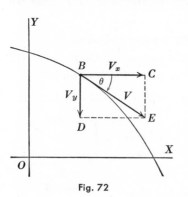

Fig. 72

Let the motion of a particle P in an xy-plane be defined by specifying the coordinates of P at any instant as functions of the time, t,

$$x = \phi(t) \quad and \quad y = \psi(t), \tag{1}$$

where $\phi(t)$ and $\psi(t)$ have continuous first and second derivatives.   Then, (1) gives parametric equations for the path of P.   At any instant, let

$$v_x = \frac{dx}{dt} \quad and \quad v_y = \frac{dy}{dt}, \tag{2}$$

and call v_x and v_y simply the *x-rate of change* and *y-rate of change*, respectively.   At any instant t, when the particle is at B, in Figure 72, define a *vector* V_x whose length is $|v_x|$, with V_x directed to the right or the left according as $v_x > 0$ or $v_x < 0$.   Similarly, define a vector V_y, whose length is $|v_y|$, with V_y directed upward or downward according as $v_y > 0$ or $v_y < 0$. We call V_x the **x-velocity**, and V_y the **y-velocity** for P.   Then, at any instant, the **velocity** of P is defined as the **vector** V which is the resultant of V_x and V_y.   We call V_x and V_y the *vector components*, and v_x and v_y the *scalar components* of V in the directions of the axes.

In Figure 72, the velocity vector V shows the path which P would cover in the next unit of time if the instantaneous velocities V_x and V_y at B should continue unchanged.   We refer to the direction of V at any instant as the *instantaneous direction* of the motion of P.

In Figure 72, the length of BC is $|v_x|$, and of BD is $|v_y|$.   Hence,

$$\overline{BE}^2 = \overline{BC}^2 + \overline{BD}^2 = v_x^2 + v_y^2. \tag{3}$$

At any instant t, we define the **instantaneous speed,** v, of P, or simply its *speed,* as *the magnitude of the velocity vector* V, or the length of BE in Figure 72. Hence, $v = |V|$ and, from (3),

$$\textbf{speed} = v = \sqrt{v_x^2 + v_y^2}, \textit{ or} \tag{4}$$

$$\textbf{speed} = v = \sqrt{\left(\frac{dx}{dt}\right)^2 + \left(\frac{dy}{dt}\right)^2}. \tag{5}$$

Let θ be an angle from the positive x-direction to the direction of V, in Figure 72. Then, with reference to B as an origin, rectangular coordinates for E are v_x and v_y. Hence, by the definitions of the trigonometric functions,

$$\tan\theta = \frac{v_y}{v_x} = \frac{\dfrac{dy}{dt}}{\dfrac{dx}{dt}} = \frac{dy}{dx}. \tag{6}$$

Thus, the slope of V is the slope of the tangent to the path at B, and we have the following result.

$$\left\{ \begin{array}{l} \textit{If the particle P is at point B, and if the velocity V is drawn} \\ \textit{from B, then V lies along the tangent to the path at B. Or, the} \\ \textit{instantaneous direction of motion at B is along the tangent.} \end{array} \right\} \tag{7}$$

Note 1. We may recall relation (4) between $|v_x|$, $|v_y|$, and v by thinking of a right triangle, as in Figure 73.

In a later chapter, we shall prove that *the speed* v *is* *the time-rate of change of distance for the particle P, meas-* *ured along the path of P.*

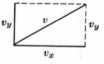

Fig. 73

Note 2. The linear unit will be one *foot,* and the time unit one *second* in all problems involving motion of particles in this text.

EXAMPLE 1. A particle P has the equations of motion

$$x = 3t^3 - 2t^2 \quad \textit{and} \quad y = 2t - t^3. \tag{8}$$

Investigate the velocity and speed at $t = 2$.

SOLUTION. 1. At $t = 2$, we have $x = 16$ and $y = -4$. From (8),

$$\frac{dx}{dt} = v_x = 9t^2 - 4t \bigg|_{t=2} = 28; \quad \frac{dy}{dt} = v_y = 2 - 3t^2 \bigg|_{t=2} = -10.$$

2. At $A:(16, -4)$, as in Figure 74 on page 117, construct the vectors V_x and V_y, and the velocity V. From (6), a direction angle θ for V satisfies

$$\tan\theta = \frac{-10}{28} = -.357, \textit{ and } \theta \textit{ is in quadrant } \text{IV}.$$

From Table VI, $\tan 19.6° = .357$. Hence, $\theta = 360° - 19.6° = 340.4°$.

3. From (5), the speed is $v = \sqrt{28^2 + 10^2} = \sqrt{884} = 29.7'$ per second.

If a particle P moves in the xy-plane along a path C which is described to us by its xy-equation, then we may meet problems involving *the related rates of change dx/dt and dy/dt.*

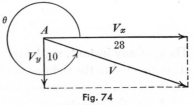

Fig. 74

EXAMPLE 2.   A particle P travels *upward* on the parabola $y^2 = 4x$ with the constant speed $4\sqrt{2}$ feet per second. Find v_x and v_y at $(1, -2)$.

SOLUTION.   1. In $y^2 = 4x$, consider x and y as functions of the time, t, and differentiate on both sides with respect to t:

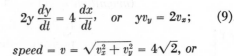

Fig. 75

$$2y\frac{dy}{dt} = 4\frac{dx}{dt}, \quad or \quad yv_y = 2v_x; \qquad (9)$$

$$speed = v = \sqrt{v_x^2 + v_y^2} = 4\sqrt{2}, \, or$$

$$v_x^2 + v_y^2 = 32. \qquad (10)$$

2. At $(1, -2)$, we have (9) with $y = -2$, and equation (10):

$$-2v_y = 2v_x \quad and \quad v_x^2 + v_y^2 = 32. \qquad (11)$$

Solve (11) simultaneously for v_x and v_y:

$$2v_x^2 = 32, \quad or \quad v_x = \pm 4; \quad v_y = \mp 4.$$

From Figure 75 and the data, $v_x < 0$ at $(1, -2)$, because P is moving to the *left.* Hence, $v_x = -4'$ per second and $v_y = 4'$ per second.

EXAMPLE 3.   A particle P moves along the hyperbola $x^2 - y^2 = 3$.   When P is at the point $(-2, 1)$, the x-rate of change is $-3'$ per second.   Find the y-rate of change, and the speed at $(-2, 1)$.

SOLUTION.   1. Differentiate with respect to t in $x^2 - y^2 = 3$:

$$2x\frac{dx}{dt} - 2y\frac{dy}{dt} = 0, \quad or \quad xv_x - yv_y = 0. \qquad (12)$$

2. Substitute $x = -2$, $y = 1$, and $v_x = -3$ in (12): $6 - v_y = 0$ or $v_y = 6$.

Hence, $$speed = \sqrt{v_x^2 + v_y^2} = \sqrt{9 + 36} = 3\sqrt{5}.$$

The y-rate of change is $6'$ per second; the speed is $3\sqrt{5}$ feet per second.

60. Introduction to vector acceleration

Let the motion of a particle P in an xy-plane be determined by

$$x = \phi(t) \quad and \quad y = \psi(t), \qquad (1)$$

as in the preceding section.   Each coordinate has a time-rate of change, v_x and v_y.   Denote their time-rates of change by a_x and a_y:

$$a_x = \frac{dv_x}{dt} = \frac{d}{dt}\left(\frac{dx}{dt}\right) = \frac{d^2x}{dt^2}, \ or$$

$$a_x = \frac{d^2x}{dt^2}; \quad a_y = \frac{d^2y}{dt^2}. \tag{2}$$

Then, at any instant, we define a *vector* A_x, where the length of A_x is $|a_x|$ and A_x is directed to the right or the left according as $a_x > 0$ or $a_x < 0$. Similarly, we define A_y in association with a_y. Finally, at any point B in the path, we define the **acceleration** of P as the **vector** A *which is the resultant of* A_x *and* A_y, as in Figure 76. The magnitude or length of A will be represented by a, that is, $a = |A|$. Then, as in the discussion of speed,

$$(magnitude \ of \ A) = |A| = a = \sqrt{a_x^2 + a_y^2}. \tag{3}$$

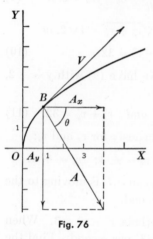

If θ is a direction angle of A measured from the positive x-direction, as in Figure 76,

$$\tan \theta = \frac{a_y}{a_x}. \tag{4}$$

In general, $\tan \theta$ *will not equal* dy/dx, or *the acceleration is not directed along the tangent to the path*.

Note 1. We describe $|A|$ in *linear units, per second per second*, in the terminology of physics.

EXAMPLE 1. Investigate the acceleration at $t = 2$ for a particle P whose motion in an xy-plane is defined by

Fig. 76

$$x = t^3 - t^2 \quad and \quad y = 2t^2 - t^3. \tag{5}$$

SOLUTION. At any instant t, $\qquad v_x = 3t^2 - 2t; \quad v_y = 4t - 3t^2;$

$$a_x = 6t - 2; \quad a_y = 4 - 6t; \quad a = |A| = \sqrt{(6t-2)^2 + (4 - 6t)^2}.$$

If $t = 2$, then $x = 4$, $y = 0$, $a_x = 10$, $a_y = -8$, and $a = \sqrt{164} = 12.8$.

EXAMPLE 2. A particle P moves on the curve $y^2 = 4x$. When P is at $B:(1, 2)$, $v_x = 4$ and $a_x = 3$. Find v_y and a_y at B.

SOLUTION. 1. In $y^2 = 4x$, differentiate twice in succession with respect to t, recalling (2):

$$2y \frac{dy}{dt} = 4 \frac{dx}{dt}, \quad or \quad y \frac{dy}{dt} = 2 \frac{dx}{dt}; \quad \left(\frac{dy}{dt}\right)^2 + y \frac{d^2y}{dt^2} = 2 \frac{d^2x}{dt^2}.$$

Thus, $\qquad\qquad\qquad yv_y = 2v_x \quad and \quad v_y^2 + ya_y = 2a_x. \tag{6}$

2. At $(x = 1, y = 2)$ with $v_x = 4$ and $a_x = 3$, from (6) we obtain $v_y = 4$ and then $a_y = -5$. The velocity V, and the accelerations A_x, A_y, and A are shown at B in Figure 76.

EXERCISE 31

The equations define the motion of a particle P in an xy-plane. At the indicated value of the time t, find the values of x, y, v_x, v_y, v, a_x, a_y, and a. Then, plot the velocity and acceleration vectors at the instantaneous location (x, y).

1. $x = 3t + t^3$, $y = t - t^2$; $t = 2$.   2. $x = 4t^2 + 4$, $y = \frac{1}{6}t^3 + 4t$; $t = 3$.

3. $x = 12 - t^2$, $y = 12t - t^3$; $t = 1$. Also, plot the path from its xy-equation, obtained by using $t = y/x$.

4. $x = \frac{8}{9}t^3$, $y = \frac{8}{9}t^2$; $t = 2$. Also, plot the path from its xy-equation.

5. $x = t^2 + 4$, $y = t - t^2$; $t = 0$. Also, find the minimum speed.

6. $x = \dfrac{3}{2 - t}$, $y = \dfrac{2}{3 - t}$; $t = 4$.

7. In an xy-plane, the x-axis is horizontal and the y-axis is vertical, directed upward. Under idealized conditions, the motion of a certain projectile is defined by $x = 60t$ and $y = 80t - 16t^2$. (a) Carry out the directions preceding Problem 1, at $t = 3$. (b) Find the speed of the projectile at $t = 0$. (c) Find when the speed is a minimum.

8. Find when the magnitude of the acceleration of a particle P is a minimum if its equations of motion are $x = \frac{1}{3}t^3 + \frac{1}{2}t^2$ and $y = 3t^2 - \frac{1}{6}t^3$.

Use the instantaneous location of the particle P as the initial point for the vectors. Graph the path and any vectors V or A which are found.

9. A particle P moves to the right on the curve $x^2 = 8y$, with a constant speed of $10\sqrt{2}$ feet per second. Find the velocity at (a) $(-4, 2)$; (b) $(4, 2)$.

10. A particle P moves clockwise with a constant speed of $15'$ per second on the ellipse $2x^2 + 3y^2 = 21$. Find the velocity at $(-3, -1)$.

11. A particle P moves upward on the curve $x^3 = 2y^2$, with a constant speed of $6\sqrt{13}$ feet per second. (a) Find the velocity when P is at $(2, -2)$. (b) How fast is P approaching the origin at $(2, -2)$?

12. A particle P moves on the upper branch of the hyperbola $xy = 4$, with $v_x = 4$. (a) Find v_y and the speed, and plot the velocity at $(4, 1)$. (b) How fast is P receding from the origin at $(4, 1)$?

13. A particle P moves clockwise on the curve $y^2 = (x - 2)(4 - x)$, with a speed of $8'$ per second. Find the velocity at (a) $(3, 1)$; (b) $(4, 0)$.

14. A particle P moves on the lower branch of the curve $xy = -6$, with $v_y = 4$ at all points. Find v_x, a_x, a_y, v, and $|A|$ when P is at $(3, -2)$.

15. A particle P moves on the curve $9y^3 = 8x^2$. When P is at $(-3, 2)$, $v_y = 4$ and $a_y = 12$. Find v_x, a_x, v, and $|A|$ when P is at $(-3, 2)$.

16. A particle P moves downward on the curve $y^2 = 16x$ with a speed of $15\sqrt{2}$ feet per second. When P is at $(4, -8)$, find v_x, v_y, a_x, a_y, and $|A|$.

17. A ladder $40'$ long rests against a wall. A man has his feet halfway up the ladder. Its top slides down the wall at a speed of $.5'$ per second. Find the speed of his feet when the foot of the ladder is $32'$ from the wall.

REVIEW EXERCISE 32

For Chapters 6 and 7

Find the equations of the tangent and normal to the curve.

1. $y = 4x^3 + 6x^2 - 9x + 5$, (a) at $x = -2$; (b) at the inflection point.
2. $x^2 + 3xy - y^2 + 3 = 0$, at the point where $x = 2$.
3. Find the angle of intersection of $x^2 + y^2 = 2$ and $y = x^2$.
4. Obtain a simplified equation for the tangent to $4x^2 - 9y^2 = 36$ at (x_1, y_1).
5. Prove that every cubic curve $y = ax^3 + bx^2 + cx + d$, where $a \neq 0$, has just one inflection point, and either one maximum and one minimum or no extremum.
6. Find the absolute maximum and absolute minimum of the function $y = 3x - 5$, where x is restricted to the range $-2 \leqq x \leqq 3$.
7. Graph the function $y = 4x^3 + 6x^2 - 9x + 5$.

Test for extrema and inflection points of the curve.

8. $y = (x + 3)^6$.   9. $y = x^3(x - 1)^2$.   10. $y = (x - 5)^{\frac{2}{3}}$.

Graph by use of asymptotes, intercepts, and vertical or horizontal tangents.

11. $x = y^3 + 2y^2 - 4y + 5$.   12. $2x^2 + 2xy + y^2 = 10$.

13. $y = \dfrac{1}{(x - 2)(x + 1)}$.   14. $y = \dfrac{x - 2}{3x + 4}$.   15. $x^2 = \dfrac{y^3}{4 - y}$.

16. Find the shape of the right triangle of maximum area, with a given hypotenuse.
17. Find the maximum area for an isosceles triangle whose perimeter is $24''$.
18. A piece of linoleum forms a quadrant of a circle with radius r. A rectangular piece will be cut having two sides along the perpendicular sides of the quadrant. Find the maximum area for the rectangle.
19. The perpendicular sides of a right triangle are $7''$ and $24''$ long. The shorter side is increasing at the rate of $.2''$ per second and the longer side is decreasing at the rate of $.3''$ per second. Find the rate of change of (a) the length of the hypotenuse; (b) the area.
20. A fire department ladder $75'$ long extends from the ground against a factory building. The bottom of the ladder is being shoved toward the factory at the rate of $1.5'$ per second. How fast is the top of the ladder rising when the bottom is $21'$ from the structure?
21. An automobile A_1 is traveling north at the rate of 60 miles per hour. An automobile A_2 is traveling east at 40 miles per hour on a road intersecting A_1's road at point P. At what rate is the distance A_1A_2 changing when A_1 is 80 miles north of P and A_2 is 60 miles west of P?
22. A curve is defined by the equations $x = 6t^2 - 2t^3$ and $y = t^2 - 3t$, where t is a parameter. Without eliminating t, (a) find equations for the tangent and normal to the curve where $t = 3$; (b) obtain all points where the tangent is horizontal or vertical; (c) find $D_x^2 y$.

23. A trapezoidal gutter is to be made from a strip of tin 15″ wide by bending up equal sides at an angle of 60°. Find the width of the base of the gutter for maximum capacity.

24. A page in a book is to contain 4800 square picas of print (where 1 *pica*, the printer's unit of length, is $\frac{1}{6}$ inch). The margins are to be 6 picas wide at the sides and 8 picas high at the top and bottom. Find the dimensions of the page for minimum area.

Find the differential of the function.

25. $x^{\frac{3}{2}} + (2x - 1)^3$.

26. $\sqrt[3]{4x^2 - 5}$.

27. $(2 + 3t)\sqrt{3t + 2}$.

28. $\dfrac{x^2 + 5x}{(3 - 2x)^4}$.

29. $\dfrac{\sqrt{3 + 4t}}{(2t - 5)^4}$.

30. $\sqrt{\dfrac{2x + 1}{x - 4}}$.

Solve Problems 31–36 by use of differentials.

31. A building consists of a cylinder of height 30′ and base radius 10′, with a hemisphere as the roof. The side walls and the roof are 1″ thick. Find the volume of the material in the wall and roof, approximately.

32. If a body has fallen a distance s feet from rest in a vacuum near the earth's surface, the body's velocity, v, in feet per second is given by $v = \sqrt{64s}$, approximately. If we measure $s = s_0$ with an error ds, and compute v, find approximately the error in v.

33. The maximum horsepower of the boiler which can be served by a chimney of given cross-section area is proportional to the square root of the height of the chimney. Find approximately the percentage increase in the horsepower due to a 6% increase in the height.

34. A monument 40′ high is a pyramid with a square base. A side of the base is measured as 8.7′, with accuracy to one decimal place. Find approximately the maximum possible error and percentage error in the volume of the monument, as computed from these data.

35. The radius of a sphere will be measured with an error of at most 2%. Find approximately the maximum percentage error (*a*) in the computed volume; (*b*) in the computed surface area.

36. The force of attraction between two spheres of masses m and M is given by $F = k/r^2$, where k is a constant depending on the physical units employed, and r is the distance between the centers of the spheres. If r is increased by 3%, find approximately the percentage change in F.

37. Write parametric equations for the line through $(2, 3)$ and $(- 4, 2)$.

The equations define the motion of a particle P in an xy-plane. At $t = 3$, find the magnitudes of the velocity and acceleration and plot them.

38. $x = 3t^2 - 2t$; $y = 4t - t^2$.

39. $x = (t + 3)^2$, $y = t^3 - t^2$.

40. A particle P moves to the left with a speed of $2\sqrt{73}$ feet per second on a branch of the curve $4y^2 - x^2 = 7$. Plot the path. Find v_x and v_y when P is at $(3, - 2)$, and plot the velocity at this point.

8

DIFFERENTIATION OF TRANSCENDENTAL FUNCTIONS

61. Derivatives of the elementary transcendental functions

In Chapter 4, we defined the algebraic functions. To complete a classification of functions, we state that any function which is *not* an algebraic function is called a **transcendental function.** In particular, trigonometric, inverse trigonometric, exponential, and logarithmic functions are referred to as the **elementary transcendental functions.** These functions and the algebraic functions then are called the **elementary functions of mathematical analysis.** In the following fundamental forms for differentiating the elementary transcendental functions, u and v represent differentiable functions of x. We use "ln u" for "log$_e$ u," as discussed later.

$$\frac{d}{dx}(\sin u) = \cos u \frac{du}{dx}. \tag{IX}$$

$$\frac{d}{dx}(\cos u) = -\sin u \frac{du}{dx}. \tag{X}$$

$$\frac{d}{dx}(\tan u) = \sec^2 u \frac{du}{dx}. \tag{XI}$$

$$\frac{d}{dx}(\cot u) = -\csc^2 u \frac{du}{dx}. \tag{XII}$$

$$\frac{d}{dx}(\sec u) = \sec u \tan u \frac{du}{dx}. \tag{XIII}$$

$$\frac{d}{dx}(\csc u) = -\csc u \cot u \frac{du}{dx}. \tag{XIV}$$

$$\frac{d}{dx}(\text{Arcsin } u) = \frac{1}{\sqrt{1 - u^2}} \frac{du}{dx}. \tag{XV}$$

$$\frac{d}{dx}(\text{Arccos } u) = -\frac{1}{\sqrt{1 - u^2}} \frac{du}{dx}. \tag{XVI}$$

$$\frac{d}{dx}(\text{Arctan } u) = \frac{1}{1 + u^2} \frac{du}{dx}. \tag{XVII}$$

$$\frac{d}{dx}(\text{Arccot } u) = -\frac{1}{1+u^2}\frac{du}{dx}. \qquad \text{(XVIII)}$$

$$\frac{d}{dx}(\ln u) = \frac{1}{u}\frac{du}{dx}. \qquad \text{(XIX)}$$

$$\frac{d}{dx}(\log_a u) = \frac{\log_a e}{u}\frac{du}{dx}. \qquad \text{(XX)}$$

$$\frac{d}{dx}(e^u) = e^u \frac{du}{dx}. \qquad \text{(XXI)}$$

$$\frac{d}{dx}(a^u) = a^u(\ln a)\frac{du}{dx}. \qquad \text{(XXII)}$$

$$\frac{d}{dx}(u^v) = vu^{v-1}\frac{du}{dx} + (\ln u)u^v\frac{dv}{dx}. \qquad \text{(XXIII)}$$

62. Review of the general angle and angular measurement

Suppose that a half-line or ray, issuing from a fixed point O, rotates about O either clockwise or counterclockwise from an initial position OA to a terminal position OB, as in Figure 77. Then, this rotation is said to generate an angle AOB with the *initial side OA* and *terminal side OB*. The *measure* of $\angle AOB$ is defined as the measure of the amount of rotation used in generating the angle, where we agree to consider counterclockwise rotation as positive and clockwise rotation negative. As a unit for measuring rotation, we define $1°$ as $1/360$ of a complete revolution.

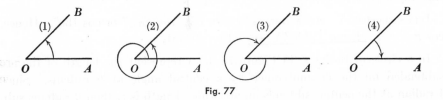

Fig. 77

ILLUSTRATION 1. In Figure 77, the configuration AOB is the same in each diagram. In (1), $\angle AOB = 45°$. In (2), $\angle AOB = 360° + 45° = 405°$. In (3), $\angle AOB = -315°$. In (4), $\angle BOA = -45°$. Any positive angle whose value lies between $0°$ and $90°$ is called an *acute* angle. Any positive angle between $90°$ and $180°$ is called an *obtuse* angle. Any angle with the value $k\cdot(90°)$, where k is any integer, is called a *quadrantal angle*.

In formulas of calculus, it proves convenient to use *radian measure* for angles, where the unit, a *radian*, is described as follows.

DEFINITION I. *One* **radian** *is the measure of an angle which, if its vertex is placed at the center of a circle, subtends on the circumference an arc whose length is equal to the radius of the circle.*

ILLUSTRATION 2. In Figure 78, the measure of ∠*BOC* is one radian, because the length of the subtended *arc BC* is *r*.

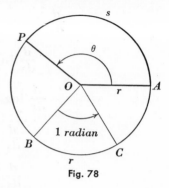

Fig. 78

Since an arc of length *r* subtends an angle of one radian at the center of a circle whose radius is *r*, hence the whole circumference, with length $2\pi r$, subtends an angle of $2\pi \times$ (*one radian*) or 2π **radians**. In degree measure, the whole circumference subtends an angle of 360° at the center. Thus,*

$$360° = 2\pi \text{ radians; } \quad 180° = \pi \text{ radians;} \tag{1}$$

$$1° = \frac{\pi}{180} \text{ radians} = .0174533 \text{ radians, } approximately; \tag{2}$$

$$1 \text{ radian} = \frac{180°}{\pi} = 57.2958°, \; approximately. \tag{3}$$

ILLUSTRATION 3. $\frac{5}{6}\pi$ radians $= \frac{5}{6}(180°) = 150°$.

$$90° = \frac{1}{2}(180°) = \frac{1}{2}\pi \; radians = \frac{\pi}{2} \; radians = 1.5708 \; radians.$$

$$3.2 \text{ rad.} = 3.2 \frac{180°}{\pi} = \frac{(2.3)(180°)}{3.1416} = 183.35°, \; by \; logarithms.$$

Hereafter, when no unit is indicated in giving the value of an angle, assume that the unit of measurement is a *radian*.

ILLUSTRATION 4. cos π means *"cosine of π radians,"* or cos 180°. Hence, cos $\pi = -1$. From Table IV, sin 1.18 = .92461.

In a circle of radius *r*, in Figure 78, let *s* represent the length of the arc subtended on the circumference by a central angle of θ radians. Since 1 radian at the center subtends an arc whose length is *r*, then θ radians subtend an arc whose length is $\theta \cdot r$. That is,

$$s = r\theta; \tag{4}$$

$$\text{arc} = (\text{radius}) \times (\text{angle, in radians}). \tag{5}$$

ILLUSTRATION 5. If $r = 25'$ and $s = 75'$, $\quad \theta = \frac{s}{r} = \frac{75}{25} = 3$ radians.

ILLUSTRATION 6. Suppose that $0 < \theta < 2\pi$, as in Figure 78, and let *A* represent the area of the circular sector bounded by the sides of θ and the arc subtended by θ. Then, since the measure of a complete rotation

---

* Equalities such as (1)–(3) are *not equations* in the ordinary sense of the word, because *equalities of numbers are not involved.* Each of (1)–(3) is merely an *abbreviation for a sentence.* Thus, (1) states that "*an angle whose measure is 360° is the same as an angle whose measure is 2π radians.*"

about a point is 2π radians, and the area of the circle is πr^2, we have

$$\frac{A}{\pi r^2} = \frac{\theta}{2\pi} \quad or \quad A = \frac{1}{2}r^2\theta. \tag{6}$$

63. Behavior of $(\sin \theta)/\theta$ as θ approaches zero

The usual formulas of calculus for trigonometric functions are based on the following result, where "$\sin \theta$" means the "*sine of θ radians*."

$$\lim_{\theta \to 0} \frac{\sin \theta}{\theta} = 1. \tag{1}$$

ILLUSTRATION 1. By use of Table IV, we compute the following table, which suggests the truth of (1). Thus, since $\sin .1 = .09983$, and since $\sin (- .1) = - \sin .1$, we obtain .9983 as listed below. Similarly, the values of $(\sin \theta)/\theta$ for any value $\theta > 0$ and for $- \theta$ are the same.

$\dfrac{\sin \theta}{\theta}$	NO VALUE	.9983	.9934	.9851	.9736	.9589
θ	0	$\pm .1$	$\pm .2$	$\pm .3$	$\pm .4$	$\pm .5$

Proof of (1). 1. With $\theta > 0$, consider Figure 79. Since $OR = OM = 1$,

$$\sin \theta = NR; \quad \cos \theta = ON; \quad \tan \theta = MP. \tag{2}$$

Also, $(area \triangle ONR) < (area\ sector\ OMR) < (area \triangle OMP).$ $\tag{3}$

From (2), $(area \triangle ONR) = \frac{1}{2}(ON)(NR) = \frac{1}{2} \sin \theta \cos \theta;$

$(area \triangle OMP) = \frac{1}{2}(OM)(MP) = \frac{1}{2} \tan \theta;$

from (6) above, $(area\ sector\ OMR) = \frac{1}{2}\theta$. Hence, from (3),

$$\tfrac{1}{2} \sin \theta \cos \theta < \tfrac{1}{2}\theta < \tfrac{1}{2} \tan \theta. \tag{4}$$

2. On dividing by $\frac{1}{2} \sin \theta$ in (4), we obtain

$$\cos \theta < \frac{\theta}{\sin \theta} < \frac{1}{\cos \theta}. \tag{5}$$

3. On taking reciprocals in (5),

since $\cos \theta < \dfrac{\theta}{\sin \theta}$, $\dfrac{\sin \theta}{\theta} < \dfrac{1}{\cos \theta};$ $\tag{6}$

since $\dfrac{\theta}{\sin \theta} < \dfrac{1}{\cos \theta}$, $\cos \theta < \dfrac{\sin \theta}{\theta}.$ $\tag{7}$

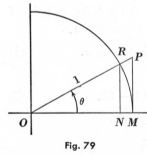

Fig. 79

From (6) and (7), $\cos \theta < \dfrac{\sin \theta}{\theta} < \dfrac{1}{\cos \theta}.$ $\tag{8}$

4. If $\theta \to 0$ in (8), then $\cos \theta \to 1$ and $(1/\cos \theta) \to 1$. Hence, the central member in (8) has the limit 1 as $\theta \to 0$, which proves (1) for $\theta > 0$. Since $(\sin \theta)/\theta$ has the same value at a value θ as at $- \theta$, then (1) is true if $\theta \to C$ and $\theta < 0$. Thus, (1) is true as $\theta \to 0$, with θ unrestricted.

ILLUSTRATION 2. By use of (1), $\lim\limits_{\theta \to 0} \dfrac{\sin 3\theta}{\theta} = \lim\limits_{\theta \to 0} 3 \cdot \dfrac{\sin 3\theta}{3\theta} = 3 \cdot 1 = 3;$

$$\lim\limits_{\Delta x \to 0} \dfrac{\sin \Delta x}{\Delta x} = 1; \quad \lim\limits_{\Delta x \to 0} \dfrac{\sin \frac{1}{2}\Delta x}{\frac{1}{2}\Delta x} = 1.$$

ILLUSTRATION 3. Let ϕ be the measure of an angle in degrees, and let θ be the corresponding measure in radians. Then, $\theta = \pi\phi/180$ and

$$\sin \phi^\circ = \sin (\pi\phi/180),$$

where radian measure is involved on the right. Thus,

$$\lim\limits_{\phi \to 0} \dfrac{\sin \phi^\circ}{\phi} = \lim\limits_{\phi \to 0} \dfrac{\pi}{180} \dfrac{\sin \dfrac{\pi\phi}{180}}{\dfrac{\pi\phi}{180}} = \dfrac{\pi}{180} \cdot 1 = \dfrac{\pi}{180}. \tag{9}$$

The simplicity of the limit "1" in (1) as compared to "$\pi/180$" in (9) is the source of the convenience in use of radian measure later.

64. Derivatives of the direct trigonometric functions

To prove (IX)–(XIV) on page 122, first we shall prove their following special cases, where we place $u = x$ in (IX)–(XIV).

$$\dfrac{d \sin x}{dx} = \cos x. \qquad \text{(IX)}' \qquad \Big\| \qquad \dfrac{d \cot x}{dx} = -\csc^2 x. \qquad \text{(XII)}'$$

$$\dfrac{d \cos x}{dx} = -\sin x. \qquad \text{(X)}' \qquad \Big\| \qquad \dfrac{d \sec x}{dx} = \sec x \tan x. \qquad \text{(XIII)}'$$

$$\dfrac{d \tan x}{dx} = \sec^2 x. \qquad \text{(XI)}' \qquad \Big\| \qquad \dfrac{d \csc x}{dx} = -\csc x \cot x. \qquad \text{(XIV)}'$$

Proof of (IX)'. Let $y = \sin x$. With (x, y) and $(x + \Delta x, y + \Delta y)$ as pairs of corresponding values of x and y, and x held fixed for the moment,

$$y + \Delta y = \sin (x + \Delta x); \quad \Delta y = \sin (x + \Delta x) - \sin x. \tag{1}$$

2. From trigonometry, we have the identity

$$\sin A - \sin B = 2 \cos \tfrac{1}{2}(A + B) \sin \tfrac{1}{2}(A - B). \tag{2}$$

Hence, by use of (2) with $A = x + \Delta x$ and $B = x$, (1) gives

$$\Delta y = 2 \cos (x + \tfrac{1}{2}\Delta x) \sin \tfrac{1}{2}\Delta x;$$

$$\dfrac{\Delta y}{\Delta x} = \cos (x + \tfrac{1}{2}\Delta x) \dfrac{\sin \frac{1}{2}\Delta x}{\frac{1}{2}\Delta x}. \tag{3}$$

If $\Delta x \to 0$, then $\cos (x + \tfrac{1}{2}\Delta x) \to \cos x$, and $\tfrac{1}{2}\Delta x \to 0$. Hence, from (1) on page 125 with $\theta = \tfrac{1}{2}\Delta x$, by use of (3) we obtain (IX)':

$$\dfrac{d \sin x}{dx} = \lim\limits_{\Delta x \to 0} \dfrac{\Delta y}{\Delta x} = (\cos x) \left(\lim\limits_{\Delta x \to 0} \dfrac{\sin \frac{1}{2}\Delta x}{\frac{1}{2}\Delta x} \right) = (\cos x) \cdot 1 = \cos x.$$

Proof of (IX). Let u be a differentiable function of x, and let $y = \sin u$. Then, by use of (IX)$'$ and the formula for the derivative of a composite function, we obtain (IX):

$$\frac{dy}{dx} = \frac{dy}{du} \cdot \frac{du}{dx} = \frac{d \sin u}{du} \cdot \frac{du}{dx} = \cos u \, \frac{du}{dx}. \tag{4}$$

ILLUSTRATION 1.
$$\frac{d \sin 3x}{dx} = (\cos 3x) \frac{d(3x)}{dx} = 3 \cos 3x.$$

$$\frac{d \sin (3 - 5x)}{dx} = \cos (3 - 5x) \frac{d(3 - 5x)}{dx} = - 5 \cos (3 - 5x).$$

Proof of (X)$'$. 1. Let $y = \cos x$. Then, by a cofunction identity of trigonometry, $\cos x = \sin (\tfrac{1}{2}\pi - x)$. Hence, by use of (IX),

$$\frac{d \cos x}{dx} = \frac{d \sin (\tfrac{1}{2}\pi - x)}{dx} = \cos (\tfrac{1}{2}\pi - x) \frac{d(\tfrac{1}{2}\pi - x)}{dx}$$

$$= - \cos (\tfrac{1}{2}\pi - x) = - \sin x.$$

Then, by the method of (4), from (X)$'$ we obtain (X).

Proof of (XI)$'$. From (IX)$'$, (X)$'$, and the formula for the derivative of a quotient,

$$\frac{d \tan x}{dx} = \frac{d}{dx}\left(\frac{\sin x}{\cos x}\right) = \frac{\cos x \dfrac{d \sin x}{dx} - \sin x \dfrac{d \cos x}{dx}}{\cos^2 x}$$

$$= \frac{\cos x \cos x + \sin x \sin x}{\cos^2 x} = \frac{\cos^2 x + \sin^2 x}{\cos^2 x} = \frac{1}{\cos^2 x} = \sec^2 x,$$

which proves (XI)$'$. Then, as in (4), we obtain (XI) from (XI)$'$.

Note 1. In the next exercise, the student will prove (XII)$'$, (XIII)$'$ by use of $\sec x = 1/\cos x$, and (XIV)$'$, and then (XII)–(XIV).

ILLUSTRATION 2. By use of (X) with $u = (3x^2 + 2)$,

$$\frac{d}{dx} \cos (3x^2 + 2) = - \sin (3x^2 + 2) \frac{d}{dx}(3x^2 + 2) = - 6x \sin (3x^2 + 2).$$

To indicate powers of trigonometric functions of an angle x, place the exponent, n, of the power with the name of the function, except when $x = - 1$. The reason for this exception will appear later.

ILLUSTRATION 3. $(\sin x)^3$ is written $\sin^3 x$.

$$\frac{1}{\tan^4 x} \quad \textit{may be written} \quad \tan^{-4} x.$$

However, the reciprocal of $\sin x$, or its $(- 1)$th power, is written

$$\frac{1}{\sin x} = (\sin x)^{-1} \quad \textit{and is not written} \quad \sin^{-1} x.$$

ILLUSTRATION 4. By use of the power formula first,

$$\frac{d}{dx} \tan^3 (2x + 3) = 3 \tan^2 (2x + 3) \frac{d}{dx} \tan (2x + 3)$$

$$= 3 \cdot 2 \tan^2 (2x + 3) \sec^2 (2x + 3). \qquad [(XI), \text{ with } u = 2x + 3]$$

ILLUSTRATION 5. We use the power formula first:

$$\frac{d}{dz}\left(\frac{5}{\sqrt{\csc 3z}}\right) = \frac{d}{dz} 5(\csc 3z)^{-\frac{1}{2}} = 5 \cdot (-\tfrac{1}{2})(\csc 3z)^{-\frac{3}{2}} \frac{d \csc 3z}{dz}$$

$$= -\frac{5}{2}(\csc 3z)^{-\frac{3}{2}}(- \csc 3z \cot 3z) \frac{d(3z)}{dz} \qquad [\text{Using (XIV)}]$$

$$= \frac{15}{2}(\csc 3z)^{-\frac{1}{2}} \cot 3z.$$

ILLUSTRATION 6. By use of the product formula,

$$\frac{d}{dt}(\cot^2 4t \tan \sqrt{1 - 2t}) =$$

$$(\tan \sqrt{1 - 2t})\left[2(\cot 4t) \frac{d \cot 4t}{dt}\right] + (\cot^2 4t)(\sec^2 \sqrt{1 - 2t})\left(\frac{d\sqrt{1 - 2t}}{dt}\right) =$$

$$- 8(\csc^2 4t \cot 4t)\tan \sqrt{1 - 2t} - (\cot^2 4t)(\sec^2 \sqrt{1 - 2t})(1 - 2t)^{-\frac{1}{2}}.$$

EXAMPLE 1. Obtain dy/dx if y is defined as a function of x by

$$\sin (2x + 3y) + \cos (x - 2y) = 2. \qquad (5)$$

SOLUTION. Differentiate with respect to x on each side in (5):

$$\cos (2x + 3y) \frac{d(2x + 3y)}{dx} - \sin (x - 2y)\frac{d(x - 2y)}{dx} = 0, \text{ or}$$

$$(2 + 3y')\cos (2x + 3y) - (1 - 2y')\sin (x - 2y) = 0, \text{ or}$$

$$y'[3 \cos (2x + 3y) + 2 \sin (x - 2y)] = \sin (x - 2y) - 2 \cos (2x + 3y);$$

$$y' = \frac{\sin (x - 2y) - 2 \cos (2x + 3y)}{3 \cos (2x + 3y) + 2 \sin (x - 2y)}.$$

EXERCISE 33

Find the derivative of the function.

1. $\sin 5x$. **2.** $\cos \tfrac{3}{2}x$. **3.** $\tan 4t$. **4.** $\sec 5t$.

5. $\csc \tfrac{3}{2}t$. **6.** $\sin^4 x$. **7.** $\cot^5 z$. **8.** $\sec^3 4t^2$.

9. $\sqrt{\sin x}$. **10.** $\sqrt[3]{\tan x}$. **11.** $\sqrt[4]{\cos 2x}$. **12.** $\sqrt{\sec 3x}$.

13. $\dfrac{1}{\sin^3 4x}$. **14.** $\dfrac{3}{\tan^2 6z}$. **15.** $\dfrac{1}{\cos \sqrt{x}}$. **16.** $-\dfrac{5}{\sec^2 x}$.

Note 1. In Problem 13, we could write $\sin^{-3} 4x$ and use the power formula with exponent $- 3$. Or, first we could use $\csc 4x = 1/\sin 4x$, to obtain $\csc^3 4x$, and then apply the power formula with exponent 3.

17. $\sin (2x^2 + x)$.

18. $\cot (3 - 5x)$.

19. $7 \csc^2 x$.

20. $a \csc k\theta$.

21. $\sqrt{\cos (2x - 3)^2}$.

22. $\sec^2 (4x + 3)^2$.

23. $x^3 \sin x$.

24. $\sin 3x \cos 2x$.

25. $\cos^2 x \sin 4x$.

26. $(\tan 2x)\sqrt{\cos 3x}$.

27. $(\sec^2 x)(3 + 4x)^2$.

28. $\cos 3x \sin \sqrt{x}$.

29. $\dfrac{1 - \cos x}{1 + \cos x}$.

30. $\dfrac{1 - \tan x}{1 + \tan x}$.

31. $\dfrac{\cos (\frac{1}{2}\pi - 2x)}{3 - \sec 2x}$.

32. $\dfrac{\sin^2 3x}{4x^2 - x}$.

33. $\dfrac{\sin (3t - 1)}{t + \cos t}$.

34. $\dfrac{t^3 \tan t}{2 + \cos^2 t}$.

35. $\dfrac{1}{3 \sin 2x - 1}$.

36. $\dfrac{a}{4x - \cos 3x}$.

37. $\dfrac{2}{x^2 + \tan x}$.

38. $x \cos \dfrac{1}{x}$.

39. $\dfrac{\sin 2x}{1 + \tan 2x}$.

40. $\tan \dfrac{2x}{x - 1}$.

Find dy/dx at the given value of x.

41. $y = 2x + \cos 2x;\ x = \frac{3}{4}\pi$.

42. $y = x \sin^2 x;\ x = \frac{5}{6}\pi$.

43. $y = x(\cos x - \sin x);\ x = \frac{1}{4}\pi$.

44. $y = \tan 2x + \cot 4x;\ x = \frac{1}{3}\pi$.

45. $y = \tan x \sin 2x;\ x = \frac{1}{6}\pi$.

46. $y = \cos \frac{1}{2}x \sec 3x;\ x = \frac{1}{3}\pi$.

Find the second derivative of the function.

47. $f(x) = \cos 3x$.

48. $f(t) = x \sin x$.

49. $g(x) = x^2 \tan x$.

50. $F(x) = \dfrac{\cos 2x}{x}$.

51. $h(z) = \dfrac{\tan 3z}{z^2}$.

52. $f(x) = \dfrac{\sec x}{3x + 3}$.

Find dy/dx from the given equation.

53. $\sin x - \cos y = 3y - 1$.

54. $\tan x + \sin y = 2y^3$.

55. $x = \sin (x + 3y)$.

56. $\cos (2x + 3y) = x$.

57. $\tan (x^2 - y) + \cot y = 5$.

58. $x \tan (x + 2y) = 3 + x^2$.

59. $\tan (x^2 - 2y) + \cot (2x - y^2) = 4$.

60. Prove formulas (XII), (XIII), and (XIV).

★61. By mathematical induction, prove that

$$\frac{d^n \sin x}{dx^n} = \sin \left(x + \frac{n\pi}{2}\right); \quad \frac{d^n \cos x}{dx^n} = \cos \left(x + \frac{n\pi}{2}\right).$$

HINT. Use $\cos \theta = \sin (\theta + \frac{1}{2}\pi)$ or $\sin \theta = - \cos (\theta + \frac{1}{2}\pi)$, after each differentiation.

65. Graphs involving trigonometric functions

Trigonometric equations are likely to arise when we test a trigonometric function for extrema, or seek inflection points in graphing the function.

EXAMPLE 1. Use derivatives to study the graph of $y = \sin x$.

SOLUTION. 1. Since $\sin x$ is a periodic function with the period 2π, restrict details to the range $0 \leq x < 2\pi$. We have

$$y' = \cos x; \quad y'' = - \sin x. \tag{1}$$

2. *Extrema.* Critical values of x satisfy $\cos x = 0$, which gives $x = \frac{1}{2}\pi$ and $x = \frac{3}{2}\pi$. Since $y'' < 0$ at $x = \frac{1}{2}\pi$ and $y'' > 0$ at $x = \frac{3}{2}\pi$, there is a maximum at $x = \frac{1}{2}\pi$ and a minimum at $x = \frac{3}{2}\pi$.

3. *Inflection points.* $y'' = 0$ leads to $\sin x = 0$, or $x = 0$ and $x = \pi$. Since $\sin x$ changes sign at $x = 0$ and at $x = \pi$, hence y'' changes sign, and there are inflection points at $x = 0$ and $x = \pi$. At $x = 0$, $y' = 1$ and thus the inflection tangent has slope 1. The tangent at $x = \pi$ has slope -1. The preceding details check with the graph in Figure 80.

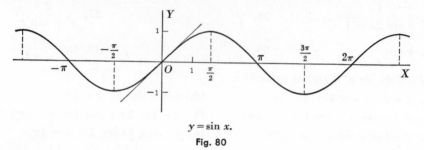

$$y = \sin x.$$

Fig. 80

EXAMPLE 2. Study the graph of $y = \sec x$.

SOLUTION. 1. We restrict x to the range $0 \leqq x < 2\pi$, as in Example 1. Since $\cos x = 0$ at $x = \frac{1}{2}\pi$ and $x = \frac{3}{2}\pi$, hence $|\sec x| \to \infty$ as $x \to \frac{1}{2}\pi$ and as $x \to \frac{3}{2}\pi$. Thus, the graph has the lines $x = \frac{1}{2}\pi$ and $x = \frac{3}{2}\pi$ as vertical asymptotes.

2. We obtain $y' = \sec x \tan x$ and

$$y'' = \sec x \, (\sec^2 x + \tan^2 x). \tag{2}$$

Since $\sec x \neq 0$ at any value of x, the critical values of x for extrema satisfy $\tan x = 0$. By the 2d derivative test, there is a minimum at $x = 0$ and a maximum at $x = \pi$. In (2), $\sec x \neq 0$ and hence $y'' \neq 0$ at any value of x, so that the graph has no inflection points. The results check with the graph on page 591.

EXAMPLE 3. If $0 \leqq x < 2\pi$, test for extrema and inflection points:

$$y = \sin x + \cos x. \tag{3}$$

SOLUTION. 1. We obtain

$$y' = \cos x - \sin x \quad and \quad y'' = -\sin x - \cos x. \tag{4}$$

2. Critical values for extrema satisfy the equation

$$\cos x - \sin x = 0, \quad or \quad 1 = \frac{\sin x}{\cos x}, \quad or \quad \tan x = 1. \tag{5}$$

Hence, $x = \frac{1}{4}\pi$ and $x = \frac{5}{4}\pi$. From (4),

$$at \; x = \tfrac{1}{4}\pi, \;\; y'' = -\sqrt{2}; \;\; at \; x = \tfrac{5}{4}\pi, \;\; y'' = \sqrt{2}.$$

Thus, there is a maximum at $x = \frac{1}{4}\pi$ and a minimum at $x = \frac{5}{4}\pi$.

3. Critical values for inflection points satisfy $y'' = 0$, or

$$- \sin x - \cos x = 0, \quad or \quad \tan x = - 1, \tag{6}$$

which gives $x = \frac{3}{4}\pi$ and $x = \frac{7}{4}\pi$. To test these values, write

$$y'' = - \cos x \left(1 + \frac{\sin x}{\cos x}\right) = - \cos x \ (\tan x + 1). \tag{7}$$

If x is near $\frac{3}{4}\pi$, or $\frac{7}{4}\pi$, then $\cos x$ remains of constant sign. At each of these values of x, $\tan x$ increases, or decreases, through the value $- 1$; hence, $(\tan x + 1)$ and y'' change sign. Therefore, there are inflection points at $x = \frac{3}{4}\pi$ and $x = \frac{7}{4}\pi$. A graph of (3) is given in Figure 81. The graph was checked by *composition* (addition) *of ordinates* of the curves $y = \sin x$ and $y = \cos x$. Thus, the graph of (3) crosses the graph of $y = \cos x$ when $\sin x = 0$, and crosses the graph of $y = \sin x$ when $\cos x = 0$.

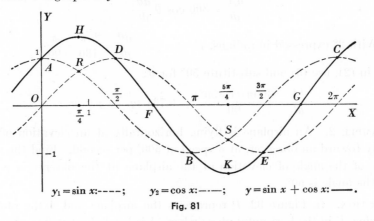

$y_1 = \sin x$:----; $y_2 = \cos x$:--·--; $y = \sin x + \cos x$:——.

Fig. 81

EXERCISE 34

Graph the equation with the aid of extrema, and inflection points where convenient. At each inflection point, obtain the equation of the tangent, and draw it. Cover a range somewhat greater than $0 \leq x \leq 2\pi$.

1. $y = \cos x$.   2. $y = \tan x$.   3. $y = \cot x$.   4. $y = \csc x$.

5. $y = \sin x - \cos x$.   6. $y = x - \sin x$.   7. $y = \tan^2 x$.

8. $y = \sin x + \sqrt{3} \cos x$.   9. $y = 4 \cos x + \cos 2x$.

10. $y = \sin x \cos^2 x$.   11. $y = \tan x - \sin x$.

12. $y^2 = \sin x$, on the range $- 2\pi \leq x \leq 3\pi$. It will be useful to employ dx/dy as well as dy/dx.

Find the angle of intersection of the curves.

13. $y = \sin x$ and $y = \cos x$.   14. $y = \tan x$ and $y = \cot x$.

Find all extrema of the function on the range $0 \leq x \leq 2\pi$.

15. $2 \sin x + \sin 2x$.   16. $3 \sin x - 4 \cos x$.   17. $\sin x \cos^3 x$.

66. Applications involving trigonometric functions

Hereafter, in solving verbal problems, it will be desirable to inspect the corresponding figure to learn whether or not some angle will be convenient as a fundamental variable.

EXAMPLE 1. In a triangle, two sides have the lengths 20″ and 30″, and the included angle is increasing at the rate of 2° per hour. At what rate is the area of the triangle changing when the angle is 50°?

SOLUTION. 1. At any time t, let θ be the radian measure of the angle with sides 20″ and 30″, and let A be the area of the triangle. Then

$$A = \tfrac{1}{2}(20 \sin \theta)(30), \quad or \quad A = 300 \sin \theta. \tag{1}$$

2. With A and θ considered as functions of the time t in hours, differentiate with respect to t in (1):

$$\frac{dA}{dt} = 300 \cos \theta \, \frac{d\theta}{dt}. \tag{2}$$

3. With 2° expressed in radians, $\qquad \dfrac{d\theta}{dt} = \dfrac{2 \cdot \pi}{180} = \dfrac{\pi}{90}. \tag{3}$

Then, in (2), use (3) and substitute 50° for θ:

$$\frac{dA}{dt} = \frac{300\pi(\cos 50°)}{90} = 6.731 \; sq. \; in. \; per \; hr. \tag{4}$$

EXAMPLE 2. An airplane is flying horizontally at an elevation of 8000′ directly toward an observer, at a speed of 500′ per second. Find the rate of change of the angle of elevation of the airplane at the observer's position when the angle is 60°.

SOLUTION. In Figure 82, P represents the airplane and A the observer; B is below P in the horizontal plane where A is located. Let θ be the radian measure of the angle of elevation of P at any instant and let $x = AB$. Then

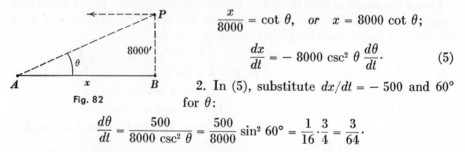

Fig. 82

$$\frac{x}{8000} = \cot \theta, \quad or \quad x = 8000 \cot \theta;$$

$$\frac{dx}{dt} = - 8000 \csc^2 \theta \, \frac{d\theta}{dt}. \tag{5}$$

2. In (5), substitute $dx/dt = - 500$ and 60° for θ:

$$\frac{d\theta}{dt} = \frac{500}{8000 \csc^2 \theta} = \frac{500}{8000} \sin^2 60° = \frac{1}{16} \cdot \frac{3}{4} = \frac{3}{64}.$$

Thus, θ is increasing at the rate of $\frac{3}{64}$ radians, or 2.7° per sec.

Note 1. Recall the double angle identities of trigonometry:

$$\sin 2\theta = 2 \sin \theta \cos \theta; \quad \cos 2\theta = \cos^2 \theta - \sin^2 \theta, \; or$$

$$\cos 2\theta = 1 - 2 \sin^2 \theta, \quad or \quad \cos 2\theta = 2 \cos^2 \theta - 1.$$

EXAMPLE 3. Find the relative dimensions of the cylinder of maximum curved surface area which can be inscribed in a sphere of radius r.

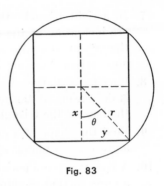

Fig. 83

SOLUTION. 1. Figure 83 shows a cross section through the center of a sphere with an inscribed cylinder. Let θ be the radian measure of the angle subtended at the center of the circle by the radius of the base of the cylinder. Let y be this radius and x be one-half of the altitude of the cylinder; let S be its curved surface area. Then,

$$x = r \cos \theta; \quad y = r \sin \theta; \quad S = 4\pi r^2 \sin \theta \cos \theta. \tag{6}$$

In (6), $2 \sin \theta \cos \theta = \sin 2\theta$. Let $W = S/2\pi r^2$. Then, $W = \sin 2\theta$.

2. Instead of minimizing S, we shall minimize W:

$$W' = 2 \cos 2\theta; \quad W'' = -4 \sin 2\theta. \tag{7}$$

3. For a minimum, $W' = 0$ or $\cos 2\theta = 0$. Hence, $W' = 0$ if $2\theta = \frac{1}{2}\pi$ or $2\theta = \frac{3}{2}\pi$, that is, if $\theta = \frac{1}{4}\pi$ or $\theta = \frac{3}{4}\pi$. Since $0 \leq \theta \leq \frac{1}{2}\pi$, the only possible critical value is $\theta = \frac{1}{4}\pi$. In (7), $W'' = -4$ when $\theta = \frac{1}{4}\pi$; thus, there is a maximum for W, and hence for S at $\theta = \frac{1}{4}\pi$. Then, from Figure 83, $x = y$, and the altitude of the cylinder is equal to the diameter of the base, for maximum curved surface area.

EXERCISE 35

1. Given that x and θ are functions of t, with $dx/dt = 3$ and $d\theta/dt = .2$, and that $y = x \sin \theta$. Find dy/dt when $x = 5$ and $\theta = \frac{2}{3}\pi$.

2. Given that x and y are functions of t with $dx/dt = 2$ and $dy/dt = -3$, and that $\tan \theta = x/y^2$. Find $d\theta/dt$ when $x = 3$ and $y = 2$.

HINT. Find $\sec \theta$, when needed, from a right triangle.

Solve by use of an angular variable at the calculus stage.

3. In a lighthouse 6000 yards west of point A on a straight shore running north and south, a horizontal searchlight is revolving counterclockwise at the rate of 3° per second. When the light beam hits a point 5000 yards north of A, how fast is the beam moving north on the shore?

4. A ladder 25′ long leans against a wall, with the upper end sliding down at the rate of .5′ per second. Find the rate of change of the acute angle made by the ladder with the ground, when the upper end is 20′ above the ground.

5. Find the maximum volume of a cylinder inscribed in a given sphere.

6. A horizontal reservoir has a cross section which is an inverted isosceles triangle, where the length of a leg is 60′. Find the angle between the equal legs to give maximum capacity. (Use one-half of the angle.)

7. In a right triangle, the horizontal and vertical sides of the right angle are increasing at the rates of 2″ and 3″ per second, respectively. Find the rate at which the smaller acute angle is changing when the horizontal and vertical sides are 25″ and 15″, respectively.

8. Each leg of an isosceles triangle is 50″ long, and a base angle of the triangle is decreasing at the rate of 2° per minute. Find the rate of change of the base of the triangle when the base angle is 40°.

9. Find the shape of a cylinder with maximum curved surface inscribed in a given hemisphere, where the cylinder's base is on the plane face.

10. A reservoir has a horizontal plane bottom and a cross section as shown in Figure 84. Find the angle of inclination of the sides from the horizontal, to give maximum capacity.

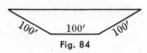

Fig. 84

11. A wall rises from a horizontal plane, and a fence 16′ high is 2′ from the wall. A beam to brace the wall will extend from the ground over the fence to the wall. Find the minimum length for the beam.

12. Ship S_1 is 120 miles south of ship S_2 at noon. S_1 sails north at 20 miles per hour, and S_2 sails east at 30 miles per hour. At 2 P.M., find the rate of change of the smaller angle between the north direction and the direction from S_1 to S_2.

13. A boat is being drawn into a dock by a mooring rope, which passes through a retaining hole on the dock, and is attached to the boat at a point 20′ lower than the hole. If the rope is pulled in at the rate of 1.5′ per second, find the rate of change of the acute angle made by the rope with the horizontal, (a) when there are 60′ of rope out; (b) when the angle is 45°.

14. In a triangle, one side is 10″ long and the opposite angle is 30°. A second angle is 45° and is increasing at the rate of .3° per second. Find the rate at which the side opposite the second angle is changing. (Recall the law of sines.)

15. In a variable triangle, a 1st side is 30″, a 2d side is 20″ and is decreasing at the rate of 2″ per minute; the included angle is $\frac{1}{3}\pi$ and is increasing at the rate of .05 radians per minute. At what rate is the 3d side changing?

16. When light from a point source strikes a plane surface, the intensity of the illumination is proportional to the cosine of the angle of incidence and inversely proportional to the square of the distance from the source. How high should a light be located above the center of a circle of radius 25′ to give the best illumination along the circumference? (The angle of incidence is measured from the normal to the plane.)

17. A wire of negligible diameter and mass M forms a circle of radius r in a horizontal plane. A particle, P, of mass m is above the center of the circle. Then, in physics, it is shown that P is attracted vertically by the wire with a force inversely proportional to the square of the distance from P to a point on the circle, and directly proportional to the

cosine of the acute angle between the vertical and a line from P to a point on the circle. Find the height of P above the circle to maximize the vertical attraction.

18. A sector is cut from a circle of radius r, and is bent to form the lateral surface of a cone of maximum volume. Find the sector's angle.

19. The minute hand of a clock is $3''$ long and the hour hand is $2''$ long. At what rate are the ends of the hands approaching each other at 4 P.M.?

20. An artillery battery is in a horizontal plane, 5 miles east of a hill rising to the west at an angle α, where $\tan \alpha = \frac{5}{12}$. An enemy tank travels due west up the hill at the rate of $\frac{1}{3}$ mile per minute. Just when the tank has traveled 1 mile up the hill, find the rate of change (in *mils*) of the angle of elevation of the tank as observed at the battery. Approximately, the angular unit called the *mil*, employed in military practice, satisfies the relation (1 *radian*) = (1000 *mils*).

21. In a 120° sector of a circle, an inscribed rectangle has one side as a chord perpendicular to the radius which bisects the sector, and the opposite side has its end points on the boundary radii of the sector. Find the angle subtended by the chord at the center of the circle, and the area of the rectangle, when its area is a maximum.

22. In a hotel, a straight hall is $3'$ wide. A rectangular dining room, $80'$ long and $24'$ wide, has a $24'$ side open on the hall, as in Figure 85. Find the length of the longest banquet table top which can be carried horizontally on edge into the room. The hall extends $40'$ on each side.

23. An iron girder $64'$ long must be carried horizontally along a straight hall $8'$ wide into a second hall meeting it at right angles. Find the minimum width of the second hall.

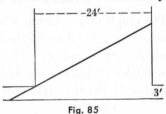
Fig. 85

24. Find the altitude of a conical goblet of minimum capacity, to permit a ball of given radius r to be completely submerged in the goblet when it is filled.

Find du/dt without eliminating x, y, or z.

25. $u = x^2 + 8xy$, when $x = 3t - t^2$ and $y = \sin 2t - t$.

26. $u^2 = x^2 + y^2 + z^2$, when $x = \sin t - t^3$, $y = \cos t$, and $z = \tan t$.

67. Inverse trigonometric functions

Let the variables x and y be related by the equation $x = \sin y$, which gives x explicitly as a function of y. The equation also defines an *inverse* function y as a function of x, to be denoted by $y = \arcsin x$, and called the "**arcsine function of x**," or the "**inverse sine of x**." Then, by definition of arcsin x, the equations

$$x = \sin y \quad and \quad y = \arcsin x \quad are\ equivalent. \tag{1}$$

Occasionally, we read "arcsin x" as "*an angle whose sine is x,*" but we prefer the phrase "*arcsine x.*" In arcsin x, the range for x is $|x| \leqq 1$, because x is the sine of an angle. The graph of $y = $ arcsin x in Figure 86 is the sine curve $x = \sin y$ along the y-axis, because of (1).

EXAMPLE 1.   Find all values of arcsin $\frac{1}{2}$.

SOLUTION.   Let $y = $ arcsin $\frac{1}{2}$. Then $\sin y = \frac{1}{2}$. With $0 \leqq y < 2\pi$, we obtain $y = \frac{1}{6}\pi$ and $y = \frac{5}{6}\pi$. Since $\sin y$ has the period 2π, the complete set of values of arcsin $\frac{1}{2}$ is as follows, where the range of k is all integers:

$$\text{arcsin } \tfrac{1}{2} = \tfrac{1}{6}\pi + 2k\pi; \quad \text{arcsin } \tfrac{1}{2} = \tfrac{5}{6}\pi + 2k\pi. \tag{2}$$

The values in (2) would be the ordinates of the points of intersection of the curve $y = $ arcsin x and a line $x = \frac{1}{2}$, in Figure 86.

Similarly, we introduce the inverses of the functions $x = \cos y$, $x = \tan y$, $x = \cot y$, $x = \sec y$, and $x = \csc y$, as follows:

$$\text{arccos } x; \quad \text{arctan } x; \quad \text{arccot } x; \quad \text{arcsec } x; \quad \text{arccsc } x. \tag{3}$$

Each of the six inverse trigonometric functions is infinitely many-valued, as illustrated in Example 1.

ILLUSTRATION 1.   The functions $x = \tan y$ and $y = $ arctan x are inverse functions, and the equations are equivalent. Since $\tan y$ has the period π,

$$\text{arctan } 1 = \tfrac{1}{4}\pi + k\pi, \quad where \; k = 0, \pm 1, \pm 2, \cdots. \tag{4}$$

The graph of $y = $ arctan x is the graph of $x = \tan y$, as in Figure 87. The range for x is all real values, indicated symbolically as the set of values x where $-\infty < x < \infty$. The range for y is all real values except the odd multiples of $\frac{1}{2}\pi$, because $\tan y$ is not defined at these values; the graph in Figure 87 has the asymptotes $y = \frac{1}{2}\pi$, $y = \frac{3}{2}\pi$, etc.

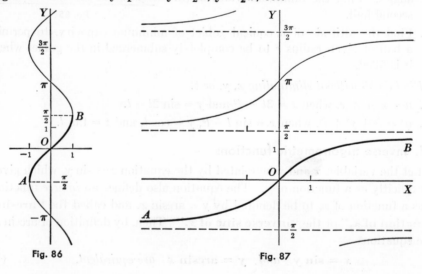

Fig. 86   Fig. 87

ILLUSTRATION 2. The equations $x = \sec y$ and $y = \text{arcsec } x$ are equivalent. Hence, the graph of $y = \text{arcsec } x$ is the secant curve $x = \sec y$. Since $|\sec y| \geqq 1$ at all values of y, the range for x in $y = \text{arcsec } x$ is $|x| \geqq 1$.

ILLUSTRATION 3. Let $y = \arccos(-\frac{1}{2})$. To find all values of y on the range $0 \leqq y < 2\pi$, first write $\cos y = -\frac{1}{2}$. If α is acute, and $\cos \alpha = +\frac{1}{2}$, then $\alpha = \frac{1}{3}\pi$. Hence, y is an angle in quadrant II or quadrant III, with $\frac{1}{3}\pi$ as the acute reference angle (see page 562). Thus, $y = \pi \pm \frac{1}{3}\pi$, or

$$\arccos(-\tfrac{1}{2}) = \tfrac{2}{3}\pi \quad and \quad \arccos(-\tfrac{1}{2}) = \tfrac{4}{3}\pi.$$

EXAMPLE 2. Find $\sec \arctan(-\frac{12}{5})$.

SOLUTION. Let $\theta = \arctan(-\frac{12}{5})$. Then, $\tan \theta = -\frac{12}{5}$ and

$$\sec \theta = \pm\sqrt{1 + \tan^2 \theta} = \pm\sqrt{1 + \tfrac{144}{25}} = \pm\tfrac{13}{5}. \qquad (5)$$

Hence, $\sec \arctan(-\frac{12}{5}) = \pm\frac{13}{5}$, where "$+$" or "$-$" would depend on the quadrant (II or IV) selected for θ. Instead of (5), we could use the right triangle in Figure 88 to find the absolute value of $\sec \theta$; in the figure,

$$\sec \alpha = |\sec \theta| = \tfrac{13}{5}.$$

In contrast to the *inverse* trigonometric functions, we may refer to $\sin \theta$, $\cos \theta$, $\tan \theta$, $\cot \theta$, $\sec \theta$, and $\csc \theta$ as the **direct trigonometric functions**.

Fig. 88

Note 1. Instead of "arcsin x," the notation "$\sin^{-1} x$" is used frequently for the *inverse of the sine function* (and similarly for the other inverse trigonometric functions). In this text we shall use "arcsin x" *exclusively*. Either "arcsin x" or "$\sin^{-1} x$" may be read "*the inverse sine of x.*" On account of the use of the superior "-1" in this fashion to denote the *inverse*, to avoid confusion it is customary to write $(\sin x)^{-1}$ for $1/\sin x$, although we use $\sin^n x$ for the nth power of $\sin x$ when $n \neq -1$.

68. Principal values of inverse trigonometric functions

In calculus, the theory is developed for the case of *single-valued* functions, with any many-valued function then treated as a collection of single-valued functions. Hence, since the inverse trigonometric functions are *infinitely many-valued*, usually we shall select a *single-valued branch* of each of the functions for applications in calculus. Each function value of the single-valued branch then is called a *principal value* of the corresponding inverse function. As standard notation hereafter, any inverse trigonometric function will be written with small "a" in the name, such as "*arcsin*," on the rare occasions when the *complete, infinitely many-valued function is involved*, and with capital "A," as in "*Arcsin*," to indicate the *principal value branch*. We define principal values as follows, where (I) overlaps (II) and (III).

I. *If* $x \geq 0$, *the principal value of any inverse trigonometric function of* x *is that value which is on the range from* 0 *to* $\frac{1}{2}\pi$, *inclusive.*

II. *For any value of* x, *the principal value of* arcsin x *or* arctan x *is that value which is on the range from* $-\frac{1}{2}\pi$ *to* $\frac{1}{2}\pi$ *inclusive, or is that function value having the least absolute value.*

III. *For any value of* x, *the principal value of* arccos x *or* arccot x *is that value which is on the range* 0 *to* π, *inclusive.*

The preceding definitions are summarized as follows: *

Principal values:
$$-\tfrac{1}{2}\pi \leq \text{Arcsin } x \leq \tfrac{1}{2}\pi. \tag{1}$$
$$-\tfrac{1}{2}\pi < \text{Arctan } x < \tfrac{1}{2}\pi. \tag{2}$$
$$0 \leq \text{Arccos } x \leq \pi. \tag{3}$$
$$0 < \text{Arccot } x < \pi. \tag{4}$$

ILLUSTRATION 1.   Arcsin $\frac{1}{2} = \frac{1}{6}\pi$.   Arctan $1 = \frac{1}{4}\pi$.   Arccot $\sqrt{3} = \frac{1}{6}\pi$.

ILLUSTRATION 2.   Arcsin $(-\frac{1}{2}) = -\frac{1}{6}\pi$ because
$$\sin(-\tfrac{1}{6}\pi) = -\sin\tfrac{1}{6}\pi = -\tfrac{1}{2}.$$
Arctan $(-\sqrt{3}) = -\frac{1}{3}\pi$ *because* $\tan(-\frac{1}{3}\pi) = -\tan\frac{1}{3}\pi = -\sqrt{3}.$
Arccos $(-\frac{1}{2}\sqrt{2}) = \frac{3}{4}\pi$, *because* $\cos\frac{3}{4}\pi = -\frac{1}{2}\sqrt{2}.$

From (1), the graph of $y = $ Arcsin x is simply the heavy arc AOB in Figure 86 on page 136.   Similarly, the graphs of $y = $ Arctan x, $y = $ Arccos x, and $y = $ Arccot x are the heavy arcs in Figures 87, 89, and 90, respectively.

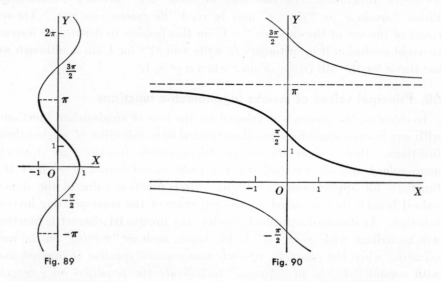

Fig. 89   Fig. 90

* The rarely used functions Arcsec x and Arccsc x will be discussed in problems.

REVIEW EXERCISE 36

In Problems 1–24, the complete inverse functions are involved.
Write an equivalent equation in the notation of inverse functions.

1. $\tan y = \frac{3}{4}$. 2. $\csc y = -5$. 3. $\sin \theta = \frac{1}{3}$. 4. $\cot \theta = x$.

Find two positive or zero values and two negative values, if any, for each expression. State the results in radian measure.

5. $\arccos 1$. 6. $\arctan (-1)$. 7. $\arcsin 0$. 8. $\mathrm{arccsc}\ 2$.
9. $\arcsin 1$. 10. $\arccos (-1)$. 11. $\mathrm{arccsc}\ (-1)$. 12. $\arctan \sqrt{3}$.
13. $\mathrm{arcsec}\ (-2)$. 14. $\arcsin (-\frac{1}{2}\sqrt{2})$. 15. $\arccos (\frac{1}{2}\sqrt{2})$.
16. $\arctan (\frac{1}{3}\sqrt{3})$. 17. $\arcsin (-\frac{1}{2}\sqrt{3})$. 18. $\arccos (\frac{1}{2}\sqrt{3})$.
19. $\arcsin 3$. 20. $\mathrm{arcsec}\ \frac{1}{3}$. 21. $\arctan (-\sqrt{3})$.

By use of Table IV, find two positive values for the expression, using $\pi = 3.142$.

22. $\arcsin .2051$. 23. $\arctan .2247$. 24. $\arcsin (-.8371)$.

Obtain the value of the expression. Use Table IV if necessary.

25. $\mathrm{Arcsin}\ 1$. 26. $\mathrm{Arcsin}\ (-1)$. 27. $\mathrm{Arctan}\ \sqrt{3}$. 28. $\mathrm{Arccos}\ \frac{1}{2}$.
29. $\mathrm{Arccos}\ (-1)$. 30. $\mathrm{Arccot}\ (\frac{1}{3}\sqrt{3})$. 31. $\mathrm{Arctan}\ (-\sqrt{3})$.
32. $\mathrm{Arcsin}\ (-\frac{1}{2}\sqrt{2})$. 33. $\mathrm{Arccos}\ 0$. 34. $\mathrm{Arcsin}\ 0$.
35. $\mathrm{Arctan}\ (-\frac{1}{3}\sqrt{3})$. 36. $\mathrm{Arccos}\ (-\frac{1}{2}\sqrt{2})$. 37. $\mathrm{Arccot}\ (-1)$.
38. $\mathrm{Arctan}\ 1.3133$. 39. $\mathrm{Arcsin}\ (-.40776)$. 40. $\mathrm{Arccos}\ (-.66746)$.

69. Derivatives of inverse trigonometric functions

Hereafter, unless otherwise specified, in any reference to an inverse trigonometric function, its *principal value branch* will be implied. We proceed to obtain the derivatives of these inverse functions.

Proof of (XV) *on page* 122. 1. Let $y = \mathrm{Arcsin}\ u$, where u is a differentiable function of x. Then, by (1) on page 138,

$$u = \sin y \quad and \quad -\tfrac{1}{2}\pi \leqq y \leqq \tfrac{1}{2}\pi. \tag{1}$$

2. Differentiate with respect to x on both sides of $u = \sin y$, with u and y implicitly functions of x, and use (IX):

$$\frac{du}{dx} = (\cos y)\frac{dy}{dx}, \quad or \quad \frac{dy}{dx} = \frac{1}{\cos y}\frac{du}{dx}. \tag{2}$$

3. In dividing by $\cos y$ in (2), we rule out $y = \pm \tfrac{1}{2}\pi$, where $\cos y = 0$ and $u = \sin y = \pm 1$. Otherwise, from (1) we notice that

$$\cos y = \pm \sqrt{1 - \sin^2 y} = \pm \sqrt{1 - u^2}. \tag{3}$$

Since $-\tfrac{1}{2}\pi < y < \tfrac{1}{2}\pi$, then $\cos y > 0$. Hence, in (3), $\cos y = +\sqrt{1 - u^2}$.
Then, from (2) and (3) with $y = \mathrm{Arcsin}\ u$,

$$\frac{d}{dx} \mathrm{Arcsin}\ u = \frac{1}{\sqrt{1 - u^2}}\frac{du}{dx}. \tag{XV}$$

Proof of (XVII) *on page* 122. 1. Let $y = $ Arctan u. Then,

$$u = \tan y \quad and \quad -\tfrac{1}{2}\pi < y < \tfrac{1}{2}\pi. \tag{4}$$

By use of (XI), $\qquad\qquad \dfrac{du}{dx} = (\sec^2 y)\dfrac{dy}{dx}, \quad or \quad \dfrac{dy}{dx} = \dfrac{1}{\sec^2 y}\dfrac{du}{dx}. \tag{5}$

2. From trigonometry and (4), $\sec^2 y = 1 + \tan^2 y = 1 + u^2$. Hence, from (5) with $y = $ Arctan u,

$$\frac{d}{dx}(\text{Arctan } u) = \frac{1}{1+u^2}\frac{du}{dx}. \tag{XVII}$$

The student will prove (XVI) and (XVIII) later. We proceed to use all of (IX)–(XVIII). As special cases of (XV)–(XVIII) with $u = x$, we obtain

$$\frac{d \text{ Arcsin } x}{dx} = \frac{1}{\sqrt{1-x^2}}; \qquad \frac{d \text{ Arccos } x}{dx} = \frac{-1}{\sqrt{1-x^2}}; \tag{6}$$

$$\frac{d \text{ Arctan } x}{dx} = \frac{1}{1+x^2}; \qquad \frac{d \text{ Arccot } x}{dx} = \frac{-1}{1+x^2}. \tag{7}$$

It is interesting to use (6) and (7) in checking the graphs of the inverse functions, even though these graphs are familiar to us.

ILLUSTRATION 1. To study the graph of $y = $ Arcsin x, we have

$$\frac{dy}{dx} = \frac{1}{\sqrt{1-x^2}}; \qquad \frac{d^2y}{dx^2} = \frac{x}{(1-x^2)^{\frac{3}{2}}}. \tag{8}$$

From (8), $y' \neq 0$ at any value of x, and thus there is no extremum with $|x| \neq 1$. From (8), $y'' = 0$ at $x = 0$, and y'' changes sign from "$-$" to "$+$" at $x = 0$. Hence, there is an inflection point at $x = 0$ where the graph changes from concave downward to concave upward. From (8), y' does not exist at $x = \pm 1$, and $y' \to \infty$ as $x \to -1+$ and as $x \to +1-$. From $y = $ Arcsin x, we have

$x = \sin y$ and hence $\qquad\qquad \dfrac{dx}{dy} = \cos y = \sqrt{1 - \sin^2 y} = \sqrt{1 - x^2}.$

Thus, $dx/dy = 0$ at $x = \pm 1$, and the graph has a vertical tangent at $x = \pm 1$.

ILLUSTRATION 2. From (XV) with $u = x^2$,

$$\frac{d \text{ Arcsin } x^2}{dx} = \frac{1}{\sqrt{1-x^4}}\frac{dx^2}{dx} = \frac{2x}{\sqrt{1-x^4}}.$$

With $u = \sin x$ in (XVII), $\qquad \dfrac{d \text{ Arctan } (\sin x)}{dx} = \dfrac{1}{1+\sin^2 x}\cdot \cos x.$

From (XVI), $\qquad \dfrac{d \text{ Arcos }\sqrt{1+3x}}{dx} = \dfrac{-1}{\sqrt{1-(1+3x)}}\cdot\dfrac{1}{2}\dfrac{3}{\sqrt{1+3x}}$

$$= -\frac{3}{2}\frac{1}{\sqrt{1+3x}\sqrt{-3x}} = \frac{-3}{2\sqrt{-3x-9x^2}}.$$

On page 132, various problems were solved by use of direct trigonometric functions. Some problems of this nature can be solved with greater convenience by use of inverse trigonometric functions.

EXAMPLE 1. A searchlight S is situated 4000 yards west of point A on a north-south road. The beam of light is following a fugitive F who is running north at the rate of 5 yards per second. Find the rate at which the searchlight is revolving when F is 2000 yards north of A.

SOLUTION. 1. Figure 91 shows a position of F, at any instant. From Figure 91, where $dx/dt = 5$,

$$\tan \theta = \frac{x}{4000}, \quad \text{or} \quad \theta = \text{Arctan} \frac{x}{4000}.$$

The rate of revolution is $d\theta/dt$. We find

$$\frac{d\theta}{dt} = \frac{d}{dt}\left(\text{Arctan} \frac{x}{4000}\right) = \frac{1}{1 + \dfrac{x^2}{(4000)^2}} \cdot \frac{1}{4000} \cdot \frac{dx}{dt}.$$

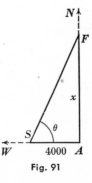

2. With $x = 2000$ and $dx/dt = 5$,

$$\frac{d\theta}{dt} = \frac{4000}{(4000)^2 + (2000)^2} \cdot 5 = \frac{1}{1000}.$$

That is, the searchlight revolves at the rate of .001 radians per second.

Fig. 91

EXAMPLE 2. A statue 8′ high stands on a pedestal 4′ above the eye level of an observer. How far from the pedestal should he stand to obtain the best view of the statue? (We assume that the view is best where the statue subtends the greatest angle.)

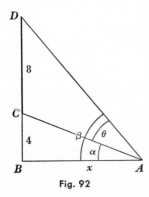

Fig. 92

SOLUTION. 1. In Figure 92, A represents the observer's eye, and θ is the radian measure of the angle subtended by the statue, CD, at a distance of x feet. Let $\alpha = \angle BAC$ and $\beta = \angle BAD$. Then,

$$\theta = \beta - \alpha, \text{ or } \theta = \text{Arccot} \frac{x}{12} - \text{Arccot} \frac{x}{4}. \quad (9)$$

Hence, we obtain

$$\frac{d\theta}{dx} = \frac{-1}{1 + (\frac{1}{12}x)^2} \cdot \frac{1}{12} + \frac{1}{1 + (\frac{1}{4}x)^2} \cdot \frac{1}{4};$$

$$\frac{d\theta}{dx} = \frac{8(48 - x^2)}{(144 + x^2)(16 + x^2)}. \quad (10)$$

2. From (10), $d\theta/dx = 0$ at $x = 4\sqrt{3}$, and $d\theta/dx$ changes sign from "$+$" to "$-$" as x increases through $x = 4\sqrt{3}$. Hence, θ is a maximum when the observer stands $4\sqrt{3}$ feet from the pedestal.

EXERCISE 37

Find the derivative of the function. Early letters of the alphabet represent positive constants.

1. Arcsin $4x$.   **2.** Arctan $2x$.   **3.** Arccos x^3.   **4.** Arccot x^2.

5. Arctan $(3x + 2)$.   **6.** Arcsin $(x^2 + 1)$.   **7.** Arccos $(4 - 3x)$.

8. Arctan $(\cos x)$.   **9.** Arccos $(\sec x)$.   **10.** Arcsin $(\tan^2 x)$.

11. Arcsin $\dfrac{z}{3}$.   **12.** Arctan $\dfrac{1}{x^2}$.   **13.** Arccos $\dfrac{1}{\sqrt{x}}$.   **14.** Arccot $\dfrac{\sqrt[3]{x}}{2}$.

15. Arcsin $\dfrac{3z}{2 - z}$.   **16.** Arctan $\dfrac{2t}{t^2 - 1}$.   **17.** Arccos $\dfrac{3}{x + x^2}$.

18. Arcsin $\dfrac{x}{a}$.   **19.** $\dfrac{1}{a}$ Arctan $\dfrac{x}{a}$.   **20.** Arccot $\dfrac{3}{2z}$.

21. Arccos $\dfrac{\sqrt{2}}{1 - x}$.   **22.** v Arctan $\dfrac{2}{v}$.   **23.** $\dfrac{1}{t^2}$ Arcsin t.

24. x^2 Arcsin $3x$.   **25.** $\sin 3x$ Arcsin $\sqrt{x}$.   **26.** $\tan^3 x$ Arctan x^2.

27. $\dfrac{a^2}{2}$ Arcsin $\dfrac{x}{a} + \dfrac{x}{2} \sqrt{a^2 - x^2}$.   **28.** $\dfrac{x}{\sqrt{a^2 - x^2}} -$ Arcsin $\dfrac{x}{a}$.

29. Arcsin $\dfrac{x}{a} + \dfrac{\sqrt{a^2 - x^2}}{x}$.   **30.** $\dfrac{x - a}{2} \sqrt{2ax - x^2} + \dfrac{a^2}{2}$ Arccos $\left(1 - \dfrac{x}{a}\right)$.

Obtain dy/dx by use of the equation.

31. Arctan $y +$ Arcsin $x = x^3$.

32. Arccos $x +$ Arctan $3y = 1$.

33. Arctan $(x + 2y) + \sin x = \cos y - 1$.

Find the second derivative of the function.

34. Arcsin $2x$.   **35.** Arctan $4x$.   **36.** x Arccot x.

37. Prove formulas (XVI) and (XVIII).

Check the graph of the function for extrema and inflection points. Also, find the slope at any inflection point. Then, graph the function by use of just a few accurately located points and general characteristics.

38. $y =$ Arctan x.   **39.** $y =$ Arccos x.   **40.** $y =$ Arccot x.

Solve by use of an inverse trigonometric function.

41. A helicopter leaves the ground 1000′ from an observer and rises vertically at the rate of 20′ per second. At what rate is the angle of elevation of the helicopter changing at the observer's position, when the helicopter is 800′ above the ground?

42. A jet airplane is flying south at an elevation of 3000′, with a speed of 600′ per second, in a vertical plane with a searchlight on the ground. To keep the beam of light on the airplane, what would be the necessary rate of revolution of the searchlight when the airplane is due south, at an airline distance of 5000′?

43. A boat is sailing at the rate of 6 miles per hour in the direction of a tower whose top is 300' above the base of a cliff on the shore. Find the rate of change, per minute, of the angle of elevation of the top of the tower from the boat when it is 1800' from shore.

44. An airplane is flying south at a constant elevation of 12,000' toward an antiaircraft gun on the ground. An automatic sighting mechanism at the gun keeps a direction indicator pointed at the airplane. The airline distance from the airplane to the gun is decreasing at the rate of 500' per second. Find the rate of revolution of the direction indicator when the distance is 13,000'.

45. Solve Problem 13 on page 134 by the present method.

46. A 100' aerial ladder for firemen projects from its truck toward a burning building at an angle of inclination α from the horizontal, where $\cos \alpha = \frac{7}{25}$. The bottom of the ladder is at eye level for an observer 288' away, in a vertical plane with the ladder. A fireman with a hose climbs the ladder at the rate of .5' per second. At the instant when he has advanced 75' up the ladder, at what rate in degrees is the observer's head bending backward as he looks at the fireman?

47. A picture with a rectangular frame 5' high hangs on a wall, and the lower edge of the frame is 10' above eye level of an observer. How far from the wall should he stand to obtain the best view?

48. A set of enemy trenches starts 900 yards from the base and extends 100 yards upward on a hill which rises to the north at an angle of 30° from a horizontal plane. To maximize the vertical angle subtended by the trenches at a machine gun emplacement south of the hill, how far from its base should the emplacement be located by the attacking force?

49. Without eliminating x, y, or z, find du/dt if $u = \text{Arcsin } xyz$, with $x = \sin 2t$, $y = \cos 2t$, and $z = \sec t$.

Note 1. Definitions of the principal values Arcsec x and Arccsc x are not uniform in mathematical texts. This is of small importance because, where Arcsec x or Arccsc x might be used, usually it is convenient to use Arccos x or Arcsin x, respectively. We defined the principal values of arcsec x and arccsc x for $x \geq 1$ in (I) on page 138. The following agreements complete our specification of Arcsec x and Arccsc x:

Principal value, when $x \leq -1$: $\quad \begin{cases} -\pi \leq \text{Arcsec } x < -\frac{1}{2}\pi; \\ -\pi < \text{Arccsc } x \leq -\frac{1}{2}\pi. \end{cases}$

★50. (*a*) Draw a graph of the complete function arcsec x for the range $-\pi \leq x \leq 2\pi$, and then mark heavily the principal value Arcsec x. (*b*) Repeat the problem for arccsc x and Arccsc x.

★51. Recall the method used in proving (XV), and prove the following formulas, where u is a function of x:

$$\frac{d \text{ Arcsec } u}{dx} = \frac{1}{u\sqrt{u^2 - 1}} \frac{du}{dx}; \quad \frac{d \text{ Arccsc } u}{dx} = \frac{-1}{u\sqrt{u^2 - 1}} \frac{du}{dx}.$$

70. Logarithmic and exponential functions

We introduced powers with rational exponents on page 45. A logical foundation for the use of *irrational numbers as exponents* is beyond the level of this text. Hence, without discussion, we mention that, if x is irrational and $a > 0$, then a^x can be defined as the limit of a certain sequence of numbers, and the resulting value of a^x is positive. **If $a \leq 0$ and x is irrational, we shall not define a^x.** Without proof, we shall assume the fact that the laws of exponents hold if the exponents are any real numbers, rational or irrational, provided that the bases for the exponents are positive.

ILLUSTRATION 1. We may use our intuition safely with a symbol such as $10^{\sqrt{2}}$. Closer and closer approximations to $10^{\sqrt{2}}$ are obtained if the successive decimal approximations to $\sqrt{2} = 1.414 \cdots$ are used as exponents. Or, $10^{\sqrt{2}}$ is the limit of the sequence

$$10^1,\ 10^{1.4},\ 10^{1.41},\ 10^{1.414},\ \cdots.$$

For our future purposes, we make the following assumption, whose proof must be reserved for more advanced courses.

$$\left\{ \begin{array}{l} \textit{If } a > 0, a \neq 1, \textit{ and } y > 0, \textit{ there exists} \\ \textit{just one number } x \textit{ such that } y = a^x. \end{array} \right\} \tag{1}$$

Suppose that $a > 0$ and $a \neq 1$; let x and y be variables, where the range for x is all real numbers, and $y = a^x$. Then, we call a^x an *exponential function* of x. Because of (1), the range for y is all positive numbers, and there is a one to one correspondence between the values for x and those for y. We shall assume that the function $y = a^x$ is continuous at all values of x.

ILLUSTRATION 2. A graph of $y = 2^x$ is seen in Figure 93.

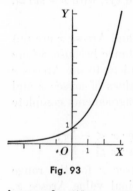

Fig. 93

From Figure 93, as a typical graph for a function $y = a^x$ with $a > 1$,

$$a^0 = 1; \quad \lim_{x \to -\infty} a^x = 0; \quad \lim_{x \to \infty} a^x = \infty. \tag{2}$$

A perpendicular to the y-axis at any point $y = y_0$, where $y_0 > 0$, meets the curve in Figure 93 at just one point, as an illustration of (1). Or, if $y = a^x$, then there is just one value of x for each value of y. Thus, the equation $y = a^x$ defines y as an exponential function of x, and also defines an *inverse function* x implicitly as a function of y. We shall denote this inverse by "$\log_a y$," explicitly defined as follows.

DEFINITION II. *Suppose that $a > 0$ and $a \neq 1$, and that x and y are such that $y = a^x$. Then, x is called the **logarithm** of y to the base a. That is, the logarithm of a number y to the base a is the exponent of the power to which the base a must be raised in order to obtain y.*

To abbreviate "*the logarithm of y to the base a*," we write "$\log_a y$." Then,

$$y = a^x \quad and \quad x = \log_a y \quad are\ equivalent;\tag{3}$$

that is, the exponential function $y = a^x$ and the logarithmic function $x = \log_a y$ are *inverse functions*, each the *inverse* of the other.

ILLUSTRATION 3. From (3), if $N = 4^5$, then $\log_4 N = 5$. Since $64 = 2^6$, then $\log_2 64 = 6$. If $\log_a 10{,}000 = 2$, then $a^2 = 10{,}000$ or $a = \sqrt{10{,}000} = 100$.

If $\log_a 2 = -\dfrac{1}{3}$, then $2 = a^{-\frac{1}{3}} = \dfrac{1}{\sqrt[3]{a}}, \quad \sqrt[3]{a} = \dfrac{1}{2}, \quad or \quad a = \dfrac{1}{8}.$

ILLUSTRATION 4. For any base a, since $a^0 = 1$ and $a^1 = a$, then

$$\log_a 1 = 0 \quad and \quad \log_a a = 1.\tag{4}$$

From (3), $$y = a^{\log_a y}.\tag{5}$$

Notice that $y > 0$ in Definition II. That is, *we do not define or use logarithms of negative numbers or zero.*

We recall the following properties of logarithms, where M and N are any positive numbers, k is any real number, and no denominator is zero.

$$\log_a MN = \log_a M + \log_a N.\tag{6}$$

$$\log_a \frac{M}{N} = \log_a M - \log_a N.\tag{7}$$

$$\log_a M^k = k \log_a M.\tag{8}$$

Logarithms to the base 10 are called **common logarithms** and are the most useful variety when logarithms are used as aids in computation. We shall find that, for purposes in calculus, the most convenient base for logarithms is a certain irrational number $e = 2.71828 \cdots$, an endless nonrepeating decimal. Logarithms to the base e are called **natural logarithms.** Hereafter, instead of using $\log_e N$ for the natural logarithm of N, we shall use simply "**ln N**," read "*natural logarithm of N.*"

Now, let x and y be variables, with $x > 0$. Then

$$y = \ln x \quad and \quad x = e^y \quad are\ equivalent.\tag{9}$$

Hence, to graph $y = \ln x$, more conveniently we may graph $x = e^y$, as in Figure 94. The line $x = 0$ is an asymptote of the graph and

$$\lim_{x \to 0+} \ln x = -\infty; \quad \lim_{x \to \infty} \ln x = \infty.\tag{10}$$

We shall accept without proof the fact that $\ln x$ is continuous at all values $x > 0$. Then, at every point $x = a > 0$,

$$\lim_{x \to a} \ln x = \ln a.\tag{11}$$

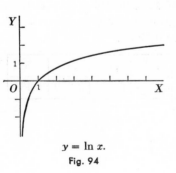

$y = \ln x.$

Fig. 94

As a special case of (5) on page 145, if $x > 0$ then

$$x = e^{\ln x}. \tag{12}$$

THEOREM I. *If $a > 0$, $a \neq 1$, $b > 0$, $b \neq 1$, and $N > 0$, then*

$$\log_a N = (\log_a b)(\log_b N). \tag{13}$$

Proof. Let $y = \log_b N$; then $N = b^y$. Hence, we obtain (13):

$$\log_a N = \log_a b^y = y \log_a b = (\log_a b)(\log_b N).$$

In (13), if $N = a$ then $\log_a a = 1$ and $1 = (\log_a b)(\log_b a)$, or

$$\log_a b = \frac{1}{\log_b a}. \tag{14}$$

We refer to (13) as *the formula for change of base.* In (13), we call $\log_a b$ the **modulus** of the system of logarithms of base a with respect to the system of base b. Given a table of logarithms to the base b, we could form a table for the base a by multiplying each entry of the given table by $\log_a b$. In particular, from (13) with $a = 10$ and $b = e$,

$$\log_{10} N = (\log_{10} e) \ln N, \quad or \quad \ln N = \frac{\log_{10} N}{\log_{10} e}. \tag{15}$$

From (14) with $b = e$, $$\log_a e = \frac{1}{\ln a}. \tag{16}$$

71. The base for natural logarithms

With the aid of advanced methods, it can be proved that the following limit exists, and is equal to the irrational number $2.71828\cdots$, an endless nonrepeating decimal. We let $e = 2.71828\cdots$; thus, e is defined as follows:

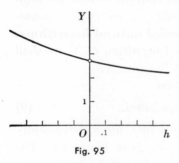

Fig. 95

$$\lim_{h \to 0} (1 + h)^{\frac{1}{h}} = e. \tag{1}$$

Let $f(h) = (1 + h)^{\frac{1}{h}}$. Then, we appreciate the preceding result by inspection of the following table. A graph of $y = f(h)$ for $h > -.5$ is in Figure 95. The graph has a hole where $h = 0$ because $f(0)$ is not defined.

h	$-.5$	$-.1$	$-.01$	$-.001$	$\cdots$	$.001$	$.01$	$.1$	$.5$	5
$f(h)$	4.000	2.868	2.732	2.718	$\cdots$	2.717	2.705	2.594	2.250	1.431

ILLUSTRATION 1. By use of (1), we obtain

$$\lim_{k \to 0} (1 + 2k)^{\frac{1}{k}} = \lim_{2k \to 0} \left[(1 + 2k)^{\frac{1}{2k}} \right]^2 = e^2.$$

Note 1. We could define e as follows, by using $h = \dfrac{1}{k}$ in (1):

$$e = \lim_{k \to \infty} \left(1 + \frac{1}{k}\right)^{k}. \tag{2}$$

EXERCISE 38

Write an equivalent logarithmic equation.

1. $N = 3^5$. **2.** $M = 5^{\frac{1}{2}}$. **3.** $N = 10^{-2}$. **4.** $.001 = 10^{-3}$.

Find the number whose logarithm is given.

5. $\log_6 N = 2$. **6.** $\log_{125} N = \frac{1}{3}$. **7.** $\log_8 N = \frac{5}{3}$.

8. Find $\log_9 81$; $\log_3 81$; $\log_{10} 1000$; $\log_7 \frac{1}{7}$; $\log_2 \frac{1}{16}$.

9. Find the base a if $\log_a 64 = 3$; $\log_a 10{,}000 = -2$; $\log_a 4 = \frac{1}{3}$.

Obtain the limit by use of the definition of e.

10. $\lim\limits_{h \to 0} (1 + h)^{\frac{3}{h}}$. **11.** $\lim\limits_{k \to 0} (1 + k)^{\frac{1}{2k}}$. **12.** $\lim\limits_{x \to 0} (1 + \sin x)^{\csc x}$.

72. Differentiation of logarithmic functions

Suppose that $a > 0$ and $a \neq 1$, and let x and y be variables, with $x > 0$ and $y = \log_a x$. We shall prove that

$$\frac{d}{dx} \log_a x = \frac{\log_a e}{x}. \tag{1}$$

Proof. 1. Assume that x has any particular positive value, and that Δx is a variable increment such that $x + \Delta x > 0$. Then,

$$y = \log_a x \quad and \quad y + \Delta y = \log_a (x + \Delta x);$$

from (7), page 145, $\quad \Delta y = \log_a (x + \Delta x) - \log_a x = \log_a \dfrac{x + \Delta x}{x}; \tag{2}$

$$\frac{\Delta y}{\Delta x} = \frac{1}{\Delta x} \log_a \left(1 + \frac{\Delta x}{x}\right) = \frac{1}{x}\left[\frac{x}{\Delta x} \log_a \left(1 + \frac{\Delta x}{x}\right)\right]. \tag{3}$$

2. From (3), and (8) on page 145 with $x/\Delta x$ as the exponent,

$$\frac{\Delta y}{\Delta x} = \frac{1}{x} \log_a \left(1 + \frac{\Delta x}{x}\right)^{\frac{x}{\Delta x}}. \tag{4}$$

In (4), let $h = \Delta x/x$; then $x/\Delta x = 1/h$. To say that $\Delta x \to 0$ is equivalent to stating that $h \to 0$. Hence, by use of Section 71 we obtain (1):

$$\frac{dy}{dx} = \lim_{\Delta x \to 0} \frac{\Delta y}{\Delta x} = \frac{1}{x} \lim_{h \to 0} \log_a (1 + h)^{\frac{1}{h}} = \frac{1}{x} \log_a \left[\lim_{h \to 0} (1 + h)^{\frac{1}{h}}\right] = \frac{1}{x} \log_a e.$$

If $a = e$ in (1), then $\log_a e = \log_e e = 1$, and (1) becomes

$$\frac{d \ln x}{dx} = \frac{1}{x}. \tag{XIX}'$$

Hence, a very simple formula (XIX)' is obtained for $D_x \log_a x$, **if $a = e$.** For this reason, we decide that, hereafter in calculus, *we shall use logarithms to the base e wherever possible.*

Proof of (XIX) *on page* 123. Let u be a differentiable function of x. Then, by use of (XIX)' and the derivative of a composite function,

$$\frac{d}{dx} \ln u = \frac{d \ln u}{du} \cdot \frac{du}{dx} = \frac{1}{u} \frac{du}{dx}.$$

Similarly, we could prove (XX) by use of (1).

ILLUSTRATION 1. $\dfrac{d}{dx} \ln (1 + 4x) = \dfrac{1}{1 + 4x} \dfrac{d(1 + 4x)}{dx} = \dfrac{4}{1 + 4x}.$

$$\frac{d}{dx} \ln (\sin x) = \frac{1}{\sin x} \frac{d \sin x}{dx} = \frac{\cos x}{\sin x} = \cot x.$$

$$\frac{d}{dx} \ln [\ln (3x - 2)] = \frac{1}{\ln (3x - 2)} \frac{d \ln (3x - 2)}{dx} = \frac{3}{(3x - 2) \ln (3x - 2)}.$$

EXAMPLE 1. Differentiate $\ln [(3 + 5x)\sqrt[3]{2x + 7}]$.

SOLUTION. Let $y = \ln [(3 + 5x)\sqrt[3]{2x + 7}]$, where we insert redundant brackets for greater clarity. By use of the properties of logarithms in (6) and (8) on page 145, with $\sqrt[3]{2x + 7}$ rewritten as $(2x + 7)^{\frac{1}{3}}$,

$$y = \ln (3 + 5x) + \tfrac{1}{3} \ln (2x + 7).$$

$$\frac{dy}{dx} = \frac{5}{3 + 5x} + \frac{1}{3} \cdot \frac{2}{2x + 7} = \frac{40x + 111}{3(3 + 5x)(2x + 7)}.$$

Comment. In the solution, **notice the simplification due to using properties of logarithms before differentiation.**

EXAMPLE 2. Obtain y' from the relation

$$\ln x + \ln (3y + 2) = 16x^2. \tag{5}$$

SOLUTION. The equation defines y implicitly as a function of x. Differentiate on both sides of (5) with respect to x:

$$\frac{1}{x} + \frac{1}{3y + 2} \frac{d(3y + 2)}{dx} = 32x, \quad or \quad \frac{1}{x} + \frac{1}{3y + 2}(3y') = 32x, \text{ or}$$

$$y' = \frac{96x^2y + 64x^2 - 3y - 2}{3x}.$$

To obtain the derivative of a function $f(x)$ which is a complicated product or quotient, it may be convenient to start by finding $\ln f(x)$. This method is referred to as *logarithmic differentiation.*

EXAMPLE 3. Differentiate $\qquad y = (3 + 2x)^3(5 - x)^2\sqrt[3]{2 - 4x}. \tag{6}$

SOLUTION. 1. From (6), and properties of logarithms,

$$\ln y = 3 \ln (3 + 2x) + 2 \ln (5 - x) + \tfrac{1}{3} \ln (2 - 4x). \tag{7}$$

2. Differentiate with respect to x on both sides of (7), with y considered implicitly a function of x:

$$\frac{1}{y} \frac{dy}{dx} = \frac{6}{3 + 2x} - \frac{2}{5 - x} - \frac{4}{3(2 - 4x)}$$

$$= \frac{84 - 376x + 128x^2}{3(3 + 2x)(5 - x)(2 - 4x)}. \tag{8}$$

Multiply both sides of (8) by y, with (6) employed for y:

$$y' = \tfrac{1}{3}(84 - 376x + 128x^2)(3 + 2x)^2(5 - x)(2 - 4x)^{-\frac{2}{3}}.$$

EXERCISE 39

Differentiate. Avoid expanding where possible. Where convenient, use properties of logarithms before differentiating.

1. $\ln (3 + 5x)$.   **2.** $\ln 7x$.   **3.** $\ln (4 - 3x)$.   **4.** $\ln (z^2 + 2z)$.

5. $\ln (z^2 - 4)$.   **6.** $\log_{10} (2 - x)$.   **7.** $\log_a (1 + x^2)$.   **8.** $\log_a \cot x$.

9. $\log_{10} \sin 2x$.   **10.** $\ln \sec 3x$.   **11.** $\ln \cos \tfrac{1}{2}x$.   **12.** $\ln \tan \tfrac{1}{3}x$.

13. $\ln (\ln x)$.   **14.** $\ln (\ln \csc x)$.   **15.** $\ln (\ln \sec x)$.

16. $\ln x^3$.   **17.** $(\ln x)^3$.   **18.** $(\ln x)^{-2}$.

19. $\ln (2 + 3x)^2$.   **20.** $\ln (1 - 3x)^4$.   **21.** $\ln \sqrt{4 + 5x}$.

22. $\ln \sqrt[4]{1 - x^3}$.   **23.** $\ln \sin^3 x$.   **24.** $\ln \tan^2 x$.

25. $\ln \sqrt{\sec x}$.   **26.** $(\ln x)\ln (3x - 2)$.   **27.** $(\ln 2x)\ln \sin x$.

28. $\ln (2 + 3x)(5 + 7x)$.   **29.** $\ln (1 + x^2)(2 - 5x)$.

30. $\ln (1 - x)^2(2 - 5x)^3$.   **31.** $\ln (3 + z^3)^2(2 - 4z)^5$.

32. $\ln (1 + \sin x)(1 + \cos x)^2$.   **33.** $\ln (3 + x^2)\sqrt[4]{1 - 2x}$.

34. $\ln (\sin^3 x)(2 + \cos x)^2$.   **35.** $\ln \tan^3 x \sin^2 2x \cos 3x$.

36. $\ln \sqrt{4 + 7x}\sqrt[3]{2 + 5x}$.   **37.** $\ln \sqrt{\sin x}\sqrt[3]{1 - \cos x}$.

38. $[\ln (1 - 4x)]^2$.   **39.** $(\ln \tan x)^3$.   **40.** $\sqrt{\ln (3x + 2)}$.

41. $\dfrac{5}{\ln x}$.   **42.** $\dfrac{3}{(\ln x)^2}$.   **43.** $\dfrac{2}{\ln \cos x}$.   **44.** $\dfrac{\sin x}{\ln \cos x}$.

45. $\ln \dfrac{2 + 3x}{5 - x}$.   **46.** $\ln \dfrac{1 - t^2}{2 + 3t}$.   **47.** $\dfrac{\ln \sin x}{\ln \cos x}$.

48. $\ln \sqrt{\dfrac{2 - x}{3 + x}}$.   **49.** $\ln \sqrt[3]{\dfrac{1 + x^2}{1 - x^2}}$.   **50.** $\ln \dfrac{1 - \sin x}{1 + \cos x}$.

51. $\ln \sqrt{\dfrac{\sin x}{1 - \cos x}}$.   **52.** $\ln \sqrt[3]{\dfrac{1 - \cos x}{1 + \cos x}}$.   **53.** $\dfrac{\ln (3x - 1)^3}{(3x - 1)^2}$.

Evaluate y' at the specified point, perhaps by use of Table III.

54. $y = x^2 \ln x$; at $x = 3$.   **55.** $y = x \ln \sqrt{3 - x}$; at $x = 1$.

56. $y = \dfrac{\ln x}{x}$; at $x = 4$.   **57.** $y = \dfrac{x^2}{\ln x}$; at $x = 2$.

Find the second derivative of the function.

58. $x^2 \ln (x + 1)$.   **59.** $x \ln \sin 3x$.   **60.** $\sqrt{x} \ln (2x + 5)$.

Find y' by implicit function differentiation.

61. $\ln x + \ln y = 5$.

62. $\ln (x + 2y) + \sin x = y^2$.

63. $\ln \sqrt{2x + 3y} - x^2 = \ln x^2$.

64. $\sin \ln y + \cos x = 5$.

Obtain dy/dx by differentiating $\ln y$.

65. $y = (2 + x)^3 (2x - 3)^8$.

66. $y = (3 + 4x)^7 (1 - 2x)^9$.

67. $y = \dfrac{(x + 2)^3}{(3x - 1)^4}$.

68. $y = \dfrac{(2x + 3)^5}{(4x - 3)^4}$.

69. $y = \sqrt{\dfrac{2x - 1}{3x + 2}}$.

70. $y = \dfrac{(5x + 1)^{\frac{2}{3}}}{(1 - 2x)^{\frac{2}{3}}}$.

71. $y = \dfrac{\sqrt[5]{1 - 3x}}{\sqrt[3]{2 + 4x}}$.

72. $y = \dfrac{\sqrt[3]{1 + \sin 2x}}{(3 + \cos x)^2}$.

Differentiate the function of x.

73. $\dfrac{1}{a(a + bx)} - \dfrac{1}{a^2} \ln \dfrac{a + bx}{x}$.

74. $\sqrt{x^2 + a^2} - a \ln \left(\dfrac{a + \sqrt{x^2 + a^2}}{x} \right)$.

75. $\frac{1}{2} x \sqrt{x^2 + a^2} + \frac{1}{2} a^2 \ln (x + \sqrt{x^2 + a^2})$.

76. $\ln \dfrac{\sqrt{x^2 + a^2} - x}{\sqrt{x^2 + a^2} + x}$.   (Rationalize the denominator.)

Obtain the nth derivative of the function, and prove the result by induction.

77. $\ln x$.   **78.** $\ln (1 - x)$.   **79.** $\ln (1 + x)$.

80. The vapor pressure, p, in millimeters of mercury, of carbon tetrachloride is well represented by the equation $\log_{10} p = - \dfrac{1706.4}{T} - 7.7760$,

where $T°$ Centigrade is the absolute temperature. Find the temperature-rate of change of p when $T = 300$.

81. Suppose that the demand function for a commodity is $p = 30/\ln x$. Find the marginal revenue when $x = 5.5$. See Note 1 on page 43.

82. Suppose that the total-cost function for a factory is $C = 15 \ln x + 2$. Find the marginal cost when $x = 3$. See Note 1 on page 43.

73. Differentiation of exponential functions

Proof of (XXI) *on page* 123. Let u be a differentiable function of x, and let $y = e^u$. Then,

$$u = \ln y, \tag{1}$$

where u and y are implicitly functions of x. On differentiating with respect to x on both sides in (1), and using (XIX), we obtain (XXI):

$$\frac{du}{dx} = \frac{1}{y} \frac{dy}{dx}, \quad \text{or} \quad \frac{dy}{dx} = y \frac{du}{dx} = e^u \frac{du}{dx}. \tag{2}$$

Proof of (XXII). If $y = a^u$ then $u = \log_a y$. By (XX),

$$\frac{du}{dx} = \frac{\log_a e}{y}\frac{dy}{dx} = \frac{1}{y \ln a}\frac{dy}{dx}, \tag{3}$$

because of (16) on page 146. Hence, from (3) we obtain (XXII):

$$\frac{dy}{dx} = y(\ln a)\frac{du}{dx} = a^u(\ln a)\frac{du}{dx},$$

ILLUSTRATION 1. From (XXI) with $u = 3x$,

$$\frac{de^{3x}}{dx} = e^{3x}\frac{d(3x)}{dx} = 3e^{3x}.$$

$$\frac{de^{\sin^2 4x}}{dx} = e^{\sin^2 4x}\frac{d \sin^2 4x}{dx} = 8e^{\sin^2 4x}\sin 4x \cos 4x.$$

$$\frac{de^{e^{\tan x}}}{dx} = e^{e^{\tan x}}\frac{de^{\tan x}}{dx} = e^{\tan x}\,e^{e^{\tan x}}\sec^2 x.$$

From (12) on page 146, $\quad\dfrac{de^{\ln\,(2x+3)}}{dx} = \dfrac{d(2x+3)}{dx} = 2.$

We have proved the power formula

$$\frac{d}{dx}u^n = nu^{n-1}\frac{du}{dx} \tag{III}$$

only when n is a rational number. Now we are prepared to prove (III) for any real number n, provided that $u > 0$.

Proof of (III). Let $y = u^n$, where u is a differentiable function of x, with $u > 0$ at all values of x. Then, $u = e^{\ln u}$ and

$$y = (e^{\ln u})^n = e^{n \ln u}. \tag{4}$$

Hence, from (4) and (XXI) we obtain (III):

$$\frac{dy}{dx} = e^{n \ln u}\left[\frac{d(n \ln u)}{dx}\right] = \frac{n}{u}(e^{n \ln u})\frac{du}{dx}$$

$$= \frac{nu^n}{u}\cdot\frac{du}{dx} = nu^{n-1}\frac{du}{dx}.$$

EXAMPLE 1. Find y' if $y = x^{\sin x}$.

SOLUTION. Use logarithmic differentiation:

$$\ln y = (\sin x)\ln x. \tag{5}$$

Differentiate with respect to x on both sides of (5):

$$\frac{1}{y}\frac{dy}{dx} = \frac{\sin x}{x} + (\ln x)\cos x;$$

or, since $y = x^{\sin x}$, $\qquad\dfrac{dy}{dx} = x^{\sin x}\left[\dfrac{\sin x}{x} + (\cos x)\ln x\right].$

By the method of the preceding solution, in the next exercise the student will derive the general exponential formula (XXIII) on page 123. Need for (XXIII) arises rarely, so that the formula is not recommended for memorization. Any particular case may be solved as in Example 1. On the right in (XXIII), the first term is what we would obtain if v were a constant; the second term is what we would obtain from (XXII) if u were a constant. Formulas (III) and (XXII) thus are special cases of (XXIII).

74. Graphing of logarithmic and exponential functions

EXAMPLE 1. Graph the function $y = xe^{-x}$, given that

$$\lim_{x \to \infty} xe^{-x} = 0. \tag{1}$$

SOLUTION. 1. The range for x is $-\infty < x < \infty$. We find

$$y' = e^{-x}(1 - x); \quad y'' = e^{-x}(x - 2). \tag{2}$$

2. *Extrema.* $y' = 0$ just at $x = 1$, because e^{-x} is never zero. Then, at $x = 1$, we find $y'' < 0$. Hence, there is a maximum at $x = 1$, with the maximum value $y = e^{-1} = .37$, approximately.

3. *Inflection points.* $y'' = 0$ just when $x = 2$. Also, y'' changes sign from "$-$" to "$+$" as x increases through 2. Hence, there is an inflection point at $x = 2$, where the graph changes from concave downward to concave upward as x increases through $x = 2$. At $x = 2$, the slope is $-e^{-2}$ or $-.14$.

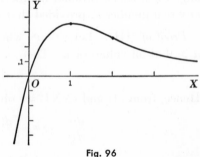

Fig. 96

4. From (1), whose proof will be given in a later chapter, the graph has the line $y = 0$ as an asymptote, approached as $x \to \infty$. If $x \to -\infty$, then $y \to -\infty$. Values of y for a few values of x were computed with the aid of Table V. The graph is given in Figure 96.

ILLUSTRATION 1. The graph of $y = \ln |x|$ is symmetrical to the y-axis, because $|-x| = |x|$ and hence y is unaltered if x is changed to $-x$. When $x > 0$, $|x| = x$ and we have $y = \ln x$. Thus, the graph of $y = \ln |x|$ would consist of the graph of $y = \ln x$, when $x > 0$, and the reflection of this graph in the y-axis when $x < 0$. The student will draw this graph later.

In graphing exponential or logarithmic functions, investigation of extrema and inflection points frequently leads to the necessity for solving logarithmic or exponential equations.

ILLUSTRATION 2. To solve $e^{2x} = \frac{1}{2}$, take logarithms and use Table III:

$$\ln e^{2x} = \ln \tfrac{1}{2}, \quad or \quad 2x = -\ln 2; \quad x = -\tfrac{1}{2}\ln 2 = -.34658.$$

EXAMPLE 2. Graph the function $y = \ln \cos x$.

SOLUTION.   1. Since y is periodic with the period 2π, consider just the graph on the range $-\frac{1}{2}\pi < x < \frac{3}{2}\pi$. Since $\ln N$ is defined only when $N > 0$, the range for x in $y = \ln \cos x$ is $-\frac{1}{2}\pi < x < \frac{1}{2}\pi$, where $\cos x > 0$. Since $\cos x \to 0$ as $x \to \frac{1}{2}\pi$ and as $x \to -\frac{1}{2}\pi$, hence

$$\lim_{x \to \frac{1}{2}\pi-} \ln \cos x = -\infty = \lim_{x \to -\frac{1}{2}\pi+} \ln \cos x.$$

Thus, the lines $x = \pm \frac{1}{2}\pi$ are asymptotes of the curve.

2. *Extrema and inflection points.* We find

$$y' = -\tan x; \quad y'' = -\sec^2 x.$$

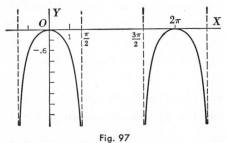

If $y' = 0$, then $\tan x = 0$ and $x = 0$ or $x = \pi$, where only $x = 0$ applies. At $x = 0$, $y'' = -\sec^2 \theta = -1$, and thus there is a maximum. Since $-\sec^2 x \neq 0$ at any value of x, there is no inflection point. The graph is in Figure 97.

Fig. 97

EXERCISE 40

Differentiate the function.   Any letter except x, z, or t is a constant.

1. e^{4x}.
2. e^{2x+3}.
3. $e^{\cot x}$.
4. $e^{\ln t^2}$.

5. e^{-2x}.
6. $e^{-\sqrt{z}}$.
7. a^{4t}.
8. $10^{\cos x}$.

9. $e^{\sec z}$.
10. $e^{(\ln x)^2}$.
11. 4^{-3z}.
12. $10^x e^x$.

13. e^{3x-x^2}.
14. $e^{-2z^{-1}}$.
15. $x^3 e^{-x^3}$.
16. $\ln e^{4x}$.

17. $e^{x \ln x}$.
18. $\sin e^x$.
19. $\cos a^t$.
20. Arcsin e^{2t}.

21. $\dfrac{\ln x}{e^{3x}}$.
22. $\dfrac{a^x e^x}{\ln x}$.
23. $\dfrac{\sin x}{e^{\sqrt{2x}}}$.
24. $\dfrac{\ln z^3}{e^{z^3}}$.

25. Arctan (xe^{2x}).
26. Arcsin $(e^{x^2} \ln x)$.
27. Arccos (xe^{-3x}).

28. $e^{3x} \sin 4x$.
29. $e^{-2t} \cos 5t$.
30. $e^{2x} \ln \cos x$.

31. $\dfrac{\tan x + \sec x}{e^{-2x}}$.
32. $\dfrac{e^x + e^{-2x}}{e^x - e^{-2x}}$.
33. $\dfrac{e^{3x} - 1}{e^{3x} + 1}$.

34. $(3x + e^{-2x})^5$.
35. $\sqrt{5 - 2e^{-3t}}$.
36. $e^x \sqrt{1 + \ln x}$.

Find y'' for each function.

37. $y = e^{2x} \ln x$.
38. $y = xe^{2x-3}$.
39. $y = 5/xe^{-x}$.

Find y' from the given relation.

40. $e^{x+2y} - \ln x = 3$.
41. $xy - \ln y = e^{-y}$.

Compute y' to two significant digits, and write the equation of the tangent to the graph of the equation at the specified point.

42. $y = x^2 e^{-3x}$; at $x = \frac{1}{3}$.
43. $y = (2x - 1)e^{-\frac{1}{4}x}$; at $x = -2$.

Find y′ by differentiating ln *y.* *Check by use of* (XXIII).

44. $y = x^{x^2}$.   **45.** $y = \sqrt{x^x}$.   **46.** $y = x^{\cos x}$.   **47.** $y = (\sin x)^{\cos x}$.

48. $y = (\sin x)^x$.   **49.** $y = (\ln x)^x$.   **50.** $y = (\ln x)^{e^x}$.   **51.** $y = x^{e^x}$.

Find an expression for the n*th derivative of the function.*

52. e^x.   **53.** xe^x.   **54.** xe^{-x}.

Specify the value of the limit.

55. $\lim_{x \to 0+} \ln \sin x$.   **56.** $\lim_{x \to \frac{1}{2}\pi -} e^{\tan x}$.   **57.** $\lim_{x \to \frac{1}{2}\pi +} e^{\tan x}$.

Apply tests for extrema and inflection points, and graph the function. Find the slope at any inflection point and draw the inflection tangent.

58. $y = \ln (x - 3)$.   **59.** $y = e^x$.   **60.** $y = e^{-x}$.

61. $x = \ln (y + 2)$.   **62.** $x = e^{2y}$.   **63.** $y = \ln x^2$.

64. $y = xe^x$, given that $y \to 0$ as $x \to -\infty$.

65. $y = \ln (4 + x^2)$.   **66.** $y = x - \ln x$.

67. The **hyperbolic sine** of x: $y = \frac{1}{2}(e^x - e^{-x})$.

68. The **hyperbolic cosine** of x: $y = \frac{1}{2}(e^x + e^{-x})$.

69. $y = \dfrac{1}{\sqrt{2\pi}} e^{-\frac{1}{2}x^2}$, the **normal probability density function** of statistics.

70. $y = \ln \sin x$.   **71.** $y = \ln \sec x$.   **72.** $y = \ln \tan x$.

73. Recall Note 1 on page 43. Let the average-cost curve for a commodity be $A = 3x \ln x - 8x + 18$. Find the minimum value of A.

75. Applications to rectilinear motion

Let the position of a particle at time t in motion on an s-axis be given by

$$s = k \sin (\omega t - \alpha), \tag{1}$$

where k, ω, and α are constants, with $k > 0$ and $\omega > 0$. Then, the motion is called **simple harmonic motion.**

EXAMPLE 1. For $t \geqq 0$, study the motion defined by

$$s = 5 \sin (3t - \tfrac{1}{4}\pi) = 5 \sin 3(t - \tfrac{1}{12}\pi). \tag{2}$$

SOLUTION. 1. In (2), if $s = s_1$ at $t = t_1$, then also $s = s_1$ at $t = t_1 + \frac{2}{3}\pi$, because addition of $\frac{2}{3}\pi$ to t_1 adds 2π to $(3t_1 - \frac{1}{4}\pi)$, and thus does not change the sine factor in (2). Hence, the motion (2) is periodic, with the period $\frac{2}{3}\pi$.

2. By trigonometry, we graph (2) in Figure 98 on page 155. The range for s is from -5 to $+5$, inclusive, with

$$s = 5 \quad at \quad 3t - \tfrac{1}{4}\pi = \tfrac{1}{2}\pi + 2n\pi, \text{ or} \qquad t = \tfrac{1}{4}\pi + n(\tfrac{2}{3}\pi), \tag{3}$$

$$s = -5 \quad at \quad 3t - \tfrac{1}{4}\pi = \tfrac{3}{2}\pi + 2n\pi, \text{ or} \qquad t = \tfrac{7}{12}\pi + n(\tfrac{2}{3}\pi), \tag{4}$$

$$s = 0 \quad at \quad 3t - \tfrac{1}{4}\pi = n\pi, \text{ or} \qquad t = \tfrac{1}{12}\pi + n(\tfrac{1}{3}\pi), \tag{5}$$

where n takes on all integral values $n \geqq 0$.

3. *The velocity, v, and acceleration, a:*

$$v = \frac{ds}{dt} = 15 \cos (3t - \tfrac{1}{4}\pi); \quad a = \frac{d^2s}{dt^2} = -45 \sin (3t - \tfrac{1}{4}\pi) = -9s. \quad (6)$$

Hence, $v = 0$ when $3t - \tfrac{1}{4}\pi = \tfrac{1}{2}\pi + n\pi$, where we found $s = \pm 5$ in (3) and (4). Also, the speed $|v|$ has its maximum, 15, when $3t - \tfrac{1}{4}\pi = n\pi$, where $s = 0$. Since $a = -9s$, a and s have *opposite signs* when not equal to zero. The acceleration attains its minimum -45 whenever $s = 5$, and maximum 45 whenever $s = -5$.

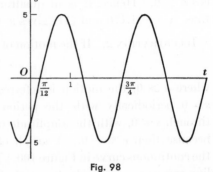

4. From (2) and (6), and Figure 98, the particle P starts at the point $s = -\tfrac{5}{2}\sqrt{2} = -3.5$ on the s-axis of Figure 99 when $t = 0$, with $v > 0$, and moves to $s = 5$, where $v = 0$ and $a = -45$. Then, v becomes negative and P moves to $s = -5$; thereafter, P oscillates between $s = -5$ and $s = 5$. The speed $|v|$ attains its maximum value 15 whenever P is at $s = 0$.

Fig. 98

Comment. In Example 1, if P has mass m, then the force, F, acting on P at the instant t is $F = ma = -9ms$. Thus, in simple harmonic motion about the origin $s = 0$, $|F|$ is proportional to the distance of P from the origin $s = 0$, and F is always directed at the origin when $s \ne 0$, since $F > 0$ when $s < 0$, and $F < 0$ when $s > 0$.

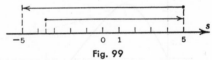

Fig. 99

Similarly, as in Example 1, the motion determined by (1) is periodic with the period $2\pi/\omega$, and the particle oscillates between $s = k$ and $s = -k$. In (1), we call k the **amplitude** and α the **phase constant** of the motion. The graph of s as a function of t is a sine curve shifted a distance α/ω along the t-axis. In (1), $\cos (\omega t - \alpha)$ could be used instead of $\sin (\omega t - \alpha)$ with similar conclusions.

Note 1. If $s = A \cos \omega t + B \sin \omega t$, where A and B are not both zero and $\omega > 0$, we can find constants α and $k > 0$, with $-\pi < \alpha \le \pi$, so that $s = k \sin (\omega t - \alpha)$. For this purpose, we write

$$A \cos \omega t + B \sin \omega t = k (\sin \omega t \cos \alpha - \cos \omega t \sin \alpha), \quad (7)$$

where $$k \cos \alpha = B \quad \text{and} \quad k \sin \alpha = -A. \quad (8)$$

Then, $$k^2 = A^2 + B^2, \quad \text{and we select} \quad k = \sqrt{A^2 + B^2}. \quad (9)$$

From (8), $$\sin \alpha = -\frac{A}{k} \quad \text{or} \quad \cos \alpha = \frac{B}{k}. \quad (10)$$

With $k > 0$ from (9), find α from an equation in (10), where both of (10) are used to specify the quadrant of α. Thus,

$$s = A \cos \omega t + B \sin \omega t \quad becomes \quad s = k \sin (\omega t - \alpha). \tag{11}$$

Hence, the standard form (1) is equivalent to the form at the left in (11). Form (1) usually is more desirable.

ILLUSTRATION 1. To change $\qquad s = 5 \sin 2t + 12 \cos 2t \qquad$ (12)

to the form (1), we use (9) to obtain $k = 13$; (10) gives $\sin \alpha = -\frac{12}{13}$ and $\cos \alpha > 0$. Hence, α is in quadrant IV. From Table IV, $\frac{12}{13} = \sin 1.176$; thus, $\alpha = -1.176$ and (11) gives $s = 13 \sin (2t + 1.176)$.

ILLUSTRATION 2. If the motion of a particle P on an s-axis is determined by

$$s = e^{-at} \sin (\omega t - \alpha), \tag{13}$$

where $a > 0$, the motion is referred to as a **damped vibration.** In (13), $s = 0$ periodically with the period $2\pi/\omega$ as t increases, and P oscillates through $s = 0$, with the amplitude of oscillation approaching zero as $t \to \infty$, because then $e^{-at} \to 0$. A graph of (13) with $a = .5$, $\alpha = 0$, and $\omega = 2$ is the continuous curve in Figure 100. The graph of (13) is tangent to the broken-line curves $s = e^{-at}$ and $s = -e^{-at}$ of Figure 100 at common points.

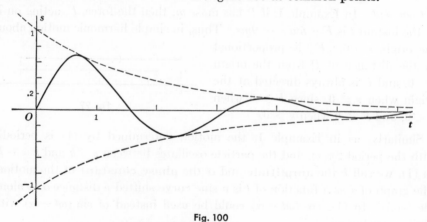

Fig. 100

EXERCISE 41

Find the velocity, v, and acceleration, a, of a particle P at the indicated values of the time t, if P has the given equation for motion on an s-axis. Also, graph s as a function of t without using calculus and describe the motion when $t \geqq 0$. State the period of the motion. Use Note 1 of page 155 where appropriate.

1. $s = 3 \sin 2t$; find v and a at $t = 0, \frac{1}{4}\pi, \frac{1}{2}\pi, \frac{3}{4}\pi, \pi$.

2. $s = 5 \sin (t - \frac{1}{4}\pi)$; find v and a at $t = 0, \frac{1}{4}\pi, \frac{1}{2}\pi, \frac{3}{4}\pi, \pi$.

3. $s = 4 \cos (2t - \frac{1}{3}\pi)$; find v and a at $t = 0, \frac{1}{3}\pi, \frac{2}{3}\pi, \pi, \frac{5}{3}\pi$.

4. $s = \cos t - \sqrt{3} \sin t$; find v and a at $t = 0, \frac{1}{6}\pi, \frac{1}{3}\pi, \frac{5}{6}\pi$.

5. $s = 3 \sin 2t - 3 \cos 2t$; find v and a at $t = 0, \frac{1}{4}\pi, \frac{1}{2}\pi, \frac{3}{4}\pi$.

6. $s = 3 \sin t + 4 \cos t$; find v and a at $t = 0, \frac{1}{2}\pi, \pi$.

★7. The equation of motion for a particle P is $s = e^{-t} \sin t$. (a) Locate all extrema and graph s as a function of t; also graph $s = e^{-t}$ and $s = -e^{-t}$ on the same coordinate system. (b) Prove that the curve $s = e^{-t} \sin t$ is tangent to each of the exponential curves at any common point. (c) Describe the motion of P on the s-axis.

★8. Repeat Problem 7 for the equation of motion $s = e^{-.5t} \cos .5t$.

76. Differentials of transcendental functions

Corresponding to each of the derivative formulas (I)–(XXIII), omitting (VIII), on pages 38 and 122, we obtain a differential formula, labeled with the subscript d below, on multiplying both sides of the derivative formula by dx. From page 103, we recall that (VII)$_d$ includes each of the later differential formulas as a special case. In the following results, u and v represent differentiable functions of x, and k is a constant; (I)$_d$–(VII)$_d$ were met on page 102.

SUMMARY OF FUNDAMENTAL DIFFERENTIALS

$d(k) = 0.$ (I)$_d$ | $d(ku) = k\ du.$ (II)$_d$

$d(u^n) = nu^{n-1}\ du.$ (III)$_d$ | $d(u + v) = du + dv.$ (IV)$_d$

$d(uv) = u\ dv + v\ du.$ (V)$_d$ | $d\left(\dfrac{u}{v}\right) = \dfrac{v\ du - u\ dv}{v^2}.$ (VI)$_d$

Suppose that $y = \phi(u)$, and $u = g(x)$, where ϕ and g are differentiable functions. Then, with $du = g'(x)dx$,

$$dy = \phi'(u)du. \qquad \text{(VII)}_d$$

$d \sin u = \cos u\ du.$ (IX)$_d$ | $d \cos u = -\sin u\ du.$ (X)$_d$

$d \tan u = \sec^2 u\ du.$ (XI)$_d$ | $d \cot u = -\csc^2 u\ du.$ (XII)$_d$

$d \sec u = \sec u \tan u\ du.$ (XIII)$_d$

$d \csc u = -\csc u \cot u\ du.$ (XIV)$_d$

$d \operatorname{Arcsin} u = \dfrac{du}{\sqrt{1 - u^2}}.$ (XV)$_d$ | $d \operatorname{Arccos} u = \dfrac{-du}{\sqrt{1 - u^2}}.$ (XVI)$_d$

$d \operatorname{Arctan} u = \dfrac{du}{1 + u^2}.$ (XVII)$_d$ | $d \operatorname{Arccot} u = \dfrac{-du}{1 + u^2}.$ (XVIII)$_d$

$d \ln u = \dfrac{du}{u}.$ (XIX)$_d$ | $d \log_a u = \dfrac{\log_a e}{u}\ du.$ (XX)$_d$

$d(e^u) = e^u\ du.$ (XXI)$_d$ | $d(a^u) = a^u \ln a\ du.$ (XXII)$_d$

$d(u^v) = vu^{v-1}\ du + (\ln u)u^v\ dv.$ (XXIII)$_d$

ILLUSTRATION 1. By $(IX)_d$ with $u = x^2 + e^x$, and $du = (2x + e^x)dx$,

$$d \sin (x^2 + e^x) = [\cos (x^2 + e^x)](2x + e^x)dx.$$

From $(XIX)_d$, $d \ln \csc x = \dfrac{1}{\csc x} d \csc x = - \dfrac{\csc x \cot x}{\csc x} dx = - \cot x \, dx.$

From $(XXI)_d$, $de^{\text{Arcsin } x} = e^{\text{Arcsin } x} d \text{ Arcsin } x = e^{\text{Arcsin } x}\left(\dfrac{dx}{\sqrt{1 - x^2}}\right).$

From $(V)_d$, $d(e^{-3x} \ln x) = (\ln x)de^{-3x} + e^{-3x}d \ln x = - 3(\ln x)e^{-3x} + \dfrac{e^{-3x}}{x}.$

EXAMPLE 1. The base, AC, of a right triangle, as in Figure 101, is 7.4′ long. The angle α is measured as 35.3°, with an error not larger than .5°. Find approximately the maximum possible error in the area of the triangle as computed from the data.

Fig. 101

SOLUTION. 1. Let W be the area. Then, from Figure 101,

$$BC = 7.4 \tan \alpha; \quad W = \tfrac{1}{2}(7.4)^2 \tan \alpha. \tag{1}$$

2. An error $d\alpha$ radians in α causes an error ΔW in W, where

$$\Delta W \approx dW = \tfrac{1}{2}(7.4)^2 \sec^2 \alpha \, d\alpha. \tag{2}$$

We use (2) with α as the radian equivalent of 35.3°; $|\, d\alpha \,|$ is at most the radian equivalent of .5°, or $\tfrac{1}{2}(\pi/180)$. Hence,

$$|\, \Delta W \,| \approx \tfrac{1}{2}(7.4)^2(\sec^2 \alpha)|\, d\alpha \,| \leqq \tfrac{1}{2}(7.4)^2(\sec^2 35.3°) \cdot \frac{\pi}{360} = .36,$$

by logarithms. Or, approximately, the error is at most .36 square feet.

EXAMPLE 2. Compute sin 32° approximately by differentials.

SOLUTION. 1. Let $y = \sin x$, where $\sin x$ means the sine of x radians. We know sin 30°. We shall obtain sin 32° by adding to sin 30° the increment Δy, approximated as dy, due to an increase of 2° in the angle. First, we change the angular data to radian measure:

$$30° = \frac{1}{6} \pi \text{ radians}; \quad 2° = 2\frac{\pi}{180} \text{ radians} = \frac{\pi}{90} \text{ radians}.$$

2. We desire dy corresponding to $x = \frac{1}{6} \pi$ and $dx = \pi/90$:

$$dy = \cos x \, dx; \quad \Delta y \approx dy = \left(\cos \frac{1}{6} \pi\right)\frac{\pi}{90} = \left(\frac{1}{2} \sqrt{3}\right)\left(\frac{\pi}{90}\right) = .0302.$$

Hence, $\sin 32° = \sin 30° + \Delta y \approx .5000 + .0302 = .5302.$

(A four-place trigonometric table gives sin 32° = .5299.)

Consider a differentiable function $y = f(x)$, where we think of measuring the value of x and computing the corresponding value of y, from $y = f(x)$. Then, on page 105, we used dy/y as an approximation to the *relative error* in y, due to an error dx in x. We notice that $d \ln y = dy/y$. Hence,

$$\left\{ \begin{array}{c} \textit{relative error in } y \\ \textit{due to error } dx \textit{ in } x \end{array} \right\} \approx \frac{dy}{y} = d \ln y. \tag{3}$$

Use of $d \ln y$ instead of dy/y in (3) is particularly convenient if $d \ln y$ is expressible simply in terms of dx/x.

EXAMPLE 3. A cone has the altitude h units. The base radius of the cone is measured as r units, with an error of at most 3%. Find approximately the maximum possible percentage error in the computed volume.

SOLUTION. 1. With V as the volume, and h a constant,

$$V = \tfrac{1}{3}\pi r^2 h; \quad \ln V = \ln \tfrac{1}{3}\pi + \ln h + 2 \ln r. \tag{4}$$

$$\left\{ \begin{array}{c} \textit{Relative} \\ \textit{error in } V \end{array} \right\} \approx d \ln V = 0 + 0 + 2\frac{dr}{r}. \tag{5}$$

2. The percentage error in r is the relative error expressed as a percentage, and thus is the value of dr/r. Hence, from (5)

$$|\, d \ln V \,| \leq 2\left|\frac{dr}{r}\right| \leq 2(.03) = .06,$$

or the error in V does not exceed 6%, approximately.

EXERCISE 42

1. Check the standard differential forms $(IX)_d$–$(XXIII)_d$ by reference to the corresponding derivative formulas.

Calculate the differential.

2. de^{4x}.   3. $d \cos 5x$.   4. $d \tan 2x$.   5. $d \sin \tfrac{1}{3}x$.

6. $d \ln 8y$.   7. $d \ln (x+3)^5$.   8. $d \ln \cos z$.   9. $d \ln (\ln x)$.

10. $d \operatorname{Arcsin} \tfrac{1}{2}z$.   11. $d \operatorname{Arctan} 3t$.   12. $de^{\sin x}$.

Calculate the differential of the function.

13. $\cos (e^{2x} + x)$.   14. $e^x \sin 3x$.   15. $(\tan x)\ln x$.

16. $e^{-2x} \ln x$.   17. $(\sin \theta + \cos \theta)e^{3\theta}$.   18. $\ln \operatorname{Arctan} x$.

19. $\dfrac{e^x - 1}{e^x + 1}$.   20. $\dfrac{\sin t + \cos t}{\sin t - \cos t}$.   21. $\dfrac{\ln x}{x^2 + 1}$.

22. $10^{4x} \sin 3x$.   23. $a^z \ln \sin z$.   24. $\dfrac{x^2 + 1}{\operatorname{Arctan} x}$.

Solve Problems 25–29 by use of differentials. Recall (3) of Section 76.

25. From a point on a shore of a lake, the angle of elevation of the top of a wall $75'$ high on the opposite shore is measured as $30°$, with an error not larger than $6'$. Find approximately the maximum possible error in the distance across the lake as computed from these data.

26. The angle at the vertex in a cross-section through the vertex of a cone perpendicular to its base is measured as 40°, with an error not larger than .2°. The radius of the base is 10′. Find approximately the maximum possible error in (*a*) the volume and (*b*) the lateral area of the cone as computed from the data. Use logarithms.

27. If a certain metal sphere of radius *r* is heated to a specified temperature, the radius will increase by .3%. Find approximately the percentage increase in (*a*) the surface area and (*b*) the volume of the sphere.

28. Suppose that the time *T*, in seconds, for one oscillation of a pendulum *l* feet long is given by $T = \pi\sqrt{l/g}$ where $g = 32$. If *l* is measured with an error not larger than 2.5%, find approximately the maximum possible percentage error in the value computed for *T*.

29. Find approximately the maximum percentage error which is permissible in the measurement of the radius of a circle if the computed area is to be in error by not more than 3%.

30. The power, *P*, in foot-pounds per second available in a jet of water with a cross-section area of *A* square feet, discharging with a velocity of *v* feet per second, is approximated by $P = (v^3wA)/2g$, where $g = 32$ and *w* is the weight in pounds of one cubic foot of water. It is estimated that the measured value of *v* possibly is in error by 3%. Find approximately the maximum possible percentage error in *P* as computed from the formula.

Find the quantity approximately by use of differentials. Check by a table.

31. tan 47°.   **32.** cos 61°.   **33.** sin 148°.   **34.** $e^{.03}$.

35. ln 1.02.   **36.** ln .99.   **37.** $e^{1.03}$.   **38.** $e^{.98}$.

Calculate dy in terms of x, y, and dx without solving for y in terms of x.

39. $\sin x + \cos y = 1.4$.   **40.** $\ln (x + y) + \sin x = 2$.

41. $e^{3x-2y} + \sin x = \cos y$.   **42.** $\ln (x^2 + 2y) + e^{3x} = 5$.

17. Parametric form involving transcendental functions

Sometimes, a geometric definition of a locus in an *xy*-plane may lead easily to parametric equations, and only with difficulty to an *xy*-equation.

ILLUSTRATION 1. If a circle rolls on a straight line in a plane, any point on the circumference traces out a curve called a **cycloid.** To obtain parametric equations for it, let the line be the *x*-axis, let the radius of the circle be *r*, and suppose that, at some fixed instant, the moving point *P* is at the origin. At a later instant when the circle is tangent to *OX* at *K*, let *H* be the center of the circle, and let *P*:(*x*, *y*) be the position of the moving point, in Figure 102. Let *θ* be the value, in radian measure, of angle *PHK*, considered positive in the direction indicated by the arrow. Let all vertical and horizontal line segments be *directed*, with the usual directions specified as positive. Then, since the circle has rolled from O to K, we have $arc\ KSP = OK$;

$$MK = PN = r \sin \theta \quad and \quad OK = arc\ KSP = r\theta;$$

$$x = OM = OK - MK = r\theta - r \sin \theta; \tag{1}$$

$$y = MP = KH - NH = r - r \cos \theta. \tag{2}$$

Therefore,
$$\begin{cases} x = r(\theta - \sin \theta), & (3) \\ y = r(1 - \cos \theta), & (4) \end{cases}$$

are parametric equations for the cycloid. To eliminate θ in (3) and (4), solve (4) for θ:

$$\cos \theta = \frac{r - y}{r}, \quad or \quad \theta = \arccos \frac{r - y}{r}; \quad \sin \theta = \pm \frac{\sqrt{2ry - y^2}}{r}, \tag{5}$$

where we used $\sin \theta = \pm \sqrt{1 - \cos^2 \theta}$. On using (5) in (3), we find

$$x = r \arccos \frac{r - y}{r} \pm \sqrt{2ry - y^2} \tag{6}$$

as the xy-equation of the cycloid. In (6), "$arccos$" refers to the complete, infinitely many-valued function. The cycloid consists of an endless sequence of arches to the left and right of the y-axis, where those on the left are obtained when $\theta < 0$.

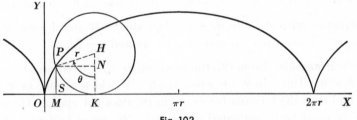

Fig. 102

EXAMPLE 1. Obtain an xy-equation for the curve

$$x = a \cos t \quad and \quad y = b \sin t, \tag{7}$$

where $a > 0$, $b > 0$, and t is a variable. By use of (7), locate the points where the tangent is horizontal or vertical.

SOLUTION. 1. $dx = - a \sin t\ dt; \quad dy = b \cos t\ dt.$

$$y' = \frac{dy}{dx} = - \frac{b}{a} \cdot \frac{\cos t}{\sin t}; \quad \frac{dx}{dy} = - \frac{a}{b} \cdot \frac{\sin t}{\cos t}.$$

2. To eliminate t in (7), square in both equations, and add:

$$\cos^2 t + \sin^2 t = \frac{x^2}{a^2} + \frac{y^2}{b^2}, \quad or \quad \frac{x^2}{a^2} + \frac{y^2}{b^2} = 1.$$

Thus, (7) gives parametric equations for the ellipse with semi-axes a and b along the coordinate axes, and center at the origin.

3. *Horizontal and vertical tangents.* Since x and y are periodic functions of t, with the period 2π, we get all points of the ellipse by use of $0 \leqq t < 2\pi$.

$$\frac{dy}{dx} = 0 \quad gives \quad \cos t = 0; \quad t = \frac{1}{2}\pi \quad and \quad t = \frac{3}{2}\pi;$$

$$\frac{dx}{dy} = 0 \quad gives \quad \sin t = 0; \quad t = 0 \quad and \quad t = \pi.$$

If $t = \frac{1}{2}\pi$, then (7) gives $(x = 0, y = b)$; etc. The tangent to (7) is horizontal at $(0, \pm b)$, and vertical at $(\pm a, 0)$, which verifies known features of (7).

EXAMPLE 2. With $0 \leqq \theta \leqq 2\pi$, obtain the points on the cycloid $[(3), (4)]$ where the tangent is horizontal or vertical, and test for concavity.

SOLUTION. 1. From $[(3), (4)]$,

$$dx = r(1 - \cos \theta)d\theta; \quad dy = r \sin \theta \, d\theta; \tag{8}$$

$$\frac{dy}{dx} = \frac{\sin \theta}{1 - \cos \theta}; \quad \frac{dx}{dy} = \frac{1 - \cos \theta}{\sin \theta}. \tag{9}$$

From (9), the cycloid has a tangent at all values of θ except possibly where

$$both \quad \sin \theta = 0 \quad and \quad 1 - \cos \theta = 0. \tag{10}$$

The solutions of $\sin \theta = 0$ are $\theta = 0$, $\theta = \pi$, and $\theta = 2\pi$. The solutions of $1 = \cos \theta$ are $\theta = 0$ and $\theta = 2\pi$. Thus, (10) is true at $\theta = 0$ and $\theta = 2\pi$.

2. *Horizontal tangents.* $dy/dx = 0$ when $\sin \theta = 0$ and $1 - \cos \theta \neq 0$, or when $\theta = \pi$. Then, from (3) and (4), $x = \pi r$ and $y = 2r$.

3. *Vertical tangents.* From (9), the equation $dx/dy = 0$ requires $1 - \cos \theta = 0$ and $\sin \theta \neq 0$. But, $\sin \theta = 0$ when $\cos \theta = 1$, which occurs at $\theta = 0$ and $\theta = 2\pi$, and thus the formula for dx/dy in (9) does not apply. Hence, $\theta = 0$ and $\theta = 2\pi$ must be investigated otherwise. By use of half-angle formulas,

$$\lim_{\theta \to 0} \frac{dx}{dy} = \lim_{\theta \to 0} \frac{1 - \cos \theta}{\sin \theta} = \lim_{\theta \to 0} \frac{2 \sin^2 \frac{1}{2}\theta}{2 \sin \frac{1}{2}\theta \cos \frac{1}{2}\theta} = \lim_{\theta \to 0} \tan \frac{1}{2}\theta = 0.$$

Hence, we conclude * that $dx/dy = 0$ at $\theta = 0$, or the curve has a vertical tangent at $\theta = 0$, and similarly at $\theta = 2\pi$. Thus, from the nature of a cycloid, there is a cusp with a vertical tangent at $\theta = 2k\pi$, for all integral values of k.

4. *Concavity.* Let $y' = dy/dx$. Then, from (9),

$$y'' = \frac{dy'}{dx} = -\frac{1}{r(1 - \cos \theta)^2}.$$

If $0 < \theta < 2\pi$, then $(1 - \cos \theta)^2 > 0$, $y'' < 0$, and hence the cycloid is concave downward at all points except the cusps.

---

* Our reasoning is not complete here. Essentially, we assume that dx/dy exists at $\theta = 0$ because $dx/dy \to 0$ as $\theta \to 0$. This is true in the case involved but is not a general result.

EXERCISE 43

Find dy/dx in terms of the other variable in the equations.

1. $x = 3 \sin \theta$, $y = 2 \cos \theta$.
2. $x = 2 \cos^3 t$, $y = 2 \sin^3 t$.
3. $x = 1 + \sin t$, $y = t + \cos t$.
4. $x = 2 \sin t$, $y = 2(1 - \cos t)$.
5. $x = t^3$, $y = 2 \ln t$; also find $D_x^2 y$.
6. $x = e^\theta \cos \theta$, $y = e^\theta \sin \theta$; also find $D_x^2 y$.

Find equations for the tangent and normal to the curve with the given parametric equations, at the specified point. The letters r and a represent constants.

7. $x = 1 - \cos t$, $y = t + \sin t$; where $t = \frac{3}{2}\pi$.
8. $x = a \cos^3 t$, $y = a \sin^3 t$, with $a > 0$; where $t = \frac{3}{4}\pi$.
9. $x = r \cos t + rt \sin t$, $y = r \sin t - rt \cos t$, with $r > 0$; where $t = \frac{3}{4}\pi$.

Plot the curve given in parametric form, without changing to the xy-form. Take account of the routine on page 111; r and a represent constants.

10. $x = 2 + 5 \sin \theta$, $y = 3 \cos \theta - 1$; also, find the xy-equation.
11. $x = 3 \cos^3 t$, $y = 3 \sin^3 t$; also, find the xy-equation.
12. $x = a \cos^4 t$, $y = a \sin^4 t$, where $a > 0$; also, find the xy-equation.
13. $x = a(\theta + \sin \theta)$, $y = a(1 - \cos \theta)$, where $a > 0$.
14. $x = 2 \sin^2 t$, $y = 2 \cot t$; also, find the xy-equation.
15. $x = r \cos \theta + r\theta \sin \theta$, $y = r \sin \theta - r\theta \cos \theta$, where $r > 0$.
16. $x = 2t + t^{-1}$, $y = \ln t - t^2 - 1$.

The equations define the motion of a particle P in an xy-plane, with t as the time in seconds and with 1 foot as the unit for length. At the specified value of t, find the values of x, y, v_x, v_y, the speed v, a_x, a_y, and the magnitude of the acceleration, a. Then, plot the velocity and acceleration vectors at the location found for P.

17. $x = 2 \sin 2t$, $y = 3 \cos 2t$; at $t = \frac{1}{6}\pi$.
18. $x = (\cos t)(1 + \sin t)$, $y = (\sin t)(1 + \sin t)$; at $t = \frac{1}{3}\pi$.
19. $x = e^{-t} \sin 2t$, $y = e^{-t} \cos 2t$; at $t = \frac{1}{4}\pi$.

HINT. Use Table V to obtain e^t to two decimal places.

20. A particle P moves in an xy-plane, according to the equations $x = k \cos ht$ and $y = k \sin ht$, where k and h are constants with $k > 0$ and $h > 0$, and t is the time. (a) Find the xy-equation of the path. (b) Obtain the speed at any instant t. (c) Find the magnitude and direction of the acceleration at any instant t.

★21. Let P be the moving point, thought of as a particle, which traces the cycloid of Illustration 1 on page 160. Assume that the generating circle rolls with constant angular velocity about its center, that is, $d\theta/dt = h$, a positive constant, where t is the time. For the moving particle P, (a) find v_x, v_y, v, a_x, a_y, and a, at any instant t. (b) With θ on the range $0 \le \theta \le 2\pi$, find the location of P when its speed is a minimum, and a maximum. (c) Prove that the magnitude of the acceleration is a constant.

9

APPLICATIONS TO POLAR COORDINATES

78. Review of polar coordinates

In the plane, select a fixed point O, called the **pole,** and a fixed half-line or directed ray OI, called the **initial ray.** Let the whole line through OI be called the **polar axis,** drawn horizontal in the typical Figure 103, with OI directed to the right. Let P be a given point, not the pole. Let θ be any angle whose initial side is OI and whose terminal side falls on the line OP. Let r be the corresponding value of the *directed distance* OP, considered *positive* or *negative* according as P is on the terminal side of θ or on the extension of this side through O. Then, we call θ a **vectorial angle** or **polar angle** for P, r the corresponding **radius vector** for P, and the pair $[r, \theta]$ a set of **polar coordinates** for P. The pole O is assigned the coordinates $[0, \theta]$, where θ may have *any* value. The notation $P:[r, \theta]$, with square brackets, will mean *"point P with polar coordinates r, θ,"* and is read simply *"P, r, θ."* To plot an assigned point $P:[r, \theta]$, lay off θ by rotation from the initial ray OI, and then locate P on the terminal side of θ by use of the value of r. In applications of polar coordinates, *we cannot avoid using negative values for r.*

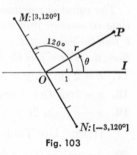

Fig. 103

ILLUSTRATION 1. Figure 103 shows $M:[3, 120°]$ and $N:[-3, 120°]$. Figure 104 shows $A:[2, 135°]$; other coordinates for A are $[2, -225°]$ and $[-2, 315°]$.

Let θ be any vectorial angle for P. Then, other possible vectorial angles are $(\theta + k \cdot 180°)$, where k may be any integer, because the terminal side of any one of these angles falls on the line through OP.

Note 1. In the symbol $P:[3, 5]$ where no indication of degrees is given, we have $\theta = 5$ radians. In $A:[2, \frac{1}{2}\pi]$, $\theta = \frac{1}{2}\pi$ radians.

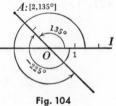

Fig. 104

The graph of an equation $G(r, \theta) = 0$ consists of all points for which there exists *at least one set* of coordinates $[r, \theta]$ satisfying $G(r, \theta) = 0$. An equation for a given locus in an $r\theta$-plane is an equation $G(r, \theta) = 0$ whose graph is the given locus.

ILLUSTRATION 2. An equation for the circle with radius a and center at the pole, in Figure 105, is $r = a$. For any value of θ, $P:[a, \theta]$ is on the locus of $r = a$; as θ varies from $0°$ to $360°$, P traces out the circle. Another equation for the circle is $r = -a$, because any point $[-a, \theta]$ also is on the circle. Thus, the equations $r = a$ and $r = -a$ have the same graph although they are not equivalent algebraically.

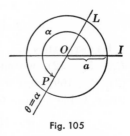

Fig. 105

ILLUSTRATION 3. If an angle from OI to a line L through the pole is α, an equation for L is $\theta = \alpha$. Another equation for L is $\tan \theta = \tan \alpha$. Notice that any point $P:[a, \alpha]$ is determined geometrically as one of the intersections of the circle $r = a$ and the line $\theta = \alpha$ (Figure 105).

ILLUSTRATION 4. The locus of the equation $\theta = 90°$, or $\theta = \frac{1}{2}\pi$, or $\theta = 270°$, etc., is the line s perpendicular to the polar axis at the pole. We call s the $90°$-line. The polar axis has the equations $\theta = 0°$, $\theta = 180°$, etc.

ILLUSTRATION 5. The graph of the equation $r = 4 \sin \theta$ is the circle in Figure 106. As θ varies from $0°$ to $180°$, $P:[r, \theta]$ traces out the whole circle, from the pole in the direction of the arrowheads. The points obtained for θ on the range $180° \leq \theta \leq 360°$ repeat those just mentioned. Thus, if $\theta = 210°$ then $r = -2$; if $\theta = 30°$ then $r = 2$; the points $P:[-2, 210°]$ and $R:[2, 30°]$ coincide.

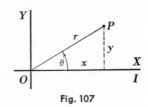

Fig. 106

Let a system of polar coordinates be given. Then, in Figure 107, introduce an xy-system of rectangular coordinates with the pole O as the origin, the polar axis as the x-axis, with its positive half along the initial ray OI, and the y-axis perpendicular to OI. Let the same unit of length be used for all distances in both systems. Any point P in the plane now has two sets of coordinates, (x, y) and $[r, \theta]$. The following relations are true, even when r is negative, except at points where a zero denominator eliminates certain formulas:

Fig. 107

$$x = r \cos \theta; \quad y = r \sin \theta; \tag{1}$$

$$r^2 = x^2 + y^2; \quad \tan \theta = \frac{y}{x} \quad or \quad \theta = \arctan \frac{y}{x}. \tag{2}$$

Whenever we consider rectangular and polar coordinates in the same problem, Figure 107 will apply, with relations (1) and (2).

ILLUSTRATION 6. To find x and y for $P:[r = 2, \theta = \frac{2}{3}\pi]$, use (1):

$$x = 2 \cos \tfrac{2}{3}\pi = -1;$$

$$y = 2 \sin \tfrac{2}{3}\pi = 2(\tfrac{1}{2}\sqrt{3}) = \sqrt{3}.$$

ILLUSTRATION 7. To obtain polar coordinates for $P:(-5, -12)$, we plot P in Figure 108. Then, from (2), $r^2 = 169$; $\tan \theta = \frac{12}{5} = 2.40$; θ is in quadrant III. From Table VI, $\tan 67.4° = 2.40$, and

$$\theta = 180° + 67.4° = 247.4°.$$

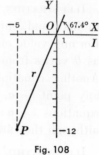

Fig. 108

P has the polar coordinates $[13, 247.4°]$. Also, P has the coordinates $[-13, 67.4°]$, etc.

If a given locus has the equation $f(x, y) = 0$, we obtain an equation $G(r, \theta) = 0$ for the locus by using (1) in $f(x, y) = 0$. If $G(r, \theta) = 0$ is a given equation for a locus, we obtain an equation $f(x, y) = 0$ for the locus by using (2) in $G(r, \theta) = 0$. In either case, we call $f(x, y) = 0$ and $G(r, \theta) = 0$ *equivalent equations* and each is said to be the *transformation* of the other into the corresponding system of coordinates. To investigate a locus, we use either $f(x, y) = 0$ or $G(r, \theta) = 0$, whichever offers the greater convenience.

ILLUSTRATION 8. To transform the circle $x^2 + y^2 = a^2$, with $a > 0$, into polar coordinates, use (1) and obtain $r^2 = a^2$, which is equivalent to $r = a$ and $r = -a$. The locus of each of these is the given circle.

ILLUSTRATION 9. The lines of the form $x = a$ and $y = b$ become

$$r \cos \theta = a \quad and \quad r \sin \theta = b.$$

EXAMPLE 1. Prove that $r = a \sin \theta$ is the equation of a circle.

SOLUTION. On multiplying both sides by r, we obtain $r^2 = a(r \sin \theta)$. By use of (1) and (2), we obtain the equivalent equation

$$x^2 + y^2 = ay \quad or \quad x^2 + (y - \tfrac{1}{2}a)^2 = \tfrac{1}{4}a^2.$$

Hence, the locus of $r = a \sin \theta$ is the circle with radius $\frac{1}{2}a$ and center $(0, \frac{1}{2}a)$. Notice that the multiplication by r at worst could have added just the locus of $r = 0$, the pole, to the original locus. However, $r = a \sin \theta$ is satisfied by $[r = 0, \theta = 0]$, or the pole is on the given locus. Thus, $r = a \sin \theta$ and $r^2 = ar \sin \theta$ are equivalent equations.

Let $f(\theta)$ be any periodic function of θ with the period 360°, so that $f(\theta) = f(\theta \pm 360°)$. Then, if we graph $r = f(\theta)$ for $0° \leqq \theta \leqq 360°$, or for θ on any interval of length 360°, we obtain all of the graph. Similarly, if $f(\theta)$ has the period 720°, we obtain all of the graph of $r = f(\theta)$ by use of $0° \leqq \theta \leqq 720°$.

With any equation $r = f(\theta)$ of the type to be met in this text, the following useful rule is valid.

$$\left\{ \begin{array}{l} \textit{If } f(\theta) = 0 \textit{ when } \theta = \theta_0, \textit{ then the line } \theta = \theta_0 \\ \textit{is tangent to the graph of } r = f(\theta) \textit{ at the pole.} \end{array} \right\} \tag{3}$$

Proof of (3). Let $P:[r, \theta]$ be on the graph of $r = f(\theta)$, as in Figure 109, where the equation of OT is $\theta = \theta_0$. By hypothesis, $[r = 0, \theta = \theta_0]$ satisfies $r = f(\theta)$. With the assumption that θ is a continuous function of r on the arc OP, then $\theta \to \theta_0$ when $r \to 0$. Or, the secant OP has the line OT as a limiting position when $r \to 0$. Hence, the arc OP has OT as the tangent line at the pole.

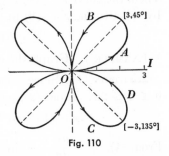

Fig. 109

ILLUSTRATION 10. Consider the four-leaved rose

$$r = 3 \sin 2\theta, \tag{4}$$

whose graph is in Figure 110. In (4), $r = 0$ when $\sin 2\theta = 0$, or $2\theta = 0°, 180°,$ 360°, or 540°, and then $\theta = 0°, 90°, 180°,$ or 270°. Thus, the lines $\theta = 0°, \theta = 90°, \theta = 180°,$ and $\theta = 270°$ are tangent to the graph at the pole; this yields two tangent lines, the polar axis and the 90°-line. The maximum $|r| = 3$ occurs when $\sin 2\theta = \pm 1$, or $\theta = 45°, 135°,$ etc. The point $P:[r, \theta]$ satisfying (4) traces the curve from the pole in the direction of the arrowheads as θ varies from 0° to 360°.

Fig. 110

ILLUSTRATION 11. The **lemniscate** (of BERNOUILLI) is shown in Figure 12 in Table VIII, and has the equation $r^2 = a^2 \cos 2\theta$, where $a > 0$. We have $\cos 2\theta = 0$ when $\theta = 45°$ and when $\theta = 135°$, which gives corresponding tangents at the pole. There are no points on the graph when $90° < 2\theta < 270°$, or $45° < \theta < 135°$, because then $\cos 2\theta < 0$ and r is imaginary.

EXERCISE 44

Review of Polar Coordinates

Plot the point whose polar coordinates are given. Also, give one other set of coordinates $[r, \theta]$ for the point, with $0° \leq \theta < 360°$.

1. $[3, 120°]$.   **2.** $[2, 240°]$.   **3.** $[-1, \frac{3}{2}\pi]$.   **4.** $[2, -\frac{1}{4}\pi]$.

Graph the equation.

5. $r = 3$.   **6.** $\theta = \frac{1}{4}\pi$.   **7.** $r = 2 \sin \theta$.   **8.** $r = -4 \cos \theta$.

9. $\tan \theta = -1$.   **10.** $\cos \theta = \frac{1}{2}$.   **11.** $r = 3 \cos 2\theta$.   **12.** $r = 2 \sin 3\theta$.

Find the corresponding rectangular coordinates for the point.

13. $[2, 30°]$.   **14.** $[1, \frac{5}{4}\pi]$.   **15.** $[2, \frac{11}{6}\pi]$.   **16.** $[-2, -\frac{3}{4}\pi]$.

Find two sets of polar coordinates for the point with the given rectangular coordinates.

17. $(-2, 2)$.   **18.** $(1, -\sqrt{3})$.   **19.** $(-4, -3)$.   **20.** $(-12, 5)$.

Transform the equation into rectangular coordinates, and then graph the equation. Rationalize if necessary.

21. $r = 16$.   **22.** $r \cos \theta = 2$.   **23.** $r \sin \theta = 6$.

24. $r = 4 \sin \theta$.   **25.** $2 \cos \theta = 1$.   **26.** $r = 2/(1 - \cos \theta)$.

Transform into polar coordinates.

27. $x^2 + y^2 = 4x$.   **28.** $x^2 + y^2 = -6y$.

79. Parametric equations related to polar coordinates

In an $r\theta$-system of polar coordinates, consider a curve $r = f(\theta)$. With the corresponding xy-system of rectangular coordinates, we have

$$x = r \cos \theta \quad and \quad y = r \sin \theta. \tag{1}$$

Then, the curve $r = f(\theta)$ is given in parametric form, with θ as the parameter, by substituting $r = f(\theta)$ in (1):

$$x = f(\theta)\cos \theta \quad and \quad y = f(\theta)\sin \theta. \tag{2}$$

EXAMPLE 1.   Graph the **cardioid** $r = 1 - \cos \theta.$ (3)

SOLUTION.   1. Since $\cos \theta$ has the period 2π, restrict θ to the range $0 \leq \theta \leq 2\pi$. From (2), parametric equations for the cardioid are

$$x = (1 - \cos \theta)\cos \theta \quad and \quad y = (1 - \cos \theta)\sin \theta. \tag{4}$$

From (4), $\dfrac{dx}{d\theta} = -\sin \theta + 2 \sin \theta \cos \theta = (\sin \theta)(2 \cos \theta - 1);$ (5)

$$\frac{dy}{d\theta} = \cos \theta - \cos^2 \theta + \sin^2 \theta = 1 + \cos \theta - 2 \cos^2 \theta, \text{ or}$$

$$\frac{dy}{d\theta} = (1 + 2 \cos \theta)(1 - \cos \theta); \tag{6}$$

$$\frac{dy}{dx} = \frac{(1 + 2 \cos \theta)(1 - \cos \theta)}{(2 \cos \theta - 1)\sin \theta}; \quad \frac{dx}{dy} = \frac{(2 \cos \theta - 1)\sin \theta}{(1 + 2 \cos \theta)(1 - \cos \theta)}. \tag{7}$$

2. *Horizontal and vertical tangents.* From (5), $dx/d\theta = 0$ when $\sin \theta = 0$ and when $\cos \theta = \frac{1}{2}$, or when $\theta = 0, \pi, 2\pi, \frac{1}{3}\pi$, and $\frac{5}{3}\pi$. From (6), $dy/d\theta = 0$ when $\cos \theta = 1$ and when $\cos \theta = -\frac{1}{2}$, or when $\theta = 0, 2\pi, \frac{2}{3}\pi$, and $\frac{4}{3}\pi$. Since $dx/d\theta = dy/d\theta = 0$ at $\theta = 0$ and $\theta = 2\pi$, special attention must be given to these values later. Then, from (7), dy/dx is defined (denominator $\neq 0$) and is equal to zero, and thus the tangent to (3) is horizontal, when $\theta = \frac{2}{3}\pi$ and $\frac{4}{3}\pi$. Also, dx/dy is defined and is equal to zero, and thus the tangent is vertical, when $\theta = \pi, \frac{1}{3}\pi$, and $\frac{5}{3}\pi$.

3. When $\theta = 0$ or $\theta = 2\pi$, from (3) we obtain $r = 0$. Hence, the line $\theta = 0$, or $\theta = 2\pi$, is tangent to the cardioid at the origin; there is a cusp with a horizontal tangent at $[0, 0]$.

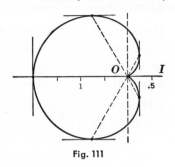

Fig. 111

4. We compute points from (3) with convenient values of θ, including the critical values from Step 2. The graph of (3) is in Figure 111.

The parametric form (2) may be used where the direction of a tangent is desired. "*Slope*" will relate to the xy-coordinate system.

EXAMPLE 2. Find the slope of the cardioid (3) where $\theta = \frac{5}{6}\pi$.

SOLUTION. We refer to (4), and obtain (5) and (6). From (7),

$$\text{(slope at } \theta = \tfrac{5}{6}\pi) = \frac{dy}{dx}\bigg|_{\theta = \frac{5}{6}\pi} = \frac{(1 - \sqrt{3})(1 + \frac{1}{2}\sqrt{3})}{(-\sqrt{3} - 1)(\frac{1}{2})} = 1.$$

EXAMPLE 3. Find the smallest positive angle, ψ, formed by the tangent and the radius vector at the point on (3) where $\theta = \frac{5}{6}\pi$.

SOLUTION. The slope of the radius vector at $P:[r, \theta]$ is $\tan \theta$. Hence, by (2) on page 65, with $m_1 = 1$ from Example 2, and $m_2 = \tan \frac{5}{6}\pi = -\frac{1}{3}\sqrt{3}$,

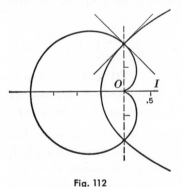

Fig. 112

$$\tan \psi = \left| \frac{-\frac{1}{3}\sqrt{3} - 1}{1 - \frac{1}{3}\sqrt{3}} \right| = 2 + \sqrt{3}.$$

From Table VI, we find $\psi = 75°$.

EXAMPLE 4. Find the angle of intersection of (3) and the parabola

$$r = \frac{1}{1 - \cos \theta}. \tag{8}$$

SOLUTION. 1. *Intersections.* Solve (3) and (8) simultaneously. In (3) and (8), r is a periodic function of θ, with the period 2π. Hence, restrict θ to the range $0 \le \theta < 2\pi$. From (3) and (8),

$(1 - \cos \theta)^2 = 1$ *or* $1 - \cos \theta = \pm 1$; $\cos \theta = 0$ *or* $\cos \theta = 2$.

Since $\cos \theta = 2$ is impossible, we have $\cos \theta = 0$, or $\theta = \frac{1}{2}\pi$ and $\theta = \frac{3}{2}\pi$ for intersections. If $\theta = \frac{1}{2}\pi$, then $r = 1$; if $\theta = \frac{3}{2}\pi$ then $r = 1$. Hence, the intersections are $[1, \frac{1}{2}\pi]$ and $[1, \frac{3}{2}\pi]$, as in Figure 112.

2. *Slopes at* $[1, \frac{1}{2}\pi]$. For the cardioid, from (7), the slope is $m_1 = -1$. For the parabola (8), the parametric form (2) becomes

$$x = \frac{\cos \theta}{1 - \cos \theta} \quad and \quad y = \frac{\sin \theta}{1 - \cos \theta}. \tag{9}$$

From (9),
$$\frac{dy}{dx} = \frac{1 - \cos\theta}{\sin\theta}.$$
(10)

Hence, with $\theta = \frac{1}{2}\pi$ in (10), the slope of the parabola is $m_2 = 1$. Thus, $m_1m_2 = -1$, and the tangents to the cardioid and parabola are perpendicular, or the curves intersect orthogonally. From symmetry, the same situation is met at the intersection $[1, \frac{3}{2}\pi]$.

★THEOREM I. *If ψ is the smallest positive angle made by the radius vector of a point $P:[r, \theta]$ on a curve $r = f(\theta)$, and the tangent to the curve at P, then*

$$\tan\psi = \left|\frac{r}{r'}\right|,$$
(11)

where $r' = dr/d\theta = f'(\theta)$.

Proof. 1. Let C be the curve $r = f(\theta)$. A parametric form for C is

$$x = r\cos\theta \quad and \quad y = r\sin\theta,$$
(12)

where we understand that $r = f(\theta)$. Then,

$$\frac{dx}{d\theta} = r'\cos\theta - r\sin\theta; \quad \frac{dy}{d\theta} = r'\sin\theta + r\cos\theta.$$

$\left\{\begin{array}{l}\textbf{Slope of tangent}\\ \textbf{to curve } r = f(\theta)\end{array}\right\}$ $\quad\dfrac{dy}{dx} = \dfrac{r'\sin\theta + r\cos\theta}{r'\cos\theta - r\sin\theta}.$ (13)

2. In Figure 113, the slope of the line OP is $\tan\theta$, or $\sin\theta/\cos\theta$. To find $\tan\psi$, we use

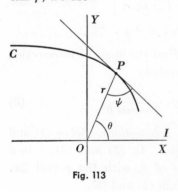

$$\tan\psi = \left|\frac{m_2 - m_1}{1 + m_1m_2}\right|,$$
(14)

with $m_1 = dy/dx$ from (13) and $m_2 = \tan\theta$. After elementary simplification, by use of $\sin^2\theta + \cos^2\theta = 1$, we obtain (11) from (14).

★*Note 1.* We could use (11) to solve Examples 3 and 4, and (13) to solve Example 2. Formula (13) is particularly useful if r is defined *implicitly* as a function of θ, instead of explicitly in the form $r = f(\theta)$.

Fig. 113

EXERCISE 45

Interpret r and θ as polar coordinates, with an associated xy-system of rectangular coordinates. "Slope" or "inclination" involves the xy-system.

Write parametric equations for the curve, find its slope at the specified point, and obtain the xy-equation of the tangent at the point.

1. $r = 6\cos\theta$; where $\theta = \frac{1}{4}\pi$.   2. $r = 4\sin\theta$; where $\theta = \frac{1}{3}\pi$.
3. $r = 2\cos 3\theta$; where $\theta = \frac{1}{3}\pi$.   4. $r = 3\sin 2\theta$; where $\theta = \frac{3}{4}\pi$.
5. $r = 2(1 - \cos\theta)$; where $\theta = \frac{2}{3}\pi$.   6. $r = 3(1 + \sin\theta)$; where $\theta = \pi$.

7. $r = \dfrac{4}{1 - \cos \theta}$; where $\theta = \tfrac{2}{3}\pi$.   8. $r = \dfrac{2}{1 + \sin \theta}$; where $\theta = \tfrac{1}{3}\pi$.

9. $r = \tan \theta$; where $\theta = \tfrac{3}{4}\pi$.   10. $r = \cot \theta$; where $\theta = \tfrac{1}{4}\pi$.

By use of calculus, applied to the corresponding parametric form, and by use of (3) on page 167, find the points on the curve where the tangent is horizontal or vertical and plot the curve.

11. $r = 3(1 + \cos \theta)$.   12. $r = 3(1 - \sin \theta)$.   13. $r = \tan \theta$.

Hint for Problem 13. If $\theta \to \tfrac{1}{2}\pi-$, we find $x \to 1$, $y \to +\infty$, and $D_x y \to +\infty$. Thus, the line $x = 1$ is a vertical asymptote. There is another asymptote. The graph is called a **kappa curve.**

14. $r = \dfrac{3}{1 + \sin \theta}$.   15. $r = \dfrac{6}{2 - \sin \theta}$.   16. $r = \dfrac{6}{3 - 2 \cos \theta}$.

17. $r = 2 - \cos \theta$.   18. $r = 2 + 4 \sin \theta$.   19. $r^2 = \cos \theta$.

Note 1. With $a \neq 0$ and $b \neq 0$, the graph of $r = a + b \cos \theta$, or of $r = a + b \sin \theta$, is called a **limaçon** (see Figure 13 in Table VIII). If $a = b$ then the limaçon becomes a cardioid. Problems 17–18 illustrate limaçons of two types which are not cardioids.

20. Find the inclination of the tangent to the **spiral of Archimedes,** $r = a\theta$, at the points where $\theta = 0$, $\tfrac{1}{2}\pi$, π, and $\tfrac{3}{2}\pi$. Also, plot the curve on the range $-2\pi \leq \theta \leq 2\pi$. See Figure 32 in Table VIII.

Comment. In graphing an equation such as $r = a\theta$ in polar coordinates, where θ occurs algebraically, it is customary to interpret any value of θ as the radian measure of an angle in the coordinate system.

Find the angle of intersection of the curves at each common point. If desired, use (13) on page 170 in finding slopes. Draw a figure showing the curves and each angle.

21. $r = 2 \cos 2\theta$ and $r = 1$.   22. $r^2 = 4 \cos 2\theta$ and $r = 2 \cos \theta$.

23. $r = 2(1 + \sin \theta)$ and $r = \dfrac{2}{1 + \sin \theta}$.

★80. Angular velocity and acceleration

Suppose that a particle P is moving in a plane. Let O be a fixed point, and set up an $r\theta$-system of polar coordinates with O as the pole and any directed ray radiating from O as the polar axis. At any instant, P has coordinates r and θ which are functions of the time, t; or $r = g(t)$ and $\theta = h(t)$, where we assume that g and h have continuous second derivatives. Then, the *time-rate of change of θ*, or $d\theta/dt$, is called the **angular velocity** of P with respect to O. If we let $\omega = d\theta/dt$, the time-rate of change of ω, or $d\omega/dt$, is called the **angular acceleration** of P with respect to O. Thus, ω is the time-rate of revolution of the radius vector OP about the pole, or ω can be called the *angular velocity of the radius vector to P*. At present, we shall refer to dr/dt merely as the time-rate of change of the radius vector of P, and we shall not use $\dfrac{d^2r}{dt^2}$ until later in the text.

Note 1. When we consider a particle P moving in an xy-plane, we imply use of the related polar coordinates $[r, \theta]$ in any reference to angular velocity or acceleration for P.

EXAMPLE 1. A particle P moves on the cardioid $r = a(1 - \cos \theta)$ with constant angular velocity, k radians per second. (*a*) Find the time-rate of change of the radius vector when $\theta = \frac{1}{4}\pi$. (*b*) Find v_x, v_y, and the speed when $\theta = \frac{1}{2}\pi$. Figure 111 on page 169 shows the nature of the path.

SOLUTION. 1. Since $d\theta/dt = k$,

$$\frac{dr}{dt} = \frac{dr}{d\theta} \cdot \frac{d\theta}{dt} = ak \sin \theta.$$

Hence, at $\theta = \frac{1}{4}\pi$, $dr/dt = \frac{1}{2}ak\sqrt{2}$ feet per second.

2. Parametric equations for the path are

$$x = a(1 - \cos \theta)\cos \theta \quad and \quad y = a(1 - \cos \theta)\sin \theta. \tag{1}$$

Hence, $\qquad v_x = \dfrac{dx}{dt} = \dfrac{dx}{d\theta} \cdot \dfrac{d\theta}{dt} = -ak(\sin \theta - 2 \sin \theta \cos \theta);$

$$v_y = ak(\cos \theta - \cos^2 \theta + \sin^2 \theta).$$

Or, $\qquad v_x = ak(\sin 2\theta - \sin \theta); \quad v_y = ak(\cos \theta - \cos 2\theta).$

By use of trigonometric identities, the student may verify that, with v as the speed, $a > 0$ and $k > 0$,

$$v^2 = v_x^2 + v_y^2 = 4a^2k^2 \sin^2 \tfrac{1}{2}\theta.$$

Thus, if $0 \leq \theta \leq 2\pi$ so that $\sin \frac{1}{2}\theta \geq 0$, we have $v = 2ak \sin \frac{1}{2}\theta$. If $\theta = \frac{1}{2}\pi$, then $v = ak\sqrt{2}$ feet per second.

★EXERCISE 46

A particle P moves on the given curve so that the radius vector of P revolves with constant angular velocity, k radians per second. Sketch the path. For the specified values of θ, (a) find v_x, v_y, a_x and a_y; (b) construct the velocity V and acceleration A; (c) compute dr/dt.

1. The circle $r = 4 \cos \theta$; at $\theta = 0$, $\frac{1}{8}\pi$, $\frac{1}{4}\pi$; $k = \frac{1}{2}$.

2. The three-leaved rose $r = 5 \sin 3\theta$; at $\theta = 0$, $\frac{1}{6}\pi$, and $\frac{1}{3}\pi$; $k = \frac{1}{4}$.

3. The cardioid $r = 2(1 + \sin \theta)$; at $\theta = \frac{1}{4}\pi$, $\frac{1}{2}\pi$, π; $k = \frac{1}{4}$.

4. The parabola $r = 4/(1 + \cos \theta)$, with the range $-\pi < \theta < \pi$; at $\theta = -\frac{1}{2}\pi$, 0, $\frac{1}{2}\pi$; $k = \frac{1}{4}$.

5. The limaçon $r = 3 + \cos \theta$; at $\theta = 0$, $\frac{1}{2}\pi$, π; $k = \frac{1}{10}$.

6. The limaçon $r = 1 - 2 \sin \theta$; at $\theta = 0$, $\frac{1}{6}\pi$, $\frac{1}{2}\pi$, $\frac{3}{2}\pi$; $k = \frac{1}{10}$.

EXERCISE 47

Review of Chapters 8 and 9

Differentiate the function, or find dy/dx from the equation.

1. $\sin^2 (3x^3 - x)$. **2.** $\sqrt{\tan 5x}$. **3.** Arctan $(\sin 2x)$.

4. $\cos (\ln x)$. **5.** $\sec e^{3x}$. **6.** $\cot (\frac{1}{2}x^3 + 4x)$.

7. Arcsin e^{2t}. **8.** $\csc^2 (x + 3)^3$. **9.** $e^{3x} \sin 4x$.

10. $\ln \sin^4 3z$. **11.** $e^{3 \cos 4x}$. **12.** $\sqrt{\sin^2 x + \cos x}$.

13. $x \sin \dfrac{3}{x}$. **14.** $\dfrac{5}{\cos 4x}$. **15.** $\dfrac{\ln t}{\sin t - 1}$.

16. $\log_{10} \sin x$. **17.** $\ln (\cos^3 x \sin^2 x)$. **18.** $\ln (3x^2 - 5)^5$.

19. $\sqrt{\ln (2z - 3)^2}$. **20.** $a^{5 \sin z}$. **21.** Arcsin $(\ln x^2)$.

22. $\sin y + \ln xy = 5$. **23.** $e^y + \ln x = y^2 - 5$.

24. Arccos $(e^{3x} - e^{-x})$. **25.** Arctan $(e^x + e^{-x})$.

26. $(x^3 + x^2) \ln 3x$. **27.** $(\sin 4z)$ Arcsin $2z$.

28. $\ln [\ln(3 \sin x)]^2$. **29.** $\tan (x + 2y) - \sin (x + y) = 4$.

30. $(\sin x)^{\tan x}$. **31.** $(\ln x)^{\cos x}$. **32.** $(e^x)^{e^x}$. **33.** $e^{\ln 6x}$.

34. $\sqrt[3]{3x - 5}(x^2 - 1)^6$. **35.** $\ln [(2x^2 + 5)^3(\sin 2x - 1)^5]$.

Find the second derivative of the function.

36. x Arctan $2x$. **37.** $[\ln (\ln x)]^2$. **38.** $e^{2x} \ln x$.

Find all extrema of the function. If trigonometric functions are involved, consider only the range $0 \leqq x < 2\pi$.

39. $y = 4 \cos x - \cos 2x$. **40.** $y = x \ln x$. **41.** $y = 5 \sin x - 12 \cos x$.

42. $y = x^3 \ln x$. **43.** $y = \ln \sin 2x$. **44.** $y = e^x + 4e^{-x}$.

45. A bomber is flying south at an elevation of 5000 yards, with a speed of 200 yards per second. The automatic bomb sight is focused on an enemy bridge south of the plane, and continuously measures the angle of depression, θ, of the bridge as seen from the bomber. Find the rate of change of θ when $\theta = 45°$, (a) without using an inverse function; (b) by use of an inverse function at the calculus stage.

46. Find the minimum value of $y = 3e^{4x} + 5e^{-4x}$.

Find the differential of the function.

47. $e^{-2x} \ln (\ln x)$. **48.** Arctan $(\ln \sin x)$. **49.** $10^{2x} \cot 3x$.

50. $\dfrac{\tan x}{e^{3x} + 1}$. **51.** $\dfrac{\ln \tan^3 x}{\cos x + 1}$. **52.** $\dfrac{e^{-2x} + 1}{\ln x^2}$.

53. A pyramid has a square base, whose side is measured as 90′, with essentially no error. The inclination of a side of the pyramid from the horizontal is measured as 60°, with an error not larger than 10′. By differentials, find approximately the maximum possible error in the volume of the pyramid as computed from the measurements.

54. The electromotive force E, in volts, which is necessary to produce a current of I amperes in a certain circuit with wire of diameter d inches is given by $E = .1137I/d^2$. For a given value of I, if d is measured with an error of at most 2%, and if E then is computed, find the maximum possible percentage error in E, approximately by use of differentials.

55. Find equations for the tangent and normal where $t = \frac{1}{4}\pi$ on the curve C defined parametrically by

$$x = 2 \sin t - 2t \cos t \quad and \quad y = 2 \cos t + 2t \sin t.$$

Also, find the sense of concavity of C where $t = \frac{1}{4}\pi$.

56. A curve C is defined by $x = 4 \cos^2 \theta$ and $y = 4 \cos \theta \sin \theta$, where θ is a parameter. Without eliminating θ, obtain the points on C where the tangent is horizontal or vertical, and plot C. Also, eliminate θ, to obtain an xy-equation for C.

57. A given radioactive substance decomposes at such a rate that, if h is the initial number of atoms of the substance and x is the number remaining at the end of t hours, then $x = he^{-.15t}$. Find the time-rate of change of x when $t = 5$. By use of differentials, find approximately the decrease in x when t increases from $t = 5$ to $t = 5.2$.

58. If an electrical circuit contains a resistance R and inductance L in series, and is connected across a steady voltage E, it can be proved that the current I satisfies $I = (E/R)(1 - e^{-RtL^{-1}})$, with proper units for E, L, R, I, and the time t. Find the time-rate of change of I.

59. In an $r\theta$-system of polar coordinates, find the slope of the parabola $r = 3/(1 - \cos \theta)$ where $\theta = \frac{1}{2}\pi$. Also, find the tangent of the acute angle between the parabola and the line $y = 3 + 2x$ where they intersect.

60. Find the tangent of the acute angle of intersection of the curves $r = 2(1 - \cos \theta)$ and $r = 2 \cos \theta$, in an $r\theta$-system of polar coordinates.

61. An ellipse C in an $r\theta$-system of polar coordinates has the equation $r = 12/(3 + \cos \theta)$. Write parametric equations for the corresponding variables (x, y) in terms of the parameter θ. Then, find all values of θ where C has a horizontal or vertical tangent.

62. Find the ratio of the altitude to the radius of the base in a conical tent of given capacity, which requires minimum material. Solve by the implicit function method of page 89, with the radius and a base angle in a cross section taken as variables.

63. A conical goblet has altitude h and generating angle α (half-angle at vertex), and is full of water. A sphere of radius r is lowered into the goblet. Find r, to cause the maximum overflow of water. [Recall that, in a sphere of radius r, the volume of a segment of one base with altitude y is $\frac{1}{3}\pi(3ry^2 - y^3)$].

64–66. Draw graphs of the equations in Problems 39, 43, and 44, respectively.

10

MEAN VALUE THEOREM

81. Law of the mean

The following result is needed for proving a later theorem.

THEOREM I. (**Rolle's theorem.**) *Suppose that the function $f(x)$ is continuous on an interval $T:(a \leq x \leq b)$, and has a derivative if $a < x < b$. Then, if $f(a) = 0$ and $f(b) = 0$, there exists at least one point $x = \xi$ **between** a and b such that $f'(\xi) = 0$.*

Geometric interpretation. In Figure 114, let the curve be the graph of $y = f(x)$. Theorem I states that, if the graph meets the x-axis at $x = a$ and $x = b$, and has a *nonvertical tangent* at all points *between* $x = a$ and $x = b$, then there is at least one point $x = \xi$ *between* a and b where the tangent is horizontal.

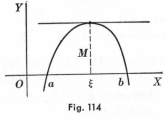

Fig. 114

Proof of Theorem I. 1. If $f(x) = 0$ at *all points* on the interval T, then $f'(x) = 0$ at all points on T, and hence Theorem I is true with ξ taken as any point between a and b.

2. Suppose, now, that $f(x) \neq 0$ at some point x_1 on T. Since $f(x)$ is continuous, it has an absolute maximum M and an absolute minimum m, where at least one of m and M is *not zero*, because $f(x_1) \neq 0$.

3. Consider the case $M \neq 0$, and let ξ be a value of x where $f(x) = M$. Certainly, $a < \xi < b$, because $f(a) = f(b) = 0$. Thus, $f(x)$ assumes its maximum M at the *interior* point $x = \xi$ of T. Hence, by Theorem II on page 69, $f'(\xi) = 0$. Similar remarks apply to prove Theorem I if $m \neq 0$.

ILLUSTRATION 1. Consider the graph of $y = \sin x$ in Figure 80, page 130. Then, $\sin x$ satisfies the hypotheses of Theorem I when $0 \leq x \leq 2\pi$, with $d(\sin x)/dx = \cos x$. Hence, Theorem I states that $\cos x$ has the value zero *at least once* between $x = 0$ and $x = 2\pi$. However, in this case, we have two points, $\xi = \frac{1}{2}\pi$ and $\xi = \frac{3}{2}\pi$, where $\cos x = 0$.

ILLUSTRATION 2. Figure 115 shows a graph of

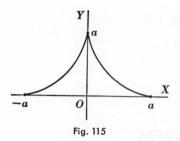

Fig. 115

$$y = \sqrt{(a^{\frac{2}{3}} - x^{\frac{2}{3}})^3}, \qquad (1)$$

where $y = 0$ at $x = a$ and at $x = -a$. There
is no value $x = \xi$ between $x = -a$ and $x = a$
where the slope of the graph is zero. This
does not contradict Theorem I, because its
hypothesis about the derivative is *not satisfied*
by y' for (1). That is, we notice that y' does
not exist at $x = 0$, where there is a vertical cusp.

ILLUSTRATION 3. Let a function $y = f(x)$ be defined by

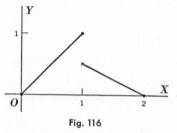

Fig. 116

$$\left. \begin{array}{l} f(x) = x \quad if \quad 0 \leqq x \leqq 1; \\ f(x) = 1 - \tfrac{1}{2}x \quad if \quad 1 < x \leqq 2. \end{array} \right\} \quad (2)$$

A graph of $y = f(x)$ is given in Figure 116.
We have $f(0) = f(2) = 0$. However, the hypotheses of Theorem I are violated by (2) in
two respects. First, $f(x)$ is *discontinuous* at
$x = 1$. Second, $f(x)$ *does not have a derivative*
at $x = 1$. Hence, we have no reason to expect that $f'(x) = 0$ at some point
between $x = 0$ and $x = 2$.

THEOREM II. (**Law of the mean.**) *Suppose that the function $f(x)$ is continuous for x on an interval $T:(a \leqq x \leqq b)$, and has a derivative if x is
between a and b. Then, there exists at least one point ξ **between** a and b
such that*

$$f(b) - f(a) = (b - a)f'(\xi). \qquad (a < \xi < b). \qquad (3)$$

Geometric interpretation. From (3), $\dfrac{f(b) - f(a)}{b - a} = f'(\xi). \qquad (4)$

Consider the graph of $y = f(x)$, in Figure 117. The fraction in (4) is the
slope of the chord RS through the points $[a, f(a)]$ and $[b, f(b)]$ on the
graph. Then, in geometrical termi-
nology, Theorem II is as follows:

*If $f(x)$ is continuous on $a \leqq x \leqq b$,
and if the graph of $y = f(x)$ has a
nonvertical tangent at each point x
between a and b, then there exists at
least one point ξ between a and b
where the corresponding tangent to the
graph is parallel to the chord through
the points where $x = a$ and $x = b$.*

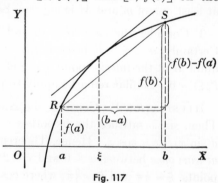

Fig. 117

Thus, with any *secant* of the graph playing the role occupied by the x-axis in Theorem I, the geometrical significance of Theorem II is the same as that of Theorem I.

Proof of Theorem II. Consider the function

$$\phi(x) = \frac{f(b) - f(a)}{b - a}(x - a) + f(a) - f(x). \tag{5}$$

On substituting $x = a$, and then $x \sim b$ in (5), we verify that $\phi(a) = 0$ and $\phi(b) = 0$. Also, from (5),

$$\phi'(x) = \frac{f(b) - f(a)}{b - a} - f'(x), \tag{6}$$

which exists if $a < x < b$. Thus, $\phi(x)$ satisfies the hypotheses of Theorem I. Hence, there exists a point $x = \xi$ between a and b such that

$$\phi'(\xi) = 0, \quad or \quad \frac{f(b) - f(a)}{b - a} - f'(\xi) = 0,$$

which proves (3).

Note 1. If ξ is between a and b, then $\xi = a + \theta(b - a)$, where $0 < \theta < 1$. Then, Theorem II states that there is a number θ such that $0 < \theta < 1$ and

$$f(b) - f(a) = (b - a)f'[a + \theta(b - a)]. \tag{7}$$

ILLUSTRATION 4. Let the curve RBS in Figure 118 be the graph of a certain function $y = f(x)$. At the corner point B, where $x = c$, there is no tangent to the curve $y = f(x)$, and hence $f'(c)$ does not exist. Thus, the hypothesis in Theorem II about the derivative is not satisfied. Hence, we have no reason to expect a point $x = \xi$ between a and b where the tangent is parallel to the secant RS.

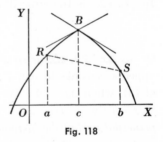

Fig. 118

The following theorem will be very useful.

THEOREM III. *Assume that $\phi(x)$ and $F(x)$ are continuous on $a \leq x \leq b$, and have derivatives if $a < x < b$, where $\phi'(x) = F'(x)$. Then, there exists a constant C such that $\phi(x) = F(x) + C$ when $a \leq x \leq b$.*

Proof. Let $G(x) = \phi(x) - F(x)$. Then, $G(x)$ is continuous on $a \leq x \leq b$, and has a derivative $G'(x) = \phi'(x) - F'(x) = 0$ when $a < x < b$. Hence, by the law of the mean, if x is on $a < x \leq b$, and ξ is chosen properly,

$$G(x) - G(a) = (x - a)G'(\xi) = 0; \quad or, \quad G(x) = G(a)$$

at all values of x, because $G'(\xi) = 0$. That is,

$$\phi(x) - F(x) = G(a), \quad or \quad \phi(x) = F(x) + G(a),$$

which proves Theorem III with $C = G(a)$.

EXAMPLE 1. If $f(x) = x^2 - 6x + 7$, with $a = 2$ and $b = 5$, obtain all values of ξ satisfying (3).

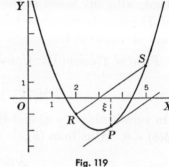

Fig. 119

SOLUTION. $\dfrac{f(5) - f(2)}{3} = \dfrac{2 + 1}{3} = 1.$

Since $f'(x) = 2x - 6$, equation (3) becomes

$$2\xi - 6 = 1 \quad or \quad \xi = \tfrac{7}{2}.$$

We verify that $f'(\tfrac{7}{2}) = 1$, which is the slope of the graph of $y = f(x)$ at P where $x = \tfrac{7}{2}$, in Figure 119, and is equal to the slope of RS.

★82. Analytic motivation for differentials

Consider a function $f(x)$ which possesses a derivative, $f'(a)$, at $x = a$. Let $\Delta f = f(a + \Delta x) - f(a)$. Then,

$$\lim_{\Delta x \to 0} \frac{\Delta f}{\Delta x} = f'(a). \tag{1}$$

Let $\epsilon = \dfrac{\Delta f}{\Delta x} - f'(a). \tag{2}$

From (1) and (2), $\epsilon \to 0$ as $\Delta x \to 0$. By use of (2),

$$\Delta f = f'(a)\Delta x + \epsilon \Delta x. \tag{3}$$

In (3), $\epsilon \Delta x$ is the *error* if we take $f'(a)\Delta x$ as an approximation to Δf. Also,

$$\lim_{\Delta x \to 0} \frac{\epsilon \Delta x}{\Delta x} = \lim_{\Delta x \to 0} \epsilon = 0.$$

Or, as $\Delta x \to 0$, $\epsilon \Delta x$ is *so small relative to Δx that* $[(\epsilon \Delta x)/\Delta x] \to 0$. Hence, it appears sensible to call $f'(a)\Delta x$ the **principal part** of the right-hand side of (3), when $\Delta x \to 0$. We recognize that $f'(a)\Delta x$ is the expression for $df(x)$ at $x = a$, with $dx = \Delta x$. Thus, we are led to the differential of $f(x)$ as *the principal part of the increment Δf*, when $\Delta x \to 0$. Notice that (3) is obtained if (4) on page 176 is used with $b = a + \Delta x$ and $f'(\xi) = f'(a) + \epsilon$.

★*Note 1.* Consider a function $g(v)$ which is defined when v is near $v = 0$, except possibly at the point $v = 0$. If $\lim_{v \to 0} g(v) = 0$, sometimes it is said that $g(v)$ is an **infinitesimal,** relative to v as the *independent infinitesimal.* If $[g(v)/v] \to 0$ as $v \to 0$, then we say that $g(v)$ is an infinitesimal of *higher order* than v. If $[g(v)/v] \to L \neq 0$ as $v \to 0$, we say that $g(v)$ is an infinitesimal of the *same order* as v. In (3), when $\Delta x \to 0$, if $f'(a) \neq 0$ then $f'(a)\Delta x$ is an infinitesimal of the same order as Δx, and $\epsilon \Delta x$ is of higher order, because

$$\lim_{\Delta x \to 0} \frac{f'(a)\Delta x}{\Delta x} = f'(a) \quad and \quad \lim_{\Delta x \to 0} \frac{\epsilon \Delta x}{\Delta x} = \lim_{\Delta x \to 0} \epsilon = 0.$$

Hence, we refer to $f'(a)\Delta x$ as the *principal infinitesimal* on the right in (3), while the error $(\Delta f - df)$, or $\epsilon \Delta x$, is an infinitesimal of *higher order* than Δx.

EXERCISE 48

With the specified values for a and b, find explicitly all values of ξ satisfying statement (3) of page 176 for the law of the mean (including Rolle's theorem as a special case). Exhibit the secant corresponding to a and b, and the tangent at $x = \xi$ with a graph of $f(x)$.

1. $f(x) = 15 - 8x + x^2$; $a = 3$ and $b = 5$.
2. $f(x) = \cos x$; $a = \frac{1}{2}\pi$ and $b = \frac{5}{2}\pi$.
3. $y = x^2 - 4x + 7$; $a = 0$ and $b = 2$.
4. $y = 6x - x^2 + 4$; $a = 3$ and $b = 5$.

Graph the function $f(x)$ defined by the formula, or formulas. With the specified values of a and b, state which hypothesis, or hypotheses, of the law of the mean are not satisfied on the interval (a, b).

5. $f(x) = |x|$; $a = -3$ and $b = 2$.
6. $f(x) = \tan x$; $a = 0$ and $b = \frac{3}{4}\pi$.
7. $f(x) = 1$ when $0 \leqq x \leqq 2$ and $f(x) = 2$ when $2 < x \leqq 4$; $a = 0$ and $b = 3$.
8. $f(x) = -x$ when $x \leqq 0$ and $f(x) = 3x$ when $x > 0$; $a = -2$ and $b = 1$.
9. $f(x) = (x - 2)^{\frac{2}{3}}$; $a = 1$ and $b = 4$.

10. Write the formula of the law of the mean with $a = 0$ and $b = x$.

Note 1. An efficient routine, called Newton's method, for solving an equation $f(x) = 0$ of general type, can be motivated by the law of the mean. The method is presented on page 569 of the Appendix, with an associated exercise, which would be appropriate for treatment at this point in the course.

83. Limits of fractions

In a fraction $F(t) = \psi(t)/\phi(t)$, suppose that $\phi(t) \to L$ and $\psi(t) \to M$ as $t \to a$, where we allow L, M, and a to be finite or $\pm \infty$. When a is finite, we do not demand that $\phi(t)$ and $\psi(t)$ be defined at $t = a$. However, in such a case, if $\phi(t)$ and $\psi(t)$ are continuous at $t = a$ then $L = \phi(a)$ and $M = \psi(a)$. Suppose that we do *not* have $L = M = 0$, or $L = \pm \infty$ and $M = \pm \infty$. Then, the fundamental theorem on the limit of a quotient (*L and M finite, and $L \neq 0$*) or simple direct reasoning immediately specifies a limit, finite or infinite, for $F(t)$ or for $|F(t)|$.

ILLUSTRATION 1. Consider $$\lim_{x \to 0+} \frac{\ln x}{\sin x}. \tag{1}$$

Recall that $\sin x \to 0+$ (or, $\sin x$ approaches zero through positive values) when $x \to 0+$. Also, $\ln x \to -\infty$ when $x \to 0+$, as recalled from the graph of $y = \ln x$ on page 145. Since the denominator in (1) decreases and is positive, while the numerator becomes negatively infinite,

$$\lim_{x \to 0+} \frac{\ln x}{\sin x} = -\infty.$$

If $L = M = 0$, we say that $\psi(t)/\phi(t)$ tends to the (**indeterminate**) **form 0/0,** where this symbol has *no meaning except as an abbreviation for the facts that* $\phi(t) \to 0$ *and* $\psi(t) \to 0$. Similarly, if $L = \pm \infty$ and $M = \pm \infty$, we say that $\psi(t)/\phi(t)$ tends to the (**indeterminate**) **form** * ∞/∞, read "*infinity over infinity*." For either of these cases, in the next section we shall find that $\psi(t)/\phi(t)$ may have a limit, finite or infinite, as $t \to a$.

Note 1. If $\phi(t)$ and $\psi(t)$ are defined and continuous at $t = a$, and $\psi(t)/\phi(t)$ tends to the form $0/0$ as $t \to a$, then $\phi(a) = \psi(a) = 0$. In this case, $\psi(t)/\phi(t)$ assumes the meaningless form $0/0$ at $t = a$.

84. L'Hospital's rule

The following result is due to the French mathematician GUILLAUME FRANÇOIS ANTOINE L'HOSPITAL, 1661–1704.

THEOREM IV. (**L'Hospital's rule.**) *Suppose that* $\phi(t)$ *and* $\psi(t)$ *are differentiable on some interval* $T:(c < t < a)$, *or* $T:(a < t < c)$, *where* a *is finite. Assume that* $\phi(t) \neq 0$ *and* $\phi'(t) \neq 0$ *on* T, *and* †

$$\phi(t) \to 0 \quad and \quad \psi(t) \to 0 \quad as \quad t \to a, \tag{1}$$

or that $$\phi(t) \to \pm \infty \quad and \quad \psi(t) \to \pm \infty \quad as \quad t \to a. \tag{2}$$

Then, as $t \to a$, *if* $\psi'(t)/\phi'(t)$ *has a limit, finite or infinite, the fraction* $\psi(t)/\phi(t)$ *also has a limit and*

$$\lim_{t \to a} \frac{\psi(t)}{\phi(t)} = \lim_{t \to a} \frac{\psi'(t)}{\phi'(t)}. \tag{3}$$

EXAMPLE 1. Evaluate: $$\lim_{t \to 2} \frac{\ln(t-1)}{t-2}. \tag{4}$$

SOLUTION. As $t \to 2$, we have

$$\ln(t-1) \to \ln 1 = 0; \quad (t-2) \to 0.$$

Hence, the fraction in (4) tends to the form $0/0$ and (3) applies:

$$\lim_{t \to 2} \frac{\ln(t-1)}{t-2} = \lim_{t \to 2} \frac{\dfrac{1}{t-1}}{1} = 1.$$

Note 1. Geometrical interpretation of a special case of L'Hospital's rule under assumption (1). Let T be the interval $a < t < c$. Extend $\phi(t)$ and $\psi(t)$ of Theorem IV by specifying $\phi(a) = \psi(a) = 0$. In an xy-plane, let W be the curve defined parametrically by

$$x = \phi(t) \quad and \quad y = \psi(t), \tag{5}$$

---

* In our notations for indeterminate forms, we shall not use any sign, $\pm$, with the symbol ∞. We take care of signs in the details of calculation.
† We interpret "$t \to a$" as $t \to a+$ or $t \to a-$ according as $t = a$ is at the left-hand or right-hand end of the interval T. If the hypotheses hold on both sides of a, then in (3) we imply the usual meaning for "$t \to a$."

with $a \leq t < c$. Since $\phi(a) = \psi(a) = 0$, W goes through the origin when $t = a$, as in Figure 120. From (5), if $t > a$, at the corresponding point $P:(x, y)$ on W, there is a tangent PT where

$$\text{(slope of tangent } PT) = \frac{dy}{dx} = \frac{\psi'(t)}{\phi'(t)}.$$

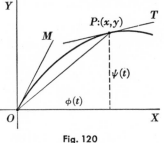

Fig. 120

In Figure 120, $\quad$ (slope of $OP) = \dfrac{\psi(t)}{\phi(t)}.$

Then, (3) states that, if the slope of the tangent PT has a limit λ, the slope of the chord OP has the same limit, which would be the slope of the tangent OM to the curve (5) in Figure 120.

On page 565 of the Appendix, Theorem IV is discussed not only for the case where $t = a$ is a finite value, but also when "a" is replaced by $+ \infty$ or $- \infty$. In (2), the hypothesis "$\psi(t) \to \pm \infty$" is redundant, but will be satisfied usually wherever (3) is to be used with $\phi(t) \to \pm \infty$ as $t \to a$.

Note 2. In applying (3), if it is found that $\psi'(t)/\phi'(t)$ tends to a form $0/0$ or ∞/∞ as $t \to a$, then we reapply L'Hospital's rule to $\psi'(t)/\phi'(t)$, and investigate $\psi''(t)/\phi''(t)$, provided that the derivatives satisfy proper hypotheses. Thus, we may be led to any number of successive applications of (3); it is possible to meet an endless sequence of indeterminate forms, and thus reach no conclusion about the limit. We may summarize (3) in the following working rule.

To evaluate $\lim_{t \to a} [\psi(t)/\phi(t)]$, if it tends to the form $0/0$ or ∞/∞, differentiate the numerator for a new numerator, and the denominator for a new denominator, and obtain the limit of the new fraction as $t \to a$.

EXAMPLE 2. Evaluate: $\qquad\qquad\qquad \lim\limits_{x \to 0} \dfrac{1 - \cos x}{\sin x}.$

SOLUTION. *Test of form.* As $x \to 0$, $(1 - \cos x) \to 0$ and $\sin x \to 0$; thus the fraction tends to the form $0/0$. By use of (3),

$$\lim_{x \to 0} \frac{1 - \cos x}{\sin x} = \lim_{x \to 0} \frac{\sin x}{\cos x} = \frac{0}{1} = 0.$$

EXAMPLE 3. Evaluate: $\qquad\qquad\qquad \lim\limits_{x \to +\infty} \dfrac{x^3}{e^{2x}}.$

SOLUTION. The fraction tends to the form ∞/∞, because

$$\lim_{x \to +\infty} x^3 = +\infty; \qquad \lim_{x \to +\infty} e^{2x} = +\infty.$$

Hence, by (3), $\qquad\qquad \lim\limits_{x \to +\infty} \dfrac{x^3}{e^{2x}} = \lim\limits_{x \to +\infty} \dfrac{3x^2}{2e^{2x}};$ $\qquad\qquad$ (form, ∞/∞)

[applying (3) twice] $\qquad = \lim\limits_{x \to +\infty} \dfrac{6x}{4e^{2x}} = \lim\limits_{x \to +\infty} \dfrac{6}{8e^{2x}} = 0.$

After any application of (3), before evaluating the limit, *we are at liberty to simplify the new fraction*, and *to perform any legitimate transformations*, for instance, trigonometric transformations.

ILLUSTRATION 1. After one application of (3) to the following case where the form ∞/∞ arises, we obtain

$$\lim_{x\to 0+}\frac{\ln x}{x^{-\frac{1}{2}}} = \lim_{x\to 0+}\frac{\dfrac{1}{x}}{-\frac{1}{2}x^{-\frac{3}{2}}} = \lim_{x\to 0+}(-2x^{\frac{1}{2}}) = 0. \tag{6}$$

Notice that, if we had not simplified algebraically in (6), an endless sequence of fruitless steps would have arisen, because each new fraction would tend to the form ∞/∞, as follows:

$$\lim_{x\to 0+}\frac{\dfrac{1}{x}}{-\frac{1}{2}x^{-\frac{3}{2}}} = \lim_{x\to 0+}\frac{-\dfrac{1}{x^2}}{+\frac{3}{4}x^{-\frac{5}{2}}} = \lim_{x\to 0+}\frac{\dfrac{2}{x^3}}{-\frac{15}{8}x^{-\frac{7}{2}}} = etc.$$

EXAMPLE 4. Evaluate: $\displaystyle\lim_{\theta\to\frac{1}{2}\pi}\frac{\tan 3\theta}{\tan \theta}$.

SOLUTION. The fraction tends to the form ∞/∞. We apply (3).

$$\lim_{\theta\to\frac{1}{2}\pi}\frac{\tan 3\theta}{\tan \theta} = \lim_{\theta\to\frac{1}{2}\pi}\frac{3\sec^2 3\theta}{\sec^2 \theta}; \qquad \left(use\ \sec \alpha = \frac{1}{\cos \alpha}\right)$$

$$= \lim_{\theta\to\frac{1}{2}\pi}\frac{3\cos^2 \theta}{\cos^2 3\theta}; \qquad\qquad (form,\ 0/0)$$

$$= \lim_{\theta\to\frac{1}{2}\pi}\frac{6\sin \theta \cos \theta}{6\sin 3\theta \cos 3\theta} = \lim_{\theta\to\frac{1}{2}\pi}\frac{\sin 2\theta}{\sin 6\theta}, \tag{7}$$

where we used the identity $\sin 2\alpha = 2\sin \alpha \cos \alpha$ in both numerator and denominator. In (7), we arrive at the form $0/0$. From (7),

$$\lim_{\theta\to\frac{1}{2}\pi}\frac{\tan 3\theta}{\tan \theta} = \lim_{\theta\to\frac{1}{2}\pi}\frac{2\cos 2\theta}{6\cos 6\theta} = \frac{\cos \pi}{3\cos 3\pi} = \frac{1}{3}.$$

EXERCISE 49

Evaluate the limit by inspection, if it exists. L'Hospital's rule is not involved.

1. $\displaystyle\lim_{\theta\to\frac{1}{2}\pi}\frac{\sin 2\theta}{\sin \theta}$.

2. $\displaystyle\lim_{x\to 0-}\frac{\sec x}{x}$.

3. $\displaystyle\lim_{x\to 0+}\frac{\sec x}{x}$.

4. $\displaystyle\lim_{x\to\infty}\frac{e^{-(1/x)}}{x}$.

5. $\displaystyle\lim_{x\to\infty}\frac{\sin x}{x}$.

6. $\displaystyle\lim_{x\to 0+}\frac{\ln x}{x}$.

Evaluate the limit. Use L'Hospital's rule **if it applies.**

7. $\displaystyle\lim_{t\to 0}\frac{1-\cos 2t}{t-1}$.

8. $\displaystyle\lim_{x\to -3}\frac{x^2-9}{x-3}$.

9. $\displaystyle\lim_{x\to 0}\frac{\tan x}{x}$.

10. $\displaystyle\lim_{x\to 1}\frac{\ln x}{x-1}$.

11. $\displaystyle\lim_{x\to\frac{1}{2}\pi}\frac{1-\sin x}{x-\frac{1}{2}\pi}$.

12. $\displaystyle\lim_{\theta\to\frac{1}{4}\pi}\frac{\tan \theta-1}{\theta-\frac{1}{4}\pi}$.

13. $\lim\limits_{x \to 1} \dfrac{\ln (2x - 1)}{1 - x^2}$.

14. $\lim\limits_{x \to 0} \dfrac{\sin x}{e^x - e^{-x}}$.

15. $\lim\limits_{x \to 0-} \dfrac{x^2}{\sin x - x}$.

16. $\lim\limits_{x \to 0+} \dfrac{x}{\sin^2 x}$.

17. $\lim\limits_{x \to 0-} \dfrac{x}{\sin^2 x}$.

18. $\lim\limits_{x \to 0+} \dfrac{x^2}{\sin x - x}$.

19. $\lim\limits_{x \to \infty} \dfrac{x - 2x^3}{x^2}$.

20. $\lim\limits_{x \to \infty} \dfrac{x^2}{e^x}$.

21. $\lim\limits_{x \to \infty} \dfrac{x}{\ln x}$.

22. $\lim\limits_{x \to \infty} \dfrac{e^x}{x^3}$.

23. $\lim\limits_{x \to \infty} \dfrac{\ln x}{x^3}$.

24. $\lim\limits_{x \to \infty} \dfrac{e^x}{\ln x}$.

25. $\lim\limits_{x \to 0} \dfrac{e^x + e^{-x} - 2}{\cos x - 1}$.

26. $\lim\limits_{x \to 0} \dfrac{2^x - 3^x}{x}$.

27. $\lim\limits_{|x| \to \infty} \dfrac{x^4 + 3}{2x^4 - 5x}$.

28. $\lim\limits_{x \to \frac{1}{2}\pi+} \dfrac{\sin 2x}{\sin x - 1}$.

29. $\lim\limits_{x \to 0} \dfrac{1 + \csc x}{\cot x}$.

30. $\lim\limits_{x \to \infty} \dfrac{e^{-x}}{x^8}$.

31. $\lim\limits_{x \to 0} \dfrac{x - \sin x}{2x^3}$.

32. $\lim\limits_{x \to \infty} \dfrac{(\ln x)^2}{x}$.

33. $\lim\limits_{x \to 0+} \dfrac{\cot x}{\ln x}$.

34. $\lim\limits_{x \to 0} \dfrac{\sin 3x}{\sin 2x}$.

35. $\lim\limits_{x \to 0} \dfrac{\tan x}{\tan 2x}$.

36. $\lim\limits_{x \to \infty} \dfrac{\tan x}{x}$.

37. $\lim\limits_{x \to 0} \dfrac{\csc^2 2x}{\csc^2 x}$.

38. $\lim\limits_{x \to 0} \dfrac{\cot 3x}{\cot x}$.

HINT for Problem 37. Sines are more convenient than cosecants.

39. $\lim\limits_{x \to 0+} \dfrac{\ln \sin x}{\ln \sin 2x}$.

40. $\lim\limits_{x \to \frac{1}{2}\pi+} \dfrac{\cot^2 (x - \frac{1}{2}\pi)}{x - \frac{1}{2}\pi}$.

41. $\lim\limits_{\theta \to \frac{1}{2}\pi-} \dfrac{\ln \tan \theta}{e^{\sec^2 \theta}}$.

42. $\lim\limits_{x \to 0} \dfrac{x \sin x}{1 - \cos x}$.

43. $\lim\limits_{x \to 0} \dfrac{\sin 3x}{\ln (1 - x)}$.

44. $\lim\limits_{\theta \to 0} \dfrac{\sin^2 \theta}{\sin \theta^2}$.

45. $\lim\limits_{x \to 0} \dfrac{e^x \tan x}{x}$.

46. $\lim\limits_{x \to 0} \dfrac{\tan 2x}{x \sec x}$.

47. $\lim\limits_{x \to 0} \dfrac{\ln \cos x}{\sin^2 x}$.

48. $\lim\limits_{x \to 1} \dfrac{\tan \pi x}{x - 1}$.

49. $\lim\limits_{x \to 0} \dfrac{\text{Arcsin } 2x}{\text{Arcsin } 3x}$.

50. $\lim\limits_{x \to 0} \dfrac{\ln (1 + x)}{\cot x}$.

51. $\lim\limits_{x \to 0+} \dfrac{\ln x}{10^x}$.

52. $\lim\limits_{x \to +\infty} \dfrac{\sin (1/x)}{\ln x}$.

53. $\lim\limits_{\theta \to \frac{1}{2}\pi} \dfrac{\tan 5\theta}{\tan \theta}$.

54. $\lim\limits_{x \to 0} \dfrac{\sin x - x}{x^3}$.

55. $\lim\limits_{x \to \infty} \dfrac{(\ln x)^2}{e^x}$.

56. $\lim\limits_{x \to 0-} \dfrac{\tan x}{\sec x - 1}$.

57. $\lim\limits_{x \to -\infty} \dfrac{\text{Arctan } x + \frac{1}{2}\pi}{\sin (1/x)}$.

58. $\lim\limits_{x \to \infty} \dfrac{\sin e^{-x}}{\sin (1/x)}$.

59. Prove that $\lim_{x \to \infty} (x^n / e^x) = 0$, if n is any real number. That is, prove that e^x grows large faster than any power of x, as $x \to \infty$.

60. Evaluate $\lim_{x \to \infty} [(\ln x)/x^n]$, for any real number n.

61. Prove that $(\tan x - x)$ differs from $\frac{1}{3}x^3$ by as small a percentage of $\frac{1}{3}x^3$ as we please, if $|x|$ is sufficiently small. That is, prove that

$$\lim\limits_{x \to 0} \frac{\tan x - x}{\frac{1}{3}x^3}$$

exists, and has the proper value. Explain why it is proper.

85. Limits of products and sums

If $\phi(t) \to +\infty$ and $\psi(t) \to -\infty$ as $t \to a$, we say that $[\phi(t) + \psi(t)]$ tends to the (**indeterminate**) **form** $(\infty - \infty)$ as $t \to a$. If $\phi(t) \to \pm\infty$ and $\psi(t) \to 0$ as $t \to a$, we say that $\phi(t)\psi(t)$ tends to the (**indeterminate**) **form** $0 \cdot \infty$ as $t \to a$.

In order to evaluate the limit of a product or sum which tends to the form $0 \cdot \infty$ or $(\infty - \infty)$, we try to rewrite the given expression as a fraction, which may tend to the form $0/0$ or ∞/∞. Then, we apply L'Hospital's rule to the fraction.

EXAMPLE 1. Evaluate: $\qquad\qquad \lim\limits_{x \to 0+} (\csc x - \cot x)$.

SOLUTION. *Test of form:* as $x \to 0+$, $\csc x \to +\infty$ and $\cot x \to +\infty$. Hence, $(\csc x - \cot x)$ tends to the form $(\infty - \infty)$. We obtain

$$\lim_{x \to 0+} (\csc x - \cot x) = \lim_{x \to 0+} \left(\frac{1}{\sin x} - \frac{\cos x}{\sin x} \right)$$

$$= \lim_{x \to 0+} \frac{1 - \cos x}{\sin x}; \qquad\qquad (form,\ 0/0)$$

$$= \lim_{x \to 0+} \frac{\sin x}{\cos x} = \frac{0}{1} = 0. \qquad (apply\ L'Hospital's\ rule)$$

Comment. Similarly, the limit as $x \to 0-$ also is found to be 0. Hence, $\lim_{x \to 0} (\csc x - \cot x) = 0$, with "$x \to 0$" indicating the *unrestricted, two-sided limit* as usual.

EXAMPLE 2. Evaluate: $\qquad\qquad \lim\limits_{x \to 0} x^2 \cot x$.

SOLUTION. The expression tends to the form $0 \cdot \infty$. Then,

$$\lim_{x \to 0} x^2 \cot x = \lim_{x \to 0} \frac{x^2}{\tan x} \qquad\qquad (form,\ 0/0)$$

$$= \lim_{x \to 0} \frac{2x}{\sec^2 x} = \frac{0}{1} = 0. \qquad (by\ L'Hospital's\ rule)$$

EXAMPLE 3. Evaluate: $\qquad\qquad \lim\limits_{x \to \infty} x \tan \frac{1}{x}$.

SOLUTION. The expression tends to the form $\infty \cdot 0$. Then,

$$\lim_{x \to \infty} x \tan \frac{1}{x} = \lim_{x \to \infty} \frac{\tan \dfrac{1}{x}}{\dfrac{1}{x}} \qquad\qquad (form,\ 0/0)$$

(because sec 0 = 1) $\qquad = \lim\limits_{x \to \infty} \dfrac{-\left(\sec^2 \dfrac{1}{x} \right) \dfrac{1}{x^2}}{-\dfrac{1}{x^2}} = \lim\limits_{x \to \infty} \sec^2 \dfrac{1}{x} = 1.$

86. Limits of exponential forms

If $b > 0$, recall that $$b = e^{\ln b}. \qquad (1)$$

Then, if h is any real number, $(e^{\ln b})^h = e^{h \ln b}$ and

$$b^h = e^{h \ln b}. \qquad (2)$$

If $b \neq 0$, then $b^0 = 1$, by definition. However, we have mentioned on page 45 that 0^0 is not defined, and hence has *no meaning as a number*. Also, if h is an irrational number, we do not define the symbol b^h when $b < 0$.

Now, consider functions $\phi(t)$ and $\psi(t)$, where $\phi(t) > 0$, and let

$$W(t) = \phi(t)^{\psi(t)}; \quad \text{then} \quad \ln W(t) = \psi(t) \ln \phi(t). \qquad (3)$$

If $\phi(t) \to 0+$ and $\psi(t) \to 0$ as $t \to a$, then $W(t)$ tends to the form 0^0, and $\ln W(t)$ tends to the form $0 \cdot \infty$, because $\ln \phi(t) \to -\infty$ when $\phi(t) \to 0+$. If $\phi(t) \to 1$ and $\psi(t) \to \pm\infty$, then $W(t)$ tends to the form 1^∞ as $t \to a$, and again $\ln W(t)$ tends to the form $0 \cdot \infty$. If $\phi(t) \to +\infty$ and $\psi(t) \to 0$, then $W(t)$ tends to the form ∞^0, and again $\ln W(t)$ tends to the form $0 \cdot \infty$. Thus, we refer to 0^0, 1^∞, and ∞^0 as *indeterminate forms* because the corresponding logarithms tend to the form $0 \cdot \infty$, and special investigation is demanded in evaluating any particular case of $\lim_{t \to a} W(t)$.

Note 1. From (1), $W(t) = e^{\ln W(t)}$. Suppose that $\ln W(t) \to L$ as $t \to a$, where L is finite. Then, since e^x is continuous at $x = L$,

$$\lim_{t \to a} e^{\ln W(t)} = e^{\lim_{t \to a} \ln W(t)} = e^L, \qquad (4)$$

or there exists $$\lim_{t \to a} W(t) = e^L. \qquad (5)$$

From (3) and (5), we are led to the following procedure.

To evaluate $\lim_{t \to a} W(t)$ where $W(t) = \phi(t)^{\psi(t)}$ and $W(t)$ tends to one of the forms 0^0, 1^∞, and ∞^0 as $t \to a$, first calculate $\ln W(t)$. Then, evaluate $\lim_{t \to a} \ln W(t) = L$, and use (5).

EXAMPLE 1. Evaluate: $$\lim_{x \to \frac{1}{2}\pi} (\sin x)^{\tan x}.$$

SOLUTION. 1. The expression tends to the form 1^∞.

2. Let $W(x) = (\sin x)^{\tan x}$. Then, $\ln W(x) = \tan x \ln \sin x$.

As $x \to \frac{1}{2}\pi$, $\ln W(x)$ tends to the form $\infty \cdot 0$, because $\sin x \to 1$, and $\ln 1 = 0$.

$$\lim_{x \to \frac{1}{2}\pi} \ln W(x) = \lim_{x \to \frac{1}{2}\pi} \frac{\ln \sin x}{\cot x} \qquad (\textit{form, } 0/0)$$

$$= \lim_{x \to \frac{1}{2}\pi} -\frac{\frac{\cos x}{\sin x}}{\csc^2 x} = \lim_{x \to \frac{1}{2}\pi} -\cos x \sin x = 0. \qquad (\textit{by L'Hospital's rule})$$

Hence, $$\lim_{x \to \frac{1}{2}\pi} W(x) = e^{\lim_{x \to \frac{1}{2}\pi} \ln W(x)} = e^0 = 1.$$

Note 2. In (5), let us understand that, if $L = +\infty$ then e^L is replaced by $+\infty$; if $L = -\infty$ then e^L is replaced by 0.

EXAMPLE 2. Evaluate: $\lim\limits_{x\to 0+} (\sin x)^x.$

SOLUTION. 1. The form involved is 0^0. Let $W(x) = (\sin x)^x$. Then,

$$\ln W(x) = x \ln \sin x,$$

which tends to the form $0\cdot\infty$ as $x \to 0+$.

2. By L'Hospital's rule, $\lim\limits_{x\to 0+} \ln W(x) = \lim\limits_{x\to 0+} \dfrac{\ln \sin x}{\dfrac{1}{x}}$ (*form,* ∞/∞)

$$= \lim_{x\to 0+} \frac{\dfrac{\cos x}{\sin x}}{-x^{-2}} = \lim_{x\to 0+} -\frac{x^2 \cos x}{\sin x} \qquad (\textit{form, } 0/0)$$

$$= -\lim_{x\to 0+} \frac{2x \cos x - x^2 \sin x}{\cos x} = \frac{0}{1} = 0.$$

Hence, $\lim\limits_{x\to 0+} W(x) = e^{\lim_{x\to 0} \ln W(x)} = e^0 = 1.$

EXAMPLE 3. Evaluate: $\lim\limits_{t\to 0} (1 + 3t)^{\frac{1}{t}}.$

SOLUTION. 1. The form involved is 1^∞. Let $W(t) = (1 + 3t)^{\frac{1}{t}}$. Then,

$$\ln W(t) = \frac{\ln (1 + 3t)}{t},$$

which tends to the form $0/0$ as $t \to 0$.

2. By L'Hospital's rule, $\lim\limits_{t\to 0} \ln W(t) = \lim\limits_{t\to 0} \dfrac{\dfrac{3}{1 + 3t}}{1} = 3.$

Hence, $\lim\limits_{t\to 0} W(t) = e^3.$

MISCELLANEOUS EXERCISE 50

Evaluate the limit, by use of L'Hospital's rule when desirable.

1. $\lim\limits_{x\to\infty} xe^{-x}.$

2. $\lim\limits_{x\to 0} \csc 2x.$

3. $\lim\limits_{x\to 0} x \cot x.$

4. $\lim\limits_{x\to 0+} x \ln x.$

5. $\lim\limits_{x\to 0+} x^3 \ln x.$

6. $\lim\limits_{x\to -\infty} x^2 e^x.$

7. $\lim\limits_{x\to \frac{1}{2}\pi} (\pi - 2x) \sec x.$

8. $\lim\limits_{x\to 0+} (\sin x)\ln \sin x.$

9. $\lim\limits_{x\to 0} (\csc x)\ln (1 + \sin x).$

10. $\lim\limits_{x\to\infty} x \sin 2x^{-1}.$

11. $\lim\limits_{x\to \frac{1}{2}\pi} (\sec x - \tan x).$

12. $\lim\limits_{x\to 1} \left(\dfrac{1}{\ln x} - \dfrac{x}{x - 1} \right).$

13. $\lim\limits_{x\to 1} \left(\dfrac{x}{\ln x} - \dfrac{1}{x-1}\right).$

14. $\lim\limits_{x\to 0} \left(\dfrac{1}{x\tan x} - \dfrac{1}{x^2}\right).$

15. $\lim\limits_{x\to 0+} \left(\dfrac{1}{e^x - 1} - \dfrac{2}{x}\right).$

16. $\lim\limits_{h\to\infty} \left(1 + \dfrac{1}{2h}\right)^{3h}.$

17. $\lim\limits_{x\to 0} (1 + 4x)^{\frac{3}{x}}.$

18. $\lim\limits_{x\to 0} (\sec x)^{\frac{1}{x}}.$

19. $\lim\limits_{x\to\frac{1}{2}\pi} (\sin^2 x)^{\tan x}.$

20. $\lim\limits_{x\to\infty} (1 + x)^{\frac{4}{x}}.$

21. $\lim\limits_{x\to 0} (x + e^{2x})^{-\frac{2}{x}}.$

22. $\lim\limits_{x\to 0+} x^x.$

23. $\lim\limits_{x\to\frac{1}{2}\pi} (1 + 2\cot x)^{\tan x}.$

24. $\lim\limits_{x\to\frac{1}{2}\pi-} (\cos x)^{\cos x}.$

25. $\lim\limits_{x\to\infty} e^{-x} \tan \dfrac{1}{x}.$

26. $\lim\limits_{x\to\infty} x \tan \dfrac{a}{x}.$

27. $\lim\limits_{x\to\infty} \left(\cos \dfrac{1}{x}\right)^x.$

28. $\lim\limits_{x\to\frac{1}{2}\pi-} (\cos x)^{\tan x}.$

29. $\lim\limits_{x\to 1} x^{\tan \frac{1}{2}\pi x}.$

30. $\lim\limits_{x\to\frac{1}{2}\pi} (\sin x)^{4\tan^2 x}.$

31. $\lim\limits_{x\to 0} (\csc 2x)\text{Arcsin } x.$

32. $\lim\limits_{x\to\frac{1}{2}\pi} (x - \tfrac{1}{2}\pi)\tan x.$

33. $\lim\limits_{x\to 0} x(\sin x^{-1}).$

34. $\lim\limits_{x\to\frac{1}{2}\pi} (\csc^2 x)^{-\tan^2 x}.$

35. $\lim\limits_{\theta\to\frac{1}{2}\pi+} e^{-\tan\theta} \sec\theta.$

36. $\lim\limits_{t\to\frac{1}{4}\pi} (1 - \cot t)\tan 2t.$

37. $\lim\limits_{x\to 0} (\csc x)\ln (1 + 2x).$

38. $\lim\limits_{x\to 0+} (\text{Arctan } x^{-1} - \tfrac{1}{2}\pi)\csc 2x.$

39. $\lim\limits_{t\to\frac{1}{2}\pi-} (\sec^3 t - \tan^3 t).$

40. $\lim\limits_{\theta\to\frac{1}{2}\pi} \left(\dfrac{1}{1 - \sin\theta} - \dfrac{2}{\cos^2\theta}\right).$

41. $\lim\limits_{\theta\to\alpha} \dfrac{\tan\theta - \tan\alpha}{\theta - \alpha}.$

42. $\lim\limits_{x\to 0} \dfrac{\cos x - 1 + \frac{1}{2}x^2}{\sin^2 x}.$

43. $\lim\limits_{x\to 0} \dfrac{\tan x - x}{x^3}.$

44. $\lim\limits_{x\to 0-} \dfrac{\sin x - 1}{\tan^3 x}.$

45. $\lim\limits_{x\to 0-} \dfrac{\ln (1 + x)}{e^x - 1 - x}.$

46. $\lim\limits_{x\to 0} (\sin x + \cos x)^{\frac{3}{x}}.$

47. $\lim\limits_{x\to 0} (1 - \tan x)^{3\cot x}.$

48. $\lim\limits_{x\to 0} \left(\dfrac{1}{x^2} - \dfrac{1}{x\sin x}\right).$

49. $\lim\limits_{x\to 0+} \left(\ln x - \dfrac{1}{x}\right).$

50. $\lim\limits_{x\to 0} \left(\dfrac{1}{\text{Arctan } x} - \dfrac{1}{x}\right).$

51. $\lim\limits_{x\to\infty} \dfrac{\sin e^{-x}}{\sin x^{-2}}.$

Graph the equation. Investigate asymptotes of the form $y = k$, where k is a constant, by evaluating $\lim_{x\to\infty} y$ and $\lim_{x\to-\infty} y$. Obtain extrema and inflection points wherever the derivatives are convenient.

52. $y = x^2 e^x.$ **53.** $y = xe^{-x^2}.$ **54.** $y = e^{-\frac{1}{x}}.$ **55.** $y = xe^{-\frac{1}{x}}.$

HINT for Problems 54–55. Define y at $x = 0$ as $\lim_{x\to 0+} y$, and also investigate $\lim_{x\to 0-} y$.

56. Graph the equation $y = x \sin x^{-1}$, with the value of y at $x = 0$ defined by $y = \lim_{x\to 0} x \sin x^{-1}$. Show that there is a horizontal asymptote. Instead of finding all extrema, prove that the graph is tangent to the lines $y = x$ and $y = -x$, and there is no extremum if $|x| > 2/\pi$.

11

INTRODUCTION TO DEFINITE INTEGRALS

87. Orientation for the definite integral

Calculus deals primarily with two fundamental concepts, the notion of a *derivative*, with which we have been concerned up to this point, and the notion of a *definite integral*, which we proceed to introduce. We emphasize that the definite integral of a function is defined independently of the notion of a derivative.

88. Summation notation

To abbreviate a sum like $u_1 + u_2 + \cdots + u_n$, we write

$$\sum_{i=1}^{n} u_i, \quad or \quad \sum_{i=1}^{n} u_i,$$

which is read *"the sum of u_i for $i = 1$ to $i = n$."* We refer to Greek sigma, $\sum$, as the *sign of summation*, and call i the *index of summation*. The letter used for the index of summation is immaterial.

ILLUSTRATION 1. $\quad \sum_{i=1}^{5} a_i = a_1 + a_2 + a_3 + a_4 + a_5 = \sum_{k=1}^{5} a_k.$

ILLUSTRATION 2. A common factor of each term of a summation may be removed and placed before the summation sign:

$$\sum_{i=1}^{4} kf(\xi_i) = kf(\xi_1) + kf(\xi_2) + kf(\xi_3) + kf(\xi_4) = k \sum_{i=1}^{4} f(\xi_i).$$

89. The definite integral

On an x-axis, consider all numbers x such that $a \leq x \leq b$, to be called *the interval (a, b)*. Let (a, b) be divided into n subintervals $\{T_i\}$ by the points $x_0, x_1, x_2, \cdots, x_{n-1}, x_n$, where

$$a = x_0 < x_1 < x_2 < \cdots < x_{i-1} < x_i < \cdots < x_{n-1} < x_n = b, \qquad (1)$$

as indicated in Figure 121. We shall refer to this subdivision as a **partition** of (a, b), and shall denote such a partition by P.

The ith subinterval, T_i, of P consists of the values of x where

$$x_{i-1} \leqq x \leqq x_i; \quad length = \Delta_i x = x_i - x_{i-1}. \tag{2}$$

Let d_P be the maximum of the lengths $\Delta_i x$, and call d_P the **norm** of P. Thus, if d_P is small, all $\Delta_i x$ are small. We read "d_P" as "d sub P," and "$\Delta_i x$" as "*delta i of x*."

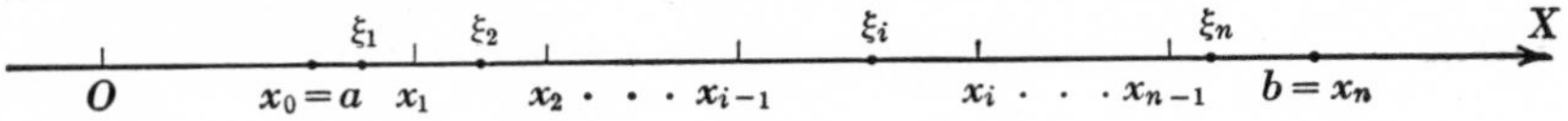

Fig. 121

ILLUSTRATION 1. If the interval $2 \leqq x \leqq 8$ is divided into 18 equal parts by a partition P, as in (1), then $n = 18$ and $d_P = \frac{6}{18} = \frac{1}{3}$.

Let $f(x)$ be defined on an interval (a, b). Let P be any partition (1) of (a, b), and select arbitrarily a point ξ_i on the ith subinterval, T_i, for $i = 1, 2, 3, \cdots, n$, as in Figure 121. For each value of i, form the product $f(\xi_i)\Delta_i x$, and denote the sum of these products by S_P:

$$S_P = f(\xi_1)\Delta_1 x + f(\xi_2)\Delta_2 x + \cdots + f(\xi_n)\Delta_n x = \sum_{i=1}^{n} f(\xi_i)\Delta_i x. \tag{3}$$

ILLUSTRATION 2. Let $f(x) = 1 + x^2$, and restrict x to satisfy $0 \leqq x \leqq 2$. Subdivide this interval by the points

$$(Partition\ P) \qquad\qquad 0 < \tfrac{1}{2} < 1 < \tfrac{3}{2} < 2, \tag{4}$$

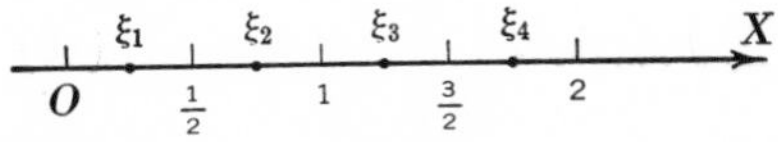

Fig. 122

as in Figure 122. On the ith subinterval in (4), let ξ_i be the mid-point, to give $\xi_1 = \frac{1}{4}$, $\xi_2 = \frac{3}{4}$, $\xi_3 = \frac{5}{4}$, and $\xi_4 = \frac{7}{4}$. Then, $\Delta_i x = \frac{1}{2}$ and

$$f(\xi_i)\Delta_i x = f(\xi_i) \cdot \tfrac{1}{2}, \tag{5}$$

$$f(\xi_1) = 1 + (\tfrac{1}{4})^2; \qquad f(\xi_2) = 1 + (\tfrac{3}{4})^2; \qquad f(\xi_3) = 1 + (\tfrac{5}{4})^2; \qquad f(\xi_4) = 1 + (\tfrac{7}{4})^2;$$

$$f(\xi_1)\Delta_1 x = \tfrac{17}{16} \cdot \tfrac{1}{2}; \qquad\qquad f(\xi_2)\Delta_2 x = \tfrac{25}{16} \cdot \tfrac{1}{2}; \qquad\qquad f(\xi_3)\Delta_3 x = \tfrac{41}{16} \cdot \tfrac{1}{2}; \quad etc.$$

$$S_P = \frac{17}{32} + \frac{25}{32} + \frac{41}{32} + \frac{65}{32} = \frac{37}{8} = 4.625. \tag{6}$$

With P as in (4), the smallest value of S_P of (3) is obtained if we choose ξ_i as the left-hand end-point of the ith subinterval, because then $f(\xi_i)$ is the minimum of $f(x)$ on this subinterval. Let $\underline{S}_P$ be the corresponding least value of S_P; we find $\underline{S}_P = \frac{15}{4}$. The greatest value, $\overline{S}_P$, of S_P for (4) is obtained if ξ_i is chosen as the right-hand end-point of the ith subinterval, and we find $\overline{S}_P = \frac{23}{4}$. In place of (4), let P be the partition obtained by dividing the interval $(0, 2)$ into 8 equal parts:

$$(Partition\ P) \qquad 0 < \tfrac{1}{4} < \tfrac{1}{2} < \tfrac{3}{4} < 1 < \tfrac{5}{4} < \tfrac{3}{2} < \tfrac{7}{4} < 2. \tag{7}$$

Then, with each ξ_i as the mid-point of its subinterval, we obtain $S_P = 4.656$.

Sums of the form (3) occur frequently in applications. Numerical experimentation, as in Illustration 2, convinces us that, under favorable circumstances, S_P of (3) will approach some limiting value if $d_P \to 0$. Hence, we are led to introduce terminology about limits for sums of the type S_P.*

DEFINITION I.   *To say that S_P has a limit L as $d_P \to 0$ means that S_P is as near L as we please for all partitions P where d_P is sufficiently small. Then, we write*

$$S_P \to L \text{ as } d_P \to 0, \quad \text{or} \quad \lim_{d_P \to 0} S_P = L. \tag{8}$$

Note 1.   Instead of saying "*as $d_P \to 0$*" in (8), we could say "*as the lengths of all subintervals of P approach zero,*" because d_P is the maximum of these lengths. Also, if $d_P \to 0$, the number of subintervals in P becomes infinite. However, a statement merely that $n \to \infty$ in (1) would *not* imply that all $\Delta_i x \to 0$. For instance, x_1 might remain fixed in (1) while $n \to \infty$, and then we would not have $d_P \to 0$.

DEFINITION II.   *Let P be any partition of the interval (a, b), as in (1), and let ξ_i be selected arbitrarily on the ith subinterval, T_i, of P. Let $S_P = \sum_{i=1}^{n} f(\xi_i)\Delta_i x$, where $\Delta_i x$ is the length of T_i. Then, if S_P approaches a limit as $d_P \to 0$, we call this limit "the **integral** of $f(x)$ from a to b," denoted by $\int_a^b f(x)dx$:*

$$\int_a^b f(x)dx = \lim_{d_P \to 0} S_P, \text{ or} \tag{9}$$

$$\int_a^b f(x)dx = \lim_{(as \text{ all } \Delta_i x \to 0)} \sum_{i=1}^{n} f(\xi_i)\Delta_i x. \tag{10}$$

ILLUSTRATION 3.   If $f(x) \geq 0$ at all values of x, then $f(\xi_i) \geq 0$, every $S_P \geq 0$, and hence $\int_a^b f(x)dx \geq 0$. Similarly, if $f(x) \leq 0$ at all values of x, then the integral is negative or zero.

In (9), we call a and b the **limits of integration,** $f(x)$ the **integrand,** and x the **variable of integration.** We refer to S_P in (3) as an **approximating finite sum** for the integral in (9). A term like $f(\xi_i)\Delta_i x$ is called an **element** of such a sum. Observe that $\int_a^b f(x)dx$ does not depend on x, but represents that number which is the limit of S_P as $d_P \to 0$. Thus, *the letter used for the variable of integration is immaterial.* For instance,

$$\int_a^b f(x)dx = \int_a^b f(t)dt = \int_a^b f(z)dz = \text{ etc.}$$

Sometimes, the variable in the integrand is called a *dummy variable.*

If the limit in (9) exists, we say that $f(x)$ is *integrable* over (a, b). The following theorem, stating a condition for integrability, harmonizes with our

---

* For any value of d_P, there exist infinitely many values for S_P, or S_P is an infinitely many-valued function of d_P.

intuitions, as developed by numerical work such as we met in Illustration 2. We shall use the theorem without proof.*

THEOREM I. *If $f(x)$ is continuous on the interval (a, b), then $f(x)$ is integrable on (a, b), or $\int_a^b f(x)\,dx$ exists.*

The operation of computing an integral is referred to as **integration.** Later, we shall call $\int_a^b f(x)dx$ a **definite integral,** instead of simply an *integral*, whenever there is danger of confusing it with another type of expression which then will be called an *indefinite integral*. Then the computation of a definite integral may be called **definite integration.**

ILLUSTRATION 4. Recall the sum S_P of (6) on page 189. We note that $S_P = 4.625$ is an approximating sum for $\int_0^2 (1 + x^2)dx$. From (7) on page 189, another approximating sum for this integral is $S_P = 4.656$.

Let $\{P_k\}$, $k = 1, 2, \cdots$, be any infinite sequence of partitions where P_k has the norm d_k, and $d_k \to 0$ as $k \to \infty$. Let σ_k represent S_P when P is P_k. Then, from Definition I and (9), σ_k will be as near $\int_a^b f(x)dx$ as we please if k is *so large* that d_k is *sufficiently small*, or

$$\lim_{k \to \infty} \sigma_k = \int_a^b f(x)dx. \tag{11}$$

Thus, the integral is equal to *the limit of any sequence of approximating sums,* $\{\sigma_k\}$, *for which the norm $d_k \to 0$ as $k \to \infty$.*

ILLUSTRATION 5. Consider $\int_0^2 (1 + x^2)dx$, and refer to Illustration 2. Let P_k be the partition of $(0, 2)$ obtained on dividing the interval into 2^k equal parts. Then P_2 is (4) on page 189, P_3 is (7) on page 189, $\sigma_2 = 4.625$, $\sigma_3 = 4.656$, and (11) shows that

$$\sigma_k \to \int_0^2 (1 + x^2)dx \quad as \quad k \to \infty. \tag{12}$$

By later methods, the exact value of the integral in (12) is found to be 4.667, to three decimal places. Hence, σ_3 is in error by only .011.

EXERCISE 51

For the specified integrand, compute S_P of (3) on page 189 accurately to three significant digits, when P has the given number of equal subintervals, and ξ_i is the indicated point of the ith subinterval of P.

1. $\int_0^2 \left(1 + \frac{1}{2}x^2\right)dx$; P has 4 intervals; ξ_i as the mid-point.

2. $\int_0^2 \left(1 + \frac{1}{2}x^2\right)dx$; P has 8 intervals; (a) ξ_i as the mid-point; (b) ξ_i as the left-hand end-point; (c) ξ_i as the right-hand end-point.

* For a proof, see texts on functions of real variables.

3. $\int_{-1}^{1} (4 - x^2)dx$; P has 6 intervals; ξ_i as the mid-point.

4. $\int_{0}^{3} \dfrac{dx}{1 + x}$; P has 9 intervals; ξ_i as the mid-point.

5. $\int_{1}^{6} \dfrac{dx}{x}$; P has 10 intervals; ξ_i as the mid-point.

Comment. Compare the result in Problem 5 with ln 6 from Table III. Later, we shall find that ln 6 is the exact value of the integral.

6. $\int_{-1}^{2} x^3\, dx$; P has 6 intervals; ξ_i as the mid-point.

★90. Computation of integrals as limits

The exact values of certain integrals can be found directly from the definition of an integral. However, the details involved are complicated even with simple integrands. The following examples emphasize the need for developing some other means for computing integrals.

EXAMPLE 1. With $a < b$, obtain $\int_{a}^{b} k\, dx$, where k is a constant.

SOLUTION. In (3) on page 189, for any partition P, $f(\xi_i) = k$ and

$$S_P = \sum_{i=1}^{n} f(\xi_i)\Delta_i x = \sum_{i=1}^{n} k\Delta_i x = k \sum_{i=1}^{n} \Delta_i x = k(b - a);$$

$$\int_{a}^{b} k\, dx = \lim_{d_P \to 0} S_P = \lim_{d_P \to 0} k(b - a) = k(b - a).$$

EXAMPLE 2. With $a < b$, obtain $\int_{a}^{b} x\, dx$.

SOLUTION. Let P_n be the partition obtained if (a, b) is divided into n equal parts. On the ith subinterval of P_n, let ξ_i be the right-hand end-point. Let $h = (b - a)/n$. Then, in P_n, $\Delta_i x = h$ for all values of i. In (3) of page 189 with $f(x) = x$, let σ_n represent S_P when P is P_n, and let d_n be the norm of P_n.

Then, $\xi_1 = a + h, \quad \xi_2 = a + 2h, \cdots, \quad \xi_n = a + nh = b;$ (1)

$$\sigma_n = (a + h)h + (a + 2h)h + \cdots + (a + nh)h$$

$$= nah + h^2(1 + 2 + \cdots + n); \tag{2}$$

$\left(\text{using } h = \dfrac{b - a}{n}\right)$ $\sigma_n = ab - a^2 + \dfrac{(b - a)^2}{n^2} \cdot \dfrac{n(n + 1)}{2},$ (3)

where we used formula (4) of page 435 for an arithmetic progression. Since the function $f(x) = x$ is continuous, the desired integral exists. Hence, from (11) on page 190, since $\lim_{n \to \infty} d_n = 0$,

$$\int_{a}^{b} x\, dx = \lim_{n \to \infty} \sigma_n = ab - a^2 + \frac{(b - a)^2}{2}\left[\lim_{n \to \infty} \frac{n(n + 1)}{n^2}\right]$$

$$= ab - a^2 + \frac{(b - a)^2}{2} \cdot 1 = \tfrac{1}{2}(b^2 - a^2).$$

★EXERCISE 52

Obtain the exact value of each integral by evaluating the limit (11) on page 191.

1. $\int_0^5 2x \, dx.$ **2.** $\int_0^3 (2 + 3x)dx.$

3. $\int_0^b 3x^2 \, dx.$ **4.** $\int_0^x t^3 \, dt.$ **5.** $\int_a^b e^x \, dx.$

HINTS. In Problems 3 and 4, recall that

$$1^2 + 2^2 + \cdots + n^2 = \tfrac{1}{6}n(n + 1)(2n + 1); \quad 1^3 + 2^3 + \cdots + n^3 = \tfrac{1}{4}n^2(n + 1)^2.$$

In Problem 5, recall the sum of a geometric progression, page 435.

91. Areas of simple regions

The notion of the area of a plane figure is intuitively apparent, but requires careful definition. The following introduction will cover all cases to be met at present. Our most general definition will occur in the chapter on double integrals.

In a plane, let C be a closed curve which does not cross itself, as in Figure 123. Then, the points of the plane *inside or on C* will be referred to as a **region** of points. We shall call C the **boundary** of the region. If C is a familiar named *curve*, such as a circle, an ellipse, or a rectangle, sometimes we shall use its name to refer *also to the region* which has the curve as the boundary, when the context prevents ambiguity.

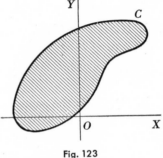

Fig. 123

We commence our introduction of the notion of area by *defining the area of any rectangle*, with dimensions h and k linear units, *to be hk "square units"*; we call hk the *measure of this area*. Then, for any region R, we agree that the area of R will be defined as the limit of the sum of the areas of a finite number of associated rectangles, which do not overlap except at boundaries,

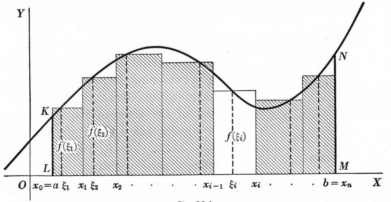

Fig. 124

as the number of rectangles becomes infinite in some fashion. Also, if a set of points S in a plane consists of a finite number of regions which overlap at most in boundary points, we define the area of S as the sum of the areas of the specified regions.

Consider the region R with the boundary $KLMN$ in Figure 124, page 193, bounded by the x-axis, the lines $x = a$ and $x = b$, and a curve $y = f(x)$, where $f(x)$ is continuous and $f(x) \geq 0$. Let a single unit be used for measuring all distances in the xy-plane. Then, our definition of the area of R is as follows:

1. *Take any partition P of the interval (a, b), as in Section 89. On the ith sub-interval, $x_{i-1} \leq x \leq x_i$, whose length is $\Delta_i x$, choose arbitrarily a point ξ_i. Construct a rectangle, as in Figure 124, with base $\Delta_i x = x_i - x_{i-1}$ and altitude $f(\xi_i)$. Then, the area * of this rectangle is $f(\xi_i)\Delta_i x$. Let S_P be the sum of the areas of the rectangles just described. That is, let*

$$S_P = \sum_{i=1}^{n} f(\xi_i)\Delta_i x. \tag{1}$$

2. *If S_P has a limit, A, when the norm, d_P, of P approaches zero, we define the area of R as A area units:*

$$A = \lim_{(as\ all\ \Delta_i x \to 0)} \sum_{i=1}^{n} f(\xi_i)\Delta_i x. \tag{2}$$

In (1), S_P is the same as S_P in (3) on page 189. Also, since $f(x)$ is continuous, $\int_a^b f(x)dx$ exists. Hence, our definition of the area A can be abbreviated as follows:

$$\left\{ \begin{array}{l} area\ of\ region\ bounded\ by\ x = a,\ x = b, \\ x\text{-}axis,\ and\ curve\ y = f(x);\ f(x) \geq 0 \end{array} \right\} \qquad A = \int_a^b f(x)dx. \tag{3}$$

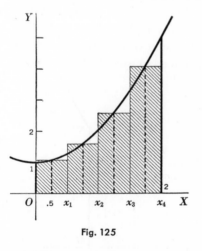

Fig. 125

ILLUSTRATION 1. In Figure 125, R is bounded by the x-axis, the curve $y = 1 + x^2$, and the lines $x = 0$ and $x = 2$. From (3),

$$(area\ of\ R) = A = \int_0^2 (1 + x^2)dx. \tag{4}$$

We approximated A in Illustration 2 on page 189. When P is the partition with division points $0, \frac{1}{2}, 1, \frac{3}{2},$ and 2, and each ξ_i is chosen as the mid-point of the corresponding subinterval, then S_P of (1) is the sum of the areas of the ruled rectangles in Figure 125. From (6) on page 189, $S_P = 4.625$. The figure was drawn with a reduced vertical unit.

In this text, we agree that the area, A, of any region R will be defined as

* Hereafter, the single word "*area*" will abbreviate "*measure of the area.*"

positive or zero. Thus, if $f(x) \leq 0$ when $a \leq x \leq b$, we define the area, A, of the region R described in (3) by the equation *

$$[f(x) \leq 0] \qquad\qquad A = - \int_a^b f(x)dx. \qquad\qquad (5)$$

Note 1. For a region of the type in (3), we have defined the concept of *area* as a *definite integral.* Later, we shall define many other quantities as definite integrals; for instance, the *volume* of a region in space, the *work* done by a force, the *probability* of an event, in mathematical statistics, etc.

EXERCISE 53

Compute the approximating sum S_P of (1) on page 194, for the area of the region bounded by the x-axis and the curve $y = f(x)$, between the specified values of x. Use the mid-point of any interval T_i as ξ_i and let the partition P consist of, first, four equal intervals and, second, eight equal intervals. Draw a figure.

1. $f(x) = 2x - x^2$, between $x = 0$ and $x = 2$.
2. $f(x) = 4/x$, between $x = 2$ and $x = 6$.
3. $f(x) = (x+1)(x-3)$, between $x = -1$ and $x = 3$.

92. Properties of integrals

In the definition of $\int_a^b f(x)dx$, we assumed that $a < b$. If $b < a$, or if $b = a$, we employ the following definitions.

If $b < a$; $\qquad\qquad \int_a^b f(x)dx = - \int_b^a f(x)dx. \qquad\qquad (1)$

Equal limits of integration: $\qquad\qquad \int_a^a f(x)dx = 0. \qquad\qquad (2)$

ILLUSTRATION 1. $\qquad \int_3^1 f(x)dx = - \int_1^3 f(x)dx.$

Hereafter, in any integral, we shall assume that the integrand is a continuous function, unless otherwise stated. Then, by Theorem I, the integral will exist. Also, we observe that the fundamental theorems on limits, from page 19, could be restated for limits of the type "$S_P \to L$ *as* $d_P \to 0$." In the proofs of the following properties, for convenience we shall assume usually that the lower limit of integration is less than the upper limit in any integral. The properties are true for other limits of integration because of (1) and (2).

THEOREM II. *If k is any constant,* $\qquad \int_a^b kf(x)dx = k\int_a^b f(x)dx.$

Proof. With usual notation, from (10) on page 190,

$$\int_a^b kf(x)dx = \lim_{d_P \to 0} \sum_{i=1}^n kf(\xi_i)\Delta_i x = \lim_{d_P \to 0} k \sum_{i=1}^n f(\xi_i)\Delta_i x = k\int_a^b f(x)dx.$$

---

* In some texts, for the case in (5), A is defined by (3), which would imply that $A < 0$ if R is below the x-axis.

Theorem III. $\int_a^b [f(x) + g(x)]dx = \int_a^b f(x)dx + \int_a^b g(x)dx.$

Proof. From (10) on page 190,

$$\int_a^b [f(x) + g(x)]dx = \lim_{d_p \to 0} \sum_{i=1}^n [f(\xi_i) + g(\xi_i)]\Delta_i x$$

$$= \lim_{d_p \to 0} \sum_{i=1}^n f(\xi_i)\Delta_i x + \lim_{d_p \to 0} \sum_{i=1}^n g(\xi_i)\Delta_i x = \int_a^b f(x)dx + \int_a^b g(x)dx. \qquad (3)$$

Theorem IV. *For any a, b, c on an interval where f(x) is continuous,*

$$\int_a^b f(x)dx + \int_b^c f(x)dx = \int_a^c f(x)dx. \qquad (4)$$

Comment. A formal proof of (4) would involve consideration of corresponding partitions of the intervals (a, b), (b, c), and (a, c). We shall omit the details. With $a < b < c$ and $f(x) \geq 0$, if each integral in (4) is interpreted as an *area*, then (4) becomes evident as a statement that the sum of the areas from a to b, and from b to c, is equal to the area from a to c. Suppose that (4) has been proved if $a < b < c$. Then, to prove (4) when $a < c < b$, we first apply (4) with (a, c, b) replacing (a, b, c), and use (1):

$$\int_a^b f(x)dx = \int_a^c f(x)dx + \int_c^b f(x)dx = \int_a^c f(x)dx - \int_b^c f(x)dx.$$

On transposing the last term above to the left, we obtain (4). Similarly, (4) could be proved for any order of a, b, and c on the number scale.

Theorem V. *Suppose that f(x) is continuous and a < b. Let M be the absolute maximum and m be the absolute minimum of f(x) on (a, b). Then*

$$m(b - a) \leq \int_a^b f(x)dx \leq M(b - a). \qquad (5)$$

Comment. Let $\int_a^b f(x)dx$ be interpreted as an area in Figure 126, for the case where $f(x) \geq 0$. Then, (5) is equivalent to the geometric fact that the area of the region bounded by the lines $x = a$, and $x = b$, the x-axis, and the curve $y = f(x)$ lies between the area of the small rectangle with height m and the large rectangle with height M, in Figure 126. A formal proof of (5) is suggested in a later exercise.

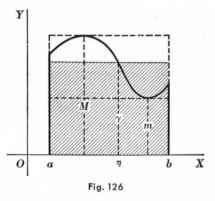

Fig. 126

Theorem VI. (**Mean Value Theorem for Integrals.**) *If f(x) is continuous when x is on (a, b), there exists a number η on (a, b) such that*

$$\int_a^b f(x)dx = (b - a)f(\eta). \qquad (6)$$

Proof of Theorem VI. Suppose that $a < b$. Then, from (5), there exists a number γ such that $m \leqq \gamma \leqq M$ and

$$\int_a^b f(x)dx = (b-a)\gamma, \tag{7}$$

where m is the absolute minimum and M is the absolute maximum of $f(x)$ on (a, b). Hence, since $f(x)$ is continuous, there exists at least one value $x = \eta$ on (a, b) such that $f(\eta) = \gamma$, and then (7) gives (6).

Comment. For Figure 126 on page 196, (6) states that the area of the region bounded by $x = a$, $x = b$, the x-axis, and the curve $y = f(x)$ is equal to the area of the ruled rectangle with altitude $f(\eta)$, represented by γ.

93. Integral with variable upper limit

THEOREM VII. *Suppose that the function $f(t)$ is continuous when t is on the interval (a, b), let x also have the range (a, b), and let*

$$\phi(x) = \int_a^x f(t)dt. \tag{1}$$

Then, $\phi(x)$ has a derivative, and $\phi'(x) = f(x)$.

Proof. 1. For Figure 127, which shows a graph of $y = f(t)$ where $f(t) > 0$, $\phi(x)$ is the measure of the area of the region marked by horizontal rulings. To obtain $\phi'(x)$, we shall use the Δ-process.

2. Let x be fixed temporarily. Then, for any Δx,

$$\Delta\phi = \phi(x + \Delta x) - \phi(x) = \int_a^{x+\Delta x} f(t)dt - \int_a^x f(t)dt. \tag{2}$$

From Theorem IV, page 196, with "a, b, c" as "$a, x, (x + \Delta x)$,"

$$\int_a^{x+\Delta x} f(t)dt = \int_a^x f(t)dt + \int_x^{x+\Delta x} f(t)dt. \tag{3}$$

Hence,
$$\Delta\phi = \int_x^{x+\Delta x} f(t)dt. \tag{4}$$

In Figure 127, $\Delta\phi$ is the area of the region ruled obliquely.

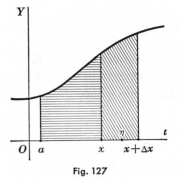

3. In (4), by Theorem VI, there exists a number η on the range from x to $(x + \Delta x)$, inclusive, as in Figure 127, such that

$$\Delta\phi = f(\eta)(x + \Delta x - x) = f(\eta)\Delta x. \tag{5}$$

If $\Delta x \to 0$ then $\eta \to x$, and hence $f(\eta) \to f(x)$, because $f(t)$ is continuous at the point $t = x$. Thus, from (5),

$$\lim_{\Delta x \to 0} \frac{\Delta\phi}{\Delta x} = \lim_{\Delta x \to 0} f(\eta) = f(x).$$

That is, $\phi(x)$ has a derivative, and $\phi'(x) = f(x)$.

Fig. 127

ILLUSTRATION 1. $\dfrac{d}{dx} \displaystyle\int_a^x (3t + \cos^3 t)dt = 3x + \cos^3 x.$

Note 1. Interval (a, b), or $a \leq x \leq b$, in Theorem VII may be replaced by $b \leq x \leq a$, with no change in the proof, because (2), (3), and (5) remain unaltered if $b < a$. That is, in (1), we may have $x < a$.

Note 2. Recall Theorem III on page 177: *if $\phi(x)$ and $F(x)$ are such that $F'(x) = \phi'(x)$, when x is on an interval (a, b), then there exists a constant C such that $\phi(x) = F(x) + C$ when x is on (a, b).*

THEOREM VIII. (**Fundamental Theorem of Integral Calculus.**) *If $f(x)$ is continuous, and $F(x)$ is any function such that $F'(x) = f(x)$, then*

$$\int_a^b f(x)dx = F(b) - F(a). \tag{6}$$

Proof. 1. Let $\phi(x) = \int_a^x f(t)dt.$ Then, $\phi'(x) = f(x).$ Since $F'(x) = f(x)$, we have $F'(x) = \phi'(x).$ Hence, there exists a constant C such that, when x is on (a, b),

$$\phi(x) = F(x) + C, \text{ or} \tag{7}$$

$$\int_a^x f(t)dt = F(x) + C. \tag{8}$$

2. If $x = a$ in (8), we obtain $0 = F(a) + C; \quad C = - F(a).$

Then, from (8), $\displaystyle\int_a^x f(t)dt = F(x) - F(a). \tag{9}$

When $x = b$ in (9), $\displaystyle\int_a^b f(t)dt = F(b) - F(a), \tag{10}$

which proves (6).

Note 3. If $F(x)$ is any function of x, we use the symbol

$$F(x)\Big]_a^b \qquad \text{to abbreviate} \qquad [F(b) - F(a)]. \tag{11}$$

ILLUSTRATION 2. To obtain $\int_3^5 2x\, dx$, notice that, if $F(x) = x^2$, then $F'(x) = 2x.$ Hence, from (6),

$$\int_3^5 2x\, dx = x^2\Big]_3^5 = 25 - 9 = 16.$$

Note 4. The importance of Theorem VIII cannot be overemphasized. It establishes a connection between differentiation and integration which welds differential calculus and integral calculus into a single discipline.

94. Antiderivatives

To use Theorem VIII, it becomes important to investigate how to find a function whose derivative is known. In this connection, we introduce the following terminology.

DEFINITION III. *To say that $F(x)$ is an **antiderivative** of a function $f(x)$ means that $F'(x) = f(x)$. The process of finding an antiderivative is called* **antidifferentiation,** *and is referred to as the inverse of differentiation.*

To verify that a function $F(x)$ is an antiderivative of a given function $f(x)$, we may differentiate $F(x)$ to check that $F'(x) = f(x)$. Thus,

$$(\text{if } n \neq -1) \qquad \text{an antiderivative of } x^n \text{ is } \quad \frac{x^{n+1}}{n+1}, \tag{1}$$

$$\text{because} \qquad \frac{d}{dx}\left(\frac{x^{n+1}}{n+1}\right) = \frac{n+1}{n+1}\, x^n = x^n. \tag{2}$$

ILLUSTRATION 1. An antiderivative of $2x$ is x^2 because the derivative of x^2 is $2x$. Also, if C is any constant, then $(x^2 + C)$ is an antiderivative of $2x$ because the derivative of C is zero.

ILLUSTRATION 2. From (1),

$$(\text{with } n = 3) \qquad\qquad \text{an antiderivative of } x^3 \text{ is } \tfrac{1}{4}x^4;$$

$$(\text{with } n = -3) \qquad \text{an antiderivative of } \frac{1}{x^3}, \text{ or } x^{-3}, \text{ is } -\frac{x^{-2}}{2} \text{ or } -\frac{1}{2x^2};$$

$$(\text{with } n = \tfrac{2}{3}) \qquad \text{an antiderivative of } \sqrt[3]{x^2}, \text{ or } x^{\frac{2}{3}}, \text{ is } \frac{1}{\frac{5}{3}}\, x^{\frac{5}{3}} \text{ or } \tfrac{3}{5}x^{\frac{5}{3}}.$$

ILLUSTRATION 3. If k is a constant, an antiderivative of k is kx because the derivative of kx is k.

At present, we shall determine antiderivatives by use of (1) and the following easily appreciated facts, which will be discussed later.

$$\left\{ \begin{array}{l} \textit{An antiderivative of a sum of functions is} \\ \textit{the sum of antiderivatives of the functions.} \end{array} \right\} \tag{3}$$

$$\left\{ \begin{array}{l} \textit{An antiderivative of } kf(x), \textit{ where } k \textit{ is a constant,} \\ \textit{is equal to } k \textit{ times an antiderivative of } f(x). \end{array} \right\} \tag{4}$$

EXAMPLE 1. Integrate: $\int_{-1}^{2} (x^2 - 3x + 5)\,dx$.

SOLUTION. 1. An antiderivative of x^2 is $\tfrac{1}{3}x^3$; of $3x$, is $3\cdot\tfrac{1}{2}x^2$; of 5, is $5x$. Hence, an antiderivative of $(x^2 - 3x + 5)$ is $(\tfrac{1}{3}x^3 - \tfrac{3}{2}x^2 + 5x)$.

2. By use of the fundamental theorem of integral calculus,

$$\int_{-1}^{2} (x^2 - 3x + 5)\,dx = \frac{1}{3}\,x^3 - \frac{3}{2}\,x^2 + 5x \,\bigg]_{-1}^{2} = 6\tfrac{2}{3} - (-6\tfrac{5}{6}) = 13\tfrac{1}{2}.$$

ILLUSTRATION 4. $\displaystyle \int_{1}^{3} (2x^4 + 2x - 1)\,dx = \left(\frac{2}{5}\,x^5 + x^2 - x\right)\bigg]_{1}^{3} = \frac{514}{5}.$

$$\text{because} \qquad \frac{d}{dx}\left(\frac{2}{5}\,x^5 + x^2 - x\right) = 2x^4 + 2x - 1.$$

EXAMPLE 2. Find the area of the finite region above the x-axis, and of the finite * region below the x-axis, bounded by the x-axis and the curve $y = x^3 - x^2 - 2x$.

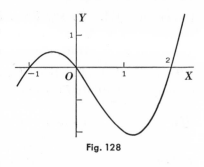

Fig. 128

SOLUTION. 1. Since $y = x(x^2 - x - 2)$, or $y = x(x - 2)(x + 1)$, the graph of this equation has the x-intercepts 0, -1, and 2, as in Figure 128.

2. From (3) and (5) in Section 91,

$$(area, \text{ } above \text{ } x\text{-}axis) = \int_{-1}^{0} (x^3 - x^2 - 2x)dx = \left(\frac{1}{4}x^4 - \frac{1}{3}x^3 - x^2\right)\Big]_{-1}^{0} = \frac{5}{12};$$

$$(area, \text{ } below \text{ } x\text{-}axis) = -\int_{0}^{2} (x^3 - x^2 - 2x)dx = \left(-\frac{1}{4}x^4 + \frac{1}{3}x^3 + x^2\right)\Big]_{0}^{2} = \frac{8}{3}.$$

ILLUSTRATION 5. $\int_{-1}^{8} \sqrt[3]{x} \text{ } dx = \int_{-1}^{8} x^{\frac{1}{3}} \text{ } dx$

$$= \frac{3}{4}x^{\frac{4}{3}}\Big]_{-1}^{8} = \frac{3}{4}[8^{\frac{4}{3}} - (-1)^{\frac{4}{3}}] = \frac{3}{4}(16 - 1) = \frac{45}{4},$$

where we used (1) with $n = \frac{1}{3}$ to obtain the antiderivative $\frac{3}{4}x^{\frac{4}{3}}$.

Note 1. Hereafter, unless otherwise specified, any integral should be computed by use of the fundamental theorem of integral calculus.

EXERCISE 54

Obtain an antiderivative of the function by use of (1) on page 199.

1. $2x^4$.   **2.** $3x^{\frac{1}{2}}$.   **3.** $5x^{-3}$.   **4.** $2\sqrt[3]{x}$.

5. $3x^5 - 2x^2 - 2\sqrt{x} + 6$.   **6.** $2x^{-3} - 3x^4 - 5\sqrt[3]{x} + 3$.

Integrate by use of the fundamental theorem of integral calculus.

7. $\int_{2}^{4} 3x^2 \text{ } dx$.   **8.** $\int_{-2}^{1} 4y^3 \text{ } dy$.   **9.** $\int_{6}^{2} 5x \text{ } dx$.

10. $\int_{-1}^{1} (3x^2 - x + 4)dx$.   **11.** $\int_{-3}^{0} (x^3 + 2x^2 - x + 2)dx$.

12. $\int_{2}^{5} y^{-3} \text{ } dy$.   **13.** $\int_{1}^{9} 3y^{\frac{1}{2}} \text{ } dy$.   **14.** $\int_{-8}^{1} 2\sqrt[3]{x} \text{ } dx$.

Find the area of the region bounded by the x-axis and the given curve, between the specified values of x.

15. $y = 3x - x^2$; between $x = 0$ and $x = 3$.

16. $y = 9 - x^2$; between $x = -3$ and $x = 3$.

17. $y = x^2 - 4x$; between $x = 0$ and $x = 4$.

18. $y = x^2 - 6x + 8$; between (a) $x = 2$ and $x = 4$; (b) $x = 0$ and $x = 3$.

---

* Hereafter, the word *"finite"* will be omitted in descriptions of regions. Unless otherwise specified, any region will be a *finite*, or *bounded region*.

19. $y = x^3 - 4x$; between (a) $x = -2$ and $x = 0$; (b) $x = -2$ and $x = 1$.

20. $y = (x^2 - 4)(x - 5)$; between (a) $x = -2$ and $x = 0$; (b) $x = 4$ and $x = 6$.

21. $y = 1/x^2$; between $x = 1$ and $x = 3$.

★22. If $f(x)$ and $g(x)$ are continuous, and $f(x) \le g(x)$ when x is on the interval (a, b), prove that $\int_a^b f(x)dx \le \int_a^b g(x)dx$. Use (3) on page 189.

★23. Let $\phi(x) = \int_a^x f(t)dt$, where $f(x)$ is continuous when $a \le x \le b$. Apply the law of the mean from page 176 to show that

$$\phi(b) - \phi(a) = \int_a^b f(t)dt = f(\eta)(b - a),$$

where $a < \eta < b$. (In Theorem VI, page 196, we concluded merely that $a \le \eta \le b$, where $\eta = a$ and $\eta = b$ would be possibilities.)

★24. Prove Theorem V on page 196. Make use of the fact that, in (10) on page 190, $m \le f(\xi_i) \le M$ for each value of i; multiply by $\Delta_i x$ and sum for $i = 1$ to $i = n$.

★25. If a is a constant, prove that $\dfrac{d}{dx} \int_x^a f(t)dt = -f(x)$.

95. Area between two curves

Let R represent the region in Figure 129 bounded by the ordinates $x = a$ and $x = b$, and the curves $y_1 = g(x)$ and $y_2 = f(x)$, where $y_1 \le y_2$ and y_1 and y_2 are continuous when $a \le x \le b$. We shall define the area of R in a fashion consistent with the definition of area on page 194.

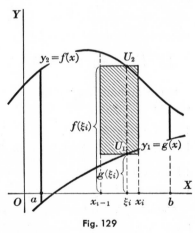

Fig. 129

Form a partition P of the interval (a, b), as in (1) on page 188, with the subintervals $\{T_i\}$ where T_i is the interval $x_{i-1} \le x \le x_i$. On each interval T_i, select a point ξ_i arbitrarily. The line $x = \xi_i$, as in Figure 129, intersects the given curves in points U_1 and U_2 with ordinates $g(\xi_i)$ and $f(\xi_i)$, respectively. Construct the rectangle with

$$altitude = U_1 U_2 = f(\xi_i) - g(\xi_i); \quad base = \Delta_i x = x_i - x_{i-1};$$

$$area = \Delta_i A = [f(\xi_i) - g(\xi_i)]\Delta_i x. \tag{1}$$

Then, we define the *area*, A, of the region R to be *the limit of the sum of all elements of area*, $\Delta_i A$, for the partition P, as all $\Delta_i x \to 0$. By comparison with (10) on page 190, we recognize (1) as the typical element in an approximating sum for the integral of $[f(x) - g(x)]$ from $x = a$ to $x = b$. Thus, we have defined A as follows:

$$\left\{ \begin{array}{l} \textit{Region bounded by } x = a, \; x = b, \; y_1 = g(x), \\ \quad \textit{and } y_2 = f(x); \; y_1 \leqq y_2 \textit{ and } a < b \end{array} \right\} \quad A = \int_a^b (y_2 - y_1)dx. \quad (2)$$

We obtain (3) of page 194 as a special case of (2) by using $y_1 = 0$, and $y_2 = y$ where $y = f(x)$ and $f(x) \geqq 0$:

$$\left\{ \begin{array}{l} \textit{Region bounded by } x = a, \; x = b, \; y = 0, \\ \quad \textit{and } y = f(x); \; f(x) \geqq 0 \textit{ and } a < b \end{array} \right\} \quad A = \int_a^b y \, dx. \quad (3)$$

EXAMPLE 1. Find the total area of the region bounded by

$$y = x(x + 1)(x - 3) \quad \textit{and} \quad y = 5x. \quad (4)$$

SOLUTION. 1. *Intersections.* Solve equations (4) simultaneously:

$$5x = x(x + 1)(x - 3); \quad \textit{hence,}$$

$$x = 0 \quad \textit{or} \quad 5 = x^2 - 2x - 3.$$

We obtain $x = 0, -2$, and 4; then, from (4), $y = 0, -10$, and 20, respectively, as shown on the graphs of (4) in Figure 130.

2. To find the area of the region with inclined rulings, use (2) with $y_2 = 5x$ and $y_1 = x(x + 1)(x - 3)$, so that $y_1 \leqq y_2$; reverse these roles for the region with vertical rulings. The total area A is

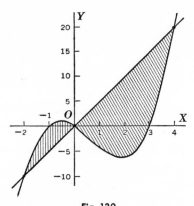

Fig. 130

$$A = \int_{-2}^0 [x(x + 1)(x - 3) - 5x]dx + \int_0^4 [5x - x(x + 1)(x - 3)]dx = \frac{148}{3}.$$

On interchanging the roles of x and y in (2) and (3), we obtain the following results.

$$\left\{ \begin{array}{l} \textit{Region bounded by } y = c, \; y = d, \; x_1 = g(y), \\ \quad \textit{and } x_2 = f(y); \; x_1 \leqq x_2 \textit{ and } c < d \end{array} \right\} \quad A = \int_c^d (x_2 - x_1)dy. \quad (5)$$

$$\left\{ \begin{array}{l} \textit{Region bounded by } y = c, \; y = d, \; x = 0, \\ \quad \textit{and } x = f(y); \; f(y) \geqq 0 \textit{ and } c < d \end{array} \right\} \quad A = \int_c^d x \, dy. \quad (6)$$

Note 1. Formula (2) applies only when there is an upper boundary and a lower boundary where each is given as *the graph of a single function over the whole range for x.* Similarly, (5) can be employed only for a region with a left-hand boundary and a right-hand boundary, where each is given as the graph of a single function. Sometimes, both (2) and (5) apply conveniently for a given region. This matter will be discussed again later.

EXAMPLE 2. Find the area, A, of the region bounded by the parabolas

$$x = -\tfrac{1}{4}y^2 \quad \textit{and} \quad x = \tfrac{1}{4}(y^2 - 8). \quad (7)$$

SOLUTION. 1. The curves intersect at $(-1, -2)$ and $(-1, 2)$, as in Figure 131. Let Δy be the length of a typical subinterval of a partition of the interval $-2 \leqq y \leqq 2$. Let ΔA be the area of the corresponding rectangle in the background of an approximating sum for the integral in (5) related to (7). Let $x_2 = -\frac{1}{4}y^2$ and $x_1 = \frac{1}{4}(y^2 - 8)$, so that $x_1 \leqq x_2$. Then, in Figure 131,

$$\Delta A = (x_2 - x_1)\Delta y = [-\frac{1}{4}y^2 - \frac{1}{4}(y^2 - 8)]\Delta y. \tag{8}$$

2. Hence, from (5),

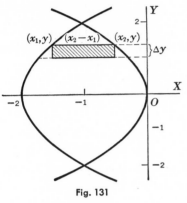

$$A = \int_{-2}^{2} \left[-\frac{1}{4}y^2 - \frac{1}{4}(y^2 - 8) \right] dy$$

$$= \frac{16}{3} \; sq. \; units. \tag{9}$$

Comment. The element ΔA in (8) and the ruled rectangle in Figure 131 were not essential for writing (9). However, ΔA in (8) leads naturally to (9), and the student is advised to give a similar background for at least several of the problems in the next exercise.

Fig. 131

EXERCISE 55

Draw graphs in an xy-plane exhibiting the region R bounded by the given curves. Find the area of R. Use whichever variable is best for integration, except when a particular variable is specified.

1. The parabola $y = 4x^2$ and the line $y = 9$.

2. $y = (x - 3)^2$ and $y = 4$.   **3.** The y-axis and $x = y^2 - 3y$.

4. $y + 2x + 6 = 0$ and $y = 9 - x^2$.   **5.** $y = x^2 + 5$ and $y = 2x^2 - 4$.

6. $y = 6x$ and $y = 2x^2$. Compute by integrating (*a*) with respect to x; (*b*) with respect to y.

7. $y^2 = 3x$ and $3y = x^2$, by integrating (*a*) with respect to x; (*b*) with respect to y.

8. $x = (y - 1)^2$ and $2 - x = (y - 1)^2$.

9. $y = x(x + 1)(x - 5)$ and $y = 7x$.   **10.** $x = (y + 2)^2$ and $x = 9$.

11. $x = y(y - 3)(y + 2)$ and $x = 0$.

12. $2y = -x^2$ and $3x + 2y + 4 = 0$.

13. $4y^3 = x^2$ and $y = 1$.   **14.** $y = x^3$ and $x = y^3$.

15. The region bounded by segments of the axes and an arc of $x^{\frac{1}{2}} + y^{\frac{1}{2}} = 2$.

16. $8y^2 = 9x^3$ and $x = 2$.

17. Find the area of the region between the parabolas $y^2 = 3(4 - x)$ and $y^2 = 3x$, by integrating with respect to y.

Note 1. Let the function $f(x)$ be continuous when $a \leqq x \leqq b$. Let P be a partition of the interval (a, b) into n equal subintervals, each of length Δx, so that $n\Delta x = b - a$. Then, with $\{x_i\}$, $i = 0, 1, 2, \cdots, n$, as the division points of P, let

$$\mu_n = \frac{f(x_1) + f(x_2) + \cdots + f(x_n)}{n}, \; or \tag{1}$$

$$\mu_n = \frac{f(x_1)\Delta x + f(x_2)\Delta x + \cdots + f(x_n)\Delta x}{n\Delta x} = \frac{\sum_{i=1}^{n} f(x_i)\Delta x}{b - a}. \tag{2}$$

In (1), μ_n is the *arithmetic mean* of $f(x_1)$, $f(x_2)$, $\cdots$, $f(x_n)$. The numerator in (2) is a particular value of S_P of (3) on page 189, and hence approaches $\int_a^b f(x)dx$ when $n \to \infty$. Let $\gamma = \lim_{n\to\infty} \mu_n$. Then,

$$\gamma = \frac{\int_a^b f(x)dx}{b - a}. \tag{3}$$

On account of the arithmetic mean μ_n in the background of (3), sometimes γ is called the **mean value** of $f(x)$ over the interval (a, b). Recognize that γ in (3) has the same value as γ in the mean value theorem for $\int_a^b f(x)dx$, in (7) on page 197.

Find the mean value of $f(x)$ over the given interval.

18. $f(x) = x^2 + 4x$; $0 \leq x \leq 6$.   **19.** $f(x) = \sqrt{x}$; $0 \leq x \leq 9$.

20. $f(x) = (2x - 1)^3$; $-1 \leq x \leq 2$.   **21.** $f(x) = (2 - x)^3$; $-2 \leq x \leq 2$.

96. Volume of a region

Let W be the set of points, to be called a *region*, inside or on a closed surface S in three-dimensional space. The notion of the *volume* of W is intuitively apparent. However, it is essential to define the *"measure of the volume,"* hereafter abbreviated simply as the *"volume."* Any definition of volume which will be met in later sections will be based on a limiting process, leading to a definite integral. In each case, the element in any approximating sum for the integral will be computed directly or indirectly on the following basis, where (II) clearly includes (I) as a special case.

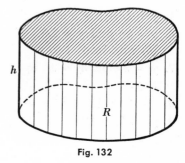

Fig. 132

I. *If W is a rectangular parallelepiped, with dimensions a, b, and c, we define the volume of W as abc volume units.*

II. *Let W be a region, as in Figure 132, swept out if a plane region R, with area A, is moved h linear units perpendicular to the plane of R. Then, we define the volume of W as * Ah volume units. We refer to W as a slab.*

* In Chapter 19, this formula will be proved by use of (I), instead of being taken as a definition.

. *Note 1.* We accept the fact that the area of a circle of radius r is πr^2. This result will be proved later, on the basis of the definition of area in Section 91.

ILLUSTRATION 1. Consider a circular cylinder with altitude h and r as the radius of the base. From (II), the volume of the cylinder is $h(\pi r^2)$, or $\pi r^2 h$.

97. Volume of a solid of revolution

In an xy-plane, let R be the region bounded by the x-axis, the lines $x = a$ and $x = b$, and a curve $y = f(x)$, where $f(x)$ is continuous when $a \leqq x \leqq b$. In Figure 133, the boundary of R is $MUWN$. If R is revolved about the x-axis, the curve $y = f(x)$ sweeps out a so-called *surface of revolution*, as in Figure 134; the ordinates MN and UW sweep out circles. Thus, R sweeps out a *solid of revolution*, H, bounded by a surface of revolution, and two circular plane regions.

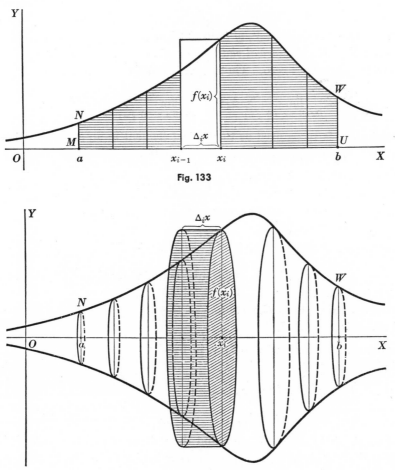

Fig. 133

Fig. 134

To arrive at a definition for the *volume* of H, first form any partition P of the interval $a \leq x \leq b$ into n subintervals $\{T_i\}$, as in (1) on page 188, where T_i is the interval $x_{i-1} \leq x \leq x_i$ with length $\Delta_i x$. In Figure 133, construct a perpendicular to OX at each division point x_i of P, and thus divide R into n vertical strips corresponding to the n subintervals $\{T_i\}$ of P. When R is revolved about OX, the section corresponding to T_i generates a *slab* of thickness $\Delta_i x$, as in Figure 134, with vertical circular faces having the radii

$$|y_{i-1}| = |f(x_{i-1})| \quad and \quad |y_i| = |f(x_i)|, \tag{1}$$

where absolute value signs are necessary because $f(x)$ may have negative values. Now, in Figure 133, with each subinterval T_i as a base, construct a rectangle with its vertical side as the ordinate y_i, or * $f(x_i)$. Revolution of this rectangle about OX generates a cylindrical slab C_i, as in Figure 134, with base radius $|y_i|$, thickness $\Delta_i x$, and volume $\Delta_i V$, where

$$\Delta_i V = \pi y_i^2 \Delta_i x, \quad or \quad \Delta_i V = \pi [f(x_i)]^2 \Delta_i x. \tag{2}$$

Then, *we define the volume, V, of the solid H as the limit of the sum of all of the volumes $\Delta_i V$ of the cylindrical slabs C_i corresponding to a partition P*, as the norm of P approaches zero. That is, by definition

$$V = \lim_{(as\ all\ \Delta_i x \to 0)} \sum_{i=1}^{n} \Delta_i V = \lim_{(as\ all\ \Delta_i x \to 0)} \sum_{i=1}^{n} \pi [f(x_i)]^2 \Delta_i x. \tag{3}$$

Expression (2) is recognized as the typical element in an approximating sum for an integral of $\pi [f(x)]^2$. Thus, in (3) *we defined V as a definite integral:*

$$\left\{ \begin{array}{l} Revolve\ y = f(x) \\ about\ x\text{-}axis;\ a < b \end{array} \right\} \quad V = \pi \int_a^b [f(x)]^2\, dx, \quad or \quad V = \pi \int_a^b y^2\, dx. \tag{4}$$

On interchanging the roles of x and y, from (4) we obtain

$$\left\{ \begin{array}{l} Revolve\ x = g(y) \\ about\ y\text{-}axis;\ c < d \end{array} \right\} \quad V = \pi \int_c^d [g(y)]^2\, dy, \quad or \quad V = \pi \int_c^d x^2\, dy. \tag{5}$$

EXAMPLE 1. The region in quadrant I bounded by the x-axis, the parabola $y^2 = 2x$, and the ordinate $x = 8$ is revolved about the x-axis. Find the volume of the solid which is generated.

SOLUTION. A graph of $y^2 = 2x$ is in Figure 135. From (4),

$$V = \pi \int_0^8 y^2\, dx = \pi \int_0^8 2x\, dx = \pi x^2 \Big]_0^8$$

$$= 64\pi,\ cubic\ units.$$

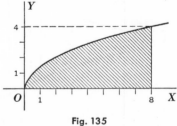

Fig. 135

Comment. In Example 1, we found the volume of a region bounded by a paraboloid of revolution and a plane perpendicular to its axis (see page 350).

* Instead of $f(x_i)$, we could take any point ξ_i on T_i and use $f(\xi_i)$, with the same final result.

EXAMPLE 2. The region in quadrant I bounded by $y^2 = 2x$, the y-axis, and the line $y = 4$ is revolved about the y-axis. Find the volume of the solid which is generated.

SOLUTION. Refer to Figure 135 for a graph of $y^2 = 2x$. From (5),

$$V = \pi \int_0^4 x^2 \, dy = \pi \int_0^4 \frac{y^4}{4} \, dy = \frac{\pi}{20} y^5 \Big]_0^4 = \frac{256\pi}{5}, \text{ cubic units.}$$

Note 1. If a region W is enclosed by a surface S, for brevity we may refer to "*the volume of S*" instead of "*the volume of W which is enclosed by S.*"

EXERCISE 56

1. Find the volume of a sphere of radius r, by revolving the region bounded by the circle $x^2 + y^2 = r^2$ about the x-axis.

Find the volume of the solid generated if the region R in the xy-plane bounded by the given curve or curves is revolved about the specified axis.

2. $x = 2y$, $x = 4$, and the x-axis. Revolve about the x-axis.

3. $y = x^3$, the x-axis, and $x = 2$. Revolve about the x-axis.

4. $y = x^3$, the y-axis, and $y = 8$. Revolve about the y-axis.

5. The x-axis and $y = x^2 - 3x$. Revolve about the x-axis.

6. $4x^2 + y^2 = 36$. Revolve about (a) the x-axis; (b) the y-axis.

Note 1. If an ellipse is rotated about one of its axes, the surface thus generated is called an **ellipsoid** of revolution. Moreover, the surface is called a *prolate* or an *oblate spheroid* according as the major axis or the minor axis is the axis of revolution.

7. $y^2 = 4x$ and $x = 4$. Revolve about the x-axis.

8. $x^2 = 3y$ and $y = 3$. Revolve about the y-axis.

9. $x^{\frac{1}{2}} + y^{\frac{1}{2}} = 3$ and the coordinate axes. Revolve about the y-axis.

10. $x^{\frac{2}{3}} + y^{\frac{2}{3}} = a^{\frac{2}{3}}$, where $a > 0$. Revolve about the x-axis.

11. The x-axis, $xy = 4$, $x = 1$, and $x = 4$. Revolve about the x-axis.

12. $y = 2$, $y = 0$, and $x^2 - 4y^2 = 16$. Revolve about the y-axis.

13. $x = 3$, $x = 0$, and $9y^2 - x^2 = 36$. Revolve about the x-axis.

14. A spheroid is generated by revolving the ellipse $b^2x^2 + a^2y^2 = a^2b^2$ about the x-axis. Find the volume of the spheroid.

15. Find the volume of a right circular cone with altitude h, and a as the radius of the base, by use of integration.

16. A *spherical segment* is that part of the region bounded by a sphere which is included between two parallel planes, called the faces of the segment. If one of these planes is tangent to the sphere, the segment has just one face. Find the volume of a spherical segment of altitude h, with just one face, in a sphere of radius a.

CHAPTER

12

INTEGRATION BY STANDARD FORMS

98. Indefinite integrals

In the following discussion, the range for x is some finite interval, say $h \leq x \leq k$, or perhaps an interval of infinite extent.

THEOREM I. *If $F(x)$ is a particular antiderivative of a function $f(x)$, that is, if $F'(x) = f(x)$, then the set of all antiderivatives of $f(x)$ is given by $[F(x) + C]$, where C is an arbitrary constant.*

Proof. 1. For any C, $[F(x) + C]$ is an antiderivative of $f(x)$, since

$$\frac{d[F(x) + C]}{dx} = F'(x) + \frac{dC}{dx} = f(x). \tag{1}$$

2. Now, let $G(x)$ be any antiderivative of $f(x)$. Then $G'(x) = f(x)$, or $G'(x) = F'(x)$. Hence, by Theorem III on page 177, there exists a constant C so that $G(x) = F(x) + C$, which proves Theorem I.

ILLUSTRATION 1. An antiderivative of $3x^2$ is x^3. Hence, the set of all antiderivatives of $3x^2$ is the family of functions $(x^3 + C)$.

THEOREM II. *If $f(x)$ is continuous when x is on the interval (h, k), then $f(x)$ has antiderivatives, consisting of all functions of the form*

$$\int_a^x f(t)dt + C, \tag{2}$$

where a is any point on (h, k) and C is an arbitrary constant.

Proof. By Theorem VII on page 197, if we let

$$\phi(x) = \int_a^x f(t)dt,$$

then $\phi'(x) = f(x)$ at all values of x on (h, k). Hence, by Theorem I with $\phi(x)$ in place of $F(x)$, all antiderivatives of $f(x)$ are given by (2).

If a function $f(x)$ is integrable on an interval $h \leq x \leq k$, any function of x of the form (2) is called an **indefinite integral** of $f(x)$. In this text, in any reference to an *indefinite integral* of a function $f(x)$, it will be assumed that $f(x)$ is *continuous*. Then, by Theorem II, "*an indefinite integral of $f(x)$*" *means the same* as "an antiderivative of $f(x)$,*" and we have the following result:

$$\left\{ \begin{array}{l} An \textbf{ indefinite integral } of \ a \ continuous \ function \\ f(x) \ is \ any \ function \ F(x) \ whose \ derivative \ is \ f(x) \\ or, \ equally \ well, \ whose \ differential \ is \ f(x)dx. \end{array} \right\} \qquad (3)$$

In the future, generally we shall use the name "indefinite integral" instead of "antiderivative." By Theorem I, we see that, if $f(x)$ has a particular indefinite integral $F(x)$, then the set of all indefinite integrals of $f(x)$ is the family of functions $[F(x) + C]$, where C is an arbitrary constant. We introduce the symbol $\int f(x)dx$ to represent any one of these functions, or

$$\int f(x)dx = F(x) + C, \quad where \quad F'(x) = f(x), \qquad (4)$$

and C is a constant of integration. Sometimes, we shall use "$\int f(x)dx$" to represent *just a particular function*, and then "$\int f(x)dx$" should be read "**AN** *indefinite integral of $f(x)$.*" We read "$\int f(x)dx$" as "**THE** *indefinite integral of $f(x)$*" when the integral represents *any function* $[F(x) + C]$ in (4), and this meaning should be inferred when no contrary information is at hand. In any formula for indefinite integration, C will represent an arbitrary constant.

In $\int f(x)dx$, we call x the *variable of integration* and $f(x)$ the **integrand.** To calculate $\int f(x)dx$, we search for a function $F(x)$ such that $F'(x) = f(x)$, and then add an arbitrary constant to $F(x)$. The process of finding indefinite integrals is called **indefinite integration,**† or simply *integration*, when there is no danger of confusion with *definite integration*. We emphasize that *indefinite integration* and *differentiation* are *inverse operations*. Thus, $\int f(x)dx$ is a function of x such that

$$\frac{d}{dx} \int f(x)dx = f(x), \quad or \quad d\left[\int f(x)dx\right] = f(x)dx. \qquad (5)$$

In contrast, for fixed a and b, the definite integral $\int_a^b f(x)dx$ is some particular number, and is not a function of the dummy variable x.

ILLUSTRATION 2. $\int 3x^2 \, dx = x^3 + C$. *An* indefinite integral of $\cos x$ is $\sin x$; *THE* indefinite integral of $\cos x$ is $(\sin x + C)$, or $\int \cos x \, dx = \sin x + C$.

Let $v(x)$ be a function with a continuous derivative, $v'(x)$. Then, from (4),

$$\int v'(x)dx = v(x) + C, \ or \qquad (6)$$

$$\int dv(x) = v(x) + C. \qquad (7)$$

---

* If $f(x)$ is *not* assumed to be continuous, the notions of an indefinite integral and an antiderivative (or, *primitive*) of $f(x)$ are not identical. See page 90, *Theory of Functions of Real Variables*, by L. M. Graves; McGraw-Hill Book Company, publishers.
† Previously called "antidifferentiation."

By means of (7), we shall obtain a standard indefinite integral from each of the following differentials, where u is any differentiable function of x.

$$\left.\begin{array}{ll} du^{n+1} = (n+1)u^n\, du. & d\ln u = \frac{1}{u}\, du. \\[2mm] da^u = (a^u \ln a)du. & de^u = e^u\, du. \\[2mm] d\cos u = -\sin u\, du. & d\sin u = \cos u\, du. \\[2mm] d\tan u = \sec^2 u\, du. & d\cot u = -\csc^2 u\, du. \\[2mm] d\sec u = \sec u \tan u\, du. & d\csc u = -\csc u \cot u\, du. \\[2mm] d\,\text{Arctan}\, u = \frac{du}{1+u^2}. & d\,\text{Arcsin}\, u = \frac{du}{\sqrt{1-u^2}}. \end{array}\right\} \quad (8)$$

ILLUSTRATION 3. If u is a differentiable function of x and $n \neq -1$,

$$d\left(\frac{u^{n+1}}{n+1}\right) = u^n\, du.$$

Hence, by (7),
$$\int u^n\, du = \int d\left(\frac{u^{n+1}}{n+1}\right) = \frac{u^{n+1}}{n+1} + C.$$

ILLUSTRATION 4. From (8), $d(-\cos u) = \sin u\, du$. Hence,

$$\int \sin u\, du = \int d(-\cos u) = -\cos u + C.$$

The results of Illustrations 3 and 4, and other formulas obtainable similarly. are as follows. Additional results will be derived from (8) later.

The power formula $(n \neq -1)$:
$$\int u^n\, du = \frac{u^{n+1}}{n+1} + C. \qquad (9)$$

$$\int \sin u\, du = -\cos u + C. \qquad \int \cos u\, du = \sin u + C. \qquad (10)$$

$$\int \sec^2 u\, du = \tan u + C. \qquad \int \csc^2 u\, du = -\cot u + C. \qquad (11)$$

99. Properties of indefinite integrals

After an indefinite integration, we may verify the result by differentiating it, to show that thus we obtain the given integrand.

I. *If k is any constant, then*

$$\int kf(x)dx = k \int f(x)dx. \qquad (1)$$

Proof.
$$\frac{d}{dx}\left[k \int f(x)dx\right] = k\frac{d}{dx}\left[\int f(x)dx\right] = kf(x), \qquad (2)$$

which is the integrand on the left in (1). Hence, (1) is true.

ILLUSTRATION 1. By use of (1), and the power formula with $n = -\frac{2}{5}$,

$$\int \frac{3x}{\sqrt[5]{x^7}}\, dx = 3\int x^{1-\frac{7}{5}}\, dx = 3\int x^{-\frac{2}{5}}\, dx = 3\cdot\frac{1}{\frac{3}{5}} x^{\frac{3}{5}} + C = 5x^{\frac{3}{5}} + C.$$

II. *The indefinite integral of a sum of functions is the sum of their indefinite integrals. Thus,*

$$\int [f(x) + g(x) + h(x)]dx = \int f(x)dx + \int g(x)dx + \int h(x)dx. \quad (3)$$

Proof. $\qquad \dfrac{d}{dx}\left[\int f(x)dx + \int g(x)dx + \int h(x)dx\right] =$

$$\frac{d}{dx}\int f(x)dx + \frac{d}{dx}\int g(x)dx + \frac{d}{dx}\int h(x)dx = f(x) + g(x) + h(x), \quad (4)$$

where we used (5) of page 209. On the right in (4), we obtained the integrand on the left in (3), which proves (3). In using (3), all arbitrary constants on the right can be added to give a single arbitrary constant.

ILLUSTRATION 2. By use of (1) and (3), with (9) of page 210,

$$\int (3x^2 - 5x - x^3 + 3)dx = \int 3x^2\, dx - 5\int x\, dx - \int x^3\, dx + \int 3\, dx$$

$$= x^3 - \tfrac{5}{2}x^2 - \tfrac{1}{4}x^4 + 3x + C.$$

ILLUSTRATION 3. $\qquad \displaystyle\int \frac{2x^3 - x}{x^5}\, dx = \int \frac{2}{x^2}\, dx - \int \frac{dx}{x^4}$

$$= 2\int x^{-2}\, dx - \int x^{-4}\, dx = -2x^{-1} + \tfrac{1}{3}x^{-3} + C. \quad (5)$$

The fundamental theorem of integral calculus can be restated as follows.

SUMMARY. **Computation of $\int_a^b f(x)dx$.** *Find an indefinite integral of $f(x)$, that is, find a function $F(x)$ such that $F'(x) = f(x)$. Then,*

$$\int_a^b f(x)dx = F(b) - F(a). \quad (6)$$

EXAMPLE 1. Obtain the area of the region bounded by the x-axis and the curve $y = x(x + 1)(x - 4)$ from $x = -1$ to $x = 4$.

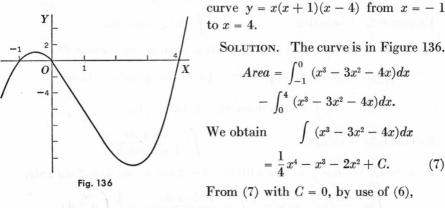

Fig. 136

SOLUTION. The curve is in Figure 136.

$$Area = \int_{-1}^{0} (x^3 - 3x^2 - 4x)dx$$

$$- \int_{0}^{4} (x^3 - 3x^2 - 4x)dx.$$

We obtain $\qquad \displaystyle\int (x^3 - 3x^2 - 4x)dx$

$$= \frac{1}{4}x^4 - x^3 - 2x^2 + C. \quad (7)$$

From (7) with $C = 0$, by use of (6),

$$area = \left(\frac{1}{4}x^4 - x^3 - 2x^2\right)\Big]_{-1}^{0} - \left(\frac{1}{4}x^4 - x^3 - 2x^2\right)\Big]_{0}^{4} = 32\tfrac{3}{4}\ square\ units. \quad (8)$$

Comment. We could retain C in (7), and notice that C cancels in (8).

100. Substitution in fundamental forms

In obtaining an indefinite integral, $\int f(x)dx$, by direct use of a fundamental form for integration, such as (9)–(11) on page 210, first decide on the function $u(x)$ involved. Then, adjust constant multipliers before and after the integral sign, in order to exhibit du.

EXAMPLE 1. Evaluate: $\qquad\qquad \int t(2t^2 + 1)^{15}\, dt.$ $\qquad\qquad$ (1)

SOLUTION. Work toward $\int u^{15}\, du$ with $u = 2t^2 + 1$. Since $du = 4t\, dt$, multiply by 4 in the integrand, and divide by 4 before the integral:

$$\int t(2t^2 + 1)^{15}\, dt = \frac{1}{4}\int (2t^2 + 1)^{15}(4t\, dt) = \frac{1}{4}\int u^{15}\, du$$

$$= \frac{1}{4}\cdot\frac{u^{16}}{16} + C = \frac{1}{64}(2t^2 + 1)^{16} + C.$$

ILLUSTRATION 1. In $\displaystyle\int \frac{dx}{\sqrt[3]{4x + 1}},$ if $u = 4x + 1$ then $du = 4\, dx$ and

$$\int \frac{dx}{\sqrt[3]{4x + 1}} = \frac{1}{4}\int (4x + 1)^{-\frac{1}{3}}(4\, dx) =$$

$$\frac{1}{4}\int u^{-\frac{1}{3}}\, du = \frac{1}{4}\frac{u^{\frac{2}{3}}}{\frac{2}{3}} + C = \frac{3}{8}(4x + 1)^{\frac{2}{3}} + C.$$

ILLUSTRATION 2. $\qquad\qquad \int \sin 2x\, dx = \frac{1}{2}\int (\sin 2x)(2\, dx)$

(with $u = 2x$) $\qquad = \frac{1}{2}\int \sin u\, du = -\frac{1}{2}\cos u + C = -\frac{1}{2}\cos 2x + C.$

For rapid work, we prefer the following details:

$$\int \sin 2x\, dx = \frac{1}{2}\int (\sin 2x)d(2x) = -\frac{1}{2}\cos 2x + C.$$

EXAMPLE 2. Evaluate: $\qquad\qquad \int \sin^4 x \cos x\, dx.$

SOLUTION. Work toward $\int u^4\, du$, with $u = \sin x$; $du = \cos x\, dx$.

$$\int \sin^4 x \cos x\, dx = \int u^4\, du = \frac{1}{5}u^5 + C = \frac{1}{5}\sin^5 x + C, \text{ or}$$

$$\int (\sin x)^4 d(\sin x) = \frac{1}{5}\sin^5 x + C.$$

EXAMPLE 3. Evaluate: $\qquad\qquad \displaystyle\int \frac{\sin x\, dx}{(1 + 2\cos x)^3}.$

SOLUTION. We use $\int u^{-3}\, du$ with $u = 1 + 2\cos x$; $du = -2\sin x\, dx.$

$$\int \frac{\sin x\, dx}{(1 + 2\cos x)^3} = -\frac{1}{2}\int \frac{-2\sin x\, dx}{(1 + 2\cos x)^3} = -\frac{1}{2}\int u^{-3}\, du$$

$$= -\frac{1}{2}\left(-\frac{1}{2}u^{-2}\right) + C = \frac{1}{4}(1 + 2\cos x)^{-2} + C.$$

ILLUSTRATION 3. $\displaystyle\int \cot^3 2x \sec^2 2x \, dx = \int \frac{1}{\tan^3 2x} \sec^2 2x \, dx$

$(u = \tan 2x; \; du = 2 \sec^2 2x \, dx)$

$$= \frac{1}{2} \int (\tan^{-3} 2x)(2 \sec^2 2x \, dx) = \frac{1}{2} \int u^{-3} \, du = -\frac{1}{4} \tan^{-2} 2x + C.$$

ILLUSTRATION 4. With $u = \ln x$ and $du = dx/x$,

$$\int \frac{1}{(\ln x)^3} \cdot \frac{dx}{x} = \int u^{-3} \, du = -\frac{1}{2u^2} + C = -\frac{1}{2(\ln x)^2} + C.$$

ILLUSTRATION 5. $\displaystyle\int (2 + e^{3x})^4 e^{3x} \, dx = \frac{1}{3} \int (2 + e^{3x})^4 (3 e^{3x} \, dx)$

$\left(u = 2 + e^{3x}; \; form, \; \displaystyle\int u^4 \, du\right)$ $\qquad = \dfrac{1}{3} \cdot \dfrac{1}{5}(2 + e^{3x})^5 + C.$

EXERCISE 57

Verify the equality by differentiating the right-hand side, where C is an arbitrary constant.

1. $\int \cos 3x \, dx = \frac{1}{3} \sin 3x + C.$
   2. $\int e^{4x} \, dx = \frac{1}{4} e^{4x} + C.$

3. $\int \sin u \, du = -\cos u + C.$
   4. $\int \sec^2 \frac{1}{2}t \, dt = 2 \tan \frac{1}{2}t + C.$

5. $\displaystyle\int \frac{du}{\sqrt{a^2 - u^2}} = \text{Arcsin}\, \frac{u}{a} + C.$
   6. $\displaystyle\int \frac{e^t \, dt}{1 + e^{2t}} = \text{Arctan}\, e^t + C.$

Integrate. Radicals should be changed to fractional powers. Avoid expanding before integrating, if possible. Any letter other than t, u, v, w, x, etc., represents a constant.

7. $\displaystyle\int \frac{1}{2x^3} \, dx.$
   8. $\displaystyle\int \frac{x^2}{x^{\frac{1}{3}}} \, dx.$
   9. $\displaystyle\int \frac{\sqrt[4]{x^3}}{3x^2} \, dx.$
   10. $\displaystyle\int \frac{2x^3}{\sqrt{x}} \, dx.$

11. $\displaystyle\int \frac{2 + 3u}{u^3} \, du.$
    12. $\displaystyle\int \frac{(2 - t)^2}{\sqrt{t}} \, dt.$
    13. $\displaystyle\int \frac{(3 + \sqrt{u})^2}{u^3} \, du.$

14. $\int (x + 5)^7 \, dx.$
    15. $\int (3 + t)^{-5} \, dt.$
    16. $\int (2x + 3)^4 (2dx).$

17. $\int (3 - 4x)^3 \, dx.$
    18. $\int (3x + 2)^{\frac{3}{4}} \, dx.$
    19. $\int \sqrt{2 + 5x} \, dx.$

20. $\int \sqrt[3]{5x - 7} \, dx.$
    21. $\int (3x^2 + 1)^3 x \, dx.$
    22. $\int (2x^3 + 5)^4 x^2 \, dx.$

23. $\displaystyle\int \frac{du}{(3u + 2)^5}.$
    24. $\displaystyle\int \frac{w \, dw}{(2w^2 - 7)^2}.$
    25. $\displaystyle\int \frac{dz}{\sqrt{3 - 5z}}.$

26. $\int \sin 5x \, dx.$
    27. $\int \cos 4x \, dx.$
    28. $\int \cos \frac{1}{3}x \, dx.$

29. $\int_{-\frac{1}{4}\pi}^{\frac{3}{4}\pi} \sin t \, dt.$
    30. $\int_{-\frac{1}{4}\pi}^{\frac{3}{4}\pi} \cos 2x \, dx.$
    31. $\int \sec^2 3x \, dx.$

32. $\int \csc^2 4x \, dx.$
    33. $\int \csc^2 \frac{1}{4}t \, dt.$
    34. $\int \sec^2 \frac{1}{2}x \, dx.$

35. $\int (x^2 + 2x - 3)^7 (x + 1) dx.$
    36. $\int (5 - 3x - x^3)^4 (1 + x^2) dx.$

37. $\int v\sqrt{3v^2 + 2} \, dv.$
    38. $\int \sin^6 x \cos x \, dx.$
    39. $\int \cos^3 x \sin x \, dx.$

40. $\int \tan^3 x \sec^2 x \, dx.$ **41.** $\int \cot^4 x \csc^2 x \, dx.$ **42.** $\int \cos^4 2x \sin 2x \, dx.$

43. $\int \sin^2 3x \cos 3x \, dx.$ **44.** $\int (3 + \sin x)^8 \cos x \, dx.$

45. $\int (2 + 5 \cos x)^3 \sin x \, dx.$ **46.** $\int (3 + 2 \tan y)^6 \sec^2 y \, dy.$

47. $\int (3 + 5e^t)^6 e^t \, dt.$ **48.** $\int (\sin x^2) x \, dx.$ **49.** $\int (\sec^2 y^3) y^2 \, dy.$

50. $\int \sqrt{x} \cos x^{\frac{3}{2}} \, dx.$ **51.** $\int x^2 \cos x^3 \, dx.$ **52.** $\int e^{2x} \sin e^{2x} \, dx.$

53. $\int \cos mx \, dx.$ **54.** $\int \sec^2 kx \, dx.$ **55.** $\int \csc^2 au \, du.$

56. $\int \dfrac{4 \, dy}{\cos^2 2y}.$ **57.** $\int \dfrac{3 \, dx}{\sin^2 x}.$ **58.** $\int \dfrac{\sin x \, dx}{\cos^5 x}.$

59. $\int \dfrac{\cos 2x \, dx}{\sin^4 2x}.$ **60.** $\int \dfrac{(t - 1) dt}{\sqrt{2t^2 - 4t}}.$ **61.** $\int \dfrac{\sec^2 2t \, dt}{\tan^4 2t}.$

62. $\int_1^3 (\ln x)^4 \dfrac{dx}{x}.$ **63.** $\int \dfrac{\sin t \, dt}{\sqrt{2 - 3 \cos t}}.$ **64.** $\int \dfrac{\sec^2 t \, dt}{\sqrt[3]{2 + \tan t}}.$

65. $\int (2t + 1)\sin (t^2 + t) dt.$ **66.** $\int x^{-2}(1 - x^{-1})^6 \, dx.$

67. $\int \dfrac{(\text{Arctan } x)^2 \, dx}{1 + x^2}.$ **68.** $\int \dfrac{\text{Arcsin } x}{\sqrt{1 - x^2}} \, dx.$

69. $\int \cos t \sqrt[4]{\sin t} \, dt.$ **70.** $\int_{-5}^{-8} \sqrt[3]{2 - 5x} \, dx.$

71. $\int \dfrac{du}{\tan^5 u \cos^2 u}.$ **72.** $\int \dfrac{e^{-x} \, dx}{(3 + e^{-x})^4}.$ **73.** $\int \dfrac{e^x - e^{-x}}{(e^x + e^{-x})^2} \, dx.$

Find the differential or derivative as stated.

74. $\dfrac{d}{dx}\left[\int (4x^{\frac{10}{3}} - 1)^7 \sin x \, dx \right].$ **75.** $\dfrac{d}{dt}\left[\int (2t^5 + \cos t)^8 \, dt \right].$

76. $d\left[\int \dfrac{\cos (\ln x)}{\sec x} \, dx \right].$ **77.** $d\left[\int \dfrac{(\sec u)e^{u^2}}{\ln u} \, du \right].$

Find the area of the region in the xy-plane described in the problem. Draw a rough graph to aid in the solution.

78. Bounded by the x-axis and one arch of $y = \sin x.$

79. Bounded by the y-axis, and the curves $y = \sin x$ and $y = \cos x$ from $x = 0$ to the first intersection of the curves where $x > 0.$

80. Bounded by $y = x + \sin 2x$ and the line $y = x$, from $x = 0$ to $x = \pi.$

81. Bounded by the x-axis, the lines $x = \frac{3}{2}$ and $x = 4$, and the curve $y = \sqrt{2x + 1}.$ Obtain the result correct to three decimal places.

82. Find the volume of the solid of revolution obtained if the region in an xy-plane bounded by the coordinate axes, the curve $y = \sec x$, and the line $x = \frac{1}{4}\pi$ is revolved about the x-axis.

83. Prove the results for $\int \cos u \, du, \int \sec^2 u \, du,$ and $\int \csc^2 u \, du.$

84. Find the mean value of the function $\cos 3x \sin^3 3x$ over the interval $0 \leq x \leq \frac{3}{2}\pi.$

101. Standard indefinite integrals

$$\int u^n \, du = \frac{u^{n+1}}{n+1} + C. \qquad (n \neq -1) \tag{I}$$

$$\int \frac{du}{u} = \ln |u| + C. \tag{II}$$

$$\int a^u \, du = \frac{a^u}{\ln a} + C. \qquad (a > 0, \, a \neq 1) \tag{III}$$

$$\int e^u \, du = e^u + C. \tag{III}'$$

$$\int \sin u \, du = -\cos u + C. \tag{IV}$$

$$\int \cos u \, du = \sin u + C. \tag{V}$$

$$\int \tan u \, du = -\ln |\cos u| = \ln |\sec u| + C. \tag{VI}$$

$$\int \cot u \, du = \ln |\sin u| = -\ln |\csc u| + C. \tag{VII}$$

$$\int \sec^2 u \, du = \tan u + C. \tag{VIII}$$

$$\int \csc^2 u \, du = -\cot u + C. \tag{IX}$$

$$\int \sec u \, du = \ln |\sec u + \tan u| + C. \tag{X}$$

$$\int \csc u \, du = \ln |\csc u - \cot u| + C. \tag{XI}$$

$$\int \sec u \tan u \, du = \sec u + C. \tag{XII}$$

$$\int \csc u \cot u \, du = -\csc u + C. \tag{XIII}$$

$$\int \frac{du}{a^2 + u^2} = \frac{1}{a} \operatorname{Arctan} \frac{u}{a} + C. \tag{XIV}$$

$$\int \frac{du}{\sqrt{a^2 - u^2}} = \operatorname{Arcsin} \frac{u}{a} + C. \tag{XV}$$

$$\int \frac{du}{u^2 - a^2} = \frac{1}{2a} \ln \left| \frac{u-a}{u+a} \right| + C. \tag{XVI}$$

$$\int \frac{du}{a^2 - u^2} = \frac{1}{2a} \ln \left| \frac{a+u}{a-u} \right| + C. \tag{XVI$_j$}$$

$$\int \frac{du}{\sqrt{u^2 \pm a^2}} = \ln |u + \sqrt{u^2 \pm a^2}| + C. \tag{XVII}$$

$$\int \frac{du}{u\sqrt{u^2 - a^2}} = \frac{1}{a} \operatorname{Arcsec} \frac{u}{a} + C. \tag{XVIII}$$

The student will wish to memorize the preceding standard forms (I)–(XV), and possibly the remaining forms. In later sections, we shall consider proofs for those of the formulas which are not obtained instantaneously from fundamental differentials. In each formula, u may be any differentiable function of the independent variable, which may be u itself as a simple special case. No result in the list is to be used with any value of u for which the integrand or the right-hand side is imaginary, or otherwise undefined. Formula (XVIII) is the least essential for work in this text.

Note 1. In any formula where a *positive constant* is denoted by a^2, we agree to let a represent a *positive number*. In (XVII), "$+ a^2$" and "$- a^2$" on the left correspond to "$+ a^2$" and "$- a^2$" on the right, respectively.

102. Exponential forms

If u is any differentiable function of x, and $a > 0$ and $a \neq 1$,

$$\int a^u \, du = \frac{a^u}{\ln a} + C. \tag{III}$$

Proof. From (8) on page 210, $da^u = a^u(\ln a)du$. Hence,

$$\int a^u \, du = \int d\left(\frac{a^u}{\ln a}\right) = \frac{a^u}{\ln a} + C.$$

If $a = e$ then $\ln a = 1$ and (III) gives

$$\int e^u \, du = e^u + C. \tag{III}$$

ILLUSTRATION 1. From (III), $\qquad \int 2^x \, dx = \frac{2^x}{\ln 2} + C.$

ILLUSTRATION 2. With $u = 3 - 4x$, then $du = - 4 \, dx$ and

$$\int e^{3-4x} \, dx = -\frac{1}{4} \int e^{3-4x}(- 4 \, dx) = -\frac{1}{4} \int e^u \, du$$

$$= - \tfrac{1}{4}e^u + C = - \tfrac{1}{4}e^{3-4x} + C.$$

ILLUSTRATION 3. With $u = \tan 3x$ in (III)′,

$$(du = 3 \sec^2 3x \, dx) \qquad \int e^{\tan 3x} \sec^2 3x \, dx = \frac{1}{3} \int e^{\tan 3x} (3 \sec^2 3x \, dx)$$

$$= \frac{1}{3} \int e^u \, du = \frac{1}{3} e^u + C = \frac{1}{3} e^{\tan 3x} + C.$$

ILLUSTRATION 4. $\qquad \int \frac{dx}{\sqrt[4]{e^{3x}}} = \int e^{-\frac{3}{4}x} \, dx$

$$= -\frac{4}{3} \int e^{-\frac{3}{4}x} \cdot \left(-\frac{3}{4} \, dx\right) = -\frac{4}{3} e^{-\frac{3}{4}x} + C,$$

where we used (III)′ with $u = - \tfrac{3}{4}x$.

EXERCISE 58

Integrate. Any letter other than t, x, y, z, and u represents a constant.

1. $\int e^{3x}\,dx.$ 2. $\int 3^x\,dx.$ 3. $\int 10^x\,dx.$ 4. $\int e^{-x}\,dx.$

5. $\int e^{2+5x}\,dx.$ 6. $\int 2^x e^x\,dx.$ 7. $\int a^x e^x\,dx.$ 8. $\int e^{-4x}\,dx.$

9. $\int \dfrac{dx}{e^{2x}}.$ 10. $\int \dfrac{(2+e^x)\,dx}{e^{3x}}.$ 11. $\int \dfrac{4\,dx}{e^{\frac{1}{2}x}}.$

12. $\int x^3 e^{x^4}\,dx.$ 13. $\int x^2 e^{-x^3}\,dx.$ 14. $\int \sqrt{e^t}\,dt.$

15. $\int \dfrac{e^{\sqrt{x}}}{\sqrt{x}}\,dx.$ 16. $\int \dfrac{dt}{\sqrt[3]{e^t}}.$ 17. $\int \dfrac{x\,dx}{e^{x^2}}.$

18. $\int e^{3-4t}\,dt.$ 19. $\int \sqrt{x}\,e^{x\sqrt{x}}\,dx.$ 20. $\int 5^{3u}\,du.$

21. $\int 10^{cx}\,dx.$ 22. $\int_{-2}^{0} 3xe^{-x^2}\,dx.$ 23. $\int x^{-2}e^{\frac{1}{x}}\,dx.$

24. $\int e^{3\ln x}\,dx.$ 25. $\int e^{\sin u}\cos u\,du.$ 26. $\int be^{-nt}\,dt.$

27. $\int (e^x - e^{-2x})^2\,dx.$ 28. $\int e^{\cot z}\csc^2 z\,dz.$

29. $\int (2x-1)e^{x^2-x+3}\,dx.$ 30. $\int e^{\sin 2y}\cos 2y\,dy.$

31. $\int_{\pi}^{\frac{3}{4}\pi} e^{\tan z}\sec^2 z\,dz.$ 32. $\int e^{-y^2+\ln y}\,dy.$

33. $\int e^z\sqrt{3+4e^z}\,dz.$ 34. $\int (e^{ax}+e^{-ax})^2\,dx.$

35. $\int \dfrac{e^u\,du}{(2-3e^u)^3}.$ 36. $\int \dfrac{e^{\cos^2 y}}{\csc 2y}\,dy.$

37. $\int \dfrac{e^{\text{Arctan } y}}{2+2y^2}\,dy.$ 38. $\int \dfrac{e^{-\tan 2u}}{\cos^2 2u}\,du.$

Find the area of the region of the xy-plane which is described.

39. The region bounded by the x-axis, the curve $y = e^x$, and the lines $x = -1$ and $x = 2$.

40. The region bounded by the coordinate axes, the curve $y = e^{-x}$, and the line $x = 3$.

41. The region between $y = \frac{1}{2}(e^x + e^{-x})$ and $y = \frac{1}{2}e^x$, from $x = 0$ to $x = 1$.

42. The region bounded by the catenary $y = \frac{1}{2}a(e^{\frac{x}{a}} + e^{-\frac{x}{a}})$, the lines $x = \pm\frac{1}{2}a$, and the x-axis.

43–44. Find the volumes of the solids of revolution obtained if the regions of Problems 39 and 40, respectively, are revolved about the x-axis.

45. Find the mean value of $e^{\frac{1}{2}x}$ over the interval $1 \leqq x \leqq 3$.

103. The logarithmic form

If u is any differentiable function of x, where $u \neq 0$ at any value of x which is involved, then

$$\int \frac{du}{u} = \ln|u| + C. \tag{II}$$

Proof. 1. We recall that $\ln u$ is defined only when $u > 0$. Then, $d \ln u = du/u$. Hence, by (7) on page 209,

$$(if\ u > 0) \qquad \int \frac{du}{u} = \int d(\ln u) = \ln u + C. \qquad (1)$$

2. Now, suppose that $u < 0$. Then, since $d(-u) = -du$, by use of (1) with u replaced by $-u$ we obtain

$$(if\ u < 0) \qquad \int \frac{du}{u} = \int \frac{-du}{-u} = \int \frac{d(-u)}{(-u)} = \ln (-u) + C. \qquad (2)$$

3. If $u > 0$ then $|u| = u$. If $u < 0$ then $|u| = -u$. Hence, in both (1) and (2), the right-hand side can be written $\ln |u| + C$, which proves (II) for any function $u(x)$ which is always of one sign.

Note 1. For any constant $C \neq 0$, let $k > 0$ be defined by $k = e^C$, or $\ln k = C$. Then, from (II),

$$\int \frac{du}{u} = \ln |u| + C = \ln |u| + \ln k, \ or$$

$$\int \frac{du}{u} = \ln k|u|. \qquad (II)$$

ILLUSTRATION 1. $\qquad \int_1^{e^2} \frac{dx}{x} = \ln |x| \Big]_1^{e^2} = \ln e^2 - \ln 1 = 2.$

ILLUSTRATION 2. $\qquad \int_{-5}^{-2} \frac{dx}{x} = \ln |x| \Big]_{-5}^{-2} = \ln |-2| - \ln |-5|$

(Table III) $\qquad\qquad = \ln 2 - \ln 5 = -.91629.$

ILLUSTRATION 3. With $u = 1 + 3x$ and $du = 3\ dx$,

$$\int \frac{dx}{1 + 3x} = \frac{1}{3} \int \frac{3\ dx}{1 + 3x} = \frac{1}{3} \int \frac{du}{u} = \frac{1}{3} \ln |1 + 3x| + C.$$

ILLUSTRATION 4. $\qquad\qquad \int \frac{(2x + 1)dx}{2x^2 + 2x + 3} = \frac{1}{2} \int \frac{(4x + 2)dx}{2x^2 + 2x + 3}$

$[u = 2x^2 + 2x + 3;\ du = (4x + 2)dx] \qquad = \frac{1}{2} \int \frac{du}{u} = \frac{1}{2} \ln |u| + C$

$$= \tfrac{1}{2} \ln |2x^2 + 2x + 3| + C.$$

ILLUSTRATION 5. With $u = 1 + 3 \sec 2x$,

$(du = 6 \sec 2x \tan 2x\ dx) \qquad \int \frac{\sec 2x \tan 2x\ dx}{1 + 3 \sec 2x} = \frac{1}{6} \int \frac{du}{u}$

$$= \tfrac{1}{6} \ln |1 + 3 \sec 2x| + C.$$

EXAMPLE 1. Obtain $\int \frac{6x^2 + 5}{2x - 2}\ dx.$

SOLUTION. In the integrand, first carry out long division until the remainder is of lower degree than the denominator:

$$\int \frac{6x^2 + 5}{2x - 2} \, dx = \int \left(3x + 3 + \frac{11}{2x - 2} \right) dx$$

$$= \tfrac{3}{2}x^2 + 3x + \tfrac{11}{2} \ln \mid 2x - 2 \mid + C.$$

ILLUSTRATION 6. $\int \dfrac{3e^{2x}}{1 + 4e^{2x}} \, dx = \dfrac{3}{8} \int \dfrac{8e^{2x} \, dx}{1 + 4e^{2x}}.$

$(u = 1 + 4e^{2x};\ du = 8e^{2x} \, dx)$ $= \tfrac{3}{8} \ln (1 + 4e^{2x}) + C.$

No absolute value signs from (II) are used with $(1 + 4e^{2x})$, because it is positive for all values of x.

ILLUSTRATION 7. $\displaystyle\int_{.235}^{1} \frac{dx}{x} = \ln x \Big]_{.235}^{1} = \ln 1 - \ln .235 = 1.44817.$

To obtain $\ln .235$ from Table III, we wrote $.235 = 2.35/10$:

$$\ln .235 = \ln 2.35 - \ln 10 = .85442 - 2.30259 = -1.44817.$$

(Similar details would give $\ln .0235 = \ln 2.35 - 2 \ln 10.$)

EXERCISE 59

1. Compute by use of Table III if possible: $\displaystyle\int_{2}^{7} \frac{du}{u};\ \int_{-4}^{2} \frac{du}{u}.$

HINT. The second integral is not admissible at this stage because the range for u includes $u = 0$, where the integrand $1/u$ is undefined.

Integrate. Any letter other than t, x, y, z, and u represents a constant.

2. $\displaystyle\int \frac{dx}{x + 2}.$ 3. $\displaystyle\int \frac{dt}{2t + 1}.$ 4. $\displaystyle\int \frac{du}{1 - 3u}.$

5. $\displaystyle\int \frac{2x \, dx}{1 + x^2}.$ 6. $\displaystyle\int \frac{\cos x \, dx}{1 + \sin x}.$ 7. $\displaystyle\int \frac{\sec^2 x \, dx}{1 - 2 \tan x}.$

8. $\displaystyle\int \frac{x^2 \, dx}{2 - 5x^3}.$ 9. $\displaystyle\int \frac{\sec t \tan t \, dt}{1 + 4 \sec t}.$ 10. $\displaystyle\int \frac{e^x \, dx}{1 + 2e^x}.$

11. $\displaystyle\int \frac{\cos u}{\sin u} \, du.$ 12. $\displaystyle\int \frac{\sin t}{\cos t} \, dt.$ 13. $\displaystyle\int \frac{\sin 2t}{\cos 2t} \, dt.$

14. $\displaystyle\int \frac{4x^2 + 2}{2x + 1} \, dx.$ 15. $\displaystyle\int \frac{t^3 + 4t^2}{t + 3} \, dt.$ 16. $\displaystyle\int_{1}^{3} \frac{(2x + 4)dx}{x^2 + 4x}.$

17. $\displaystyle\int \frac{(6x + 2)dx}{3x^2 + 2x + 5}.$ 18. $\displaystyle\int \frac{(x + 2)dx}{3 - 4x - x^2}.$

19. $\displaystyle\int \frac{e^x + e^{-x}}{e^x - e^{-x}} \, dx.$ 20. $\displaystyle\int \frac{\csc^2 y \, dy}{1 + 2 \cot y}.$ 21. $\displaystyle\int \frac{e^{2u} \, du}{3 + 4e^{2u}}.$

22. $\displaystyle\int \frac{(2 + \sin z)dz}{2z - \cos z}.$ 23. $\displaystyle\int \frac{\sec^2 3t \, dt}{2 + \tan 3t}.$ 24. $\displaystyle\int \frac{\sin kt \, dt}{a + b \cos kt}.$

25. $\displaystyle\int \frac{dy}{y(2 + \ln y)}.$

26. $\displaystyle\int \frac{(1 + \ln y)dy}{1 + y \ln y}.$

27. $\displaystyle\int \frac{\cos u \sin u\; du}{1 + \cos^2 u}.$

28. $\displaystyle\int \frac{2 \sin \frac{1}{2}x\; dx}{3 + 5 \cos \frac{1}{2}x}.$

29. $\displaystyle\int \frac{e^{2x}\; dx}{2e^x + 1}.$

30. $\displaystyle\int \frac{e^{-3x}\; dx}{1 + e^{-x}}.$

31. $\displaystyle\int \frac{\sin 2x\; dx}{5 + \sin^2 x}.$

32. $\displaystyle\int \frac{\csc 2y \cot 2y\; dy}{1 + 3 \csc 2y}.$

33. $\displaystyle\int \frac{dx}{(1 + x^2)\, \mathrm{Arctan}\; x}.$

34. $\displaystyle\int \frac{du}{\sqrt{1 - 4u^2}\, \mathrm{Arcsin}\; 2u}.$

Find the area of the region of the xy-plane which is described.

35. The region bounded by the hyperbola $xy = 4$, the x-axis, and the lines $x = 1$ and $x = 5$. Compute accurately to 3 decimal places.

36. The region bounded by the curve $y = 1/(x - 1)$, the x-axis, and the lines $x = 1.463$ and $x = 4$.

37. The region between the curves $xy = 1$ and $x^2 y = 1$, from the line $x = 1$ to the line $x = 3$.

38. Find the mean value of the function $2/(x - 3)$ over the interval $4 \leqq x \leqq 9$.

104. Standard trigonometric forms

Formulas (IV), (V), (VIII), and (IX) of page 215 have been met before.

ILLUSTRATION 1. By use of (IV) with $u = \frac{1}{3}x$,

$$\int \sin \frac{1}{3} x\; dx = 3 \int \left(\sin \frac{1}{3} x \right)\left(\frac{1}{3}\, dx \right) = - 3 \cos \frac{1}{3} x + C.$$

If u is any differentiable function of x,

$$\int \tan u\; du = \ln | \sec u | + C. \tag{VI}$$

Proof of (VI). $\displaystyle\qquad \int \tan u\; du = \int \frac{\sin u\; du}{\cos u} = - \int \frac{- \sin u\; du}{\cos u}.$

With $v = \cos u$ and $dv = - \sin u\; du$, we obtain

$$\int \tan u\; du = - \int \frac{dv}{v} = - \ln | \cos u | + C. \tag{1}$$

Since $\displaystyle\qquad \sec u = \frac{1}{\cos u}, \quad and \quad \ln 1 = 0,$

$$\ln | \sec u | = \ln 1 - \ln | \cos u | = - \ln | \cos u |.$$

Hence, from (1), $\displaystyle\qquad \int \tan u\; du = \ln | \sec u | + C.$

The student will prove (VII) of page 215 similarly as an exercise.

We obtain (XII) and (XIII) of page 215 immediately from

$$d \sec u = \sec u \tan u\; du \quad and \quad d(- \csc u) = \csc u \cot u\; du.$$

ILLUSTRATION 2. By use of (VII) of page 215, we obtain

$$\int \cot \frac{1}{2} x \ dx = 2 \int \left(\cot \frac{1}{2} x \right) \left(\frac{1}{2} dx \right) = -2 \ln \left| \csc \frac{1}{2} x \right| + C.$$

Proof of (X), *page* 215. $\displaystyle \int \sec u \ du = \int \frac{\sec u \ (\sec u + \tan u) du}{\sec u + \tan u}.$

If we let $v = \sec u + \tan u,$ *then* $dv = (\sec u \tan u + \sec^2 u) du.$

Hence, $\displaystyle \int \sec u \ du = \int \frac{dv}{v} = \ln |v| + C$

$$= \ln | \sec u + \tan u | + C.$$

Similarly, the student will prove (XI) later.

ILLUSTRATION 3. $\displaystyle \int \frac{3 + \sin 2x}{\cos 2x} \ dx = 3 \int \sec 2x \ dx + \int \tan 2x \ dx$

$$= \frac{3}{2} \int (\sec 2x)(2 \ dx) + \frac{1}{2} \int (\tan 2x)(2 \ dx)$$

$$= \tfrac{3}{2} \ln | \sec 2x + \tan 2x | + \tfrac{1}{2} \ln | \sec 2x | + C.$$

ILLUSTRATION 4. $\displaystyle \int_{\frac{1}{4}\pi}^{\frac{3}{8}\pi} \tan 2x \ dx = \frac{1}{2} \int_{\frac{1}{4}\pi}^{\frac{3}{8}\pi} (\tan 2x)(2 \ dx)$

$$= \frac{1}{2} \ln | \sec 2x | \ \Big]_{\frac{1}{4}\pi}^{\frac{3}{8}\pi} = \frac{1}{2} (\ln | \sec \tfrac{3}{4}\pi | - \ln | \sec \tfrac{2}{3}\pi |)$$

$$= \tfrac{1}{2}(\ln \sqrt{2} - \ln 2) = -\tfrac{1}{4} \ln 2 = -.17329 \qquad \text{(Table III)}$$

105. Elementary trigonometric transformations

The following identities will prove useful at present:

$$2 \sin^2 \alpha = 1 - \cos 2\alpha; \quad 2 \cos^2 \alpha = 1 + \cos 2\alpha; \qquad (1)$$

$$\sin^2 \alpha + \cos^2 \alpha = 1; \quad 1 + \tan^2 \alpha = \sec^2 \alpha; \quad 1 + \cot^2 \alpha = \csc^2 \alpha. \qquad (2)$$

To evaluate integrals of the form $\int \sin^2 u \ du$ or $\int \cos^2 u \ du$, where u is a differentiable function of x, use (1) to introduce the double angle.

ILLUSTRATION 1. By use of (1) with $\alpha = 2x$,

$$\int \cos^2 2x \ dx = \frac{1}{2} \int (1 + \cos 4x) dx = \frac{1}{2} \int dx + \frac{1}{2} \int \cos 4x \ dx$$

$$= \frac{1}{2} x + \frac{1}{8} \int (\cos 4x)(4 \ dx) = \frac{1}{2} x + \frac{1}{8} \sin 4x + C.$$

ILLUSTRATION 2. From (2), $\tan^2 3x = \sec^2 3x - 1.$ Hence,

$$\int \tan^2 3x \ dx = \int (\sec^2 3x - 1) dx = \int \sec^2 3x \ dx - \int dx$$

$$= \tfrac{1}{3} \int (\sec^2 3x)(3 \ dx) - x = \tfrac{1}{3} \tan 3x - x + C.$$

EXERCISE 60

Integrate. Letters a, b, and k represent constants.

1. $\int \tan 2x \, dx.$ **2.** $\int \csc 3x \, dx.$ **3.** $\int \cot \frac{1}{4}x \, dx.$

4. $\int \sec 5x \, dx.$ **5.** $\int \csc^2 4t \, dt.$ **6.** $\int \tan ku \, du.$

7. $\int \dfrac{dv}{\sin v}.$ **8.** $\int \dfrac{dy}{\cos 2y}.$ **9.** $\int \dfrac{dv}{\sec 3v}.$ **10.** $\int \dfrac{dx}{\cot 5x}.$

11. $\int \sec \frac{1}{2}x \tan \frac{1}{2}x \, dx.$ **12.** $\int \csc 4x \cot 4x \, dx.$

13. $\int \sec ax \, dx.$ **14.** $\int \csc bx \, dx.$ **15.** $\int \cos^2 x \, dx.$

16. $\int \sin^2 x \, dx.$ **17.** $\int \cos^2 3x \, dx.$ **18.** $\int \tan^2 x \, dx.$

19. $\int \cot^2 x \, dx.$ **20.** $\int \sin^2 3x \, dx.$ **21.** $\int \cos^2 \frac{1}{2}x \, dx.$

22. $\int \cos^2 ax \, dx.$ **23.** $\int \tan^2 4u \, du.$ **24.** $\int \cot^2 \frac{1}{2}u \, du.$

25. $\int (\sec y - \tan y)^2 \, dy.$ **26.** $\int (\tan x + \cot x)^2 \, dx.$

27. $\int \dfrac{\sec^2 t \, dt}{4 + 3 \tan t}.$ **28.** $\int \dfrac{2 + \cos 3x}{\sin 3x} \, dx.$

29. $\int_{-\frac{1}{4}\pi}^{\frac{1}{4}\pi} \tan y \, dy.$ **30.** $\int_{\frac{1}{3}\pi}^{\frac{2}{3}\pi} \sec u \, du.$

31. $\int (\sec 2t - 1)^2 \, dt.$ **32.** $\int (\tan u + 2)^2 \, du.$ **33.** $\int (\sin x - 3)^2 \, dx.$

34. $\int \dfrac{e^x}{\cot e^x} \, dx.$ **35.** $\int \dfrac{\sec 2e^{-x}}{e^x} \, dx.$ **36.** $\int \dfrac{x^2}{\tan x^3} \, dx.$

37. $\int \dfrac{\cot (\ln x)}{x} \, dx.$ **38.** $\int \dfrac{\sin e^{-x}}{e^x} \, dx.$ **39.** $\int \dfrac{e^{2x} \, dx}{\cot e^{2x}}.$

40. $\int \dfrac{(2 + \sec^2 \frac{1}{2}y) dy}{2y + 2 \tan \frac{1}{2}y}.$ **41.** $\int \dfrac{(3 + 2x) dx}{\csc (3x + x^2)}.$

Find the area of the region of the xy-plane which is described.

42. The region bounded by the x-axis, the curve $y = \tan x$, and the lines $x = -\frac{1}{4}\pi$ and $x = \frac{1}{3}\pi$.

43. The region bounded below by the curve $y = \sec x$ and above by the line $y = \sqrt{2}$, between $x = -\frac{1}{4}\pi$ and $x = \frac{1}{4}\pi$.

Find the volume of the solid of revolution obtained by revolving the specified region of the xy-plane about the x-axis.

44. Bounded by the x-axis and one arch of $y = \sin x$.

45. Bounded by $y = \sec x$, the coordinate axes, and the line $x = \frac{1}{4}\pi$.

46. Bounded by $y = \tan x$, the x-axis, and the line $x = \frac{1}{3}\pi$.

Find the mean value of the function over the given x-interval.

47. $\sin x; \ 0 \leqq x \leqq 2\pi.$ **48.** $\sin x; \ 0 \leqq x \leqq \frac{3}{2}\pi.$

49. $\tan x; \ 0 \leqq x \leqq \frac{1}{4}\pi.$ **50.** $\sec x; \ 0 \leqq x \leqq \frac{1}{4}\pi.$

51. Prove (VII) of page 215.

106. Inverse trigonometric forms

At this point it is important to recall that the principal value functions Arcsin v and Arctan v have the following ranges:

$$-\tfrac{1}{2}\pi \le \text{Arcsin } v \le \tfrac{1}{2}\pi; \qquad -\tfrac{1}{2}\pi < \text{Arctan } v < \tfrac{1}{2}\pi. \tag{1}$$

We recall the graphs in Figures 137 and 138.

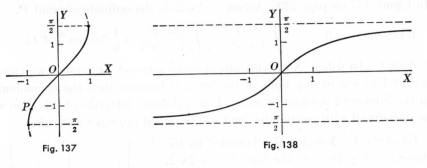

Fig. 137   Fig. 138

If u is any differentiable function of x,

$$\int \frac{du}{a^2 + u^2} = \frac{1}{a} \text{ Arctan } \frac{u}{a} + C. \tag{XIV}$$

In particular,
$$\int \frac{du}{1 + u^2} = \text{Arctan } u + C. \tag{2}$$

Proof of (XIV). From (8) on page 210,

$$d \text{ Arctan } \frac{u}{a} = \frac{1}{1 + \dfrac{u^2}{a^2}} \cdot d \left(\frac{u}{a}\right) = \frac{a \, du}{a^2 + u^2}, \text{ or}$$

$$\frac{du}{a^2 + u^2} = d \left(\frac{1}{a} \text{ Arctan } \frac{u}{a}\right). \tag{3}$$

From (7) on page 209,

$$\int \frac{du}{a^2 + u^2} = \int d \left(\frac{1}{a} \text{ Arctan } \frac{u}{a}\right) = \frac{1}{a} \text{ Arctan } \frac{u}{a} + C.$$

Similarly, we obtain

$$\int \frac{du}{\sqrt{a^2 - u^2}} = \text{Arcsin } \frac{u}{a} + C, \tag{XV}$$

by first verifying that $d \left(\text{Arcsin } \dfrac{u}{a}\right) = \dfrac{du}{\sqrt{a^2 - u^2}}.$

ILLUSTRATION 1. By use of (XIV) with $a = \sqrt{5}$ and $u = 2x$,

$$\int \frac{dx}{5 + 4x^2} = \frac{1}{2} \int \frac{2 \, dx}{5 + (2x)^2} = \frac{1}{2\sqrt{5}} \text{ Arctan } \frac{2x}{\sqrt{5}} + C.$$

ILLUSTRATION 2. By use of $a = 2$ and $u = 3x$ in (XV),

$$\int_{-\frac{1}{3}\sqrt{3}}^{\frac{1}{3}\sqrt{2}} \frac{dx}{\sqrt{4 - 9x^2}} = \frac{1}{3} \int_{-\frac{1}{3}\sqrt{3}}^{\frac{1}{3}\sqrt{2}} \frac{3 \, dx}{\sqrt{2^2 - (3x)^2}} = \frac{1}{3} \operatorname{Arcsin} \frac{3x}{2}\bigg]_{-\frac{1}{3}\sqrt{3}}^{\frac{1}{3}\sqrt{2}}$$

$$= \frac{1}{3}\left[\operatorname{Arcsin} \frac{\sqrt{2}}{2} - \operatorname{Arcsin}\left(-\frac{\sqrt{3}}{2}\right)\right] = \frac{1}{3}\left[\frac{\pi}{4} - \left(-\frac{\pi}{3}\right)\right] = \frac{7\pi}{36}.$$

In Figure 137 on page 223, $\operatorname{Arcsin}\left(-\frac{1}{2}\sqrt{3}\right)$ is the ordinate of point P.

ILLUSTRATION 3. $\qquad \int \frac{x^2 \, dx}{4 + x^6} = \frac{1}{3} \int \frac{3x^2 \, dx}{4 + (x^3)^2} = \frac{1}{6} \operatorname{Arctan} \frac{x^3}{2} + C.$

Note 1. In using (XV) with any definite integral, at present we cannot permit $|u| = a$ in any limit of the integral because then the denominator in the integrand is equal to zero. Later, definite integrals of this type will be introduced with restrictions, and will be called *improper integrals*.

EXAMPLE 1. A region R is bounded by the curve $y = 4/\sqrt{16 - x^2}$, the lines $x = \pm 2\sqrt{2}$, and the x-axis. Find the area, A, of R.

SOLUTION. The graph of $y = 4/\sqrt{16 - x^2}$, in Figure 139, has the lines $x = \pm 4$ as asymptotes, and y is not defined if $|x| = 4$. From symmetry, A is twice the area between $x = 0$ and $x = 2\sqrt{2}$:

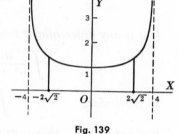

Fig. 139

$$A = 2 \int_0^{2\sqrt{2}} y \, dx = 2 \int_0^{2\sqrt{2}} \frac{4 \, dx}{\sqrt{16 - x^2}} = 8 \operatorname{Arcsin} \frac{x}{4}\bigg]_0^{2\sqrt{2}} = 8\left(\frac{\pi}{4}\right) = 2\pi.$$

Note 2. We could express

$$\int -\frac{du}{a^2 + u^2} \quad and \quad \int -\frac{du}{\sqrt{a^2 - u^2}}$$

in terms of the Arccotangent function and Arccosine function, respectively. However, such formulas are not needed. Instead, we merely multiply by -1 on each side in (XIV) and (XV).

EXERCISE 61

Integrate.

1. $\displaystyle\int \frac{dx}{x^2 + 4}.$

2. $\displaystyle\int \frac{dx}{\sqrt{9 - x^2}}.$

3. $\displaystyle\int \frac{dx}{\sqrt{9 - 25x^2}}.$

4. $\displaystyle\int \frac{dx}{4 + 25x^2}.$

5. $\displaystyle\int \frac{dy}{\sqrt{16 - 9y^2}}.$

6. $\displaystyle\int \frac{dt}{\sqrt{121 - 9t^2}}.$

7. $\displaystyle\int_{-\frac{1}{2}}^{\frac{1}{2}} \frac{dt}{\sqrt{1 - t^2}}.$

8. $\displaystyle\int_1^{\sqrt{3}} \frac{du}{1 + u^2}.$

9. $\displaystyle\int_{-1}^{\sqrt{2}} \frac{dx}{\sqrt{4 - x^2}}.$

10. $\displaystyle\int_{-1}^{3} \frac{dz}{3 + z^2}$.

11. $\displaystyle\int_{0}^{-1} \frac{dv}{\sqrt{2 - v^2}}$.

12. $\displaystyle\int_{-\frac{2}{3}}^{0} \frac{dz}{4 + 9z^2}$.

13. $\displaystyle\int_{0}^{.228} \frac{dx}{\sqrt{1 - 4x^2}}$.

14. $\displaystyle\int_{-\frac{1}{2}}^{\frac{1}{6}\sqrt{3}} \frac{dx}{\sqrt{3 - 9x^2}}$.

15. $\displaystyle\int \frac{\cos\theta \, d\theta}{49 + 4\sin^2\theta}$.

16. $\displaystyle\int \frac{\sec^2 t \, dt}{1 + 9\tan^2 t}$.

17. $\displaystyle\int \frac{x^2 \, dx}{9 + x^6}$.

18. $\displaystyle\int \frac{\csc^2 x \, dx}{\sqrt{5 - \cot^2 x}}$.

19. $\displaystyle\int \frac{x \, dx}{4 + x^4}$.

20. $\displaystyle\int \frac{e^{\frac{1}{3}u} \, du}{9 + \sqrt[3]{e^{2u}}}$.

21. $\displaystyle\int \frac{(8x^2 + 4)dx}{25 + 4x^2}$.

22. $\displaystyle\int \frac{\sec u \tan u \, du}{\sqrt{4 - \sec^2 u}}$.

23. $\displaystyle\int \frac{du}{u\sqrt{1 - (\ln u)^2}}$.

24. $\displaystyle\int \frac{e^x \, dx}{\sqrt{16 - 9e^{2x}}}$.

25. $\displaystyle\int \frac{dx}{\sqrt{4 - (2 + x)^2}}$.

26. $\displaystyle\int \frac{dz}{121 + (2z + 1)^2}$.

27. $\displaystyle\int \frac{dx}{9 + 25(2x + 3)^2}$.

28. $\displaystyle\int \frac{dx}{\sqrt{9 - 4(2 - 3x)^2}}$.

Find the area of the region of the xy-plane which is described.

29. Bounded by the x-axis, $y = 1/\sqrt{4 - x^2}$, and the lines $x = \pm 1$.

30. Bounded by the x-axis, $y = 1/\sqrt{9 - 25x^2}$, and the lines $x = \pm \frac{3}{10}\sqrt{3}$.

31. Bounded by $y = 1/(9 + 4x^2)$, and the lines $x = -\frac{3}{2}\sqrt{3}$, $x = \frac{3}{2}$, and $y = 0$.

32. Bounded by $y = 1/(1 + 9x^2)$, and the lines $x = -\frac{1}{3}\sqrt{3}$, $x = .43$, and $y = 0$.

33. Bounded by the x-axis, the y-axis, $y = 1/\sqrt{3 - x^2}$, and the line $x = \frac{1}{2}\sqrt{6}$.

★34. Prove formula (XVIII), and use it to obtain the following integrals:

$$\int \frac{dy}{y\sqrt{4y^2 - 9}} \, ; \qquad \int \frac{dx}{x\sqrt{9x^2 - 25}} \, ; \qquad \int \frac{dx}{x\sqrt{x^2 - 4}}.$$

107. Certain logarithmic formulas

If u is any differentiable function of x, then

$$\int \frac{du}{u^2 - a^2} = \frac{1}{2a} \ln\left|\frac{u - a}{u + a}\right| + C; \qquad\qquad \text{(XVI)}$$

$$\int \frac{du}{a^2 - u^2} = \frac{1}{2a} \ln\left|\frac{a + u}{a - u}\right| + C. \qquad\qquad \text{(XVI)}'$$

Proof of XVI. We verify the identity

$$\frac{1}{u^2 - a^2} = \frac{1}{2a}\left(\frac{1}{u - a} - \frac{1}{u + a}\right).$$

Hence,
$$\int \frac{du}{u^2 - a^2} = \frac{1}{2a}\left[\int \frac{du}{u - a} - \int \frac{du}{u + a}\right]$$

$$= \frac{1}{2a}(\ln|u - a| - \ln|u + a|) + C = \frac{1}{2a}\ln\left|\frac{u - a}{u + a}\right| + C.$$

Proof of (XVI)'. From (XVI),

$$\int \frac{du}{a^2 - u^2} = - \int \frac{du}{u^2 - a^2} = - \frac{1}{2a} \ln \left| \frac{u - a}{u + a} \right| + C. \tag{1}$$

We recall that $\qquad \ln \frac{1}{N} = \ln 1 - \ln N = - \ln N.$

Hence, $\qquad - \ln \left| \frac{u - a}{u + a} \right| = \ln \left| \frac{u + a}{u - a} \right| = \ln \left| \frac{a + u}{a - u} \right|.$

Thus, the right-hand sides of (1) and (XVI)' are identical.

ILLUSTRATION 1. From (XVI) with $u = 3x$,

$$\int \frac{dx}{9x^2 - 4} = \frac{1}{3} \int \frac{3\,dx}{(3x)^2 - 2^2} = \frac{1}{3} \int \frac{du}{u^2 - 2^2} = \frac{1}{12} \ln \left| \frac{u - 2}{u + 2} \right| + C$$

$$= \frac{1}{12} \ln \left| \frac{3x - 2}{3x + 2} \right| + C.$$

ILLUSTRATION 2. $\qquad \int_{-3}^{2} \frac{dt}{t^2 - 36} = \frac{1}{12} \ln \left| \frac{t - 6}{t + 6} \right| \Big]_{-3}^{2}$

$$= \tfrac{1}{12} (\ln \tfrac{1}{2} - \ln 3) = - \tfrac{1}{12} \ln 6 = - .14931. \qquad \text{(Table III)}$$

EXERCISE 62

Integrate.

1. $\displaystyle \int \frac{du}{u^2 - 4}.$

2. $\displaystyle \int \frac{dt}{9 - t^2}.$

3. $\displaystyle \int \frac{dz}{16z^2 - 9}.$

4. $\displaystyle \int \frac{dx}{25 - 9x^2}.$

5. $\displaystyle \int_{-2}^{1} \frac{du}{u^2 - 16}.$

6. $\displaystyle \int_{3}^{6} \frac{dy}{9 - 4y^2}.$

7. $\displaystyle \int_{-5}^{-10} \frac{dz}{25 - 4z^2}.$

8. $\displaystyle \int_{-1}^{0} \frac{dt}{9t^2 - 25}.$

9. $\displaystyle \int \frac{e^x\,dx}{9e^{2x} - 5}.$

10. $\displaystyle \int \frac{y\,dy}{7 - 4y^4}.$

11. $\displaystyle \int \frac{x^2\,dx}{x^6 - 9}.$

12. $\displaystyle \int \frac{y^{\frac{1}{2}}\,dy}{9 - 4y^3}.$

13. $\displaystyle \int \frac{dx}{4 - (3x - 1)^2}.$

14. $\displaystyle \int \frac{dx}{4(2x + 3)^2 - 25}.$

15. $\displaystyle \int \frac{\sec^2 x\,dx}{\tan^2 x - 9}.$

16. Find the area of the region of the xy-plane bounded by the x-axis, the curve $y = 1/(x^2 - 9)$, and the lines $x = -4$ and $x = -9$.

108. Integration by substitution

We have used substitution of a new variable when employing the fundamental indefinite integrals. We proceed to extend the substitution method.

In a differential expression $f(x)dx$, if we let $x = \phi(u)$ where $\phi'(u)$ exists, then $dx = \phi'(u)du$ and $f(x)dx = f[\phi(u)]\phi'(u)du$. Thus,

[when $x = \phi(u)$] $\qquad f(x)dx = g(u)du, \quad where \quad g(u) = f[\phi(u)]\phi'(u).$ (1)

The preceding notations apply in the following discussion.

THEOREM III. *Assume that $f(x)$ is continuous when $a \leq x \leq b$, and that $\phi(u)$ has a continuous derivative $\phi'(u)$, with*

$$\phi(\alpha) = a, \quad \phi(\beta) = b, \quad and \quad a \leq \phi(u) \leq b \quad when \text{*} \quad \alpha \leq u \leq \beta. \quad (2)$$

Let $g(u)du$ be the transformation of $f(x)dx$ when the substitution $x = \phi(u)$ is used. Then, when $\alpha \leq u \leq \beta$,

$$[\text{with } x = \phi(u)] \qquad \int_a^x f(t)dt = \int_\alpha^u g(s)ds. \qquad (3)$$

Proof. 1. Let $\qquad F(x) = \int_a^x f(t)dt \quad and \quad G(u) = \int_\alpha^u g(s)ds. \qquad (4)$

Then, $\qquad\qquad \dfrac{dF}{dx} = f(x) \quad and \quad \dfrac{dG(u)}{du} = g(u). \qquad (5)$

2. If we let $x = \phi(u)$, then $F(x)$ becomes a function of u. By use of (1),

$$\frac{dF}{du} = \frac{dF}{dx}\frac{dx}{du} = f(x)\phi'(u) = f[\phi(u)]\phi'(u) = g(u), \; or$$

$$[\text{with } x = \phi(u)] \qquad\qquad \frac{dF(x)}{du} = \frac{dG(u)}{du}. \qquad (6)$$

Hence, by Theorem III on page 177, there is a constant C such that

$$[\text{with } x = \phi(u)] \qquad\qquad F(x) = G(u) + C. \qquad (7)$$

3. If $u = \alpha$, then $x = \phi(\alpha) = a$. Also, from (4), $F(a) = 0$ and $G(\alpha) = 0$. Hence, from (7) with $u = \alpha$, $F(a) = G(\alpha) + C$, or $C = 0$. Thus, from (7), at all values of u, we obtain (3) in the form

$$[\text{when } x = \phi(u)] \qquad\qquad F(x) = G(u). \qquad (8)$$

COROLLARY 1. *If $x = \phi(u)$ transforms $f(x)dx$ into $g(u)du$, then*

$$\int_a^b f(x)dx = \int_\alpha^\beta g(u)du. \qquad (9)$$

Proof. Place $u = \beta$ in (3). Then $x = \phi(\beta) = b$, and (3) becomes (9).

Now, assume that the transformation $x = \phi(u)$ of Theorem III defines a single-valued inverse function $u = \psi(x)$, with $f(x)dx = g(u)du$. By Theorem II on page 208, the general indefinite integrals of $f(x)$ and $g(u)$, respectively, are of the forms

$$\int f(x)dx = \int_a^x f(t)dt + C = F(x) + C; \qquad (10)$$

$$\int g(u)du = \int_\alpha^u g(s)ds + C = G(u) + C. \qquad (11)$$

From (8), observe that $F(x) + C = G(u) + C$ when $x = \phi(u)$. Hence,

$$[\text{with } u = \psi(x)] \qquad\qquad \int f(x)dx = \int g(u)du. \qquad (12)$$

---

* Or, when $\beta \leq u \leq \alpha$. That is, we may have either $\alpha < \beta$ or $\beta < \alpha$.

Thus, we have justified the following statement:

$$\begin{cases} \textit{If the substitution } x = \phi(u), \textit{ or } u = \psi(x), \textit{ transforms } f(x)dx \\ \textit{into } g(u)du, \textit{ then } \int f(x)dx \textit{ is obtained by first calculating} \\ \int g(u)du \textit{ and then substituting } u = \psi(x) \textit{ in the result.} \end{cases} \quad (13)$$

ILLUSTRATION 1. To obtain $\int \sin^4 2x \cos 2x \, dx$ by use of (12), make the substitution $u = \sin 2x$. Then, $du = 2 \cos 2x \, dx$ and

$$\int \sin^4 2x \cos 2x \, dx = \int \frac{1}{2} u^4 \, du = \frac{1}{10} u^5 + C = \frac{1}{10} \sin^5 2x + C. \quad (14)$$

In (14), we illustrated the fact that our usual method in applying standard integration forms is a simple case of (13). We shall use (13) in more complicated cases hereafter.

109. Elementary rationalizing substitutions

Suppose that the integrand in $\int f(x)dx$ is an algebraic function, and involves just one radical $\sqrt[n]{ax + b}$, with a *linear radicand*, as the only irrational feature. Then, by substituting $u = \sqrt[n]{ax + b}$, we change to a new integral where the integrand is a rational function of u.

EXAMPLE 1. Integrate: $\qquad J = \int \dfrac{x \, dx}{\sqrt{3x + 1}}.$

SOLUTION. Let $u = \sqrt{3x + 1}$. Then, by use of (12) of page 227,

$$u^2 = 3x + 1; \quad x = \tfrac{1}{3}(u^2 - 1); \quad dx = \tfrac{2}{3}u \, du;$$

$$J = \frac{1}{3} \cdot \frac{2}{3} \int \frac{(u^2 - 1)u \, du}{u} = \frac{2}{9} \int (u^2 - 1)du \quad (1)$$

$$= \tfrac{2}{27}u^3 - \tfrac{2}{9}u + C = \tfrac{2}{27}(3x + 1)^{\frac{3}{2}} - \tfrac{2}{9}(3x + 1)^{\frac{1}{2}} + C. \quad (2)$$

EXAMPLE 2. Integrate: $\qquad J = \int x^2(2x + 1)^{\frac{2}{3}}dx.$

SOLUTION. Note that $(2x + 1)^{\frac{2}{3}} = (\sqrt[3]{2x + 1})^2$. Thus, substitute $u = \sqrt[3]{2x + 1}$. Then, by use of (12) on page 227,

$$u^3 = 2x + 1; \quad x = \tfrac{1}{2}(u^3 - 1); \quad dx = \tfrac{3}{2}u^2 \, du;$$

$$J = \frac{1}{4} \cdot \frac{3}{2} \int (u^3 - 1)^2 u^2 (u^2 \, du) = \frac{3}{88} u^{11} - \frac{3}{32} u^8 + \frac{3}{40} u^5 + C$$

$$= \tfrac{3}{88}(2x + 1)^{\frac{11}{3}} - \tfrac{3}{32}(2x + 1)^{\frac{8}{3}} + \tfrac{3}{40}(2x + 1)^{\frac{5}{3}} + C.$$

110. Substitution in a definite integral

Consider obtaining $\int_a^b f(x)dx$ by use of a substitution $x = \phi(u)$, or $u = \psi(x)$, subject to the hypotheses of Theorem III on page 227:

$$\phi(\alpha) = a \quad and \quad \phi(\beta) = b; \quad a \leqq \phi(u) \leqq b \quad when* \quad \alpha \leqq u \leqq \beta. \quad (1)$$

* We may have $\beta < \alpha$ so that the range for u is $\beta \leqq u \leqq \alpha$.

Then, the following method is justified by (9) on page 227.

1. *Use $x = \phi(u)$, or $u = \psi(x)$, to transform $f(x)dx$ into $g(u)du$.*

2. *Simultaneously, change the limits of integration from $x = a$ and $x = b$ to $u = \alpha$ and $u = \beta$, by use of $u = \psi(x)$. Then,*

$$\int_a^b f(x)dx = \int_\alpha^\beta g(u)du. \tag{2}$$

EXAMPLE 1. Calculate $\displaystyle\int_5^8 \frac{x\,dx}{\sqrt{3x+1}}.$ $\tag{3}$

SOLUTION. Let $u = \sqrt{3x+1}$. Then,

$$u^2 = 3x + 1; \quad x = \tfrac{1}{3}(u^2 - 1); \quad dx = \tfrac{2}{3}u\,du. \tag{4}$$

When $x = 5$, then $u = 4$; when $x = 8$, then $u = 5$. We notice that u increases from 4 to 5 as x increases from 5 to 8. Then, from (3) and (4),

$$\int_5^8 \frac{x\,dx}{\sqrt{3x+1}} = \frac{2}{9}\int_4^5 (u^2 - 1)du = \frac{2}{27}u^3 - \frac{2}{9}u\bigg]_4^5 = \frac{116}{27}. \tag{5}$$

EXERCISE 63

Integrate. Use a substitution if necessary.

1. $\int x\sqrt{2+x}\,dx.$

2. $\int v\sqrt{3+4v}\,dv.$

3. $\int x\sqrt[3]{1+2x}\,dx.$

4. $\int \dfrac{(2x+1)dx}{\sqrt{2x+3}}.$

5. $\int \dfrac{(6x-1)dx}{\sqrt{1-3x}}.$

6. $\int \dfrac{(x+2)dx}{(\sqrt{x+1})^3}.$

7. $\int \dfrac{u\,du}{\sqrt{3+4u}}.$

8. $\int \dfrac{(3+5w)dw}{\sqrt[3]{2-w}}.$

9. $\int \dfrac{x\,dx}{\sqrt[3]{5+2x}}.$

10. $\int x(2x+5)^{\frac{3}{2}}\,dx.$

11. $\int x(3-x)^{\frac{2}{3}}\,dx.$

12. $\int \dfrac{(x^{\frac{3}{4}} - x^{\frac{5}{2}})dx}{3x^{\frac{1}{4}}}.$

13. $\int \dfrac{(4x+3)dx}{(1+4x)^{\frac{3}{2}}}.$

Compute by use of a substitution and a change in limits of integration.

14. $\int_2^7 x\sqrt{2+x}\,dx.$

15. $\int_{-8}^{-1} x\sqrt{1-3x}\,dx.$

16. $\int_{-4}^{-1} \dfrac{z\,dz}{\sqrt{2-4z}}.$

17. $\int_{-1}^{11} \dfrac{x^2\,dx}{\sqrt{2x+3}}.$

18. $\int_{-11}^{-4} \dfrac{t^2\,dt}{\sqrt[3]{t+3}}.$

19. $\int_2^7 (6x+5)\sqrt{3x-1}\,dx.$

20. $\int_{-7}^0 x\sqrt{4-3x}\,dx.$

111. Certain radical forms

If u is any differentiable function of x, then

$$\int \frac{du}{\sqrt{u^2 \pm a^2}} = \ln|u + \sqrt{u^2 \pm a^2}| + C. \tag{XVII}$$

Proof of (XVII) *for* $\sqrt{u^2 + a^2}$. Let $u = a \tan \theta$, with the agreement that $a > 0$, and that we choose θ on the range

$$-\tfrac{1}{2}\pi < \theta < \tfrac{1}{2}\pi, \quad where \quad \sec \theta > 0. \tag{1}$$

Then,

$$du = a \sec^2 \theta \, d\theta; \quad \sqrt{u^2 + a^2} = a\sqrt{\tan^2 \theta + 1} = a \sec \theta; \tag{2}$$

$$\int \frac{du}{\sqrt{u^2 + a^2}} = \int \frac{\sec^2 \theta \, d\theta}{\sec \theta} = \int \sec \theta \, d\theta$$

$$= \ln |\sec \theta + \tan \theta| + C', \tag{3}$$

where C' is an arbitrary constant. From $u = a \tan \theta$, (1), and (2),

$$\tan \theta = \frac{u}{a}; \quad \sec \theta = \frac{\sqrt{u^2 + a^2}}{a}.$$

Hence, from (3),

$$\int \frac{du}{\sqrt{u^2 + a^2}} = \ln \left| \frac{\sqrt{u^2 + a^2} + u}{a} \right| + C'$$

$$= \ln (u + \sqrt{u^2 + a^2}) + (C' - \ln a). \tag{4}$$

On letting $C = C' - \ln a$, from (4) we obtain (XVII), for the case where "$+$" is used on both sides in the radical. We omitted absolute value signs with $(u + \sqrt{u^2 + a^2})$ in (4) because

$$\sqrt{u^2 + a^2} > |u| \quad and \ hence \quad \sqrt{u^2 + a^2} + u > 0.$$

Proof of (XVII) *for the case of* $\sqrt{u^2 - a^2}$. 1. Observe that the range for u must be an interval where

$$u^2 - a^2 > 0, \quad or \quad u^2 > a^2, \quad or \quad |u| > a.$$

Hence, we deal with either $u > a$ or $u < -a$.

2. Substitute $u = a \sec \theta$, with the agreement that $0 < \theta < \tfrac{1}{2}\pi$ when $u > a$, and $\pi < \theta < \tfrac{3}{2}\pi$ when $u < -a$, so that in either case

$$\tan \theta > 0 \quad and \quad \tan \theta = +\sqrt{\sec^2 \theta - 1}. \tag{5}$$

Then,

$$du = a \sec \theta \tan \theta \, d\theta; \quad \sqrt{u^2 - a^2} = a\sqrt{\sec^2 \theta - 1} = a \tan \theta.$$

In Problem 22 in Exercise 64, the student will verify that details similar to those in the case of $\sqrt{u^2 + a^2}$ lead again to (XVII) for $\sqrt{u^2 - a^2}$.

ILLUSTRATION 1.

$$\int \frac{dt}{\sqrt{4t^2 - 25}} = \frac{1}{2} \int \frac{2 \, dt}{\sqrt{4t^2 - 25}}$$

[(XVII) with $u = 2t$]

$$= \tfrac{1}{2} \ln |2t + \sqrt{4t^2 - 25}| + C.$$

ILLUSTRATION 2.

$$\int_{-5}^{-4} \frac{dx}{\sqrt{x^2 - 9}} = \ln |x + \sqrt{x^2 - 9}| \Big]_{-5}^{-4}$$

$$= \ln |-4 + \sqrt{7}| - \ln |-5 + 4| = \ln 1.354 - \ln 1 = .3028,$$

where we used Table III.

EXERCISE 64

Integrate.

1. $\int \dfrac{dx}{\sqrt{x^2 + 4}}.$

2. $\int \dfrac{du}{\sqrt{u^2 - 25}}.$

3. $\int \dfrac{dz}{\sqrt{z^2 + 16}}.$

4. $\int \dfrac{dx}{\sqrt{4x^2 + 9}}.$

5. $\int \dfrac{dt}{\sqrt{9t^2 + 25}}.$

6. $\int \dfrac{dw}{\sqrt{4w^2 + 1}}.$

7. $\int \dfrac{dt}{\sqrt{9t^2 - 121}}.$

8. $\int \dfrac{dx}{\sqrt{25x^2 - 1}}.$

9. $\int \dfrac{dy}{\sqrt{1 + 36y^2}}.$

10. $\int \dfrac{\sin x \, dx}{\sqrt{\cos^2 x + 4}}.$

11. $\int \dfrac{\sec^2 t \, dt}{\sqrt{\tan^2 t + 9}}.$

12. $\int \dfrac{e^t \, dt}{\sqrt{4e^{2t} + 49}}.$

13. $\int \dfrac{\cos 2x \, dx}{\sqrt{16 + \sin^2 2x}}.$

14. $\int \dfrac{dx}{x\sqrt{(\ln x)^2 + 25}}.$

15. $\int_5^{10} \dfrac{du}{\sqrt{u^2 - 16}}.$

16. $\int_0^4 \dfrac{dx}{\sqrt{x^2 + 9}}.$

17. $\int_5^6 \dfrac{dt}{\sqrt{t^2 - 9}}.$

18. $\int_{-6}^{-5} \dfrac{du}{\sqrt{u^2 - 16}}.$

19. $\int_{-5}^{-4} \dfrac{dx}{\sqrt{x^2 - 9}}.$

20. $\int_{-\frac{5}{2}}^{\frac{5}{2}} \dfrac{dw}{\sqrt{4w^2 + 25}}.$

21. A region R is bounded by the curve $y = 1/\sqrt{x^2 + 16}$, the x-axis, and the lines $x = 3$ and $x = 4$. (*a*) Find the area of R. (*b*) Find the volume of the solid generated if R is revolved about the x-axis.

22. Finish the proof of (XVII) for the case of $\sqrt{u^2 - a^2}$.

112. Certain integrands involving quadratic functions

By completing a square based on the terms in x, we can write any quadratic function $Ax^2 + Bx + C$ in one of the forms $(a^2 + u^2)$, $(a^2 - u^2)$, $(u^2 - a^2)$, or $(- a^2 - u^2)$, perhaps multiplied by a constant, where u is some linear function of x. Then, (XIV)–(XVII) enable us to evaluate integrals of the types

$$\int \dfrac{dx}{Ax^2 + Bx + C} \quad and \quad \int \dfrac{dx}{\sqrt{Ax^2 + Bx + C}}. \tag{1}$$

ILLUSTRATION 1. $\quad \displaystyle\int \dfrac{dx}{7 - 4x^2 + 12x} = \int \dfrac{dx}{7 + 9 - (4x^2 - 12x + 9)}$

$[(\text{XVI})', u = 2x - 3] \qquad = \dfrac{1}{2} \int \dfrac{2 \, dx}{16 - (2x - 3)^2} = \dfrac{1}{2} \int \dfrac{du}{16 - u^2}$

$$= \dfrac{1}{2} \cdot \dfrac{1}{8} \ln \left| \dfrac{4 + 2x - 3}{4 - (2x - 3)} \right| + C = \dfrac{1}{16} \ln \left| \dfrac{1 + 2x}{7 - 2x} \right| + C.$$

Note 1. To complete a square with $(x^2 + Bx)$, we add $B^2/4$. If $A > 0$, we complete a square with $(Ax^2 + Bx)$ by adding the square of $B/2\sqrt{A}$:

$$Ax^2 + Bx + \dfrac{B^2}{4A} = \left(x\sqrt{A} + \dfrac{B}{2\sqrt{A}} \right)^2.$$

If A is not a perfect square, we may prefer to remove A as a factor before completing a square. When $A < 0$, group the terms involving x within parentheses preceded by a minus sign, before completing a square.

ILLUSTRATION 2. $$\int \frac{dx}{5x^2 + 30x + 55} = \frac{1}{5} \int \frac{dx}{x^2 + 6x + 11}$$

[(XIV), $u = x + 2$] $$= \frac{1}{5} \int \frac{dx}{(x + 3)^2 + 2} = \frac{1}{5\sqrt{2}} \operatorname{Arctan} \frac{x + 3}{\sqrt{2}} + C.$$

ILLUSTRATION 3. $$\int \frac{dx}{\sqrt{16 - x^2 - 6x}} = \int \frac{dx}{\sqrt{16 + 9 - (x^2 + 6x + 9)}}$$

$$= \int \frac{dx}{\sqrt{25 - (x + 3)^2}} = \operatorname{Arcsin} \frac{x + 3}{5} + C.$$

ILLUSTRATION 4. $$\int \frac{dx}{\sqrt{10x - x^2 - 29}} = \int \frac{dx}{\sqrt{-4 - (x - 5)^2}}.$$

We stop, because the radicand is *negative*, and hence the integrand is *imaginary, at all values of x*. Thus, *the integral has no meaning*.

If $A < 0$, the graph of $y = Ax^2 + Bx + C$ is a parabola which is concave *downward*. If, besides, the discriminant $(B^2 - 4AC)$ is *negative*, the equation $Ax^2 + Bx + C = 0$ has *imaginary roots*. Then, the parabola lies entirely below the x-axis, as in Figure 140. Or, $(Ax^2 + Bx + C)$ *is negative at all values of x in case $A < 0$ and $B^2 - 4AC < 0$.* This result enables us to discover a situation like that of Illustration 4 without completing a square.

ILLUSTRATION 5. In $10x - x^2 - 29$ in Illustration 4, the discriminant is $(10^2) - 4(1)(29) = -16$. Hence, immediately, we know that the radicand is negative at all values of x.

Fig. 140

To evaluate an integral of the form

$$\int \frac{(hx + k)dx}{Ax^2 + Bx + C} \quad \text{or} \quad \int \frac{(hx + k)dx}{\sqrt{Ax^2 + Bx + C}}, \tag{2}$$

where $A \neq 0$, first express the integrand as the sum of two simpler fractions, having the given denominator. For one of these fractions, we *automatically write the numerator by differentiating* $(Ax^2 + Bx + C)$, and then multiplying by a constant chosen to give hx as the coefficient of x. The integral of this fraction then is of the form $\int u^n du$ or $\int du/u$, perhaps multiplied by a constant. The second new fraction which is met can be integrated as in Illustrations 1–3.

ILLUSTRATION 6. $$\int \frac{(3x + 5)dx}{4x^2 + 9} = \frac{3}{8} \int \frac{8x \, dx}{4x^2 + 9} + \frac{5}{2} \int \frac{2 \, dx}{4x^2 + 9}$$

[$u = 2x$ in (XIV)] $$= \frac{3}{8} \ln (4x^2 + 9) + \frac{5}{6} \operatorname{Arctan} \frac{2}{3}x + C.$$

EXAMPLE 1. Integrate: $\displaystyle\int \frac{(2x + 5)dx}{\sqrt{8 - 6x - 9x^2}}.$

SOLUTION. Since $\dfrac{d}{dx}(8 - 6x - 9x^2) = -6 - 18x,$ write

$$T = \int \frac{(2x + 5)dx}{\sqrt{8 - 6x - 9x^2}} = h\int \frac{(-6 - 18x)dx}{\sqrt{8 - 6x - 9x^2}} + \int \frac{k\,dx}{\sqrt{8 - 6x - 9x^2}}, \quad (3)$$

where h and k are to be determined. Select h so that, in (3), $2x$ on the left will equal $-18hx$ on the right, or $2 = -18h$; $h = -\frac{1}{9}$. Then, on the right, $-6h = \frac{2}{3}$ and we must have $5 = \frac{2}{3} + k$, or $k = \frac{13}{3}$. In the denominator of the second term on the right in (3), complete a square. Thus,

$$T = -\frac{1}{9}\int (8 - 6x - 9x^2)^{-\frac{1}{2}}d(8 - 6x - 9x^2) + \frac{13}{3}\int \frac{dx}{\sqrt{9 - (3x + 1)^2}}$$

$$= -\frac{2}{9}(8 - 6x - 9x^2)^{\frac{1}{2}} + \frac{13}{9}\,\text{Arcsin}\,\frac{3x + 1}{3} + C.$$

EXERCISE 65

Integrate.

1. $\displaystyle\int \frac{dx}{x^2 + 6x + 13}.$ 2. $\displaystyle\int \frac{dx}{x^2 + 8x + 12}.$ 3. $\displaystyle\int \frac{dx}{3 - x^2 - 2x}.$

4. $\displaystyle\int \frac{dx}{\sqrt{4x - x^2 - 3}}.$ 5. $\displaystyle\int \frac{dx}{\sqrt{9 - x^2 - 8x}}.$ 6. $\displaystyle\int \frac{dx}{\sqrt{x^2 - x - 2}}.$

7. $\displaystyle\int \frac{dx}{\sqrt{4x - x^2 - 5}}.$ 8. $\displaystyle\int \frac{dy}{y^2 - y + 1}.$

9. $\displaystyle\int \frac{dt}{4t^2 - 4t + 5}.$ 10. $\displaystyle\int \frac{dz}{9z^2 + 6z - 5}.$

11. $\displaystyle\int \frac{dx}{\sqrt{10 + 4x^2 - 4x}}.$ 12. $\displaystyle\int \frac{dx}{\sqrt{15 - 9x^2 - 6x}}.$

13. $\displaystyle\int \frac{dw}{4w - w^2}.$ 14. $\displaystyle\int \frac{dx}{4x^2 - 4x}.$ 15. $\displaystyle\int \frac{dx}{\sqrt{-x^2 - 6x}}.$

16. $\displaystyle\int \frac{dz}{\sqrt{7 - 4z^2 + 12z}}.$ 17. $\displaystyle\int \frac{du}{9u^2 + 6u - 1}.$

18. $\displaystyle\int \frac{dx}{\sqrt{x^2 + 3x + 3}}.$ 19. $\displaystyle\int \frac{dx}{\sqrt{-9x^2 - 12x - 1}}.$

20. $\displaystyle\int \frac{dv}{3v^2 + 2v - 5}.$ 21. $\displaystyle\int \frac{dx}{2x^2 - 6x + 5}.$

22. $\displaystyle\int \frac{dt}{\sqrt{3t^2 + 2t + 2}}.$ 23. $\displaystyle\int \frac{dx}{\sqrt{1 - 2x^2 + x}}.$

24. $\displaystyle\int \frac{dx}{\sqrt{4 - 9x^2 + 6x}}.$ 25. $\displaystyle\int \frac{\sec^2 x\,dx}{\tan^2 x + 4\tan x + 3}.$

26. $\displaystyle\int \frac{(3 + 2x)dx}{4 + x^2}.$

27. $\displaystyle\int \frac{(4x - 2)dx}{\sqrt{x^2 - 1}}.$

28. $\displaystyle\int \frac{(3t + 5)dt}{\sqrt{9 - t^2}}.$

29. $\displaystyle\int \frac{(3 - 5x)dx}{4x^2 + 9}.$

30. $\displaystyle\int \frac{(4z + 6)dz}{z^2 - 4}.$

31. $\displaystyle\int \frac{(3 - 4z)dz}{16 - z^2}.$

32. $\displaystyle\int \frac{(6t + 2)dt}{\sqrt{9t^2 + 5}}.$

33. $\displaystyle\int \frac{(4 - 8y)dy}{\sqrt{1 - 16y^2}}.$

34. $\displaystyle\int \frac{(3x - 7)dx}{\sqrt{4 - 3x^2}}.$

35. $\displaystyle\int \frac{(3 - 6x)dx}{x^2 + 4x - 5}.$

36. $\displaystyle\int \frac{(13 - 5x)dx}{x^2 + 3x + 2}.$

37. $\displaystyle\int \frac{(4z - 5)dz}{\sqrt{4z^2 + 4z + 13}}.$

38. $\displaystyle\int \frac{(9t + 16)dt}{\sqrt{9t^2 + 12t + 3}}.$

39. $\displaystyle\int \frac{(8x + 5)dx}{\sqrt{7 - x^2 + 6x}}.$

40. $\displaystyle\int \frac{(15 - 3x)dx}{\sqrt{4x - x^2 - 7}}.$

41. $\displaystyle\int \frac{(11 - 12y)dy}{\sqrt{24 - 9y^2 + 6y}}.$

42. $\displaystyle\int \frac{(6x - 5)dx}{\sqrt{5x - x^2 - 6}}.$

113. Simple differential equations

Sometimes, an unknown function, y, of an independent variable x may be defined only through a relation satisfied by x, y, and derivatives of y. Such a relation is called a *differential equation in x and y*, defining y as a function of x. The order of the derivative of *highest order* in the equation is called the **order** of the equation.

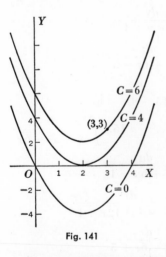

Fig. 141

EXAMPLE 1. Obtain the function, y, of x whose graph passes through the point $(3, 3)$ and has the slope $(2x - 4)$ at each value of x.

SOLUTION. 1. We are given

$$\frac{dy}{dx} = 2x - 4, \tag{1}$$

with $y = 3$ *when* $x = 3$.   (2)

2. From (1), and the definition of an indefinite integral,

$$y = \int (2x - 4)dx, \quad or \quad y = x^2 - 4x + C, \tag{3}$$

where C is an arbitrary constant. On substituting (2) in (3), we find $3 = 9 - 12 + C$, or $C = 6$, and obtain $y = x^2 - 4x + 6$.

Comment. Figure 141 shows several curves of the family (3). We call (1) *the differential equation of the family of curves* (3), and refer to (2) as **initial conditions.** The differential equation (1) determines a family of functions, depending on an arbitrary constant. We call (3) the **general**

solution of (1). Then, the initial conditions pick out a **particular solution** of (1). The following terminology was illustrated in Example 1.

DEFINITION I. *A **solution** of a differential equation for y as a function of x is a function y = f(x) such that, if y and its derivatives are expressed in terms of x and are substituted in the differential equation, it becomes an identity in x. To say that an equation F(x, y) = 0 is a solution, means that the function y, of x, defined by F(x, y) = 0 is a solution of the differential equation.*

Briefly, Definition I states that a *solution* is a function $y = f(x)$ which *satisfies* the differential equation. We shall consider only those solutions possessing continuous derivatives of all orders involved.

EXAMPLE 2. Verify that the function $y = x^2 + x^{-3}$ is a solution of

$$x \frac{dy}{dx} + 3y = 5x^2. \tag{4}$$

SOLUTION. From $y = x^2 + x^{-3}$, we obtain $y' = 2x - 3x^{-4}$. On substituting for y and y' in (4), we find that (4) is satisfied:

$$x(2x - 3x^{-4}) + 3(x^2 + x^{-3}) = 5x^2, \quad or \quad 5x^2 = 5x^2.$$

EXAMPLE 3. Solve

$$\frac{d^2y}{dx^2} = 12x - 4, \tag{5}$$

with the initial conditions

$$y = 4 \quad and \quad y' = 3 \quad at \quad x = 2. \tag{6}$$

SOLUTION. 1. Since $y'' = dy'/dx$, equation (5) becomes

$$\frac{dy'}{dx} = 12x - 4; \quad hence, \quad y' = \int (12x - 4)dx = 6x^2 - 4x + C_1. \tag{7}$$

2. On using ($y' = 3$ *at* $x = 2$) in (7), we find $3 = 24 - 8 + C_1$, or $C_1 = -13$. Then, from (7),

$$\frac{dy}{dx} = 6x^2 - 4x - 13. \tag{8}$$

Hence,

$$y = \int (6x^2 - 4x - 13)dx = 2x^3 - 2x^2 - 13x + C_2.$$

By use of ($y = 4$ *at* $x = 2$) from (6), we find

$$4 = C_2 - 18, \quad or \quad C_2 = 22.$$

Thus, the desired *particular solution* is $y = 2x^3 - 2x^2 - 13x + 22$.

Comment. Without initial conditions, and thus with C_1 remaining arbitrary, from (7) we obtain a solution involving two arbitrary constants:

$$y = \int (6x^2 - 4x + C_1)dx, \quad or \quad y = 2x^3 - 2x^2 + C_1x + C_2,$$

which is the *general solution* of (5). With given initial conditions, it was more desirable to determine the value of C_1, as in (8), before proceeding to the next stage. Notice that (5) is of the *second order*.

As a characteristic feature, a differential equation of order n for y as a function of x may be expected to possess infinitely many solutions, forming a family of functions defined by an equation involving *just n arbitrary constants.** The following terminology was illustrated in Examples 1 and 3.

A **general solution** *of a differential equation of the nth order is a solution involving exactly n arbitrary constants. A* **particular solution** *is a solution obtained by assigning a special value to each arbitrary constant in a general solution.*

For any differential equation in this text, it will be safe to refer to "THE" general solution instead of to "A" general solution, because just one result or its equivalent will arise. *To solve* a differential equation will mean to obtain its *general solution.* To solve a differential equation *together with given initial conditions* will mean to find the *particular solution* satisfying these conditions.

Note 1. A differential equation may possess so-called **singular solutions,** not obtainable as particular cases of the general solution. A few illustrations of singular solutions will be met later, but as a rule the possibility of their existence will be disregarded. Hence, we shall speak of any general solution as if it gave rise to all solutions of the corresponding differential equation.

EXERCISE 66

Verify the given solution of the differential equation.

1. $y'' - 3xy' + 3y = 2 - 3x^2$; solution, $y = x^2 + 3x$.

2. $xy'' - xy' + 2x = 2x + 12x^2 - 6x^3$; solution, $y = 2x^3 + 5$.

3. $y'' - 9y = 0$; solution, $y = 2e^{3x} - 3e^{-3x}$.

4. $y'' + 4y = 0$; solution, $y = c_1 \sin 2x + c_2 \cos 2x$, where c_1 and c_2 are arbitrary constants.

Find the solution of the differential equation satisfying the initial conditions.

5. $y' = 4x + 7$; $y = 3$ at $x = 2$.
6. $y' = -x^2 - 3$; $y = 4$ at $x = -1$.

7. $\dfrac{ds}{dt} = -\sin t$; $s = 2$ at $t = \dfrac{1}{4}\pi$.
8. $\dfrac{dv}{dt} = -2t + 3$; $v = 4$ at $t = 3$.

9. $\dfrac{d^2y}{dx^2} = 3x - 2$; $y = 4$ and $\dfrac{dy}{dx} = -2$ at $x = 4$.

10. $\dfrac{d^2y}{dx^2} = -5$; $y = -1$ and $\dfrac{dy}{dx} = 3$ at $x = -2$.

11. $\dfrac{d^2u}{dt^2} = -2t^2 + 5$; $u = 4$ and $\dfrac{du}{dt} = -2$ at $t = -1$.

Find the general solution of the equation.

12. $\dfrac{d^2y}{dx^2} = 3x + 2$.
13. $\dfrac{d^2s}{dt^2} = 3e^{2t}$.

* We assume that the constants are *independent*, where we accept this phraseology informally to mean that we could not define the family by use of *fewer* than n parameters.

Obtain the function, y, of x whose graph passes through the given point, and has the indicated slope at any value of x. In Problems 14 and 15, also graph the desired function and two other curves of the family determined by the differential equation which is used.

14. Slope $= 4x + 4$; through the point $(2, -12)$.

15. Slope $= -6x - 12$; through the point $(1, -22)$.

16. Slope $= 9x^2 - 10x - 2$; through the point $(1, 3)$.

17. Slope $= -4/x^2$; through the point $(-2, -2)$.

18. Slope $= -2/\sqrt{x+1}$; through the point $(0, 2)$.

19. Slope $= 2/\sqrt{x+1}$; through the point $(0, -2)$.

Comment. Graph the functions in Problems 18 and 19 and compare.

20. Slope $= \sin x$; through the point $(0, 3)$.

21. Slope $= e^{-2x}$; through the point $(1, e^2)$.

22. Slope $= 1/x$; (a) through $(e, 0)$; (b) through $(-e, 0)$.

Comment. Graph the function in Problem 22. Use of the absolute value in $\int dx/x = \ln |x| + C$ gives both branches of the graph.

23. Find the function, y, of x for which $y'' = 3$ at all values of x, if the tangent to the graph of the function at $(2, 3)$ is $y = 3x - 3$.

24. Find the function, y, of x for which $y'' = -2$ at all values of x, if the tangent to the graph of the function at $(-1, 2)$ is parallel to the line $4x - 2y = 5$.

25. Find the equation of the family of curves in an xy-plane whose slope at any point (x, y) is $3x^2 - 5x$. Also, find the equation of that curve of the family passing through the point $(2, 5)$.

114. Differential equations of motion

Suppose that a particle is moving on an s-axis. If s represents the coordinate of the particle at the time t, then s is a function of t. We recall that the velocity v and the acceleration a at time t are given by

$$v = \frac{ds}{dt}; \quad a = \frac{d^2s}{dt^2}, \quad or \quad a = \frac{dv}{dt}. \tag{1}$$

EXAMPLE 1. A particle moves on an s-axis with the acceleration

$$\frac{d^2s}{dt^2} = 6t - 4. \tag{2}$$

At $t = 1$, $s = 4$ and the velocity is $v \approx 3$. Find the coordinate s of the particle at any time t.

SOLUTION. 1. We refer to (2) as *the differential equation of the motion.* From (1) and (2),

$$\frac{dv}{dt} = 6t - 4; \quad v = \int (6t - 4)dt, \quad or \quad v = 3t^2 - 4t + C_1, \tag{3}$$

where C_1 is an arbitrary constant. From the initial conditions $v = 3$ at $t = 1$, we obtain $3 = 3 - 4 + C_1$ or $C_1 = 4$.

2. From (3), at any time t, $\qquad\qquad \dfrac{ds}{dt} = 3t^2 - 4t + 4;$

$$s = \int (3t^2 - 4t + 4)dt, \quad or \quad s = t^3 - 2t^2 + 4t + C_2, \tag{4}$$

where C_2 is an arbitrary constant. From the initial conditions, $s = 4$ at $t = 1$; hence, from (4), $C_2 = 1$ and $s = t^3 - 2t^2 + 4t + 1$.

Unless otherwise stated, in any problem relating to a falling body in the earth's atmosphere, we shall take account only of the effect of gravity, and thus shall neglect air resistance and other disturbing features. Then, the acceleration of the body will be a constant, g, approximately 32 feet per second per second, directed downward. Thus, if distance is measured in feet with the positive direction upward, and if time t is measured in seconds, the differential equation for the motion of a falling body is

$$\frac{d^2s}{dt^2} = -g. \tag{5}$$

EXAMPLE 2. A balloon is rising at the rate of 64' per second. A stone is dropped from the balloon when it is 3072' above the ground. With what speed, and how many seconds later will the stone hit the ground?

SOLUTION. 1. Measure time in seconds from the instant when the stone is dropped. Measure distance in feet, positive downward, from the point where the stone is dropped, as in Figure 142. Then,

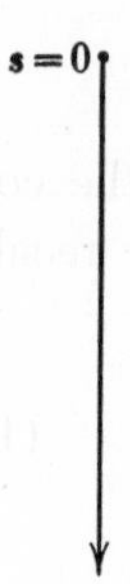

$s = 0$

$$\frac{d^2s}{dt^2} = 32, \tag{6}$$

with $s = 0$ and $v = -64$ at $t = 0$.

2. From (6), $\qquad \dfrac{dv}{dt} = 32; \quad v = \int 32\,dt = 32t + C_1. \tag{7}$

Since $v = -64$ at $t = 0$, from (7) we obtain $C_1 = -64$.

3. Hence, $\qquad\qquad v = \dfrac{ds}{dt} = 32t - 64; \tag{8}$

Fig. 142

$$s = \int (32t - 64)dt = 16t^2 - 64t + C_2.$$

Since $s = 0$ at $t = 0$, we obtain $C_2 = 0$. Thus, at any time t, $s = 16t^2 - 64t$.

4. The stone hits the ground when

$$16t^2 - 64t = 3072; \quad or \quad t^2 - 4t - 192 = 0;$$

$$(t - 16)(t + 12) = 0; \quad t = 16 \ seconds.$$

Then, from (8), $v = 448$ ft. per sec.

EXERCISE 67

A particle moves on an s-axis, with the velocity v and the acceleration a at any time t. Find s as a function of t, to satisfy the conditions. The units are 1 foot for distance and 1 second for time.

1. $v = 3t + 4$; $s = 2$ at $t = 0$.

2. $v = -2t + 3$; $s = -3$ at $t = 1$.

3. $a = -t$; $s = 2$ and $v = 3$ at $t = 0$.

4. $a = 3$; $s = 3$ and $v = 4$ at $t = 2$.

5. $a = 3t + 1$; $s = 0$ and $v = 3$ at $t = 1$.

6. $a = -2t + 4$; $s = -2$ and $v = 1$ at $t = -3$.

7. $a = 3t^2 + 6t$; $s = 3$ and $v = -2$ at $t = 2$.

8. $a = \sqrt{t} + 3$; $s = 1.3$ and $v = 0$ at $t = 9$.

9. $a = 6t + 3$; $s = 18$ at $t = 2$, and $s = -2$ at $t = 0$.

HINT. Integrate twice, and thus introduce two constants of integration before substituting the initial conditions.

10. $a = 24t - 4$; $s = -13$ at $t = -1$, and $s = 95$ at $t = 3$.

Solve by use of a differential equation. Be explicit in your choice of the origin and the positive direction for measuring distance.

11. A soldier is descending with a parachute at the rate of 80′ per second. He drops his 60-pound knapsack when he is 2400′ above the ground. How many seconds later, and with what speed, will his knapsack hit the ground?

12. A projectile is shot vertically upward from the ground with an initial speed of 160′ per second. (*a*) When will the projectile reach its greatest height above the ground? (*b*) How many seconds after the shot is fired, and with what speed, will the projectile hit the ground?

13. A balloon is rising at the rate of 20′ per second. A projectile is shot vertically upward from the balloon with a speed of 108′ per second relative to the balloon, when it is 3840 feet above the ground. How many seconds later will the projectile hit the ground?

14. A soldier is descending with a parachute at the rate of 20′ per second. He drops his revolver and it hits the ground 8 seconds later. How high was he above the ground when the revolver was dropped?

15. A particle is projected upward along an inclined plane, with an initial speed of 24′ per second along the plane. Friction, and other forces applied to the particle cause it to be affected by a constant acceleration of 4′ per second per second directed downward along the plane. When will the particle start to slide downward, and how far will it travel upward along the plane?

★16. A projectile is shot with an initial velocity of v_0 feet per second in a direction elevated at an angle α from the horizontal. Disregard all forces except that of gravity. (*a*) Find parametric equations for the path (*trajectory*) of the projectile in terms of the time t in seconds as a parameter, with t measured from the instant of firing. (*b*) Eliminate t between the resulting equations to find an equation for the trajectory in rectangular coordinates.

HINT. Set up xy-coordinates, with the x-axis horizontal and the projectile shot from the origin into quadrant I in the xy-plane. Let v_x, v_y, a_x, and a_y be defined as on page 118. The motion is determined by the simultaneous differential equations $a_x = 0$ and $a_y = -g$.

★17. By use of Problem 16, show that the range of the projectile, when fired at elevation α, is $(v_0^2 \sin 2\alpha)/g$. With what angle of elevation will maximum range be obtained?

115. Differential equations of the separable type

A differential equation of the first order in the variables x and y is said to be of the *first degree* if the derivative involved, dy/dx or dx/dy, occurs only to the first degree. Thus, the equation is of the form

$$Q(x, y) \frac{dy}{dx} + P(x, y) = 0, \quad or \quad P(x, y) \frac{dx}{dy} + Q(x, y) = 0, \tag{1}$$

where P and Q are functions of x and y. From either equation in (1),

$$P(x, y)dx + Q(x, y)dy = 0, \tag{2}$$

which we shall refer to as the *differential form* for a differential equation of the first order and first degree in x and y. If each of the functions P and Q is a product of a function of x and a function of y, we may change (2) to the following standard form on dividing by appropriate factors and rearranging terms:

$$f(x)dx = g(y)dy. \tag{3}$$

In (4), we say that *the variables are separated*. To state that an equation $P\,dx + Q\,dy = 0$ is of the *separable type* will mean that the equation is equivalent * to an equation (3) where the variables are separated.

ILLUSTRATION 1. The following equation is of the separable type:

$$(1 - x)(1 + y^2) + 2xy \frac{dy}{dx} = 0, \ or$$

$$(1 - x)(1 + y^2)dx + 2xy\,dy = 0. \tag{4}$$

In (4), we separate the variables by dividing both sides by $x(1 + y^2)$:

$$\frac{1 - x}{x} dx + \frac{2y}{1 + y^2} dy = 0.$$

* That is, has the same general solution as (3). Logically, the possibility of zero values for $P(x, y)$ and $Q(x, y)$ should be considered in any special case, to rule out corresponding values of x or y in the equivalence statement. As a rule, we shall omit such complications of the routine for solving (2).

We shall consider (3) when $f(x)$ and $g(y)$ are continuous. Also, when (3) is thought of as defining y as a function of x, assume that $g(y) \neq 0$ on the range for y, so that $y' = f(x)/g(y)$, which is continuous. Similarly, assume that $f(x) \neq 0$ on the range for x if (3) is thought of as defining x as a function of y. Then, if $\int f(x)dx$ and $\int g(y)dy$ denote any particular indefinite integrals of the corresponding integrands, we shall show that the general solution of (3) is as follows, where * C is an arbitrary constant:

$$\int f(x)dx = \int g(y)dy + C. \tag{5}$$

ILLUSTRATION 2. By (5), the general solution of $2x\ dx = -2y\ dy$ is

$$\int 2x\ dx = -\int 2y\ dy + C, \quad or \quad x^2 + y^2 = C.$$

In this case, the range for C is $C > 0$. Thus, $2x\ dx + 2y\ dy = 0$ is the differential equation of the family of circles $x^2 + y^2 = C$.

Proof of (5). 1. Suppose that C has a value for which (5) defines y as a function of x, say $y = \phi(x)$, where $\phi'(x)$ is continuous. Then, with $y = \phi(x)$, the two sides of (5) are functions of x for which

$$d\left[\int f(x)dx\right] = d\left[\int g(y)dy + C\right], \quad or \quad f(x)dx = g(y)dy,$$

because $d(C) = 0$. Hence, $y = \phi(x)$ satisfies (3).

2. Conversely, suppose that (3) is satisfied by $y = \phi(x)$ where $\phi'(x)$ is continuous. Then, if we use the substitution $y = \phi(x)$ in $\int f(x)dx$, by use of (12) on page 227 we obtain (5) for some value of C, because $f(x)dx = g(y)dy$. Thus, we have shown that (3) and (5) are satisfied by the same functions of x, or (5) is the general solution of (3). Similar reasoning applies if (3) defines x as a function of y.

Note 1. In place of (3), we may prefer the standard form

$$f(x)dx + g(y)dy = 0, \quad \textit{whose solution is}$$

$$\int f(x)dx + \int g(y)dy = C. \tag{6}$$

To obtain the solution in (5) or (6) for a differential equation of separable type, first separate the variables, and then integrate on both sides of the equation, with an arbitrary constant added on just one side. In this operation it is not necessary to group together the terms involving dx and those involving dy.

ILLUSTRATION 3. The solution of $3\ dx - 2y\ dy = x^3\ dx$ is

$$\int 3\ dx - \int 2y\ dy = \int x^3\ dx, \quad or \quad 3x - y^2 = \tfrac{1}{4}x^4 + C.$$

* C may have only those values for which (4) defines x or y as a differentiable function of the other variable, with the derivative continuous.

EXAMPLE 1.   Solve $$2y(1 - x)dy + (1 + y^2)dx = 0,\qquad(7)$$

with the initial conditions that $y = 3$ when $x = -2$.

SOLUTION.   1. To separate the variables, divide by $(1 - x)(1 + y^2)$:

$$\frac{2y\,dy}{1 + y^2} + \frac{dx}{1 - x} = 0.\qquad(8)$$

Integrate in (8): $$\int \frac{2y\,dy}{1 + y^2} + \int \frac{dx}{1 - x} = C, \text{ or}$$

$$\ln(1 + y^2) - \ln|1 - x| = C.\qquad(9)$$

In (9), let $C = \ln K$, where $K > 0$; then

$$\ln\left|\frac{1 + y^2}{1 - x}\right| = \ln K, \quad or \quad \left|\frac{1 + y^2}{1 - x}\right| = K.\qquad(10)$$

Hence, the fraction in (10) is equal to some constant C_1, where $C_1 > 0$ or $C_1 < 0$ according as $x < 1$ or $x > 1$. That is, the general solution of (6) is (*with* $x \neq 1$) $$1 + y^2 = C_1(1 - x).\qquad(11)$$

2. On substituting $x = -2$ and $y = 3$ in (11), we obtain $C_1 = \frac{10}{3}$. Hence, the desired particular solution of (7) is $1 + y^2 = \frac{10}{3}(1 - x)$.

Comment.   When $x = 1$, (8) is not defined. If we look upon (7) as defining x to be a function of y, the constant function $x = 1$ is a solution. This is true because, if $x = 1$, then $dx/dy = 0$ and $dx = 0$, so that (7) is satisfied. The solution $x = 1$ is not given by the general solution (11) for any value of C_1. For this reason, a solution such as $x = 1$ is called a *singular solution*.

Note 2.   The equation $y' = f(x)$, or $dy = f(x)dx$, is a special case of (3), and has the solution $y = \int f(x)dx$, where we let $\int f(x)dx$ involve the arbitrary constant. Problems in Section 113 illustrated this simple method of solution, where merely the definition of an indefinite integral is involved, and the terminology about separable equations is not needed.

EXERCISE 68

Find the general solution of the differential equation, or the particular solution satisfying the given initial conditions. Obtain an answer not involving logarithms, where convenient.

1. $2x\,dy + y\,dx = 0$.

2. $(1 + x)dx + (2 + y)dy = 0$.

3. $x(3 + y)dx = (1 + x^2)dy$.

4. $xy\,dy = (1 + x^2)dx$.

5. $\sqrt{4 + x}\,dy = \sqrt{9 - y}\,dx$.

6. $(1 + 3y)^2\,dx = (2 - x)dy$.

7. $x \cot y\,dx + (1 + x^2)dy = 0$.

8. $(1 + y^2)dx = (1 + x^2)dy$.

9. $\csc x \cos y\,dx + \sin x \sec y\,dy = 0$.

10. $y^2\,dy + \sin x\,dx = \tan y\,dy$.

11. $\dfrac{dy}{dx} = \dfrac{y^2}{x^4}$.

12. $\dfrac{dy}{dx} = \dfrac{2 + y}{3 + x}$.

13. $\dfrac{dy}{dx} = \dfrac{\sin y}{\sin x}$.

14. $y^2 \dfrac{dy}{dx} = \dfrac{x^2 y^3 + x^2}{x^3 + 1}.$

15. $\dfrac{dy}{dx} = \sqrt{\dfrac{4 - y^2}{9 - x^2}}.$

16. $\dfrac{dy}{dx} = \dfrac{4 + y^2}{2 + x^2}.$

17. $\dfrac{x}{y}\, dx - 4\, dy = 0;$ the solution where $y = 2$ at $x = 5$.

18. $\sqrt{y}\, dx + \sqrt{1 + x}\, dy = 0;$ the solution where $y = 4$ when $x = 8$.

19. $2y + x \dfrac{dy}{dx} + 6 = 0;$ the solution where $y = -1$ at $x = 2$.

20. $3e^x\, dy + ye^x\, dy = e^x\, dx - 3\, dy - y\, dy.$

Find an equation for the curve in the xy-plane through the given point, with the given slope at any point (x, y).

21. Slope, $-4x/9y;$ through $(2, -4)$.

22. Slope, $(1 - y)/(x - 1);$ through $(2, -3)$.

23. Slope, $(2y + 1)/(6 - 2x);$ through $(2, -2)$.

24. Slope, $x/y;$ through $(2, 4)$.   **25.** Slope, $2x/3y^2;$ through $(-2, 4)$.

26. Slope, $2/y^2;$ through $(2, 3)$.   **27.** Slope, $-xy;$ through $(0, 1/\sqrt{2\pi})$.

REVIEW EXERCISE 69

Integrate.

1. $\int (2x + 3)^{27}\, dx.$ **2.** $\int \cos^3 u \sin u\, du.$ **3.** $\int_{-\pi}^{\frac{3}{2}\pi} \sin \tfrac{1}{2}x\, dx.$

4. $\int (x - \sqrt[4]{x})^2\, dx.$ **5.** $\int x^2 \sec x^3\, dx.$ **6.** $\int \cot 5x\, dx.$

7. $\int \dfrac{\cos x\, dx}{(1 - 3 \sin x)^4}.$ **8.** $\int \dfrac{\sec^2 \tfrac{1}{2}t\, dt}{1 + 2 \tan \tfrac{1}{2}t}.$ **9.** $\int \dfrac{dz}{(2 - 6z)^{\frac{2}{3}}}.$

10. $\int \dfrac{dv}{4 + 5v}.$ **11.** $\int \dfrac{dv}{\cos 3v}.$ **12.** $\int_{-\frac{2}{3}\sqrt{3}}^{\frac{2}{3}} \dfrac{du}{\sqrt{16 - 9u^2}}.$

13. $\int \dfrac{dz}{\sqrt[3]{4z^2}}.$ **14.** $\int \dfrac{(2x - 3)dx}{\sqrt{4 + 49x^2}}.$ **15.** $\int \dfrac{(2x^2 + 3x)dx}{x^2 + 16}.$

16. $\int \dfrac{(x + 3)dx}{\sqrt{1 + 2x}}.$ **17.** $\int_{-4}^{2} \dfrac{(3x - 2)dx}{(9 - 4x)^{\frac{3}{2}}}.$ **18.** $\int \dfrac{(3x + 4)dx}{\sqrt{4x - x^2}}.$

19. $\int \cot^2 2x\, dx.$ **20.** $\int_{-\frac{1}{2}\pi}^{\pi} \cos^2 3x\, dx.$ **21.** $\int \tan^2 4x\, dx.$

22. $\int \dfrac{du}{17 + 4u + 4u^2}.$ **23.** $\int \dfrac{dx}{\sqrt{5 - x^2 - 4x}}.$

24. $\int \dfrac{dt}{\sqrt{3 + 9t^2 + 6t}}.$ **25.** $\int \dfrac{du}{2u^2 + 8u - 5}.$

26. $\int \dfrac{(2x + 1)dx}{12x - 4x^2 + 7}.$ **27.** $\int \dfrac{(13 - x)dx}{7x - 3 - 2x^2}.$

28. Find an equation for the curve in an xy-plane whose slope at any point (x, y) is $4/y$, if the curve passes through the point $(2, -3)$.

29. A particle moves on an s-axis with the acceleration $(3t + 2)$ at any time t. At $t = 1$, the velocity is $v = -2$ and $s = 3$. Find the coordinate s at any instant t.

13

INTEGRATION BY SPECIAL METHODS

116. Integration by parts

If u and v are differentiable functions of an independent variable x, then, from page 102,

$$d(uv) = u\,dv + v\,du. \tag{1}$$

Hence, by the definition of an indefinite integral,

$$uv = \int d(uv) = \int [u\,dv + v\,du] = \int u\,dv + \int v\,du, \text{ or}$$

$$\int u\,dv = uv - \int v\,du, \tag{2}$$

which is referred to as the formula for *integration by parts*. In a typical application of (2), we think of $\int u\,dv$ as specified for evaluation, but not of a standard form, while v and $\int v\,du$ can be found with ease.

EXAMPLE 1. Integrate: $\int x \sin 2x\,dx$.

SOLUTION. Let $u = x$ and $dv = \sin 2x\,dx$. Then,

$$v = \int \sin 2x\,dx = -\tfrac{1}{2}\cos 2x; \quad du = dx; \tag{3}$$

$$\int \underset{u}{\underbrace{x}}\,\underset{dv}{\underbrace{\sin 2x\,dx}} = -\tfrac{1}{2}x\cos 2x - \int (-\tfrac{1}{2}\cos 2x)\cdot dx$$

$$= -\tfrac{1}{2}x\cos 2x + \tfrac{1}{4}\sin 2x + C. \tag{4}$$

In (3), we avoided introduction of an arbitrary constant in specifying v, because any indefinite integral v is satisfactory for use in (2).

In making choices for u and dv in applying (2), we are guided by the following considerations, wherever possible.

1. *Choose dv so that $\int dv$ is easily obtainable.*

2. *Choose u so that du/dx is* **simpler than u,** *for integration.*

It may be necessary to apply integration by parts two or more times in obtaining an integral.

Note 1. The derivatives and integrals with respect to t of the functions e^t, $\sin t$, and $\cos t$ are as simple as the given functions. Hence, they are useful in either u or dv in applying (2). The derivatives of $\ln t$, Arcsin t, Arctan t, and t^n, with the integer $n > 0$, usually are more desirable than the given functions in connection with integration. Hence, these functions are useful as choices for u.

EXAMPLE 2. Integrate: $\int x^2 e^{3x}\, dx.$

SOLUTION. Let $u = x^2$ and $dv = e^{3x}\, dx;\ \ v = \int e^{3x}\, dx = \tfrac{1}{3}e^{3x}.$

$$\int \underset{u}{\underbrace{x^2}} \cdot \underset{dv}{\underbrace{e^{3x}\, dx}} = \frac{1}{3}\,x^2 e^{3x} - \frac{2}{3}\int \underset{u}{\underbrace{x}} \cdot \underset{dv}{\underbrace{e^{3x}\, dx}}$$

$$= \frac{1}{3}\,x^2 e^{3x} - \frac{2}{3}\left(\frac{1}{3}\,xe^{3x} - \frac{1}{3}\int e^{3x}\, dx\right) = \frac{1}{27}\,e^{3x}(9x^2 - 6x + 2) + C.$$

Comment. The student should try a solution in Example 2 using $dv = x^2\, dx$ and $u = e^{3x}$; the resulting term $\int v\, du$, in (2), is more complicated than the original integral.

EXAMPLE 3. Integrate: $\int x$ Arctan $2x\, dx.$

SOLUTION. With $u =$ Arctan $2x$ and $dv = x\, dx$, then $v = \int x\, dx = \tfrac{1}{2}x^2$, and

$$du = \frac{2\, dx}{1 + 4x^2};\ \ \int \underset{u}{\underbrace{(\text{Arctan } 2x)}} \cdot \underset{dv}{\underbrace{x\, dx}} = \frac{1}{2}\,x^2 \text{ Arctan } 2x - \int \frac{x^2\, dx}{4x^2 + 1}$$

$$= \frac{1}{2}\,x^2 \text{ Arctan } 2x - \frac{1}{4}\left(\int dx - \int \frac{dx}{4x^2 + 1}\right)$$

$$= \tfrac{1}{2}x^2 \text{ Arctan } 2x - \tfrac{1}{4}x + \tfrac{1}{8} \text{ Arctan } 2x + C.$$

EXAMPLE 4. Integrate: $I = \int e^{3x} \sin 2x\, dx.$

SOLUTION. 1. Use (2) with $u = \sin 2x$ and $dv = e^{3x}\, dx$; then $v = \tfrac{1}{3}e^{3x}$ and

$$I = \frac{1}{3}\,e^{3x} \sin 2x - \frac{2}{3}\int e^{3x} \cos 2x\, dx. \tag{5}$$

2. With $u = \cos 2x$ and $dv = e^{3x}\, dx$ on the right in (5),

$$I = \frac{3}{9}\,e^{3x} \sin 2x - \frac{2}{3}\left(\frac{1}{3}\,e^{3x} \cos 2x + \frac{2}{3}\int e^{3x} \sin 2x\, dx\right). \tag{6}$$

In (4), the integral on the right is I. Hence,

$$I + \frac{4}{9}\,I = \frac{13I}{9} = \frac{e^{3x}(3 \sin 2x - 2 \cos 2x)}{9};$$

$$I = \frac{e^{3x}(3 \sin 2x - 2 \cos 2x)}{13} + C,$$

where we added an arbitrary constant to our particular indefinite integral.

ILLUSTRATION 1. $\displaystyle\int_1^2 x^2 \ln x\, dx = \int_1^2 \underbrace{(\ln x)}_{u}\underbrace{(x^2\, dx)}_{dv}$

$$= \frac{1}{3} x^3 \ln x \Big]_1^2 - \frac{1}{3}\int_1^2 x^2\, dx = \frac{8}{3}\ln 2 - \frac{7}{9}.$$

EXAMPLE 5.   Prove the formula

$$\int \sec^3 x\, dx = \tfrac{1}{2}\sec x \tan x + \tfrac{1}{2}\ln |\sec x + \tan x| + C. \qquad \text{(XIX)}$$

SOLUTION.   Let $I = \int \sec^3 x\, dx = \int (\sec x)(\sec^2 x\, dx)$, and employ integration by parts with $u = \sec x$ and $dv = \sec^2 x\, dx$:

$$I = \sec x \tan x - \int \tan x\, (\sec x \tan x)dx. \qquad (7)$$

Use $\tan^2 x = \sec^2 x - 1$ in the integrand in (7):

$$I = \sec x \tan x - \int \sec^3 x\, dx + \int \sec x\, dx, \qquad (8)$$

where $- I$ appears on the right.   Hence,

$$I + I = \sec x \tan x + \ln |\sec x + \tan x| + C'. \qquad (9)$$

On dividing by 2 in (9), and letting $\tfrac{1}{2}C' = C$, we obtain (XIX).   In the next exercise, the student will derive the similar formula

$$\int \csc^3 x\, dx = -\tfrac{1}{2}\cot x \csc x + \tfrac{1}{2}\ln |\csc x - \cot x| + C. \qquad \text{(XX)}$$

A formula which expresses an integral of a certain type in terms of a simpler integral, of similar form, is called a **reduction formula**.   Some reduction formulas can be derived by use of integration by parts.

EXAMPLE 6.   Prove the following formula, where $m + n \neq 0$:

$$\int \sin^m x \cos^n x\, dx = \frac{\sin^{m+1} x \cos^{n-1} x}{m+n} + \frac{n-1}{m+n}\int \sin^m x \cos^{n-2} x\, dx. \qquad (10)$$

SOLUTION.   Let $I = \int \sin^m x \cos^n x\, dx = \int \cos^{n-1} x \sin^m x\, (\cos x\, dx)$.

Integrate by parts with $u = \cos^{n-1} x \quad and \quad dv = \sin^m x\, d(\sin x)$.

Then, $\displaystyle v = \int \sin^m x\, d(\sin x) = \frac{\sin^{m+1} x}{m+1}.$

$$I = \frac{\sin^{m+1} x \cos^{n-1} x}{m+1} + \frac{n-1}{m+1}\int \sin^{m+2} x \cos^{n-2} x\, dx. \qquad (11)$$

In (11), use $\sin^{m+2} x = \sin^m x \sin^2 x = \sin^m x(1 - \cos^2 x)$:

$$(m+1)I = \sin^{m+1} x \cos^{n-1} x + (n-1)\int \sin^m x \cos^{n-2} x\, dx - (n-1)I;$$

$$(m+1+n-1)I = \sin^{m+1} x \cos^{n-1} x + (n-1)\int \sin^m x \cos^{n-2} x\, dx. \qquad (12)$$

On dividing both sides in (12) by $(m+n)$, we obtain (10).

EXERCISE 70

Integrate. Letters a, k, and n represent constants.

1. $\int xe^x \, dx.$ **2.** $\int_1^3 xe^{2x} \, dx.$ **3.** $\int x \cos x \, dx.$

4. $\int x \sin 3x \, dx.$ **5.** $\int xe^{-x} \, dx.$ **6.** $\int x \sec^2 x \, dx.$

7. $\int_{\frac{1}{4}\pi}^{\frac{3}{4}\pi} x \sin x \, dx.$ **8.** $\int \ln x \, dx.$ **9.** $\int x \ln x \, dx.$

10. $\int x^2 e^{2x} \, dx.$ **11.** $\int x^2 \ln x \, dx.$ **12.** $\int x^2 \sin x \, dx.$

13. $\int x^n \ln x \, dx$, with $n \neq -1.$ **14.** $\int y \sec y \tan y \, dy.$

15. $\int x^2 \cos 2x \, dx.$ **16.** $\int \text{Arctan } x \, dx.$ **17.** $\int \text{Arcsin } 3x \, dx.$

18. $\int_{-1}^1 x \text{ Arctan } x \, dx.$ **19.** $\int_{-\frac{1}{2}\pi}^0 x \sec^2 \frac{1}{2}x \, dx.$ **20.** $\int x(2^x) \, dx.$

21. $\int x \text{ Arccot } 2x \, dx.$ **22.** $\int (\ln x)^3 \, dx.$ **23.** $\int x^3 \sin x \, dx.$

24. $\int u \csc 2u \cot 2u \, du.$ **25.** $\int \text{Arcsin } 2x \, dx.$

26. $\int x^4 e^{-x} \, dx.$ **27.** $\int x \sin kx \, dx.$ **28.** $\int x \text{ Arctan } \frac{1}{2}x \, dx.$

29. $\int xa^x \, dx.$ **30.** $\int x \csc^2 \frac{1}{2}x \, dx.$ **31.** $\int x^2 e^{-2x} \, dx.$

32. $\int_{\frac{1}{4}\pi}^{\frac{3}{4}\pi} \frac{x \cot x}{\sin x} \, dx.$ **33.** $\int \frac{x^3}{\sqrt{4 + x^2}} \, dx.$

34. $\int u^3 \sqrt{a^2 \pm u^2} \, du.$ **35.** $\int x^{-\frac{1}{2}} \text{ Arcsin } \sqrt{x} \, dx.$ **36.** $\int (\text{Arcsin } x)^2 \, dx.$

37. $\int \frac{\ln x \, dx}{(x + 2)^2}.$ **38.** $\int \frac{\ln (x + 3)}{\sqrt[3]{x + 3}} \, dx.$

39. $\int \frac{x \text{ Arctan } x}{\sqrt{1 + x^2}} \, dx.$ **40.** $\int x \text{ Arctan } \frac{1}{x} \, dx.$

41. $\int \frac{\text{Arccot } \sqrt{x}}{\sqrt{x}} \, dx.$ **42.** $\int \text{Arcsin } \frac{1}{x} \, dx.$

Obtain the integral by using successive integrations by parts.

43. $\int e^x \sin 3x \, dx.$ **44.** $\int e^{2x} \cos 4x \, dx.$ **45.** $\int e^{-2x} \sin x \, dx.$

46. $\int e^{-x} \cos 2x \, dx.$ **47.** $\int e^{-2x} \sin \frac{1}{2}x \, dx.$ **48.** $\int e^{ax} \cos bx \, dx.$

49. $\int e^{ax} \sin bx \, dx.$ **50.** $\int \csc^3 x \, dx.$ **51.** $\int e^{\frac{1}{2}x} \cos \frac{1}{3}x \, dx.$

(a) Compute the area of the region R bounded by the given curves in an xy-plane. (b) Find the volume of the solid obtained if R is revolved about the x-axis.

52. The x-axis, the curve $y = \ln x$, and the line $x = e^2$.

53. The x-axis, the curve $y = xe^{-x}$, and the lines $x = 1$ and $x = 3$.

54. The x-axis and the curve $y = x \sin x$ from $x = 0$ to $x = \pi$.

55. Prove formulas (125) and (126) of Table VII, and then obtain the results in Problems 43–49 by substitution in these formulas.

56. Derive the formulas (113)–(115) of Table VII.

57. Apply formula (108) of Table VII to find $\int \sec^5 x \, dx.$

117. Trigonometric integrands

Suppose that $f(x)$ is a function of the fundamental trigonometric functions of a single angle. Then, if $\int f(x)dx$ is not in a standard form for integration, our first hope is that

$$\left\{ \begin{array}{l} \textbf{substitution of a new variable } u \textbf{ for} \\ \textbf{one of the trigonometric functions} \end{array} \right\} \tag{1}$$

will change $\int f(x)dx$ to a form $\int g(u)du$ which can be integrated easily. If (1) is not immediately useful, we then consider applying trigonometric identities to alter the form of $f(x)$, with the objective of ultimately using (1). The following alterations of $f(x)$ should be kept in mind as possibilities.

A. *Express all trigonometric functions in terms of sines and cosines by use of the identities*

$$\tan \theta = \frac{\sin \theta}{\cos \theta}, \quad \cot \theta = \frac{\cos \theta}{\sin \theta}, \quad \sec \theta = \frac{1}{\cos \theta}, \quad \csc \theta = \frac{1}{\sin \theta}. \tag{2}$$

B. *Express all trigonometric functions in terms of a single function.*

C. *Use the double-angle* * *identities*

$$1 + \cos 2\theta = 2 \cos^2 \theta, \quad 1 - \cos 2\theta = 2 \sin^2 \theta, \quad \sin 2\theta = 2 \sin \theta \cos \theta, \tag{3}$$

and other identities from page 563.

ILLUSTRATION 1. To perform the following integration, finally substitute $u = \cos x$, with $du = -\sin x \, dx$:

$$\int \sin x \tan^2 x \, dx = \int \frac{\sin x \sin^2 x}{\cos^2 x} \, dx = \int \frac{(1 - \cos^2 x)\sin x \, dx}{\cos^2 x}$$

$$= -\int \frac{1 - u^2}{u^2} \, du = u + \frac{1}{u} + C = \cos x + \sec x + C.$$

118. Various integrands involving sines and cosines

In order to perform an integration of the type

$$\int \sin^m u \cos^n u \, du, \tag{1}$$

we may consider employing the identity $\sin^2 \theta + \cos^2 \theta = 1$, or the double-angle identities. In any case, our first objective is to express (1) in terms of integrals where the sine or cosine of an angle can be taken conveniently as a new variable of integration. We emphasize the following simple possibilities.

I. *If m is a positive odd integer in (1), use*

$$\sin^{m-1} u \cos^n u \, (\sin u \, du) = -\sin^{m-1} u \cos^n u \, d(\cos u).$$

and express $\sin^{m-1} u$ in terms of $\cos u$.

* When read from right to left, (3) may be called *half-angle* identities.

II. *If n is a positive odd integer in* (1), *use*

$$\sin^m u \cos^{n-1} u \ (\cos u \ du) = \sin^m u \cos^{n-1} u \ d(\sin u),$$

and express $\cos^{n-1} u$ *in terms of* $\sin u$.

III. *If m and n are nonnegative even integers in* (1), *transform the integrand by use of the double-angle identities.*

ILLUSTRATION 1. $\displaystyle\int \sin^2 x \cos^3 x \ dx = \int \sin^2 x \cos^2 x \ (\cos x \ dx)$

$$= \int \sin^2 x \ (1 - \sin^2 x) d(\sin x) = \tfrac{1}{3} \sin^3 x - \tfrac{1}{5} \sin^5 x + C.$$

ILLUSTRATION 2. $\displaystyle\int \sin^5 2x \ dx = \frac{1}{2} \int \sin^4 2x \ [(\sin 2x)(2 \ dx)]$

$$= -\frac{1}{2} \int (\sin^2 2x)^2 \ d(\cos 2x) = -\frac{1}{2} \int (1 - \cos^2 2x)^2 \ d(\cos 2x)$$

$$= -\frac{1}{2} \int d(\cos 2x) + \int \cos^2 2x \ d(\cos 2x) - \frac{1}{2} \int \cos^4 2x \ d(\cos 2x)$$

$$= -\tfrac{1}{2} \cos 2x + \tfrac{1}{3} \cos^3 2x - \tfrac{1}{10} \cos^5 2x + C.$$

ILLUSTRATION 3. $\displaystyle\int \frac{\cos^3 x \ dx}{\sin x} = \int \frac{(1 - \sin^2 x)(\cos x \ dx)}{\sin x}$

$$= \int \frac{d(\sin x)}{\sin x} - \int \sin x \ d(\sin x) = \ln | \sin x | - \frac{1}{2} \sin^2 x + C.$$

ILLUSTRATION 4. $\displaystyle\int \sin^4 x \cos^2 x \ dx = \int \sin^2 x \ (\sin^2 x \cos^2 x) dx$

[formulas (3), page 248] $\displaystyle = \int \frac{1}{2}(1 - \cos 2x) \left(\frac{1}{4} \sin^2 2x \right) dx$

$$= \frac{1}{8} \int \frac{1}{2}(1 - \cos 4x) dx - \frac{1}{16} \int \sin^2 2x \ [(\cos 2x)(2 \ dx)]$$

$$= \tfrac{1}{16}x - \tfrac{1}{64} \sin 4x - \tfrac{1}{48} \sin^3 2x + C.$$

In (1), if m and n are even integers and at least one is negative, use of the double-angle identities may lead to an inconvenient form. Then, we may try simple devices based on the identity $\sin^2 \theta + \cos^2 \theta = 1$.

ILLUSTRATION 5. $\displaystyle\int \frac{\cos^4 x}{\sin^2 x} \ dx = \int \frac{1 - \sin^2 x}{\sin^2 x} \cos^2 x \ dx$

$$= \int \cot^2 x \ dx - \int \cos^2 x \ dx = \int \left[\csc^2 x - 1 - \frac{1}{2}(1 + \cos 2x) \right] dx$$

$$= - \cot x - \tfrac{3}{2}x - \tfrac{1}{4} \sin 2x + C.$$

With integrals of form (1), whenever the preceding methods lead to inconvenient integrals, the reduction formulas (109)–(112) of the Table of Integrals are available for obtaining the result.

ILLUSTRATION 6. In the following integration, we apply (114) of Table VII with $m = -4$ and $n = -2$, to increase the exponent of $\cos x$ by 2:

$$\int \frac{dx}{\sin^2 x \cos^4 x} = \frac{1}{3 \sin x \cos^3 x} + \frac{4}{3} \int \frac{dx}{\sin^2 x \cos^2 x}$$

$$\left(\text{since } \sin^2 x \cos^2 x = \frac{1}{4} \sin^2 2x\right) \qquad = \frac{1}{3 \sin x \cos^3 x} + \frac{16}{3} \int \csc^2 2x \, dx$$

$$= \frac{1}{3 \sin x \cos^3 x} - \frac{8}{3} \cot 2x + C.$$

EXERCISE 71

Integrate without introducing a radical.

1. $\int \sin^3 x \cos x \, dx.$ **2.** $\int \cos^2 x \sin x \, dx.$

3. $\int \tan^3 x \csc^2 x \, dx.$ **4.** $\int \cot^2 x \sec x \, dx.$

5. $\int \sin^3 x \cos^2 x \, dx.$ **6.** $\int \sin^4 x \cos^3 x \, dx.$

7. $\int \sin \frac{1}{3}x \cos \frac{1}{3}x \, dx.$ **8.** $\int \sin 2x \cos^3 2x \, dx.$

9. $\int \sin^2 3x \, dx.$ **10.** $\int \cos^2 2x \, dx.$ **11.** $\int \sin^2 \frac{1}{2}x \, dx.$

12. $\int \cos^3 x \, dx.$ **13.** $\int \sin^5 x \, dx.$ **14.** $\int \cos^5 x \, dx.$

15. $\int \frac{\sin^3 x}{\cos^2 x} \, dx.$ **16.** $\int \frac{\sin^5 x}{\cos^4 x} \, dx.$ **17.** $\int \frac{\sin^2 2x}{\cot 2x} \, dx.$

18. $\int \cos^4 x \, dx.$ **19.** $\int \sin^4 x \, dx.$ **20.** $\int \sin^3 hx \, dx.$

21. $\int \sin^2 x \cos^2 x \, dx.$ **22.** $\int \sin^2 x \cos^4 x \, dx.$

23. $\int \sin^4 x \cos^6 x \, dx.$ **24.** $\int \sin^2 \frac{1}{2}x \cos^2 \frac{1}{2}x \, dx.$

25. $\int \sin^4 2x \cos^2 2x \, dx.$ **26.** $\int \sin^6 2x \, dx.$

27. $\int \sin^4 3x \cos^4 3x \, dx.$ **28.** $\int \sin 2x \cos 4x \, dx.$

29. $\int \sin 2x \sin 4x \, dx.$ **30.** $\int \cos 4x \cos 6x \, dx.$

31. $\int \sin hx \cos kx \, dx.$ **32.** $\int (2 \sin x + \cos 2x)^2 \, dx.$

33. $\int \frac{\cos^4 2x}{\sin^2 2x} \, dx.$ **34.** $\int \frac{\cos^6 x}{\sin^2 x} \, dx.$ **35.** $\int \frac{\tan^3 2x}{\cos^2 2x} \, dx.$

36. $\int \frac{\cos 2x}{\tan^2 2x} \, dx.$ **37.** $\int \frac{\cot 2x}{\csc^4 2x} \, dx.$ **38.** $\int \frac{\sin x}{\cot x} \, dx.$

39. $\int \frac{dx}{1 - \cos 2x}.$ **40.** $\int \frac{dy}{1 + \cos y}.$ **41.** $\int \frac{dz}{1 - \cos z}.$

42. $\int \frac{dx}{\sqrt{1 + \cos x}}.$ **43.** $\int \frac{dx}{\sqrt{1 - \cos 4x}}.$ **44.** $\int \frac{dx}{1 + \sin x}.$

45. $\int_0^{2\pi} \sqrt{1 - \cos x} \, dx.$ **46.** $\int_0^{\frac{1}{2}\pi} \sqrt{1 - \cos 4x} \, dx.$

47. $\int_0^{2\pi} \sqrt{1 + \cos x} \, dx.$ **48.** $\int \sin^3 x \sqrt[3]{\cos x} \, dx.$

HINT for Problem 47. If $\pi \leqq x \leqq 2\pi$, $\sqrt{1 + \cos x} = -\sqrt{2} \cos \frac{1}{2}x.$

119. Integrands of the types $\tan^m u \sec^n u$, and $\cot^m u \csc^n u$

In order to perform integrations of the types

$$\int \tan^m n \sec^n u \, du \quad and \quad \int \cot^m u \csc^n u \, du, \tag{1}$$

we frequently employ the identities

$$\tan^2 \theta + 1 = \sec^2 \theta \quad and \quad \cot^2 \theta + 1 = \csc^2 \theta, \tag{2}$$

with the aim of obtaining integrands where $\tan u$, $\sec u$, $\cot u$, or $\csc u$ can be taken conveniently as a new variable.

I. *To obtain $\int \tan^m u \, du$ and $\int \cot^m u \, du$, if m is an integer greater than 1, use*

$$\tan^m u = \tan^{m-2} u \tan^2 u = \tan^{m-2} u \, (\sec^2 u - 1);$$

$$\cot^m u = \cot^{m-2} u \cot^2 u = \cot^{m-2} u \, (\csc^2 u - 1).$$

ILLUSTRATION 1. $\displaystyle \int \tan^4 x \, dx = \int \tan^2 x \, (\sec^2 x - 1) dx$

$$= \int \tan^2 x \, d(\tan x) - \int \tan^2 x \, dx = \tfrac{1}{3} \tan^3 x - \int (\sec^2 x - 1) dx$$

$$= \tfrac{1}{3} \tan^3 x - \tan x + x + C.$$

ILLUSTRATION 2. $\displaystyle \int \cot^5 x \, dx = \int \cot^3 x \, (\csc^2 x - 1) dx$

$$= - \int \cot^3 x \, d(\cot x) - \int \cot^3 x \, dx = - \tfrac{1}{4} \cot^4 x - \int \cot x \, (\csc^2 x - 1) dx$$

$$= - \tfrac{1}{4} \cot^4 x + \tfrac{1}{2} \cot^2 x + \ln | \sin x | + C.$$

II. *If n is a positive even integer in (1), use*

$$\tan^m u \sec^n u \, du = \tan^m u \sec^{n-2} u \, (\sec^2 u \, du) = \tan^m u \sec^{n-2} u \, d(\tan u),$$

and express $\sec^{n-2} u$ in terms of $\tan u$ by use of (2). Similarly, express $\cot^m u \csc^n u \, du$ in terms of $\cot u$ and $d(\cot u)$.

ILLUSTRATION 3. $\displaystyle \int \tan^3 2x \sec^4 2x \, dx = \tfrac{1}{2} \int \tan^3 2x \sec^2 2x \, [(\sec^2 2x)(2 \, dx)]$

$$= \tfrac{1}{2} \int \tan^3 2x \, (\tan^2 2x + 1) \, d(\tan 2x) = \tfrac{1}{12} \tan^6 2x + \tfrac{1}{8} \tan^4 2x + C.$$

ILLUSTRATION 4. $\displaystyle \int \frac{\sec^4 x \, dx}{\tan^5 x} = \int \frac{(\tan^2 x + 1)(\sec^2 x \, dx)}{\tan^5 x}$

$$= - \frac{1}{2 \tan^2 x} - \frac{1}{4 \tan^4 x} + C.$$

III. *If m is a positive odd integer in (1), use*

$$\tan^m u \sec^n u \, du = \tan^{m-1} u \sec^{n-1} u \, (\tan u \sec u \, du)$$

$$= \tan^{m-1} u \sec^{n-1} u \, d(\sec u),$$

and express $\tan^{m-1} u$ in terms of $\sec u$ by use of (2). Similarly, express $\cot^m u \csc^n u \, du$ in terms of $\csc u$ and $d(\csc u)$.

ILLUSTRATION 5. $\displaystyle\int \cot^5 x \csc^3 x \, dx = \int \cot^4 x \csc^2 x \, (\cot x \csc x \, dx)$

$= -\displaystyle\int (\csc^2 x - 1)^2 \csc^2 x \, d(\csc x) = -\tfrac{1}{7} \csc^7 x + \tfrac{2}{5} \csc^5 x - \tfrac{1}{3} \csc^3 x + C.$

ILLUSTRATION 6. $\displaystyle\int \frac{\csc^3 x}{\cot x} \, dx = \int \frac{\csc^2 x}{\cot^2 x} (\csc x \cot x \, dx)$

(let $u = \csc x$) $= \displaystyle\int \frac{u^2 \, du}{1 - u^2} = -\int du + \int \frac{du}{1 - u^2}$

$= -u + \dfrac{1}{2} \ln \left| \dfrac{1 + u}{1 - u} \right| + C = -\csc x + \dfrac{1}{2} \ln \left| \dfrac{1 + \csc x}{1 - \csc x} \right| + C.$

ILLUSTRATION 7. In the following integration, we apply (16) of page 563.

$\displaystyle\int \sin 3t \cos 4t \, dt = \tfrac{1}{2} \int [\sin 7t + \sin (-t)] dt$

$= \tfrac{1}{2} \displaystyle\int (\sin 7t - \sin t) dt = -\tfrac{1}{14} \cos 7t + \tfrac{1}{2} \cos t + C.$

Sometimes, in an integration of types (I), it may be convenient to express the integrand in terms of the sine and cosine. On the other hand, in obtaining $\int \sin^m u \cos^n u \, du$ when m and n are even integers, one of which is negative, it may be best to express the integrand in terms of sec u, csc u, tan u, cot u.

ILLUSTRATION 8. $\displaystyle\int \frac{\sin^2 x}{\cos^4 x} \, dx = \int \tan^2 x \sec^2 x \, dx = \frac{1}{3} \tan^3 x + C.$

ILLUSTRATION 9. $\displaystyle\int \frac{\sec^2 2x}{\tan^5 2x} \, dx = \int \frac{\cos^2 2x \cos 2x \, dx}{\sin^5 2x}$

$= \dfrac{1}{2} \displaystyle\int \frac{1 - \sin^2 2x}{\sin^5 2x} (\cos 2x)(2 \, dx)$ (Let $u = \sin 2x$)

$= \dfrac{1}{2} \displaystyle\int (u^{-5} - u^{-3}) du = -\frac{1}{8} \csc^4 2x + \frac{1}{4} \csc^2 2x + C.$

To obtain $\int \sec^n x \, dx$ if n is an odd integer greater than 1, use (102) or the reduction formula (108) of Table VII.

EXERCISE 72

Integrate without introducing radicals.

1. $\int \tan^2 2x \, dx.$ 2. $\int \tan^3 x \, dx.$ 3. $\int \cot^3 y \, dy.$

4. $\int \cot^4 x \, dx.$ 5. $\int \tan^5 x \, dx.$ 6. $\int \tan^6 2z \, dz.$

7. $\int \cot^5 \tfrac{1}{2}x \, dx.$ 8. $\int \sec^4 x \, dx.$ 9. $\int \csc^6 x \, dx.$

10. $\int \csc^4 2x \, dx.$ 11. $\int \sec^4 3x \, dx.$ 12. $\int \csc^6 \tfrac{1}{2}x \, dx.$

13. $\int \tan^2 t \sec^4 t \, dt.$ 14. $\int \cot^4 y \csc^4 y \, dy.$

15. $\int \cot 2t \csc^4 2t \, dt.$ 16. $\int \cot^3 x \csc^6 x \, dx.$

17. $\int \tan^3 \theta \sec^3 \theta \, d\theta.$ 18. $\int \tan 2x \sec^7 2x \, dx.$

19. $\int \tan^3 3t \sec^5 3t \, dt.$ **20.** $\int \tan^5 z \sec^3 z \, dz.$

21. $\int \cot^4 2x \csc^6 2x \, dx.$ **22.** $\int \cot^3 \frac{1}{2}x \csc^3 \frac{1}{2}x \, dx.$

23. $\int \dfrac{\sec^4 x}{\tan^2 x} \, dx.$ **24.** $\int \dfrac{\csc^4 x}{\sqrt{\cot x}} \, dx.$ **25.** $\int \dfrac{\csc^4 2x}{\cot^5 2x} \, dx.$

26. $\int \dfrac{\sec^6 x}{\sqrt[3]{\tan x}} \, dx.$ **27.** $\int \dfrac{\csc^4 y}{\tan^3 y} \, dy.$ **28.** $\int \dfrac{\sec^6 x}{\cot^3 x} \, dx.$

29. $\int \dfrac{\csc^2 x}{\cot^5 x} \, dx.$ **30.** $\int \dfrac{\sec^2 \frac{1}{2}x}{\tan^3 \frac{1}{2}x} \, dx.$ **31.** $\int \left(\dfrac{\tan \theta}{\cot \theta}\right)^3 d\theta.$

32. $\int \sec^4 x \sqrt[3]{\tan x} \, dx.$ **33.** $\int \csc^6 2x \sqrt{\cot 2x} \, dx.$

34. $\int \dfrac{\sin^4 x}{\cos^6 x} \, dx.$ **35.** $\int \dfrac{\cos^2 x}{\sin^6 x} \, dx.$ **36.** $\int \dfrac{\sin^3 x}{\cos^7 x} \, dx.$

37. $\int \dfrac{\sec^4 x}{\tan x} \, dx.$ **38.** $\int \dfrac{\csc^4 x}{\cot x} \, dx.$ **39.** $\int \dfrac{\sec^4 2x}{\tan^4 2x} \, dx.$

40. $\int \dfrac{\sec^3 x}{\tan x} \, dx.$ **41.** $\int \dfrac{\tan^3 x}{\sec^3 x} \, dx.$ **42.** $\int \dfrac{\cot^5 3y}{\csc^5 3y} \, dy.$

43. $\int \tan^3 x \sqrt{\sec x} \, dx.$ **44.** $\int \cot^3 x \sqrt[3]{\csc x} \, dx.$

45. $\int \sec^3 2x \, dx.$ **46.** $\int \sec^5 2x \, dx.$ **47.** $\int \sec^{-3} \frac{1}{2}x \, dx.$

48. $\int x \sec^4 x \, dx.$ **49.** $\int x \csc^4 2x \, dx.$ **50.** $\int x \tan^2 x \, dx.$

51. $\int z \sec^3 z \tan z \, dz.$ **52.** $\int x \csc^4 2x \cot 2x \, dx.$

120. Rationalization by trigonometric substitutions

In $\int f(x)dx$, suppose that $f(x)$ is an irrational function, which is a *rational function* of x and the square root of a quadratic function of x. Then, by a suitable trigonometric substitution it is possible to alter the radical to a constant times a trigonometric function of a new variable, without introducing any new radical in the integrand. Hence, the change of variable is called a *rationalizing substitution*. We are led to the desired change in such cases by recollection of the identities

$$\cos^2 \theta = 1 - \sin^2 \theta, \quad \sec^2 \theta = 1 + \tan^2 \theta, \quad \tan^2 \theta = \sec^2 \theta - 1. \qquad (1)$$

For radicals of the following forms, we use the indicated substitutions.

$$\sqrt{a^2 - u^2}: \qquad \textit{substitute } u = a \sin \theta. \qquad (2)$$

$$\sqrt{a^2 + u^2}: \qquad \textit{substitute } u = a \tan \theta. \qquad (3)$$

$$\sqrt{u^2 - a^2}: \qquad \textit{substitute } u = a \sec \theta. \qquad (4)$$

ILLUSTRATION 1. To rationalize $\sqrt{x^2 - 4}$, substitute $x = 2 \sec \theta$:

(if $\tan \theta > 0$) $\sqrt{4 \sec^2 \theta - 4} = \sqrt{4(\sec^2 \theta - 1)} = 2 \tan \theta.$

To rationalize $\sqrt{9 + 4x^2}$, substitute $2x = 3 \tan \theta$. If $\sec \theta > 0$,

$$\sqrt{9 + (2x)^2} = \sqrt{9 + 9 \tan^2 \theta} = 3\sqrt{1 + \tan^2 \theta} = 3 \sec \theta.$$

EXAMPLE 1. Integrate: $\displaystyle\int \frac{du}{(a^2 + u^2)^{\frac{3}{2}}}.$ $(a > 0)$

SOLUTION. 1. Let $u = a \tan \theta$, with $\sec \theta > 0$; then $du = a \sec^2 \theta \, d\theta$;

$$(\sqrt{a^2 + u^2})^3 = (\sqrt{a^2 + a^2 \tan^2 \theta})^3 = a^3(\sqrt{1 + \tan^2 \theta})^3 = a^3 \sec^3 \theta;$$

$$\int \frac{du}{(a^2 + u^2)^{\frac{3}{2}}} = \frac{1}{a^2} \int \frac{\sec^2 \theta}{\sec^3 \theta} d\theta = \frac{1}{a^2} \int \cos \theta \, d\theta = \frac{1}{a^2} \sin \theta + C. \qquad (5)$$

2. Figure 143 is useful in changing back from θ to u in (5):

$$\sin \theta = \frac{u}{\sqrt{a^2 + u^2}}; \quad \int \frac{du}{(a^2 + u^2)^{\frac{3}{2}}} = \frac{u}{a^2\sqrt{a^2 + u^2}} + C.$$

Comment. In $u = a \tan \theta$, with $a > 0$, we agree to use the *principal value*
$\theta = \text{Arctan } u/a$, so that $-\frac{1}{2}\pi < \theta < \frac{1}{2}\pi$, where
$\theta < 0$ if $u < 0$. The triangle in Figure 143 actually
is valid only if $u \geqq 0$, so that $0 \leqq \theta < \frac{1}{2}\pi$. However, the formulas obtained from Figure 143 for the
functions of θ are valid also if $u < 0$. In this case,
$-\frac{1}{2}\pi < \theta < 0$, and u gives the proper sign to all
the functions of θ which are negative.

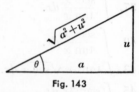

Fig. 143

EXAMPLE 2. Integrate: $\displaystyle\int \frac{x^2 \, dx}{(4 - x^2)^{\frac{3}{2}}}.$

SOLUTION. 1. Let $x = 2 \sin \theta$, with $\cos \theta > 0$; then $dx = 2 \cos \theta \, d\theta$;

$$(4 - x^2)^{\frac{1}{2}} = \sqrt{4 - 4 \sin^2 \theta} = 2\sqrt{1 - \sin^2 \theta} = 2 \cos \theta;$$

$$\int \frac{x^2 \, dx}{(4 - x^2)^{\frac{3}{2}}} = \int \frac{\sin^2 \theta \cos \theta \, d\theta}{\cos^3 \theta} = \int \tan^2 \theta \, d\theta$$

$$= \int (\sec^2 \theta - 1)d\theta = \tan \theta - \theta + C. \qquad (6)$$

Fig. 144

2. From $x = 2 \sin \theta$ and Figure 144, $\theta = \text{Arcsin } \frac{1}{2}x$;

$$\tan \theta = \frac{x}{\sqrt{4 - x^2}}; \quad \int \frac{x^2 \, dx}{(4 - x^2)^{\frac{3}{2}}} = \frac{x}{\sqrt{4 - x^2}} - \text{Arcsin } \frac{x}{2} + C.$$

ILLUSTRATION 2. To rationalize the integrand in $\int \sqrt{5 - x^2 + 4x} \, dx$, we
would complete a square and apply (2):

$$\sqrt{5 - x^2 + 4x} = \sqrt{9 - (x - 2)^2}; \quad then, \ let \quad x - 2 = 3 \sin \theta.$$

EXAMPLE 3. Compute $\displaystyle\int_{-1}^{\sqrt{3}} \frac{x^2 \, dx}{(4 - x^2)^{\frac{3}{2}}}.$

SOLUTION. Let $x = 2 \sin \theta$, with $\theta = \text{Arcsin } \frac{1}{2}x$. If $x = -1$, then
$\theta = -\frac{1}{6}\pi$; if $x = \sqrt{3}$, then $\theta = \frac{1}{3}\pi$. Hence, from (6) in Example 2,

$$\int_{-1}^{\sqrt{3}} \frac{x^2 \, dx}{(4 - x^2)^{\frac{3}{2}}} = \int_{-\frac{1}{6}\pi}^{\frac{1}{3}\pi} \tan^2 \theta \, d\theta = \tan \theta - \theta \Big]_{-\frac{1}{6}\pi}^{\frac{1}{3}\pi} = \frac{4}{3}\sqrt{3} - \frac{1}{2}\pi.$$

Substitutions (2), (3), and (4) apply conveniently with integrals of the following types, where n is a positive integer:

$$\int \frac{du}{(u^2 + a^2)^n}; \quad \int \frac{du}{(u^2 - a^2)^n}.$$

EXERCISE 73

Integrate. Perhaps use formulas (28) and (41) of Table VII, after deriving them.

1. $\displaystyle\int \frac{dx}{(9 - x^2)^{\frac{3}{2}}}.$

2. $\displaystyle\int \frac{dx}{x^2\sqrt{4 + x^2}}.$

3. $\displaystyle\int \frac{\sqrt{x^2 - 9}}{x}\, dx.$

4. $\displaystyle\int \frac{\sqrt{t^2 - 16}}{t^2}\, dt.$

5. $\displaystyle\int \frac{dy}{y\sqrt{9 + 4y^2}}.$

6. $\displaystyle\int \frac{dt}{t\sqrt{t^2 - 16}}.$

7. $\displaystyle\int \frac{dy}{y\sqrt{1 - 9y^2}}.$

8. $\displaystyle\int \frac{u^2\, du}{(a^2 + u^2)^{\frac{3}{2}}}.$

9. $\displaystyle\int \frac{x^2\, dx}{\sqrt{25 - x^2}}.$

10. $\displaystyle\int \frac{dy}{(9 + 49y^2)^{\frac{3}{2}}}.$

11. $\displaystyle\int \frac{u^3\, du}{\sqrt{2 - u^2}}.$

12. $\displaystyle\int \frac{z^2\, dz}{\sqrt{1 - 4z^2}}.$

13. $\displaystyle\int \frac{dx}{(x^2 + 9)^2}.$

14. $\displaystyle\int \frac{du}{(a^2 + u^2)^2}.$

15. $\displaystyle\int \frac{dy}{y^2\sqrt{9 + y^2}}.$

16. $\displaystyle\int \frac{dy}{y\sqrt{y^2 - 5}}.$

17. $\displaystyle\int_{-2}^{2\sqrt{3}} \frac{x^2\, dx}{(16 - x^2)^{\frac{3}{2}}}.$

18. $\displaystyle\int_{-\frac{4}{3}}^{\frac{4}{3}\sqrt{3}} \frac{dz}{(9z^2 + 16)^{\frac{3}{2}}}.$

19. $\displaystyle\int \sqrt{a^2 + 9x^2}\, dx.$

20. $\displaystyle\int \sqrt{4x^2 - a^2}\, dx.$

21. $\displaystyle\int \sqrt{4a^2 - x^2}\, dx.$

22. $\displaystyle\int_{\frac{1}{6}}^{\frac{1}{6}\sqrt{2}} \frac{dx}{x^2\sqrt{1 - 9x^2}}.$

23. $\displaystyle\int \frac{dx}{(5 - x^2 - 4x)^{\frac{3}{2}}}.$

24. $\displaystyle\int \frac{\sqrt{49t^2 - 1}}{t^2}\, dt.$

25. $\displaystyle\int \frac{x^2\, dx}{\sqrt{4x^2 - 49}}.$

26. $\displaystyle\int \frac{u^3\, du}{\sqrt{a^2 - u^2}}.$

27. $\displaystyle\int \frac{\sec^2 t\, dt}{(4 - \tan^2 t)^{\frac{3}{2}}}.$

28. $\displaystyle\int \frac{e^{-x}\, dx}{(9 + 4e^{-2x})^{\frac{3}{2}}}.$

29. $\displaystyle\int \frac{(3x + 5)dx}{(9 + 4x^2)^2}.$

30. $\displaystyle\int \frac{\sqrt{9 + z^2}}{z}\, dz.$

31. $\displaystyle\int \frac{(3 - 6x)dx}{(25 + 4x^2)^{\frac{3}{2}}}.$

32. $\displaystyle\int \frac{dx}{x\sqrt{2x - x^2}}.$

33. $\displaystyle\int \frac{dx}{(4x^2 - 24x + 27)^{\frac{3}{2}}}.$

34. $\displaystyle\int \frac{(16x + 5)dx}{(4x^2 + 12x + 25)^2}.$

35. $\displaystyle\int \frac{(2x - 3)dx}{(9x^2 + 12x + 5)^{\frac{3}{2}}}.$

36. $\displaystyle\int \frac{dy}{(y - 2)\sqrt{y^2 - 4y - 5}}.$

37. $\displaystyle\int (8x - 5)\sqrt{4x^2 - 4x}\, dx.$

38. $\displaystyle\int \sqrt{x^2 - 2ax}\, dx.$

39. Obtain the area of a circle of radius r by integration.

40. Find the area of the ellipse $4x^2 + 9y^2 = 36$.

41. Find the area of the ellipse $b^2x^2 + a^2y^2 = a^2b^2$.

14

APPLICATIONS OF DEFINITE INTEGRALS

121. Formulation of areas

Let R be the region in an xy-plane bounded by the x-axis, the graph of a function $y = f(x)$, where $f(x) \geq 0$, and the lines $x = a$ and $x = b$, where $a \leq b$. Then, we have defined the area, A, of R so that

$$[\text{with } y = f(x)] \qquad\qquad A = \int_a^b y \, dx. \qquad\qquad (1)$$

Also, if $y_1 = g(x)$ and $y_2 = f(x)$ are two functions such that $y_1 \leq y_2$, then the area, A, of the region bounded by the curves $y_1 = g(x)$, $y_2 = f(x)$, and the lines $x = a$ and $x = b$ is given by

$$(\text{with } y_1 \leq y_2) \qquad\qquad A = \int_a^b (y_2 - y_1) dx. \qquad\qquad (2)$$

Similarly, with the roles of x and y interchanged, we have the areas

$$(\text{with } c \leq d) \qquad A = \int_c^d x \, dy \quad and \quad A = \int_c^d (x_2 - x_1) dx; \qquad (3)$$

where $x = g(y)$ in the first integral; $x_1 = g(y)$ and $x_2 = f(y)$, with $x_1 \leq x_2$, in the second integral.

EXAMPLE 1. Find the area, A, of the region bounded by $y = \tan x$ and $y = \sin x$, and the lines $x = 0$ and $x = \frac{1}{3}\pi$.

SOLUTION. A graph of $y_1 = \sin x$ and $y_2 = \tan x$ is given in Figure 145. We shall use (2). Figure 145 exhibits a typical elementary rectangle, whose area is $(y_2 - y_1)\Delta x$. This recalls the form of the element of area when (2) is expressed as the limit of a finite sum. From (2),

$$A = \int_0^{\frac{1}{3}\pi} (\tan x - \sin x) dx = .1932.$$

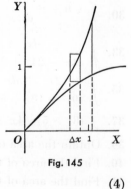

Fig. 145

Consider a curve C defined parametrically by

$$x = \phi(t) \quad and \quad y = \psi(t), \qquad\qquad (4)$$

256

with $y \geq 0$ when $\alpha \leq t \leq \beta$, $(x = a, y = c)$ at $t = \alpha$, and $(x = b, y = d)$ at $t = \beta$. Assume that $\phi(t)$ has a continuous derivative $\phi'(t)$ and that the equation $x = \phi(t)$ defines a single valued inverse $t = h(x)$. Then, with $t = h(x)$, the equation $y = \psi(t)$ implicitly defines y as a function of x, say $y = f(x)$, where $f(x) \geq 0$ when $a \leq x \leq b$. Let R be the region bounded by the x-axis, the curve C, and the lines $x = a$ and $x = b$; let A be the area of R. In the integral (1), transform by the substitution $x = \phi(t)$, which satisfies the hypotheses of Theorem III on page 227. Then, $y = f(x)$ becomes $y = \psi(t)$; $dx = \phi'(t)dt$, and the limits in (1) change to α and β:

$$A = \int_{\alpha}^{\beta} \psi(t)\phi'(t)\,dt. \tag{5}$$

Hereafter, we shall abbreviate (5) by writing

[with $x = \phi(t)$, $y = \psi(t)$]
$$A = \int_{t=\alpha}^{t=\beta} y \, dx, \tag{6}$$

with t as the variable of integration, as shown by the limits. That is, to obtain A when C is given in the form (4), *first formulate A in terms of the variables x and y, as in (1), and then change the variable of integration from x to t by use of* (4). Similarly, we use (4) with (2) and (3).

EXAMPLE 2. Obtain the area of the ellipse defined by

$$x = 4 \cos t \quad and \quad y = 3 \sin t. \tag{7}$$

SOLUTION. 1. The ellipse, in Figure 146, is traced out from B to D as t varies from $t = 0$ to $t = \frac{1}{2}\pi$. The area A of the ellipse is equal to four times the area of the region bounded by the x-axis, the curve (7), and the lines $x = 0$ and $x = 4$. Thus,

$$A = 4 \int_0^4 y \, dx. \tag{8}$$

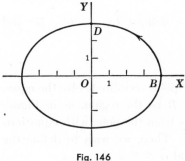

Fig. 146

2. *Transform* (8) *by use of* (7). Then, $dx = -4 \sin t \, dt$; $x = 0$ when $t = \frac{1}{2}\pi$ and $x = 4$ when $t = 0$. Thus, as x ranges from 0 to 4 in (8), the variable t ranges from $\frac{1}{2}\pi$ to 0, and

$$A = 4 \int_{\frac{1}{2}\pi}^{0} (3 \sin t)(-4 \sin t \, dt) \tag{9}$$

$$= -48 \int_{\frac{1}{2}\pi}^{0} \sin^2 t \, dt = 48 \int_0^{\frac{1}{2}\pi} \sin^2 t \, dt$$

$$= 48 \int_0^{\frac{1}{2}\pi} \frac{1}{2}(1 - \cos 2t)dt = 24\left(t - \frac{1}{2}\sin 2t\right)\Big]_0^{\frac{1}{2}\pi} = 12\pi.$$

Comment. In using the preceding method, it is essential to start, as in (8), *with the limits as specified for x* (or for y), and then get the corresponding limits for the parameter, as in (9).

EXERCISE 74

Find the area of the specified region in an xy-plane.

1. Bounded by $y = \sqrt[3]{x}$, the x-axis, and the lines $x = 0$ and $x = 8$.
2. Bounded by $y = x^3$, the x-axis, and the lines $x = -2$ and $x = 3$.
3. Bounded by $x = \ln y$, the y-axis, and the lines $y = 2$ and $y = 4$.
4. Bounded by $xy = 4$, the y-axis, and the lines $y = 1$ and $y = 3$.
5. Between $y = x^3 + x^2 - 6x$ and $y = 6x$.
6. Between $y^2 = 12 - 3x$ and $y = 3x$.
7. Bounded by $y = e^{2x}$, the y-axis, and the lines $y = 1$ and $y = e$.
8. Enclosed by the loop of the curve $y^2 = x(x - 2)^2$.
9. Enclosed by the loop of the curve $y^2 = x^2(x + 2)$.
10. Bounded below by the line $y = \frac{1}{2}$ and above by one arch of the curve $y = \sin x$.
11. Between the line $y = 2$ and one branch of $y = \sec x$.

In the following problems, t or θ is a parameter.

12. Find the area of the ellipse defined by $x = a \cos t$ and $y = b \sin t$, where $a > 0$ and $b > 0$.
13. Find the area of the hypocycloid of four cusps defined by $x = a \cos^3 t$ and $y = a \sin^3 t$, where $a > 0$.
14. Find the area of the region between the x-axis and one arch of the cycloid defined by $x = a(\theta - \sin \theta)$ and $y = a(1 - \cos \theta)$ where $a > 0$.
15. Find the area of the region between the x-axis and the witch, defined by $x = 2a \tan t$ and $y = 2a \cos^2 t$, where $a > 0$, from $x = -2a$ to $x = 2a$.
16. Find the area of the region bounded by the semicubical parabola defined by $(x = \frac{27}{4}t^2, \ y = \frac{27}{4}t^3)$ and the line $x = 3$.
17. Find the area of the loop of the curve defined by $x = 6t - \frac{1}{2}t^3$ and $y = \frac{1}{2}t^2 - 6$.

122. Areas, in polar coordinates

Let a curve C be defined in an $r\theta$-system of polar coordinates by the equation $r = f(\theta)$, where $f(\theta)$ is continuous. Let R be the region, as in Figure 147 on page 259, bounded by C and two rays from the pole, with equations $\theta = \alpha$ and $\theta = \beta$, respectively, where $\alpha \leq \beta$. Then, we wish to define the area of R. Let P be a partition of the interval $\alpha \leq \theta \leq \beta$:

Partition P: $\alpha = \theta_0 < \theta_1 < \cdots < \theta_{i-1} < \theta_i < \cdots < \theta_n = \beta.$ (1)

Let $r_i = f(\theta_i)$, and let τ_i be the point $[r_i, \theta_i]$ on C. Draw a ray from the pole to each point τ_i; the ith ray has the equation $\theta = \theta_i$. The rays divide R into irregular sectors, where the ith sector has the angle $\Delta_i\theta = \theta_i - \theta_{i-1}$. For the ith piece of R, construct an arc of a circle with radius * $| r_i | = | f(\theta_i) |$,

* Perhaps $f(\theta_i) < 0$. Hence, the absolute value signs are necessary.

and thus form a circular sector with the angle $\Delta_i\theta$. From (6) on page 125, the area of this sector is $\frac{1}{2}r_i^2\Delta_i\theta$. Let S_P be the sum of the areas of all sectors thus formed, corresponding to the partition P:

$$S_P = \sum_{i=1}^{n} \tfrac{1}{2}r_i^2\Delta_i\theta = \sum_{i=1}^{n} \tfrac{1}{2}[f(\theta_i)]^2\Delta_i\theta. \tag{2}$$

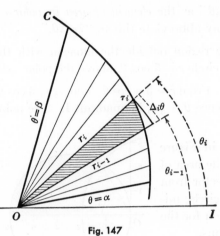

Fig. 147

Then, we define the area, A, of the region R as *the limit, if it exists, of S_P as all $\Delta_i\theta$ tend to zero*, or

$$A = \lim_{(as\ all\ \Delta_i\theta\to0)} \sum_{i=1}^{n} \frac{1}{2}[f(\theta_i)]^2\Delta_i\theta. \tag{3}$$

Compare the preceding details with those on page 189 leading to the definition of a definite integral. It is verified that S_P in (2) is a special instance (with $\xi_i = \theta_i$) of S_P on page 189, for the case of the function $\frac{1}{2}[f(\theta)]^2$. Hence,

$$A = \frac{1}{2}\int_\alpha^\beta [f(\theta)]^2\ d\theta, \text{ or}$$

[with $r = f(\theta)$]

$$A = \frac{1}{2}\int_\alpha^\beta r^2\ d\theta. \tag{4}$$

EXAMPLE 1. Find the area of the cardioid $r = 2(1 - \sin\theta)$.

SOLUTION. The cardioid is shown in Figure 148. The right-hand half of the curve is traced as θ varies from $\theta = -\frac{1}{2}\pi$ to $\theta = \frac{1}{2}\pi$. The desired area A is equal to twice that of the region bounded by the line $\theta = \frac{1}{2}\pi$ and the right-hand half of the curve, or

$$A = \int_{-\frac{1}{2}\pi}^{\frac{1}{2}\pi} [2(1 - \sin\theta)]^2\ d\theta = 6\pi.$$

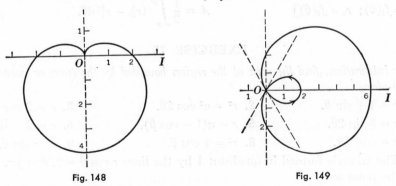

Fig. 148   Fig. 149

EXAMPLE 2. Find the area of the inner loop of the limaçon whose equation is $r = 2 + 4\cos\theta$, shown in Figure 149.

SOLUTION. Since $r = 0$ when $\cos \theta = -\frac{1}{2}$, or $\theta = \frac{2}{3}\pi$ and $\theta = \frac{4}{3}\pi$, hence the lines $\theta = \frac{2}{3}\pi$ and $\theta = \frac{4}{3}\pi$ are tangents to the limaçon at the pole. The loop is traced in the direction of the arrowheads as θ varies from $\frac{2}{3}\pi$ to $\frac{4}{3}\pi$. Thus, the desired area, A, is given by

$$A = \int_{\frac{2}{3}\pi}^{\frac{4}{3}\pi} \frac{1}{2}(2 + 4 \cos \theta)^2 \, d\theta = 4\pi - 6\sqrt{3}.$$

Note 1. In (2), we refer to "$\frac{1}{2}r_i^2 \Delta_i \theta$" as the *element of area in polar coordinates*. For future purposes, we may abbreviate this to "$\frac{1}{2}r^2 \Delta \theta$."

EXAMPLE 3. Find the area of the region outside the limaçon with the equation $r = 3 - \cos \theta$ and inside the circle $r = 5 \cos \theta$, above the polar axis.

PARTIAL SOLUTION. 1. *Intersection.* From $r = 3 - \cos \theta$ and $r = 5 \cos \theta$, we obtain $6 \cos \theta = 3$ or $\cos \theta = \frac{1}{2}$; hence $\theta = \frac{1}{3}\pi$, in quadrant I. The point of intersection, P, is $[r = \frac{5}{2}, \theta = \frac{1}{3}\pi]$.

2. The specified region R is ruled in Figure 150. The area, A, of R is equal to the area of the region swept out by the radius vector from the origin to the point $[r, \theta]$ on the circle, minus the area of the corresponding region for the limaçon, as θ varies from 0 to $\frac{1}{3}\pi$. Thus,

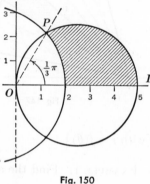

$$A = \frac{1}{2} \int_0^{\frac{1}{3}\pi} 25 \cos^2 \theta \, d\theta - \frac{1}{2} \int_0^{\frac{1}{3}\pi} (3 - \cos \theta)^2 \, d\theta$$

$$= \frac{1}{2} \int_0^{\frac{1}{3}\pi} (24 \cos^2 \theta + 6 \cos \theta - 9) d\theta.$$

Fig. 150

Let R be the region bounded by the lines $\theta = \alpha$ and $\theta = \beta$, with $\alpha < \beta$, and the curves $r = f_1(\theta)$ and $r = f_2(\theta)$, where $0 \leq f_1(\theta) \leq f_2(\theta)$. Then, by the method of Example 3, the area, A, of R is given by

$$[r_1 = f_1(\theta); \ r_2 = f_2(\theta)] \qquad A = \frac{1}{2} \int_\alpha^\beta (r_2^2 - r_1^2) d\theta. \qquad (5)$$

EXERCISE 75

By integration, find the area of the region bounded by the curve or curves in an $r\theta$-plane.

1. $r = 1 + \sin \theta$.   2. $r^2 = a^2 \cos 2\theta$.   3. $r = 2 \cos 3\theta$.

4. $r = 3 \sin 2\theta$.   5. $r = a(1 - \cos \theta)$.   6. $r = 2 - \sin \theta$.

7. $r = \cos^2 \frac{1}{2}\theta$.   8. $r^2 = 4 \cos \theta$.   9. $r^2 = \sin \theta$.

10. The triangle formed in quadrant I by the lines $r \cos \theta = 2$, $\theta = \frac{1}{6}\pi$, and the polar axis.

11. Bounded by the parabola $r = 3/(1 + \cos \theta)$ and the line $\theta = \frac{1}{2}\pi$.

12. Bounded above by the line $\theta = \frac{1}{6}\pi$ and below by the circle $r = 4 \sin \theta$.

Find the area of the region swept out by the radius vector from the pole to the
point $[r,\ \theta]$ *on the curve when* θ *varies as specified.*

13. The *spiral* of ARCHIMEDES $r = k\theta$, with $k > 0$; θ varies from 0 to π.

14. The *logarithmic spiral* $r = e^{k\theta}$, with $k > 0$; θ varies from 0 to 2π.

15. The *hyperbolic spiral* $r\theta = a$, with $a > 0$; θ varies from $\frac{1}{2}\pi$ to $\frac{3}{2}\pi$.

16. The hyperbola $r^2 \cos 2\theta = 4$; θ varies from 0 to $\frac{1}{6}\pi$, with $r > 0$.

Find the area of the region which is described.

17. The smaller segment of the circle $r = 4 \cos \theta$ cut off by the line $r \cos \theta = 3$.

18. The region bounded above by the cardioid $r = 2(1 + \sin \theta)$ and below by the circle $r = 2$, with $0 \le \theta \le \pi$.

19. The region in quadrant I inside the circle $r = \cos \theta$ and the cardioid $r = 1 - \cos \theta$.

20. The three-sided region above the polar axis bounded by the circle $r = -2 \cos \theta$, the parabola $r = 2 \csc^2 \frac{1}{2}\theta$, and the line $\theta = \frac{1}{2}\pi$.

21. The region interior to the lemniscate $r^2 = 2 \sin 2\theta$ and exterior to the circle $r = 1$.

22. The region in quadrant I bounded by the polar axis, the line $r \cos \theta = \frac{1}{2}a$, and the *kappa curve* $r = a \tan \theta$, where $a > 0$.

23. The whole region bounded by the curve $r = 3 + 2 \cos 2\theta$.

24. The whole region bounded by the curve $r = 3 + \sin 3\theta$.

Find the area of the region interior to both of the curves.

25. $r = \sqrt{3} \cos \theta$; $r = \sin \theta$.   **26.** $r^2 = 4 \cos 2\theta$; $r^2 = 4 \sin 2\theta$.

27. Find the area of the region between the inner loop and the outer part of the limaçon in Example 2 on page 259. Use that example's result.

28. The area of the loop of the *conchoid* of NICOMEDES $r = \csc \theta - 2$.

123. Infinite interval of integration

In the definition of a definite integral on page 190, the interval of integration is specified to be finite. Now, we shall introduce symbols such as $\int_a^\infty f(x)dx$, which we call an **improper integral**, and which we read as "*the integral of $f(x)$ from $x = a$ to infinity,*" where the range of x is an *infinite interval*. For contrast, sometimes we shall refer to an integral as a *proper definite integral*, if it exists according to Definition II on page 190.

DEFINITION I. *Let a be a fixed number, and suppose that $f(x)$ is continuous on any range involved for x. Then, we define the value of each of the following improper integrals as the limit on the right in the corresponding equation, provided that this limit exists:*

$$\int_a^\infty f(x)dx = \lim_{h \to \infty} \int_a^h f(x)dx. \tag{1}$$

$$\int_{-\infty}^a f(x)dx = \lim_{h \to -\infty} \int_h^a f(x)dx. \tag{2}$$

In (1) or (2), if the limit on the right exists (is *finite*), we say that the improper integral on the left *exists*, or **converges**, and that it *converges to the specified limit*. Otherwise, we say that the improper integral **diverges**, or that it *fails to exist*.

ILLUSTRATION 1. By Definition I,

$$\int_2^\infty \frac{dx}{x^3} = \lim_{h \to \infty} \int_2^h \frac{dx}{x^3} = \lim_{h \to \infty} \left(-\frac{1}{2x^2}\right)\Big]_2^h = \lim_{h \to \infty} \left(\frac{1}{8} - \frac{1}{2h^2}\right) = \frac{1}{8} - 0 = \frac{1}{8}.$$

ILLUSTRATION 2. By equation (1),

$$\int_1^\infty \frac{dx}{\sqrt{x}} = \lim_{h \to \infty} \int_1^h \frac{dx}{\sqrt{x}} = \lim_{h \to \infty} 2\sqrt{x}\Big]_1^h = \lim_{h \to \infty} (2\sqrt{h} - 2) = \infty.$$

Hence, the improper integral diverges, or has no value.

ILLUSTRATION 3. $\int_{-\infty}^0 \sin x \, dx = \lim_{h \to -\infty} \int_h^0 \sin x \, dx$

$$= \lim_{h \to -\infty} - \cos x \Big]_h^0 = \lim_{h \to -\infty} (\cos h - 1). \tag{3}$$

In (3), cos h oscillates between -1 and $+1$ as $h \to -\infty$, and thus *does not have a limit*, finite or infinite, or the improper integral diverges.

DEFINITION II.   *If $f(x)$ is continuous on the whole real axis, $-\infty < x < \infty$, and a is any number, we define the improper integral $\int_{-\infty}^\infty f(x)dx$ as follows, provided that both integrals on the right converge:*

$$\int_{-\infty}^\infty f(x)dx = \int_{-\infty}^a f(x)dx + \int_a^\infty f(x)dx. \tag{4}$$

If either integral on the right in (4) fails to exist, we say that the integral on the left fails to exist, or that it diverges.

EXAMPLE 1. Test for convergence: $\int_{-\infty}^\infty x^3 \, dx$.

SOLUTION. By Definition II, $\int_{-\infty}^\infty x^3 \, dx = \int_{-\infty}^0 x^3 \, dx + \int_0^\infty x^3 \, dx,$

provided that both integrals on the right converge. We obtain

$$\int_0^\infty x^3 \, dx = \lim_{h \to \infty} \int_0^h x^3 \, dx = \lim_{h \to \infty} \frac{1}{4} x^4 \Big]_0^h = \lim_{h \to \infty} \frac{1}{4} h^4 = \infty.$$

Hence, $\int_0^\infty x^3 \, dx$ does not exist. Thus, without considering $\int_{-\infty}^0 x^3 \, dx$, we may state that $\int_{-\infty}^\infty x^3 \, dx$ does not exist.

Comment. Notice the fallacy which arises when, *incorrectly*, we act as if the given improper integral could be defined as follows:

$$\int_{-\infty}^\infty x^3 \, dx = \lim_{h \to \infty} \int_{-h}^h x^3 \, dx = \lim_{h \to \infty} \tfrac{1}{4} x^4 \Big]_{-h}^h = \lim_{h \to \infty} 0 = 0,$$

which is not true. Thus, we must avoid thinking of $\int_{-\infty}^\infty f(x)dx$ as a *single limit* of an integral over a *finite interval* of the x-axis.

By use of improper integrals, we may define the notion of *area* for certain types of *unbounded regions* in an xy-plane. Assume that $f(x) \geq 0$ when $x \geq a$. Let R be the unbounded region between the x-axis and the graph of $y = f(x)$ when $x \geq a$. For any number $h > a$, let R_h be the ruled region in Figure 151, between $x = a$ and $x = h$, and let A_h be the area of R_h. Then, we define the area, A, of the unbounded region R as *the limit of A_h as $h \to \infty$*, provided that this limit exists. Or, by definition,

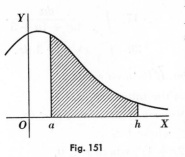

Fig. 151

$$A = \lim_{h \to \infty} A_h = \lim_{h \to \infty} \int_a^h f(x)dx, \text{ or} \quad (5)$$

from (1),

$$A = \int_a^\infty f(x)dx. \quad (6)$$

If the limit in (6) is ∞, we say that *the area of R is infinite*, which is merely a convenient way of remarking that the area of R does not exist, and that $\lim_{h \to \infty} A_h = \infty$. If $f(x) \geq 0$ when $x \leq a$, or when $-\infty < x < \infty$, similar remarks apply to the areas of the corresponding unbounded regions between the graph of $y = f(x)$ and the x-axis.

EXAMPLE 2. Find the area of the region bounded by the x-axis and the curve $y = 3/(1 + x^2)$, on the range $0 \leq x < \infty$.

SOLUTION. A graph of the function is shown in Figure 152. With notation such as was used in (5) and (6),

$$A = \int_0^\infty \frac{3\,dx}{1 + x^2} = \lim_{h \to \infty} \int_0^h \frac{3\,dx}{1 + x^2}$$

$$= \lim_{h \to \infty} 3 \text{ Arctan } x \Big]_0^h$$

$$= \lim_{h \to \infty} 3(\text{Arctan } h - \text{Arctan } 0) = \frac{3}{2}\pi,$$

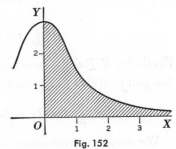

Fig. 152

because Arctan $0 = 0$ and Arctan $h \to \frac{1}{2}\pi$ when $h \to \infty$, as shown on page 223.

EXERCISE 76

Find the value of the integral, or demonstrate that it diverges.

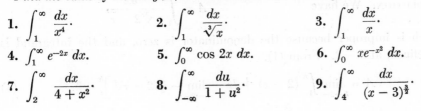

1. $\int_1^\infty \dfrac{dx}{x^4}$.

2. $\int_1^\infty \dfrac{dx}{\sqrt[3]{x}}$.

3. $\int_1^\infty \dfrac{dx}{x}$.

4. $\int_1^\infty e^{-2x}\,dx$.

5. $\int_0^\infty \cos 2x\,dx$.

6. $\int_0^\infty xe^{-x^2}\,dx$.

7. $\int_2^\infty \dfrac{dx}{4 + x^2}$.

8. $\int_{-\infty}^\infty \dfrac{du}{1 + u^2}$.

9. $\int_4^\infty \dfrac{dx}{(x - 3)^{\frac{3}{2}}}$.

10. $\int_0^\infty \dfrac{dx}{(2x+3)^2}$. **11.** $\int_1^\infty \dfrac{dx}{x^2+2x+2}$. **12.** $\int_3^\infty \dfrac{du}{u^2-4}$.

13. $\int_1^\infty \dfrac{dx}{x^n}$, where $n < 1$. **14.** $\int_1^\infty \dfrac{dx}{x^n}$, where $n > 1$.

15. $\int_0^\infty \dfrac{x^2\,dx}{1+x^3}$. **16.** $\int_{\frac{3}{2}}^\infty \dfrac{dt}{9+4t^2}$. **17.** $\int_{-\infty}^\infty \dfrac{du}{4u^2+4u+5}$.

18. $\int_{-\infty}^\infty \sin 2x\,dx$. **19.** $\int_{-\infty}^\infty x^2 e^{-x^3}\,dx$. **20.** $\int_{-\infty}^\infty x\sqrt{x^2+3}\,dx$.

Find the area of the specified unbounded region, if the area exists.

21. Between the x-axis and the curve $y = e^x$ on the range $x \leq 0$.

22. Between the x-axis and the curve $y = 1/(9 + x^2)$, with $-\infty < x < \infty$.

23. Between the x-axis and the curve $y = 1/x^2$, where $1 \leq x$.

24. Between the x-axis and the curve $y = 1/(2x + 1)^3$, where $x \geq 0$.

25. Find the value of $\int_0^\infty xe^{-x}\,dx$, or prove that it diverges.

124. Integrals where the integrand becomes infinite

Assume that $f(x)$ is continuous when $a \leq x < b$. We suppose that $f(x)$ is not defined at $x = b$; possibly, $|f(x)| \to \infty$ as $x \to b-$. Then, we shall call $\int_a^b f(x)dx$ an **improper integral,** and define it as follows, provided that the limit on the right exists:

$$\int_a^b f(x)dx = \lim_{h \to b-} \int_a^h f(x)dx; \ or \tag{1}$$

$$\int_a^b f(x)dx = \lim_{\epsilon \to 0+} \int_a^{b-\epsilon} f(x)dx. \tag{2}$$

Similarly, if $f(x)$ is continuous when $a < x \leq b$, we define the improper integral $\int_a^b f(x)dx$ as follows:

$$\int_a^b f(x)dx = \lim_{h \to a+} \int_h^b f(x)dx = \lim_{\epsilon \to 0} \int_{a+\epsilon}^b f(x)dx. \tag{3}$$

We employ terminology about *convergence* or *divergence* with improper integrals of the present type similarly as in Section 123. Also, we define the areas of unbounded regions related to (1) and (3) by improper integrals.

EXAMPLE 1. Obtain the area, A, of the unbounded region between the x-axis and the curve $y = 1/\sqrt[3]{2 - x}$ from $x = 1$ to $x = 2$.

SOLUTION. We have

$$A = \int_1^2 \frac{dx}{\sqrt[3]{2-x}},$$

which is improper because the denominator is zero, and the integrand is undefined, at $x = 2$. From (1),

$$A = \lim_{h \to 2-} \int_1^h (2-x)^{-\frac{1}{3}}\,dx = \lim_{h \to 2-} -\tfrac{3}{2}(2-x)^{\frac{2}{3}}\Big]_1^h = \tfrac{3}{2}. \tag{4}$$

Comment. In Figure 153, showing a graph of $y = 1/\sqrt[3]{2-x}$, let A_h be the area of the ruled region, between $x = 1$ and $x = h$. The proper integral from 1 to h in (4) is equal to A_h. We de-fine $A = \lim_{h \to 2-} A_h$, and this is precisely what is found in (4). Instead of (1) we could use (2) in Example 1, to obtain

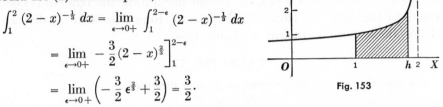

Fig. 153

$$\int_1^2 (2-x)^{-\frac{1}{3}}\, dx = \lim_{\epsilon \to 0+} \int_1^{2-\epsilon} (2-x)^{-\frac{1}{3}}\, dx$$

$$= \lim_{\epsilon \to 0+} \left. -\frac{3}{2}(2-x)^{\frac{2}{3}}\right]_1^{2-\epsilon}$$

$$= \lim_{\epsilon \to 0+} \left(-\frac{3}{2}\epsilon^{\frac{2}{3}} + \frac{3}{2}\right) = \frac{3}{2}.$$

In $\int_a^b f(x)dx$, suppose that $f(x)$ is discontinuous or undefined at some point $x = c$ where $a < c < b$, and that $f(x)$ otherwise is continuous. Then, we call the integral *improper* and define it as the sum of two improper integrals, as below, if both of them exist:

$$\int_a^b f(x)dx = \int_a^c f(x)dx + \int_c^b f(x)dx. \tag{5}$$

Similarly, suppose that $f(x)$ is continuous when $a \leq x \leq b$ except at a finite number of points. Then, we define $\int_a^b f(x)dx$ as the sum of a corresponding set of improper integrals where, in each integral, $f(x)$ is continuous on the interval of integration except at one of the end points.

ILLUSTRATION 1. From (5), since $1/(x-3)^2$ becomes infinite as $x \to 3$,

$$\int_2^4 \frac{dx}{(x-3)^2} = \int_2^3 \frac{dx}{(x-3)^2} + \int_3^4 \frac{dx}{(x-3)^2}. \tag{6}$$

Then, $$\int_2^3 \frac{dx}{(x-3)^2} = \lim_{h \to 3-} \int_2^h \frac{dx}{(x-3)^2} = +\infty.$$

Similarly, the second integral on the right in (6) diverges. Hence, the integral on the left in (6) does not converge. Notice the following fallacious result which is obtained by failure to start with (6):

$$\int_2^4 \frac{dx}{(x-3)^2} = \left. -\frac{1}{x-3}\right]_2^4 = -1 - 1 = -2!$$

We have introduced improper integrals of two types. In one case, an integral is called improper because the interval of integration is infinite, although the integrand is continuous. In the second case, an integral with a finite interval of integration is said to be improper because the integrand is not defined, or is discontinuous at certain points. An integral may exhibit both of the preceding characteristics. In such a case, the integral is defined as the sum of corresponding improper integrals where each one exhibits just one of the two characteristics by which we have earmarked improper integrals.

ILLUSTRATION 2. The integrand is undefined at $x = 2$ in the following improper integral on the left. Hence, the integral on the left is equal to the sum of the improper integrals on the right, if both exist:

$$\int_2^\infty \frac{dx}{(x-2)^2} = \int_2^3 \frac{dx}{(x-2)^2} + \int_3^\infty \frac{dx}{(x-2)^2}. \qquad (7)$$

By the method of Section 123, the second integral on the right in (7) converges to the value 1. However, the integral from 2 to 3 in (7) diverges. Hence, the integral on the left in (7) diverges.

EXERCISE 77

Compute the value of the integral, or prove it divergent.

1. $\int_0^2 \frac{dx}{\sqrt{2-x}}.$
2. $\int_0^3 \frac{dx}{(3-x)^2}.$
3. $\int_0^4 \frac{dx}{x}.$

4. $\int_0^2 \frac{dx}{x^{\frac{1}{3}}}.$
5. $\int_{-2}^3 \frac{dx}{(x-3)^{\frac{1}{3}}}.$
6. $\int_{-1}^1 \frac{dx}{x^2}.$

7. $\int_0^2 \frac{u\,du}{\sqrt{4-u^2}}.$
8. $\int_0^1 \frac{dx}{\sqrt{1-x^2}}.$
9. $\int_{-\frac{3}{4}}^{\frac{3}{4}} \frac{du}{\sqrt{9-16u^2}}.$

10. $\int_0^{\frac{1}{4}\pi} \tan 2t\,dt.$
11. $\int_0^{\frac{1}{2}\pi} \cot u\,du.$
12. $\int_0^{\frac{1}{4}\pi} \sec^2 t\,dt.$

13. $\int_{-1}^3 \frac{du}{u-2}.$
14. $\int_0^4 \frac{du}{u^2-4}.$
15. $\int_3^5 \frac{du}{\sqrt{u^2-9}}.$

16. $\int_{-a}^a \frac{dx}{\sqrt{a^2-x^2}}; \; a > 0.$
17. $\int_0^1 \frac{du}{u^k}; \; 0 < k < 1.$

18. $\int_{\frac{1}{4}\pi}^{\frac{1}{2}\pi} \sec 2x\,dx.$
19. $\int_{\frac{1}{4}\pi}^{\frac{1}{2}\pi} \csc^2 3t\,dt.$
20. $\int_0^{\frac{1}{4}\pi} \tan^2 t \sec^2 t\,dt.$

21. $\int_{-3}^0 \frac{dx}{\sqrt{3-x^2-2x}}.$
22. $\int_3^6 \frac{dx}{\sqrt{x^2-3x}}.$

23. $\int_{\frac{1}{2}a}^a \frac{x^2\,dx}{\sqrt{a^2-x^2}}.$
24. $\int_4^8 \frac{du}{u\sqrt{u^2-16}}.$

HINT. Introduce a trigonometric substitution. Then the improper integral is equal to a proper integral involving the new variable.

Investigate the area of the specified unbounded region.

25. Between the x-axis and the curve $y = \tan x$ where $0 \leq x < \frac{1}{2}\pi$.
26. Between the x-axis and the curve $y = (x-3)^{-\frac{1}{2}}$ where $3 < x \leq 5$.
27. Between the x-axis and the curve $y = 1/\sqrt{16-9x^2}$ where $-\frac{2}{3} \leq x < \frac{4}{3}$.
28. Between the x-axis and the curve $y = \csc x$ where $0 < x \leq \frac{1}{2}\pi$.
29. Between the x-axis, the kappa curve defined by $r = \tan \theta$ in polar coordinates, and the curve's asymptote, in quadrant I.
30. Between the x-axis and the curve $y = \ln x$ where $0 < x \leq 1$. (An indeterminate form will have to be evaluated.)
31. Between the x-axis and the curve $y = 1/(x\sqrt{4-x})$ where $0 < x < 4$.

125. Volumes obtained from known plane sections

Let S be a closed surface in space of three dimensions. By a *plane section* of S, or simply a *section* of S, we mean the curve of intersection of S and some plane. Consider all plane sections of S by planes perpendicular to a specified line in space, where this line is provided with a number scale, and is labeled as an x-axis. Let the closed curve C be the section of S by a plane perpendicular to the x-axis at an arbitrary point x where $a \leqq x \leqq b$, and assume that the area of C is $A(x)$, a known continuous function. A surface S in an xyz-system of rectangular coordinates is represented in Figure 154. The base of S is in the xy-plane and MNU is the plane section of S perpendicular to the x-axis at the point x'. Let T be the region bounded by S and the planes perpendicular to the x-axis at $x = a$ and $x = b$, as in Figure 154. We shall visualize T as a *solid* in future remarks. Then, we shall define the volume, V, of T in such a way that we shall obtain

$$V = \int_a^b A(x)dx. \tag{1}$$

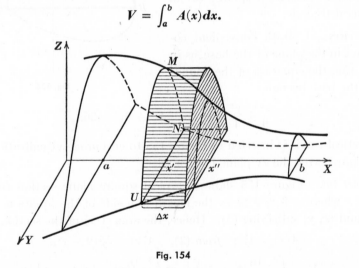

Fig. 154

ILLUSTRATION 1. If a curve E with the equation $y = f(x)$ in an xy-plane is revolved in space about the x-axis, then E generates a surface of revolution, S, as considered earlier. Any plane section of S perpendicular to the x-axis is a circle. Thus, for the solid represented in Figure 134 on page 205, we would have $A(x) = \pi y^2$, where $y = f(x)$, and (1) becomes $\int_a^b \pi y^2\, dx$.

Derivation of (1). Let the interval from x' to x'', as in Figure 154, be a subinterval of a partition, P, of the interval $a \leqq x \leqq b$, with $x'' - x' = \Delta x$. Then, plane sections perpendicular to the x-axis at x' and at x'' cut out a slab with thickness Δx from the solid T. In Figure 154, one face of this slab is MNU whose area is $A(x')$. Suppose that the plane face at the point x' is moved in the direction of the x-axis to the point x''. This motion sweeps out a second slab, which we now substitute for the *actual slab* of the solid. By (II) on page 204, the volume, ΔV, of the substituted slab is

$$\Delta V = A(x')\Delta x. \tag{2}$$

For any partition P of the interval (a, b), let S_P be the sum of the elements of volume ΔV, as in (2), corresponding to all subintervals of P. Then, we define the volume, V, of the solid T as *the limit of S_P as the lengths of all subintervals of P approach zero.* From (2), we then observe that V has been defined to be the definite integral in (1).

EXAMPLE 1. The base of a solid T is an ellipse with major axis 6 and minor axis 4. Find the volume, V, of T if every plane section of T perpendicular to the major axis is (a) a square; (b) an equilateral triangle.

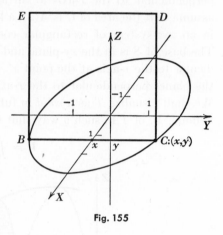

Fig. 155

SOLUTION. 1. With convenient coordinates in the plane of the base, as in Figure 155, the equation of the boundary of the base becomes

$$\frac{x^2}{9} + \frac{y^2}{4} = 1, \quad or \quad 4x^2 + 9y^2 = 36. \tag{3}$$

The vertical z-axis is inserted in Figure 155 to encourage visualization of the space figure, with the xy-plane horizontal.

2. *Part* (a). Figure 155 shows a typical square plane section $BCDE$, at a point x where $-3 \leqq x \leqq 3$; the length of a side of the square is $2y$, with $y \geqq 0$ and (x, y) satisfying (3). Hence, the area $A(x)$ of the section is

$$A(x) = 4y^2; \quad from \ (3), \quad A(x) = \tfrac{16}{9}(9 - x^2). \tag{4}$$

By (1), $\qquad V = \int_{-3}^{3} \frac{16}{9}(9 - x^2)dx = 2\int_{0}^{3} \frac{16}{9}(9 - x^2)dx = 64. \tag{5}$

3. *Part* (b). A typical plane section is $\triangle BCF$, in Figure 156, where BC duplicates BC in Figure 155. With $2y$ as the side, the altitude of $\triangle BCF$ is $y\sqrt{3}$. Hence, the area of $\triangle BCF$ is $A(x) = y^2\sqrt{3}$; etc.

Comment. In Part (a), the elementary slab whose volume is the element ΔV, of (2), would be a parallelepiped with two square faces and thickness Δx, so that $\Delta V = 4y^2\Delta x$. In Part (b), the elementary slab would have two triangular faces, so that $\Delta V = y^2\sqrt{3}\Delta x$.

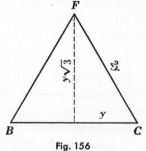

Fig. 156

In many problems of the next exercise, it would be difficult to draw the solids involved. Hence, as a rule, the student is advised to concentrate on drawing just the base of any solid, and a typical plane section. If this figure necessarily distorts the section, then a separate undistorted sketch of the section should be drawn, as a basis for calculating $A(x)$ for (1). A sketch of the surface might be given, but ordinarily will not be needed.

EXAMPLE 2. The plane of a variable isosceles right triangle is perpendicular to the x-axis of an xy-plane, the vertex of the 90° angle is on the x-axis, one side is in the xy-plane, and a vertex is on the curve $y = \sin x$. Find the volume of the region T in space swept out by the triangle as its 90° vertex moves from $x = 0$ to $x = \pi$ on the x-axis.

PARTIAL SOLUTION. In Figure 157, CB is the base of the triangle in a typical position, with C as the vertex of the right angle. Figure 157 also shows the complete triangle BCF. Its area is $\frac{1}{2}y^2$ where we have $y = \sin x$. Hence, in (1), we use $A(x) = \frac{1}{2} \sin^2 x$, with $a = 0$ and $b = \pi$.

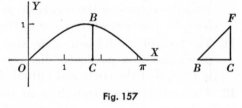

Fig. 157

EXERCISE 78

Find the volume of the solid, T, which is described. For convenience in a figure, it can be assumed that the base of T is in a horizontal xy-plane.

1. The base is the region bounded by the ellipse $4x^2 + 9y^2 = 36$. Every plane section of T perpendicular to the minor axis of the ellipse is an isosceles triangle whose altitude is twice its base in the xy-plane.

2. The base is the region bounded by the x-axis, the curve $x^2 = 6y$, and the line $x = 6$. Every plane section of T perpendicular to the x-axis is (*a*) an isosceles right triangle with the 90°-vertex on the x-axis; (*b*) a quadrant of a circle with its center on the x-axis.

3. The base is a circle with radius 6. Every plane section of T perpendicular to a particular diameter of the base is (*a*) a semicircle; (*b*) a rectangle whose altitude is twice the base in the plane of the given circle; (*c*) an equilateral triangle.

4. The base is the region bounded by the x-axis, the curve $y = \tan x$, and the line $x = \frac{1}{4}\pi$. Every plane section perpendicular to the x-axis is (*a*) an isosceles right triangle with its hypotenuse in the xy-plane; (*b*) an isosceles triangle with altitude 10, and base in the xy-plane.

5. The base is the triangle in quadrant I bounded by the x-axis, the y-axis, and the line $4x + 3y = 12$. Every plane section perpendicular to the y-axis is (*a*) an equilateral triangle; (*b*) a semicircle; (*c*) a sector of a circle with the angle $\frac{1}{4}\pi$.

6. The base is bounded by the axes, the curve $y = e^x$, and the line $x = 3$. Every plane section perpendicular to the x-axis is a semicircle.

7. The plane of a variable isosceles triangle is perpendicular to the x-axis in an xy-plane. The altitude of the triangle is 12, one end of the base is on the x-axis, and the other end is on the line $2y - 3x = 0$. Find the volume swept out by the triangle as the base moves from $x = 0$ to $x = 8$.

8. Find the volume of a pyramid with altitude 50′ and a square base whose side is 20′.

9. A variable circle has its plane perpendicular to the x-axis of an xy-plane, with a diameter of the circle joining two points on the curve $8y^2 = 9x^3$. Find the volume of the horn which is swept out by the circle as its center moves from $x = 0$ to $x = 2$.

10. The plane of a variable circular disk is perpendicular to the y-axis of an xy-plane, and the ends of a diameter are on the lines $y = x$ and $y = \frac{1}{3}x$. Find the volume of the region swept out in space by the disk as it moves from the position where $y = 0$ to the location where $y = 8$.

11. The base of a solid is a circle with radius r. Every plane section perpendicular to a particular diameter is an isosceles triangle whose base is a chord of the circle and altitude is 10. Find the volume of the solid.

12. The vertices of a tetrahedron are the points $(0, 0, 0)$, $(3, 0, 0)$, $(0, 5, 0)$, and $(0, 0, 15)$ in an xyz-system of rectangular coordinates. Find the volume of the tetrahedron by taking sections perpendicular to the z-axis.

13. Find the volume of an elliptical cone with altitude 25′ whose base is an ellipse with major axis 8′ and minor axis 6′.

    HINT. The cone's axis is the line perpendicular to the base at its center. Plane sections perpendicular to this axis are ellipses where, in each case, the ratio of the major axis to the minor axis is $\frac{4}{3}$.

14. The base radius is 5′ and the altitude is 20′ in a solid circular cone. A wedge is cut from the cone by two half-planes through the cone's axis. If the angle between the planes is $\frac{1}{6}\pi$, find the volume of the wedge.

15. The plane of a variable isosceles right triangle is perpendicular to the y-axis of a horizontal xy-plane, the vertex of the 90°-angle is on the y-axis, and another vertex is on the curve $xy = 4$. Find the volume of the region T swept out by the triangle as the 90°-vertex moves (a) from $y = 1$ to $y = 3$ on the y-axis; (b) from $y = 1$ through all values of $y \geq 1$ on the y-axis. (c) For part (b), find the area (if it exists) of the xy-base of the solid. The volume is finite in (b) but the area is infinite in (c).

16. In chopping down a tree with a cylindrical trunk, a lumberjack saws a horizontal cut perpendicular to the axis halfway through the tree. Then, he makes a second cut along a plane meeting the first cut at the axis of the tree. If the tangent of the angle between the planes of the two cuts is $\frac{2}{3}$, find the volume of the wedge cut out, if the tree's diameter is 2′. Solve by use of (a) triangular sections; (b) rectangular sections.

126. Volumes obtained by use of cylindrical slabs or washers

In an xy-plane, let R be the region bounded by the x-axis, the lines $x = a$ and $x = b$, and a curve $y = f(x)$, where $f(x)$ is continuous when $a \leqq x \leqq b$. Let V be the volume of the solid generated by revolving R about the x-axis. Then, on page 206, we defined V as the limit of a sum of the volumes of elementary cylindrical slabs, and obtained

[with $y = f(x)$]
$$V = \pi \int_a^b y^2 \, dx. \tag{1}$$

We mentioned in Section 125 that (1) is equivalent to use of the method of plane sections, with each section as a circle. Similarly, let R be the region bounded by the y-axis, the lines $y = c$ and $y = d$, and the curve $x = g(y)$. Then, if R is revolved about the y-axis, the volume, V, of the solid thus generated is given by

[with $x = g(y)$]
$$V = \pi \int_c^d x^2 \, dy. \tag{2}$$

ILLUSTRATION 1. Let R be the region bounded by the x-axis, the lines $x = \pm 2$ and the catenary (see Table VIII) $y = \frac{1}{4}(e^{2x} + e^{-2x})$. From (1), the volume of the solid generated by revolving R about the x-axis is

$$V = \pi \int_{-2}^{2} \frac{1}{16}(e^{2x} + e^{-2x})^2 \, dx.$$

EXAMPLE 1. By use of the parametric form

$$x = a \cos t \quad and \quad y = b \sin t \tag{3}$$

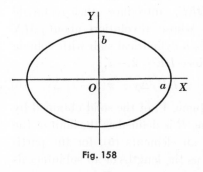

Fig. 158

for an ellipse, find the volume of the solid generated if the region bounded by the ellipse is revolved about the x-axis.

SOLUTION. 1. By symmetry, as verified in Figure 158, the volume, V, is twice that which is obtained if we revolve just the region in quadrant I bounded by the ellipse. Hence, from (1),

$$V = 2\pi \int_0^a y^2 \, dx. \tag{4}$$

2. In (4), transform the variable of integration from x to t by use of (3). If x goes from 0 to a, then t goes from $\frac{1}{2}\pi$ to 0. Hence,

$$V = 2\pi \int_{\frac{1}{2}\pi}^{0} b^2(\sin^2 t)(-a \sin t)dt;$$

$$V = 2\pi ab^2 \int_0^{\frac{1}{2}\pi} (\sin t)(1 - \cos^2 t)dt$$

$$= 2\pi ab^2 \left(-\cos t + \frac{1}{3}\cos^3 t\right)\Big]_0^{\frac{1}{2}\pi} = \frac{4}{3}\pi ab^2.$$

If a region in an xy-plane is revolved about a line other than the x-axis or the y-axis, then (1) and (2) do not apply. However, in such a case, it may be possible to obtain the corresponding volume by the general method involving plane sections, or equivalent reasoning concerning elements of volume.

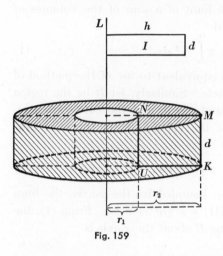

Fig. 159

Note 1. In Figure 159, revolution of the narrow rectangle (I) about the line L would generate a *cylindrical slab* with volume $\pi h^2 d$. Rectangle $KMNU$ has two sides parallel to L. Revolution of $KMNU$ about L would generate a cylindrical "*washer*," whose volume is

$$(\pi r_2^2 d - \pi r_1^2 d), \quad or \quad \pi d(r_2^2 - r_1^2). \quad (5)$$

EXAMPLE 2. Find the volume of the solid which is generated if the region R in an xy-plane bounded by the line $x = 2$ and the curve $y^2 = 8x$ is revolved about the line $x = 2$.

SOLUTION. 1. The line $x = 2$ intersects the parabola where $y = \pm 4$.

2. Let $D:(x, y)$ be any point on the curve $y^2 = 8x$, in Figure 160. Let Δy be a subinterval of a partition P of the interval $-4 \leq y \leq 4$. When the strip $CDEF$ of R is revolved about MN, a slab is generated. As a substitute

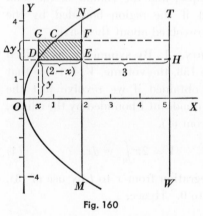

Fig. 160

for $CDEF$, introduce the rectangle $DEFG$, whose revolution about MN produces a cylindrical slab with volume ΔV. Since $DE = 2 - x$,

$$\Delta V = \pi (DE)^2 \Delta y = \pi (2 - x)^2 \Delta y. \quad (6)$$

The volume, V, of the solid obtained by revolving R is defined as the limit of the sum of all elements (6), for the partition P, as the lengths of all subintervals of P approach zero. From symmetry, the volume will be twice that obtained when $0 \leq y \leq 4$. From (6),

(with $y^2 = 8x$) $V = 2\pi \int_0^4 (2 - x)^2 \, dy = 2\pi \int_0^4 \left(2 - \frac{1}{8}y^2\right)^2 dy = \frac{256}{15}\pi.$

EXAMPLE 3. Find the volume of the solid generated by revolving the region R of Example 2 about the line $x = 5$.

SOLUTION. Revolution of the elementary rectangle $DEFG$ of Figure 160 about the line WT generates a cylindrical washer, with inner radius $EH = 3$, outer radius $DH = 5 - x$, and volume ΔV. From (5),

(with $y^2 = 8x$) $\Delta V = \pi[(5 - x)^2 - 3^2]\Delta y.$ (7)

Then, by inspection of the element of volume ΔV, we obtain

$$V = 2\pi \int_0^4 \left(16 - \frac{5}{4} y^2 + \frac{1}{64} y^4\right) dy = etc.$$ (8)

Comment. In Example 3, the typical plane section perpendicular to the *y*-axis is a region between two circles, with the area $\pi[(5 - x)^2 - 3^2]$. Then, (8) is obtained immediately by use of (1) on page 267.

Note 2. The solutions of Examples 2 and 3 illustrate the abbreviated manner in which a definite integral frequently is introduced for a result. First, the desired quantity (a *volume* in Examples 2 and 3) is recognized as *the limit of a sum of elements* corresponding to a partition, P, of an interval of values of a corresponding variable. Then, a general expression is obtained for the *typical element* (ΔV in Examples 2 and 3). Finally, by observation of this element, we write the integral which is the limit of the sum of elements as the lengths of all subintervals of P approach 0. In the preceding method, we omit the complications of notation and most of the details corresponding to the definition of a definite integral.

EXERCISE 79

The specified region R is in an xy-plane. Compute the volume of the solid obtained by revolving R as indicated. Use a figure showing an interval Δx, or Δy, of the range of integration, and a corresponding rectangle whose revolution produces the typical element of volume for the integral. Also, write an expression for this element as the first step in the solution.

1. R is bounded above by the parabola $y = 4 - x^2$ and below by the *x*-axis. Revolve R about the line $y = 4$.

2. R is bounded by the curve $y = \cos x$ and the coordinate axes, from $x = 0$ to $x = \frac{1}{2}\pi$. Revolve R about the line $y = 2$.

3. R is bounded by the parabola $y = (x + 3)(1 - x)$ and the line $y = 3$. Revolve R about (a) the line $y = 3$; (b) the line $y = 0$.

4. R is bounded by the curve $y = 6x - x^2$ and the line $y = 5$. Revolve R about (a) the *x*-axis; (b) the line $y = 5$.

5. R is bounded by the parabola $x = y(4 - y)$ and the line $x = -5$. Revolve R about the line $x = -5$.

6. R is bounded by the curve $y = e^x$, the coordinate axes, and the line $x = 1$. Revolve R about the line $y = e$.

7. R is in quadrant I and is bounded by the curve $8y^2 = 9x^3$, the *x*-axis, and the line $x = 2$. Revolve R about (a) the *x*-axis; (b) the *y*-axis; (c) the line $x = 2$.

8. R is bounded by the curve $y = \sin x$ and the x-axis from $x = 0$ to $x = \pi$. Revolve R about the line $y = 1$.

9. R is bounded by the curve $y = \frac{1}{4}x^3$, the x-axis, and the line $x = 4$. Revolve R about (a) the y-axis; (b) the line $y = 16$; (c) the line $x = 4$.

10. R is bounded by the curve $y = \tan x$, the x-axis, and the line $x = \frac{1}{4}\pi$. Revolve R about the line $y = 1$.

11. R is bounded by one branch of the curve $y = \csc x$ above the x-axis and the line $y = 2$. Revolve R about the line $y = 2$.

12. R is bounded by the curve $x^2 = 6y$ and the line $y = 6$. Revolve R about (a) the y-axis; (b) the x-axis; (c) the line $y = 6$; (d) the line $y = 8$.

13. R is bounded by the hypocycloid defined parametrically by $x = a \cos^3 t$ and $y = a \sin^3 t$, where $a > 0$. Revolve R about the y-axis. Use an integral with respect to t.

14. R is bounded by the x-axis and one arch of the cycloid defined parametrically by $x = a(t - \sin t)$ and $y = a(1 - \cos t)$, where $a > 0$. Revolve R about the x-axis.

15. R is bounded by the loop of the curve $y^2 = x(x - 1)(x - 3)$. Revolve R about the x-axis.

16. R is the smaller segment of the circle $x^2 + y^2 = 25$ cut off by the line $x = 3$. Revolve R about the line $x = 3$.

17. A region R is bounded by the parabola $x^2 + y - 2x = 1$, the y-axis, and the line $y = 2$. Find the volume of the solid obtained by revolving R about the line $y = 2$.

★*Find the volume of the unbounded solid obtained by revolving the specified region R as indicated, or prove that the volume does not exist. It is understood that the volume is defined by an improper integral.*

18. R is bounded by the curve $xy = 4$, the line $x = 1$, and the x-axis where $x \geq 1$. Revolve R about the x-axis.

19. R is bounded by the curve $y = e^x$, the y-axis, and the x-axis where $x \leq 0$. Revolve R about the x-axis.

20. R is bounded by the x-axis where $x \geq a$, the line $x = a$, and the hyperbola defined parametrically by $x = a \cot \theta$ and $y = a \tan \theta$, with $a > 0$. Revolve R about the x-axis, and use an integral with respect to θ.

21. R is the region in quadrant I between the curve $y(x + 2) = x$ and its horizontal asymptote. Revolve R about the asymptote.

22. R is bounded by the curve $y = 1/\sqrt[3]{x - 2}$, the x-axis, and the lines $x = 2$ and $x = 4$. Revolve R about the x-axis.

23. R is bounded by the curve $x = 1/\sqrt{y - 3}$, the y-axis, and the lines $y = 3$ and $y = 5$. Revolve R about the y-axis.

24. R is the region in quadrant I bounded by the coordinate axes and the *witch* of AGNESI, defined parametrically by $x = 2a \tan t$ and $y = 2a \cos^2 t$. Revolve R about the y-axis.

★*A region R is described in an rθ-system of polar coordinates. Express the given curve in parametric form in rectangular coordinates as on page* 168. *Then, compute the volume of the solid obtained on revolving the region as specified.*

25. R is bounded by the circle $r = a \cos \theta$, the polar axis, and the line $\theta = \frac{1}{4}\pi$, with $a > 0$. Revolve R about the x-axis.

26. R is bounded by the polar axis, the curve $r = \tan \theta$, and the line $r \cos \theta = \frac{1}{2}$. Revolve R about the x-axis.

27. R is bounded by that part of the cardioid $r = a(1 - \sin \theta)$ which is in quadrant I, and the polar axis. Revolve R about the polar axis.

28. R is bounded by the cardioid $r = a(1 + \cos \theta)$ in quadrant I, the polar axis, and the line $\theta = \frac{1}{2}\pi$. Revolve R about the polar axis.

127. Volumes obtained by use of cylindrical shells

In Figure 161, line L lies in the plane of the slender rectangle CDEF, which has two sides parallel to L. Revolution of CDEF about L generates a cylindrical shell. We shall use the following result.

$$\left\{ \begin{array}{l} \textit{The volume of a cylindrical shell of inner radius } r_1, \\ \textit{outer radius } r_2, \textit{ altitude } h, \textit{ and thickness } k, \textit{ is } 2\pi\rho h k, \\ \textit{where } \rho = \frac{1}{2}(r_1 + r_2), \textit{ which is the average of } r_1 \textit{ and } r_2. \end{array} \right\} \quad (1)$$

Proof of (1). In Figure 161, let $WD = r_1$ and $WC = r_2$. The volume, V, of the shell is the difference of the volumes of two cylinders, or

$$V = \pi r_2^2 h - \pi r_1^2 h = \pi h (r_2^2 - r_1^2)$$

$$= \pi h (r_2 - r_1)(r_2 + r_1) = 2\pi h (r_2 - r_1) \frac{r_1 + r_2}{2} = 2\pi\rho h k,$$

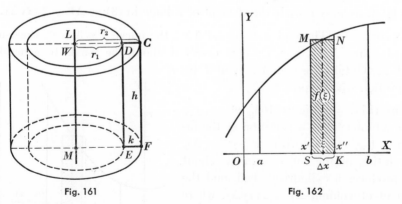

Fig. 161   Fig. 162

where we let $k = r_2 - r_1$ and $\rho = \frac{1}{2}(r_1 + r_2)$. (We notice that $2\pi\rho$ is the circumference of a circle midway between the inner and outer circles at the base of the cylindrical shell.)

In Figure 162, let R be the region bounded by the curve $y = f(x)$, the x-axis, and the lines $x = a$ and $x = b$. We assume that the function $f(x)$ is continuous and $xf(x) \geqq 0$ when $a \leqq x \leqq b$. Let T be the solid obtained by revolving R about the y-axis. Then, we shall define the volume, V, of T in such a way that we shall obtain

$$[\text{with } xy = xf(x) \geqq 0] \qquad\qquad V = 2\pi \int_a^b xy \, dx. \qquad\qquad (2)$$

Derivation of (2). Let the interval from x' to x'', as in Figure 162, be a subinterval of a partition of the interval $a \leqq x \leqq b$, with $x' < x''$ and $x'' - x' = \Delta x$. The ordinates of the graph of $y = f(x)$ at x' and x'' cut a vertical strip from the region R. Let ξ be the mid-point of the interval $x' \leqq x \leqq x''$, and construct a rectangle $MNKS$ having the altitude $f(\xi)$, on this interval as a base. In the following limiting process, take $MNKS$ as a substitute for the strip of R with the interval (x', x'') as the base. Revolution of $MNKS$ about the y-axis generates a cylindrical shell with thickness Δx whose volume, ΔV, is obtained from (1) with $\rho = \xi$:

$$\Delta V = 2\pi \xi f(\xi) \Delta x. \qquad\qquad (3)$$

For any partition P of interval (a, b), let S_P be the sum of the elements of volume ΔV, as in (3), corresponding to all subintervals of P. Then, we define the volume, V, of the solid T as the limit of S_P as the lengths of all subintervals of P approach zero. Hence, by inspection of the element of volume in (3), we conclude that V has been defined as the integral in (2).

Note 1. In (2) and its derivation, for convenience we assumed that $xf(x) \geqq 0$, so that (3) would be positive. If we do not have $xf(x) \geqq 0$, then we alter (2) by using $|xy|$ in place of xy in the integrand. For rapid recollection later, we may rewrite the element of volume in (3) as $\Delta V = 2\pi xy \Delta x$.

EXAMPLE 1. The region R bounded by the curve $y = 3 + x^2$, the x-axis, and the lines $x = 1$ and $x = 4$ is revolved about the y-axis to generate a solid T. Obtain the volume, V, of T by integration with respect to x.

SOLUTION. In Figure 163, let (x', x'') be a subinterval of a partition of the interval $1 \leqq x \leqq 4$, with $x'' - x' = \Delta x$. Revolution of the ruled rectangle about OY produces a cylindrical shell, and the element of volume $\Delta V = 2\pi xy \Delta x$, where we use simply x for the *mid-point* of the interval (x', x'') instead of ξ as in (3). Thus, we are led to

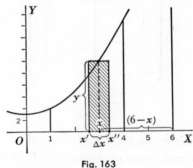

Fig. 163

$$(\text{with } y = 3 + x^2) \qquad V = 2\pi \int_1^4 xy \, dx = 2\pi \int_1^4 (3x + x^3) dx = \frac{345}{2} \pi.$$

ILLUSTRATION 1. Let the region R of Example 1 be revolved about the line $x = 6$, to produce a solid T with volume V. Then, on revolving the ruled rectangle of Figure 163 about the line $x = 6$, we obtain a cylindrical shell where the radius to the mid-point of the base is $(6 - x)$. Thus, the element of volume for the integral is $\Delta V = 2\pi(6 - x)y\Delta x$ and

$$V = 2\pi \int_1^4 (6 - x)y \, dx, \quad with \quad y = 3 + x^2.$$

EXERCISE 80

The specified region R is in an xy-plane. Compute the volume of the solid obtained by revolving R as indicated. Use a figure showing a typical interval Δx, or Δy, with an elementary rectangle whose revolution creates a cylindrical shell as the basis for the integral.

1. R is bounded by the curve $y = 3x^2$, the x-axis, and the lines $x = 1$ and $x = 3$. Revolve R about (*a*) the y-axis; (*b*) the line $x = 5$. Use integrals with respect to x.

2. R is the region in quadrant I bounded by the curve $y^2 = 4x$, the x-axis, and the line $x = 4$. Revolve R about (*a*) the y-axis; (*b*) the line $x = 6$. Use integrals with respect to x.

3. R is bounded by the parabola $y = x(x - 6)$ and the x-axis. Revolve R about (*a*) the y-axis; (*b*) the line $x = -2$.

4. R is bounded by the parabola $x = (y - 2)(y - 4)$ and the y-axis. Revolve R about (*a*) the x-axis; (*b*) the line $y = -1$. Use integrals with respect to y.

5. R is bounded by the curve $y = e^x$, the x-axis, and the lines $x = 1$ and $x = 4$. Revolve R about the y-axis. Notice that integration by parts is available.

6. R is bounded by the curve $x = \ln y$, the y-axis, and the line $y = e^2$. Revolve R about the x-axis.

7. R is the region bounded by the hyperbola $x^2 - y^2 = 9$ and the lines $y = 1$ and $y = 4$. Revolve R about the x-axis.

8. R is bounded by the curve $y = \sin 2x$, the x-axis, and the lines $x = \frac{1}{4}\pi$ and $x = \frac{1}{2}\pi$. Revolve R about the y-axis.

9. R is the region bounded by the circle $x^2 + y^2 = a^2$, with $a > 0$. Revolve R about the line $x = a$. That is, obtain the volume of the solid generated by revolution of a circle about one of its tangents.

10. If a circle is revolved in space about a line in the plane of the circle but not intersecting it, the surface thus generated is called a **torus**, which can be compared to the surface of an anchor ring, or a doughnut. Find the volume of the torus generated by revolution of the circle $x^2 + y^2 = a^2$ about the line $x = h$, where we take $a > 0$ and $h > a$.

11. Solve Problem 10 by use of a parametric form $x = a \cos t$ and $y = a \sin t$, and integration with respect to t.

12. R is the region bounded by the x-axis and the cycloid $x = \theta - \sin \theta$ and $y = 1 - \cos \theta$ on the range $0 \leq x \leq 2\pi$. Revolve R about the y-axis.

13. R is the smaller segment of the circle $x^2 - 2ax + y^2 = 0$ cut off by the line $x = \frac{3}{2}a$, where $a > 0$. Revolve R about the y-axis.

Find the volume of the solid generated by revolution of the specified region R in an xy-plane. Use cylindrical slabs, or washers, or shells as the elements of volume, with the choice dictated by the simplicity of the integral obtained, or by the requirements of the problem.

14. R is the region bounded by the curve $y = x^3 - 8$, and the lines $y = -8$, $x = 1$, and $x = 2$. Revolve R about the line $x = 2$.

15. R is the region bounded by the parabolas $x^2 = 2y$ and $x^2 = 4y - 8$. Revolve R about the y-axis.

16. R is the region bounded by the curve $xy = 8$ and the line $x + y = 6$. Revolve R about the x-axis, and use integration (a) with respect to x; (b) with respect to y.

17. R is the region bounded by the witch $y = 8/(4 + x^2)$, the lines $x = 2$ and $x = 4$, and the x-axis. Revolve R about (a) the y-axis; (b) the x-axis. For Part (b), use a trigonometric substitution when integrating.

18. R is the region bounded by the curve $y = \text{Arctan } x$, the x-axis, and the line $x = 1$. Revolve R about the y-axis.

★19. R is the region in quadrant I bounded by the kappa curve $r = \tan \theta$, in polar coordinates, the polar axis, and the line $r \cos \theta = \frac{1}{2}\sqrt{3}$. Revolve R about the associated y-axis. Employ θ when integrating.

★20. R is the region in an $r\theta$-plane bounded by the polar axis and the rose curve $r = 3 \cos 2\theta$ for $0 \leq \theta \leq \frac{1}{4}\pi$. Revolve R about the line $\theta = \frac{1}{2}\pi$.

128. Work as an integral

Suppose that a particle T moves a distance x along a line while T is acted upon by a constant force * which is directed along the line. Let the magnitude of the force be F units, and suppose that the direction of the motion is the same as that of the force. Then, we define the *work*, W, done by the force F as follows:

$$W = Fx, \text{ units of work.} \tag{1}$$

If the direction of the force is opposite to that of the motion, we define $W = -Fx$. In (1), the unit for work is named by joining the name of the distance unit to the name of the force unit by a hyphen: foot-pound, inch-pound, centimeter-dyne, etc. Colloquially, because of (1), we state that *work is equal to force times distance.*

Note 1. To state that an object *weighs* w pounds means that gravitational attraction acts vertically downward on the object with a force of w pounds. That is, the weight is measured in force units.

---
* We accept the concept of *force* without definition.

ILLUSTRATION 1. Suppose that a 20-pound weight is raised 50′ vertically. To raise the object, a force of 20 pounds must be applied upward at the object to counteract gravity. Thus, the applied force does (20)(50) or 1000 foot-pounds of work. Simultaneously, gravity does − 1000 foot-pounds of work, where the result is negative because gravity acts in the direction opposite to that of the motion.

If a particle T is acted on by a *variable* force, definition (1) does not apply. Then, we shall define the concept of work by an *integral*, introduced as follows.

Fig. 164

Consider a particle T which moves on a straight line, labeled as an x-axis, from $x = a$ to $x = b$, where $a \leq b$. Let T be acted upon by a variable force during this motion. When T is at the point x, as in Figure 164, suppose that the magnitude of the force is $|f(x)|$, where $f(x)$ is taken positive or negative according as the direction of the force is the same as or opposite to the positive direction on the x-axis. We assume that the function $f(x)$ is continuous. Hereafter, for abbreviation we shall call $f(x)$ "*the force.*" Let P be a partition of the interval $a \leq x \leq b$:

$$\text{Partition } P: \quad x_0 = a < x_1 < \cdots < x_{i-1} < x_i < \cdots < x_n = b, \qquad (2)$$

where we let $\Delta_i x = x_i - x_{i-1}$. Let d_P be the maximum of the lengths $\Delta_i x$ in P. Select ξ_i arbitrarily on the ith subinterval of P, as in Figure 165. If a *constant force* $f(\xi_i)$ were to act from x_{i-1} to x_i, then the corresponding *element of work*, $\Delta_i W$, would be

$$\Delta_i W = f(\xi_i)\Delta_i x.$$

We think of $\Delta_i W$ as an approximation to that quantity, as yet undefined, which will be called the *work* done by the *variable force* $f(x)$ when it acts from x_{i-1} to x_i. Let

Fig. 165

$$S_P = \sum_{i=1}^{n} \Delta_i W = \sum_{i=1}^{n} f(\xi_i)\Delta_i x. \qquad (3)$$

Then, we define the work, W, done by $f(x)$ in acting from $x = a$ to $x = b$ as *the limit of S_P as $d_P \to 0$*, if the limit exists:

$$W = \lim_{d_P \to 0} \sum_{i=1}^{n} f(\xi_i)\Delta_i x. \qquad (4)$$

The limit on the right in (4) is seen to be *the integral of $f(x)$ from a to b*. Or, our definition of W has led to

$$\left\{ \begin{array}{c} \textit{work done by force} \\ f(x) \textit{ acting from a to b} \end{array} \right\} \qquad W = \int_a^b f(x)\,dx, \textit{ units of work.} \qquad (5)$$

In case $b < a$, we also accept (5) as the definition of W.

EXAMPLE 1. A cask of wine weighs 1200 pounds. When the cask is raised vertically, wine leaks from it so that, after being raised x feet, the cask weighs $(1200 - 5x)$ pounds. Find the work done by a force applied at the base of the cask to raise it $20'$.

SOLUTION. With the x-axis directed upward from the initial position of the cask, the force $f(x)$, in pounds, which acts on the cask at any point x is $f(x) = 1200 - 5x$, as in Figure 166. Hence, from (5),

$$work = \int_0^{20} (1200 - 5x)dx = \left(1200x - \frac{5}{2}x^2\right)\Big]_0^{20} = 23,000 \ ft.\text{-}lbs.$$

Fig. 166

EXAMPLE 2. A tank is a vertical elliptic cylinder $40'$ high, and is full of water. Any horizontal plane section of the tank is an ellipse with major axis $10'$ and minor axis $8'$. Find the work done in pumping the water over the top of the tank.

SOLUTION. 1. Conceive of an imaginary piston whose face is a horizontal section of the tank, where this piston moves upward from the bottom of the tank and spills the water over the top. We desire to compute the work done if the piston should empty the tank.

2. Insert an x-axis, as in Figure 167, where the vertical scale is distorted. When the piston is at elevation x feet, the height of the water is $(40 - x)$ feet and its volume * is $\pi \cdot 4 \cdot 5 \cdot (40 - x)$ cubic feet; the weight, $f(x)$, of the water is $20\pi\sigma(40 - x)$ pounds, where σ is the weight in pounds of one cubic foot of water ($\sigma = 62.3$, approximately). Then, $f(x)$ is the force in pounds applied at the piston at elevation x. Hence, the work, W, done by the force $f(x)$ in emptying the tank is

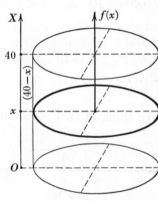

$$W = 20\pi\sigma\int_0^{40} (40 - x)dx = 16,000\pi\sigma \ ft.\text{-}lbs.$$

Fig. 167

Without using the notion of an imaginary piston, we can obtain a convenient formula for the solution of a problem like Example 2. For this purpose, consider a tank with a horizontal base and top, containing liquid weighing σ pounds per cubic foot. Insert a vertical x-axis, with its positive direction downward, and the origin at the level of the top of the tank, as in the vertical section of the tank in Figure 168 on page 281. Let $A(x)$ be the area of the horizontal cross section of the tank at the level x on the x-axis, and assume that the function $A(x)$ is continuous. We propose defining the work done by pumping out, over the top of the tank, all liquid between the levels $x = a$

* The area of an ellipse with axes $2a$ and $2b$ is πab.

and $x = b$, where $a < b$. Let the interval from x to $(x + \Delta x)$, in Figure 168, be a subinterval of a partition, P, of the interval $a \leq x \leq b$. As a substitute for the slab of liquid between the horizontal plane sections of the tank at depths x and $(x + \Delta x)$, take a slab with the element of volume $\Delta V = A(x)\Delta x$,

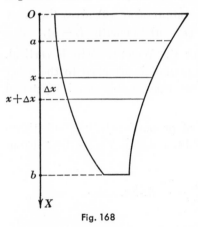

Fig. 168

$\left\{ \begin{array}{l} \text{empty tank from} \\ \text{depth } a \text{ to depth } b \end{array} \right\}$

as on page 267, and the element of weight $\sigma \Delta V$. If this weight were concentrated at depth x, the element of work, ΔW, done in raising the weight through the distance x would be

$$\Delta W = x\sigma \Delta V = \sigma x A(x)\Delta x. \qquad (6)$$

Let S_P be the sum of the elements of type (6) for all subintervals of the partition P. Then, physical intuition leads us to define the work, W, done in emptying the specified liquid, as *the limit of S_P as the lengths of all subintervals of P approach zero.* That is, we obtain

$$W = \sigma \int_a^b xA(x)dx. \qquad (7)$$

ILLUSTRATION 2. In Example 2, we may use (7) with $A(x) = 20\pi$, $a = 0$ and $b = 40$, to obtain

$$W = 20\pi\sigma \int_0^{40} x \, dx = 10\pi\sigma x^2 \Big]_0^{40} = 16{,}000\pi\sigma \; ft.\text{-}lbs.$$

Work done in deforming elastic material. Consider an elastic object such as a steel spring, a wire, a rod, etc. For discussion, we shall call the object a *spring*. Then, it has a certain natural length, L, when undisturbed. Now, think of one end of the spring as being attached to a fixed point M, and let the other end be pulled, to stretch the length by x linear units, as in Figure 169, where a certain stretching force $f(x)$ maintains the new length. Likewise, the spring pulls with a force $T(x)$, of the same magnitude as $f(x)$, and opposite direction. We call $T(x)$ the **tension** in the spring due to the elongation x. Also, if the spring is *compressed* to shorten the length by x units, a tension $T(x)$ again exists, where the compression force $f(x)$ and $T(x)$ have the same magnitude and opposite directions. Then, HOOKE's *law* in physics states that, with a certain so-called *elastic upper limit* on the value of x, there exists a constant k so that, in compressing or stretching,

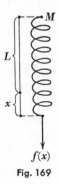

Fig. 169

$$T(x) = kx. \qquad (8)$$

Thus, in Figure 169, when the spring has the length $(L + x)$, the applied force is $f(x)$, or, equally well, has the magnitude $T(x)$. Hence, the work, W, done in stretching the spring from length $(L + a)$ to $(L + b)$, where $0 \leqq a < b$, is obtained from (5) with $f(x)$ replaced by $T(x)$:

$$W = \int_a^b T(x)\,dx. \tag{9}$$

Similarly, with $T(x)$ as the tension due to compression, (9) gives the work done in compressing the spring from length $(L - a)$ to length $(L - b)$.

EXAMPLE 3. A wire has the natural length 4′. When the wire is vertical, with one end held fast, and a weight of 10 pounds is attached to the other end, the wire's length is 4′ 3″. Find the work done if this wire is stretched from 4′ 1″ to 4′ 5″ in length.

SOLUTION. In (8), to find the constant of proportionality, k, substitute $x = \frac{1}{4}$ and $T(x) = 10$. Then, $10 = \frac{1}{4}k$ or $k = 40$, and thus $T(x) = 40x$. From (9), the specified work is given by

$$W = \int_{\frac{1}{12}}^{\frac{5}{12}} 40x \; dx = 20x^2 \Big]_{\frac{1}{12}}^{\frac{5}{12}} = \frac{10}{3} \; ft.\text{-}lbs.$$

EXERCISE 81

Give a figure showing an associated coordinate axis, with the origin and positive direction indicated. Use 62 pounds as the weight of a cubic foot of water.

1. How much work is done when an elevator raises a load weighing 2000 pounds through a distance of 25′, vertically?

2. To push a certain car along a straight rail, it is necessary to apply a force of 450 pounds for the first 3′ and, thereafter, a force of 300 pounds, for 97′. Find the work done.

3. To push a car from $x = 0$ to $x = 25$ along an x-axis, where the unit is one foot, the applied force is $(250 + 10x)$ pounds from $x = 0$ to $x = 10$, and remains constant while $10 \leqq x \leqq 25$. Find the work done.

4. A basket of sand is raised from the ground by a pulley. At ground level, the basket weighs 300 pounds, but sand spills out so that, after the basket has been raised x feet, the weight is $(300 - 2x)$ pounds. Find the work done in raising the basket 50′.

5. A tank contains 1000 cubic feet of water. Find the work done in raising the tank 40′ vertically if water leaks out at the constant rate of 5 cubic feet per foot of rise.

6. A rectangular tank has a base 4′ square, is 20′ high, and is full of water. Find the work done in pumping all of the water out over the top of the tank.

7. A vertical tank is a right circular cylinder with height 30′ and radius 10′, and contains liquid weighing 80 pounds per cubic foot. Find the work done in pumping all of the liquid out over the top of the tank if the liquid is (a) 30′ deep; (b) 20′ deep.

8. The natural length of a spring is 15″. If a force of 60 pounds stretches the spring by 3″, find the work done in stretching the length from 16″ to 20″.

9. The natural length of a spring is 6′, and the tension in the spring is 30 pounds when its length is 8′. Find the work done in stretching the length from 6′ to 9′.

10. A metal rod has the natural length 100″, and the tension in the rod is 1000 pounds when the rod is stretched by .5″. Find the work done when the length is increased from 100″ to 100.5″.

11. A vertical tank is a right circular cone with altitude 60′, base radius 8′, vertical axis, and vertex at the bottom. The tank is filled with water to a depth of 40′. Find the work done in pumping all of the water out over the top of the tank.

12. A tank is a hemisphere with the plane face horizontal, at the top, and diameter 30′. The tank is filled with liquid weighing 90 pounds per cubic foot. Find the work done in pumping out liquid over the top, to reduce the depth to 5′.

13. The surface of a tank is formed by revolving a parabola about its axis, which is vertical. The vertex of the parabola is at the bottom of the tank, which is 64′ high and has the diameter 16′ at the top. The tank is filled to a depth of 40′ by a liquid weighing 75 pounds per cubic foot. Find the work done in pumping all of the liquid out over the top.

14. Suppose that a particle P_1 with a mass of m_1 grams is at the origin, and a particle P_2 with a mass of m_2 grams is at the point x on an x-axis, where the unit is 1 centimeter. Then, it is known that P_1 attracts P_2 with a force whose magnitude is km_1m_2/x^2, in dynes, where k is a constant. Find the work done by this force when P_2 moves (a) from $x = 1$ to $x = 3$; (b) from $x = 4$ to $x = 2$.

15. Suppose that the particles P_1 and P_2 are r units apart on a line, and have the charges e_1, of positive electricity, and e_2, of negative electricity, respectively. Then, e_1 attracts e_2 with a force ke_1e_2/r^2, where k is a constant of proportionality depending on the units of measurement. How much work is done by this force when P_2 moves on the line from the distance $r = a$ to the distance $r = b$ from P_1, where $a < b$?

16. A uniform wire cable weighs 6 pounds per foot, and 100′ of the cable hangs down, without stretching, in a shaft. By increment reasoning, as in the background for (7) on page 281, obtain an integral for the work, W, done in raising all of the cable to the top. Then, compute W.

17. A given quantity of a certain gas is confined in a right circular cylinder with a piston free to move at one end. When the volume of the gas is 1500 cubic inches, the gas exerts a *pressure* (a *force*) of 10 pounds per square inch on the walls of the container. Find the work done when the gas expands from 500 cubic inches to 1500 cubic inches. Assume that conditions justify use of the law that *pressure times volume is a constant*. (Carry heights as unknown literal constants.)

129. A linear distribution of mass

We accept the physical concept of the **mass** of an object as a basic undefined notion. Mass is measured in grams, pounds, and other units. If a
mass of μ units (referred to hereafter simply as "*a mass μ*") is concentrated
at a point Q, we shall call Q a "*mass particle.*" Now conceive of mass spread
on an x-axis from $x = a$ to $x = b$. For concreteness, this distribution can
be thought of as the mass of a wire of negligible diameter. Suppose that
there is a constant δ such that the mass Δm on any interval of length Δx
is given by $\Delta m = \delta \Delta x$. Then, it is said that mass is distributed *uniformly*
on the line with the density δ.

ILLUSTRATION 1. If the density is $\delta = 4$ grams per centimeter, the mass
Δm on an interval of length $\Delta x = 5$ centimeters is $\Delta m = 4 \cdot 5 = 20$ grams.

In a uniform distribution of mass, with δ as the density, the mass Δm on
an interval $x_1 \leq x \leq x_2$, where $x_2 - x_1 = \Delta x$, is given by

$$\Delta m = \delta \Delta x = (x_2 - x_1)\delta = \int_{x_1}^{x_2} \delta \, dx. \tag{1}$$

The form of (1) suggests the notion of a variable density as follows:

DEFINITION III. *Suppose that the function $\delta(x)$ is continuous and $\delta(x) \geq 0$
when x is on the interval $T:(a \leq x \leq b)$. Then, if the mass on any subinterval $x_1 \leq x \leq x_2$ of T is equal to the integral of $\delta(x)$ from x_1 to x_2, we call
$\delta(x)$ the density of mass on T.*

When Definition III applies, it is said that there is a *continuous distribution
of mass* on T. Then, the total mass, m, of T is

$$m = \int_a^b \delta(x)dx. \tag{2}$$

On any subinterval $x_1 \leq x \leq x_2$ of T, the mass, Δm, is given by

$$\Delta m = \int_{x_1}^{x_2} \delta(x)dx, \tag{3}$$

which is consistent with (1) when $\delta(x)$ is a constant. By the mean value
theorem for an integral, on page 196, from (3) there exists a point ξ on the
interval (x_1, x_2) such that, if $x_2 - x_1 = \Delta x$, then $\Delta m = \delta(\xi)(x_2 - x_1)$, or

$$\Delta m = \delta(\xi)\Delta x; \qquad \frac{\Delta m}{\Delta x} = \delta(\xi). \tag{4}$$

Thus, on any interval of length Δx, there exists a point ξ such that
$\Delta m = \delta(\xi)\Delta x$; we call $\delta(\xi)$ the *average density* over the interval.

EXAMPLE 1. In a distribution of mass on an x-axis, the density is
$\delta(x) = 2x + 5$, grams per unit length. Find the mass, m, where $3 \leq x \leq 6$.

SOLUTION. From (2), $\qquad m = \int_3^6 (2x + 5)dx = 42 \ grams.$

If the word *mass* in Definition III is changed to *"electric charge,"* then $\delta(x)$ is the density of electric charge. In statistics, with *"density of mass"* changed to *"probability density,"* (2) gives a *"probability,"* as described later.

130. Center of mass, discrete case on a line or in a plane

Consider a system of mass particles $\{m_i\}$, $i = 1, 2, \cdots, n$, on a line, which we label as an x-axis. Suppose that m_i is at the point x_i, as in Figure 170. Then, we define the **moment** of any mass m_i *about the origin* as $m_i x_i$, and define the corresponding moment, M, for the system as

Fig. 170

$$M = \sum_{i=1}^{n} m_i x_i. \tag{1}$$

In each case where mass distributions will be considered later, on a *line*, in a *plane*, or in *three-dimensional space*, one or more varieties of moments, such as M, will be introduced. Then, the following terminology will apply.

DEFINITION IV. *The* **center of mass** *for a mass distribution is that point where the total mass would have to be concentrated in order for it to have the same moment, of any sort, as the original distribution.*

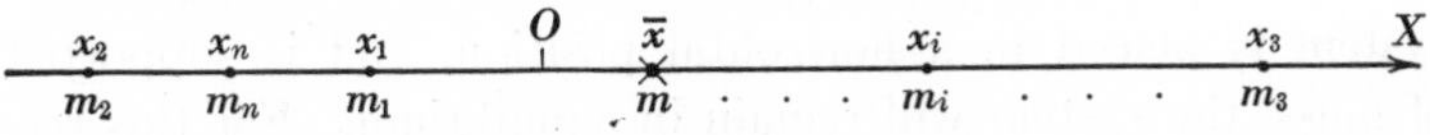

Fig. 171

Let $\bar{x}$ be the center of mass for the masses $\{m_i\}$ of Figure 171. Then, the total mass is $m = \sum_{i=1}^{n} m_i$. If the mass m were at $\bar{x}$, the moment of m with respect to the origin would be $m\bar{x}$. Hence, by Definition IV and (1),

$$m\bar{x} = M, \quad or \quad \bar{x} = \frac{\sum_{i=1}^{n} m_i x_i}{m}, \quad where \quad m = \sum_{i=1}^{n} m_i. \tag{2}$$

Note 1. It can be proved that the location of the point $x = \bar{x}$ on the line through the masses in (2) is independent of the point which may be selected as the origin, and also is independent of the positive direction selected on the line. We shall omit the proof of the preceding facts, which become evident later from physical considerations.

ILLUSTRATION 1. If masses of magnitudes 2, 5, and 7 are at $x = 3$, $x = 5$, and $x = -4$, respectively, from (2) we obtain $\bar{x} = \frac{1}{14}(6 + 25 - 28) = \frac{3}{14}$.

Now, suppose that a mass particle μ is located at a point (x, y) in an xy-system of rectangular coordinates in a *plane*. Then, *the moment of μ about either coordinate axis is defined as the product of μ and its directed distance from that axis*, as indicated in Figure 172 on page 286. Thus, the moments of μ about the x-axis and y-axis are μy and μx, respectively.

If n mass particles $\{m_i\}$ are at points (x_i, y_i) in the xy-plane, the moments

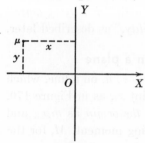

Fig. 172

M_x and M_y about the x-axis and y-axis, respectively, for the system are defined as the sums of the corresponding moments for all masses $\{m_i\}$, or

$$M_y = \sum_{i=1}^{n} m_i x_i \quad and \quad M_x = \sum_{i=1}^{n} m_i y_i. \tag{3}$$

By Definition IV, the coordinates of the center of mass, $(\bar{x}, \bar{y})$, of the system are defined by the equations

$$m\bar{x} = M_y \quad and \quad m\bar{y} = M_x, \quad where \quad m = \sum_{i=1}^{n} m_i, \, or \tag{4}$$

$$\bar{x} = \frac{\sum_{i=1}^{n} m_i x_i}{m} \quad and \quad \bar{y} = \frac{\sum_{i=1}^{n} m_i y_i}{m}. \tag{5}$$

It can be proved that the location of $(\bar{x}, \bar{y})$ in the plane of the masses is independent of the choice of coordinate axes in the plane.

Note 2. In (2), let us idealize the x-axis as having no mass, and assume that the system of masses is subject to the attraction of gravity. Then, if the system is placed in a horizontal position, and is supported at the center of mass, the system will remain in equilibrium. For this reason, the center of mass then is called the **center of gravity** of the system. A similar property holds in the case of $(\bar{x}, \bar{y})$ in (5), if the xy-plane has no mass.

ILLUSTRATION 2. Suppose that masses with measures 2, 4, and 6 are located at $(-1, 2)$, $(3, -4)$, and $(2, 6)$, respectively. Then, in (4),

$$\bar{x} = \tfrac{1}{12}(-2 + 12 + 12) = \tfrac{11}{6}; \quad \bar{y} = \tfrac{1}{12}(4 - 16 + 36) = 2.$$

The mass distributions leading to (2) and (5) are called **discrete distributions of mass** because only mass particles are involved.

131. Center of mass on a line, continuous case

Suppose that the segment T of an x-axis covers the interval $a \leq x \leq b$, as in Figure 173 on page 287, and that there is a continuous distribution of mass over T with the density $\delta(x)$. To generalize (2) of page 285, first form a partition, P, of the interval T with the representative subinterval T_i where $x_{i-1} \leq x \leq x_i$, and $x_i - x_{i-1} = \Delta_i x$, as in Figure 173. Let $\Delta_i m$ be the mass of T_i. Then, from (3) and (4) on page 284, there exists a point ξ_i on the interval T_i such that

$$\Delta_i m = \int_{x_{i-1}}^{x_i} \delta(x)dx = \delta(\xi_i)(x_i - x_{i-1}), \, or$$

$$\Delta_i m = \delta(\xi_i)\Delta_i x. \tag{1}$$

Now, let $\Delta_i m$ be thought of as concentrated at an arbitrary point η_i on T_i, as in Figure 173, and let $\Delta_i M$ be the corresponding moment of $\Delta_i m$ about the x-origin. Then,

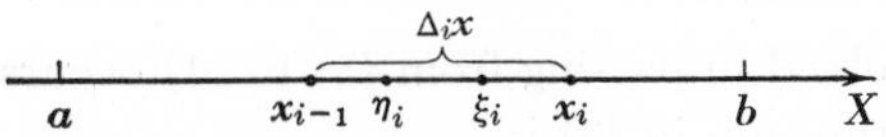

Fig. 173

$$\Delta_i M = \eta_i \, \Delta_i m = \eta_i \delta(\xi_i) \Delta_i x. \quad (2)$$

Finally, we define the moment, M, of the continuous distribution of mass over T as the following limit, where the norm d_P is the maximum of the lengths $\Delta_i x$ of the subintervals of P:

$$M = \lim_{d_P \to 0} \sum_{i=1}^{n} \Delta_i M = \lim_{d_P \to 0} \sum_{i=1}^{n} \eta_i \delta(\xi_i) \Delta_i x. \quad (3)$$

The distance between ξ_i and η_i, as in Figure 173, approaches zero as $d_P \to 0$. Hence, since $\delta(x)$ is continuous, we accept the fact that the limit in (3), if this limit exists, would not be changed if we should replace * η_i by ξ_i, or

$$M = \lim_{d_P \to 0} \sum_{i=1}^{n} \xi_i \delta(\xi_i) \Delta_i x. \quad (4)$$

By comparison with (10) on page 190, the sum (4) is recognized as an approximating sum S_P for an integral of the function "$x\delta(x)$." Thus,

$$M = \int_a^b x\delta(x)\,dx. \quad (5)$$

Let $\bar{x}$ be the center of mass for T. If the total mass m of T were at $\bar{x}$, the moment about the origin would be $m\bar{x}$. Hence, by Definition IV of page 285, $m\bar{x} = M$; from (5),

$$m\bar{x} = \int_a^b x\delta(x)\,dx, \quad where \quad m = \int_a^b \delta(x)\,dx, \; or \quad (6)$$

$$\bar{x} = \frac{\int_a^b x\delta(x)\,dx}{m}, \quad or \quad \bar{x} = \frac{\int_a^b x\delta(x)\,dx}{\int_a^b \delta(x)\,dx}. \quad (7)$$

EXAMPLE 1. On a wire of length 30 units, and negligible diameter, mass is distributed with the density of mass at any point proportional to its distance from one end, B. Find the distance of the center of mass from B.

SOLUTION. Choose B as the origin for an x-scale on the wire, with $x \geqq 0$ on the wire, as in Figure 174. We have $\delta(x) = kx$, where k is a constant of proportionality. From (5), (6), and (7),

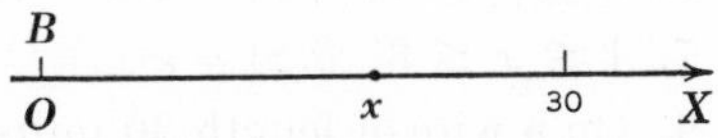

Fig. 174

$$m = k\int_0^{30} x \, dx = 450k; \quad M = k\int_0^{30} x^2 \, dx = 9000k; \quad \bar{x} = 20.$$

* By use of the advanced notion of "*uniform continuity*" for the function of *two variables* $y\delta(x)$, it can be proved that $\sum_{i=1}^{n} \eta_i \delta(\xi_i)\Delta_i x$ is equal to $\sum_{i=1}^{n} \xi_i \delta(\xi_i)\Delta_i x + (b - a)\epsilon$, where $\epsilon \to 0$ as $d_P \to 0$. This fact justifies the replacement of η_i by ξ_i above.

Note 1. It can be proved that the remarks about $\bar{x}$ for the discrete case on a line in Notes 1 and 2 of Section 130 apply to $\bar{x}$ in (7).

★*Note 2.* The type of reasoning involved in passing from (3) to (4) occurs frequently. A general expression like the sum in (3) is

$$\sigma_P = \sum_{i=1}^{n} g(\eta_i)f(\xi_i)\Delta_i x, \tag{8}$$

where the two arbitrary points ξ_i and η_i are on the subinterval T_i of the partition P, while the functions $g(x)$ and $f(x)$ are continuous when $a \leqq x \leqq b$. By continuity reasoning, as suggested in the footnote about (3), it can be proved that the *two indeterminates* ξ_i and η_i in (8) may be replaced by the *single point* ξ_i, to give

$$\lim_{d_P \to 0} \sigma_P = \lim_{d_P \to 0} \sum_{i=1}^{n} g(\xi_i)f(\xi_i)\Delta_i x = \int_a^b g(x)f(x)dx. \tag{9}$$

The final equality in (9) is a direct consequence of the definition of an integral on page 190. The result in (9) was recommended by the American mathematician, GILBERT AMES BLISS (1876–1950) as a partial substitute for a more complicated theorem usually referred to as *Duhamel's principle.* Hence, sometimes, (9) is called *Bliss' theorem.* Hereafter, in cases like (3) or in other related situations, we shall justify passage to a simplified form like (4) by recalling the continuity argument illustrated in the footnote on page 287. Such reasoning covers many cases to which Bliss' theorem would not apply.

EXERCISE 82

If the specified masses are located at the corresponding points on an x-axis, or in an (x, y) plane, find the center of mass.

1. Masses 1, 3, 2, and 7 at $x = -3$, $x = 2$, $x = 4$, and $x = 8$.
2. Masses 5, 1, 3, and 9 at $x = -4$, $x = -2$, $x = 3$, and $x = 5$.
3. Masses 2, 4, 3, and 5 at $(2, -3)$, $(1, 5)$, $(-3, 2)$, and $(4, 6)$.
4. Masses 3, 2, 4, and 10 at $(-3, 2)$, $(-4, 3)$, $(2, -3)$, and $(0, 4)$.

Mass is distributed on the given interval of an x-axis with the specified density $\delta(x)$ at any point x. Find the center of mass.

5. $2 \leqq x \leqq 7$; $\delta(x) = 4(x - 1)$.   6. $-3 \leqq x \leqq 2$; $\delta(x) = 2x^2$.
7. $1 \leqq x \leqq 8$; $\delta(x) = e^x$.   8. $-\frac{1}{2}\pi \leqq x \leqq \frac{1}{2}\pi$; $\delta(x) = 2 \cos x$.
9. On a wire of length 30 units, and negligible diameter, the density of mass at any point is equal to three times the square of its distance from a point 10 units from one end. Find the center of mass.

If the density on the interval is $\delta(x)$, find the total mass.

10. $0 \leqq x < \infty$; $\delta(x) = (4 + x^2)^{-1}$.   11. $0 \leqq x < \infty$; $\delta(x) = e^{-3x}$.
12. $0 \leqq x < \infty$; $\delta(x) = xe^{-x^2}$.   13. $0 \leqq x < 3$; $\delta(x) = (9 - x^2)^{-\frac{1}{2}}$.

★132. An application to statistics

In the terminology of statistics, let X be a **random variable**, with any particular value denoted by x, where X has the range $a \leq x \leq b$. Or, the range may be of infinite extent, such as $a \leq x < \infty$, or $-\infty < x < \infty$. Each value of X may be thought of as arising from a particular trial of some idealized experiment. Let "*the probability of the experiment producing values of X such that $h \leq X \leq k$*" be abbreviated by "$pr(h \leq X \leq k)$." Then, a continuous, nonnegative function $f(x)$ is called the **probability density function** for X in case the following conditions are satisfied:

$$\int_a^b f(x)\,dx = 1. \tag{1}$$

$$If\ a \leq h \leq k \leq b,\ then\quad pr(h \leq X \leq k) = \int_h^k f(x)\,dx. \tag{2}$$

Condition (1) specifies that the probability of the whole range for X is taken as 1. Then, in (7) on page 287 with $\delta(x) = f(x)$, the number $\bar{x}$ is called the **mean** of X, or the **expected value** of X, and is denoted by $E(X)$. From (1), $m = 1$ in (7) on page 287, and thus

$$E(X) = \bar{x} = \int_a^b xf(x)\,dx. \tag{3}$$

Also, $E(X)$ is called the **first moment** of X with respect to the x-origin.

If $g(X)$ is any continuous function of X, the expected value of $g(X)$ is defined as follows, and is denoted by $E[g(X)]$:

$$E[g(X)] = \int_a^b g(x)f(x)\,dx. \tag{4}$$

If c is a constant,
$$E(X - c) = \int_a^b (x - c)f(x)\,dx, \tag{5}$$

and we call $E(X - c)$ the first moment of X with respect to the point $x = c$. The kth moment of X with respect to the origin is denoted by μ_k', where

$$\mu_k' = \int_a^b x^k f(x)\,dx. \tag{6}$$

In statistics, the moments of X with respect to the mean $\bar{x}$ are very important. If μ_k represents the kth moment of X with respect to the point $\bar{x}$, then

$$\mu_k = \int_a^b (x - \bar{x})^k f(x)\,dx. \tag{7}$$

In particular, μ_2 is called the **variance** of X; $\sqrt{\mu_2}$ is named the **standard deviation** of X, and usually is represented by σ. Thus,

$$\sigma = \sqrt{\mu_2}; \qquad \sigma^2 = \int_a^b (x - \bar{x})^2 f(x)\,dx. \tag{8}$$

15

ADVANCED INTEGRATION

133. Facts about polynomials

Let $f(x)$ represent any polynomial of degree n in x:

$$(a_0 \neq 0) \qquad f(x) = a_0 x^n + a_1 x^{n-1} + a_2 x^{n-2} + \cdots + a_{n-1} x + a_n. \qquad (1)$$

Then, there exist n numbers $r_1, r_2, \cdots, r_n$, real or imaginary, so that

$$f(x) = a_0 (x - r_1)(x - r_2) \cdots (x - r_n). \qquad (2)$$

Each of $r_1, r_2, \cdots, r_n$, and no other number, is a root of the equation $f(x) = 0$. Thus, any integral rational equation of degree $n > 0$ has *at most n distinct roots*. This leads to the following useful result.

THEOREM I. *If each of two polynomials in x is of degree n at most, and if the polynomials are equal for more than n distinct values of x, then the polynomials are identical term by term, and hence are equal for all values of x.*

Hereafter, let us assume that the coefficients $a_0, a_1, \cdots, a_n$ in (1) are real numbers, and $n > 0$. Then, we recall that *any imaginary roots of $f(x) = 0$ occur in conjugate imaginary pairs*, say $r_1 = b + ci$ and $r_2 = b - ci$, where b and c are real, $c \neq 0$, and $i = \sqrt{-1}$. When the corresponding factors in (2) are multiplied, we obtain a real quadratic factor for $f(x)$,

$$[x - (b + ci)][x - (b - ci)] = x^2 - 2bx + b^2 + c^2. \qquad (3)$$

Then, in (2), after any imaginary factors are grouped in conjugate pairs as in (3), we may combine any identical factors into a power of the factor. Thus, we reach the following result.

THEOREM II. *Any polynomial of degree $n > 0$ in x, with real coefficients, is expressible as the product of powers of distinct real factors, where each factor is linear, or is quadratic and is not a product of real linear factors.*

Note 1. If $p \neq 0$, we recall that the quadratic equation $px^2 + qx + r = 0$ has *real roots*, or $px^2 + qx + r$ has *real linear factors, if and only if the discriminant $q^2 - 4pr \geqq 0$.* If $q^2 - 4pr < 0$, the linear factors of $px^2 + qx + r$, as given by (2), are imaginary.

134. Partial fractions

If $N(x)$ and $D(x)$ are polynomials in x, the rational function $N(x)/D(x)$ sometimes is referred to as a **rational fraction.** It is called a **proper fraction** if and only if the degree of $N(x)$ is *less than* the degree of $D(x)$; otherwise, $N(x)/D(x)$ is said to be an **improper fraction.** We say that $N(x)/D(x)$ is in its *lowest terms* if $N(x)$ and $D(x)$ have no common polynomial factor which is not a mere constant. If $N(x)/D(x)$ is an improper fraction, it can be expressed as the sum of a polynomial and a proper fraction, by dividing $N(x)$ by $D(x)$ until the remainder is of lower degree than $D(x)$.

ILLUSTRATION 1. $\qquad \dfrac{4x^3 + 5}{2x^2 + x} = 2x - 1 + \dfrac{x + 5}{2x^2 + x}.$

In integration, we may find it desirable to decompose a given rational fraction into a sum of more simple fractions, called *partial fractions.* This process is spoken of as the resolution of the given fraction into its partial fractions. We obtain them by application of the following theorem, whose proof will be omitted.

Note 1. At present, in any reference to a *fraction*, we shall mean a *rational fraction.* In connection with any polynomial in a variable x, any factor to which we refer will have real coefficients; any quadratic factor which is mentioned will have no real linear factors, although this assumption is not necessary as a basis for some of the results.

THEOREM III. *Let $N(x)/D(x)$ be a proper fraction in lowest terms. Then, there exist partial fractions, made up as follows, whose sum is equal to $N(x)/D(x)$ at all values of x for which $D(x) \neq 0$:*

If a linear factor $(\alpha x + \beta)$ occurs just k times as a factor of $D(x)$, then there are k partial fractions,

$$\frac{A_1}{\alpha x + \beta} + \frac{A_2}{(\alpha x + \beta)^2} + \cdots + \frac{A_k}{(\alpha x + \beta)^k}, \qquad (1)$$

where $A_1, A_2, \cdots, A_k$ are constants and $A_k \neq 0$.

If a quadratic factor $(px^2 + qx + r)$ occurs just h times as a factor of $D(x)$, there are h partial fractions,

$$\frac{B_1 x + C_1}{px^2 + qx + r} + \frac{B_2 x + C_2}{(px^2 + qx + r)^2} + \cdots + \frac{B_h x + C_h}{(px^2 + qx + r)^h}, \qquad (2)$$

where the B's and C's are constants and $B_h x + C_h \not\equiv 0$.

In order to calculate $\int f(x)dx$ when $f(x)$ is a *proper* fraction, first we may resolve it into its partial fractions, and then add their integrals. If $f(x)$ is an *improper* fraction, by division we may express it as the sum of a polynomial and a proper fraction, which then may be integrated to obtain $\int f(x)dx$.

135. Case I for partial fractions

Resolution of $N(x)/D(x)$ into partial fractions when $D(x)$ is a product of distinct linear factors: For each factor $(\alpha x + \beta)$, there is a partial fraction of the form $A/(\alpha x + \beta)$.

EXAMPLE 1. Resolve into partial fractions: $\dfrac{7x^2 - 23x + 10}{(3x - 1)(x - 1)(x + 2)}$.

FIRST SOLUTION. 1. By Theorem III, there exists just one set of constants A, B, C such that, at all values of x except those for which some denominators are zero,

$$\frac{7x^2 - 23x + 10}{(3x - 1)(x - 1)(x + 2)} = \frac{A}{3x - 1} + \frac{B}{x - 1} + \frac{C}{x + 2}. \tag{1}$$

2. In (1), multiply both sides by $(3x - 1)(x - 1)(x + 2)$:

$$\left. \begin{aligned} 7x^2 - 23x + 10 = \qquad\qquad\qquad\qquad\qquad\qquad\qquad\quad \\ A(x - 1)(x + 2) + B(x + 2)(3x - 1) + C(x - 1)(3x - 1). \end{aligned} \right\} \tag{2}$$

3. On account of (1), equation (2) is true at all values of x except possibly $x = 1$, $x = -2$, and $x = \frac{1}{3}$, for which denominators vanish in (1). Hence, (2) is true for *infinitely many values of x*. Therefore, by Theorem I of page 290, (2) is true for *all* values of x, *including* $x = 1$, $x = -2$, and $x = \frac{1}{3}$. Thus, we may place x equal to each of these values in (2):

when $x = 1$, $-6 = A \cdot 0 + 6B + C \cdot 0$,   *or* $B = -1$;

when $x = -2$, $84 = 21C$,   *or* $C = 4$;

when $x = \frac{1}{3}$, $\frac{28}{9} = -\frac{14}{9}A$,   *or* $A = -2$.

4. On substituting for A, B, C in (1), we obtain

$$\frac{7x^2 - 23x + 10}{(3x - 1)(x - 1)(x + 2)} = -\frac{2}{3x - 1} - \frac{1}{x - 1} + \frac{4}{x + 2}. \tag{3}$$

SECOND SOLUTION. (This method is given for later use, but is *not recommended in Case* 1.) By Theorem I of page 290, like powers of x on the two sides of (2) have equal coefficients. Hence, we may equate them,

for x^2: $7 = A + 3B + 3C$;

for x: $-23 = A + 5B - 4C$; $\left.\vphantom{\begin{aligned}1\\1\\1\end{aligned}}\right\} \tag{4}$

for the constant term: $10 = -2A - 2B + C.$

On solving system (4), we obtain $A = -2$; $B = -1$; $C = 4$.

ILLUSTRATION 1. By use of (3),

$$\int \frac{(7x^2 - 23x + 10)dx}{(3x - 1)(x - 1)(x + 2)} = -\int \frac{2\,dx}{3x - 1} - \int \frac{dx}{x - 1} + \int \frac{4\,dx}{x + 2}$$

$$= -\tfrac{2}{3}\ln|3x - 1| - \ln|x - 1| + 4\ln|x + 2| + C.$$

136. Case II for partial fractions

Resolution of $N(x)/D(x)$ into partial fractions when $D(x)$ has just linear factors, some repeated: If $(\alpha x + \beta)^k$ is a factor, there are k partial fractions,

$$\frac{A_1}{\alpha x + \beta} + \frac{A_2}{(\alpha x + \beta)^2} + \cdots + \frac{A_k}{(\alpha x + \beta)^k}. \tag{1}$$

EXAMPLE 1.   Resolve into partial fractions: $\dfrac{4x^3 + 16x^2 - 5x + 3}{(x - 1)^2(x + 2)^2}$.

SOLUTION.   1. There exists just one set of numbers A, B, C, D such that, for all values of x except $x = 1$ and $x = -2$,

$$\frac{4x^3 + 16x^2 - 5x + 3}{(x - 1)^2(x + 2)^2} = \frac{A}{(x - 1)^2} + \frac{B}{x - 1} + \frac{C}{(x + 2)^2} + \frac{D}{x + 2}. \tag{2}$$

2. On clearing of fractions in (2), we obtain

$$4x^3 + 16x^2 - 5x + 3 \tag{3}$$

$$= A(x + 2)^2 + B(x - 1)(x + 2)^2 + C(x - 1)^2 + D(x + 2)(x - 1)^2 \tag{4}$$

$$\left. \begin{aligned} &= (B + D)x^3 + (A + 3B + C)x^2 \\ &\qquad + (4A - 2C - 3D)x + (4A - 4B + C + 2D). \end{aligned} \right\} \tag{5}$$

In (5), we expanded (4) and collected corresponding powers of x.

3. By Theorem I of page 290, (3) and (4) are equal for all values of x, *even when $x = 1$ and $x = -2$.*   Thus, we obtain two of A, B, C, D by substituting $x = 1$ and $x = -2$ in (3) and (4).   Also, we find the necessary two additional equations involving A, B, C, D by equating coefficients for *two pairs of like powers of x* in (3) and (4).

Place $x = 1$ in (3) and (4): $18 = 9A$,   *or* $A = 2$. $\qquad$ (6)

Place $x = -2$ in (3) and (4): $45 = 9C$,   *or* $C = 5$. $\qquad$ (7)

Place $x = 0$ in (3) and (4): $3 = 4A - 4B + C + 2D$. $\qquad$ (8)

Equate coefficients of x^3 in (3) and (4): $4 = B + D$. $\qquad$ (9)

On using $A = 2$ and $C = 5$, from (8) and (9) we obtain

$$B + D = 4 \quad and \quad -2B + D = -5. \tag{10}$$

The solution of (10) gives $B = 3$ and $D = 1$.   Thus,

$$\frac{4x^3 + 16x^2 - 5x + 3}{(x - 1)^2(x + 2)^2} = \frac{2}{(x - 1)^2} + \frac{3}{x - 1} + \frac{5}{(x + 2)^2} + \frac{1}{x + 2}. \tag{11}$$

Comment.   By placing $x = 0$ in (3) and (4), we obtain the equivalent of equating the constant terms in (3) and (5).   Notice that (5) was not used in the solution.   We could have used (5) to write *four* linear equations for A, B, C, D, by equating the coefficients of like powers of x in (3) and (5).

ILLUSTRATION 1. By use of (11),

$$\int \frac{4x^3 + 16x^2 - 5x + 3}{(x-1)^2(x+2)^2} \, dx = \int \frac{2 \, dx}{(x-1)^2} + \int \frac{3 \, dx}{x-1} + \int \frac{5 \, dx}{(x+2)^2} + \int \frac{dx}{x+2}$$

$$= -\frac{2}{x-1} + 3 \ln |x-1| - \frac{5}{x+2} + \ln |x+2| + C.$$

The problem of factoring a denominator $D(x)$ in a rational fraction $N(x)/D(x)$ is essentially equivalent to the problem of solving the equation $D(x) = 0$. This is true because, *if $x = r$ is a root of $D(x) = 0$, then $(x - r)$ is a factor of $D(x)$.* Solutions of $D(x) = 0$ sometimes can be obtained by use of the following theorem, with synthetic division as an aid in computation.

If an equation $a_0 x^n + a_1 x^{n-1} + a_2 x^{n-2} + \cdots + a_{n-1} x + a_n = 0,$

with integral coefficients, has a rational root c/d, where c/d is in lowest terms, then c is a factor of a_n and d is a factor of a_0.

EXERCISE 83

Integrate. Use Table III if necessary.

1. $\int \frac{(5x + 16)dx}{(x-4)(2x+1)}.$

2. $\int \frac{(13x + 18)dx}{(3x+2)(x-4)}.$

3. $\int_8^{10} \frac{(2x - 5)dx}{x^2 - 5x - 14}.$

4. $\int_0^4 \frac{(7x - 14)dx}{x^2 - 3x - 10}.$

5. $\int_2^5 \frac{(2x^2 - 13x - 16)dx}{(x+2)(x-1)(2x+1)}.$

6. $\int \frac{(2x^2 - 16x + 6)dx}{x(2x^2 - 5x + 2)}.$

7. $\int \frac{2x^2 + 8x - 12}{x^2 - 4} \, dx.$

8. $\int \frac{9x^2 + 14x + 3}{2x^3 + 5x^2 + 3x} \, dx.$

9. $\int \frac{(x^2 + 1)dx}{(x-1)^3}.$

10. $\int_1^3 \frac{x^2 - 4x + 3}{x(x+1)^2} \, dx.$

11. $\int \frac{8 \, dx}{(x+2)^4}.$

12. $\int \frac{4y^2 + 14y + 18}{y(y+3)^2} \, dy.$

13. $\int \frac{3t^2 + 10t + 9}{(t+2)^3} \, dt.$

14. $\int \frac{(5x^2 - 11x + 5)dx}{(x-1)(x^2 - 3x + 2)}.$

15. $\int \frac{x^3 - 3x^2 + 2x - 2}{(x^2 - x)(x-1)^2} \, dx.$

16. $\int \frac{(x^3 - 7x + 7)dx}{(x-2)(x^2 - 3x + 2)}.$

17. $\int \frac{x^4 - 4x^3 + x + 27}{x(x^2 - 6x + 9)} \, dx.$

18. $\int \frac{(6x^2 + 6)dx}{2x^3 - 5x^2 - 4x + 3}.$

19. $\int \frac{(3 - 13x - 2x^2)dx}{3x^3 + 2x^2 - 7x + 2}.$

20. $\int \frac{(3x^2 - 5x + 6)dx}{(1 + 3x)(1 - 2x - 15x^2)}.$

21. $\int \frac{17 + 52x + 30x^2 - 24x^3}{(3x^2 - x - 2)^2} \, dx.$

22. Find the area of the region R bounded by the x-axis, the lines $x = -4$ and $x = -6$, and the curve $y = \dfrac{x + 2}{(x-1)(x+3)}.$

137. Case III for partial fractions

Resolution of $N(x)/D(x)$ into partial fractions when $D(x)$ has one or more quadratic factors, not repeated: If $(px^2 + qx + r)$ occurs just once as a factor, then there is a partial fraction

$$\frac{Bx + C}{px^2 + qx + r}. \tag{1}$$

EXAMPLE 1. Resolve into partial fractions: $\dfrac{3x^2 - x + 1}{(x + 1)(x^2 - x + 3)}.$

SOLUTION. We seek A, B, C so that

$$\frac{3x^2 - x + 1}{(x + 1)(x^2 - x + 3)} = \frac{A}{x + 1} + \frac{Bx + C}{x^2 - x + 3}. \tag{2}$$

From (2): $3x^2 - x + 1 = A(x^2 - x + 3) + (Bx + C)(x + 1).$ (3)

Place $x = -1$ in (3): $5 = 5A,$ or $A = 1.$

Place $x = 0$ in (3): $1 = 3A + C;$ hence $C = 1 - 3 = -2.$

Equate coefficients of x^2 in (3): $3 = A + B;$ hence $B = 2.$

Thus, $\dfrac{3x^2 - x + 1}{(x + 1)(x^2 - x + 3)} = \dfrac{1}{x + 1} + \dfrac{2x - 2}{x^2 - x + 3}.$ (4)

ILLUSTRATION 1. To obtain the following integral, we first resolve the integrand into its partial fractions, as in (4), and then use the method of Example 1 of page 233:

$$\int \frac{(3x^2 - x + 1)dx}{(x + 1)(x^2 - x + 3)} = \int \frac{dx}{x + 1} + \int \frac{(2x - 2)dx}{x^2 - x + 3} \tag{5}$$

$$= \ln |x + 1| + \int \frac{(2x - 1)dx}{x^2 - x + 3} - \int \frac{dx}{(x - \frac{1}{2})^2 + \frac{11}{4}}$$

$$= \ln |x + 1| + \ln |x^2 - x + 3| - \frac{2}{\sqrt{11}} \text{Arctan} \frac{2x - 1}{\sqrt{11}} + C.$$

EXERCISE 84

Integrate.

1. $\displaystyle\int \frac{3x^2 + 5x + 6}{(x + 1)(x^2 + 3)}\, dx.$

2. $\displaystyle\int \frac{x^2 - 8x - 4}{(x - 2)(x^2 + 4)}\, dx.$

3. $\displaystyle\int \frac{2x^2 + 11x - 7}{(2x - 5)(x^2 + 2)}\, dx.$

4. $\displaystyle\int \frac{(z^2 - 7z + 8)dz}{(z + 2)(2z^2 + 5)}.$

5. $\displaystyle\int \frac{4x^2 + 3x + 14}{x^3 - 8}\, dx.$

6. $\displaystyle\int \frac{4x^3 + 4x^2 + 54x + 18}{x^4 - 81}\, dx.$

7. $\displaystyle\int \frac{8x^3 + x^2 + 19x + 5}{(2x^2 + 3)(x^2 + 5)}\, dx.$

8. $\displaystyle\int \frac{x^3 + x^2 + 7x + 5}{x^4 + 4x^2 + 3}\, dx.$

9. $\displaystyle\int \frac{7x^3 + 2x^2 + 13x + 2}{4x^4 + 11x^2 + 7}\,dx.$

10. $\displaystyle\int \frac{(3x^2 - 5x + 6)\,dx}{(1 + 3x)(1 - 2x - 15x^2)}.$

11. $\displaystyle\int \frac{16y^4 + 8y}{8y^3 + 1}\,dy.$

12. $\displaystyle\int \frac{2x^3 + 6x^2 - 3x - 30}{x^3 + 6x^2 + 10x}\,dx.$

13. $\displaystyle\int_0^3 \frac{6x^2 + 5x + 12}{(x + 2)(x^2 + 9)}\,dx.$

14. $\displaystyle\int_{-1}^2 \frac{6x^2 - 9x + 27}{x^3 + 27}\,dx.$

15. $\displaystyle\int_{-\frac{1}{4}\pi}^{\frac{1}{4}\pi} \frac{4 \sec\theta \tan\theta\,d\theta}{\sec^3\theta + 4\sec\theta}.$

16. $\displaystyle\int_0^{\frac{1}{4}\pi} \frac{15 \cos^2\theta \sin\theta + 3 \sin\theta}{\cos\theta\,(4 \cos^2\theta + \sin^2\theta)}\,d\theta.$

17. $\displaystyle\int \frac{(2 + 5x^2)\,dx}{20 + x^2 - x^4}.$

18. $\displaystyle\int \frac{(x^2 + 33)\,dx}{2x^4 - 15x^2 - 27}.$

HINT for Problem 17. The integrand is a rational function of x^2. Hence, let $v = x^2$ and resolve $(2 + 5v)/(20 + v - v^2)$ into its partial fractions.

138. Case IV for partial fractions

Resolution of $N(x)/D(x)$ into partial fractions when $D(x)$ has one or more repeated quadratic factors: If $(px^2 + qx + r)$ occurs just h times as a factor, then there are h partial fractions as given in (2) on page 291.

EXAMPLE 1. Resolve into partial fractions: $\displaystyle \frac{2x^4 - 7x^2 - 37x - 28}{(x + 2)(x^2 + 2x + 5)^2}.$

SOLUTION. 1. We seek A, B, C, D, E so that

$$\frac{2x^4 - 7x^2 - 37x - 28}{(x + 2)(x^2 + 2x + 5)^2} = \frac{A}{x + 2} + \frac{Bx + C}{(x^2 + 2x + 5)^2} + \frac{Dx + E}{x^2 + 2x + 5}. \tag{1}$$

On clearing of fractions in (1), we find

$$2x^4 - 7x^2 - 37x - 28 =$$

$$A(x^2 + 2x + 5)^2 + (Bx + C)(x + 2) + (Dx + E)(x + 2)(x^2 + 2x + 5). \tag{2}$$

2. We obtain five equations involving A, B, C, D, E from (2):

Place $x = -2$: $\qquad\qquad 50 = 25A.$ $\tag{3}$

Place $x = 0$: $\qquad\qquad -28 = 25A + 2C + 10E.$ $\tag{4}$

Equate coefs. of x^4: $\qquad\qquad 2 = A + D.$ $\tag{5}$

Equate coefs. of x^3: $\qquad\qquad 0 = 4A + 4D + E.$ $\tag{6}$

Equate coefs. of x^2: $\qquad\qquad -7 = 14A + B + 9D + 4E.$ $\tag{7}$

3. From (3) $-$ (7), we obtain $A = 2$, $B = -3$, $C = 1$, $D = 0$, $E = -8$;

$$\frac{2x^4 - 7x^2 - 37x - 28}{(x + 2)(x^2 + 2x + 5)^2} = \frac{2}{x + 2} + \frac{1 - 3x}{(x^2 + 2x + 5)^2} - \frac{8}{x^2 + 2x + 5}. \tag{8}$$

In Case IV, we meet integrals of the type $\int du/(a^2 + u^2)^n$, where n is an integer and $n > 1$. Then, we may apply the reduction formula *

* Instead of applying (9), we may use a trigonometric substitution.

$$\int \frac{du}{(a^2 + u^2)^n} = \frac{1}{(2n-2)a^2}\left[\frac{u}{(a^2+u^2)^{n-1}} + (2n-3)\int \frac{du}{(a^2+u^2)^{n-1}}\right], \quad (9)$$

which gives a new integral with the exponent of $(a^2 + u^2)$ reduced by 1. By use of (9), repeated if $n > 2$, we arrive where the exponent of $(a^2 + u^2)$ is 1 and the final integral is a fundamental form. In using (9) with a denominator $(px^2 + qx + r)^n$, we apply a method like that of Example 1 on page 233, and first complete a square.

ILLUSTRATION 1. To integrate the fraction in Example 1, integrate the right-hand side in (8), where the major problem is to integrate the second fraction. If I represents its integral,

$$I = \int \frac{(1 - 3x)dx}{(x^2 + 2x + 5)^2} = -\frac{3}{2}\int \frac{(2x + 2)dx}{(x^2 + 2x + 5)^2} + 4\int \frac{dx}{[(x+1)^2 + 4]^2}; \quad (10)$$

$$I = \frac{3}{2}\cdot\frac{1}{x^2 + 2x + 5} + 4\int \frac{du}{(u^2 + 4)^2}, \quad (11)$$

where $u = x + 1$. From (9) with $n = 2$ and $a^2 = 4$,

$$\int \frac{du}{(u^2 + 4)^2} = \frac{1}{8}\left(\frac{u}{u^2 + 4} + \frac{1}{2}\operatorname{Arctan}\frac{u}{2}\right).$$

Hence, $\qquad\qquad I = \dfrac{x + 4}{2(x^2 + 2x + 5)} + \dfrac{1}{4}\operatorname{Arctan}\dfrac{x + 1}{2} + C.$

139. Nature of $\int f(x)\,dx$ when $f(x)$ is a rational function

If $f(x)$ is a rational function, then $f(x)$ is equal to the sum of a polynomial and possibly a set of partial fractions, of types met in the preceding Cases I–IV. The indefinite integral of a polynomial is a polynomial. Apart from constant factors, the indefinite integral of a partial fraction is a logarithmic function in Case I; either a logarithmic function or a rational fraction in Case II; an arctangent function, perhaps plus a rational function, in Cases III and IV. Hence, there exists an expression for $\int f(x)dx$ as a sum of elementary functions of the preceding types. Thus, we obtain the following theorem.

If $f(x)$ is a rational function of x, then there exists * an expression for $\int f(x)\,dx$ in terms of elementary functions of x.

EXERCISE 85

Integrate. Use a reduction formula if desirable.

1. $\displaystyle\int \frac{(4x + 5)dx}{(x^2 + 9)^2}.$
2. $\displaystyle\int \frac{(6t + 3)dt}{(4t^2 + 1)^2}.$
3. $\displaystyle\int \frac{dy}{(4y^2 + 9)^2}.$

4. $\displaystyle\int \frac{2x^3 + x + 3}{(x^2 + 1)^2}\,dx.$
5. $\displaystyle\int \frac{x^3 + x^2 + 2}{(x^2 + 2)^2}\,dx.$

* The expression can be found if we are able to factor all denominators involved.

6. $\displaystyle\int \frac{4x^3 + 6x - 36}{(x^2 + 2x + 5)^2}\, dx.$ **7.** $\displaystyle\int \frac{3x^4 + 20x^2 + 25x}{(x^2 + 3)^2(x - 1)}\, dx.$

8. $\displaystyle\int \frac{12x^3 - 92x^2 + 242x - 200}{x(x^2 - 6x + 10)^2}\, dx.$ **9.** $\displaystyle\int \frac{39 + 2x + 28x^2 + 5x^4}{(x^2 + 3)^3}\, dx.$

140. The half-angle substitution

If $f(u)$ is a rational function of the fundamental trigonometric functions of u, then the half-angle substitution

$$z = \tan \tfrac{1}{2}u \tag{1}$$

changes $\int f(u)du$ into the form $\int R(z)dz$, where $R(z)$ is a rational function of z.

To make use of (1), we use the identities

$$\sin u = 2 \sin \tfrac{1}{2}u \cos \tfrac{1}{2}u; \qquad \cos u = \cos^2 \tfrac{1}{2}u - \sin^2 \tfrac{1}{2}u. \tag{2}$$

From (1), we choose the solution u where

$$\tfrac{1}{2}u = \text{Arctan } z \quad or \quad u = 2 \text{ Arctan } z. \tag{3}$$

By use of (1) and a sketch like Figure 143 on page 254, we find

$$\sin \tfrac{1}{2}u = \frac{z}{\sqrt{1 + z^2}}; \quad \cos \tfrac{1}{2}u = \frac{1}{\sqrt{1 + z^2}}. \tag{4}$$

Hence, from (2), (3), and (4),

$$du = \frac{2\, dz}{1 + z^2}; \tag{5}$$

$$\sin u = \frac{2z}{1 + z^2}; \quad \cos u = \frac{1 - z^2}{1 + z^2}. \tag{6}$$

In using (1), first express sec u, csc u, tan u, and cot u, if they occur, in terms of sin u and cos u, and then use (5) and (6).

EXAMPLE 1. Obtain $\displaystyle I = \int \frac{dx}{\tan 2x + \sin 2x}.$

SOLUTION. If we let $u = 2x$, then

$$I = \frac{1}{2}\int \frac{\cos 2x\ (2\, dx)}{\sin 2x\ (1 + \cos 2x)} = \frac{1}{2}\int \frac{\cos u\ du}{\sin u\ (1 + \cos u)}.$$

To integrate, substitute $z = \tan \tfrac{1}{2}u$. Then, from (5) and (6),

$$I = \frac{1}{2}\int \frac{\dfrac{1 - z^2}{1 + z^2} \cdot \dfrac{2\, dz}{1 + z^2}}{\dfrac{2z}{1 + z^2} \cdot \dfrac{2}{1 + z^2}} = \frac{1}{4}\int \frac{dz}{z} - \frac{1}{4}\int z\, dz$$

$$= \tfrac{1}{4} \ln |z| - \tfrac{1}{8}z^2 + C = \tfrac{1}{4} \ln |\tan x| - \tfrac{1}{8} \tan^2 x + C.$$

Comment. Instead of introducing u in the preceding solution, we could have substituted $z = \tan x$.

From Section 139, by use of (1) we justify the following statement.

If $f(u)$ is any rational function of the fundamental trigonometric functions of u, then there exists an expression for $\int f(u)du$ in terms of elementary functions of u.

EXERCISE 86

Integrate by use of a half-angle substitution.

1. $\displaystyle\int \frac{dy}{3 + 5 \cos y}.$
2. $\displaystyle\int \frac{dx}{13 + 5 \cos x}.$
3. $\displaystyle\int \frac{dx}{1 - \sin x}.$

4. $\displaystyle\int \frac{dw}{1 + 3 \sin 2w}.$
5. $\displaystyle\int_0^{\frac{1}{2}\pi} \frac{dx}{13 + 12 \cos x}.$
6. $\displaystyle\int \frac{dx}{1 - \sin 2x}.$

7. $\displaystyle\int \frac{dx}{\tan 3x + \sin 3x}.$
8. $\displaystyle\int \frac{dx}{2 \sin x + \cos x}.$
9. $\displaystyle\int_{-\frac{1}{2}\pi}^{\frac{1}{2}\pi} \frac{dx}{1 + 2 \cos x}.$

10. $\displaystyle\int \frac{dx}{1 + \sin 3x}.$
11. $\displaystyle\int \frac{dx}{1 + 3 \cos 2x}.$
12. $\displaystyle\int \frac{dy}{5 \sin y + 1}.$

13. $\displaystyle\int_0^{\frac{1}{2}\pi} \frac{dx}{1 + \sin x + \cos x}.$
14. $\displaystyle\int \frac{dw}{2 \sin w + \cos w + 5}.$

15. $\displaystyle\int \frac{dx}{\tan x - \sin x}.$
16. $\displaystyle\int_0^{\frac{1}{2}\pi} \frac{du}{4 + 5 \sin u}.$
17. $\displaystyle\int \frac{dx}{\cot 2x + \cos 2x}.$

18. $\displaystyle\int_{-\frac{1}{2}\pi}^{\frac{1}{2}\pi} \frac{dw}{5 + 3 \sin w + 4 \cos w}.$
19. $\displaystyle\int \frac{dx}{5 \sin \frac{1}{2}x + 12 \cos \frac{1}{2}x + 13}.$

20. $\displaystyle\int \frac{\csc x \, dx}{\csc x - 1 - \cot x}.$
21. $\displaystyle\int \frac{dz}{5 \sec z - 4}.$

22. In an $r\theta$-system of polar coordinates, a region R is bounded by the polar axis and the parabola $r = 1/(1 - \sin \theta)$. Find the area of R.

141. Miscellaneous algebraic rationalizing substitutions

1. *If $f(x)$ is a rational function of powers of x with rational exponents, then a rationalizing substitution for $\int f(x)dx$ is*

$$u = x^{\frac{1}{n}} \quad \text{or} \quad x = u^n,$$

where the positive integer n is the lowest common denominator of the exponents of x in $f(x)$.

EXAMPLE 1. Integrate: $I = \displaystyle\int \frac{x^{\frac{1}{4}} \, dx}{1 + x^{\frac{1}{2}}}.$

SOLUTION. Let $x^{\frac{1}{4}} = u$, or $u^4 = x$. Then, $dx = 4u^3 \, du$;

$$I = \int \frac{4u^4 \, du}{1 + u^2} = 4\int (u^2 - 1)du + 4\int \frac{du}{1 + u^2}$$

$$= \tfrac{4}{3}u^3 - 4u + 4 \text{ Arctan } u + C = \tfrac{4}{3}x^{\frac{3}{4}} - 4x^{\frac{1}{4}} + 4 \text{ Arctan } x^{\frac{1}{4}} + C.$$

II. *If n is a positive integer greater than* 1, *and if $f(x)$ is a rational function of x and $\sqrt[n]{a + bx}$, then a rationalizing substitution for $\int f(x)dx$ is*

$$u = \sqrt[n]{a + bx}, \quad or \quad u_{\square}^n = a + bx. \tag{1}$$

A simple case of (II) was introduced on page 228. Also, (I) is a special case of (II), with simply x in place of $(a + bx)$.

ILLUSTRATION 1. We would substitute $u = \sqrt{2t + 3}$ in obtaining

$$\int \frac{(6t + 4)dt}{(5t - 1)\sqrt{2t + 3}}.$$

Experience leads us to conclude that, sometimes, a substitution which *simplifies the appearance* of a radicand $f(x)$ also may change $\int f(x)dx$ to a form which can be integrated easily. This elementary approach suggests (I) and (II), and also other useful substitutions.

ILLUSTRATION 2. The substitution $u = \sqrt{2 + x^3}$ would simplify

$$\int \frac{x^5 \, dx}{\sqrt{2 + x^3}}.$$

If $f(x)$ is an irrational algebraic integrand involving different radicals, it may be possible to obtain $\int f(x)dx$ by making a sequence of substitutions, where each one rationalizes one radical. Or, by algebraic manipulation, $f(x)$ may be placed in a new form which is more favorable for integration.

ILLUSTRATION 3. To obtain $\qquad I = \int \frac{x \, dx}{\sqrt{x} + \sqrt{x + 1}},$

we would first rationalize the denominator:

$$I = \int \frac{x(\sqrt{x + 1} - \sqrt{x}) \, dx}{x + 1 - x} = \int x\sqrt{x + 1} \, dx - \int x^{\frac{3}{2}} \, dx.$$

142. A table of integrals

Most of the formulas in a table of integrals, such as Table VII, can be derived by the methods presented previously in this text. However, special devices are essential for obtaining certain integration formulas, particularly various reduction formulas. Any formula in Table VII can be verified by showing that the derivatives of the two sides of the equality are equal.

When speed rather than fundamental training in methods is an essential, frequently it is desirable to use Table VII. Also, on certain occasions when our previous methods do not lead to convenient integration, some formula from Table VII may be indispensable. The details involved in applying Table VII are similar to those used with the standard forms of Chapter 12. Hereafter, use Table VII to the extent directed by the instructor.

ILLUSTRATION 1. The following integration uses (51) of Table VII:

$$\int \frac{dx}{(4x^2 - 9)^{\frac{3}{2}}} = \frac{1}{2} \int \frac{2\,dx}{(4x^2 - 9)^{\frac{3}{2}}} = \frac{1}{2} \int \frac{du}{(u^2 - 9)^{\frac{3}{2}}} \qquad (u = 2x)$$

$$= \frac{1}{2} \cdot \frac{-u}{9\sqrt{u^2 - 9}} + C = -\frac{x}{9\sqrt{4x^2 - 9}} + C.$$

143. Summary concerning indefinite integration

In early chapters, we learned how to obtain the derivative of *any* function $f(x)$ expressible in terms of the elementary functions of analysis. In contrast, it is proved at more advanced levels that many types of elementary functions $f(x)$ exist such that $\int f(x)dx$ cannot be expressed in terms of elementary functions.

Hereafter, if $f(x)$ is a given function, let us say that an *elementary formula* exists for $\int f(x)dx$ if we can prove that $\int f(x)dx$ is expressible in terms of the elementary functions. In view of preceding remarks, regardless of how many special methods are developed for obtaining elementary formulas for indefinite integrals, we must anticipate meeting integrands to which the methods do not apply.

ILLUSTRATION 1. In general, if $g(x)$ is a polynomial of degree 3 or 4 in x, and if $f(x)$ is an irrational function which is a rational function of x and $\sqrt{g(x)}$, then $\int f(x)dx$ is called an **elliptic integral**. Thus,

$$\int \sqrt{(1 - x^2)(1 - k^2x^2)}\,dx$$

is an elliptic integral. In more advanced mathematics, it is shown that elliptic integrals cannot be expressed in terms of elementary functions. However, a new class of functions, called **elliptic functions**, then is introduced and elliptic integrals are expressed in terms of these functions.

ILLUSTRATION 2. $\int \sqrt{1 - x^4}\,dx$ is an elliptic integral, and thus no elementary formula can be obtained for the integral.

Previously, we have seen that an elementary formula for $\int f(x)dx$ exists if $f(x)$ is of one of the following types.

I. *A rational function of x.*

II. *A rational function of fundamental trigonometric functions of an angle kx, where k is some constant.*

III. *A rational function of x and $\sqrt{g(x)}$, where $g(x)$ is a polynomial of degree 1 or 2 in x.*

By use of standard integration forms, the general method of substitution of a new variable, and integration by parts, we can find an elementary formula for $\int f(x)dx$ in many cases where $f(x)$ is not of one of types I–III.

EXERCISE 87

Integrate without using a trigonometric substitution.

1. $\displaystyle\int \frac{dx}{x^{\frac{1}{2}} + 2x^{\frac{1}{3}}}.$

2. $\displaystyle\int_{16}^{81} \frac{dx}{x^{\frac{3}{4}} - x^{\frac{1}{2}}}.$

3. $\displaystyle\int \frac{x^3 \, dx}{\sqrt{9 + x^2}}.$

4. $\displaystyle\int \frac{x^3 \, dx}{(4 + x^2)^{\frac{3}{2}}}.$

5. $\displaystyle\int \frac{(x + 3)\sqrt{x}}{x - 1} \, dx.$

6. $\displaystyle\int \frac{dx}{x\sqrt[3]{8 + x^3}}.$

7. $\displaystyle\int_{6}^{25} \frac{dx}{(x + 2)^{\frac{2}{3}} + (x + 2)^{\frac{1}{3}}}.$

8. $\displaystyle\int_{2}^{33} \frac{dx}{8 + \sqrt[3]{2 + 3x}}.$

9. $\displaystyle\int \frac{x^5 \, dx}{\sqrt{4 + x^3}}.$

10. $\displaystyle\int \frac{dx}{x^2(4 + x^4)^{\frac{3}{4}}}.$

11. $\displaystyle\int \frac{(1 + x^4)^{\frac{3}{4}} \, dx}{x^8}.$

Hint for Problem 10. Substitute $x = 1/u$.

Integrate by any method.

12. $\displaystyle\int \frac{x \, dx}{(x^2 - 4)^{\frac{1}{2}} + (x^2 - 4)^{\frac{3}{4}}}.$

13. $\displaystyle\int \frac{dx}{\sqrt{2x} - \sqrt{x + 4}}.$

14. $\displaystyle\int \sqrt{1 - e^x} \, dx.$

15. $\displaystyle\int \sqrt{1 + e^{2x}} \, dx.$

16. $\displaystyle\int \sqrt{\frac{1 - u}{1 + u}} \, du.$

17. $\displaystyle\int \sqrt{\frac{4 - x}{2 + x}} \, dx.$

18. $\displaystyle\int \frac{\sqrt{1 + 2e^x} \, dx}{e^x - 1}.$

19. Obtain $\displaystyle\int \frac{dx}{x^4\sqrt{1 + 4x^2}}$ by substituting $\sqrt{1 + 4x^2} = ux$.

Prove the formula in Table VII by an algebraic substitution.

20. Formula 35.   **21.** Formula 19.   **22.** Formula 20.

23–33. By use of Table VII obtain the results for Problems 2, 3, 4, 5, 6, 8, 9, 12, 15, 19, and 37, respectively, of Exercise 73, page 255.

34. Integrate Problem 18 of Exercise 73 by use of Table VII.

★*Note 1.* An expression of the form $v^h(a + bv^k)^{\frac{p}{q}} \, dv$ where h and k are rational numbers, p and q are integers, and p/q is in lowest terms, is called a *binomial differential*. If r is the lowest common denominator of the fractions represented by h and k (possibly integers), the substitution $v = u^r$ changes the given expression into one of the form $u^m(a + bu^n)^{\frac{p}{q}} \, du$, where m and n are integers. Then, Problems 35 and 36 apply to this normal form.

★*Prove that $\int u^m(a + bu^n)^{\frac{p}{q}} \, du$ can be rationalized by the specified substitution under the given hypothesis on m, n, p, q.*

35. If $(m + 1)/n$ is an integer, substitute $a + bu^n = w^q$.

36. If $\left(\dfrac{m + 1}{n} + \dfrac{p}{q}\right)$ is an integer, substitute $a + bu^n = w^q u^n$.

★**37.** Apply one of Problems 35 and 36 to $\displaystyle\int \frac{\sqrt{1 + 4x^4}}{x^3} \, dx.$

144. Approximate integration

A primary objective of indefinite integration is to provide a means for the computation of definite integrals, by use of the fundamental theorem of integral calculus,

$$\int_a^b f(x)dx = F(b) - F(a), \quad where \quad F(x) = \int f(x)dx. \tag{1}$$

The result in (1) is of utility computationally only when we have such knowledge of $F(x)$ that its values can be computed. Hence, if it is either impossible or inconvenient for us to find a formula for $F(x)$, we have recourse to numerical methods for evaluating $\int_a^b f(x)dx$ approximately, without involving $\int f(x)dx$ and (1). The ideal, then, is to employ a method which is capable of obtaining $\int_a^b f(x)dx$ with any specified degree of accuracy, provided that sufficient computation is performed.

As a basis for numerical integration, let us interpret $\int_a^b f(x)dx$ as an area. For illustration in figures, we shall assume that $f(x) \geqq 0$. If $f(x) < 0$ on a part of the interval (a, b), our future remarks should be interpreted as assigning a negative measure for the area of any region below the x-axis.

ILLUSTRATION 1. The most obvious method of numerical integration is to employ directly the definition of a definite integral as the limit of approximating sums.

145. Trapezoidal rule for approximate integration

Let $f(x)$ be a function which is continuous on an interval $a \leqq x \leqq b$. Let P be a partition of (a, b) into n equal subintervals, with the division points $\{x_i\}$, where

$$a = x_0 < x_1 < x_2 < \cdots < x_n = b. \tag{1}$$

Let the length of each interval of P be Δx. Consider the graph of $y = f(x)$ in Figure 175, where $y_i = f(x_i)$, and Q_i is the point (x_i, y_i). Construct the ordinate of each point Q_i, and join each pair (Q_{i-1}, Q_i) by a line segment. Thus, n trapezoids are formed with their bases on the x-axis and the op-

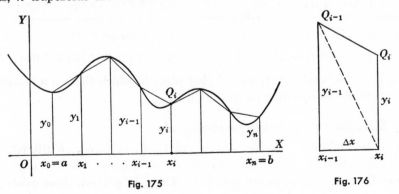

Fig. 175   Fig. 176

posite sides as chords of the graph of $y = f(x)$. Let R be the region bounded by the x-axis, the curve $y = f(x)$, and the lines $x = a$ and $x = b$. We consider the sum, τ_P, of the areas of the n trapezoids as an approximation to the area, A, of R. That is, we shall compute τ_P as an approximation to $\int_a^b f(x)dx$.

The nature of the typical trapezoid of Figure 175 is shown in Figure 176. On cutting this trapezoid into two triangles, its area is seen to be

$$\tfrac{1}{2}y_{i-1}\Delta x + \tfrac{1}{2}y_i \Delta x, \quad or \quad \tfrac{1}{2}(y_{i-1} + y_i)\Delta x. \tag{2}$$

Hence, with $i = 1, 2, \cdots, n$ in (2), we obtain

$$\tau_P = \tfrac{1}{2}\Delta x[(y_0 + y_1) + (y_1 + y_2) + \cdots + (y_{n-2} + y_{n-1}) + (y_{n-1} + y_n)]. \tag{3}$$

Each ordinate y_i, except for y_0 and y_n, occurs *twice* in (3). Hence,

$$\tau_P = \tfrac{1}{2}(y_0 + 2y_1 + 2y_2 + \cdots + 2y_{n-1} + y_n)\Delta x. \tag{4}$$

When a particular sum τ_P is accepted as an approximation to $\int_a^b f(x)dx$, it is said that the *trapezoidal rule* is being used.

Note 1. The trapezoid of Figure 176 has the same area as some rectangle on the same base with an altitude η_i where $y_{i-1} \leqq \eta_i \leqq y_i$. This altitude would be the value of $f(x)$ at some point ξ_i where $x_{i-1} \leqq \xi_i \leqq x_i$. Then, in place of (2), we could use $f(\xi_i)\Delta x$, and $\tau_P = \sum_{i=1}^n f(\xi_i)\Delta x$. Thus, each sum τ_P has the same value as a *related sum* S_P, as met in (3) on page 189, and we are assured that $\tau_P \to \int_a^b f(x)dx$ as $n \to \infty$.

ILLUSTRATION 1. In general, if $Q(x)$ is a polynomial of degree 3 in x, then $\int_a^b \sqrt{Q(x)}\,dx$ is an **elliptic integral** and we cannot express $\int \sqrt{Q(x)}\,dx$ in terms of known functions, at the level of this text. Let $H = \int_0^2 \sqrt{1 + x^3}\,dx$, which is an elliptic integral. We shall compute H by the trapezoidal rule, with the interval $0 \leqq x \leqq 2$ divided into 8 equal parts, so that $n = 8$ in (4). We obtain the following ordinates of the graph of $y = \sqrt{1 + x^3}$; $\Delta x = \tfrac{1}{4}$ for (4).

i	0	1	2	3	4	5	6	7	8
x_i	0	$\tfrac{1}{4}$	$\tfrac{1}{2}$	$\tfrac{3}{4}$	1	$\tfrac{5}{4}$	$\tfrac{3}{2}$	$\tfrac{7}{4}$	2
y_i	1.000	1.008	1.061	1.192	1.414	1.718	2.092	2.522	3

Then, from (4), we obtain the following approximation to H:

$$\tau = \tfrac{1}{2} \cdot \tfrac{1}{4}(1 + 2.016 + 2.122 + 2.384 + 2.828 + 3.436 + 4.184 + 5.044 + 3).$$

Thus, $\tau = 3.26$, where we round off that place in which there is a possibility of an error due to rounding off in the table.

146. Simpson's rule, or the parabolic rule

As a preliminary, consider three points $K_0:(-h, y_0)$, $K_1:(0, y_1)$, and $K_2:(h, y_2)$, where $h > 0$; for convenience in Figure 177 on page 305, assume that y_0, y_1, and y_2 are positive. Then, in general, there exists just one set of coefficients (a, b, c) so that the parabola $y = ax^2 + bx + c$ passes through K_0, K_1, and K_2, as seen in Figure 177. We desire to compute the area, α, bounded by this parabola, the x-axis, and the ordinates $x = -h$ and $x = h$; the result is to be expressed in terms of y_0, y_1, y_2, and h. We find

$$\alpha = \int_{-h}^{h} (ax^2 + bx + c)dx = \left(\frac{ax^3}{3} + \frac{bx^2}{2} + cx \right)\Big]_{-h}^{h} = \frac{2ah^3}{3} + 2ch. \qquad (1)$$

On the parabola,

when $x = -h$, then	$y = ah^2 - bh + c$, or	$y_0 = ah^2 - bh + c$;
when $x = 0$, then	$y = c$, or	$y_1 = c$;
when $x = h$, then	$y = ah^2 + bh + c$, or	$y_2 = ah^2 + bh + c$.

$$(2)$$

We verify that $y_0 + 4y_1 + y_2 = 2ah^2 + 6c$. From (1),*

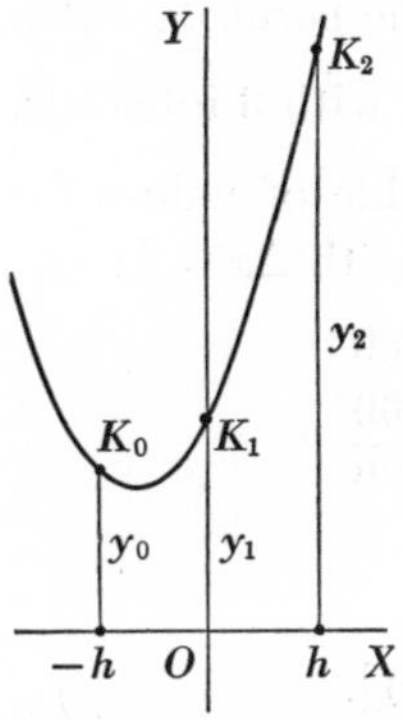

$$\alpha = \frac{1}{3} h(y_0 + 4y_1 + y_2). \qquad (3)$$

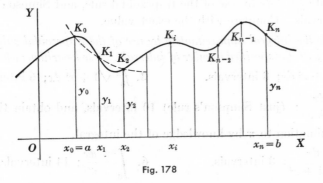

Fig. 177

Now, let $f(x)$ be continuous, and consider approximating $\int_a^b f(x)dx$ as follows. Let P be any partition of the interval (a, b), where P has an **even number of division points** $\{x_i\}$, with

$$a = x_0 < x_1 < x_2 < \cdots < x_n = b, \quad and \quad x_i - x_{i-1} = \Delta x$$

for all values of i. Let $y_i = f(x_i)$, and let K_i be the point (x_i, y_i) on the graph of $y = f(x)$, as in Figure 178. Then, pass a parabola through the points (K_0, K_1, K_2), as shown by the broken-line curve in Figure 178. The area bounded by this curve, the x-axis, and the ordinates $x = x_0$ and $x = x_2$ is found from (3) with $h = \Delta x$:

$$\tfrac{1}{3}\Delta x(y_0 + 4y_1 + y_2). \qquad (4)$$

Next, pass a parabola through (K_2, K_3, K_4). The area bounded by this curve, the x-axis, and the ordinates $x = x_2$ and $x = x_4$, is found from (3) with

Fig. 178

* It is easy to show by an independent discussion that (3) remains true if K_0, K_1, and K_2 lie on a line. In this case it is impossible to construct a parabola through the points.

$h = \Delta x$, and (y_0, y_1, y_2) replaced by (y_2, y_3, y_4):

$$\tfrac{1}{3}(\Delta x)(y_2 + 4y_3 + y_4). \tag{5}$$

Thus, pass parabolas in succession through the sets of three successive points (K_4, K_5, K_6), (K_6, K_7, K_8), $\cdots$, (K_{n-2}, K_{n-1}, K_n), and obtain the areas between these parabolas and the x-axis, over the corresponding double intervals of the partition P. Let τ_P be the sum of the areas of these $n/2$ parabolas. Then,

$$\tau_P = \tfrac{1}{3}\Delta x[(y_0 + 4y_1 + y_2) + (y_2 + 4y_3 + y_4) + \cdots + (y_{n-2} + 4y_{n-1} + y_n)];$$

$$\tau_P = \tfrac{1}{3}\Delta x(y_0 + 4y_1 + 2y_2 + 4y_3 + \cdots + 2y_{n-2} + 4y_{n-1} + y_n). \tag{6}$$

In (6), aside from the coefficients 1 for y_0 and y_n, the coefficient is 4 for y_i if i is *odd* and is 2 if i is *even*. We take τ_P as an approximation to $\int_a^b f(x)dx$, and refer to the preceding method as *Simpson's rule* (or, the *parabolic rule*).

EXAMPLE 1. Compute $\int_0^2 \sqrt{1 + x^3}\, dx$ by Simpson's rule, with 8 intervals.

SOLUTION. Let H represent the integral. From the table of values for Illustration 1 on page 304, we obtain the following values, with $\Delta x = \tfrac{1}{4}$:

$y_1 = 1.008$	$y_2 = 1.061$	$y_0 = 1.000$
$y_3 = 1.192$	$y_4 = 1.414$	$y_8 = 3.000$
$y_5 = 1.718$	$y_6 = 2.092$	$sum = 4.000$
$y_7 = 2.522$	$sum = 4.567$	
$sum = 6.440$		

From (6), $\tau = \tfrac{1}{3} \cdot \tfrac{1}{4}[4.000 + 4(6.440) + 2(4.567)].$

Or, the approximate value is $\tau = 3.24$, to two decimal places. This result may be compared with $\tau = 3.26$ in Illustration 1 on page 304. It is beyond the scope of this text * to discuss the relative accuracy of these two results, although intuition leads us to consider $\tau = 3.24$ as the more accurate.

EXERCISE 88

Perform computation with accuracy to two decimal places.

1. Compute $\int_0^3 x^2\, dx$ by use of the trapezoidal rule, and Simpson's rule, with 12 intervals. Compare with the exact value.

Compute the integral approximately by use of the trapezoidal rule and Simpson's rule, with the specified number of intervals. Use logarithms where desirable.

2. $\int_0^2 \sqrt{4 + x^3}\, dx$; 8 intervals.   3. $\int_0^2 \sqrt{1 + x^4}\, dx$; 6 intervals.

4. $\int_0^1 \dfrac{dx}{1 + x^2}$; (just Simpson's rule) 10 intervals, and obtain the resulting approximation to π by knowledge of the integral.

5. $\int_0^2 \dfrac{dx}{\sqrt{1 + x^3}}$; 8 intervals.   6. $\int_0^{2.8} \dfrac{dx}{e^{x^2}}$; 14 intervals.

---

* For a full discussion of approximate integration, including error analysis, see *Numerical Calculus*, by *William E. Milne;* Princeton University Press, publishers.

16

LENGTH OF ARC AND APPLICATIONS

147. Length of arc

In an xy-plane, consider a path C defined by parametric equations

$$x = \phi(t) \quad and \quad y = \psi(t), \tag{1}$$

where $\phi(t)$ and $\psi(t)$ are continuous, and the range for t is an interval, finite or infinite. An *arc AB* of C is defined as the set of points obtained for t on some interval $a \leq t \leq b$, where point A is obtained when $t = a$, and B when $t = b$. We shall define *arc length* on C.

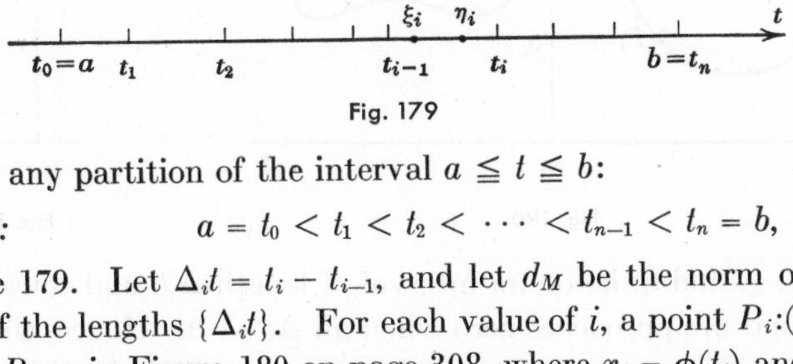

Fig. 179

Let M be any partition of the interval $a \leq t \leq b$:

Partition M: $\qquad a = t_0 < t_1 < t_2 < \cdots < t_{n-1} < t_n = b, \tag{2}$

as in Figure 179. Let $\Delta_i t = t_i - t_{i-1}$, and let d_M be the norm of M, or the maximum of the lengths $\{\Delta_i t\}$. For each value of i, a point $P_i:(x_i, y_i)$ is obtained on AB, as in Figure 180 on page 308, where $x_i = \phi(t_i)$ and $y_i = \psi(t_i)$. Join neighboring points in the sequence $P_0, P_1, \cdots, P_n$, to obtain a *polygonal line* inscribed in AB. Let $\overline{P_{i-1}P_i}$ be the length of the chord $P_{i-1}P_i$. Then, we introduce arc length as follows.

DEFINITION I. *The length, L, of arc AB is the limit of the sum of the lengths of the chords of the inscribed polygonal line corresponding to a partition M of the values of the parameter t as $d_M \to 0$, if this limit exists. Or,*

$$L = \lim_{d_M \to 0} \sum_{i=1}^{n} \overline{P_{i-1}P_i}. \tag{3}$$

THEOREM I. *If $\phi(t)$ and $\psi(t)$ in (1) have continuous derivatives, then the arc length L exists, and*

$$\left\{ \begin{array}{c} path: \\ x = \phi(t), y = \psi(t) \end{array} \right\} \qquad L = \int_a^b \sqrt{\left(\frac{dx}{dt}\right)^2 + \left(\frac{dy}{dt}\right)^2} \, dt. \tag{4}$$

307

Proof. 1. Let $\Delta_i x = \phi(t_i) - \phi(t_{i-1})$; $\Delta_i y = \psi(t_i) - \psi(t_{i-1})$.

From Figure 181,

$$\overline{P_{i-1}P_i} = \sqrt{(\Delta_i x)^2 + (\Delta_i y)^2}. \tag{5}$$

2. By the mean value theorem of page 176, there exist points ξ_i and η_i on the interval $t_{i-1} \leqq t \leqq t_i$, as in Figure 179, so that

$$\Delta_i x = \phi(t_i) - \phi(t_{i-1}) = \phi'(\xi_i)(t_i - t_{i-1}); \tag{6}$$

$$\Delta_i y = \psi(t_i) - \psi(t_{i-1}) = \psi'(\eta_i)(t_i - t_{i-1}); \tag{7}$$

$$(\Delta_i x)^2 + (\Delta_i y)^2 = \{[\phi'(\xi_i)]^2 + [\psi'(\eta_i)]^2\}(\Delta_i t)^2. \tag{8}$$

From (5), $\overline{P_{i-1}P_i} = \sqrt{[\phi'(\xi_i)]^2 + [\psi'(\eta_i)]^2}\,\Delta_i t. \tag{9}$

From (3), $L = \lim_{d_M \to 0} \sum_{i=1}^{n} \sqrt{[\phi'(\xi_i)]^2 + [\psi'(\eta_i)]^2}\,\Delta_i t. \tag{10}$

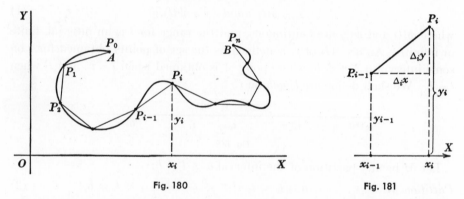

Fig. 180   Fig. 181

3. In (10), ξ_i and η_i lie on an interval of length $\Delta_i t$, and thus the distance between ξ_i and η_i approaches zero when all $\Delta_i t \to 0$. Hence, since $\phi'(t)$ and $\psi'(t)$ are continuous, we accept the fact that the limit in (10), if this limit exists, would not be changed if we should replace η_i by ξ_i, which gives

$$L = \lim_{d_M \to 0} \sum_{i=1}^{n} \sqrt{[\phi'(\xi_i)]^2 + [\psi'(\xi_i)]^2}\,\Delta_i t. \tag{11}$$

By comparison with (10) on page 190, the sum in (11) is recognized as an approximating sum, S_M, for an integral of the function $\sqrt{[\phi'(t)]^2 + [\psi'(t)]^2}$. Hence, the limit in (11) exists and is equal to the integral in (4).

EXAMPLE 1. Find the arc length from $t = 2$ to $t = 4$ on the path $(x = 3t^2,\ y = t^3)$.

SOLUTION. From (4), $L = \int_2^4 \sqrt{(6t)^2 + (3t^2)^2}\,dt = 3\int_2^4 t\sqrt{4 + t^2}\,dt \doteq 66.8$.

Note 1. We called C in (1) a *path*, and recognize that (1) may give certain parts of C more than once. Thus, with $0 \leqq t \leqq 6\pi$, the equations

($x = \cos t$, $y = \sin t$) give all of the circle $x^2 + y^2 = 1$ three times (and one point four times); then, L in (4) is three times the circumference of the circle. When we desire to indicate that such duplication is to be avoided, it will be sufficient to call the path (1) a **geometric curve** (or merely a *curve*, for brevity) in case *at most a finite number of points are obtainable more than once from* (1) *with* $a \leq t \leq b$.

If a curve C is the graph of an equation $y = f(x)$ where $f(x)$ has a continuous derivative $f'(x)$, we may *think of* C *as given by parametric equations* $[x = x, y = f(x)]$, *with x as the parameter.* Then, with t replaced by x in (4), the length of arc L between $x = a$ and $x = b$ is

$$\left\{ \begin{array}{l} \text{curve:} \\ y = f(x) \end{array} \right\} \qquad L = \int_a^b \sqrt{1 + \left(\frac{dy}{dx}\right)^2}\, dx, \qquad (12)$$

because $dx/dx = 1$. If C is defined by $x = g(y)$, where $g'(y)$ is continuous, then C is given in parametric form, *with y as the parameter*, by the equations $[x = g(y), y = y]$. The length of arc L from $y = c$ to $y = d$, with $c < d$, then is obtained from (4) with t replaced by y:

$$\left\{ \begin{array}{l} \text{curve:} \\ x = g(y) \end{array} \right\} \qquad L = \int_c^d \sqrt{\left(\frac{dx}{dy}\right)^2 + 1}\, dy. \qquad (13)$$

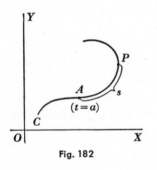

Fig. 182

EXAMPLE 2. Write integrals for the length of arc on the parabola $y^2 = 4x$ between $(0, 0)$ and $(1, 2)$ by use of an integral in two ways.

SOLUTION. (a) Since $dy/dx = x^{-\frac{1}{2}}$, from (12),

$$L = \int_0^1 \sqrt{1 + \frac{1}{x}}\, dx. \qquad (14)$$

(b) Since $x = \frac{1}{4}y^2$ and $dx/dy = \frac{1}{2}y$, from (13),

$$L = \int_0^2 \sqrt{1 + \frac{1}{4}y^2}\, dy. \qquad (15)$$

On a path C, in (1), let s be the directed distance from a point A, with $t = a$, to a general point $P:[\phi(t), \psi(t)]$, as in Figure 182, where we agree that $s \geq 0$ if $t \geq a$ and $s \leq 0$ if $t \leq a$. Then,

$$s = \int_a^t \sqrt{\left(\frac{dx}{dt}\right)^2 + \left(\frac{dy}{dt}\right)^2}\, dt. \qquad (16)$$

From Theorem VII on page 197, and (16),

$$\frac{ds}{dt} = \sqrt{\left(\frac{dx}{dt}\right)^2 + \left(\frac{dy}{dt}\right)^2}, \quad or \quad ds = \sqrt{\left(\frac{dx}{dt}\right)^2 + \left(\frac{dy}{dt}\right)^2}\, dt. \qquad (17)$$

We refer to ds as the **differential of arc.** From (17), on squaring,

$$(ds)^2 = (dx)^2 + (dy)^2. \qquad (18)$$

Notice that dx, dy, ds are related *formally* as if dx and dy were the legs, and ds the hypotenuse in a right triangle, as suggested by Figure 183. On dividing by $(dx)^2$ on the right in (18), and then multiplying by $(dx)^2$, and acting similarly with $(dy)^2$, we obtain

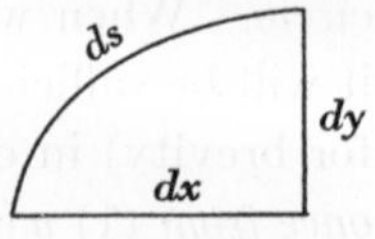

$$(ds)^2 = \left[1 + \left(\frac{dy}{dx}\right)^2\right](dx)^2, \quad and \quad (ds)^2 = \left[\left(\frac{dx}{dy}\right)^2 + 1\right](dy)^2;$$

Fig. 183

$$ds = \pm \sqrt{1 + \left(\frac{dy}{dx}\right)^2}\, dx; \qquad ds = \pm \sqrt{\left(\frac{dx}{dy}\right)^2 + 1}\, dy. \qquad (19)$$

In (19), we use the plus sign if s is to increase when x (or, y) increases. We may abbreviate (4), (12), and (13) by writing

$$L = \int_{t=a}^{t=b} ds, \qquad L = \int_{x=a}^{x=b} ds, \qquad L = \int_{y=c}^{y=d} ds, \qquad (20)$$

where ds is expressed in terms of t, x, or y, respectively, as indicated by the limits. Unless otherwise specified, we choose the sign of any radical from (19) so that L will be positive.

★*Note 2.* In (3), it was implied that L is finite. At an advanced level, it is proved that the limit on the right in (3) exists, finite or infinite, if $\phi(t)$ and $\psi(t)$ in (1) are continuous. Also, the limit is shown to be finite under hypotheses not including the assumption that $\phi(t)$ and $\psi(t)$ have derivatives. Peculiar functions $\phi(t)$ and $\psi(t)$ exist for which the limit in (3) is infinite, so that the arc AB does not have a length. If we substitute $\tau = h(t)$ as a new parameter, in (1), this may alter L as obtained from Definition I. To avoid such a change, in advanced treatments it is found desirable to restrict the admissible changes in the parameter t. The length L obtained from (4) is unaltered if, in (1), we substitute $\tau = h(t)$ where $h'(t)$ is continuous and $h'(t) \geqq 0$. Such a change results merely in the corresponding substitution $\tau = h(t)$ in the integrand of (4).

EXERCISE 89

Find the length of the arc of the curve in an xy-plane defined by the given xy-equation or parametric equations. Any constant a or b is positive.

1. $x = 3t^2$ and $y = 2t^3$. From $t = 0$ to $t = 3$.
2. $x = a \cos t$ and $y = a \sin t$. Complete length.
3. $x = 2 - t$ and $y = t^2$. From $t = 0$ to $t = 3$.
4. $x^2 + y^2 = a^2$. Complete length.
5. $y^3 = x^2$. From $y = 0$ to $y = 4$. Inspect the two possible integrals.
6. $8y = x^2$. From $x = 0$ to $x = 4$.
7. $y = \frac{1}{2}a(e^{\frac{x}{a}} + e^{-\frac{x}{a}})$. From $x = -a$ to $x = a$.
8. $x = a(t - \sin t)$ and $y = a(1 - \cos t)$. Length of one arch.
9. $x = a \cos^3 t$ and $y = a \sin^3 t$. Complete length.

10. $x^{\frac{2}{3}} + y^{\frac{2}{3}} = a^{\frac{2}{3}}$. Length in one quadrant, without using Problem 9.

11. $27y^2 = x(x-9)^2$. The loop from $x = 0$ to $x = 9$.

12. $x = \ln(y^2 - 1)$. From $y = 2$ to $y = 10$.

13. $6xy = y^4 + 3$. From $y = 1$ to $y = 3$.

14. $x = a(\cos\theta + \theta\sin\theta)$ and $y = a(\sin\theta - \theta\cos\theta)$; from $\theta = 0$ to $\theta = 2\pi$.

15. $y = x - x^2$. From $x = 0$ to $x = 1$.

16. $y = \ln\cos x$. From $x = 0$ to $x = \frac{1}{3}\pi$.

17. $x = e^t \sin t$ and $y = e^t \cos t$. From $t = -1$ to $t = 1$.

★18. Obtain the length of arc for one quadrant of the ellipse $x = 2\cos t$ and $y = \sin t$, where t is a parameter, approximately by use of Simpson's rule with 10 intervals. A so-called **elliptic integral** is involved.

148. Length of arc in polar coordinates

Consider a curve C defined by the equation $r = f(\theta)$ in an $r\theta$-system of polar coordinates. Then, by use of the relations

$$x = r\cos\theta \quad and \quad y = r\sin\theta, \tag{1}$$

we may write parametric equations for C in the related rectangular coordinates, with θ as the parameter and r replaced by $f(\theta)$ in (1):

$$x = f(\theta)\cos\theta \quad and \quad y = f(\theta)\sin\theta. \tag{2}$$

With $r = f(\theta)$, we obtain ds from (1), thought of as abbreviating (2):

$$dx = (\cos\theta)dr - r(\sin\theta)d\theta; \quad dy = (\sin\theta)dr + r(\cos\theta)d\theta;$$

$$(ds)^2 = [(\cos\theta)dr - r(\sin\theta)d\theta]^2 + [(\sin\theta)dr + r(\cos\theta)d\theta]^2, \text{ or} \tag{3}$$

$$(ds)^2 = (dr)^2 + r^2(d\theta)^2. \tag{4}$$

In (4), since $r = f(\theta)$, we have $dr = f'(\theta)d\theta = r'd\theta$. Hence,

$$(ds)^2 = (r'^2 + r^2)(d\theta)^2, \quad or \quad ds = \sqrt{r^2 + r'^2}\, d\theta, \tag{5}$$

where we choose the positive radical with the convention that s will increase when θ increases.

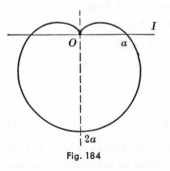

Fig. 184

EXAMPLE 1. Find the perimeter, L, of the cardioid $r = a(1 - \sin\theta)$.

SOLUTION. The right-hand half of the curve, in Figure 184, is traced as θ varies from $-\frac{1}{2}\pi$ to $\frac{1}{2}\pi$. From (4) with $dr = -a\cos\theta\, d\theta$,

$$(ds)^2 = a^2[\cos^2\theta + (1 - \sin\theta)^2](d\theta)^2$$

$$= 2a^2(1 - \sin\theta)(d\theta)^2. \tag{6}$$

Since $1 - \sin\theta = (\cos\frac{1}{2}\theta - \sin\frac{1}{2}\theta)^2$, then $ds = a\sqrt{2}(\cos\frac{1}{2}\theta - \sin\frac{1}{2}\theta)d\theta$. Hence,

$$L = 2\int_{-\frac{1}{2}\pi}^{\frac{1}{2}\pi} a\sqrt{2}(\cos\tfrac{1}{2}\theta - \sin\tfrac{1}{2}\theta)d\theta = 8a.$$

Divide, and then multiply by $(dr)^2$ on the right in (4):

$$(ds)^2 = \left[1 + r^2\left(\frac{d\theta}{dr}\right)^2\right](dr)^2, \quad or \quad \boldsymbol{ds} = \sqrt{1 + r^2\left(\frac{d\theta}{dr}\right)^2}\ \boldsymbol{dr}. \tag{7}$$

We may use (7) to obtain s by integration with respect to r.

Note 1. With $d\theta$ as an increment, Figure 185 shows two neighboring points $P:[r, \theta]$ and $Q:[r + \Delta r, \theta + d\theta]$ on the graph of a curve $r = f(\theta)$, where

$$(arc\ PQ) = \Delta s; \quad MQ = \Delta r; \quad PM = r\ d\theta. \tag{8}$$

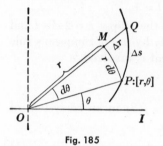

Fig. 185

The "curvilinear" triangle PQM reminds us of a right triangle with hypotenuse PQ, and suggests that $(\Delta s)^2$ is approximately equal to $(\Delta r)^2 + (r\ d\theta)^2$. Also, with Δr and Δs approximated by dr and ds, respectively, the "curvilinear" triangle PQM is a convenient device for recalling (4), in the form

$$(ds)^2 = (dr)^2 + (r\ d\theta)^2.$$

EXERCISE 90

Find the length of the specified arc of the given curve in an $r\theta$-system of polar coordinates. Integrate with respect to r or θ. Any constant a or k is positive.

1. The circle $r = 2a \cos \theta$. Complete length.
2. The cardioid $r = k \cos^2 \frac{1}{2}\theta$. Complete length.
3. The cardioid $r = a(1 - \cos \theta)$. Complete length.
4. The curve $r = k \sin^3 \frac{1}{3}\theta$. Complete length.
5. The circle $r = a(\cos \theta + \sin \theta)$. Complete length.
6. The spiral $r = a\theta$. From $\theta = 0$ to $\theta = \pi$.
7. The spiral $r = e^{k\theta}$. From $\theta = 0$ to $\theta = 1$. First express the result in two different ways, and then integrate the most convenient form.
★8. The parabola $r = a/(1 + \sin \theta)$. From $\theta = 0$ to $\theta = \pi$.
★9. The cissoid $r = 2a \tan \theta \sin \theta$. From $\theta = 0$ to $\theta = \frac{1}{3}\pi$.

149. Area of a surface of revolution

In an xy-plane, let C be a curve defined by

$$x = \phi(t) \quad and \quad y = \psi(t), \tag{1}$$

with $a \leq t \leq b$, where $\phi(t)$ and $\psi(t)$ satisfy the hypotheses which led to (4) on page 307. Let C be revolved about the x-axis to generate a surface of revolution, S. We proceed to define the notion of area for S.

Let M be any partition of the interval $a \leq t \leq b$:

$$a = t_0 < t_1 < \cdots < t_{i-1} < t_i < \cdots < t_n = b, \quad where \quad \Delta_i t = t_i - t_{i-1}. \tag{2}$$

When $t = t_i$, point $P_i:(x_i, y_i)$ is obtained on C, with $x_i = \phi(t_i)$ and $y_i = \psi(t_i)$. In Figure 186, $\alpha = \phi(a)$ and $\beta = \phi(b)$. Then, inscribe a polygonal line $P_0P_1 \cdots P_{i-1}P_i \cdots P_n$ in C, as in Figure 180 on page 308. The representative chord $P_{i-1}P_i$, corresponding to the interval $T_i:(t_{i-1} \leq t \leq t_i)$, is shown in Figure 186. When C is revolved about the x-axis, chord $P_{i-1}P_i$ generates a *frustum of a cone*. For this frustum, the slant height is $\overline{P_{i-1}P_i}$; the circumference of a midsection is $2\pi\overline{y}_i$ where $\overline{y}_i = \frac{1}{2}(y_i + y_{i-1})$; from page 567, the lateral area, Δ_iA, is

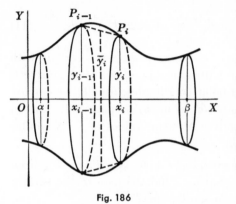

Fig. 186

$$\Delta_iA = 2\pi\overline{y}_i\overline{P_{i-1}P_i}. \qquad (3)$$

In (3), we assumed that, in (1), $\psi(t) \geq 0$ so that $\overline{y}_i \geq 0$. Then, we define the area, A, of the surface S as *the limit of the sum of the lateral areas of the inscribed frustums of cones generated by all the chords $\overline{P_{i-1}P_i}$,* corresponding to a partition M, as all $\Delta_it \rightarrow 0$, or

$$A = \lim_{d_M \to 0} \sum_{i=1}^{n} \Delta_iA. \qquad (4)$$

Since $y_{i-1} \leq \overline{y}_i \leq y_i$, or $y_i \leq \overline{y}_i \leq y_{i-1}$, there is a point σ_i on T_i where $y = \psi(\sigma_i) = \overline{y}_i$. Also, there exist points ξ_i and η_i on T_i so that $\overline{P_{i-1}P_i}$ can be expressed as in (9) on page 308, and thus (3) gives

$$\sum_{i=1}^{n} \Delta_iA = 2\pi \sum_{i=1}^{n} \psi(\sigma_i)\sqrt{[\phi'(\xi_i)]^2 + [\psi'(\eta_i)]^2}\Delta_it. \qquad (5)$$

It is seen in Figure 187 that the distances between ξ_i and σ_i, and ξ_i and η_i, approach zero when $\Delta_it \rightarrow 0$. Hence, since $\psi(t)$, $\phi'(t)$, and $\psi'(t)$ are continuous, we accept the fact that the limit in (4), if it exists, would not be changed if we should replace σ_i and η_i by ξ_i. With this replacement, (4) and (5) give

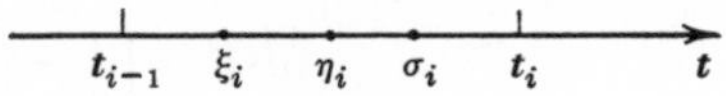

$$t_{i-1} \quad \xi_i \quad \eta_i \quad \sigma_i \quad t_i \qquad t$$

Fig. 187

$$A = 2\pi \lim_{d_M \to 0} \sum_{i=1}^{n} \psi(\xi_i)\sqrt{[\phi'(\xi_i)]^2 + [\psi'(\xi_i)]^2}\Delta_it. \qquad (6)$$

By comparison with (10) on page 190, the sum in (6) is recognized as an approximating sum for the integral which appears below. Hence,

$$A = 2\pi\int_a^b \psi(t)\sqrt{[\phi'(t)]^2 + [\psi'(t)]^2}\, dt, \text{ or}$$

$$\left\{ \begin{array}{l} \textit{revolve about x-axis} \\ x = \phi(t), y = \psi(t) \end{array} \right\} \qquad A = 2\pi\int_{t=a}^{t=b} y\, ds, \qquad (7)$$

where

$$ds = \sqrt{\left(\frac{dx}{dt}\right)^2 + \left(\frac{dy}{dt}\right)^2}\, dt. \qquad (8)$$

If the curve C defined by (1) is revolved about the y-axis, to generate a surface S, similarly we define the area, A, of S so that

$$\left\{ \begin{array}{l} \textit{revolve about y-axis} \\ x = \phi(t),\ y = \psi(t) \end{array} \right\} \qquad A = 2\pi \int_{t=a}^{t=b} x\ ds. \qquad (9)$$

With ds expressed in terms of dx, or dy, as in (19) on page 310,

$$\left\{ \begin{array}{l} \textit{revolve } y = f(x) \\ \textit{about x-axis} \end{array} \right\} \qquad A = 2\pi \int_{x=a}^{x=b} y\ ds, \quad \textit{or} \quad A = 2\pi \int_{y=c}^{y=d} y\ ds; \qquad (10)$$

$$\left\{ \begin{array}{l} \textit{revolve } x = g(y) \\ \textit{about y-axis} \end{array} \right\} \qquad A = 2\pi \int_{x=a}^{x=b} x\ ds, \quad \textit{or} \quad A = 2\pi \int_{y=c}^{y=d} x\ ds. \qquad (11)$$

In (10) or (11), $ds = \sqrt{1 + y'^2}\ dx$ with $y' = dy/dx$, or $ds = \sqrt{1 + x'^2}\ dy$ with $x' = dx/dy$, according as the limits are values of x or of y. If the curve C of (7) and (9) is defined by $r = f(\theta)$ in polar coordinates, usually we employ (7) and (9) with ds expressed in terms of $d\theta$, as in (5) on page 311. In (7), we use $|y|$ instead of y if $\psi(t)$ is negative at some values of t. A similar change may occur in (9), (10), and (11).

EXAMPLE 1. The arc of the semicubical parabola $(x = t^2,\ y = t^3)$, from $t = 0$ to $t = \sqrt{8}$ is revolved about the y-axis. Find the area of the surface which is generated. See Table VIII for a similar curve.

SOLUTION. Since $dx = 2t\ dt$ and $dy = 3t^2\ dt$,

$$(ds)^2 = (4t^2 + 9t^4)(dt)^2, \quad \textit{or} \quad ds = t\sqrt{4 + 9t^2}\ dt.$$

From (9), $$A = 2\pi \int_0^{\sqrt{8}} t^3 \sqrt{4 + 9t^2}\ dt. \qquad (12)$$

2. To integrate in (12), substitute $\sqrt{4 + 9t^2} = u$. Then $A = 713$ sq. units.

EXAMPLE 2. Find the area of the surface generated by revolving the arc of the parabola $x^2 = 8y$ from $y = 0$ to $y = 2$ in quadrant I about OY.

SOLUTION. If $y = 0$ then $x = 0$; if $y = 2$ then $x = 4$.

$$(ds)^2 = \left[1 + \left(\frac{dy}{dx} \right)^2 \right] (dx)^2 = \frac{16 + x^2}{16} (dx)^2.$$

From (11), $$A = 2\pi \int_0^4 \frac{1}{4} x\sqrt{16 + x^2}\ dx = \frac{32\pi}{3} (2\sqrt{2} - 1).$$

★EXAMPLE 3. Find the area of the surface generated by revolving the cardioid $r = a(1 - \cos \theta)$ about the x-axis.

SOLUTION. From (5) on page 311, $$(ds)^2 = 4a^2(\sin^2 \tfrac{1}{2}\theta)(d\theta)^2.$$

The upper half of the cardioid, as in Figure 111 on page 169, is traced as θ varies from 0 to π. Hence, from (7) with t replaced by θ, and

$$y = r \sin \theta = a(1 - \cos \theta)\sin \theta,$$

we obtain $$A = 4\pi a^2 \int_0^\pi (\sin \theta - \sin \theta \cos \theta)\sin \tfrac{1}{2}\theta\ d\theta = \tfrac{32}{5}\pi a^2. \qquad (13)$$

EXERCISE 91

Find the area of the surface obtained by revolving each curve about the indicated axis, OX or OY, in an xy-plane. The constants a and b are positive.

1. $y = x^3$, from $x = 0$ to $x = 2$. Revolve about OX.

2. $3y = 4x$, from $x = 0$ to $x = 3$. Revolve about OX. Check the result by the formula for the lateral area of a cone.

3. A line segment joins the points $(0, 12)$ and $(5, 0)$ in the xy-plane. Revolve the segment about OY. Check as in Problem 2.

4. $x = a \cos t$ and $y = a \sin t$. Revolve about OX, and thus find the surface area of a sphere.

5. A circle with center $(x = a, y = 0)$ and radius b, where $b < a$, with the parametric equations $x = a + b \cos \theta$ and $y = b \sin \theta$. Revolve about OY, to form a *torus*. Find its complete area.

6. $y = \frac{1}{2}(e^x + e^{-x})$, from $x = -1$ to $x = 1$. Revolve about OX.

7. $x^2 + y^2 = a^2$, complete curve. Revolve about OY.

8. $y^2 = 4x$, from $x = 0$ to $x = 4$. Revolve about (a) OX; (b) OY.

9. $y^2 = 20 + 4x$, from $x = -5$ to $x = -2$. Revolve about OX.

10. $x^2 = 8 - 4y$, from $y = \frac{3}{4}$ to $y = 2$. Revolve about OY.

11. $x = y^3$, from $y = 0$ to $y = 2$. Revolve about OX.

12. $x^{\frac{2}{3}} + y^{\frac{2}{3}} = a^{\frac{2}{3}}$. Revolve about OY. Use an integral with respect to x.

13. Repeat Problem 12, with the parametric form $x = a \cos^3 t$, $y = a \sin^3 t$.

14. $x = a(t - \sin t)$ and $y = a(1 - \cos t)$. Revolve one arch about OX.

15. The cardioid $r = 1 - \sin \theta$. Revolve about OY.

16. A region R in an xy-plane is bounded below by the parabola $x^2 = 2y + 3$ and above by the parabola $x^2 = 8y$. Find the area of the surface of the solid generated if R is revolved about OY.

17. $y = \sin x$, from $x = 0$ to $x = 2\pi$. About OX.

18. $3x^2 + 4y^2 = 12$. Revolve about OX.

19. $x^2 - y^2 = 16$, from $x = 4$ to $x = 8$. Revolve about OX.

20. $x = 1 - 3t^2$ and $y = t - 3t^3$. Revolve from $x = 0$ to $x = 1$ about OX.

21. $y^3 = x^2$, from $y = 0$ to $y = \frac{4}{3}$. Revolve about OX.

22. $x = \ln(y^2 - 1)$, from $y = \sqrt{2}$ to $y = 3$. Revolve about OX.

23. The complete circle $r = 2a \cos \theta$. Revolve about OY.

24. The lemniscate $r^2 = a^2 \cos 2\theta$. Revolve about (a) OX; (b) OY.

25. $y = e^{-x}$, from $x = 0$ to $x = +\infty$. Revolve about OX.

26. Find the surface area of the prolate spheroid obtained by revolving the ellipse $(x = a \cos t, y = b \sin t)$ about OX, with $0 < b < a$. To simplify, recall that the eccentricity η is defined by $\eta^2 = (a^2 - b^2)/a^2$.

27. Find the area of the curved surface of a zone cut from a sphere by two parallel planes k units apart.

150. Regular curves

In an xy-plane, let a path C be defined parametrically by

$$x = \phi(t) \quad and \quad y = \psi(t), \tag{1}$$

where the derivatives $\phi'(t)$ and $\psi'(t)$ are continuous and

$$[\phi'(t)]^2 + [\psi'(t)]^2 \neq 0 \tag{2}$$

at each value of t. Then, we shall call C a *regular path*.

If a curve C has the equation $y = f(x)$ where $f'(x)$ is continuous, and if C is thought of in the parametric form $[x = x$ and $y = f(x)]$, where x replaces t,

$$\{[\phi'(t)]^2 + [\psi'(t)]^2\} \quad becomes \quad \{1 + [f'(x)]^2\},$$

which is never zero. Thus, C is a regular curve. Similarly, $x = g(y)$ defines a regular curve if $g'(y)$ is continuous. The student will prove later that the equation $r = f(\theta)$, where $f'(\theta)$ is continuous, defines a regular curve in polar coordinates, except where $r = 0$ and $f'(\theta) = 0$.

At any point P on a regular path C defined by (1), there exists

$$\frac{dy}{dx} = \frac{\psi'(t)}{\phi'(t)} \quad or \quad \frac{dx}{dy} = \frac{\phi'(t)}{\psi'(t)}, \tag{3}$$

or both exist, because (2) shows that $\phi'(t)$ and $\psi'(t)$ cannot equal zero simultaneously. Hence, C has a tangent at each point. In (3), $dy/dx = \tan\omega$, where ω is an angle between the x-axis and the tangent to C, and $dx/dy = \tan\beta$, where $\beta = \frac{1}{2}\pi - \omega$ and β is an angle between the y-axis and the tangent to C, as in Figure 188. Also, $\beta = 0$ when $\omega = \frac{1}{2}\pi$. Since at least one of the functions $\tan\omega$ and $\tan\beta$ is continuous at each point P of C, *the tangent at P turns continuously as P moves on a regular path C.*

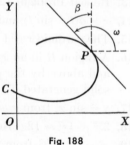

Fig. 188

On a regular path C defined by (1), let s be the arc distance measured from any fixed point, where $t = a$. Then

$$s = h(t), \quad where \quad h(t) = \int_a^t \sqrt{[\phi'(t)]^2 + [\psi'(t)]^2} \, dt. \tag{4}$$

Hence,

$$\frac{ds}{dt} = h'(t) = \sqrt{[\phi'(t)]^2 + [\psi'(t)]^2}, \tag{5}$$

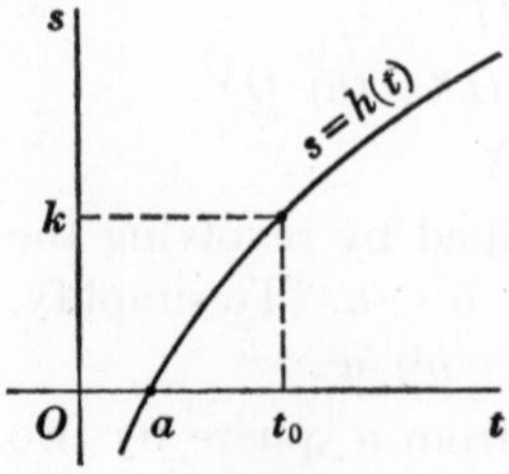

Fig. 189

where $h'(t) > 0$ because of (2). Thus, the equation $s = h(t)$ defines a single-valued inverse, $t = g(s)$, because the graph of $s = h(t)$, as in Figure 189, is met in just one point by any line $s = k$. On using $t = g(s)$ in (1), we obtain a new parametric form for C, with s as the parameter,

$$x = \Phi(s) \quad and \quad y = \Psi(s). \tag{6}$$

Also,
$$\frac{dt}{ds} = \frac{1}{\dfrac{ds}{dt}} = \frac{1}{h'(t)}, \tag{7}$$

which is continuous because $h'(t) > 0$. Hence, dx/ds and dy/ds exist and are continuous, with

$$\frac{dx}{ds} = \frac{dx}{dt} \cdot \frac{dt}{ds} \quad and \quad \frac{dy}{ds} = \frac{dy}{dt} \cdot \frac{dt}{ds}. \tag{8}$$

Then, from $(dx)^2 + (dy)^2 = (ds)^2$, on dividing by $(ds)^2$ we obtain

$$\left(\frac{dx}{ds}\right)^2 + \left(\frac{dy}{ds}\right)^2 = 1. \tag{9}$$

151. Curvature and circle of curvature

In an xy-plane, let P be a fixed point and Q be a neighboring point on a regular curve C, as in Figure 190, with Δs as the length of arc PQ. Let the inclination of the tangent to C at P be * ω, and at Q be $(\omega + \Delta \omega)$, where angles are measured in *radians*. Then, $\Delta \omega / \Delta s$ is the *average rate of change of ω with respect to distance along PQ*. The *instan-*

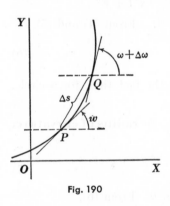

Fig. 190

taneous rate of change, dω/ds, can be taken as a measure of the bending of C at P, if $d\omega/ds$ exists. Let a number k be defined by the equation

$$k = \frac{d\omega}{ds} = \lim_{\Delta s \to 0} \frac{\Delta \omega}{\Delta s}. \tag{1}$$

For many purposes, the sign of k is immaterial, because it depends on an arbitrary selection of the direction on C in which s increases. Reversal of this direction would alter the sign of k. Hence we shall replace k by $|k|$ in the following terminology.

DEFINITION II. *At a point P on a regular curve C, the* **curvature,** K, *of C is the absolute value of the rate of change of the † direction angle ω of the tangent with respect to distance on C:*

$$K = \left|\frac{d\omega}{ds}\right|. \tag{2}$$

Note 1. In (2), K is a measure in *radians per unit distance*.

ILLUSTRATION 1. If C is a straight line, then $K = 0$ at all points of C, because ω is a constant, and hence $d\omega/ds = 0$.

---

* To obtain a continuous variation of ω, if the tangent is nearly horizontal along PQ, we would use the range $-\frac{1}{2}\pi < \omega \leqq \frac{1}{2}\pi$ instead of $0 \leqq \omega < \pi$.
† We used the *inclination* as a *direction angle* in the discussion. Any other direction angle would have been equally satisfactory.

ILLUSTRATION 2. To find the curvature at any point P on a circle of radius r, let the coordinate axes be located as in Figure 191, with P on the x-axis. Then, with $PQ = \Delta s$, we have $\Delta s = r\Delta\omega$. Hence,

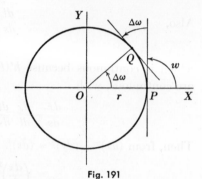

Fig. 191

$$\frac{\Delta\omega}{\Delta s} = \frac{1}{r}; \quad K = \frac{d\omega}{ds} = \lim_{\Delta s \to 0} \frac{\Delta\omega}{\Delta s} = \frac{1}{r},$$

or *the curvature K is a constant, the reciprocal of the radius.*

Let the curve C be defined by $y = f(x)$, where the derivatives $f'(x)$ and $f''(x)$ exist. Then, at $P:(x, y)$ on C,

$$\tan \omega = y' \quad or \quad \omega = \arctan y'; \tag{3}$$

$$K = \left| \frac{d\omega}{ds} \right| = \left| \frac{d (\arctan y') }{dx} \cdot \frac{dx}{ds} \right| = \left| \frac{dy'}{dx} \cdot \frac{1}{1 + y'^2} \cdot \frac{dx}{ds} \right|. \tag{4}$$

We recall that

$$\left| \frac{dx}{ds} \right| = \left| \frac{dx}{\sqrt{(dx)^2 + (dy)^2}} \right| = \frac{1}{\sqrt{1 + y'^2}}, \tag{5}$$

where we divided numerator and denominator by dx. From (4) and (5),

$$K = \frac{|y''|}{\sqrt{(1 + y'^2)^3}}. \tag{6}$$

The following terminology is in harmony with the fact that, for a circle, the curvature is the reciprocal of the radius.

DEFINITION III. *At any point $P:(x, y)$ on a curve C, the* **radius of curvature,** *R, is defined as the reciprocal of the curvature:*

$$R = \frac{1}{K}. \tag{7}$$

R is not defined where $y'' = 0$, because then $K = 0$. From (6),

$$R = \frac{(1 + y'^2)^{\frac{3}{2}}}{|y''|}. \tag{8}$$

DEFINITION IV. *The* **circle of curvature** *at $P:(x, y)$ on C is that circle, T, through P satisfying the following conditions: T has the same tangent as C at P; the radius of T is the radius of curvature of C at P, or the curvature of T is the same as the curvature of C at P; the center of T is on the concave side of C.*

The center, Q, of the circle of curvature T at a point P on a curve C is called its **center of curvature** at P. To construct T, as in Figure 192 on page 319, draw the tangent PM and normal PN for C and locate Q on PN, on the concave side of C, so that $PQ = R$, the radius of curvature. Then T is constructed with center Q and radius R.

Note 2. In Figure 192, the circle of curvature at P crosses the given curve C at P because the rate of revolution of the tangent (or, the curvature) remains constant on the circle, but increases as we move to the right on C. In any case, the circle of curvature at a point P crosses C at P unless the curvature attains a relative maximum or minimum at P.

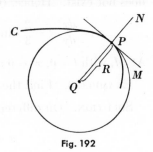

EXAMPLE 1. Compute the curvature and radius of curvature at $P:(\frac{1}{2}, \frac{1}{4})$ on the curve $y = x^2$.

Fig. 192

SOLUTION. $y' = 2x$ and $y'' = 2$. At $x = \frac{1}{2}$,

$$y' = 1; \quad y'' = 2; \quad 1 + y'^2 = 2; \quad K = \frac{2}{2\sqrt{2}}; \quad R = \sqrt{2} = 1.4.$$

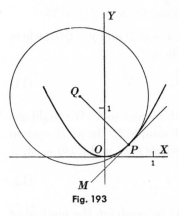

Fig. 193

In Figure 193, the tangent PM with slope 1, and the normal with slope -1, were drawn through P. Q was located so that $PQ = 1.4$, and then the circle of curvature was drawn.

If the reasoning leading to (6) and (8) were repeated with the roles of x and y interchanged, we would obtain

$$K = \frac{|x''|}{(1 + x'^2)^{\frac{3}{2}}} \quad and \quad R = \frac{(1 + x'^2)^{\frac{3}{2}}}{|x''|}, \quad (9)$$

where $\quad x' = \dfrac{dx}{dy} \quad and \quad x'' = \dfrac{d^2x}{dy^2}.$

EXAMPLE 2. Obtain the curvature of the ellipse defined by

$$x = 2 \cos t \quad and \quad y = 3 \sin t \qquad (10)$$

at the extremities of its axes.

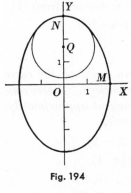

Fig. 194

SOLUTION. 1. At N in Figure 194, $t = \frac{1}{2}\pi$. We find that

$$y' = \frac{dy}{dx} = -\frac{3 \cos t}{2 \sin t} = -\frac{3}{2} \cot t;$$

$$y'' = \frac{d^2y}{dx^2} = \frac{dy'}{dx} = -\frac{3}{2} \frac{d(\cot t)}{d(2 \cos t)}$$

$$= -\frac{3}{2} \cdot \frac{\csc^2 t}{2 \sin t} = -\frac{3}{4} \csc^3 t.$$

When $t = \frac{1}{2}\pi$, $y' = 0$ and $y'' = -\frac{3}{4}$. Hence, from (6) and (8), $K = \frac{3}{4}$ and $R = \frac{4}{3}$. The circle of curvature, with center Q, is shown in the figure. Notice that the curvature attains a maximum at N, and thus the circle of curvature at N does not cross the ellipse.

2. At M in Figure 194, $t = 0$ and the tangent is vertical, so that dy/dx does not exist. Hence, (6) cannot be used. Then, we calculate

$$x' = \frac{dx}{dy} = -\frac{2}{3}\tan t; \quad x'' = \frac{d^2x}{dy^2} = \frac{dx'}{dy} = -\frac{2}{9}\cdot\frac{\sec^2 t}{\cos t} = -\frac{2}{9}\sec^3 t.$$

At M, with $t = 0$, $x' = 0$ and $x'' = -\frac{2}{9}$. From (9), $K = \frac{2}{9}$ and $R = \frac{9}{2}$.

EXAMPLE 3. Find the curvature at $(3, 2)$ on $x^2 + 4y^2 = 25$.

SOLUTION. On differentiating with respect to x, we obtain

$$x + 4y\frac{dy}{dx} = 0, \quad or \quad y' = -\frac{x}{4y};$$

$$\frac{d^2y}{dx^2} = \frac{dy'}{dx} = -\frac{1}{4}\frac{y - xy'}{y^2} = -\frac{4y^2 + x^2}{16y^3} = -\frac{25}{16y^3}.$$

At $(3, 2)$, we find $y' = -\frac{3}{8}$ and $y'' = -\frac{25}{128}$. From (6), $K = \frac{100}{5329}\sqrt{73}$.

★ Note 3. Let a regular curve C be defined by $x = \phi(t)$ and $y = \psi(t)$, where the second derivatives $\phi''(t)$ and $\psi''(t)$ exist. Then,

$$K = \frac{|x'y'' - y'x''|}{(x'^2 + y'^2)^{\frac{3}{2}}}, \tag{11}$$

where x', y', x'', and y'' represent derivatives with respect to t. We could use (11) instead of (6) or (9) in a problem such as Example 2. In an $r\theta$-system of polar coordinates, if C is defined by $r = f(\theta)$ where $f'(\theta)$ and $f''(\theta)$ exist,

$$K = \frac{|r^2 + 2r'^2 - rr''|}{(r^2 + r'^2)^{\frac{3}{2}}}, \tag{12}$$

where $r' = f'(\theta)$ and $r'' = f''(\theta)$. We obtain (11) by applying the method of Example 2 to the general curve $[x = \phi(t), y = \psi(t)]$, where at least one of $\phi'(t)$ and $\psi'(t)$ is not zero at each value of t. Then (12) is derived from (11) by writing the curve $r = f(\theta)$ in parametric form as on page 168.

EXERCISE 92

Find the curvature and radius of curvature at the given point on the curve defined by the xy-equation, or equations in terms of the parameter t. Where convenient, sketch the circle of curvature, after locating the tangent approximately. Use x instead of y as the independent variable where desirable.

1. $4y = x^2 - 4x + 4$; $(2, 0)$.   2. $xy = 4$; $(-2, -2)$.

3. $xy = 12$; $(6, 2)$.   4. $y = \sin x$; $(\frac{1}{2}\pi, 1)$.

5. $2x = y^2 - 2y + 1$; $(0, 1)$.   6. $x = y^2(2 - y)$; $(0, 0)$.

7. $y = \ln x$; $(1, 0)$.   8. $x^2 + 4y^2 = 16$; $(0, 2)$.

9. $y = \tan x$; $(\frac{1}{4}\pi, 1)$.   10. $3y = x^3$; $(3, 9)$.

11. $4x^2 + 9y^2 = 36$; $(3, 0)$ and at $(0, 2)$.

12. $4x^2 - y^2 = 16$; $(2, 0)$.   13. $4y^2 - 25x^2 = 100$; $(0, 5)$.

14. $x^2 - y^2 = 7$; $(4, 3)$.   **15.** $y = \ln \sec x$; $(\frac{1}{3}\pi, \ln 2)$.

16. $x = t^2 - 4$ and $y = 2t$; at $t = 2$.   **17.** $x = t^2$ and $y = t^3$; at $t = 1$.

18. $x = \cos t$ and $y = 2 \sin t$; at (a) $t = \frac{1}{4}\pi$; (b) $t = \frac{3}{2}\pi$.

19. $x = 2 \cos^3 t$ and $y = 2 \sin^3 t$; at $t = \frac{1}{4}\pi$.

20. $x = 2 \cos t$ and $y = \cos 2t$; at $t = \frac{1}{4}\pi$.

21. $x = 1 - \cos t$ and $y = t - \sin t$; at $t = \pi$.

22. Find the radius of curvature at each point where the following curve meets the x-axis: $y = x^4 - x^2$.

Find the point on the curve where the curvature attains a maximum. Use K^2 in the discussion, to avoid radicals.

23. $y = \ln x$.   **24.** $y = e^x$.   **25.** $y = \sin x$.

Find the curvature of the curve at the general point (x_1, y_1).

26. $y = ax^3$.   **27.** $y^2 = 2px$.   **28.** $b^2x^2 + a^2y^2 = a^2b^2$.

29. $x = a \cos^3 t$ and $y = a \sin^3 t$; at (x_1, y_1) where $t = t_1$.

30. By use of a differential, find approximately the angle through which the tangent at a point P turns as P moves a distance $\Delta s = .4$ from the point $(2, \frac{4}{3})$ on the parabola $3y = x^2$.

★*Find the curvature and radius of curvature of the given curve in an $r\theta$-system of polar coordinates, at the given point. Any constant h is positive.*

31. $r = 6 \cos \theta$; at any value of θ.   **32.** $r = h \sec \theta$; at any value of θ.

33. $r = 1 - \cos \theta$; where (a) $\theta = \pi$; (b) $\theta = \frac{1}{2}\pi$.

34. $r = h(1 + \sin \theta)$; where (a) $\theta = \frac{1}{2}\pi$; (b) $\theta = \frac{11}{6}\pi$.

35. $r^2 = 4 \cos 2\theta$; where (a) $\theta = 0$; (b) $\theta = \frac{1}{6}\pi$.

36. The parabola $r = h \sec^2 \frac{1}{2}\theta$; at (a) $\theta = 0$; (b) $\theta = \frac{1}{2}\pi$.

37. The hyperbola $r^2 = h^2 \sec 2\theta$; at (a) $\theta = 0$; (b) $\theta = \frac{1}{6}\pi$.

38. On a regular curve C in an xy-plane, let $P:(x_0, y_0)$ be a fixed point and Q be a neighboring point. Let the length of chord PQ be $\overline{PQ}$ and of arc PQ be $\widehat{PQ}$. Prove that $(\widehat{PQ}/\overline{PQ}) \to 1$ as $\overline{PQ} \to 0$.

152. Location of the center of curvature

Suppose that a curve C in an xy-plane is defined by $y = f(x)$, and that $P:(x, y)$ is a point on C at which y'' exists and is not zero. Then, we shall prove the following result.

$$\left\{ \begin{array}{l} \textit{The circle of curvature for } C \textit{ at } P \textit{ is that circle } T \textit{ through } P \\ \textit{on which } y' \textit{ and } y'' \textit{ have the same values at } P \textit{ as on the curve } C. \end{array} \right\} \quad (1)$$

Proof of (1). Suppose that T satisfies (1). Then, at P, T has the *same tangent* as C, and the *same curvature* as C because (6) on page 318 involves just y' and y''. Also, at P, the center of T is on the concave side of T, which also is the concave side for C, because y'' is the same on T and C. Hence, T satisfies Definition IV, page 318, and thus is the circle of curvature.

At any point $P:(x, y)$ on the curve C defined by $y = f(x)$, let the radius and center of curvature be R and $Q:(\alpha, \beta)$, respectively. Then, the first of the following equations is an equation for the circle of curvature, T. The next two equations are obtained by differentiating, successively, with respect to x in the equation of T.

$$(x - \alpha)^2 + (y - \beta)^2 = R^2; \tag{2}$$

$$(x - \alpha) + y'(y - \beta) = 0; \tag{3}$$

$$1 + y''(y - \beta) + y'^2 = 0. \tag{4}$$

Statement (1) shows that, corresponding to any point $P:(x, y)$ on C, we may insert in (3) and (4) the values of y' and y'' as determined from the equation $y = f(x)$ for C. Then, [(2), (3), (4)] become three equations for the unknowns R, α, and β, obtained on the basis of just (1) and (2).

EXAMPLE 1. Obtain an equation for the circle of curvature, and find the curvature, K, of the curve $xy = 2$ at the point $P:(1, 2)$.

SOLUTION. 1. $y' = -\dfrac{2}{x^2}$; $y'' = \dfrac{4}{x^3}$; at $x = 1$, $y = 2$, $y' = -2$, and $y'' = 4$.

2. From (2), (3), and (4) with the values above,

$$\begin{cases} (1 - \alpha)^2 + (2 - \beta)^2 = R^2; & \tag{5} \\ (1 - \alpha) - 2(2 - \beta) = 0; & \tag{6} \\ 1 + 4(2 - \beta) + 4 = 0. & \tag{7} \end{cases}$$

By use of (7), $\beta = \frac{13}{4}$. Then (6) gives $\alpha = \frac{7}{2}$. Then (5) gives $R^2 = \frac{125}{16}$, or $R = \frac{5}{4}\sqrt{5}$. From (2), the circle of curvature is

$$(x - \tfrac{7}{2})^2 + (y - \tfrac{13}{4})^2 = \tfrac{125}{16}.$$

3. Since $K = 1/R$, we have $K = \frac{4}{25}\sqrt{5} = .36$ radians per unit distance.

Note 1. Suppose that y'' does not exist at a point P on C, which is the case where the tangent is vertical. Then, in place of (3) and (4) we use equations obtained from (2) on differentiating twice with respect to y.

EXAMPLE 2. Obtain the circle of curvature of the ellipse $x = 2 \cos t$ and $y = 3 \sin t$, at an extremity of the minor axis.

SOLUTION. 1. We desire the circle of curvature at $M:(2, 0)$ where $t = 0$, in Figure 194 on page 319. The tangent is vertical at M. Hence, we start from (2) and differentiate twice with respect to y:

$$\begin{cases} (x - \alpha)^2 + (y - \beta)^2 = R^2; & \tag{8} \\ (x - \alpha)\dfrac{dx}{dy} + (y - \beta) = 0; & \tag{9} \\ \left(\dfrac{dx}{dy}\right)^2 + (x - \alpha)\dfrac{d^2x}{dy^2} + 1 = 0. & \tag{10} \end{cases}$$

2. From $x = 2 \cos t$ and $y = 3 \sin t$,

$$x' = \frac{dx}{dy} = -\frac{2}{3} \tan t; \quad x'' = \frac{d^2x}{dy^2} = \frac{dx'}{dy} = -\frac{2}{3} \cdot \frac{\sec^2 t}{3 \cos t} = -\frac{2}{9} \sec^3 t.$$

At $t = 0$, $x' = 0$ and $x'' = -\frac{2}{9}$. Then, on substituting $x = 2$, $y = 0$, $x' = 0$, and $x'' = -\frac{2}{9}$ in [(8), (9), (10)], we obtain a system whose solution is found to be $\alpha = -\frac{5}{2}$, $\beta = 0$, and $R^2 = \frac{81}{4}$. The circle of curvature has the equation $(x + \frac{5}{2})^2 + y^2 = \frac{81}{4}$.

153. Evolutes and involutes

At any point $P:(x, y)$ on a curve C where y has the derivatives y' and y'' with respect to x, (3) and (4) of the preceding section form a system of two equations for the unknowns α and β. Then, we solve (4) for β and use (3) to obtain α, with the following results:

$$\alpha = x - \frac{y'(1 + y'^2)}{y''}; \quad \beta = y + \frac{1 + y'^2}{y''}. \tag{1}$$

ILLUSTRATION 1. In Example 1 on page 322, with $x = 1$, $y = 2$, $y' = -2$, and $y'' = 4$, from (1) we obtain $\alpha = \frac{7}{2}$ and $\beta = \frac{13}{4}$.

For every point $P:(x, y)$ on a curve C where (1) applies, we obtain a center of curvature $Q:(\alpha, \beta)$. If a moving point P traces out C, then Q traces out a corresponding curve, described as follows.

DEFINITION V. *The **evolute**, E, of a given curve C is the locus of the centers of curvature $Q:(\alpha, \beta)$ for all points of C.*

If C is defined by parametric equations $x = \phi(t)$ and $y = \psi(t)$, (1) gives *parametric equations*, in terms of the parameter t, for the rectangular coordinates (α, β) of the general point on the evolute. If C is defined by an equation $y = f(x)$, then (1) gives parametric equations for the evolute in terms of x as a parameter. Elimination of the parameter, t or x, between equations (1) would give an $\alpha\beta$-equation for the evolute, where the former x-axis becomes the α-axis and the y-axis becomes the β-axis.

ILLUSTRATION 2. In Figure 195, the evolute of the ellipse is the curve with four cusps, as obtained in the next example. In Figure 195, centers of curvature Q_1, Q_2, etc. are shown for P_1, P_2, etc., respectively, on the ellipse. The lines P_iQ_i are normals to the ellipse; $\overline{P_iQ_i}$ is the radius of curvature at P_i on the ellipse. Notice that P_iQ_i is tangent to the evolute.

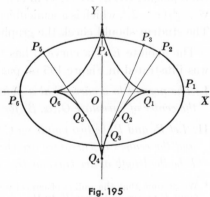

Fig. 195

EXAMPLE 1. Obtain the evolute of the ellipse

$$x = a \cos t \quad and \quad y = b \sin t, \quad where \quad a > 0 \quad and \quad b > 0. \tag{2}$$

SOLUTION. 1. From (2), and from (1),

$$y' = \frac{dy}{dx} = -\frac{b}{a} \cot t; \quad y'' = \frac{d^2y}{dx^2} = -\frac{b}{a^2} \csc^3 t; \tag{3}$$

$$\alpha = \frac{a^2 - b^2}{a} \cos^3 t; \quad \beta = \frac{b^2 - a^2}{b} \sin^3 t. \tag{4}$$

2. To eliminate t from the parametric equations for the evolute in (4), solve for $\sin t$ and $\cos t$, square the results, and add:

$$\alpha^{\frac{2}{3}} \left(\frac{a}{a^2 - b^2} \right)^{\frac{2}{3}} + \beta^{\frac{2}{3}} \left(\frac{b}{a^2 - b^2} \right)^{\frac{2}{3}} = 1, \quad or \quad a^{\frac{2}{3}}\alpha^{\frac{2}{3}} + b^{\frac{2}{3}}\beta^{\frac{2}{3}} = (a^2 - b^2)^{\frac{2}{3}}.$$

Finally, we may replace (α, β) by (x, y) to obtain

$$(ax)^{\frac{2}{3}} + (by)^{\frac{2}{3}} = (a^2 - b^2)^{\frac{2}{3}} \tag{5}$$

as the equation of the evolute in the given xy-system of coordinates. The graph of (5) is the curve with 4 cusps in Figure 195 on page 323.

EXAMPLE 2. Find the evolute of the parabola $y^2 = 4x$.

SOLUTION. 1. $\quad\quad y' = \frac{2}{y}; \quad y'' = -\frac{4}{y^3}; \quad 1 + y'^2 = 1 + \frac{4}{y^2} = \frac{x+1}{x}.$

From (1), $\quad\quad\quad\quad\quad\quad \alpha = 3x + 2; \quad \beta = -\frac{y^3}{4}. \tag{6}$

With $y^2 = 4x$, (6) gives parametric equations for the evolute, where x is the parameter.

2. In (6), solve for x and y and substitute in $y^2 = 4x$:

$$x = \tfrac{1}{3}(\alpha - 2) \quad and \quad y = -(4\beta)^{\frac{1}{3}}, \quad or \quad y^2 = (4\beta)^{\frac{2}{3}}.$$

From $y^2 = 4x$, $\quad\quad (4\beta)^{\frac{2}{3}} = \tfrac{4}{3}(\alpha - 2), \quad or \quad 16\beta^2 = [\tfrac{4}{3}(\alpha - 2)]^3; \quad or,$

$$\beta^2 = \tfrac{4}{27}(\alpha - 2)^3. \tag{7}$$

On replacing (α, β) by (x, y) in (7), we obtain the xy-equation of the evolute, $y^2 = \tfrac{4}{27}(x - 2)^3$, which is a semicubical parabola with its cusp at $(x = 2, y = 0)$. The student should check the graphs of $y^2 = 4x$ and $y^2 = \tfrac{4}{27}(x - 2)^3$.

The evolute E of a curve C has the following characteristics; Property I was illustrated in Figure 195 on page 323.

I. *The normal to a curve C at a point $P:(x, y)$ is tangent to the evolute of C at the center of curvature $Q:(\alpha, \beta)$ for P.*

II. *Let P_1 and P_2 be two points on C where the radii of curvature are R_1 and R_2, and the centers of curvature are $Q_1:(\alpha_1, \beta_1)$ and $Q_2:(\alpha_2, \beta_2)$, respectively. Let L be the length of arc Q_1Q_2 on E. Then,* $L = | R_1 - R_2 |.$

---

* We assume that the radius of curvature on C continually increases (or, decreases) as a point P moves on C from P_1 to P_2.

Proof of (I). Let C be defined by $y = f(x)$. Then, (1) specifies parametric equations for the evolute with x as the parameter. From (1),

$$\frac{d\alpha}{dx} = \frac{y'(1+y'^2)y''' - 3y'^2y''^2}{y''^2}; \quad \frac{d\beta}{dx} = \frac{3y'y''^2 - (1+y'^2)y'''}{y''^2}. \tag{8}$$

Let $Q:(\alpha, \beta)$ be the center of curvature on E corresponding to $P:(x, y)$ on C. Then, PQ is the normal to C at P, and the slope of PQ is $-1/y'$. From (8), the slope of the tangent to E at Q simplifies to give

$$\frac{d\beta}{d\alpha} = \frac{d\beta}{dx} \Big/ \frac{d\alpha}{dx} = -\frac{1}{y'}. \tag{9}$$

Hence, the tangent to E at Q has the same slope as PQ, or PQ is tangent to E at Q, as we wished to prove.

Note 1. The student may desire to prove (II) by showing that, if σ represents arc distance on the evolute of a curve $y = f(x)$, $|d\sigma/dx| = |dR/dx|$.

ILLUSTRATION 3. In Figure 196, E is the evolute of C, where the radius of curvature increases if we move to the right on C. Conceive of a string anchored at S on E, then stretched tightly on E up to a point Q_1, and then extended along the tangent to E, up to P_1 on C. By (I) and (II), if the string is unwound and remains tangent to E, the free end traces out C. From Q_1 to Q_2, the increase in free length $(P_2Q_2 - P_1Q_1)$ is the length of arc Q_1Q_2 on E. Suppose, now, that A is any point on the segment P_1Q_1, or its extension through P_1. Then, as the string is unwound from E, A would trace out a curve which also has E as its evolute. Figure 196 shows two other curves C' and C'' obtained in this way, with E as their evolute.

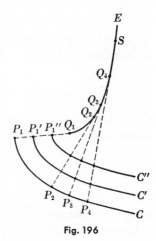

E

S

Q_4

Q_3
Q_2

$P_1\ P_1'\ P_1''\ Q_1$

C''

P_2

$P_3\ \ P_4$

C'

C

Fig. 196

If a curve C has E as its evolute, we call C an **involute** of E. Then, from Illustration 3, we observe that there are infinitely many involutes for any given curve E which is known to be an evolute of some curve. In particular, Figure 196 shows three involutes of the given curve E.

EXERCISE 93

Find the center and radius of curvature, and the curvature for the curve at the given point, and write an equation for the circle of curvature. Solve on the basis of (1) and (2) in Section 152.

1–21. Problems 1–21, respectively, in Exercise 92 on page 320.

Obtain parametric equations, or an equation for the evolute of the curve.

22. $x^2 = y$.   23. $y^2 = 6x$.   24. $y^2 = 2px$.

25. $x = 3 \cos t$ and $y = 2 \sin t$.   **26.** $4x^2 + 9y^2 = 36$.

27. $x = a \cos^3 t$ and $y = a \sin^3 t$.   **28.** $y = 2x^3$.

29. $x = 8t$ and $y = 4/t$.   **30.** $x = 2t$ and $y = t^2 + 2$.

31. $x = a \sec t$ and $y = b \tan t$.   **32.** $x = 3 \csc t$ and $y = 2 \cot t$.

33. $x = a(\cos t + t \sin t)$ and $y = a(\sin t - t \cos t)$.   (Involute of a circle.)

34. $x = a(\theta - \sin \theta)$ and $y = a(1 - \cos \theta)$.

35. $b^2x^2 + a^2y^2 = a^2b^2$.   **36.** $b^2x^2 - a^2y^2 = a^2b^2$.

37. $x^{\frac{2}{3}} + y^{\frac{2}{3}} = a^{\frac{2}{3}}$.   **38.** $2xy = a^2$.

★154. The velocity and acceleration vectors in curvilinear motion

Let the motion of a particle M on a path C in an xy-plane be defined by specifying the coordinates of M as functions of the time t:

$$x = \phi(t) \quad and \quad y = \psi(t), \tag{1}$$

where we assume that $\phi(t)$ and $\psi(t)$ have continuous second derivatives. At any instant t, there are the time-rates of change

$$v_x = \frac{dx}{dt}, \quad v_y = \frac{dy}{dt}, \quad a_x = \frac{d^2x}{dt^2} = \frac{dv_x}{dt}, \quad a_y = \frac{d^2y}{dt^2} = \frac{dv_y}{dt}. \tag{2}$$

On page 115, the velocity, V, of M at any instant t was defined as *the resultant of the velocities V_x and V_y*. The *scalar components* of V_x and V_y are dx/dt and dy/dt, respectively. The *speed*, v, of M at any instant was defined as *the magnitude of V*:

$$v = \sqrt{\left(\frac{dx}{dt}\right)^2 + \left(\frac{dy}{dt}\right)^2}. \tag{3}$$

If s indicates arc distance measured on the path C from a given point, in a direction where t increases, then (3) shows that

$$v = \frac{ds}{dt}. \tag{4}$$

That is, the speed, or the magnitude of the velocity vector, can be described as the time-rate of change of distance measured along the path.

Assume, now, that $v \neq 0$ at any point. Then, (1) defines a regular path C, as described on page 316. Suppose that the moving particle M is at P where $s = s_0$ when $t = t_0$, and at Q where $s = s_0 + \Delta s$ when $t = t_0 + \Delta t$, with $\Delta t > 0$. In Figure 197 on page 327, consider PQ as a directed line segment, with the direction *from P to Q*. Let α' be an angle from the positive x-direction at P to the direction PQ. Let ΔG be the length of PQ. Then,

$$\cos \alpha' = \frac{\Delta x}{\Delta G} = \frac{\Delta x}{\sqrt{(\Delta x)^2 + (\Delta y)^2}} = \left[\frac{\Delta x}{\Delta s} \div \sqrt{\left(\frac{\Delta x}{\Delta s}\right)^2 + \left(\frac{\Delta y}{\Delta s}\right)^2}\right]. \tag{5}$$

If $\Delta s \to 0$, then $\Delta x/\Delta s$ and $\Delta y/\Delta s$ approach the limits dx/ds and dy/ds, respectively, and the radical at the right in (5) approaches the limit 1, because of (9) on page 317. Hence,

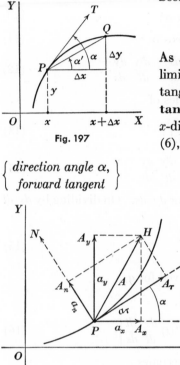

Fig. 197

$$\lim_{\Delta s \to 0} \cos \alpha' = \frac{dx}{ds}. \qquad (6)$$

As $\Delta s \to 0$, the directed segment PQ tends to a limiting position, which falls on a ray PT of the tangent to C at P. We call this ray the **forward tangent** at P. If α is an angle from the positive x-direction to PT, we obtain $\cos \alpha$ as the limit in (6), and $\sin \alpha$ similarly:

$\left\{ \begin{array}{l} \textit{direction angle } \alpha, \\ \textit{forward tangent} \end{array} \right\}$

$$\cos \alpha = \frac{dx}{ds}; \qquad \sin \alpha = \frac{dy}{ds}. \qquad (7)$$

At any point P on the path (1), as in Figure 198, let A_x and A_y be defined as vectors along the x-axis and y-axis with the scalar components a_x and a_y of (2), respectively. Then, at P, define the acceleration vector A as the resultant of the accelerations A_x and A_y in the directions of the axes, as in Figure 198. The magnitude, a, of A is given by

$$a = \sqrt{a_x^2 + a_y^2}. \qquad (8)$$

Fig. 198

At P, let A also be resolved into components A_r and A_n along the tangent and normal, respectively, as in Figure 198. Let a_r be the magnitude of A_r and a_n the magnitude of A_n. Then, we shall prove that

$$a_r = \left| \frac{d^2 s}{dt^2} \right| \quad and \quad a_n = \frac{v^2}{R}, \qquad (9)$$

where v is the speed at P and R is the radius of curvature of the path at P.

Proof of (9), *for* a_r. 1. In Figure 198, at any point P on the path, establish a *local system* of rectangular coordinates with the same directions for the axes as in the xy-system. Then, the local coordinates for point H on A are (a_x, a_y). Now, consider a *second local system* of coordinates at P obtained by revolving the first local axes about P through the angle α as described previously for the forward tangent PT. For convenience, assume that the normal ray PN, directed to the concave side of the path at P, is obtained by revolving PT through $\frac{1}{2}\pi$ radians counterclockwise, so that PT and PN are oriented like the x-axis and y-axis, respectively, in a usual xy-system of coordinates. Let the coordinates of H with axes PT and PN be (b_r, b_n).

2. From equations (5) and (6) on page 562 for transformation of co-ordinates by rotation,

$$b_\tau = a_x \cos \alpha + a_y \sin \alpha; \tag{10}$$

$$b_n = - a_x \sin \alpha + a_y \cos \alpha. \tag{11}$$

From (2), (7), and (10) $\qquad\qquad b_\tau = \frac{d^2x}{dt^2} \cdot \frac{dx}{ds} + \frac{d^2y}{dt^2} \cdot \frac{dy}{ds}. \tag{12}$

By differentiating with respect to t on both sides of

$$\left(\frac{ds}{dt}\right)^2 = \left(\frac{dx}{dt}\right)^2 + \left(\frac{dy}{dt}\right)^2, \tag{13}$$

we obtain $\qquad\qquad \frac{ds}{dt} \cdot \frac{d^2s}{dt^2} = \frac{d^2x}{dt^2} \cdot \frac{dx}{dt} + \frac{d^2y}{dt^2} \cdot \frac{dy}{dt}. \tag{14}$

Recall $dx/ds = (dx/dt)/(ds/dt)$, and similarly for dy/ds. On dividing by ds/dt in (14), from (12) we find that

$$b_\tau = \frac{d^2s}{dt^2}. \tag{15}$$

We notice that $|\, b_\tau\,| = a_\tau$. Hence, (9) has proved for a_τ.

Proof of (9), *for* a_n. From (11), (7), and (2),

$$|\, b_n\,| = \left|- \phi''(t)\, \frac{dy}{dt} \cdot \frac{dt}{ds} + \psi''(t)\, \frac{dx}{dt} \cdot \frac{dt}{ds}\right|. \tag{16}$$

Hence, from (11) on page 320 and (13), (16) becomes

$$|\, b_n\,| = K\{[\phi'(t)]^2 + [\psi'(t)]^2\}^{\frac{3}{2}}\{[\phi'(t)]^2 + [\psi'(t)]^2\}^{-\frac{1}{2}} = \frac{1}{R}\left(\frac{ds}{dt}\right)^2 = \frac{v^2}{R},$$

where K is the curvature and R is the radius of curvature at P.

Note 1. The normal component of the acceleration is intimately con-nected with the concept of *centrifugal force* as met in physics.

★ EXERCISE 94

In Problems 1 and 2, θ is a parameter.

1. A particle P moves with constant speed on the circle $x = 25 \cos \theta$ and $y = 25 \sin \theta$. (a) Prove that the magnitude of the acceleration is a con-stant. (b) Is the velocity a constant?

2. A particle P moves with constant speed on the ellipse $x = 12 \cos \theta$ and $y = 16 \sin \theta$. Find the points on the path where the magnitude of the acceleration attains its absolute (a) maximum; (b) minimum. Also, ob-tain the maximum and minimum just mentioned, in terms of v.

3. A particle P moves with a constant speed of 4 units per second upward from below the x-axis on the parabola $y^2 = 2x$. Find the magnitude of the acceleration at the point where this magnitude attains its maximum.

17

SOLID ANALYTIC GEOMETRY

155. Rectangular coordinates in three dimensions

To define rectangular coordinates in space of three dimensions, first specify a unit for distance. Then, through a fixed point O, called the *origin*, construct three mutually perpendicular directed lines OX, OY, and OZ, and call them the x-axis, y-axis, and z-axis, respectively. On each axis, let distance be measured from O as the zero point. These axes determine three mutually perpendicular *coordinate planes*, the xy-plane OXY, xz-plane OXZ, and yz-plane OYZ. Think of the yz-plane as vertical, facing us, with the positive direction on OX projecting toward us,* as in Figure 199, so that the xy-plane is horizontal. We agree that any line segment or distance parallel to a coordinate axis will be *directed*, with the same positive direction as on the axis. Then, the coordinates (x, y, z) of a point P are defined as the *directed distances* of P from the yz-plane, xz-plane, and xy-plane, respectively. To construct Figure 199, draw OX with $\angle XOY$ about 135°. On OX, take a foreshortened unit of length, about $\frac{2}{3}$ of the actual unit on OY. Then, locate $P:(x, y, z)$ by drawing $OA = x$, $AR = y$, $RP = z$, where AR and RP are parallel to OY and OZ, respectively. We call OP the **radius vector** of P.

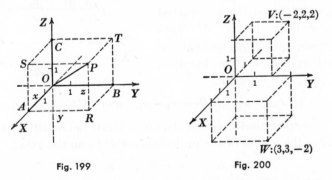

Fig. 199　　　　　　　　Fig. 200

* This gives a **right-handed system,** in harmony with custom in applications. A right-handed screw with its head at O and screw point on the positive part of OZ would advance along OZ if rotated from OX to OY.

ILLUSTRATION 1. Figure 200, page 329, shows W:$(3, 3, -2)$; V:$(-2, 2, 2)$.

The **projection** * of a point P on a line L is defined as the point where a plane (or line) through P perpendicular to L meets L.
The projection of a line segment PQ on L is the segment $P'Q'$ joining the projections of P and Q on L, as in Figure 201.

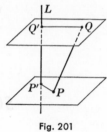

ILLUSTRATION 2. In Figure 199, page 329, A, B, and C are the projections of P on the axes. The coordinates x, y, and z of P are the values of the directed line segments OA, OB, and OC, respectively, which are the projections of the radius vector OP on the axes.

Fig. 201

The coordinate planes divide space into eight **octants.** The *visible octant*, where all coordinates are positive, is called the *first octant.*

Note 1. It can be proved † that the agreements for Figure 199, page 329, are equivalent to projecting all points of space onto the yz-plane by a family of parallel lines. This method is called **parallel projection.** Configurations in any plane parallel to the yz-plane are undistorted by parallel projection. Any line in space is represented by a line on the figure. Lines parallel in space become parallel lines in a figure.

156. The distance formula

Through each of two given points P_1:(x_1, y_1, z_1) and P_2:(x_2, y_2, z_2), as in Figure 202, pass a plane parallel to each coordinate plane. The planes intersect to form a rectangular parallelepiped with P_1P_2 as a diagonal and each edge parallel to a coordinate axis. We shall call this parallelepiped the **associated box** for P_1 and P_2. Figure 202 shows the projections A_1A_2, B_1B_2, and C_1C_2 of the directed segment P_1P_2 on the axes. Since $OA_1 = x_1$, $OA_2 = x_2$, etc.,

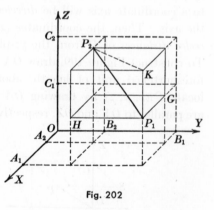

Fig. 202

$$A_1A_2 = x_2 - x_1, \quad B_1B_2 = y_2 - y_1, \quad and \quad C_1C_2 = z_2 - z_1.$$

On the box, observe that $P_1G = A_1A_2$, etc. Thus, the dimensions (positive) of the box are the *lengths* of the projections of P_1P_2 on the axes:

$$| x_2 - x_1 |, \quad | y_2 - y_1 |, \quad | z_2 - z_1 |. \tag{1}$$

* Understood to imply *perpendicular* projection unless otherwise stated.
† See page 243, *Elements of Analytic Geometry*, by *William L. Hart;* D. C. Heath and Company, publishers.

Hence, if d represents the length of the diagonal of the box, or the distance between P_1 and P_2, we obtain

$$d = \sqrt{(x_2 - x_1)^2 + (y_2 - y_1)^2 + (z_2 - z_1)^2}. \tag{2}$$

ILLUSTRATION 1. The distance between $(1, 1, -3)$ and $(-1, -2, 1)$ is

$$d = \sqrt{(-2)^2 + (-3)^2 + 4^2} = \sqrt{29}.$$

The length, ρ, of the radius vector OP in Figure 199, page 329, is

$$\rho = \sqrt{x^2 + y^2 + z^2}.$$

EXERCISE 95

Plot the point and find the length of its radius vector.

1. $(3, -2, 4)$.   **2.** $(2, 3, -2)$.   **3.** $(-2, -1, 4)$.   **4.** $(-1, 2, -3)$.

Compute the distance between the points.

5. $(0, 0, 0)$; $(2, 4, 3)$.   **6.** $(0, 0, 0)$; $(3, 5, -1)$.
7. $(-1, 2, 3)$; $(-3, 4, 4)$.   **8.** $(-1, 2, 0)$; $(2, 4, 2)$.
9. $(1, -2, -1)$; $(3, 1, -2)$.   **10.** $(-1, 2, 1)$; $(-1, -2, 3)$.

157. The angle made by two directions or two lines

Let S and T be two directions in space, and represent them by rays, or directed half-lines, PS and PT in Figure 203, with a common initial point P. Then, *the angle made by the directions S and T* is defined as the smallest angle θ, positive or zero, which has PS and PT as sides. Thus, $0° \leq \theta \leq 180°$. If S_1 is the direction opposite to S, the angle θ_1, made by S_1 and T, is the supplement of θ, or $\theta_1 = 180° - \theta$, as in Figure 203.

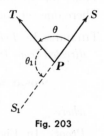

Fig. 203

If L and M are directed lines, the angle *made by L and M*, or *between L and M*, is defined as the angle θ made by their positive directions. If L and M intersect at P, θ is the angle between the positive rays of L and M. If L and M are skew lines, that is, if they do not intersect, first construct intersecting lines L' and M' with the same directions as L and M, respectively; then, the angle between L and M is the angle θ made by L' and M'. If the direction of L (or of M) is reversed, the angle formed by the new directions is $(180° - \theta)$, as observed in Figure 203.

ILLUSTRATION 1. Two directed lines L and M are parallel if and only if the angle θ between them is $0°$ or $180°$ where $\theta = 0°$ when L and M have the same direction, and $\theta = 180°$ when the directions are opposite.

Unless otherwise stated, if we refer to the angle made by two *undirected* lines L and M, we shall mean an angle θ where $0° \leq \theta \leq 90°$, which is made by properly selected positive directions on L and M.

158. The direction cosines of a directed line

If L is a directed line, the **direction angles** α, β, and γ of L are defined as the angles made by L with the x-axis, y-axis, and z-axis, respectively, as shown in Figure 204 where lines PX', PY', and PZ' parallel to the axes are drawn through P on L. We call $\cos \alpha$, $\cos \beta$, and $\cos \gamma$ the **direction cosines** of L. If the direction cosines are given, there exists just one corresponding set of direction angles, because there is just one angle between $0°$ and $180°$, inclusive, with a given cosine.

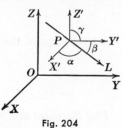

Fig. 204

ILLUSTRATION 1. The direction angles of OX are $\alpha = 0°$, $\beta = 90°$, and $\gamma = 90°$, where $\cos \alpha = 1$, $\cos \beta = 0$, and $\cos \gamma = 0$.

If L is an undirected line, first we may designate either direction on L as positive and obtain direction angles α, β, γ for L. If we reverse the direction on L, and obtain direction angles α', β', γ', then

$$\alpha' = 180° - \alpha, \quad \beta' = 180° - \beta, \quad \gamma' = 180° - \gamma;$$
$$\cos \alpha' = -\cos \alpha, \quad \cos \beta' = -\cos \beta, \quad \cos \gamma' = -\cos \gamma.$$

Thus, for an *undirected* line L, the direction cosines are either of *two sets*, where one set consists of the negatives of the other set.

THEOREM I. *Let $P_1:(x_1, y_1, z_1)$ and $P_2:(x_2, y_2, z_2)$ be distinct points on a line L directed from P_1 to P_2. Then, the direction cosines of L are*

$$\cos \alpha = \frac{x_2 - x_1}{d}, \quad \cos \beta = \frac{y_2 - y_1}{d}, \quad \cos \gamma = \frac{z_2 - z_1}{d}, \qquad (1)$$

where $d = \sqrt{(x_2 - x_1)^2 + (y_2 - y_1)^2 + (z_2 - z_1)^2}.$

Proof. In Figure 205, $P_1G = x_2 - x_1$, $P_1H = y_2 - y_1$, and $P_1K = z_2 - z_1$. Triangle P_1KP_2 from Figure 205 is drawn as Figure 206, where we observe

$$\cos \gamma = \frac{z_2 - z_1}{d}; \quad similarly, \quad \cos \alpha = \frac{x_2 - x_1}{d}; \quad \cos \beta = \frac{y_2 - y_1}{d}.$$

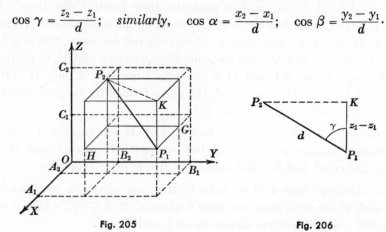

Fig. 205   Fig. 206

THEOREM II. *For any line,*

$$\cos^2 \alpha + \cos^2 \beta + \cos^2 \gamma = 1. \tag{2}$$

Proof. Square and add corresponding sides in (1) to obtain

$$\cos^2 \alpha + \cos^2 \beta + \cos^2 \gamma = \frac{(x_2 - x_1)^2 + (y_2 - y_1)^2 + (z_2 - z_1)^2}{d^2} = 1.$$

ILLUSTRATION 2. To find the direction cosines of the direction from $(3, 2, -6)$ to $(1, -2, 4)$, use (1) with $P_1:(3, 2, -6)$ and $P_2:(1, -2, 4)$:

$$\cos \alpha = -\frac{1}{\sqrt{30}}, \quad \cos \beta = -\frac{2}{\sqrt{30}}, \quad \cos \gamma = \frac{5}{\sqrt{30}}. \tag{3}$$

From (1) with P_1 as $(0, 0, 0)$ and P_2 as $P:(x, y, z)$, we obtain the direction cosines of the *radius vector OP*:

$$\cos \alpha = \frac{x}{\rho}, \quad \cos \beta = \frac{y}{\rho}, \quad \cos \gamma = \frac{z}{\rho}, \tag{4}$$

where

$$\rho = \sqrt{x^2 + y^2 + z^2}. \tag{5}$$

EXAMPLE 1. Obtain $\cos \beta$ and β if $\alpha = 45°$ and $\gamma = 120°$.

SOLUTION. $\cos \alpha = \frac{1}{2}\sqrt{2}$; $\cos \gamma = -\frac{1}{2}$. Hence, from (2),

$$\cos^2 \beta = 1 - \tfrac{1}{2} - \tfrac{1}{4} = \tfrac{1}{4}; \quad \cos \beta = \pm \tfrac{1}{2}; \quad \beta = 60° \quad or \quad \beta = 120°.$$

Let the ordered triad λ, μ, ν represent a set of direction cosines:

$$\lambda = \cos \alpha, \quad \mu = \cos \beta, \quad \nu = \cos \gamma.$$

Then,

$$\lambda^2 + \mu^2 + \nu^2 = 1. \tag{6}$$

For brevity, we may refer to *"the direction λ, μ, ν."* The direction $-\lambda$, $-\mu$, $-\nu$ is opposite to the direction λ, μ, ν. Any three numbers λ, μ, ν which satisfy (6) can be taken as direction cosines.

EXERCISE 96

Find the direction cosines of the radius vector for the point.

1. $(2, -2, 1)$.   2. $(-2, 1, 2)$.   3. $(9, 6, -2)$.

4. $(14, -2, 5)$.   5. $(-3, 0, 0)$.   6. $(3, -4, 0)$.

Obtain the direction cosines of the direction from the first point to the second.

7. $(-1, 2, 3)$; $(1, 4, 2)$.   8. $(3, -2, 5)$; $(4, -4, 7)$.

9. $(-2, 3, 0)$; $(1, 1, -6)$.   10. $(2, -4, -7)$; $(-4, -2, 2)$.

11. $(-4, 6, -3)$; $(4, -6, 6)$.   12. $(-3, 9, 0)$; $(2, -5, 2)$.

13. Find the direction angles and the direction cosines of the y-axis; z-axis; the negative direction on the x-axis.

Obtain the missing direction angle and all the direction cosines.

14. $\beta = 45°$; $\gamma = 45°$.   15. $\alpha = 60°$; $\gamma = 135°$.

159. Direction numbers for a line

The statement "*a, b, c are proportional to r, s, t*," or

$$a : b : c = r : s : t,$$

means that there exists a constant of proportionality $k \neq 0$ so that

$$a = kr, \quad b = ks, \quad c = kt. \tag{1}$$

Whenever the denominators below are not zero, (1) is equivalent to

$$\frac{a}{r} = \frac{b}{s} = \frac{c}{t}. \tag{2}$$

We agree that (2) abbreviates (1) *even when zero appears as a denominator in* (2). Then, any denominator in (2) is zero if and only if the corresponding numerator is zero, because of (1).*

ILLUSTRATION 1. If $a : b : c = \frac{2}{3} : -\frac{1}{2} : \frac{5}{6}$, we may simplify by multiplying by 6 on the right. Then, $a : b : c = 4 : -3 : 5$.

If a, b, c are proportional to $\cos \alpha, \cos \beta, \cos \gamma$ for a line L, we call a, b, c *direction numbers* (or, *direction ratios*) for L. Then

$$a : b : c = \cos \alpha : \cos \beta : \cos \gamma, \tag{3}$$

and there exists a constant of proportionality $k \neq 0$ so that

$$\cos \alpha = ka, \quad \cos \beta = kb, \quad \cos \gamma = kc. \tag{4}$$

To emphasize that an ordered triad a, b, c gives direction numbers, we shall write them "$a : b : c$" as in (3), but read them merely "a, b, c."

THEOREM III. *If $a : b : c$ are direction numbers for a line, then*

$$\left. \cos \alpha = \frac{a}{\pm \sqrt{a^2 + b^2 + c^2}}, \quad \cos \beta = \frac{b}{\pm \sqrt{a^2 + b^2 + c^2}}, \right\}$$
$$\left. \cos \gamma = \frac{c}{\pm \sqrt{a^2 + b^2 + c^2}}, \right\} \tag{5}$$

where "+" is used throughout, or "−" throughout.

Proof. From (4),

$$\cos^2 \alpha + \cos^2 \beta + \cos^2 \gamma = 1 = k^2(a^2 + b^2 + c^2). \tag{6}$$

Hence, $k = 1/\pm \sqrt{a^2 + b^2 + c^2}$. If we use the *plus* sign, we obtain *one set* of cosines in (5), and *one direction* for the line; we obtain the cosines for the *opposite direction* if the *minus* sign is used.

ILLUSTRATION 2. If the direction numbers are $3 : -2 : 1$,

$$\cos \alpha = \frac{3}{\pm \sqrt{14}}, \quad \cos \beta = -\frac{2}{\pm \sqrt{14}}, \quad \cos \gamma = \frac{1}{\pm \sqrt{14}}.$$

* No division by zero is implied. Hence, no algebraic rule is being violated.

From (5), *any* numbers a, b, c, *not all zero*, may be taken as direction numbers. One set of direction numbers for a line is its *direction cosines*. For them, the radical in (5) is equal to 1.

THEOREM IV. *A set of direction numbers for the line through two distinct points P_1:(x_1, y_1, z_1) and P_2:(x_2, y_2, z_2) is*

$$(x_2 - x_1) : (y_2 - y_1) : (z_2 - z_1). \tag{7}$$

Proof. If $d = | P_1P_2 |$, from (1) on page 332 we obtain

$$d \cos \alpha = x_2 - x_1, \quad d \cos \beta = y_2 - y_1, \quad d \cos \gamma = z_2 - z_1.$$

Hence, (4) is true for the numbers (7), if $k = 1/d$.

ILLUSTRATION 3. The line L through $(2, -3, 4)$ and $(-1, 2, -2)$ has the direction $(-1-2) : (2+3) : (-2-4)$, or $-3 : 5 : -6$.

From (7) with P_1 as $(0, 0, 0)$ and P_2 as P:(x, y, z), a set of direction numbers for the radius vector OP are $x : y : z$. Hence, *to construct a line with direction numbers $a : b : c$, plot P:(a, b, c) and draw OP.*

ILLUSTRATION 4. If $\frac{2}{3} : -\frac{5}{6} : -\frac{1}{2}$ are direction numbers, we may multiply them by 6, and obtain the convenient set $4 : -5 : -3$.

THEOREM V. *If direction numbers for a line l_1 are $a_1 : b_1 : c_1$, and for l_2 are $a_2 : b_2 : c_2$, then l_1 and l_2 are parallel if and only if*

$$a_1 : b_1 : c_1 = a_2 : b_2 : c_2. \tag{8}$$

Proof. 1. If l_1 and l_2 are parallel, their direction cosines are *the same*, or those for l_1 are *the negatives of those for l_2*. Hence, the cosines of l_1 and l_2 are proportional, or (8) is true.

2. If (8) is true, then $a_1 : b_1 : c_1$ are direction numbers for *both* l_1 and l_2. Hence, with (5) used for $a_1 : b_1 : c_1$, we obtain the cosines for both l_1 and l_2. Thus, l_1 and l_2 have the same direction or opposite directions, or are parallel.

ILLUSTRATION 5. The directions $2 : -3 : 5$ and $-4 : 6 : -10$ are parallel.

EXERCISE 97

Plot a line having the given direction, and find its direction cosines.

1. $3 : 2 : -6$.   **2.** $-\frac{2}{5} : \frac{2}{5} : -\frac{1}{5}$.   **3.** $6 : -9 : -2$.

4. $\frac{8}{7} : -\frac{12}{7} : \frac{9}{7}$.   **5.** $-\frac{5}{2} : \frac{11}{4} : -\frac{1}{2}$.   **6.** $4 : -3 : 0$.

Obtain direction numbers for the line through the points.

7. $(2, -3, 2)$; $(-1, 2, -4)$.   **8.** $(-1, 2, -3)$; $(-4, 2, -5)$.

9. $(0, 0, 0)$; $(3, -2, 4)$.   **10.** $(-3, 0, -2)$; $(0, 0, 0)$.

11. $(-3, 1, -2)$; $(-5, 4, 7)$.   **12.** $(2, -3, -3)$; $(4, -3, 5)$.

Are the two given directions parallel?

13. $-3 : 2 : -1$ and $6 : -4 : 2$.   **14.** $\frac{1}{2} : -\frac{3}{4} : 2$ and $-2 : 3 : -8$.

160. Cosine of the angle between two lines

THEOREM VI. *If θ is the angle made by two directed lines l_1 and l_2, with direction angles α_1, β_1, γ_1 and α_2, β_2, γ_2, respectively, then*

$$\cos \theta = \cos \alpha_1 \cos \alpha_2 + \cos \beta_1 \cos \beta_2 + \cos \gamma_1 \cos \gamma_2. \tag{1}$$

Proof. 1. Let λ_1, μ_1, ν_1 and λ_2, μ_2, ν_2 represent the direction cosines of l_1 and l_2, respectively. Plot $P_1:(\lambda_1, \mu_1, \nu_1)$ and $P_2:(\lambda_2, \mu_2, \nu_2)$, as in Figure 207, draw OP_1 and OP_2, and let $d = \overline{P_1P_2}$. Then,

$$OP_1 = \sqrt{\lambda_1^2 + \mu_1^2 + \nu_1^2} = 1; \quad OP_2 = 1; \tag{2}$$

$$d^2 = (\lambda_1 - \lambda_2)^2 + (\mu_1 - \mu_2)^2 + (\nu_1 - \nu_2)^2$$

$$= (\lambda_1^2 + \mu_1^2 + \nu_1^2) + (\lambda_2^2 + \mu_2^2 + \nu_2^2) - 2(\lambda_1\lambda_2 + \mu_1\mu_2 + \nu_1\nu_2);$$

$$d^2 = 2 - 2(\lambda_1\lambda_2 + \mu_1\mu_2 + \nu_1\nu_2). \tag{3}$$

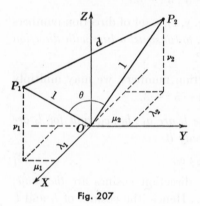

Fig. 207

2. From (4) on page 333 with $\rho = 1$, the direction cosines of OP_1 and OP_2 are λ_1, μ_1, ν_1 and λ_2, μ_2, ν_2, respectively. Hence, the angle θ made by l_1 and l_2 is the angle P_1OP_2.

3. From the law of cosines of trigonometry (on page 563), in triangle OP_1P_2,

$$d^2 = (OP_1)^2 + (OP_2)^2 - 2(OP_1)(OP_2)\cos \theta;$$

$$d^2 = 1 + 1 - 2 \cos \theta = 2 - 2 \cos \theta. \tag{4}$$

From (3) and (4), we obtain (1):

$$\cos \theta = \lambda_1\lambda_2 + \mu_1\mu_2 + \nu_1\nu_2.$$

EXAMPLE 1. Obtain the angle between two lines with the direction numbers $2 : 3 : -6$ and $2 : -6 : -9$.

SOLUTION. From (5) on page 334, one choice of direction cosines for the lines gives $\frac{2}{7}, \frac{3}{7}, -\frac{6}{7}$ *and* $\frac{2}{11}, -\frac{6}{11}, -\frac{9}{11}$.

From (1), $\quad \cos \theta = \frac{2}{7} \cdot \frac{2}{11} + \frac{3}{7} \cdot (-\frac{6}{11}) + (-\frac{6}{7})(-\frac{9}{11}) = \frac{40}{77} = .519$.

From Table VI, $\theta = 58.7°$. With other choices for signs, from (5) on page 334, we find $\cos \theta = -.519$ and $\theta = 180° - 58.7° = 121.3°$.

Since $\cos 90° = 0$, from (1) we obtain the following result.

THEOREM VII. *Lines l_1 and l_2 are perpendicular if and only if the sum of the products of corresponding direction cosines is zero:*

$$\cos \alpha_1 \cos \alpha_2 + \cos \beta_1 \cos \beta_2 + \cos \gamma_1 \cos \gamma_2 = 0. \tag{5}$$

THEOREM VIII. *If l_1 and l_2 have direction numbers $a_1 : b_1 : c_1$ and $a_2 : b_2 : c_2$, respectively, l_1 and l_2 are perpendicular if and only if*

$$a_1a_2 + b_1b_2 + c_1c_2 = 0. \tag{6}$$

Proof. With $\cos \alpha_1 = \dfrac{a_1}{\pm \sqrt{a_1^2 + b_1^2 + c_1^2}}$, $\cos \alpha_2 = \dfrac{a_2}{\pm \sqrt{a_2^2 + b_2^2 + c_2^2}}$,

etc., (5) becomes $\dfrac{a_1 a_2 + b_1 b_2 + c_1 c_2}{\pm \sqrt{a_1^2 + b_1^2 + c_1^2}\sqrt{a_2^2 + b_2^2 + c_2^2}} = 0.$ (7)

Hence, (5) is true if and only if the numerator in (7) is zero.

ILLUSTRATION 1. If direction numbers for l_1 are $9 : 6 : 2$ and for l_2 are $-2 : 6 : -9$, then l_1 and l_2 are perpendicular, because

$$(-2)(9) + 6(6) + (-9)(2) = 0.$$

161. A direction perpendicular to two given directions

EXAMPLE 1. Obtain direction numbers for a direction perpendicular to the directions $2 : -1 : 3$ and $3 : 1 : -2$.

SOLUTION. 1. Let $a : b : c$ be the desired direction, perpendicular to the directions $2 : -1 : 3$ and $3 : 1 : -2$. From (6) on page 336,

$$\begin{cases} 2a - b + 3c = 0, & (1) \\ 3a + b - 2c = 0. & (2) \end{cases}$$

Or,
$$\begin{cases} 2a - b = -3c, & (3) \\ 3a + b = 2c. & (4) \end{cases}$$

2. On solving for a and b in terms of c, we obtain $a = -\tfrac{1}{5}c$ and $b = \tfrac{13}{5}c$. Thus, if $k \neq 0$ and if we let $c = k$, then $a = -\tfrac{1}{5}k$, $b = \tfrac{13}{5}k$, $c = k$. Hence, with k as the factor of proportionality:

$$a : b : c = -\tfrac{1}{5} : \tfrac{13}{5} : 1 = -1 : 13 : 5.$$

Or, the direction $-1 : 13 : 5$ is perpendicular to each given direction.

THEOREM IX. *Let $a_1 : b_1 : c_1$ and $a_2 : b_2 : c_2$ be direction numbers for two non-parallel directions OS and OT. Then, direction numbers for a direction perpendicular to both OS and OT are*

$$\begin{vmatrix} b_1 & c_1 \\ b_2 & c_2 \end{vmatrix} : \begin{vmatrix} c_1 & a_1 \\ c_2 & a_2 \end{vmatrix} : \begin{vmatrix} a_1 & b_1 \\ a_2 & b_2 \end{vmatrix}.$$ (5)

Proof. 1. $A : B : C$ is a direction perpendicular to OS and OT if

$$\begin{cases} Aa_1 + Bb_1 + Cc_1 = 0, & (6) \\ Aa_2 + Bb_2 + Cc_2 = 0. & (7) \end{cases}$$

2. Let U, V, and W, respectively, represent the determinants from left to right in (5). If $W \neq 0$, on solving (6) and (7) for A and B in terms of C by use of determinants, we find $A = CU/W$ and $B = CV/W$. Then, if $k \neq 0$ and if we let $C = k$, we have

$$A = \frac{U}{W}k, \quad B = \frac{V}{W}k, \quad C = k.$$

Thus, $$A : B : C = \frac{U}{W} : \frac{V}{W} : 1. \tag{8}$$

From (8) we obtain $A : B : C = U : V : W$, which proves (5).

★*Note 1.* It can be proved that, if $a_1 : b_1 : c_1 \neq a_2 : b_2 : c_2$, at least one of the determinants in (5) is not zero. Thus, if the denominator in (8) is zero, we might solve (6) and (7) for B and C instead of for A and B, to obtain (5).

ILLUSTRATION 1. To solve Example 1 by (5), arrange $2 : -1 : 3$ and $3 : 1 : -2$ in rows, repeating the first two columns at the right:

$$\begin{matrix} 2 : -1 : & 3 \\ 3 : & 1 : -2 \end{matrix} \begin{matrix} 2 : -1 \\ 3 : & 1 \end{matrix} \Big];$$

$$A : B : C = \begin{vmatrix} -1 & 3 \\ 1 & -2 \end{vmatrix} : \begin{vmatrix} 3 & 2 \\ -2 & 3 \end{vmatrix} : \begin{vmatrix} 2 & -1 \\ 3 & 1 \end{vmatrix} = -1 : 13 : 5.$$

EXERCISE 98

Find the angle between the two lines with the given direction cosines.

1. $\frac{2}{3}, \frac{2}{3}, -\frac{1}{3}; \quad \frac{2}{7}, -\frac{3}{7}, \frac{6}{7}.$
2. $\frac{9}{11}, -\frac{6}{11}, \frac{2}{11}; \quad -\frac{3}{7}, \frac{2}{7}, \frac{6}{7}.$

Obtain the cosine of the angle between the directions.

3. $2 : -3 : -4; \quad -\frac{1}{2} : \frac{3}{4} : 1.$
4. $9 : -6 : 2; \quad -8 : 12 : 9.$

Determine whether or not the two directions are perpendicular.

5. $7 : 4 : -5; \quad 1 : 2 : 3.$
6. $2 : -1 : 2; \quad 7 : 4 : -5.$

7. $\frac{1}{3} : \frac{3}{2} : -2; \quad -6 : -16 : -13.$
8. $3 : 2 : -4; \quad 1 : 1 : 2.$

9. $2 : -1 : 0; \quad 0 : 3 : 1.$
10. $\frac{1}{3} : -\frac{1}{2} : \frac{1}{6}; \quad -4 : -1 : 5.$

Find direction numbers and direction cosines for a line perpendicular to two lines having the given direction numbers, or cosines.

11. $1 : -2 : 2; \quad 3 : 1 : 2.$
12. $0 : -1 : 3; \quad 2 : -2 : 3.$

13. $2 : 0 : -3; \quad -3 : 2 : -5.$
14. $-3 : 1 : 4; \quad 0 : -2 : 5.$

15. Cosines: $\frac{2}{3}, -\frac{1}{3}, \frac{2}{3}; \quad \frac{3}{7}, \frac{2}{7}, \frac{6}{7}.$
16. Cosines: $\frac{3}{5}, 0, \frac{4}{5}; \quad \frac{5}{13}, \frac{12}{13}, 0.$

162. Equation of a surface

The set of points $P:(x, y, z)$ whose coordinates satisfy a given equation $f(x, y, z) = 0$ is called the *graph* or *locus* of the equation. As a rule, if (x, y) is any pair of values in some two-dimensional region of the xy-plane, there will be one or more corresponding values of z satisfying $f(x, y, z) = 0$, and thus one or more points $P:(x, y, z)$ on its locus. Hence, in general, the locus of $f(x, y, z) = 0$ is *two-dimensional*, and will be referred to as a *surface*. An *equation for a surface* is an equation whose graph is the given surface. In referring to a *plane section*, or simply a *section* of a surface, we shall mean the curve of intersection of the surface and a plane.

ILLUSTRATION 1. Any plane section of a sphere is a circle.

The intersection of a surface and any coordinate plane is called the **trace** of the surface in that plane. We call the trace in the xy-plane the *xy-trace*, and similarly refer to the *yz-trace* and *xz-trace*.

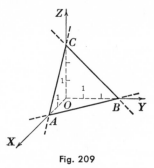

ILLUSTRATION 2. The locus of $x^2 + y^2 + z^2 = 9$ is a sphere with center at the origin and radius 3, because the equation states that the square of the length of the radius vector OP from the origin to any point $P:(x, y, z)$ on the surface is equal to 9. Each trace of the surface is a circle. In Figure 208, the xy-trace and xz-trace are distorted from circles into ellipses (see Note 9 of the Appendix).

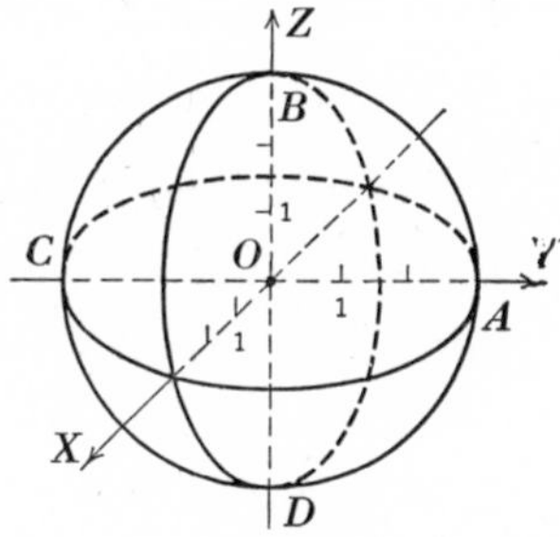

Fig. 208

In a later section, we shall prove that *the locus of any linear equation in x, y, z is a plane* and that, conversely, any plane has an equation of this type. To sketch the graph of a linear equation in x, y, z, first find the intercepts on the axes. Then, draw the traces of the plane and perhaps a few other sections parallel to coordinate planes. The aim should be to outline a triangle or quadrilateral on the desired plane.

ILLUSTRATION 3. A graph of $3x + 2y + 2z = 6$ is in Figure 209. With $y = z = 0$, we find the x-intercept $x = 2$. Similarly, with $x = z = 0$, the y-intercept is $y = 3$. The z-intercept is $z = 3$. Thus, A, B, C are on the plane. The xy-trace is AB, joining A and B, etc. for the traces AC and BC.

Fig. 209

163. Equations of a curve

The locus of a *pair of simultaneous equations* in x, y, and z is the set of points satisfying both equations. Or, the locus is *the curve of intersection of the two surfaces represented by the equations.* A pair of equations for a curve is any pair which has the curve as its locus.

ILLUSTRATION 1. The x-axis is the intersection of the planes $y = 0$ and $z = 0$. Hence, the equations of the x-axis are $y = 0$ and $z = 0$.

ILLUSTRATION 2. The sphere in Figure 208 and the plane $x = 0$ intersect in circle $ABCD$. Its *equations* are $x^2 + y^2 + z^2 = 9$ and $x = 0$.

ILLUSTRATION 3. In Figure 209, the xy-trace AB is the curve defined by

$$3x + 2y + 2z = 6 \quad and \quad z = 0. \tag{1}$$

On using $z = 0$ in the first equation, we obtain $3x + 2y = 6$ as an equation whose locus in the xy-plane is AB.

To obtain an equation whose locus in a coordinate plane is the trace of a given surface $f(x, y, z) = 0$ in that plane, proceed as follows:

1. *For the xy-trace:*   *place* $z = 0$ *in* $f(x, y, z) = 0$.

2. *For the xz-trace:*   *place* $y = 0$ *in* $f(x, y, z) = 0$.

3. *For the yz-trace:*   *place* $x = 0$ *in* $f(x, y, z) = 0$.

EXAMPLE 1.   Plot the plane $3y + 2z = 6.$ (2)

SOLUTION.   1. If $y = z = 0$, then (2) gives $0 = 6$.   Hence, (2) has no x-intercept, and thus is perpendicular to the yz-plane.

2. *The traces.*   If $x = 0$, this does not affect (2).   Hence, in Figure 210, the yz-trace is the locus, AB, of (2) in the yz-plane.   With $z = 0$ in (2), we find $y = 2$ as the equation whose locus in the xy-plane is the xy-trace.   The xz-trace is the locus, DB, of $z = 3$ in the xz-plane.

3. In Figure 210, CD is the intersection of (2) with the plane CDE through E parallel to the yz-plane. Rectangle $ABDC$ is a piece of plane (2).

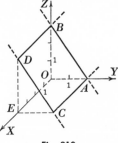

In Example 1, we illustrated the fact that the graph of a linear equation in x, y, and z, *with one variable missing*, is a plane *perpendicular to the plane of the other two variables.*

Fig. 210

<h3 style="text-align:center">EXERCISE 99</h3>

Obtain a graph of the equation.

1. $x = 2$.   2. $y = -3$.   3. $z = 2$.   4. $z = -2$.

5. $2x + y + z = 4$.   6. $3x - 2y - 2z + 6 = 0$.

7. $3x + 4y = 6z - 12$.   8. $x - y + 2z = 4$.

9. $3x + 4y = 12$.   10. $y + z = 2$.   11. $2x - 3z = 6$.

12. For the plane in Problem 6, what are the *equations* of the xy-trace; yz-trace?

164. One-point form for the equation of a plane

Let T be a given plane, and let N be a line perpendicular or *normal* to T.   Let $A : B : C$ be direction numbers for N; we shall refer to $A : B : C$ as the **normal direction** for the plane.

THEOREM X.   *Every plane has an equation linear in x, y, and z; if the normal direction for the plane is $A : B : C$, and (x_0, y_0, z_0) is any point on the plane, its equation is*

$$A(x - x_0) + B(y - y_0) + C(z - z_0) = 0. \qquad (1)$$

Proof.   1. Let M be the point (x_0, y_0, z_0) and erect the normal MN to the plane at M, as in Figure 211. Let $P:(x, y, z)$ be any point in space other than M, and draw line PM. Then, PM has the direction numbers $(x - x_0) : (y - y_0) : (z - z_0)$. MN has the direction $A : B : C$.

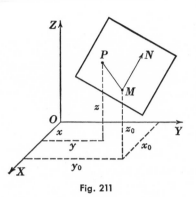

Fig. 211

2. P is on the plane *if and only if PM is perpendicular to MN* or, by (6) on page 336, *if and only if* equation (1) is true. Hence, (1) is the equation of the plane.

ILLUSTRATION 1. The equation of the plane through $(2, -3, 4)$ with the normal direction $4 : -1 : 2$ is

$$4(x - 2) - (y + 3) + 2(z - 4) = 0, \text{ or}$$
$$4x - y + 2z = 19. \tag{2}$$

THEOREM XI. *If A, B, C are not all zero, the locus of*

$$Ax + By + Cz + D = 0 \tag{3}$$

is a plane with the normal direction $A : B : C$. Thus, the locus of every linear equation in x, y, and z is a plane.

Proof. 1. There exists at least one point (x_0, y_0, z_0) on the locus of (3). Hence, these coordinates satisfy (3), or

$$Ax_0 + By_0 + Cz_0 + D = 0. \tag{4}$$

2. Since the right-hand side of (4) is zero, we may subtract the left-hand side of (4) from the left-hand side in (3), to obtain

$$A(x - x_0) + B(y - y_0) + C(z - z_0) = 0, \tag{5}$$

which is (1). Therefore the locus of (3) is a plane, as stated.

ILLUSTRATION 2. The plane $3x + 2y - 7z = 3$ has the normal direction $3 : 2 : -7$, and $2x - z = 4$ has the normal direction $2 : 0 : -1$.

EXAMPLE 1. Obtain the equation of the plane T through $(2, -3, 1)$ which is parallel to the plane $S:[4x - 2y + z = 2]$.

SOLUTION. Since S and T are parallel, they have the same normal direction, which is $4 : -2 : 1$. Hence, from (1), the equation of T is

$$4(x - 2) - 2(y + 3) + (z - 1) = 0 \quad or \quad 4x - 2y + z = 15.$$

EXERCISE 100

Write the plane through the point with the given normal direction.

1. $(2, 1, -2)$; $\quad 3 : -1 : 4$.
2. $(-1, 2, -3)$; $\quad -1 : 2 : -1$.
3. $(2, 0, -1)$; $\quad 0 : -1 : 2$.
4. $(-3, 1, 0)$; $\quad 3 : 0 : -1$.
5. $(2, 3, 0)$; $\quad 4 : -1 : 0$.
6. $(1, 0, -3)$; $\quad -2 : 1 : -3$.

Write the equation of the specified plane.

7. Through $(-1, 2, -3)$ parallel to $2x - 3y + z = 8$.

8. Through $(0, -1, 2)$ parallel to $-x + 2y - z = 3$.

9. Through $(2, -1, 3)$ parallel to the xz-plane.

10. Through $(1, 2, -1)$ perpendicular to a line with the direction cosines $-\frac{9}{11}, \frac{2}{11}, \frac{6}{11}$.

11. Prove that the plane with x-intercept a, y-intercept b, and z-intercept c, where $abc \neq 0$, can be written in the **intercept form.**

$$\frac{x}{a} + \frac{y}{b} + \frac{z}{c} = 1.$$

12. Write the equation $3x - 2y - 5z = 20$ in the intercept form.

★13. Obtain the equation of the plane through the points

$$A : (-1, -2, -1), \quad B : (0, -2, -3), \quad and \quad C : (1, 4, 1).$$

HINT. Find direction numbers for AB and BC. Then, find direction numbers for the normal, by use of page 337.

165. Problems involving two planes

Consider two planes

$$S_1 : [A_1 x + B_1 y + C_1 z + D_1 = 0]; \tag{1}$$

$$S_2 : [A_2 x + B_2 y + C_2 z + D_2 = 0]. \tag{2}$$

Their normals have the direction numbers $A_1 : B_1 : C_1$ and $A_2 : B_2 : C_2$. If S_1 and S_2 are parallel (*coincide*, or *do not intersect*), we shall say that the angle between S_1 and S_2 is 0. In this case the normals of S_1 and S_2 are parallel. If S_1 and S_2 intersect in a line l, then S_1 and S_2 form four dihedral angles, equal in pairs. These angles are measured by plane angles which are equal to those formed by the normals to the planes. In particular, S_1 and S_2 are perpendicular if and only if their normals are perpendicular.

SUMMARY. *To find the angles formed by planes (1) and (2), obtain the angles formed by their normals. In particular the following conditions are available.*

Planes parallel: $\qquad\qquad A_1 : B_1 : C_1 = A_2 : B_2 : C_2.$ $\tag{3}$

Planes perpendicular: $\qquad A_1 A_2 + B_1 B_2 + C_1 C_2 = 0.$ $\tag{4}$

ILLUSTRATION 1. The planes

$$3x + 4y - 2z + 5 = 0 \quad and \quad 6x + 8y - 4z - 7 = 0$$

are parallel because $3 : 4 : -2 = 6 : 8 : -4$.

ILLUSTRATION 2. The planes

$$6x - 9y + 2z = 3 \quad and \quad 6x + 2y - 9z = 8$$

are perpendicular because $6(6) - 9(2) + 2(-9) = 0$.

ILLUSTRATION 3. The angles formed by the planes

$$2x - 2y + z = 3 \quad and \quad 9x - 6y + 2z = 7 \tag{5}$$

are equal to the angles formed by the normal directions $2 : -2 : 1$ and $9 : -6 : 2$. These angles are found to be $14.0°$ and $166.0°$.

The line of intersection of planes (1) and (2) is perpendicular to both of the normal directions $A_1 : B_1 : C_1$ and $A_2 : B_2 : C_2$. Hence, from page 337, *the line of intersection of* (1) *and* (2) *has the direction numbers*

$$\begin{vmatrix} B_1 & C_1 \\ B_2 & C_2 \end{vmatrix} : \begin{vmatrix} C_1 & A_1 \\ C_2 & A_2 \end{vmatrix} : \begin{vmatrix} A_1 & B_1 \\ A_2 & B_2 \end{vmatrix}. \tag{6}$$

ILLUSTRATION 4. By use of (6), direction numbers for the intersection of planes (5) are

$$\begin{vmatrix} -2 & 1 \\ -6 & 2 \end{vmatrix} : \begin{vmatrix} 1 & 2 \\ 2 & 9 \end{vmatrix} : \begin{vmatrix} 2 & -2 \\ 9 & -6 \end{vmatrix}, \quad or \quad 2 : 5 : 6.$$

EXERCISE 101

If the two planes are parallel or perpendicular, verify this fact.

1. $\begin{cases} 2x - 6y - 2z = 5, \\ 3x - 9y - 3z = 7. \end{cases}$ 2. $\begin{cases} 2x + y + 2z = 4, \\ 9x + 6y - 2z = 3. \end{cases}$

3. $\begin{cases} 3x - y + 2z = 4, \\ 2x - 3z = 9. \end{cases}$ 4. $\begin{cases} 2x - y + 4z = 5, \\ x - 2y - z = 2. \end{cases}$

5. $\begin{cases} 3x - 6y - 2z = 5, \\ 2x + y - 2z = 4. \end{cases}$ 6. $\begin{cases} 4x + 2y - 2z = 3, \\ -2x - y + z = 5. \end{cases}$

7. $\begin{cases} x - 3z = 1, \\ y - 4 = 0. \end{cases}$ 8. $\begin{cases} 3x - 4y = 5, \\ 4x + 3y = 7. \end{cases}$ 9. $\begin{cases} 2z + y = 5, \\ 3x - 2 = 0. \end{cases}$

10–11. In each of Problems 2 and 5, find the acute angle which is formed.

12. Prove that the plane $Ax + Cz + D = 0$ is perpendicular to the xz-plane, and that $By + Cz + D = 0$ is perpendicular to the yz-plane.

13–14. Find direction numbers for the line of intersection of the planes in Problems 2 and 5, respectively.

15–16. In Problems 2 and 5, respectively, obtain the equation of the plane S through $(1, 2, -1)$ perpendicular to the given planes.

★*Let T be any plane and let ON be the directed normal from the origin to* * *T, with N on T. Let ON = p, and let α, β, γ be the direction angles of ON. Then p is called the* **normal distance** *for T. Solve the following problems.*

17. Find coordinates for N and use (1) on page 340 to show that T has the equation $x \cos \alpha + y \cos \beta + z \cos \gamma - p = 0$ (called the **normal form**).

18. If T has the equation $Ax + By + Cz + D = 0$, prove that, if we divide by $\pm \sqrt{A^2 + B^2 + C^2}$, the equation takes the normal form; specify a rule for choice of the ambiguous sign if T does not pass through the origin.

* If T passes through the origin, direct a normal ON *upward*, or to the *right* if "upward" does not apply, or *forward* if "upward" and "right" do not apply.

19. Let distances perpendicular to T be *directed*, as on ON. Then, prove that the distance from T to $P_1:(x_1, y_1, z_1)$ is obtained by substituting (x_1, y_1, z_1) for (x, y, z) in the left-hand member of the normal form.

20. Write the equation of T if $p = 2$ and ON has the cosines $-\frac{1}{3}, \frac{2}{3}, \frac{2}{3}$.

21. Find the distance between $(-1, 2, 1)$ and $2x - 3y - 6z + 5 = 0$.

166. Projection planes for a line

A line l may be defined (or, *determined*) geometrically by specifying any two distinct planes R and S whose intersection is l. Algebraically, l is determined as the locus of a point $P:(x, y, z)$ satisfying the system of *two linear equations* whose loci are the planes R and S. Since infinitely many pairs of distinct planes R and S may be drawn through a given line l, we may have infinitely many different pairs of equations for l. We shall refer to any one of these pairs as *the* equations of l.

Let l be a given line and S be a given plane not perpendicular to l. Then, the projection of l on S is the line of intersection of S and the plane T through l perpendicular to S. If S is a coordinate plane, the plane T projecting l on S is called a *projection plane* for l. Any projection plane T for l is parallel to a coordinate axis, and hence *the corresponding variable x, y, or z is missing from the equation of T*. If a line l is determined by two given linear equations in x, y, and z, the equations of the projection planes for l can be found by *eliminating x, y, and z, in turn*, between the given equations.

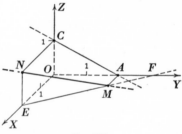

Fig. 212

ILLUSTRATION 1. The line l determined by the planes

$$U:[y + 2z = 2] \quad and \quad W:[3x + 2y = 6] \tag{1}$$

is MN in Figure 212. U and W are projection planes for l. U projects l into CA on the yz-plane and W projects l into EF on the xy-plane.

EXAMPLE 1. Obtain projection planes for the line l determined by

$$\begin{cases} 3x + 3y + 2z - 8 = 0, & (2) \\ 3x + y - 2z - 4 = 0. & (3) \end{cases}$$

SOLUTION. 1. The equation of the plane projecting l on the xy-plane will not involve z. To obtain this projection plane, eliminate z by adding in (2) and (3). We find $6x + 4y - 12 = 0$, or $3x + 2y = 6$.

2. The plane projecting l on the yz-plane is $y + 2z = 2$. Thus, (1) has been obtained from (2) and (3). Hence, the graph of the line $[(2), (3)]$ is MN in Figure 212.

EXERCISE 102

Graph the line l determined by the equations.

1. $\begin{cases} x + z = 4, \\ 4z + 3y = 12. \end{cases}$
   2. $\begin{cases} 2x + y = 4, \\ 2x + 3y = 6. \end{cases}$
   3. $\begin{cases} x + 2y = 4, \\ y + z = 3. \end{cases}$

Obtain the equations of the projection planes for the line and plot it.

4. $\begin{cases} 4x + y + 2z = 10, \\ x - 2y + 2z = -2. \end{cases}$
   5. $\begin{cases} x + y + 3z = 5, \\ x - 3y - 3z = -7. \end{cases}$

6–10. In Problems 1–5, respectively, find the coordinates of the points where the line intersects the coordinate planes.

167. Parametric and symmetric equations for a line

Let l be a line through a fixed point $P_1:(x_1, y_1, z_1)$. Assign a positive direction on l, with the direction angles α, β, γ. If $P:(x, y, z)$ is on l, let s represent the *directed distance* P_1P, as in Figure 213; that is, $P_1P = s$. Then, we shall find that l has the parametric equations

$$x = x_1 + s \cos \alpha, \qquad y = y_1 + s \cos \beta, \qquad z = z_1 + s \cos \gamma. \quad (1)$$

Proof. If $P_1P > 0$, from (1) on page 332 with $d = P_1P = s$,

$$x - x_1 = s \cos \alpha, \quad y - y_1 = s \cos \beta, \quad z - z_1 = s \cos \gamma. \quad (2)$$

If $P_1P = s < 0$, then (1) is obtained again, if we replace s by $-s$ and each cosine by its negative (which is equivalent to reversing the positive direction on l). Also, (2) is true if $P:(x, y, z)$ is taken as P_1, because (2) gives $x = x_1$, $y = y_1$, $z = z_1$ when $s = 0$. Hence, if P is *any* point on l, and $s = P_1P$, the coordinates of P satisfy (2). Conversely, for any value of s, equations (1) give the coordinates of that point P on l where $P_1P = s$. Hence, equations (1) are parametric equations for l, because (1) gives all points on l and only such points.

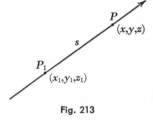

Fig. 213

THEOREM XII. *The line l through $P_1:(x_1, y_1, z_1)$ with the direction numbers $a : b : c$ has the parametric equations*

$$x = x_1 + at, \qquad y = y_1 + bt, \qquad z = z_1 + ct, \quad (3)$$

where t is the parameter. Also, l has the xyz-equations

$$\frac{x - x_1}{a} = \frac{y - y_1}{b} = \frac{z - z_1}{c}. \quad (4)$$

Proof. 1. A number $k \ne 0$ exists so that $\cos \alpha = ka$, $\cos \beta = kb$, $\cos \gamma = kc$.

Hence, from (1), $\qquad x = x_1 + aks, \quad y = y_1 + bks, \quad z = z_1 + cks. \quad (5)$

If we let $t = ks$, then (5) becomes (3). It remains to prove (4).

2. Observe that (3) is true even when one or more of a, b, c is equal to zero. If no one of a, b, c is zero, from (3) we obtain (4), because each fraction in (4) is equal to t as found from an equation in (3). If $a = 0$ in (3), then $x = x_1$ at all points $P:(x, y, z)$ on l. Then, we permit $(x - x_1)/a$ in (4) with the agreement that *zero as a denominator implies zero as a numerator*. Similar remarks apply if $b = 0$ or $c = 0$ in (4).

ILLUSTRATION 1. The line l through $A:(2, -3, 4)$ with the direction numbers $4 : 3 : -5$ has the parametric equations

$$x = 2 + 4t, \quad y = -3 + 3t, \quad z = 4 - 5t. \tag{6}$$

With $t = 1$ in (6), we obtain $B:(6, 0, -1)$ on l. The definition of s in (1), and the fact that $t = ks$ in (5), show that (6) gives the coordinates of points of l which are *on one side of A when $t > 0$*, and *on the other side when $t < 0$*.

We refer to (4) as the **symmetric form** for the equations of a line l. The equalities in (4) are equivalent to just two independent linear equations in x, y, z. Thus, in various ways, from (4) we may obtain the equations of two planes which determine l. Each of these planes will be a *projection plane* for l because one variable will be missing from the equation of the plane.

ILLUSTRATION 2. Symmetric equations for l in Illustration 1 are

$$\frac{x - 2}{4} = \frac{y + 3}{3} = \frac{z - 4}{-5}. \tag{7}$$

From (7), $\dfrac{x - 2}{4} = \dfrac{y + 3}{3}$ *and* $\dfrac{y + 3}{3} = \dfrac{z - 4}{5}$, *or*   (8)

$$3x - 4y = 18 \quad and \quad 5y - 3z = -27. \tag{9}$$

THEOREM XIII.   *The line l through $P_1:(x_1, y_1, z_1)$ and $P_2:(x_2, y_2, z_2)$ has the equations*

$$\frac{x - x_1}{x_2 - x_1} = \frac{y - y_1}{y_2 - y_1} = \frac{z - z_1}{z_2 - z_1}. \tag{10}$$

Proof. We have $(x_2 - x_1) : (y_2 - y_1) : (z_2 - z_1)$ as direction numbers for l. With this direction in place of $a : b : c$, (4) leads to (10). We call (10) the **two-point form** for the equations of a line.

ILLUSTRATION 3.   From (10), the line l through $(4, 3, -7)$ and $(-2, 3, 5)$ has the equations

$$\frac{x - 4}{-6} = \frac{y - 3}{0} = \frac{z + 7}{12}. \tag{11}$$

rom (11), l is determined by the planes

$$y - 3 = 0 \quad and \quad \frac{x - 4}{-6} = \frac{z + 7}{12}.$$

EXAMPLE 1. Change the following equations to the symmetric form:

$$\frac{3x+5}{2} = \frac{3-2y}{1} = \frac{4-z}{-3}.$$ (12)

SOLUTION. To correspond with (4), we must obtain $+1$ as the coefficient of x in each numerator. Hence, divide both numerator and denominator by 3, -2, and -1, respectively, in the fractions:

$$\frac{x+\frac{5}{3}}{\frac{2}{3}} = \frac{y-\frac{3}{2}}{-\frac{1}{2}} = \frac{z-4}{3}.$$

Then, multiply all denominators by 6:

$$\frac{x+\frac{5}{3}}{4} = \frac{y-\frac{3}{2}}{-3} = \frac{z-4}{18}.$$

Line (12) passes through $(-\frac{5}{3}, \frac{3}{2}, 4)$ with the direction $4:-3:18$.

EXERCISE 103

Plot the line l whose parametric equations are given, by finding two points on l by use of the equations.

1. $x = 1 + t,\ y = 3 - 4t,\ z = 4 + 3t.$ 2. $x = 4 + 5t,\ y = 1 - t,\ z = 5 + 7t.$

Write the equations of two projection planes which determine the line.

3. $\dfrac{x-3}{-3} = \dfrac{y}{4} = \dfrac{z-1}{1}.$

4. $\dfrac{x-1}{1} = \dfrac{y-6}{2} = \dfrac{z-1}{-1}.$

5. $\dfrac{x-2}{0} = \dfrac{y-4}{4} = \dfrac{z-2}{3}.$

6. $\dfrac{x+3}{2} = \dfrac{y-2}{0} = \dfrac{z-3}{0}.$

Write equations for the line in parametric form, and in symmetric form.

7. Through $(-1, 2, 3)$ with the direction $2:-3:1$.

8. Through $(2, -1, \frac{3}{4})$ with the direction $-1:2:-3$.

9. Through $(0, -1, 3)$ with the direction cosines $-\frac{1}{3}, -\frac{2}{3}, \frac{2}{3}$.

10. Through $(2, -1, 3)$ with the direction $2:0:-1$.

11. Through $(-1, 0, -3)$ with the direction $0:-1:3$.

12. Through the points $(-1, 2, -1)$ and $(3, 4, -2)$.

13. Through the points $(-3, 1, 0)$ and $(0, 1, -3)$.

14. Through the points $(-2, 3, 1)$ and $(0, -2, 1)$.

15. Through $(2, -1, 3)$ perpendicular to the plane $3x + 2y + 5z = 3$.

16. Through $(-1, 3, 0)$ perpendicular to the plane $x - 2y = 2$.

17. Through $(2, -1, 3)$ parallel to the line $\dfrac{x-2}{3} = \dfrac{y}{2} = \dfrac{z+1}{-1}.$

18. Through $(2, 3, -5)$ parallel to the z-axis.

19. Through $(2, -1, 2)$ parallel to the line through $(1, 3, -1)$ and $(-2, 1, 4)$.

20. Find the acute angle made by the lines in Problems 3 and 4.

21. By use of parametric equations, find where the line through $(2, -1, 3)$ with the direction $1:4:-2$ intersects $2x + y - 3z = 18$.

Change the equations of the given line to a symmetric form; then state direction numbers for the line and a point on it.

22. $\dfrac{2x-1}{3} = \dfrac{2-y}{2} = \dfrac{3z+5}{1}.$

23. $\dfrac{3x-2}{4} = \dfrac{5+y}{3} = \dfrac{1-2z}{5}.$

24. $\dfrac{3+2x}{0} = \dfrac{4-y}{3} = \dfrac{z-2}{4}.$

25. $\dfrac{2-5x}{3} = \dfrac{3+4y}{0} = \dfrac{2z-1}{4}.$

26. $\begin{cases} x+y-z = 1, \\ 4x-y+6z = 9. \end{cases}$

27. $\begin{cases} 2x+y-z = 4, \\ 2x-3y-9z = -8. \end{cases}$

HINT. Find the point where $z = 0$. Then use (6) on page 343.

28. $\begin{cases} x+2y-z = 1, \\ 3x+6y-4z = 1. \end{cases}$

29. $\begin{cases} 2x+4y-3z = 10, \\ 2x-4y+3z = -8. \end{cases}$

30. Find direction cosines for the line in Problem 27.

31. The line of Problem 1 is projected on the xy-plane. Find the equations of this line of projection.

Note 1. Directions in an xy-plane can be described by use of direction angles, direction cosines, and direction numbers, where we use just two direction angles α and β, with the same meanings as in space of three dimensions. All appropriate formulas are obtained by use of the results for three dimensional space with the third direction angle $\gamma = 90°$, or $\cos \gamma = 0$, and hence with 0 as the third direction number. Thus, for any direction, $\cos^2 \alpha + \cos^2 \beta = 1$. From (5) and (6) on page 336, the conditions for perpendicularity become

$$\cos \alpha_1 \cos \alpha_2 + \cos \beta_1 \cos \beta_2 = 0, \quad or \quad a_1 a_2 + b_1 b_2 = 0.$$

A symmetric equation for a line through (x_0, y_0) with the direction $a : b$ is

$$\frac{x-x_0}{a} = \frac{y-y_0}{b}.$$

We verify that the direction perpendicular to the direction $a : b$ has the direction numbers $b : -a$ because $(a)(b) + (b)(-a) = 0$. In many ways, the preceding setting is more convenient than that which is involved when the notions of *slope* and *inclination* are taken as basic in corresponding problems involving directions in a plane.

The following problems refer to data in an xy-plane.

Find direction numbers, and then the direction cosines of the line segment directed from the first point to the second point. Give a figure for the problem.

32. $(3, 2); (-4, 5)$.

33. $(-1, 5); (2, -6)$.

34. $(0, 3); (-1, -4)$.

35. $(-2, -4); (3, 7)$.

36–39. Write an equation in symmetric form for the line joining the points, in Problems 32–35, respectively.

40–43. In Problems 32–35, respectively, obtain a direction perpendicular to the direction of the line segment, and write a symmetric equation for a line perpendicular to the segment through the first point.

168. General equations for a sphere

Let r be the radius and let $C{:}(g, h, k)$ be the center of a sphere. Then, it has the equation

$$(x - g)^2 + (y - h)^2 + (z - k)^2 = r^2, \tag{1}$$

because (1) states that the square of the distance between $C{:}(g, h, k)$ and $P{:}(x, y, z)$ is equal to r^2. By completing squares with the terms in x, y, and z, respectively, we find that any equation of the form

$$x^2 + y^2 + z^2 + Rx + Sy + Tz + U = 0$$

represents a sphere, real (including a point-sphere) or imaginary.

169. Cylinders

A *cylinder* is defined as the surface swept out by a line L, with a fixed direction, which moves through all points of a plane curve C. Each position of L is called a *ruling*, and C is called a *directrix curve* of the cylinder. For any cylinder, we may choose any plane section perpendicular to the rulings as a directrix curve, and this will be taken as the situation hereafter. If the rulings are perpendicular to a coordinate plane, as will be the case usually in our applications, the directrix C may be taken as the trace of the cylinder in this plane. The cylinder will be referred to as *perpendicular to this plane*, or parallel to its normals. A cylinder frequently is named after its directrix.

ILLUSTRATION 1. A cylinder is called a circular, an elliptic, a hyperbolic, or a parabolic cylinder according as its directrix is a circle, an ellipse, etc.

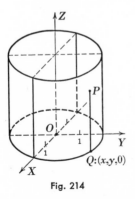

Fig. 214

ILLUSTRATION 2. Consider the surface S which is the graph of

$$x^2 + y^2 = 4. \tag{1}$$

The xy-trace is the circle which is the graph of (1) in the xy-plane, as in Figure 214. The projection of any point $P{:}(x, y, z)$ on the xy-plane is $Q{:}(x, y, 0)$. Point P is on S if and only if Q satisfies (1), or P is on a perpendicular to the xy-plane at a point Q on the circle $x^2 + y^2 = 4$. Thus, S is a circular cylinder perpendicular to the xy-plane. A similar discussion establishes the following result.

THEOREM XIV. *If an equation lacks one of the variables x, y, z, the graph of the equation is a cylinder parallel to the axis of the missing variable, or perpendicular to the plane of the other variables.*

Note 1. A section of a cylinder by a plane parallel to the plane of a directrix curve C is a curve *congruent* to C. A section of a cylinder by a plane perpendicular to the plane of C consists of one or more rulings.

ILLUSTRATION 3. The graph S of $yz = 6$ is a hyperbolic cylinder perpendicular to the yz-plane; the directrix is the graph of $yz = 6$ in the yz-plane. Figure 215 shows a piece of S bounded by arc BD of the directrix, by arc AC of a congruent section parallel to the yz-plane, and by rulings CD and AB perpendicular to the yz-plane.

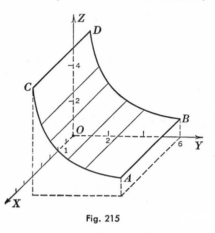

Fig. 215

ILLUSTRATION 4. A plane is a special case of a cylinder, where the directrix curve is a line. Thus, $3x + 2y = 5$ may be referred to as a *linear cylinder*, perpendicular to the xy-plane.

To write the equation of a cylinder whose directrix is a certain curve C in a coordinate plane, *write the equation in two variables whose locus in that plane is* C.

ILLUSTRATION 5. Let the directrix of a cylinder be the ellipse in the xz-plane with major axis 10 along OX, minor axis 6 along OZ, and center at the origin. Then, the equation of this cylinder is $9x^2 + 25z^2 = 225$.

EXERCISE 104

Graph the specified sphere and write its equation.

1. Center $(2, 5, 7)$; radius 2.   2. Center $(3, -4, 6)$; radius 3.

Find the center and radius of the sphere.

3. $x^2 + 2x + y^2 - 6y + z^2 - 5 = 0$.   4. $x^2 + y^2 + z^2 - 4x + 6z + 9 = 0$.

Graph the piece of the surface between the xy-plane and the plane $z = 6$.

5. $x^2 + y^2 = 16$.   6. $4x^2 + 9y^2 = 36$.   7. $x^2 = 4y$.

8. $4x^2 - 9y^2 = 0$.   9. $4y - 3x + 12 = 0$.

Graph the surface represented by the equation.

10. $9y^2 + 4z^2 = 36$.   11. $25x^2 + 4z^2 = 100$.   12. $z^2 = 6x$.

13. $z^2 - y^2 = 4$.   14. $4z^2 - 9x^2 = 36$.   15. $x = \sin z$.

170. Surfaces of revolution

If a plane curve C is revolved about a line l in its plane, the surface S thus generated is called a *surface of revolution* with l as its **axis** of revolution and C as a **generatrix**. Any section of S by a plane through l is called a **meridian section** and consists of one position of C, in its revolution, together with the symmetric reflection of C with respect to l. Any section of S by a plane perpendicular to l is a circle. If we revolve an ellipse, a hyperbola, or a parabola about an axis of symmetry of the curve, the surface obtained is called an *ellipsoid*, a *hyperboloid*, or a *paraboloid of revolution*, respectively. An ellipsoid of revolution is called an *oblate* or a *prolate spheroid* according as we revolve the ellipse of the meridian section about its *minor* or its *major* axis, and we obtain a sphere when the ellipse is a circle.

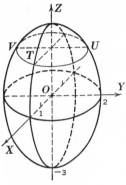

Fig. 216

ILLUSTRATION 1. If the ellipse C, which is the locus of

$$9y^2 + 4z^2 = 36 \tag{1}$$

in the yz-plane, is revolved about OZ, a prolate spheroid S is obtained, as in Figure 216. To derive an equation for S, consider Figure 217. Let $Q:(0, y_1, z_1)$ be a point on C, and let $P:(x, y, z)$ be any point into which Q revolves. Let $P_1:(x, y, 0)$ and $Q_1:(0, y_1, 0)$ be the projections of P and Q on the xy-plane. Since Q is on C,

$$9y_1^2 + 4z_1^2 = 36. \tag{2}$$

In Figure 217, $Q_1Q = P_1P$; $(OQ_1)^2 = (OP_1)^2$. Hence,

$$z_1 = z \quad and \quad y_1^2 = x^2 + y^2. \tag{3}$$

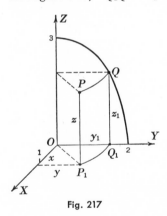

Fig. 217

A point P is on S if and only if (2) and (3) are true. Hence, an equation for S is found by using (3) in (2), which gives

$$9(x^2 + y^2) + 4z^2 = 36. \tag{4}$$

Let C be the graph of $f(y, z) = 0, f(x, y) = 0$, or $f(x, z) = 0$, in the coordinate plane of the two variables involved. Then, as in Illustration 1, the equation of the surface generated by revolving C about a coordinate axis, in its plane, is obtained as follows:

I. *Revolution about OZ:* $\begin{cases} for\ f(y, z)\ =\ 0,\ replace\ y^2\ by\ (x^2 + y^2);\ * \\ for\ f(x, z)\ =\ 0,\ replace\ x^2\ by\ (x^2 + y^2). \end{cases}$

II. *Revolution about OY:* $\begin{cases} for\ f(x, y)\ =\ 0,\ replace\ x^2\ by\ (x^2 + z^2). \\ for\ f(y, z)\ =\ 0,\ replace\ z^2\ by\ (x^2 + z^2). \end{cases}$

III. *Revolution about OX:* $\begin{cases} for\ f(x, y)\ =\ 0,\ replace\ y^2\ by\ (y^2 + z^2); \\ for\ f(x, z)\ =\ 0,\ replace\ z^2\ by\ (y^2 + z^2). \end{cases}$

ILLUSTRATION 2. If the hyperbola which is the graph of

$$y^2 - 4z^2 = 4 \tag{5}$$

in the yz-plane is revolved about OY, a hyperboloid of revolution of two

* That is, replace $|y|$ by $\sqrt{x^2 + y^2}$, and similarly in the other cases.

sheets, S, is generated, as in Figure 218. By (II), the equation of S is

$$y^2 - 4(x^2 + z^2) = 4.$$ (6)

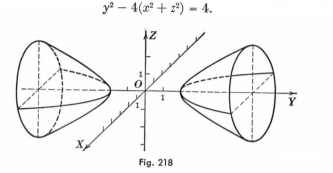

Fig. 218

ILLUSTRATION 3. By reference to (I), we see that

$$3x^2 + 3y^2 - 7z^2 = 8 \quad or \quad 3(x^2 + y^2) - 7z^2 = 8,$$

represents a hyperboloid of revolution, which is generated by revolving about OZ the locus of $3x^2 - 7z^2 = 8$ in the xz-plane.

171. Cones of revolution

Let C be a fixed plane curve and let V be a fixed point not in the plane of C. Then, the surface generated by a line t drawn through V to a point P on C, as P moves through all positions on C, is called a *cone*. For this cone, we call V the *vertex*, any position of t a *ruling*, and C a *directrix curve*. Suppose that C can be chosen as a circle, with V on a line l perpendicular to the plane of the circle at its center. Then, the cone is a surface of revolution, generated by revolving a ruling about l as the axis of revolution. Such a cone is called a *right circular cone*.

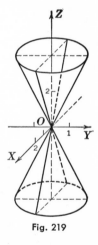

EXAMPLE 1. Obtain the equation of the cone generated by revolving about OZ the line which is the locus of $z = 2y$ in the yz-plane.

Fig. 219

SOLUTION. Replace $|y|$ by $\sqrt{x^2 + y^2}$, and obtain $\pm 2\sqrt{x^2 + y^2} = z$, where "+" applies if $z \geqq 0$ and "−" if $z < 0$. On rationalizing, we find $4x^2 + 4y^2 = z^2$ as the equation of the cone, shown in Figure 219.

EXERCISE 105

Sketch the surface obtained by revolving the locus of the given equation, in the plane of the variables involved, about the specified axis. Show the traces and several circular sections. Also, write the equation of the surface.

1. $z^2 = 4y$; about OY.   **2.** $9y^2 + 25z^2 = 225$; about OY.

3. $9x^2 + 4z^2 = 36$; about OX.   **4.** $x^2 = 6z$; about OZ.

5. $z = 4x$; about OZ.   **6.** $x = 3z$; about OX.

7. $4y^2 - 9z^2 = 36$; about OY.   **8.** $4y^2 - 9z^2 = 36$; about OZ.

First describe the locus of the equation as a surface of revolution, stating its axis and a generatrix. Then, sketch the surface.

9. $4(x^2 + y^2) + z^2 = 4$.   **10.** $z^2 + x^2 + 4y = 0$.

11. $4x^2 + 4y^2 = z^2$.   **12.** $16x^2 + 9y^2 + 9z^2 = 144$.

13. $x^2 - y^2 + z^2 = 4$.   **14.** $9x^2 - y^2 + 9z^2 = 0$.

172. Projecting cylinder for a plane section

Let C be the section of a surface $f(x, y, z) = 0$ made by a plane $z = k$, where k is a constant. Then, C is the intersection of the plane $z = k$ and the *cylinder* H whose equation is $f(x, y, k) = 0$, obtained by using $z = k$ in $f(x, y, z) = 0$. The xy-trace of H is the projection of C on the xy-plane, and is congruent to C. We call H the *projecting cylinder* for the plane section C.

Note 1. Two points P and Q are said to be *symmetric to a plane* T if T is perpendicular to the line segment PQ and bisects PQ.

EXAMPLE 1. Discuss the surface S with the equation

$$\frac{x^2}{4} + \frac{y^2}{9} + \frac{z^2}{25} = 1. \tag{1}$$

SOLUTION. 1. Since all exponents are even, if a point (x, y, z) is on S then $(-x, -y, -z)$ is on S, or S is symmetric to the origin. If (x, y, z) is on S, then $(x, y, -z)$ is on S, or S is symmetric to the xy-plane. Similarly, S is symmetric to the xz-plane and the yz-plane.

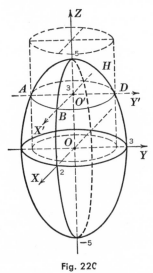

Fig. 220

2. With $z = 0$ in (1), we obtain $9x^2 + 4y^2 = 36$ as the equation whose graph in the xy-plane is the xy-trace of S. This trace is an ellipse. Similarly, the xz-trace and yz-trace are ellipses, as shown in Figure 220.

3. The plane section C of S by the plane $z = 3$ is the locus of

$$\frac{x^2}{4} + \frac{y^2}{9} + \frac{z^2}{25} = 1 \quad and \quad z = 3, or \tag{2}$$

$$\frac{x^2}{4} + \frac{y^2}{9} = 1 - \frac{9}{25} \quad and \quad z = 3. \tag{3}$$

In (3), the quadratic defines an *elliptic cylinder* H perpendicular to the xy-plane. Thus, C is defined by (3) as the intersection of the *plane* $z = 3$ and the *projecting cylinder* H, shown by broken lines in Figure 220, where C is ABD. Hence, C is an ellipse, congruent to the ellipse which is the xy-trace of H. Also, we may think of C as the locus of the quadratic from (3) in *a new system of xy-coordinates* with axes OX' and OY' as shown *in the plane* $z = 3$ in Figure 220.

4. If $z = k$ in (1), we obtain

$$\frac{x^2}{4} + \frac{y^2}{9} = 1 - \frac{k^2}{25};$$ (4)

in (4), the right-hand side is *negative* if $|k| > 5$, and then the locus of (4) is imaginary. Hence, the plane $z = k$ does not intersect (1) if $|k| > 5$, or the range for z is $|z| \leqq 5$. If $|k| \leqq 5$, the locus of (4) is an elliptic cylinder, or the section of (1) by the plane $z = k$ is an ellipse. Similarly, the range for x is $|x| \leqq 2$ and for y is $|y| \leqq 3$. Sections of (1) by planes $x = h$ or $y = g$, in the specified ranges, are ellipses. The graph of (1) is in Figure 220, and is called an *ellipsoid*.

173. The standard quadric surfaces

The locus of any equation of the second degree in x, y, z is called a *quadric surface*, or a *conicoid*, if the locus is real. It can be proved that a quadric surface is either a cylinder with a conic as a directrix curve, or a surface of one of the types which will now be illustrated, in convenient positions, or a corresponding degenerate type of surface. In the following standard forms, the constants a, b, c are positive.

Ellipsoid: $$\frac{x^2}{a^2} + \frac{y^2}{b^2} + \frac{z^2}{c^2} = 1.$$ (1)

Discussion of (1). The surface S which is the graph of (1) has the origin as a center of symmetry, and each coordinate plane as a plane of symmetry, called a *principal plane*. S is illustrated in Figures 216 and 220.

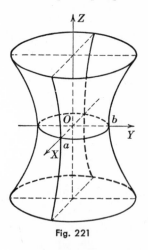

Fig. 221

Hyperboloid of one sheet:

$$\frac{x^2}{a^2} + \frac{y^2}{b^2} - \frac{z^2}{c^2} = 1.$$ (2)

Discussion of (2). The surface S, in Figure 221, which is the graph of (2), has the origin as a center of symmetry and each coordinate plane as a plane of symmetry, called a principal plane. S has no z-intercept. The section of S by any plane $z = k$ is an ellipse. In (2), x and y cannot have values for which the point $(x, y, 0)$ in the xy-plane is inside the ellipse which is the xy-trace of S. Otherwise, the ranges for x, y, z are all real values. Sections by planes $x = g$ or $y = h$ are hyperbolas.

Hyperboloid of two sheets: $$-\frac{x^2}{a^2} + \frac{y^2}{b^2} - \frac{z^2}{c^2} = 1.$$ (3)

Discussion of (3). The surface S which is the graph of (3) is illustrated in Figure 218, page 352, for a case where $a = c$. S has the origin as a center of symmetry, and each coordinate plane as a plane of symmetry. The section C of S by a plane $y = h$ is the locus of the system

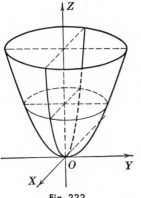

Fig. 222

$$\frac{x^2}{a^2} + \frac{z^2}{c^2} = \frac{h^2}{b^2} - 1 \quad and \quad y = h. \qquad (4)$$

In (4), if $|h| \geq b$, the quadratic defines an elliptic cylinder. The xz-trace of this projecting cylinder is an ellipse; hence, C is an ellipse. If $|h| < b$, the locus of (4) is imaginary. Thus, the range for y in (3) is $|y| \geq b$. The ranges for x and z are all values of the variables. Any section of S by a plane $x = g$, or by $z = k$, is a hyperbola, whose transverse axis in each case is parallel to the y-axis.

Elliptic paraboloid:
$$\frac{x^2}{a^2} + \frac{y^2}{b^2} = pz. \qquad (5)$$

Discussion of (5). In (5), $p \neq 0$. A graph of the surface S represented by (5) is shown in Figure 222 for a case where $p > 0$. Any plane section of S parallel to the xy-plane is an ellipse. A section of S by a plane $x = g$, or a plane $y = h$, is a parabola.

Hyperbolic paraboloid:
$$\frac{y^2}{b^2} - \frac{x^2}{a^2} = pz. \qquad (6)$$

Discussion of (6). In (6), $p \neq 0$. Figure 223 shows a graph of the surface S in (6) with $p > 0$. S is saddle-shaped. The xz-trace and yz-trace are parabolas. The xy-trace is the graph of $a^2y^2 - b^2x^2 = 0$ in the xy-plane, and consists of two lines (not shown) through the origin. If $k \neq 0$, the section C of S by the plane $z = k$ is defined by

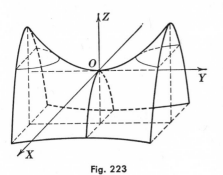

Fig. 223

$$\frac{y^2}{b^2} - \frac{x^2}{a^2} = pk \quad and \quad z = k. \qquad (7)$$

In (7), the quadratic represents a projecting hyperbolic cylinder. Hence, if $p > 0$, the plane section C is a hyperbola with its transverse axis parallel to OY when $k > 0$, and to OX when $k < 0$. Any section of S parallel to the xz-plane or yz-plane is a parabola.

Quadric cone:
$$\frac{x^2}{a^2} + \frac{y^2}{b^2} - \frac{z^2}{c^2} = 0. \qquad (8)$$

Discussion of (8).   The surface S represented by (8) is illustrated in Figure 219, page 352, for a case where $a = b$.   Sections by planes $z = k$ are ellipses, and by planes $x = g$ or $y = h$ are hyperbolas.

EXERCISE 106

Sketch the surface and state its name.   If the equation represents a surface of revolution, or a cylinder, obtain the sketch by an elementary procedure.   Otherwise, discuss the surface as done for (3) *on page 354.*

1. $\dfrac{x^2}{4} + \dfrac{y^2}{9} + \dfrac{z^2}{16} = 1.$ **2.** $-\dfrac{x^2}{4} + \dfrac{y^2}{9} - \dfrac{z^2}{16} = 1.$

3. $\dfrac{x^2}{4} + \dfrac{y^2}{9} - \dfrac{z^2}{16} = 1.$ **4.** $\dfrac{x^2}{4} + \dfrac{y^2}{9} - \dfrac{z^2}{16} = 0.$

5. $\dfrac{x^2}{9} + \dfrac{y^2}{25} = z.$ **6.** $\dfrac{x^2}{4} + \dfrac{z^2}{9} = 2y.$

7. $\dfrac{y^2}{9} - \dfrac{x^2}{25} = z.$ **8.** $\dfrac{x^2}{9} - \dfrac{y^2}{4} + \dfrac{z^2}{25} = 1.$

9. $16x^2 + 16y^2 - 25z^2 = -400.$ **10.** $4x^2 + 4y^2 - 9z^2 = 36.$

11. $\dfrac{x^2}{9} - \dfrac{y^2}{4} + \dfrac{z^2}{9} = 0.$ **12.** $\dfrac{x^2}{9} - \dfrac{y^2}{25} = z.$

13. $x^2 = 16y^2.$ **14.** $z^2 - 6y = 0.$ **15.** $x^2 - 4z^2 = 16.$

★16.   Prove that the locus of equation (8) of Section 173 is a cone, as defined on page 352, with the origin O as the vertex.

Hint.   Let C represent any section of the surface made by a plane $z = k$. Let $P':(x', y', k)$ be on C.   Prove that every point P on the line OP' lies on the locus.

174. Space curves

A space path may be defined parametrically, in terms of a parameter t, by a set of equations

$$x = f(t), \quad y = g(t), \quad z = h(t). \tag{1}$$

The straight-line case of (1) was met on page 345.

ILLUSTRATION 1.   Suppose that a point $P:(x, y, z)$ moves clockwise on the cylinder $x^2 + y^2 = a^2$ with a constant angular speed of ω radians per second about the z-axis, and a constant speed of k units per second in the vertical direction.   If P is at $(0, a, 0)$ when the time t (in seconds) is zero, the position of P at any time t is given by

$$x = a \sin \omega t; \quad y = a \cos \omega t; \quad z = kt. \tag{2}$$

The path traced by P, as in Figure 224, is called a circular **helix**.

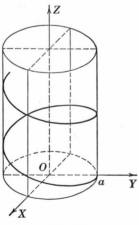

Fig. 224

Suppose that C is the curve of intersection of two surfaces

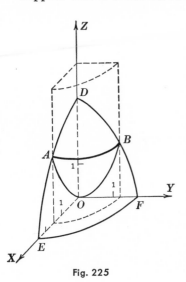

Fig. 225

$$f(x, y, z) = 0 \quad and \quad g(x, y, z) = 0. \quad (3)$$

Then, intersections of the traces of the surfaces in (3) determine points on C. Also, as an aid in visualizing C, it is useful to obtain the equations of one or more of the cylinders which would project C onto the coordinate planes. To find the equation of the cylinder projecting C onto the xy-plane, eliminate z between equations (3), etc. for the cylinders projecting C onto the yz-plane and xz-plane. However, sometimes the elimination just mentioned proves to be impossible or very inconvenient.

ILLUSTRATION 2. In Figure 225, arc AB in the 1st octant is a part of the curve of intersection of the paraboloids

$$z = 3 - \tfrac{1}{2}x^2 - y^2 \quad and \quad z = x^2 + y^2. \quad (4)$$

In Figure 225, the surface $z = 3 - \tfrac{1}{2}x^2 - y^2$ is outlined by DEF, and the surface $z = x^2 + y^2$ by ABO. The intersection of the xz-traces is A, and of the yz-traces is B. On eliminating z in (4) by subtraction, we obtain the projecting elliptic cylinder $3x^2 + 4y^2 = 6$, shown by broken lines in Figure 225, which projects C onto the xy-plane. The coordinates of A can be checked by using $y = 0$ in (4) and solving for x and z, which gives $(\sqrt{2}, 0, 2)$. Similarly, B has the coordinates $(0, \tfrac{1}{2}\sqrt{6}, \tfrac{3}{2})$.

EXERCISE 107

By eliminating t between two equations, obtain the equation of a cylinder, perpendicular to the xy-plane, on which the path C lies. Also, compute points on C by use of its parametric equations and draw an arc of C.

1. $x = 3 \sin t, y = 3 \cos t, z = 2t$.

2. $x = 2 \cos^2 t, y = 2 \sin^2 t, z = \sin t$.   3. $x = 3 - t, y = t, z = t^2$.

Draw an arc of the curve C defined by the equations. If neither of the given surfaces is a cylinder, draw a projecting cylinder for C.

4. $x^2 + y^2 = 9$ and $3z = y$.   5. $x^2 + y^2 = 9$ and $x^2 + z^2 = 9$.

6. $x^2 + y^2 + z^2 = 25$ and $x^2 + y^2 = 16$.

7. $x^2 + y^2 + z^2 = 25$ and $16x^2 + 16y^2 = 9z^2$.

8. $x^2 + y^2 + z^2 = 16$ and $x^2 + y^2 - 4y = 0$.

9. $y = 3 - z^2 - \tfrac{1}{3}x^2$ and $y = x^2 + \tfrac{1}{3}z^2$.

10. $4x^2 + 9y^2 - 4z^2 = 36$ and $x^2 + z^2 = 9$.

11. $z = x^2 + y^2$ and $z - 2x - 2y = 0$.

18

INTRODUCTION TO PARTIAL DIFFERENTIATION

175. Functions of more than one variable

The following definitions are concerned with a function $f(x, y)$, where the point (x, y) is in some rectangle in the xy-plane including the fixed point (x_0, y_0), as in Figure 226. In Definition I, $f(x, y)$ is assumed to be defined at all points involved except perhaps at (x_0, y_0).

DEFINITION I. *To say that the limit of $f(x, y)$ is L as $x \to x_0$ and $y \to y_0$, means that, when (x, y) is not (x_0, y_0), $f(x, y)$ is as near L as we please for all points (x, y) sufficiently near (x_0, y_0).*

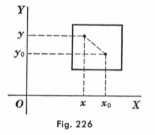

Fig. 226

When a limit exists as just described, we write

$$f(x, y) \to L \text{ as } x \to x_0 \text{ and } y \to y_0, \text{ or}$$

$$\lim_{x \to x_0; \ y \to y_0} f(x, y) = L. \tag{1}$$

Statement (1) means that, if (x, y) is not (x_0, y_0), then $|f(x, y) - L|$ is as small as we please for all points (x, y) sufficiently near (x_0, y_0).

DEFINITION II. *To say that a function $f(x, y)$ is continuous at (x_0, y_0) means that $f(x, y)$ is defined at (x_0, y_0), $f(x, y)$ has a limit as $x \to x_0$ and $y \to y_0$, and*

$$\lim_{x \to x_0; \ y \to y_0} f(x, y) = f(x_0, y_0), \text{ or} \tag{2}$$

$$\lim_{\Delta x \to 0; \ \Delta y \to 0} f(x_0 + \Delta x, y_0 + \Delta y) = f(x_0, y_0). \tag{3}$$

Suppose that the surface in Figure 227 on page 359 is a graph of $z = f(x, y)$, where $z_0 = f(x_0, y_0)$, and P_0 is the point (x_0, y_0, z_0). Then, (2) states that, as $x \to x_0$ and $y \to y_0$, the limit of the z-coordinate of P in Figure 227 is the z-coordinate of P_0.

The notions of a limit and continuity for a function of two variables extend to functions of any number of variables. Thus, we may refer to a function $f(x, y, z, w)$ being continuous at a point (x_0, y_0, z_0, w_0). The theorems on page 19 about limits of functions of a single variable extend to limits of

358

functions of any number of variables. Without proof, we accept the fact that any function of two or more variables, which is expressible in terms of the elementary functions of analysis, is a continuous function of the variables at any set of their values where the function is defined.

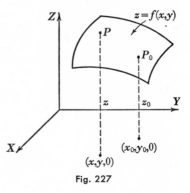

Fig. 227

ILLUSTRATION 1. $\sin (x + 2y + z^2)$ is continuous at all points (x_0, y_0, z_0).

Note 1. The limit concept in Definition I involves a condition about x and y, *simultaneously.* Thus, it is possible for a function $f(x, y)$ to be of such a nature that there exist separately $\lim_{x \to x_0} f(x, y_0)$ and $\lim_{y \to y_0} f(x_0, y)$, when (1) does not exist (see Problem 25 on page 361).

Note 2. By Definition I, equation (1) means that, for every number $\epsilon > 0$ there exists a corresponding number $\delta > 0$ such that

$$if \quad 0 < \sqrt{(x - x_0)^2 + (y - y_0)^2} < \delta \quad then \quad |f(x, y) - L| < \epsilon. \qquad (4)$$

In (4), the radical is equal to the distance between (x, y) and (x_0, y_0).

Note 3. A continuous function of two or more variables has properties similar to those mentioned in (9) on page 72 for a function of just one variable. Thus, if the function $f(x, y)$ is continuous when (x, y) is in the **closed** rectangle $R:(|x - a| \leq h, |y - b| \leq k)$, then f is *bounded*, with a least upper bound M and greatest lower bound m. Moreover, there exist points (x_1, y_1) and (x_2, y_2) in R such that $f(x_1, y_1) = m$ and $f(x_2, y_2) = M$; or, f has an *absolute minimum* m and *absolute maximum* M. Also, if γ is such that $m \leq \gamma \leq M$, there exists a point (α, β) in R such that $f(x, y) = \gamma$. That is, f *attains* each value from m to M inclusive at least once in R.

176. Partial derivatives

Consider a function $z = f(x, y)$. If y is held fast, for the moment, z becomes a function of x alone. If this function has a derivative, we call it the partial derivative of z with respect to x, and represent it by

$$\frac{\partial z}{\partial x}, \quad z_x, \quad \frac{\partial f(x, y)}{\partial x}, \quad or \quad f_x(x, y). \qquad (1)$$

In (1), we read $\frac{\partial z}{\partial x}$ or z_x as " *the partial derivative of z with respect to x.*" Also, we may read z_x as "*z sub x.*" Thus, in analytical form, at any point (x, y), we define z_x, or f_x, by the equation

$$\frac{\partial f(x, y)}{\partial x} = \lim_{\Delta x \to 0} \frac{f(x + \Delta x, y) - f(x, y)}{\Delta x}, \qquad (2)$$

if the limit exists. The numerator in (2) is the increment of $f(x, y)$ due to a change from (x, y) to $(x + \Delta x, y)$ in the xy-plane. Hence, we may call f_x the rate of change of $f(x, y)$ in the x-direction. Similarly, we define f_y. For contrast with partial derivatives, the derivative of a function of a *single independent variable* may be called an *ordinary derivative*.

If u is a function of x and any number of other independent variables, the partial derivative u_x is defined as the ordinary derivative of u with respect to x when the other independent variables are held fast. Thus, the usual formulas for differentiation apply in obtaining a partial derivative, because it is an ordinary derivative when certain variables are held constant.

ILLUSTRATION 1.   If $z = ye^x + \sin (2x + 3y)$, then

$$\frac{\partial z}{\partial x} = ye^x + 2 \cos (2x + 3y); \quad \frac{\partial z}{\partial y} = e^x + 3 \cos (2x + 3y).$$

ILLUSTRATION 2.   If $f(x, y, z) = x^2y + y^2z + xz^2$,

$$f_x = 2xy + z^2; \quad f_y = x^2 + 2yz; \quad f_z = y^2 + 2xz.$$

For a function $f(x, y)$, in place of the symbol $\dfrac{\partial f}{\partial x}$, we may write

$$\left(\frac{\partial f}{\partial x}\right)_y, \tag{3}$$

which is read "*the partial derivative of f with respect to x when y is held fast.*" The notation in (3) has the advantage of indicating both of the independent variables involved. To indicate the value of a partial derivative at a particular point, we use notations such as

$$\frac{\partial z}{\partial x}\bigg|_{(x_0,\, y_0)}, \ f_x(x_0, y_0), \ \frac{\partial f(x_0, y_0)}{\partial x}, \ \frac{\partial f(x, y)}{\partial x}\bigg|_{(x_0,\, y_0)}.$$

ILLUSTRATION 3.   In Illustration 2,

$$\frac{\partial f(x, y, z)}{\partial x} = 2xy + z^2; \quad \frac{\partial f(2, -1, 3)}{\partial x} = 5.$$

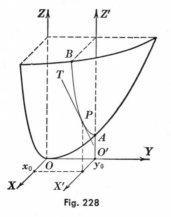

Fig. 228

In order to consider a certain geometrical interpretation for partial derivatives, let $P:(x_0, y_0, z_0)$ be a point on the surface $z = f(x, y)$, in an xyz-system of coordinates. The plane $y = y_0$ intersects the surface in a curve C, lettered APB in Figure 228, and the y-axis at O'. In the plane $y = y_0$, introduce new axes $O'X'$ and $O'Z'$ with the directions of OX and OZ, respectively. Draw the tangent line PT for C at P, and let α be the angle from the x'-axis to PT. In the plane $y = y_0$, or the $x'z'$-plane, the equation of C is $z' = f(x', y_0)$, or $z = f(x, y_0)$, where we drop the primes for convenience. Now, for temporary purposes, think of the coordinate x as the abscissa on C.

Then, the slope of PT is $\tan \alpha = z_x$, evaluated at $(x = x_0, y = y_0)$. Similarly, the value of z_y at P can be interpreted as a slope.

EXAMPLE 1. Find the slope of the curve of intersection of the plane $y = 2$ and the elliptic paraboloid $z = x^2 + \frac{1}{4}y^2$ at the point $P:(1, 2, 2)$.

SOLUTION. We find $z_x = 2x$. The plane $y = 2$ intersects the surface in a curve whose slope at P is $\tan \alpha$, where

$$slope = \tan \alpha = \frac{\partial z}{\partial x}\bigg|_{(x=1,\,y=2)} = 2x\bigg|_{(x=1)} = 2.$$

With a proper choice of units, Figure 228 corresponds to the data.

EXERCISE 108

Find the partial derivatives of the given function with respect to each of the independent variables x, y, or z which is involved.

1. $u = 3x^2y + 4x^3y$.

2. $u = \sin x \cos y$.

3. $w = e^{3x+2y}$.

4. $v = e^{2x} \ln y$.

5. $w = (x^2 + xy)^3$.

6. $u = \sqrt{x^2 + 4y^2}$.

7. $f(x, y) = (3x^2 - 2y)^{\frac{3}{2}}$.

8. $g(x, z) = e^{3x^2z}$.

9. $f(x, y) = \sin 4xy$.

10. $F(x, y) = \text{Arcsin } (2x + 3y)$.

11. $G(x, z) = ze^{-2x} + xe^{-3z}$.

12. $f(x, y) = \text{Arctan } x^2y$.

13. $H(x, y) = \tan (4x - 5y)^2$.

14. $f(x, y) = \dfrac{\sec 3xy}{e^y}$.

15. $g(x, z) = \dfrac{10^{2x}}{4x + 3z}$.

16. $\sin xy + \cos yz + \tan xz$.

17. $e^y \ln x + e^z \ln y$.

18. Find f_ρ and f_θ if $f(\rho, \theta) = \rho^3 \sin \theta + e^\rho \cos \theta$.

19. If $F(x, y) = 3x^2 + 7xy^3$, find $F_x(3, 1)$; $F_y(2, -1)$.

20. If $g(r, \theta) = 4r^2 \sin 2\theta$, find $g_r(-2, \frac{1}{4}\pi)$, $g_\theta(1, \frac{1}{2}\pi)$.

21. If $u = 3xy^2z$, find the rate of change of u in the direction of the y-axis in an xyz-system of coordinates, at $(-2, 1, 3)$.

22. Find the rates of change of the function $u = 4x^2 + 3xy$ in the x-direction and the y-direction at $(x = -2, y = 3)$ in the xy-plane.

23. The surface $z = x^2 + 4y^2$ is intersected by the plane $x = 2$ in a curve C_1. Find the slope of C_1 at $(2, 1, 8)$. The plane $y = 1$ intersects the surface in a curve C_2. Find the slope of C_2 at $(2, 1, 8)$.

24. The surface $z = x^2 - y^2$ is intersected in curves C_1 and C_2 by planes $x = 3$ and $y = 1$, respectively. Find the slopes of these curves at their point of intersection, where $x = 3$ and $y = 1$.

★25. Consider the function $f(x, y) = xy/(x^2 + y^2)$, which is not defined at $(x = 0, y = 0)$. Prove that (a) $f(x, 0) \to 0$ as $x \to 0$ and $f(0, y) \to 0$ as $y \to 0$; (b) if m has any value and $y = mx$, show that $f(x, y) \to m/(1 + m^2)$ as $x \to 0$. (c) Does $f(x, y)$ have a limit as $x \to 0$ and $y \to 0$? This example is designed to show that a function $f(x, y)$ may have no limit as "$x \to x_0$ and $y \to y_0$" although, separately, there may exist limits of $f(x, y_0)$ as $x \to x_0$, and of $f(x_0, y)$ as $y \to y_0$.

177. Partial derivatives of higher orders

Partial derivatives of partial derivatives may be considered. If just two successive partial differentiations are involved, the result is called a partial derivative of the *second order*. Similarly, we introduce partial derivatives of the third and higher orders. If $z = f(x, y)$, notations employed for the derivatives of the second order are

$$\frac{\partial^2 z}{\partial x^2} = \frac{\partial}{\partial x}\left(\frac{\partial z}{\partial x}\right) = f_{xx}; \quad \frac{\partial^2 z}{\partial y^2} = \frac{\partial}{\partial y}\left(\frac{\partial z}{\partial y}\right) = f_{yy}; \tag{1}$$

$$\frac{\partial^2 z}{\partial x\, \partial y} = \frac{\partial}{\partial x}\left(\frac{\partial z}{\partial y}\right) = f_{yx}; \quad \frac{\partial^2 z}{\partial y\, \partial x} = \frac{\partial}{\partial y}\left(\frac{\partial z}{\partial x}\right) = f_{xy}. \tag{2}$$

It can be proved that, if all derivatives which enter are continuous functions, the two results in (2) are identical for all values of x and y. That is, *the order of successive partial differentiations is immaterial.* This important result applies to partial derivatives of all orders, and will be taken without proof.

We read $\dfrac{\partial^2 z}{\partial x^2}$ as "*the second partial derivative of z with respect to x;*" $\dfrac{\partial^2 z}{\partial x\, \partial y}$, or

$\dfrac{\partial^2 z}{\partial y\, \partial x}$, is "*the second partial derivative of z with respect to x and y,*" where it is immaterial which variable is mentioned first; $\dfrac{\partial^3 z}{\partial x\, \partial y^2}$ is "*the third derivative of z with respect to x once and y twice.*"

ILLUSTRATION 1. If $z = \tan x \sin y$, then

$$\frac{\partial z}{\partial x} = \sec^2 x \sin y; \quad \frac{\partial z}{\partial y} = \tan x \cos y;$$

$$\frac{\partial^2 z}{\partial x^2} = \frac{\partial}{\partial x}(\sec^2 x \sin y) = 2 \sec^2 x \tan x \sin y;$$

$$\frac{\partial^2 z}{\partial x\, \partial y} = \frac{\partial}{\partial x}\left(\frac{\partial z}{\partial y}\right) = \frac{\partial}{\partial x}(\tan x \cos y) = \sec^2 x \cos y; \ or,$$

$$\frac{\partial^2 z}{\partial y\, \partial x} = \frac{\partial}{\partial y}\left(\frac{\partial z}{\partial x}\right) = \sec^2 x \cos y, \ as \ above.$$

$$\frac{\partial^3 z}{\partial x^2\, \partial y} = \frac{\partial}{\partial x}\left(\frac{\partial^2 z}{\partial x\, \partial y}\right) = \frac{\partial}{\partial x}(\sec^2 x \cos y) = 2 \sec^2 x \tan x \cos y; \ or$$

$$\frac{\partial^3 z}{\partial x^2\, \partial y} = \frac{\partial}{\partial y}\left(\frac{\partial^2 z}{\partial x^2}\right) = \frac{\partial}{\partial y}(2 \sec^2 x \tan x \sin y) = 2 \sec^2 x \tan x \cos y.$$

EXERCISE 109

Find all partial derivatives of the second order for the given function. The independent variables are x, y, and z.

1. $u = x^3 y^4$. **2.** $v = e^{x+3y}$. **3.** $u = \sin x^2 y$.

4. $u = \sin x \cos 2y$. **5.** $w = e^x \ln y$. **6.** $v = \text{Arcsin } xy$.

7. $f(x, y) = x^3 + 4x^2y - y^3$.   **8.** $f(x, y) = (x + 3x^3y^2)^2$.

9. $g(x, y) = \sqrt{x^2 - y^2}$.   **10.** $f(x, y, z) = x^3y^2z^4$.

11. $g(x, y, z) = \cos xyz$.   **12.** $F(x, y, z) = e^x + ye^z + ze^y$.

13. Arctan (x/y).   **14.** e^{3xyz}.   **15.** $\cos (x + 2y - 3z)$.

Obtain the third partial derivatives of z with respect to x twice and y once, and x once and y twice.

16. $z = x^2y^3 + 4xy^4$.   **17.** $z = \sin x^2y^2$.

Obtain the second partial derivative of z with respect to x and y, by differentiating in two different orders: first with respect to x, and second with respect to y; then, with the order reversed.

18. $z = \tan x \sec y$.   **19.** $z = e^x \cos y$.

20. If $u = x^3 + x^2y$, prove that $x \dfrac{\partial u}{\partial x} + y \dfrac{\partial u}{\partial y} = 3u$.

21. If $u = \text{Arcsin} \dfrac{y}{x}$, prove that $x \dfrac{\partial u}{\partial x} + y \dfrac{\partial u}{\partial y} = 0$.

The partial differential equation

$$\frac{\partial^2 u}{\partial x^2} + \frac{\partial^2 u}{\partial y^2} = 0 \tag{1}$$

is called **Laplace's equation,** *in two variables, and is important in applied mathematics. Prove that the function in the problem satisfies* (1).

22. $u = x^3 - 3xy^2$.   **23.** $u = 3x^2y - y^3$.   **24.** $u = e^x \cos y$.

178. Partial derivatives of implicit functions, single equations

The method used on page 51 for obtaining the derivative of an implicit function of a single variable applies also in the case of partial derivatives.

EXAMPLE 1. Find z_x at $(x = 2, y = -1, z = 3)$, if the variables x, y, z are related by

$$x^3 + 2xz - 2yz^2 - z^3 = 11. \tag{1}$$

SOLUTION. 1. The notation z_x specifies that x is an independent variable, and z is a dependent variable. Not more than one dependent variable can be defined as a function of other variables by *a single equation*. Hence, y also is an independent variable, and z is considered as a function of x and y, satisfying (1). Thus, z_x means the derivative of z with respect to x, *with y held fast.*

2. With y held fast in (1), differentiate both sides with respect to x:

$$3x^2 + 2z + 2x \frac{\partial z}{\partial x} - 4yz \frac{\partial z}{\partial x} - 3z^2 \frac{\partial z}{\partial x} = 0; \quad \frac{\partial z}{\partial x}(4yz + 3z^2 - 2x) = 3x^2 + 2z;$$

$$\frac{\partial z}{\partial x} = \frac{3x^2 + 2z}{4yz + 3z^2 - 2x}; \quad \frac{\partial z}{\partial x}\bigg|_{(2, -1, 3)} = \frac{18}{11}.$$

EXAMPLE 2. Find $\dfrac{\partial u}{\partial z}$ if the variables u, x, and z satisfy

$$\tan (x^2 + 3u) + \tan (3z + u^2) = 5. \tag{2}$$

SOLUTION. The problem specifies u as a dependent variable which is to be considered as a function of x and z in (2). *With x held fast,* differentiate with respect to z on both sides of (2):

$$\sec^2 (x^2 + 3u) \frac{\partial (x^2 + 3u)}{\partial z} + \sec^2 (3z + u^2) \frac{\partial (3z + u^2)}{\partial z} = 0, \; or$$

$$3[\sec^2 (x^2 + 3u)] \frac{\partial u}{\partial z} + [\sec^2 (3z + u^2)]\left(3 + 2u \frac{\partial u}{\partial z}\right) = 0, \; or$$

$$\frac{\partial u}{\partial z} = \frac{- 3 \sec^2 (3z + u^2)}{2u \sec^2 (3z + u^2) + 3 \sec^2 (x^2 + 3u)}.$$

EXERCISE 110

Find $\dfrac{\partial z}{\partial x}$ and $\dfrac{\partial z}{\partial y}$, and evaluate the derivatives at any given point. Do not expand powers.

1. $x^2 + 4y^2 + z^2 = 8.$

2. $x^3 + y^3 + z^3 = 6.$

3. $e^z + e^y + e^x = 5.$

4. $\ln x + \ln y - \ln z = e^x.$

5. $x^2 + 4y^2 - z^2 = 4$, at $(- 3, 1, 3).$

6. $z^3 - 2xz + y^2 = 6$, at $(2, 3, 1).$

7. $z^2 - xz^3 + 10yz = - 78$, at $(1, - 2, 3).$

8. $(x + 2z)^7 + (3y - z^2)^5 = 2.$

9. $x^{\frac{2}{3}} + y^{\frac{2}{3}} + z^{\frac{2}{3}} = a^{\frac{2}{3}}.$

10. $\sin x + \cos y = \tan z.$

11. $\ln x - e^z = xy^2.$

12. $\sqrt{x^2 + z^2} + \sqrt{y^2 - z^2} = 5.$

13. $\sin x \cos z + \cos y \sin z = z.$

14. $e^{2x+3z} + e^{2z-4y} = 6.$

15. $xe^{z^2+x} - ye^{2z-y} = 3.$

16. $\sin (x + 2z) + \cos (3y + 4z) = 1.$

17. $\ln (2x + z) + e^{y-3z} = 4.$

18. $\ln (4x - z^2) = \tan (x + y + 3z).$

19. $2 \tan (2x - z^2) = 1 + \cot (y^2 - 2z).$

20. $\dfrac{x + 3z}{y^2 + z^2} = e^{4z}.$

21. $\dfrac{e^x - e^{2z}}{e^y + e^z} = 2x + 5yz.$

22. If $x^2 + y^2 + z^2 = 25$, find $\dfrac{\partial^2 z}{\partial x^2}$ and $\dfrac{\partial^2 z}{\partial x \, \partial y}.$

23. Find $\dfrac{\partial^2 z}{\partial x \, \partial y}$ at $(- 3, 1, 3)$ in Problem 5.

179. Implicit functions defined by systems of equations

As a rule, n simultaneous equations in more than n variables define any n of the variables as functions of the other variables, considered independent. Under conditions as met in this text, these functions will possess continuous derivatives with respect to the independent variables. Suppose, now, that the equations are written in terms of elementary functions,* and define certain functions implicitly. Then, their derivatives can be obtained by a method similar to that employed in the preceding section.

EXAMPLE 1. Find du/dx and dv/dx if x, u, v satisfy

$$3x^2 + 2u^2v = 5, \atop xu + uv^2 = 2. \Bigg\} \tag{1}$$

SOLUTION. 1. In (1), x is the independent variable. Differentiate with respect to x in each equation, where u and v are functions of x:

$$6x + 4uv\,\frac{du}{dx} + 2u^2\,\frac{dv}{dx} = 0, \atop u + x\,\frac{du}{dx} + v^2\,\frac{du}{dx} + 2uv\,\frac{dv}{dx} = 0. \Bigg\} \tag{2}$$

Thus,

$$4uv\,\frac{du}{dx} + 2u^2\,\frac{dv}{dx} = -6x, \atop (x + v^2)\,\frac{du}{dx} + 2uv\,\frac{dv}{dx} = -u \Bigg\} \tag{3}$$

2. Solve (3) for du/dx and dv/dx by use of determinants:

$$\frac{du}{dx} = \frac{\begin{vmatrix} -6x & 2u^2 \\ -u & 2uv \end{vmatrix}}{\begin{vmatrix} 4uv & 2u^2 \\ (x + v^2) & 2uv \end{vmatrix}} = \frac{2u^3 - 12uvx}{6u^2v^2 - 2u^2x} = \frac{u^2 - 6vx}{3uv^2 - ux}; \tag{4}$$

$$\frac{dv}{dx} = \frac{\begin{vmatrix} 4uv & -6x \\ (x + v^2) & -u \end{vmatrix}}{6u^2v^2 - 2u^2x} = \frac{3x^2 + 3v^2x - 2u^2v}{3u^2v^2 - u^2x}.$$

EXAMPLE 2. Find $\dfrac{\partial u}{\partial x}$ and $\dfrac{\partial v}{\partial x}$ if the variables (x, y, u, v) satisfy

$$u^3 + v - 2x = 0, \atop v^3 + u - y = 0. \Bigg\} \tag{5}$$

SOLUTION. 1. The nature of the requested derivatives assigns u and v as *dependent* variables, and x as an *independent* variable. Hence, y also is an independent variable, because two equations can determine only two unknown functions (dependent variables). Thus, we consider (5) as defining u and v as functions of x and y.

2. Hold y fast and differentiate with respect to x on both sides in each equation in (5):

---

* If any equation is written in general functional notation, such as $f(x, y, u) = 0$, general theorems (to be met later) on partial differentiation are required to obtain results corresponding to the special cases which will be treated at present.

$$3u^2 \frac{\partial u}{\partial x} + \frac{\partial v}{\partial x} = 2, \Bigg\}$$

$$\frac{\partial u}{\partial x} + 3v^2 \frac{\partial v}{\partial x} = 0. \Bigg\}$$

$$(6)$$

On solving for the derivatives in (6) by use of determinants, we obtain

$$\left(\frac{\partial u}{\partial x}\right)_y = \frac{6v^2}{9u^2v^2 - 1}, \quad \text{and} \quad \left(\frac{\partial v}{\partial x}\right)_y = \frac{2}{1 - 9u^2v^2}. \qquad (7)$$

EXAMPLE 3.   In (5), find $\frac{\partial u}{\partial x}$ if v is an independent variable.

SOLUTION.   Now, we consider (5) as defining u and y as functions of x and v.   From (5), $u^3 = 2x - v$.   Hence, with v held fast, we obtain

$$3u^2 \frac{\partial u}{\partial x} = 2, \quad \text{or} \quad \left(\frac{\partial u}{\partial x}\right)_v = \frac{2}{3u^2}. \qquad (8)$$

Comment.   In (8), we found $\frac{\partial u}{\partial x}$ with v held fast.   In (7), y was held fast.

Thus, *the symbol for a partial derivative may have different meanings, depending on the choice of independent variables.*

EXAMPLE 4.   Find $\frac{\partial x}{\partial u}$ in (5) if v is an independent variable.

SOLUTION.   From (5), $x = \frac{1}{2}u^3 + \frac{1}{2}v$.   Hence

$$\left(\frac{\partial x}{\partial u}\right)_v = \frac{3}{2} u^2. \qquad (9)$$

In (9), $\frac{\partial x}{\partial u}$ is *not the reciprocal of* $\frac{\partial u}{\partial x}$ *in* (7), but *is the reciprocal of* $\frac{\partial u}{\partial x}$ *in* (8), which happens because the second independent variable involved is the same in (8) and (9).   *This shows the futility of trying to attach separate meanings to the symbols "∂u" and "∂x" which would apply in all situations and would make $\frac{\partial u}{\partial x}$ a true quotient.*   Hence, a partial derivative $\frac{\partial u}{\partial x}$ *always should be treated as a whole* and *never should be read like a quotient.*

EXERCISE 111

Find dy/dx and dz/dx if x, y, and z satisfy the simultaneous equations.

1. $\begin{cases} 3x + 2y + 3z = 4, \\ 2x - 3y + 5z = 2. \end{cases}$ 2. $\begin{cases} 6x - 3y + z = 4, \\ 2x + 2y - z = 3. \end{cases}$

3. $\begin{cases} x^2 + y^2 - 2z^2 = 1, \\ 3x + 2y - z = 5. \end{cases}$ 4. $\begin{cases} xy + yz + xz = 4, \\ 2x + 3y - 2z = 1. \end{cases}$

5. $\begin{cases} y^2 + xz = 3x, \\ z^2 - xy = x^2. \end{cases}$ 6. $\begin{cases} xy^2 - 3z = 4, \\ xz^2 - yz = 3. \end{cases}$

Find the derivatives of u and v with respect to x and y.

7.
$$\begin{cases} 2x + y - 3u - 5v = 2, \\ x - y + 2u + 3v = 1. \end{cases}$$

8.
$$\begin{cases} 3x - y - u - v = 4, \\ 2x + 3y - u + 4v = 7. \end{cases}$$

9.
$$\begin{cases} u^2 + v^2 - x = 0, \\ v^2 + u - y = 0. \end{cases}$$

10.
$$\begin{cases} x = u^2 + v^2, \\ y = 3uv. \end{cases}$$

11.
$$\begin{cases} ux + v^2y = 1, \\ u^2x - vy = 4. \end{cases}$$

12.
$$\begin{cases} 3u^3 + ux + vy = 5, \\ v^3 + uy - vx = 1. \end{cases}$$

13.
$$\begin{cases} x = u \cos v, \\ y = u \sin v. \end{cases}$$

14.
$$\begin{cases} \sin ux + \cos vy = x, \\ \sin vx + \cos uy = y. \end{cases}$$

15–18. Obtain $\dfrac{\partial x}{\partial u}$ and $\dfrac{\partial y}{\partial v}$ in Problems 7–10; compare with previous results.

19. Find $\dfrac{dy}{dx}$ if
$$\begin{cases} \sin x + y^2 - 3z = 0, \\ \cos x + z^2 - 2y = 0. \end{cases}$$

20. Find $\left(\dfrac{\partial u}{\partial x}\right)_y$ if
$$\begin{cases} u^2 - v + 3x - y^2 = 4, \\ v^2 - u + 2y + x^2 = 1. \end{cases}$$

21. In Problem 20, find $\dfrac{\partial u}{\partial x}$ with a different meaning for the symbol.

22. Find $\left(\dfrac{\partial u}{\partial x}\right)_y$ if
$$\begin{cases} 3 \sin (x + 2v) + \cos (y + 3u) = 1, \\ 2 \cos (2x - u) - \cos (y + 2v) = 1. \end{cases}$$

180. Total differentials

Consider a function $u = f(x, y)$, where f_x and f_y are continuous functions of x and y. At a given point $(x = x_1, y = y_1)$, with Δx and Δy as arbitrary increments for x and y, let

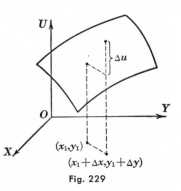

Fig. 229

$$\Delta u = f(x_1 + \Delta x, y_1 + \Delta y) - f(x_1, y_1). \quad (1)$$

Then, on page 474, it will be proved that there exist quantities ϵ_1 and ϵ_2, which are functions of Δx and Δy, such that

$$\Delta u = \frac{\partial u}{\partial x} \Delta x + \frac{\partial u}{\partial y} \Delta y + \epsilon_1 \Delta x + \epsilon_2 \Delta y, \quad (2)$$

where the derivatives are evaluated at (x_1, y_1) and

$$\epsilon_1 \to 0 \quad and \quad \epsilon_2 \to 0 \quad as \quad \Delta x \to 0 \quad and \quad \Delta y \to 0. \quad (3)$$

In (1), Δu is the increment in the ordinate on the graph of $u = f(x, y)$, due to a change from $(x = x_1, y = y_1)$ to $(x = x_1 + \Delta x, y = y_1 + \Delta y)$, as in Figure 229. Then, from (2), it is seen that $\Delta u \to 0$ as $\Delta x \to 0$ and $\Delta y \to 0$, so that u is a continuous function of x and y.

In (2), if Δx and Δy are sufficiently small, each of the terms $\epsilon_1 \Delta x$ and $\epsilon_2 \Delta y$ is a product of *two* small numbers, and is *small in comparison with Δx and Δy*. Hence, in general, when Δx and Δy are sufficiently small, the first two terms on the right in (2) form the *dominant part* of Δu, and should give a good approximation to Δu. The preceding remarks motivate the following terminology.

DEFINITION III.   *Suppose that x and y are independent variables, and that the function $u = f(x, y)$ has partial derivatives with respect to x and y.   Then, the* **total differential,** *du, of u at any point (x, y) corresponding to increments Δx and Δy, is defined by*

$$du = \frac{\partial u}{\partial x} \Delta x + \frac{\partial u}{\partial y} \Delta y. \tag{4}$$

We define the differentials dx and dy of the independent variables to be their increments, or $dx = \Delta x$ and $dy = \Delta y$.   Then, (4) becomes

$$du = \frac{\partial u}{\partial x} dx + \frac{\partial u}{\partial y} dy, \text{ or} \tag{5}$$

$[u = f(x, y)]$
$$du = \frac{\partial f}{\partial x} dx + \frac{\partial f}{\partial y} dy. \tag{6}$$

Similarly, the total differential of a function $u = f(x, y, z)$ is

$$du = \frac{\partial u}{\partial x} dx + \frac{\partial u}{\partial y} dy + \frac{\partial u}{\partial z} dz, \tag{7}$$

etc., for functions of more than three independent variables.

ILLUSTRATION 1.   If $u = 3x^2y^3$, then

$$\frac{\partial u}{\partial x} = 6xy^3; \quad \frac{\partial u}{\partial y} = 9x^2y^2; \quad du = 6xy^3 \, dx + 9x^2y^2 \, dy.$$

At $(x = 2, y = -1)$, when $dx = .1$ and $dy = -.2$,

$$du = -12(.1) + 36(-.2) = -8.4.$$

EXAMPLE 1.   If $u = xy$, find Δu and du if $x = 3$, $y = 4$, $dx = .2$, $dy = .3$.

SOLUTION.   1. $x + dx = 3.2$; $y + dy = 4.3$.   Hence,

$$\Delta u = (x + dx)(y + dy) - xy = 3.2(4.3) - 3 \cdot 4 = 1.76.$$

2. From (5) with $u = xy$,

$$\frac{\partial u}{\partial x} = y; \quad \frac{\partial u}{\partial y} = x; \quad du = y \, dx + x \, dy.$$

Hence, we obtain

$$du = 4(.2) + 3(.3) = 1.7.$$

Thus, the error of du as an approximation to Δu is $-.06$.

181. Calculation of total differentials by standard forms

The standard forms for differentials on page 157 were proved only for functions of a single variable. Fortunately, these forms apply also for functions of more than one independent variable. We shall prove the formulas for the case where there are just two independent variables. Similar proofs apply for any number of independent variables.

Note 1. Let $w = uv$, where u and v are independent variables. Then, from (5) on page 368,

$$dw = \frac{\partial w}{\partial u}\, du + \frac{\partial w}{\partial v}\, dv = v\, du + u\, dv,\ or$$

$$d(uv) = v\, du + u\, dv. \tag{1}$$

The force of the next example is that (1) is true *even when u and v are not the independent variables.*

EXAMPLE 1. Suppose that u and v are differentiable * functions of the independent variables x and y. Prove that the differential of uv with respect to the variables x and y is given by (1), where du and dv now represent differentials with respect to x and y.

Proof. Let $w = uv$. Then, by the formula for differentiating a product,

$$\frac{\partial w}{\partial x} = v\frac{\partial u}{\partial x} + u\frac{\partial v}{\partial x}; \quad \frac{\partial w}{\partial y} = v\frac{\partial u}{\partial y} + u\frac{\partial v}{\partial y}. \tag{2}$$

Hence, by (5) on page 368,

$$dw = \left(v\frac{\partial u}{\partial x} + u\frac{\partial v}{\partial x}\right)dx + \left(v\frac{\partial u}{\partial y} + u\frac{\partial v}{\partial y}\right)dy$$

$$= v\left(\frac{\partial u}{\partial x}\, dx + \frac{\partial u}{\partial y}\, dy\right) + u\left(\frac{\partial v}{\partial x}\, dx + \frac{\partial v}{\partial y}\, dy\right), \tag{3}$$

where we recognize du and dv in parentheses, as given by (5) on page 368. Hence, $d(uv) = v\, du + u\, dv$.

Similarly, as in Example 1, the student will prove (IV)$_d$ and (VI)$_d$ of page 102 in the next exercise. On page 102, it was mentioned that all of the fundamental forms for differentials in the Summary on page 157 could be obtained as special cases of (VII)$_d$, which may be written

$$d\phi(u) = \phi'(u)du, \tag{4}$$

where u was assumed to be a function of just one independent variable. We proceed to prove (4) when u is a function of any number of independent variables (two for illustration). Then, it will follow that, by use of (4), all of the fundamental forms for differentials of functions of u on page 157 remain valid when u is a function of *any number of independent variables.*

---

* Meaning, in this text, that derivatives of 1st order exist and are continuous.

THEOREM I. *Let u be a differentiable function of x and y, and assume that the function $w = \phi(u)$ has a derivative $\phi'(u)$. Then, the differential of w with respect to x and y is given by $dw = \phi'(u)du$, where du is the differential of u with respect to x and y as the independent variables.*

Proof. By (VII), page 46, for the derivative of a composite function,

$$\frac{\partial w}{\partial x} = \phi'(u) \frac{\partial u}{\partial x} \quad and \quad \frac{\partial w}{\partial y} = \phi'(u) \frac{\partial u}{\partial y}.$$

Hence,
$$dw = \frac{\partial w}{\partial x} dx + \frac{\partial w}{\partial y} dy$$

$$= \phi'(u) \frac{\partial u}{\partial x} dx + \phi'(u) \frac{\partial u}{\partial y} dy = \phi'(u) \left(\frac{\partial u}{\partial x} dx + \frac{\partial u}{\partial y} dy \right), \text{ or}$$

[by (5) on page 368] $dw = \phi'(u)\, du.$

ILLUSTRATION 1. From (1) on page 369, with $u = x^2$ and $v = y$,

$$d(x^2y) = y\, d(x^2) + x^2\, dy = 2xy\, dx + x^2\, dy.$$

EXAMPLE 1. Obtain $d \sin (x^3 + x^2y)$.

SOLUTION. We use $d \sin u = \cos u\, du$, with $u = x^3 + x^2y$:

$$d \sin (x^3 + x^2y) = [\cos (x^3 + x^2y)]d(x^3 + x^2y)$$
$$= [\cos (x^3 + x^2y)](3x^2\, dx + 2xy\, dx + x^2\, dy).$$

ILLUSTRATION 2. From $(VI)_d$ and $(XV)_d$ on page 157, if $x > 0$,

$$d \operatorname{Arcsin} \left(\frac{y}{x}\right) = \frac{1}{\sqrt{1 - \left(\frac{y}{x}\right)^2}} \, d\left(\frac{y}{x}\right)$$

$$= \frac{x}{\sqrt{x^2 - y^2}} \frac{x\, dy - y\, dx}{x^2} = \frac{x\, dy - y\, dx}{x\sqrt{x^2 - y^2}}. \quad (\text{Using } \sqrt{x^2} = x)$$

ILLUSTRATION 3. By use of $de^u = e^u\, du$,

$$de^{3x-4z} = e^{3x-4z}\, d(3x - 4z) = e^{3x-4z}(3\, dx - 4\, dz).$$

EXERCISE 112

The independent variables are x, y, and z.
Find the total differential of the function by use of (5) of Section 180.

1. $u = 5x^3 + 3x^2y^3.$ 2. $u = 2x + 4x^2y^2 - y^4.$
3. $v = \sin x \cos y.$ 4. $v = x^3 - xy^2 - xz^3.$
5. $u = (\ln x)(\ln y) \ln z.$ 6. $v = e^{2x+3y-4z}.$

Find the total differential of the function by use of Theorem I.

7. $x^2(y^4 + 3x).$ 8. $\sin^3 (2x + 5y).$ 9. $e^{4x^2+y^2}.$
10. $\ln (3y - x^2).$ 11. $(x^2 + 3y + z^2)^4.$ 12. $\tan^2 (2x - y^2).$
13. $\sqrt{x^2 + y^2 + z^2}.$ 14. $y^2 \sin (z + y^3).$ 15. $xz^2e^y.$

16. $\dfrac{x^2 + 2y}{z^3}$.   **17.** $\dfrac{\sin 2x}{1 + \cos y}$.   **18.** $\dfrac{e^{xz}}{(y^2 + z)^2}$.

19. $\ln \sqrt[3]{x^2 + y^2}$.   **20.** Arcsin xyz.   **21.** Arctan xy^{-1}.

22. If $u = 4xy^2$, compute du and Δu when $x = 3$, $y = -2$, and the increments for x and y are $dx = .2$ and $dy = -.1$.

If C is a constant, and u and v are differentiable functions of x and y, prove the specified formulas by use of (5) on page 368.

23. $d(u + v) = du + dv$.   **24.** $dC = 0$.   **25.** Formula $(VI)_d$, page 157.

182. Total differentials as approximations to increments

Consider a function $u = f(x, y)$ where f_x and f_y exist and are continuous. Then, if dx and dy are arbitrary increments,

$$\Delta u = f(x + dx, y + dy) - f(x, y); \quad du = f_x \, dx + f_y \, dy. \tag{1}$$

If dx and dy are interpreted as *errors in data*, the corresponding error in u is Δu, and the relative error is $(\Delta u)/u$. If dx and dy are small enough, we shall consider du as an approximation to Δu. Then,

(approximately)   **(error in u) = du;**   (2)

(approximately)   **(relative error in u)** $= \dfrac{du}{u} = d \ln u$,   (3)

where we noticed that $d \ln u = \dfrac{d \ln u}{du} du = \dfrac{1}{u} du$.

EXAMPLE 1. The period T, in seconds, of a simple pendulum, having small oscillations, is taken as $T = 2\pi\sqrt{l/g}$, where l is the length in feet, and g is the acceleration of gravity in feet per second per second. In a certain case, measurement gives $l = 10$ and $g = 32$, with maximum possible errors of .2 in l and .1 in g. Find approximately the maximum possible absolute values for the error and percentage error in T.

SOLUTION. 1. With l and g considered as variables,

$$dT = 2\pi \cdot \frac{1}{2} \sqrt{\frac{g}{l}} \cdot \frac{g \, dl - l \, dg}{g^2} = \frac{\pi(g \, dl - l \, dg)}{\sqrt{l}\sqrt{g^3}}; \tag{4}$$

$$\ln T = \ln 2\pi + \tfrac{1}{2} \ln l - \tfrac{1}{2} \ln g; \quad \frac{dT}{T} = d \ln T = \frac{1}{2}\left(\frac{dl}{l} - \frac{dg}{g}\right). \tag{5}$$

2. The maximum absolute values of dT and dT/T occur when dl and dg have *opposite signs*, so that no cancellation occurs in (4) and in dT/T. Hence, we use $l = 10$, $g = 32$, $dl = .2$ and $dg = -.1$ in (4) and (5):

$$(max. \mid error \mid) = (max. \mid dT \mid) = \pi \frac{(6.4 + 1.0)}{\sqrt{10}\sqrt{32^3}} = .0406 \text{ sec.}; \tag{6}$$

$$(max. \mid rel. \, error \mid) = \left(max. \left|\frac{dT}{T}\right|\right) = \frac{1}{2}\left(\frac{.2}{10} + \frac{.1}{32}\right) = .012 = 1.2\%. \tag{7}$$

EXAMPLE 2. In Example 1, suppose that l and g are measured with percentage errors of at most $1\frac{1}{2}\%$ and $\frac{1}{4}\%$, respectively. Find approximately the largest possible percentage error in the computed value of T.

SOLUTION. From (5), approximately,

$$\left(\begin{array}{c} relative\ error \\ in\ T \end{array}\right) = d \ln T = \frac{1}{2}\left(\frac{dl}{l} - \frac{dg}{g}\right). \tag{8}$$

In (8), dl/l and dg/g are the relative errors in l and g due to errors dl and dg, respectively. The maximum possible absolute value of $d \ln T$ occurs if $.015 = dl/l$ and $- .0025 = dg/g$, or (max. $| d \ln T |$) $= \frac{1}{2}(.015 + .0025) = \frac{7}{8}\%$.

EXERCISE 113

Solve each problem by use of a differential approximation. Perhaps use logarithms, or a slide rule, in computing. In the problems, "maximum error" will mean "maximum absolute value of the error."

1. The altitude of a right circular cylinder is $20''$ and its base has the radius $5''$. Find approximately the change in the volume of the cylinder if each of these dimensions is increased (*a*) by $.2''$; (*b*) by 3%.

2. The inner dimensions of a rectangular box are $10'' \times 20'' \times 5''$. The walls of the box are $.3''$ thick. Find approximately the weight of the box, if its walls weigh 6 ounces per cubic inch.

3. The radius of the base of a right circular cone was measured as $50''$ and its altitude as $20''$, subject to a possible error of as much as $.2''$ in each case. Find approximately the maximum possible error and percentage error in the computed volume of the cone.

4. For a simple pendulum, find approximately the maximum possible percentage error in the period if l and g are measured with errors possibly as large as 2% and 3%, respectively.

5. In a right triangle, we measure one acute angle as $30°$, and the hypotenuse as $40''$, with errors possibly as large as $.5°$ in the angle and $.3''$ in the side. Find approximately the maximum possible errors in the corresponding computed legs of the triangle. Remember that any increment of an angle must be expressed in radian measure.

6. It is known that the maximum safe load S, in pounds, of a certain beam is directly proportional to the breadth, in inches, and the square of the depth, in inches, and inversely proportional to the distance in feet between the beam's supports. The constant of proportionality involved is 50. If the breadth, depth, and distance between supports are measured, with possible errors of 2%, 3%, and 1%, respectively, and if S is computed, find approximately the maximum possible percentage error in S.

7. In a right triangle, we measure the two legs as $50''$ and $120''$, respectively, with an error possibly as large as $.5''$ in each case. Find approximately the range on which the true length of the hypotenuse lies.

8. In Problem 7, find approximately, in degrees, the maximum possible error in the computed value of the acute angle which has the shorter leg as one side, if we find the angle by use of its tangent.

9. The constant C in Boyle's law for gases satisfies $pv = C$, where p is the pressure and v is the volume. If p and C are known with a possible error of 2% in p and 1% in C, find the maximum possible percentage error in v as computed by use of p and C.

10. The specific gravity s of an object is given by the equation $s = a/(a - w)$, where a and w are the weights, in pounds, of the object as measured in air and water, respectively. If a and w can be read with an accuracy limit of .05 pounds, find approximately the maximum possible error and percentage error in s if observation gives $a = 3.2$ and $w = 2.7$.

11. In an electric circuit where the measures of the electromotive force in volts, resistance in ohms, and current in amperes, are E, R, and I, respectively, it is known that $E = RI$. If measurements give $E = 110$ and $I = 20$, with a possible error of 2% in each case, find the maximum possible percentage error in the computed value of R.

12. On the surface which is the graph of the function $z = f(x, y)$, find approximately the increment in the value of z due to increments dx and dy in x and y, applied to given values (x_1, y_1). Compute this approximation, and also the exact increment Δz, at the point where $x_1 = 3$ and $y_1 = 2$ on the surface $z = x^2 + 4y^2$, if $dx = .1$ and $dy = .2$.

13. The legs of a right triangle are measured as $3''$ and $4''$, respectively, with an error of at most 2% in each case. Find approximately the maximum possible percentage error in the computed hypotenuse.

14. In an xyz-system of rectangular coordinates, the coordinates of a point P are measured as $(6, -9, 2)$. Find the maximum possible error in the corresponding computed distance of P from the origin, if the maximum possible percentage error in each coordinate is 2%.

15. By measurement, we find that two sides of a triangle have the lengths $20''$ and $10''$, respectively, and that the included angle is $60°$, with errors possibly as large as $.2''$ in each side and $.1°$ in the angle. Then, we compute the area of the triangle and its third side. Find approximately the maximum possible error (a) in the area; (b) in the side.

16. When light passes from free space into a given medium, with i and r as the angles of incidence and refraction, respectively, then $(\sin i)/\sin r = n$, where n is the refractive index of the medium. If we measure $i = 32°$ and $r = 30°$, with an error in each case of at most $.1°$, find approximately the maximum possible error in the computed value of n.

17. For a perfect gas, the volume v, pressure p, and absolute temperature T are connected by the relation $pv = RT$, where R is a constant. If $T = 400°$ when $p = 50$ pounds per square inch, and $v = 600$ cubic inches, find approximately the change and the percentage change in p if T increases by $10°$ and v by 18 cubic inches.

19

DOUBLE INTEGRALS

183. Regions of points

In the next few chapters, the discussion frequently will involve regions of points in a plane,* or in space * of three dimensions. The typical region in a plane will consist of the points inside or on a closed boundary curve C, as in Figure 230, where C has a tangent everywhere except possibly at a finite number of points. We shall assume that, for any region involved, it is possible to join any pair of points P and Q of the region by a continuous curve lying wholly in the region. In such a case, the region is said to be **connected**. However, our discussion will be largely on an intuitional basis where the hypotheses about regions and boundaries will not be mentioned.

Note 1. We define the **diameter** of any region as the length of the longest line segment which can be drawn connecting two points of the region. According to this definition, the diameter of a circle or sphere is its diameter as generally considered. The diameter of a rectangle or rectangular parallelepiped is the length of a diagonal.

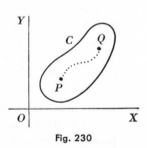

Fig. 230

184. Double integrals

Consider a function $F(x, y)$ which is defined in a region R in the xy-plane. We propose defining the integral of $F(x, y)$ over R.

Let the ranges for x and y in R be $a \leq x \leq b$ and $c \leq y \leq d$. Thus, R lies in the rectangle T having its sides on the lines $x = a$, $x = b$, $y = c$, and $y = d$. Form a partition of the x-interval (a, b), and of the y-interval (c, d), with the typical subintervals

$$x_{j-1} \leq x \leq x_j, \quad \text{where we let} \quad \Delta_j x = x_j - x_{j-1}, \text{ and} \tag{1}$$

$$y_{k-1} \leq y \leq y_k, \quad \text{where we let} \quad \Delta_k y = y_k - y_{k-1}. \tag{2}$$

Superimpose a grid on the rectangle T by constructing a line perpendicular

* We assume that just one unit is used in measuring all lengths involved.

to the x-axis at each point $x = x_j$, and perpendicular to the y-axis at each point $y = y_k$, as in Figure 231. The grid divides R into subregions, and we

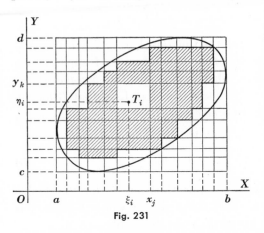

Fig. 231

shall call this subdivision of R a **partition,** P, of the region R. We define the **norm,** d_P, of P as *the maximum of the diameters of the rectangles of the grid for P.* Suppose that just n of the subregions in P consist of entire rectangles,

$$T_1, T_2, \cdots, T_i, \cdots, T_n, \quad (3)$$

which are ruled in Figure 231, except for the representative rectangle T_i. If $d_P \to 0$, then $n \to \infty$ in (3).

DEFINITION I. *Let P be any partition of the region R. In each **whole rectangle** T_i of P, select a point (ξ_i, η_i) arbitrarily, and let*

$$S_P = \sum_{i=1}^{n} F(\xi_i, \eta_i)\Delta_i A, \quad (4)$$

where $\Delta_i A$ is the area of T_i. Then, if S_P approaches a limit as $d_P \to 0$, we call this limit "the **double integral** of $F(x, y)$ over R," to be represented by the following symbol on the left:*

$$\int\int_R F(x, y)dA = \lim_{d_P \to 0} \sum_{i=1}^{n} F(\xi_i, \eta_i)\Delta_i A. \quad (5)$$

If the limit in (5) exists, $F(x, y)$ is said to be *integrable* over R. The following theorem is demonstrated at a more advanced level.

THEOREM I. *If R is a region satisfying suitable hypotheses,† and if the function $F(x, y)$ is continuous in R, then the double integral of $F(x, y)$ over R exists.*

Previously, we have introduced the notion of *area* for special regions in the xy-plane. Now, we shall define the area of a general region.

DEFINITION II. *For a region R in the xy-plane, let P be a partition created by use of a rectangular grid, as in Definition I. Then, if the sum of the areas of all of the whole rectangles in P approaches a limit as $d_P \to 0$, we define this limit as the area, A, of R:*

$$A = \lim_{d_P \to 0} \sum_{i=1}^{n} \Delta_i A. \quad (6)$$

The sum in (6) is obtained from (5) when $F(x, y) \equiv 1$. Thus, (6) is equiva-

---

* At present we use the concept of area *only for rectangles,* as on page 193.
† It is beyond the level of this text to discuss these hypotheses. They will be satisfied in all cases which we consider.

lent to the statement that *we define the area of R to be the double integral of the function $F(x, y) = 1$ over R.* That is,

$$A = \int\int_R 1 \, dA, \quad \text{or simply} \quad A = \int\int_R dA, \tag{7}$$

provided that the integral exists. Since the function $F(x, y) = 1$ is continuous, we conclude that, if R is of such a type that Theorem I applies, then *R has an area given by* (7). Hereafter, whenever we mention a *region R*, we shall assume that it satisfies the conditions of Theorem I, so that R has an area, and *any continuous function is integrable over R*.

Note 1. For future use, let τ_P be the sum in (6). Then,

$$\tau_P = \sum_{i=1}^{n} \Delta_i A \quad \text{and} \quad \tau_P \to A \text{ if } d_P \to 0. \tag{8}$$

EXAMPLE 1. By use of (4), obtain an approximation S_P for the double integral of the function $F(x, y) = x^2$, over the region R whose boundary is the circle with radius 5 and center at the origin in the xy-plane.

SOLUTION. Divide the x-interval, and the y-interval, into 10 equal parts and construct the corresponding rectangular grid, to obtain a partition P for R as shown in Figure 232. Notice that $F(x, y)$ is symmetrical to the origin. In any complete square T_i of P in quadrant I, let (ξ_i, η_i) be the lower left-hand corner, in forming the product $F(\xi_i, \eta_i)\Delta_i A$. Then, if symmetrical points (ξ_i, η_i) are chosen in the other quadrants, S_P from (4) will be equal to four times the sum taken just for quadrant I. Each area $\Delta_i A$ is 1. Hence,

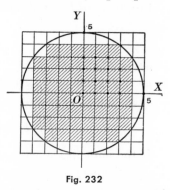

Fig. 232

$$S_P = 4[F(0, 0) + F(0, 1) + F(0, 2) + F(0, 3) + F(1, 0) + \cdots + F(3, 2)]. \tag{9}$$

We obtain $F(1, 0) = 1$, $F(0, 1) = 0$, $F(2, 0) = 4$, etc., and $S_P = 4(47) = 188$.

Comment. For the partition in Example 1, there are 60 complete squares inside the circle, and hence $\tau_P = \sum_{i=1}^{60} \Delta_i A = 60$, as an approximation to the area. The usual formula πr^2 gives 78.54. The student will obtain a better approximation in the next exercise.

As a consequence of Definition II, we may introduce a new interpretation for the expression on the right in (5).

THEOREM II. *Let P be any partition of the region R into subregions $\{T_i\}$ of **any shape,** as in Figure 233 on page 377, where T_i has an area, $\Delta_i A$, and let d_P be the maximum of the diameters of the subregions $\{T_i\}$. Let (ξ_i, η_i) be an arbitrary point in T_i. Then, if $F(x, y)$ is continuous in R, equation (5) is valid with the new meaning for P.*

We accept Theorem II on an intuitional basis. Our reaction is that, since the general notion of *area* is defined as the limit of a sum of areas of *rectangles*, then use of areas of irregular regions in Theorem II should lead to the same limit as obtained with *rectangular areas* in Definition I.

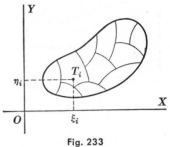

Fig. 233

185. Properties of a double integral

With the notion of a *region* replacing an *interval*, and *area* of a region replacing *length* of an interval, the following results could be verified by reasoning similar to that employed in establishing corresponding facts for simple integrals on page 195.

If $F(x, y)$ and $G(x, y)$ are integrable in R, and if c is a constant,

$$\iint_R [F(x, y) + G(x, y)]dA = \iint_R F(x, y)dA + \iint_R G(x, y)dA; \tag{1}$$

$$\iint_R cF(x, y)dA = c \iint_R F(x, y)dA. \tag{2}$$

If a region R consists of two regions R' and R'' which have only boundary points in common, and if $F(x, y)$ is continuous in R, then

$$\iint_R F(x, y)dA = \iint_{R'} F(x, y)dA + \iint_{R''} F(x, y)dA. \tag{3}$$

If $F(x, y)$ is continuous in a region R whose area is A, and if μ' and μ'' are the absolute minimum and maximum, respectively, of $F(x, y)$ in R, then

$$\mu'A \leq \iint_R F(x, y)dA \leq \mu''A. \tag{4}$$

Mean value theorem. *If $F(x, y)$ is continuous in a region R whose area is A, then there exists a point (ξ, η) in R such that*

$$\iint_R F(x, y)dA = F(\xi, \eta)A. \tag{5}$$

EXERCISE 114

1. Let R be the region bounded by the circle $x^2 + y^2 = 25$. Form a partition P of R by dividing the corresponding ranges for x and y into 20 parts of equal lengths. Compute the approximation τ_P for the area of R.

2. Let R be the region bounded by the x-axis, the curve $y^2 = 4x$, and the line $x = 2$ in quadrant I. Place a grid on R by drawing the lines $x = 0$, $x = \frac{1}{4}$, $x = \frac{1}{2}$, $\cdots$, $x = 1.75$, and $y = 0$, $y = \frac{1}{4}$, $y = \frac{1}{2}$, $\cdots$, $y = 2.75$, spaced $\frac{1}{4}$ unit apart. By use of the corresponding partition P for R, compute approximations for (*a*) the area of R; (*b*) the double integral over R of the function $F(x, y) = xy$, with (ξ_i, η_i) in (4) on page 375 taken as the lower left-hand corner in any complete square of P.

186. The notion of an iterated integral

Let $y = Y_1(x)$ and $y = Y_2(x)$ be continuous when $a \leqq x \leqq b$, and let the

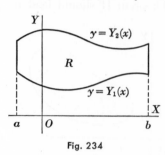

Fig. 234

function $F(x, y)$ be continuous in the region R of an xy-plane bounded by the curves $y = Y_1(x)$ and $y = Y_2(x)$, and the lines $x = a$ and $x = b$. Figure 234 for R is drawn as if $Y_1(x) \leqq Y_2(x)$ at all values of x, but this feature is not essential. Then, without proof we shall accept the fact that the expression

$$G(x) = \int_{Y_1(x)}^{Y_2(x)} F(x, y)dy \qquad (1)$$

is a continuous function of x. In (1), it is understood that x is a constant during the integration with respect to y. Then, $\int_a^b G(x)dx$ exists. That is, the following symbol has a well-defined value, obtained by two successive integrations:

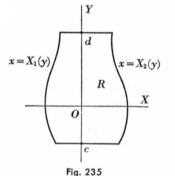

Fig. 235

$$\int_a^b \left[\int_{Y_1(x)}^{Y_2(x)} F(x, y)dy \right] dx. \qquad (2)$$

We shall refer to (2) as a **two-fold iterated integral**. Similarly, with R bounded by the curves $x = X_1(y)$ and $x = X_2(y)$, and the lines $y = c$ and $y = d$, as in Figure 235, we may use

$$\int_c^d \left[\int_{X_1(y)}^{X_2(y)} F(x, y)dx \right] dy. \qquad (3)$$

ILLUSTRATION 1. $\displaystyle\int_2^3 \left[\int_{2x}^{3x^2} xy\,dy \right] dx = \int_2^3 \frac{1}{2} xy^2 \bigg]_{y=2x}^{y=3x^2} dx$

$$= \frac{1}{2} \int_2^3 (9x^5 - 4x^3)dx = \frac{1}{2} \left(\frac{3}{2} x^6 - x^4 \right) \bigg]_2^3 = \frac{1865}{4}.$$

ILLUSTRATION 2.   If a and c are constants, then

$$\int_a^x \left[\int_c^y F(u, v)dv \right] du$$

is a function of x and y. By use of Theorem VII on page 197 with u as the variable of integration, and then with v as the variable of integration,

$$\frac{\partial}{\partial x} \left\{ \int_a^x \left[\int_c^y F(u, v)dv \right] du \right\} = \int_c^y F(x, v)dv;$$

$$\frac{\partial^2}{\partial x\, \partial y} \left\{ \int_a^x \left[\int_c^y F(u, v)dv \right] du \right\} = \frac{\partial}{\partial y} \int_c^y F(x, v)dv = F(x, y).$$

Later, we shall establish a connection between two-fold iterated integrals and double integrals. Three-fold iterated integrals will be used in Chapter 21.

ILLUSTRATION 3. $\displaystyle\int_0^2 \left[\int_{2x}^{x^2} \left(\int_2^{xy} 2xyz\, dz \right) dy \right] dx$ (4)

$$= \int_0^2 \left\{ \int_{2x}^{x^2} xyz^2 \Big]_{z=2}^{z=xy}\, dy \right\} dx = \int_0^2 \left[\int_{2x}^{x^2} (x^3y^3 - 4xy)dy \right] dx = -32.$$

Note 1. We may write (4) without parentheses, with the understanding that the differentials, *starting at the left*, indicate the order of integration:

$$\int_0^2 \int_{2x}^{x^2} \int_2^{xy} 2xyz\, dz\, dy\, dx.$$

EXERCISE 115

Compute the iterated integral.

1. $\displaystyle\int_0^3 \int_1^2 (x + 2y)dy\, dx.$

2. $\displaystyle\int_1^2 \int_0^y 3(x + y)^2\, dx\, dy.$

3. $\displaystyle\int_1^2 \int_1^{2x} x^2\, e^{xy}\, dy\, dx.$

4. $\displaystyle\int_0^{\frac{1}{2}\pi} \int_1^x x^2 \sin xy\, dy\, dx.$

5. $\displaystyle\int_{4a^2}^{9a^2} \int_1^{\sqrt{y}}\, dx\, dy.$

6. $\displaystyle\int_1^3 \int_1^x x^{-1}y^{-1}\, dy\, dx.$

7. $\displaystyle\int_{-\frac{1}{2}\pi}^{\frac{1}{2}\pi} \int_x^{3x} 2 \sin (x + 2y)dy\, dx.$

8. $\displaystyle\int_{-\frac{1}{4}\pi}^{\frac{1}{4}\pi} \int_0^r \sec^2 \theta\, d\theta\, dr.$

9. $\displaystyle\int_{\frac{1}{2}}^1 \int_0^x \sqrt{x^2 - y^2}\, dy\, dx.$

10. $\displaystyle\int_{\frac{1}{2}}^4 \int_0^x x(x^2 - y^2)^{-\frac{1}{2}}\, dy\, dx.$

11. $\displaystyle\int_{-\pi}^\pi \int_1^{\sin \theta} r\, dr\, d\theta.$

12. $\displaystyle\int_1^3 \int_{\frac{1}{2}\pi}^{2\pi} r \sin \theta\, d\theta\, dr.$

13. $\displaystyle\int_0^{\frac{1}{4}\pi} \int_1^{\sqrt{2 \cos 2\theta}} r\, dr\, d\theta.$

14. $\displaystyle\int_0^{\frac{1}{6}\pi} \int_1^{2 \cos \theta} r \sin 2\theta\, dr\, d\theta.$

15. $\displaystyle\int_0^\pi \int_2^{2(1+\sin \theta)} r \cos \theta\, dr\, d\theta.$

16. $\displaystyle\int_0^{\frac{1}{2}\pi} \int_{2 \cos \theta}^{4/(1+\cos \theta)} r^2 \sin \theta\, dr\, d\theta.$

17. $\displaystyle\int_2^3 \int_1^x \int_0^{6y} xy\, dz\, dy\, dx.$

18. $\displaystyle\int_0^2 \int_0^\pi \int_0^a r^2 \sin \phi\, dr\, d\phi\, d\theta.$

19. $\displaystyle\int_0^1 \int_0^{2\pi} \int_3^{4-r^2} r\, dz\, d\theta\, dr.$

20. If a, b, c, and d are constants, prove that the following iterated integral can be expressed as a product of two simple integrals:

$$\int_a^b \int_c^d f(x)g(y)dy\, dx.$$

187. Double integrals computed by use of iterated integrals

Hereafter, we shall refer frequently to regions of the following types in an xy-plane, as in Figures 234 and 235, respectively, on page 378.

(R of type I) $a \leqq x \leqq b$ *and* $Y_1(x) \leqq y \leqq Y_2(x).$ (1)

(R of type II) $c \leqq y \leqq d$ *and* $X_1(y) \leqq x \leqq X_2(y).$ (2)

THEOREM III. **Fundamental theorem of integral calculus for a double integral.** *If $F(x, y)$ is continuous in a region R of type I or type II,*

(R of type I) $\displaystyle\iint_R F(x, y)dA = \int_a^b \int_{Y_1(x)}^{Y_2(x)} F(x, y)dy\, dx;$ (3)

(R of type II) $\displaystyle\iint_R F(x, y)dA = \int_c^d \int_{X_1(y)}^{X_2(y)} F(x, y)dx\, dy.$ (4)

EXAMPLE 1. Let R be the region bounded by the x-axis and the curves $y^2 = x$ and $x^2 + y^2 = 2$, where $y \geqq 0$. Compute the following integral, K:

$$K = \int\int_R y \, dA. \tag{5}$$

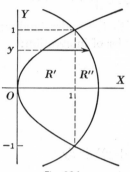

Fig. 236

SOLUTION. 1. On solving $y^2 = x$ and $x^2 + y^2 = 2$ simultaneously, we obtain the intersection $(1, 1)$ in quadrant I.

2. On the interval $0 \leqq y \leqq 1$, any perpendicular to OY meets the boundary of R in *just two points*, as shown by the arrow in Figure 236. Hence, we may consider R as of type II. The right-hand boundary is a part of $x^2 + y^2 = 2$, or $x = \sqrt{2 - y^2}$. Hence, by use of (4) with

$$X_1(y) = y^2 \quad and \quad X_2(y) = \sqrt{2 - y^2},$$

$$K = \int_0^1 \int_{y^2}^{\sqrt{2-y^2}} y \, dx \, dy = \int_0^1 xy \Big]_{x=y^2}^{x=\sqrt{2-y^2}} dy \tag{6}$$

$$= \int_0^1 (y\sqrt{2 - y^2} - y^3) dy = \left[-\frac{1}{3}(2 - y^2)^{\frac{3}{2}} - \frac{1}{4} y^4 \right]_0^1 = \frac{2}{3}\sqrt{2} - \frac{7}{12}. \tag{7}$$

Comment. We may compute K by use of (3). Then, however, the fact that two formulas are involved for y on the upper boundary forces us to divide R into two parts. Thus, we cut R into R', where $0 \leqq x \leqq 1$, and R'', where $1 \leqq x \leqq \sqrt{2}$, by drawing the line $x = 1$. Then, from (3),

$$K = \int\int_{R'} y \, dA + \int\int_{R''} y \, dA = \int_0^1 \int_0^{\sqrt{x}} y \, dy \, dx + \int_1^{\sqrt{2}} \int_0^{\sqrt{2-x^2}} y \, dy \, dx.$$

Intuitional discussion * of (3). 1. Let the region R be of type I, as in Figure 237 on page 381. Form a partition of the interval $a \leqq x \leqq b$ into g pieces, and of $c \leqq y \leqq d$ into h pieces by division points as follows:

$$x_0 = a < x_1 < x_2 < \cdots < x_{j-1} < x_j < \cdots < x_g = b; \tag{8}$$

$$y_0 = c < y_1 < y_2 < \cdots < y_{k-1} < y_k < \cdots < y_h = d. \tag{9}$$

In (8) and (9), the typical subintervals have the lengths

$$\Delta_j x = x_j - x_{j-1} \quad and \quad \Delta_k y = y_k - y_{k-1}.$$

By use of the lines $x = x_j$ and $y = y_k$, for all values of j and k, construct a grid of rectangles, arranged in g columns and h rows, as in Figure 237. This grid produces a partition P of R, as on page 375. To say that $d_P \to 0$ is equivalent to saying that, in (8) and (9), all $\Delta_j x \to 0$ and all $\Delta_k y \to 0$.

2. To form an approximating sum S_P for $\int\int_R F(x, y) dA$ in (3), consider the typical rectangle $T_{j,k}$ of P in the jth column where $x_{j-1} \leqq x \leqq x_j$, and kth row where $y_{k-1} \leqq y \leqq y_k$. The area of $T_{j,k}$ is $(\Delta_j x)(\Delta_k y)$. In $T_{j,k}$, select

* Another background for (3) will be met later. A proof of (3) and (4) is beyond the level of this text.

(x_j, y_k), shown by a black dot in Figure 237, as the arbitrary point referred to in Definition I on page 375, to obtain the element $F(x_j, y_k)\Delta_k y \Delta_j x$ for a sum S_P. Then, form the sum of the elements by adding, first, all those from the jth column of P, and then taking the sum of the column sums, for all values of j:

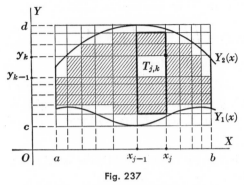

Fig. 237

$$S_P = \sum_{j=1}^{g}\left[\sum_{(k)} F(x_j, y_k)\Delta_k y\right]\Delta_j x,$$

where, for each value of j, the inner sum extends over those values of k for which there is a rectangle $T_{j,k}$ in P. In S_P, as all $\Delta_k y \to 0$, the inner sum suggests an integral of $F(x, y)$ with respect to y, between values of y depending on x; then, the outer sum suggests the integral of the preceding result with respect to x over the interval (a, b). Thus, we are led to infer that

$$\iint_R F(x, y)dA = \lim_{d_P \to 0} S_P = \int_a^b \int_{Y_1(x)}^{Y_2(x)} F(x, y)dy\; dx. \qquad (10)$$

Hereafter, we may visualize (10) as a consequence of *first summing elements by columns*, and then taking *the sum of column sums in S_P*.

If R is of Type II as in Figure 238, we would write

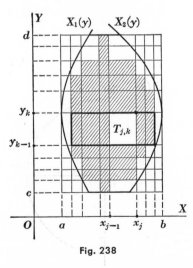

Fig. 238

$$S_P = \sum_{k=1}^{h}\left[\sum_{(j)} F(x_j, y_k)\Delta_j x\right]\Delta_k y, \qquad (11)$$

and then would be led to (4). Thus, in (4), we may visualize the inner integration with respect to x as a consequence of first summing elements $F(x_j, y_k)\Delta_j x$ by *rows;* the outer integration can be thought of as a result of taking *the sum of row sums in* (11).

Note 1. In (3) and (4), we can call "$dx\; dy$" the differential *element of area* in rectangular coordinates, as a reminder of the area $\Delta x \Delta y$ of an elementary rectangle in an approximating sum for the corresponding double integral.

188. Two dimensional distribution of mass

Consider a plane region R, and visualize mass spread over R like paint on a surface, where the mass is idealized as having no thickness. Suppose that there exists a constant δ such that, if T is any subregion of R with the area ΔA area units, then the mass, Δm, of T is $\delta \Delta A$ mass units. In this case, we say that the mass over R has *uniform density*, and that the density is δ units of mass per square unit of area. Thus, we have

$$\Delta A = \int \int_T dA \quad and \quad \Delta m = \delta \int \int_T dA = \int \int_T \delta \, dA.$$

This discussion suggests the notion of a variable density.

DEFINITION III. *Let $\delta(x, y)$ be defined, continuous, and nonnegative when (x, y) is in a given region R. Then, if the mass in any subregion T of R is equal to the double integral of $\delta(x, y)$ over T, we call $\delta(x, y)$ the **density of mass** over R.*

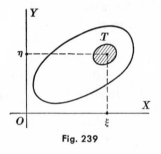
Fig. 239

In particular, by Definition III, the total mass, m, of R is

$$m = \int \int_R \delta(x, y) dA. \qquad (1)$$

Let T be any subregion of R with area ΔA and mass Δm, as in Figure 239. Then, by the mean value theorem on page 377, there exists a point (ξ, η) in T such that

$$\Delta m = \int \int_T \delta(x, y) dA = \delta(\xi, \eta) \Delta A, \quad or \quad \delta(\xi, \eta) = \frac{\Delta m}{\Delta A}. \qquad (2)$$

Hence, $\delta(\xi, \eta)$ is called the *average density* over the region T. In (2), suppose that the diameter of T is γ, and that T includes a certain fixed point (x_0, y_0). If $\gamma \to 0$, then $\delta(\xi, \eta) \to \delta(x_0, y_0)$, $\Delta A \to 0$, and (2) gives

$$\lim_{\gamma \to 0} \frac{\Delta m}{\Delta A} = \delta(x_0, y_0). \qquad (3)$$

Because of (3), we shall call $\delta(x, y)$ the density *at the point* (x, y).

EXAMPLE 1. Find the mass of the region R bounded by the y-axis and the right-hand semicircle of the circle $x^2 + y^2 = 25$, if the density at any point (x, y) is $\delta(x, y) = 5 |y|$.

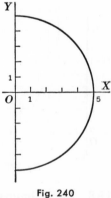
Fig. 240

SOLUTION. 1. *Symmetry*. The region R, shown in Figure 240, is symmetric with respect to OX. Also, the density has the same value at any point (x, y_1) as at (x, y_2) where $y_2 = -y_1$, because

$$\delta(x, y_1) = 5 |y_1| = 5 |y_2| = \delta(x, y_2).$$

Thus, since the *region* and the *density function* are symmetric with respect to OX, the mass of R is twice the mass in that quadrant R' where $y \geq 0$.

2. If m is the mass of R, then

$$m = 2 \int \int_{R'} 5y \, dA = 10 \int_0^5 \int_0^{\sqrt{25-x^2}} y \, dy \, dx = \frac{1250}{3}.$$

If the word "*mass*" in Definition III is changed to "*electric charge*," then $\delta(x, y)$ is the density of electric charge, and (4) becomes the total charge over R. In statistics, with the words "*density of mass*" changed to "*probability density*," the integral of $\delta(x, y)$ becomes a *probability*.

EXERCISE 116

Express the double integral of an arbitrary function $F(x, y)$ over the specified finite region R by use of an iterated integral, or more than one iterated integral, without integrating.

1. R is the region in quadrant I bounded by the parabolas $3y = x^2$ and $3x = y^2$. Give the result for each order of integration.
2. R is bounded by the parabolas $y^2 = -4x$ and $y^2 = 4(x + 2)$.
3. R is bounded by the y-axis, and the curves $y = \sin x$ and $y = \cos x$, up to their first point of intersection where $x > 0$. Give two results.

First formulate the result as a double integral, and then compute by use of an iterated integral. Use symmetry. Any constant a or k is positive.

Find the area of the region bounded by the given curves.

4–6. The regions in Problems 1–3, respectively.
7. By integration, find the area of a general right triangle.
8. Bounded by $y = x^3$ and $x = y^3$, where $y \geq 0$.
9. The region bounded by $y = 7x$ and $y = x(x + 1)(x - 5)$.
10. Bounded by $y + 2x + 6 = 0$ and $y = 9 - x^2$.
11. Bounded by $y^2 = 4 + 4x$ and $y^2 = 4 - 8x$.
12. Bounded by $x^2 + y^2 = 4$ and $y^2 = 3x$.
13. Bounded by the lines $x = 0$, $y = 0$, $x = 3$, and $y = e^x$.
14. Bounded by $xy = 1$ and $x^2y = 1$, from $x = 1$ to $x = 3$.
15. Bounded by $y = \frac{1}{2}(e^x + e^{-x})$ and $y = \frac{1}{2}e^x$, with $0 \leq x \leq 1$.
16. Bounded by $y = x^2 + 5$ and $y = 2x^2 - 4$.
17. Bounded by a circle of radius a.
18. Bounded by $x^{\frac{1}{2}} + y^{\frac{1}{2}} = 2$ and $x + y = 4$.

Find the mass of the region. $\delta(x, y)$ is the density at (x, y).

19. Bounded by $y = \sin x$ and $y = \cos x$, for $0 \leq x \leq \frac{1}{4}\pi$: $\delta = ky$.
20. Bounded by the line $y = 1$ and the curve $4y^3 = x^2$; $\delta = kx^2$.
21. Bounded by the circle $x^2 + y^2 = a^2$; $\delta = |xy|$.
22. Where $x \geq 0$, bounded by $x^2 - y^2 = 8$ and $x^2 + y^2 = 16$; $\delta = kx$.
23. Bounded by $y = 1/\sqrt{9 - 25x^2}$, and the lines $y = 0$ and $x = \pm\frac{3}{10}\sqrt{2}$; $\delta = 2y|x|$.

24. The region of Problem 2, if $\delta = 4 + x + y$.

25. Bounded by the lines $x = 0$, $y = \frac{3}{2}$, and $y = 4$, and the curve $x = \sqrt{2y + 1}$;
$\delta = 3x^2$.

26. Bounded by $y = x - \sin 2x$ and $y = x$, where $0 \leqq x \leqq \frac{1}{2}\pi$; $\delta = 2(x + y)$.

27. Find the area of the ellipse $b^2x^2 + a^2y^2 = a^2b^2$.

★*Draw a region R in an xy-system of coordinates so that the iterated integral is equal to a double integral over R.*

28. $\int_{-2}^{4} \int_{\frac{1}{4}y^2}^{\frac{1}{2}(4+y)} F(x, y)dx \, dy.$ \qquad **29.** $\int_{-3}^{3} \int_{x^2-9}^{\frac{1}{2}(9-x^2)} F(x, y)dy \, dx.$

HINT. On the right in (3) on page 379, the corresponding region R has the boundaries $x = a$, $x = b$, $y = Y_1(x)$, and $y = Y_2(x)$. In Problem 28, write the equations of the boundaries.

★*By first obtaining a corresponding double integral, derive an expression for the given integral with the order of integration reversed.*

30. $\int_{0}^{2} \int_{\frac{1}{4}y^2}^{\frac{1}{2}(8-y^2)} F(x, y)dx \, dy.$ \qquad **31.** $\int_{-1}^{0} \int_{e^x}^{e^{-x}} F(x, y)dy \, dx.$

★**32.** Suppose that a region R in an xy-plane, and a function $F(x, y)$ are symmetric with respect to the x-axis, which divides R into two regions R_1 and R_2. Prove that

$$\iint_{R_1} F(x, y)dA = \iint_{R_2} F(x, y)dA, \quad or \quad \iint_{R} F(x, y)dA = 2\iint_{R_1} F(x, y)dA.$$

HINT. Explain how to form equal approximating sums S_P and S_P' for the integrals over R_1 and R_2, and then obtain the desired result.

189. A certain volume as a double integral

In an xyz-system of rectangular coordinates, let R be a region in the xy-plane bounded by a curve C. Then, consider the cylinder formed by moving a line L parallel to the z-axis through all points on C, as in Figure 241. Let W be the region of points bounded by this cylinder, the region R, and the surface with the equation $z = F(x, y)$,

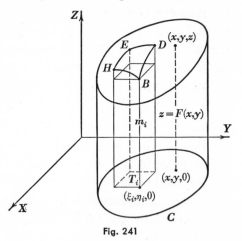

where $F(x, y)$ is continuous and $F(x, y) \geqq 0$ in R. We propose defining the notion of *volume* for W, shown in Figure 241, with the viewpoint that only the volume of a *parallelepiped* has been defined previously.

Form a partition P of R by superimposing a grid of rectangles over R, as on page 375; Figure 241 shows a representative complete rectangle T_i of P having the area $\Delta_i A$. Let d_P be the norm of P, as

Fig. 241

on page 375. For each rectangle T_i, construct planes perpendicular to the xy-plane on the sides of T_i, thus forming a column τ_i in W with base T_i and cap $HBDE$ on the surface $z = F(x, y)$. Let γ_i be the largest parallelepiped included in τ_i. If m_i is the absolute *minimum* of $F(x, y)$ at points in T_i, then m_i is the altitude of γ_i, and there exists a point $(\xi_i, \eta_i, 0)$ in the xy-plane such that $m_i = F(\xi_i, \eta_i)$. Hence, the volume $\Delta_i V$ of γ_i is given by

$$\Delta_i V = m_i \Delta_i A = F(\xi_i, \eta_i)\Delta_i A.$$

Then, we define the volume V of W as *the limit of the sum, S_P, of the volumes of all of the maximum parallelepipeds γ_i with whole rectangles of P for bases, as $d_P \to 0$. Or,*

$$V = \lim_{d_P \to 0} S_P = \lim_{d_P \to 0} \sum_{i=1}^{n} \Delta_i V = \lim_{d_P \to 0} \sum_{i=1}^{n} F(\xi_i, \eta_i)\Delta_i A. \tag{1}$$

From Definition I and Theorem I, the limit in (1) exists and

$\left\{ \begin{array}{l} \text{cylindrical region, } W; \\ \text{base, } R; \; \text{cap, } z = F(x, y) \end{array} \right\}$ $\qquad V = \int\int_R F(x, y)\,dA, \tag{2}$

which we may abbreviate by

$[z = F(x, y)]$ $\qquad\qquad\qquad V = \int\int_R z\, dA. \tag{3}$

ILLUSTRATION 1. If H is a constant and $F(x, y) = H$ in R, then W in (2) is a *slab* with thickness H, and (2) gives $V = HA$, where A is the area of R. Thus, from (2) we have proved (II) on page 204.

EXAMPLE 1. Find the volume of the region bounded by the circular cylinder $x^2 + y^2 = 4$, the xy-plane, and the plane $x - y + 2z = 4$.

SOLUTION. 1. Figure 242 shows the part of the solid in the 1st octant. AB is the yz-trace, and AC is the xz-trace of the plane. Thus, the equation of AB is $z = \frac{1}{2}(4 + y)$ in the yz-plane. BC is part of the curve of intersection of the plane and the cylinder.

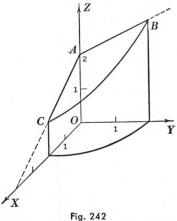

Fig. 242

2. We use (3) with $z = \frac{1}{2}(4 - x + y)$ and R as the region bounded by the circle $x^2 + y^2 = 4$, or $y = \pm \sqrt{4 - x^2}$. We take R as of type I in (3). The inner limits of integration are indicated by the arrow in Figure 243, page 386.

$$V = \int\int_R \frac{1}{2}(4 - x + y)dA = \frac{1}{2}\int_{-2}^{2} \int_{-\sqrt{4-x^2}}^{\sqrt{4-x^2}} (4 - x + y)dy\, dx = 8\pi. \tag{4}$$

Comment. In Example 1, let R_1 and R_2 be the semicircles of R where $y \geqq 0$ and $y \leqq 0$, respectively. Let P_1 be a partition of R_1, with pieces $\{T_i\}$; let

P_2 be that partition of R_2 where each piece T'_i is symmetric to T_i with respect to the x-axis, as in Figure 243. In T_i, select arbitrarily a point (x_i, y_i), and in T'_i select the symmetrical point $(x_i, -y_i)$, for applying Definition I of page 375. Then, if $\Delta_i A$ is the common area of T_i and T'_i,

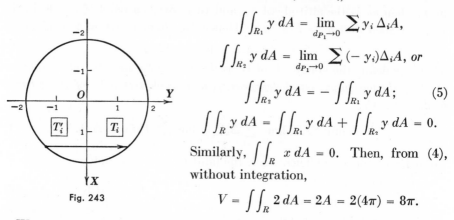

$$\iint_{R_1} y\, dA = \lim_{d_{P_1} \to 0} \sum y_i\, \Delta_i A,$$

$$\iint_{R_2} y\, dA = \lim_{d_{P_1} \to 0} \sum (-y_i) \Delta_i A, \text{ or}$$

$$\iint_{R_2} y\, dA = -\iint_{R_1} y\, dA; \qquad (5)$$

$$\iint_{R} y\, dA = \iint_{R_1} y\, dA + \iint_{R_2} y\, dA = 0.$$

Similarly, $\iint_{R} x\, dA = 0$. Then, from (4), without integration,

$$V = \iint_{R} 2\, dA = 2A = 2(4\pi) = 8\pi.$$

Fig. 243

We may use (2) to obtain a fresh viewpoint about the fundamental theorem of integral calculus for a double integral. First, recall that, on page 267, the volume V of a solid such as W in (2) was defined as the limit of a sum of volumes of *slabs*, with the result in Illustration 1 taken as a definition. The volume of each slab now is defined as a limit of a sum of volumes of parallelepipeds. Hence, we accept intuitively the fact that volume as defined on page 267, and volume as obtained by use of parallelepipeds in (2), have the same value. With this basis, we shall give a new background for (3) and (4) on page 379, where we assume first that $F(x,y) \geq 0$.

Let R be a region of type II in the xy-plane, in Figure 244:

Region R: $\qquad\qquad c \leq y \leq d; \quad X_1(y) \leq x \leq X_2(y).$ $\qquad\qquad$ (6)

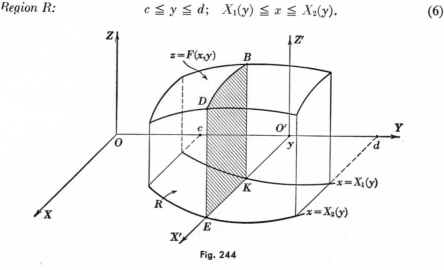

Fig. 244

Let W be the cylindrical region in space having R as a base and the surface $z = F(x, y)$ for a cap, as in Figure 244. At any point y on the y-axis, construct a plane perpendicular to the y-axis, creating the plane section $BDEK$ of W. In the plane of $BDEK$, visualize new axes $O'X'$ and $O'Z'$, as in the figure, with the directions of OX and OZ. In this new xz-plane, the equation of BD is $z = F(x, y)$, where y is fixed at the moment. At E and K, $x = X_2(y)$ and $x = X_1(y)$, respectively. Let $A(y)$ be the area of $BDEK$. Then, from (3) on page 194,

$$A(y) = \int_{X_1(y)}^{X_2(y)} F(x, y)dx.$$

Hence, from (1) on page 267, and (2),

$$V = \int_c^d A(y)dy, \quad \text{or} \quad \int\int_R F(x, y)dA = \int_c^d \int_{X_1(y)}^{X_2(y)} F(x, y)dx\, dy, \quad (7)$$

which gives (4) on page 379. Similarly, we could obtain (3) on page 379.

Note 1. With R as a region in the xz-plane, and then with R as a region in the yz-plane, from (3) we obtain, respectively, the following analogous formulas for volumes of cylindrical solids:

[*with* $y = F(x, z)$] $$V = \int\int_R y\, dA. \quad (8)$$

[*with* $x = F(y, z)$] $$V = \int\int_R x\, dA. \quad (9)$$

Note 2. If we do not have $F(x, y) \geq 0$, suppose that m is the absolute minimum for $F(x, y)$ in R. Then, let $G(x, y) = F(x, y) - m$; thus, $G(x, y) \geq 0$. If (7) is written first for $G(x, y)$, it is seen that the resulting equality leads to (7) for $F(x, y)$, now taken without the hypothesis $F(x, y) \geq 0$.

In using (2), the first question to raise is *what cylindrical surface perpendicular to the xy-plane bounds the region W whose volume is involved.* Then, the region R for the double integral is bounded by the xy-trace of the cylinder.

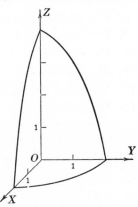

EXAMPLE 2. Find the volume of the region bounded below by the xy-plane and above by the surface T with the equation $z = 4 - x^2 - y^2$.

INCOMPLETE SOLUTION. T is a surface of revolution about the z-axis; the xy-trace of T is the circle $x^2 + y^2 = 4$, as seen in Figure 245. From symmetry, the volume, V, is four times the volume found for the 1st octant. Hence, with R as the region bounded by the circle $x^2 + y^2 = 4$ in quadrant I of the xy-plane,

Fig. 245

$$V = 4\int\int_R (4 - x^2 - y^2)dA = 4\int_0^2 \int_0^{\sqrt{4-x^2}} (4 - x^2 - y^2)dy\, dx.$$

EXAMPLE 3. In an xyz-system of rectangular coordinates, the planes $z = 0$, $x + y = 1$, $x = 1$, and $y = 1 + 3x$ intersect to form a prism with its base in the xy-plane. Find the volume of the region bounded by this prism and the surface $z = 2 + x + y^2$.

INCOMPLETE SOLUTION. The prism W involved has its base in the xy-plane, whose equation is $z = 0$. The sides of W are in the vertical planes $x + y = 1$, $x = 1$, and $y = 1 + 3x$. The xy-traces of these planes intersect to form a triangle ABC, which is the region R for use in (3) with $z = 2 + x + y^2$. No space figure is necessary. The student should verify that

$$V = \iint_R (2 + x + y^2)dA = \int_0^1 \int_{1-x}^{1+3x} (2 + x + y^2)dy\, dx.$$

EXERCISE 117

Find the volume of the region W bounded by the given surfaces in an xyz-system of rectangular coordinates. Formulate first as a double integral.

1. The surfaces $z = 0$, $2y = x$, $x = 1$, $y = 0$, and $z = x^2 + 3y + 1$.
2. Bounded by the tetrahedron in the 1st octant formed by the coordinate planes and the plane $3x + 2y + z = 6$.
3. The planes $z = 0$, $y = x$, $y = 2x$, and $y = 3$, and the surface $z = x + y^2$.
4. The cylinder $x^2 = 2y$, the planes $y = 2$ and $z = 0$, and the paraboloid $z = x^2 + 3y^2$.
5. The planes $x = 0$, $x = 1$, $y = 0$, $y = 2$, and $z = 0$, and $z = 4 - x^2$.
6. The cylinder $x^2 + y^2 = 9$ and the planes $z = 0$ and $y - x + 2z = 4$.

   HINT. $\iint_R 2\, dA = 2A$. Obtain the result without integration.

7. The cylinders $z = 1 - y^2$ and $x^2 = 4y$, and the xy-plane. (a) Solve by use of (2) on page 385. (b) Also, express the result as an iterated integral with respect to y and z, by use of (9) on page 387.
8. The surfaces $x^2 + y^2 = 25$, $y = 3$, $y = -3$, $z = 0$, and $x - y + z = 8$.
9. The surfaces $4z = x^2 + y^2$, $z = 0$, $x = 0$, $y = 4$, and $2x = y$.
10. The surfaces $y^2 = 3x$, $z = 0$, $x = 3$, and $z = x^2 + 3y^2$.
11. The surfaces $3z = 9 - x^2$, $z = 0$, $y = 0$, and $x = 3 - y$.
12. The plane $z = 0$ and the paraboloid $z = 16 - x^2 - 4y^2$.
13. The surfaces $x^2 + y^2 = k^2$, $z = 0$, and $z = k^2 - x^2$. (a) Compute by use of an integral in x and y. (b) Express as an iterated integral in x and z, but do not integrate. The constant k is positive.
14. The surfaces $z = 0$, $y = 3x$, $y = x$, and $z = 16 - x^2$.
15. The cylinders $z = 4 - x^2$ and $z = 4 - y^2$, and the xy-plane.
16. With $a > 0$, $b > 0$, and $c > 0$, W is the region bounded by the tetrahedron formed in the first octant by the coordinate planes and the plane $bcx + acy + abz = abc$.
17. The region common to the cylinders $x^2 + z^2 = a^2$ and $y^2 + z^2 = a^2$.

18. Obtain the volume of a sphere of radius a by use of a double integral.

19. In a sphere of radius a, obtain the volume of a segment with one plane face, which has altitude h.

20. Obtain the volume of the following ellipsoid by use of a double integral:

$$\frac{x^2}{a^2} + \frac{y^2}{b^2} + \frac{z^2}{c^2} = 1.$$

190. Double integrals in polar coordinates

Consider a plane where we have an $r\theta$-system of polar coordinates and also the associated xy-system of rectangular coordinates, related by

$$x = r \cos \theta \quad and \quad y = r \sin \theta. \tag{1}$$

In the plane, let R be a region where the function $z = f(r, \theta)$ is continuous. The function also may be defined as $z = F(x, y)$, with $f(r, \theta) \equiv F(x, y)$ when (1) is used. The integral of the function $z = F(x, y) = f(r, \theta)$ over R can be written in any one of the forms

$$\iint_R z\, dA, \quad \iint_R F(x, y)dA, \quad or \quad \iint_R f(r, \theta)dA. \tag{2}$$

Let P be a partition of R into subregions $\{T_i\}$ of any shape, where T_i has the area $\Delta_i A$. Select arbitrarily a point $[r = \gamma_i, \theta = \mu_i]$ in T_i. Then, instead of (5) on page 375, the defining expression for (2) becomes

$$\iint_R f(r, \theta)dA = \lim_{d_P \to 0} \sum_{i=1}^{n} f(\gamma_i, \mu_i)\Delta_i A. \tag{3}$$

We desire to express (3) by use of iterated integrals with respect to r and θ for regions of the following nature, where type I is illustrated in Figure 246 and type II in Figure 247. In each case, we assume that coordinates are chosen with $r \geq 0$.

$(R \text{ of type I})$ $\qquad\qquad \alpha \leq \theta \leq \beta; \quad h_1(\theta) \leq r \leq h_2(\theta). \tag{4}$

$(R \text{ of type II})$ $\qquad\qquad a \leq r \leq b; \quad g_1(r) \leq \theta \leq g_2(r). \tag{5}$

We shall give a background later for the following result.

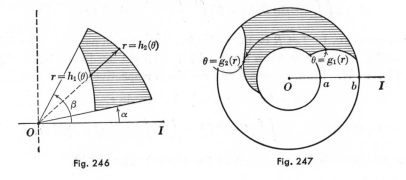

Fig. 246   Fig. 247

THEOREM IV. **Fundamental theorem of integral calculus, with polar coordinates.** *If* $f(r, \theta)$ *is continuous in a region* R, *then*

(R *of type* I) $\displaystyle \int\int_R f(r, \theta)dA = \int_\alpha^\beta \int_{h_1(\theta)}^{h_2(\theta)} rf(r, \theta)dr \, d\theta;$ (6)

(R *of type* II) $\displaystyle \int\int_R f(r, \theta)dA = \int_a^b \int_{g_1(r)}^{g_2(r)} rf(r, \theta)d\theta \, dr.$ (7)

The inner limits of integration in (6) and (7) are indicated by the corresponding straight arrow in Figure 246, and curved arrow in Figure 247.

Let A be the area of the region R in Theorem IV. Also, suppose that a total mass m is spread over R with $\delta(r, \theta)$ as the density of mass at the point $[r, \theta]$. Then,

(R *of type* I) $\displaystyle A = \int\int_R dA = \int_\alpha^\beta \int_{h_1(\theta)}^{h_2(\theta)} r \, dr \, d\theta;$ (8)

(R *of type* II) $\displaystyle m = \int\int_R \delta(r, \theta)dA = \int_a^b \int_{g_1(r)}^{g_2(r)} r\delta(r, \theta)d\theta \, dr.$ (9)

EXAMPLE 1. If R is the region bounded by the line $\theta = \frac{1}{2}\pi$ and the curves $r = \cos\theta$ and $r = 1 + \cos\theta$ in quadrants I and IV, find (*a*) the area of R; (*b*) its mass if $\delta(r, \theta) = k|y|$, where $y = r \sin\theta$.

SOLUTION. 1. R is indicated in Figure 248 and is of type I. To obtain a continuous range, choose θ on the interval $-\frac{1}{2}\pi \le \theta \le \frac{1}{2}\pi$. The arrow in Figure 248 indicates that the lower limit for the inner integration is $r = \cos\theta$, and the upper limit is $r = 1 + \cos\theta$.

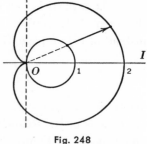

Fig. 248

$$A = \int\int_R dA = \int_{-\frac{1}{2}\pi}^{\frac{1}{2}\pi} \int_{\cos\theta}^{1+\cos\theta} r \, dr \, d\theta = 2 + \tfrac{1}{2}\pi.$$

2. At any point $[r, \theta]$, $\delta(r, \theta) = k|y| = kr|\sin\theta|$, where k is an unknown positive constant of proportionality. Since R and the values of $\delta(r, \theta)$ are symmetric with respect to the polar axis, the mass of R is twice the mass of that part, R', above the polar axis, where $|\sin\theta| = \sin\theta$. Thus,

$$M = 2\int\int_{R'} kr \sin\theta \, dA = 2k\int_0^{\frac{1}{2}\pi} \int_{\cos\theta}^{1+\cos\theta} r^2 \sin\theta \, dr \, d\theta = \tfrac{7}{3}k.$$

ILLUSTRATION 1. Let R be the region in Figure 249 on page 391 bounded by the circles $r = \cos\theta$ and $r = \sin\theta$, which intersect at $[r = \frac{1}{2}\sqrt{2}, \theta = \frac{1}{4}\pi]$. R is of type II. From $r = \cos\theta$ and $r = \sin\theta$, respectively,

$$\theta = \text{Arccos } r \quad and \quad \theta = \text{Arcsin } r.$$

Hence, from (7), $\displaystyle \int\int_R f(r, \theta)dA = \int_0^{\frac{1}{2}\sqrt{2}} \int_{\text{Arcsin } r}^{\text{Arccos } r} rf(r, \theta)d\theta \, dr,$

where the inner limits are shown by the arrow in Figure 249.

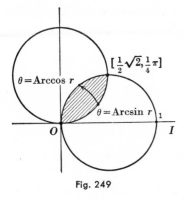

$\theta = \text{Arccos } r$

$[\frac{1}{2}\sqrt{2}, \frac{1}{4}\pi]$

$\theta = \text{Arcsin } r$

O I

Fig. 249

The student will find that use of (8) in finding an area is equivalent to the former method of page 258.

Note 1. Consider the region *BCDE* in Figure 250 between concentric circles of radii $r = r_1$ and $r = r_2$, where $r_2 = r_1 + \Delta r$, in a sector whose angle is $\Delta\theta$ radians. From page 124, the area of a sector whose angle is ϕ, in a circle of radius r, is $\frac{1}{2}r^2\phi$. Hence, the area, A, of *BCDE* is $A = \frac{1}{2}(r_2^2 \Delta\theta - r_1^2 \Delta\theta)$, or

$$A = \frac{1}{2}(r_2 + r_1)(r_2 - r_1)\Delta\theta, \text{ or}$$

(with $\Delta r = r_2 - r_1$)

$$A = r' \Delta r \Delta\theta, \tag{10}$$

where $r' = \frac{1}{2}(r_2 + r_1)$, which is the radius of a mid-section of *BCDE*. Hereafter, in any partition of a region R in an $r\theta$-plane, we shall refer to a subregion of type *BCDE* as a **regular subregion**.

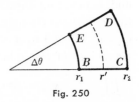

Fig. 250

Note 2. It is possible to prove (6) and (7) by direct use of (3) and Theorem II on page 376. However, any type of complete proof for Theorem IV is beyond the level of this text. The following details merely have the object of making (6) and (7) plausible.

Discussion of Theorem IV. 1. Let the ranges for r and θ in R be

$$a \leqq r \leqq b \quad and \quad \alpha \leqq \theta \leqq \beta, \tag{11}$$

as in Figure 251. Form partitions of the intervals in (11) by points $r = r_j$

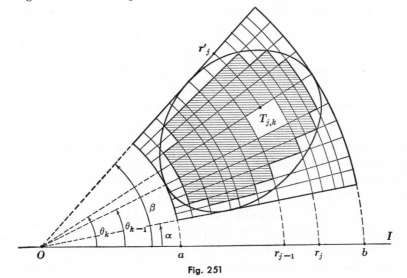

Fig. 251

for (a, b) and $\theta = \theta_k$ for (α, β). Cover R with a grid formed by lines $\theta = \theta_k$ through the pole, and circles $r = r_j$. This grid creates a partition P of R. Let $T_{j,k}$ be the regular subregion of the grid where

$$\theta_{k-1} \leqq \theta \leqq \theta_k \quad and \quad r_{j-1} \leqq r \leqq r_j. \tag{12}$$

Let $\Delta_k\theta = \theta_k - \theta_{k-1}$ and $\Delta_jr = r_j - r_{j-1}$, and let $\Delta_{j,k}A$ be the area of $T_{j,k}$. Then, by (10),

$$\Delta_{j,k}A = r_j'\Delta_jr\Delta_k\theta, \quad where \quad r_j' = \tfrac{1}{2}(r_{j-1} + r_j). \tag{13}$$

2. The partition P consists of certain regular subregions $T_{j,k}$ which lie wholly in P, and perhaps various irregular subregions. In Figure 251, the regular parts $\{T_{j,k}\}$, with one exception, are ruled. Intuition convinces us that the total area of all irregular subregions of P approaches zero if $d_P \to 0$ and, hence, that they may be omitted in setting up the right-hand side of (3) for P, without changing the equality. In any piece $T_{j,k}$ of P, select the point $[r = r_j', \theta = \theta_k]$ to serve in place of $[\gamma_i, \mu_i]$ in (3). Then, with only regular subregions of P employed, from (3) and (13) we obtain

$$\iint_R f(r, \theta)dA = \lim_{d_P \to 0} \sum_{(j,k)} f(r_j', \theta_k)\Delta_{j,k}A = \lim_{d_P \to 0} \sum_{(j,k)} [r_j'f(r_j', \theta_k)]\Delta_jr\,\Delta_k\theta, \tag{14}$$

where the sum for (j, k) extends over all values (j, k) for which $T_{j,k}$ is entirely in R. We verify that the sum in (14) is of the same form as the sum S_P on page 381, with the function "$rf(r, \theta)$" in (14) playing the role of "$F(x, y)$" in S_P on page 381, and $[r, \theta]$ in place of (x, y). Hence, we conclude that the type of reasoning employed with S_P in Section 187, on page 381, would lead from (14) to (6) or (7), according as "$\sum_{(j,k)}$" in (14) is evaluated by summing *first with respect to j* or *first with respect to k*. Thus, in (6), hereafter we may think of the inner integral arising as a consequence of writing

$$\sum_{(j,k)} r_j'f(r_j', \theta_k)\Delta_jr\Delta_k\theta = \sum_{(k)} \left[\sum_{(j)} r_j'f(r_j', \theta_k)\Delta_jr\right]\Delta_k\theta, \tag{15}$$

where we first take a sum of elements in a *fixed sector*, where k is held fast. Then, the outer integration in (6) is thought of as a consequence of taking the sum of sector sums in (15). Similar remarks apply to (7).

Note 3. For a regular subregion, in Figure 252, (13) gives $\Delta A = r\Delta r\Delta\theta$, with proper values for the factors, and the expression reminds us of the area of a rectangle with sides $r\Delta\theta$ and Δr. We think of "$r \Delta r \Delta\theta$" as a background for "$r \, dr \, d\theta$" on the right in (6) and (7), and refer to "$r \, dr \, d\theta$" as the **differential element of area in polar coordinates.** The extra factor "r" in "$rf(r, \theta)$" on the right in (6) and (7) is a consequence of r_j' in expression (13) for the area $\Delta_{j,k}A$ for a regular subregion of R.

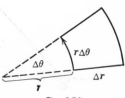

Fig. 252

EXERCISE 118

Express the double integral of an arbitrary function $f(r, \theta)$ over the specified region R by use of an iterated integral.

1. R is the smaller segment of the circle $r = 4 \cos \theta$ cut off by the line $r \cos \theta = 3$.

2. R is bounded by the cardioid $r = 1 + \sin \theta$, the circle $r = \sin \theta$, and the line $\theta = 0$.

3. R is the triangle in quadrant I bounded by the lines $\theta = \frac{1}{6}\pi$, $r \cos \theta = 2$, and the polar axis. Write a result, first, where the inner integration is with respect to r. Second, divide R into two parts by drawing the circle $r = 2$, and write the result as a sum of two iterated integrals where the inner integration is with respect to θ.

4. R is the region of points outside the limaçon $r = 3 - \cos \theta$, and inside the circle $r = 5 \cos \theta$.

5. Check the formula for the area of a circle by use of polar coordinates.

6. Check the formula for the area of a right triangle with legs u and v by use of a double integral in polar coordinates.

7. Find the mass of the region bounded by the circle $r = 4$ if the density at $[r, \theta]$ is $\delta(r, \theta) = 5r$.

First formulate the result as a double integral. Use any symmetry which exists. Where mass is requested, $\delta(r, \theta)$ is the density at $[r, \theta]$.

8. Find the area of R in Problem 1, and also the mass of R if δ is proportional to the distance of $[r, \theta]$ from the polar axis.

9. Find the mass of R in Problem 4 if $\delta = 2|\sin \theta|$.

10. Find the mass of R in Problem 3 if $\delta = kr^2$.

11. Find the area of the region R bounded above by $r = 2(1 + \sin \theta)$ and below by the upper half of $r = 2$; find the mass of R if $\delta = k|\cos \theta|$.

12. Find the mass of the region bounded by the upper semicircle of the circle $r = 1$, and by that part of $r = 1 + \sin \theta$ which is above the polar axis, if $\delta = k|\cos \theta|$.

13. R is the region inside the circle $r = 5 \cos \theta$ and outside the circle $r = \frac{5}{2}$. Find the mass of R if $\delta = kr^2$.

14. R is the region inside the cardioid $r = 1 + \cos \theta$ and outside the cardioid $r = 1 - \cos \theta$ in quadrant I. Find the mass of R if $\delta = xy$.

15. R is the region inside the lemniscate $r^2 = 2 \cos 2\theta$ and outside the circle $r = 1$ in quadrant I. Find the area of R and its mass if $\delta = kr^2$.

16. R is the region above the polar axis bounded by the circle $r = 2 \cos \theta$, the parabola $r = 4/(1 + \cos \theta)$, and the line $\theta = \frac{1}{2}\pi$. Find the area of R, and its mass if $\delta = ky$.

17. In a region R bounded by an equilateral triangle whose side is u, the density of mass at any point is proportional to the distance from one vertex. Find the mass of R by use of polar coordinates.

18. R is the region in quadrant I between the circle $r = 2$ and the parabola $r = \sec^2 \frac{1}{2}\theta$. Find the mass of R if $\delta = k/r$.

19. R is the region inside the cardioid $r = 4(1 + \sin\theta)$ and outside the parabola $r = 3/(1 - \sin\theta)$, to the right of the $\pi/2$-line. Find the mass of R if $\delta = kx$.

20. R is the region between the inner loop and the outer part of the limaçon $r = 2 - 4\cos\theta$. Find the mass of R if $\delta = k|y|$.

★*With $[r, \theta]$ interpreted as polar coordinates, draw the region R in an $r\theta$-plane, so that the given iterated integral is equal to a double integral over R, and write this integral. Then, repeat with (r, θ) as rectangular coordinates.*

21. $\displaystyle\int_2^4 \int_0^{\frac{1}{3}\pi} r^3 \sin\theta \; d\theta \; dr.$
  22. $\displaystyle\int_0^\pi \int_{\sin\theta}^{3\sin\theta} r^4 \cos\theta \; dr \; d\theta.$

23. $\displaystyle\int_{-\frac{1}{2}\pi}^{\frac{1}{2}\pi} \int_{\cos\theta}^{4/(1+\cos\theta)} \sin\theta \; dr \; d\theta.$
  24. $\displaystyle\int_{\frac{1}{4}\pi}^{\frac{3}{4}\pi} \int_{3/(1-\cos\theta)}^{4(1+\cos\theta)} \sin\theta \; dr \; d\theta.$

★*Express with the order of integration interchanged, by first obtaining a double integral in some plane.*

25. $\displaystyle\int_0^{\frac{1}{4}\pi} \int_{\sin\theta}^{\cos\theta} \cos^4\theta \; dr \; d\theta.$
  26. $\displaystyle\int_1^2 \int_0^{\frac{1}{2}\text{Arccos } \frac{1}{2}r} r \sin 2\theta \; d\theta \; dr.$

191. Cylindrical coordinates

Consider an xyz-system of rectangular coordinates and, in the xy-plane, set up an $r\theta$-system of polar coordinates related as usual to the rectangular

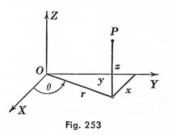

Fig. 253

coordinates (x, y). Then, the cylindrical coordinates $[r, \theta, z]$ of a point P, as in Figure 253, are defined as follows: the z-coordinate has its former meaning, the directed distance of P from the $r\theta$-plane; *the pair (r, θ) are the polar coordinates in the $r\theta$-plane of the projection of P on that plane.* The coordinates (x, y, z) and $[r, \theta, z]$ for a point P satisfy

$$z = z; \quad x = r \cos\theta; \quad y = r \sin\theta. \quad (1)$$

If (a, α, c) are constants, the locus of

$$
\left.
\begin{array}{l}
r = a \text{ is a circular cylinder, axis } OZ; \\
\theta = \alpha \text{ is a plane through the } z\text{-axis;} \\
z = c \text{ is a horizontal plane.}
\end{array}
\right\} \quad (2)
$$

The point $P:[r = a, \theta = \alpha, z = c]$ is the point of intersection of (2).

The locus of an equation $f(r, \theta) = 0$ in cylindrical coordinates is a *cylinder* whose generating lines are perpendicular to the $r\theta$-plane, along the curve which is the locus of $f(r, \theta) = 0$ in the $r\theta$-plane.

ILLUSTRATION 1. The space locus of $r = 3 \cos\theta$ is the circular cylinder perpendicular to the $r\theta$-plane whose trace in that plane is the circle $r = 3 \cos\theta$.

To change an xyz-equation to cylindrical coordinates, we use (1).

ILLUSTRATION 2.   The paraboloid of revolution $z = 4x^2 + 4y^2$ becomes

$$z = 4(x^2 + y^2) \quad or \quad z = 4r^2, \tag{3}$$

in cylindrical coordinates.   Notice that *the equation of any surface of revolution about the z-axis involves just z and r in cylindrical coordinates.*

192. Volumes by double integrals, with cylindrical coordinates

In space of three dimensions, install an xyz-system of rectangular coordinates and also the related $r\theta z$-system of cylindrical coordinates.   Let T be a surface whose equation in cylindrical coordinates is $z = f(r, \theta)$, where

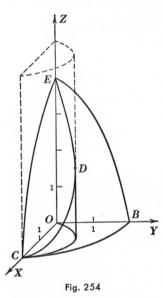

Fig. 254

$f(r, \theta) \geqq 0$.   When desirable, we may think of T also with the equation $z = F(x, y)$ where $F(x, y) \equiv f(r, \theta)$ when $x = r \cos \theta$ and $y = r \sin \theta$. Let V be the volume of the region W in (2) on page 385, capped by the surface T.   Then,

$$\left\{ \begin{array}{l} cylindrical\ region,\ W; \\ base,\ R;\ cap,\ z = f(r, \theta) \end{array} \right\} V = \iint_R z\, dA. \tag{1}$$

If the boundary of R consists of curves whose equations are convenient in polar coordinates, we consider computing V in (1) by using $z = f(r, \theta)$, and obtaining an iterated integral in polar coordinates.   Thus, if R is of type **I** as given in (4) on page 389,

$$V = \iint_R z\, dA = \int_\alpha^\beta \int_{h_1(\theta)}^{h_2(\theta)} rz\, dr\, d\theta. \tag{2}$$

EXAMPLE 1.   Find the volume of the region W which is above the xy-plane within the cylinder $r = 2 \cos \theta$ and below the paraboloid $z = 4 - x^2 - y^2$.

SOLUTION.   Figure 254 shows one-half of the region W; the surfaces intersect along arc EDC, with CD on the front and DE on the back of the cylinder. Figure 255 exhibits the base of the circular cylinder $r = 2 \cos \theta$, undistorted.   Let R be the half of the base in quadrant I. With $x = r \cos \theta$ and $y = r \sin \theta$, the equation of the paraboloid is $z = 4 - r^2$.   Since W is symmetric to the xz-plane, from (2) with $z = 4 - r^2$ we obtain

$$V = 2 \iint_R z\, dA = 2 \int_0^{\frac{1}{2}\pi} \int_0^{2 \cos \theta} r(4 - r^2)dr\, d\theta = \tfrac{5}{2}\pi.$$

Comment.   With the knowledge merely that $z \geqq 0$ on $z = 4 - x^2 - y^2$, Figure 255 alone would be sufficient. The arrow checks the inner limits of integration.

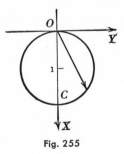

Fig. 255

396

EXERCISE 119

Write the equation of the surface in cylindrical coordinates.

1. $z = 4x^2 + 4y^2$.   **2.** $x = 3$.   **3.** $2x - y + z = 5$.

Compute by use of iterated integrals in polar coordinates.

4. Find the volume of the sphere $x^2 + y^2 + z^2 = a^2$.

5. Find the volume of a right circular cylinder with altitude h and with a as the radius of the base.

Find the volume, V, of the region W above the $r\theta$-plane within the given cylinder and below the specified surface, or the region bounded by the specified surfaces. Use polar coordinates for integration.

6. Within the cylinder $x^2 + y^2 = a^2$ and the sphere $x^2 + y^2 + z^2 = 4a^2$.

7. Within the cylinder $r = 2$, below the plane $y - x + 2z = 8$.

8. Within the cylinder $r = 3 \sin \theta$, below the plane $z = x$.

9. Within the cylinder $r = 1 - \cos \theta$, below the plane $z = y$.

10. Within the cylinder $x^2 + y^2 = 1$, below the cone $z^2 = 4x^2 + 4y^2$.

11. Within the cylinder $x^2 + y^2 = 8y$ below the paraboloid $4z = x^2 + y^2$.

12. Find the volume of the wedge of the cylinder $r = a$ bounded below by the xy-plane and above by a plane through the x-axis making an angle of $30°$ with the xy-plane.

13. Within the cylinder $r = a$, below the cylinder $z = a^2 - x^2$.

14. W is the wedge in the first octant between the planes $\theta = \frac{1}{6}\pi$ and $\theta = \frac{1}{4}\pi$, the xy-plane, and the sphere $x^2 + y^2 + z^2 = a^2$.

15. W is bounded by the planes $x = 0$, $y = 0$, $z = 0$, $x = 1$, and $y = 1$, and the paraboloid $z = 4 - x^2 - y^2$, above the xy-plane. (Divide the region of integration in the $r\theta$-plane into triangles.)

16. W is the region inside both of the cylinders $z = 4 - x^2$ and $z = 4 - y^2$.

17. W is bounded by the planes $x = 0$, $y = 0$, $z = 0$, $x = 1$, and $y = 1$, and the cone $z^2 = 9x^2 + 9y^2$.

193. Fluid pressure on a vertical surface

Consider a body of fluid which is at rest under the attraction of gravity. Let S be a horizontal plane surface immersed in the fluid. Then, S is subject to a vertical force directed downward, which is equal to the weight of the column of fluid directly over S. We accept the physical fact that, at any point in a fluid at rest, it exerts a force which is the same in all directions. This force per unit area will be referred to as the **fluid pressure.**

In a vertical plane, let R be a region immersed in a fluid whose weight is w pounds per cubic unit. Set up an xy-system of rectangular coordinates in the plane, with the x-axis vertical, and the y-axis parallel to the surface of the fluid. At any point $Q:(x, y)$ in R, let $h(x)$ be the distance of Q below the surface of the fluid. Now, consider any partition P of R. Let T be a subregion of P with area ΔA; in Figure 256, T is represented by rectangle CD. Physical intuition convinces us that T is subject to a force due to fluid pressure which is *less* than that which would exist if all of T were at its *deepest* point, and *more* than that which would exist if all of T were at its *highest* point. Thus, by intuition, we accept the fact that there is some unknown point $U:(x', y')$ in T such that, if all of T were at the depth $h(x')$ of U, the resulting force would be equal to the actual force on T. Visualize T as tipped to the horizontal position $C'D'$, in Figure 256, at the level of U, and let ΔF be the force of fluid pressure which then acts on T. We have

$$\Delta F = wh(x')\Delta A. \tag{1}$$

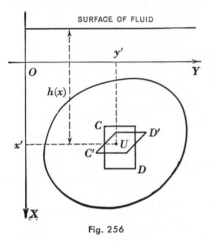

SURFACE OF FLUID

Fig. 256

With the preceding physical background, we now define the force F due to fluid pressure acting on R as the limit of the sum of all elements ΔF for a partition P as the norm $d_P \to 0$:

$$F = \lim_{d_P \to 0} \sum_{(all, \ for \ P)} \Delta F. \tag{2}$$

We recognize ΔF in (1) as the typical element of an approximating sum for the integral of $wh(x)$ over R. Hence,

$$F = w \int\int_R h(x)\,dA. \tag{3}$$

EXAMPLE 1. A cylindrical tank 12′ in diameter is lying on its side and contains water to a depth of 9′. Find the force F on one end of the tank.

SOLUTION. 1. Figure 257 shows an end of the tank. In the plane of the circle, set up coordinates as indicated. In Figure 257, BC represents the water surface.

2. At $Q:(x, y)$ in Figure 257, the depth below the surface is the value of the directed segment KD where K is $(-3, 0)$. Hence, $h(x) = x + 3$.

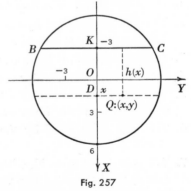

Fig. 257

3. By symmetry, the force F is equal to twice the force on the larger region R (where $y \geq 0$) bounded by the x-axis, the line $x = -3$, and circle $x^2 + y^2 = 36$, or $y = \sqrt{36 - x^2}$. From (3),

$$F = 2w \int\int_R (x + 3)\,dA = 2w \int_{-3}^{6} \int_{0}^{\sqrt{36-x^2}} (x + 3)\,dy\,dx = 9w(9\sqrt{3} + 8\pi).$$

With $w = 62.4$, we find $F = 2.29(10^4)$ pounds, by use of logarithms.

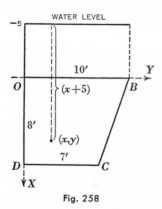

WATER LEVEL

10′

$(x+5)$

8′

(x,y)

7′

Fig. 258

EXAMPLE 2. The vertical gate in a dam $OBCD$ has the dimensions shown in Figure 258, and water is flowing over the dam with the surface 5′ above the gate. Find the force due to water pressure on the gate.

INCOMPLETE SOLUTION. Take the x-axis vertical, directed downward, with the origin at the top of the dam, as in the figure. Points B:(0, 10) and C:(8, 7) determine line BC. Its equation is

$$\frac{y - 7}{x - 8} = \frac{7 - 10}{8}, \quad or \quad 8y + 3x = 80. \quad (4)$$

At any point (x, y) on the gate, the distance below the surface of the water is $h(x) = x + 5$. Let R be the region in the gate. Then R is bounded by the lines $x = 0$, $x = 8$, $y = 0$, and $8y + 3x = 80$. From (3),

$$F = w \int\int_R (x + 5)dA = w \int_0^8 \int_0^{\frac{1}{8}(80-3x)} (x + 5)dy\, dx.$$

EXERCISE 120

Find the force due to fluid pressure.

1. The vertical end of a rectangular tank is 8′ wide and 10′ deep, and the tank is full of water. Find the force on the end of the tank.

Let the x-axis and y-axis be located in the vertical gate for a dam, with the y-axis as its top, and the x-axis directed vertically downward. Find the force on the gate in each problem. The unit for each coordinate is 1′.

2. The gate is bounded by the lines $x = 0$, $x = 10$, $y = 0$, and $x + y = 15$. The water level stands at $x = 0$.

3. Solve Problem 2, if the water level stands at $x = 3$.

4. Solve Problem 2, if water flows over the gate 2′ deep.

5. The gate has the shape of a triangle, with vertices at the points $(0, \pm 8)$ and $(20, 0)$. Water flows over the gate 5′ deep.

6. The gate is bounded by the parabola $y^2 = 400 - 4x$. The water level stands at $x = 10$.

7. The gate is a trapezoid, with the vertices at the points $(0, -5)$, $(0, 10)$, $(20, 0)$, and $(20, 5)$. The water level is flush with the top of the gate.

8. The gate is bounded on the left by the parabola $y^2 = 100 - 2x$ and on the right by the parabola $y^2 = 400 - 8x$. The water level is 10′ below the top of the gate.

9. A vertical drainage gate for a swimming pool is bounded by a circle 4′ in diameter. If the water level is 12′ above the top of the gate, find the force on the gate.

10. A horizontal cylindrical tank is 10′ in diameter and is full of oil weighing 50 pounds per cubic foot. Find the force on an end of the tank.

11. The vertical cross section of a horizontal oil tank is an ellipse with the major axis horizontal and 24′ long, and the minor axis 12′ long. The tank contains oil weighing 50 pounds per cubic foot. Find the force on one end of the tank if the oil is (a) 6′ deep; (b) 9′ deep.

★194. Improper double integrals

At a more advanced level, improper double integrals are introduced. The following illustration is very useful.

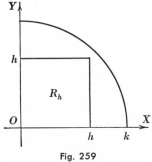

Fig. 259

Let the region R consist of all points (x, y) where $x \geqq 0$ and $y \geqq 0$. Consider

$$J = \int\int_R e^{-(x^2+y^2)} dA. \tag{1}$$

Let R_h be the square region bounded by the coordinate axes and the lines $x = h$ and $y = h$, where $h > 0$, as in Figure 259. Then, we define:

$$J = \lim_{h\to\infty} \int\int_{R_h} e^{-(x^2+y^2)} dA. \tag{2}$$

Then $\quad J = \lim_{h\to\infty} \int_0^h \int_0^h e^{-x^2} e^{-y^2}\, dx\, dy = \lim_{h\to\infty}\left(\int_0^h e^{-x^2}\,dx\right)\!\left(\int_0^h e^{-y^2}\,dy\right), \tag{3}$

Hence, $\qquad\qquad J = \lim_{h\to\infty}\left(\int_0^h e^{-x^2}\,dx\right)^2. \tag{4}$

We shall employ (4) later. First, consider a second evaluation of J.

Let S_k be the region in quadrant I bounded by the coordinate axes and the circle whose equation in polar coordinates is $r = k > 0$, as in Figure 259.

Then, we define J by $\qquad J = \lim_{k\to\infty} \int\int_{S_k} e^{-(x^2+y^2)}\, dA. \tag{5}$

Or, $\qquad J = \lim_{k\to\infty} \int_0^k \int_0^{\frac{1}{2}\pi} re^{-r^2}\,d\theta\, dr = \frac{1}{2}\pi \lim_{k\to\infty}\int_0^k re^{-r^2}\,dr = \frac{\pi}{4}. \tag{6}$

We then accept the fact that (2) should lead to the same value for J, because R_h and S_k both swell out over all points in R as $h \to \infty$ and $k \to \infty$. Thus, from (4) and (6), we conclude that

$$\lim_{h\to\infty}\left(\int_0^h e^{-x^2}\,dx\right)^2 = \frac{\pi}{4}, \quad or \quad \lim_{h\to\infty}\int_0^h e^{-x^2}\,dx = \sqrt{\frac{\pi}{4}} = \int_0^\infty e^{-x^2}\,dx.$$

Thus, by investigating (1), we have proved that

$$\int_0^\infty e^{-x^2}\,dx = \tfrac{1}{2}\sqrt{\pi}, \quad or \quad \int_{-\infty}^\infty e^{-x^2}\,dx = \sqrt{\pi}.$$

20

MOMENTS IN A PLANE

195. Center of mass in a plane, continuous case

Consider a mass particle m, located at a point (x_0, y_0) in an xy-plane. Then, from page 285, recall that the moments of m with respect to the x-axis and y-axis are defined, respectively, as my_0 and mx_0. On page 286, we introduced the notions of *moments* and *center of mass* for a discrete distribution of n mass particles in the plane. We proceed to discuss the corresponding concepts for a continuous distribution of mass.

Suppose that a total mass m is distributed over a region R in the xy-plane, with $\delta(x, y)$ as the density of mass at any point, and assume that δ is a continuous function. From page 382,

$$m = \int\int_R \delta(x, y)dA. \tag{1}$$

First, we shall define the moments of this mass with respect to the axes. Let P be a partition of R into subregions $\{T\}$, where the representative piece T has the area ΔA and mass Δm. Let the norm d_P be the maximum of the diameters of the subregions. From (2) on page 382, there exists a point (x', y') in T, as in Figure 260, so that $\Delta m = \delta(x', y')\Delta A$. By physical intuition, we decide that the moment with respect to the y-axis of the mass of T should lie between $x_1\Delta m$ and $x_2\Delta m$, where x_1 and x_2 are, respectively, the least and the greatest values for x in T, as in Figure 260. Hence, we think of concentrating all of Δm at an arbitrary point (x'', y'') in T, where x'' lies on the interval $x_1 \leq x \leq x_2$, and let ΔM_y be the corresponding moment of Δm with respect to the y-axis. Then,

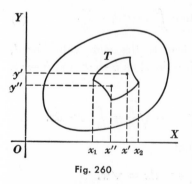

Fig. 260

$$\Delta M_y = x''\Delta m = x''\delta(x', y')\Delta A. \tag{2}$$

Finally, we define the moment, M_y, of the mass of R with respect to the

y-axis to be the limit of the sum of all elements ΔM_y corresponding to the partition P, as $d_P \to 0$. Or,

$$M_y = \lim_{d_P \to 0} \sum \Delta M_y = \lim_{d_P \to 0} \sum x''\delta(x', y')\Delta A, \qquad (3)$$

where the sum "$\sum$" involves the moment elements for all subregions of P. Since $\delta(x, y)$ is continuous, we accept the fact * that the limit in (3), if it exists, will not be altered by changing x'' to x', because $|x'' - x'| \to 0$ as $d_P \to 0$. Hence, we conclude that

$$M_y = \lim_{d_P \to 0} \sum x'\delta(x', y')\Delta A. \qquad (4)$$

From (5) on page 375, $[x'\delta(x', y')\Delta A]$ in (4) is recognized as the typical element of an approximating sum S_P for the double integral of $x\delta(x, y)$ over R. Thus, from (4), we arrive at the following definition for M_y, and similarly for M_x, the moment of the mass of R with respect to the x-axis:

$$M_y = \int\int_R x\delta(x, y)dA; \quad M_x = \int\int_R y\delta(x, y)dA. \qquad (5)$$

By Definition IV on page 285, the center of mass, $(\bar{x}, \bar{y})$, for R is that point where the whole mass m would have to be concentrated in order for it to have the same moments with respect to the axes as the mass m *when spread over* R. If a mass m were at $(\bar{x}, \bar{y})$, the moments with respect to the y-axis and x-axis would be $m\bar{x}$ and $m\bar{y}$, respectively. Hence, $\bar{x}$ and $\bar{y}$ satisfy

$$m\bar{x} = M_y \quad and \quad m\bar{y} = M_x, \text{ or}$$

$$\left\{\begin{array}{c} \textbf{center of} \\ \textbf{mass} \end{array}\right\} \qquad \bar{x} = \frac{\int\int_R x\delta(x, y)dA}{m}; \quad \bar{y} = \frac{\int\int_R y\delta(x, y)dA}{m}. \qquad (6)$$

If δ is a constant, $(\bar{x}, \bar{y})$ is called the **centroid** of R. Then, (1) becomes $m = \delta A$, where A is the area of R, and δ divides out in (6) to give

$$\textbf{(centroid)} \qquad \bar{x} = \frac{\int\int_R x\, dA}{A} \quad and \quad \bar{y} = \frac{\int\int_R y\, dA}{A}. \qquad (7)$$

Since (7) does not involve δ, the centroid depends only on the region R, and thus has a geometrical significance regardless of any mass.

Note 1. If δ is a constant in a region R, we say that *mass is distributed uniformly over* R, or that *the mass is homogeneous over* R.

If mass is distributed over a region R in an xy-plane with a given density $\delta(x, y)$, let us refer to R as a **lamina**. We shall omit proving the fact that the location of the center of mass for a lamina is independent of the choice of coordinate axes in the plane of R. The center of mass may not lie in the lamina.

* The reasoning is similar to that in the footnote on page 287 about a simple integral.

EXAMPLE 1. A region R in the 1st quadrant of the xy-plane is bounded by the x-axis, the line $x = 4$, and the parabola $y^2 = 4x$. If the density of mass in R at any point (x, y) is $\delta = 2x$, find the center of mass.

SOLUTION. From (1), (5), and (6), and Figure 261, we obtain

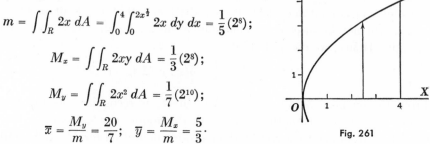

$$m = \int\int_R 2x \, dA = \int_0^4 \int_0^{2x^{\frac{1}{2}}} 2x \, dy \, dx = \frac{1}{5}(2^8);$$

$$M_x = \int\int_R 2xy \, dA = \frac{1}{3}(2^8);$$

$$M_y = \int\int_R 2x^2 \, dA = \frac{1}{7}(2^{10});$$

$$\bar{x} = \frac{M_y}{m} = \frac{20}{7}; \quad \bar{y} = \frac{M_x}{m} = \frac{5}{3}.$$

Fig. 261

THEOREM I. *If a region R has an axis of symmetry, and if the density function δ also is symmetric to this axis, then the center of mass for R lies on the axis of symmetry.*

Proof. 1. Choose the axis of symmetry as the y-axis. For any point (x, y), the symmetric point with respect to the y-axis is $(-x, y)$. By hypothesis, $\delta(x, y) = \delta(-x, y)$, for every point (x, y) in R.

2. In the details preceding (4), let P be restricted to consist of *pairs* of subregions, T and $\hat{T}$, symmetric to the y-axis, as in Figure 262. Then, with (x', y') as a point in T, and with the symmetric point $(-x', y')$ in $\hat{T}$, we obtain elements ΔM_y and $\Delta \hat{M}_y$, as in (2), where we choose $x'' = x'$ in (2) and obtain

$$\Delta M_y = x'\delta(x', y')\Delta A \quad and$$

$$\Delta \hat{M}_y = -x'\delta(-x', y')\Delta \hat{A}.$$

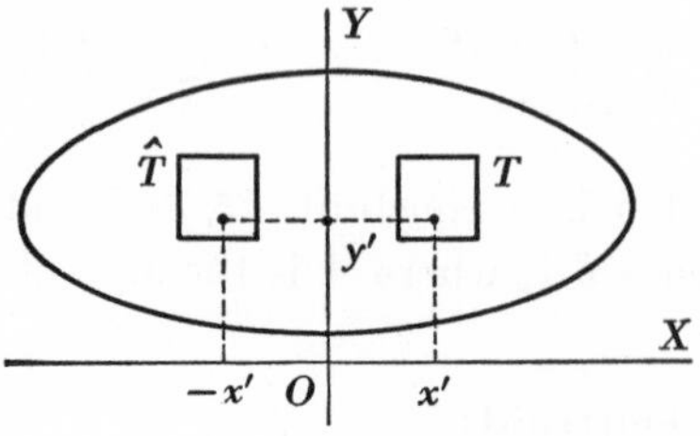

Since $\delta(x', y') = \delta(-x', y')$ and $\Delta A = \Delta \hat{A}$, we have

Fig. 262

$$\Delta M_y = -\Delta \hat{M}_y \quad or \quad \Delta M_y + \Delta \hat{M}_y = 0. \tag{8}$$

Hence, the sum in (4) is zero, because the terms cancel in pairs, as in (8). Thus, $M_y = 0$. Or, $m\bar{x} = 0$ and hence $\bar{x} = 0$, which proves Theorem I.

By Theorem I, if a region R has *two* axes of symmetry, their intersection is the centroid of R.

ILLUSTRATION 1. By Theorem I, if R is bounded by a rectangle, the centroid of R is the intersection of the diagonals of the rectangle. Similarly, the center of mass of a homogeneous circular lamina R is the center of the circle which is the boundary of R.

EXAMPLE 2. Find the center of mass for the region R bounded above by the ellipse $4x^2 + 9y^2 = 36$ and below by the x-axis, when $\delta = 3y|x|$.

SOLUTION. 1. R is symmetric to the y-axis, as seen in Figure 263. Also, at any point (x_1, y_1), where $x_1 > 0$, the density is the same as at $(-x_1, y_1)$, which is symmetric to (x_1, y_1) with respect to the y-axis. Hence, by Theorem I, $(\bar{x}, \bar{y})$ lies on the y-axis, or $\bar{x} = 0$.

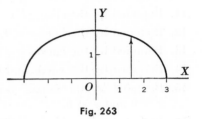

Fig. 263

2. From (1) and (6),

$$m = \iint_R 3y|x|\, dA; \quad m\bar{y} = \iint_R 3y^2|x|\, dA. \tag{9}$$

Let R_1 be that part of R where $x \geq 0$. By symmetry,

$$m = 2\iint_{R_1} 3xy\, dA = 6\int_0^3 \int_0^{\frac{2}{3}\sqrt{9-x^2}} xy\, dy\, dx = 27; \tag{10}$$

$$m\bar{y} = 2\iint_{R_1} 3xy^2\, dA = 6\int_0^2 \int_0^{3\sqrt{4-y^2}} y^2 x\, dx\, dy = \frac{144}{5}. \tag{11}$$

Then, from (10) and (11), $\bar{y} = \frac{16}{15}$. The center of mass is $(0, \frac{16}{15})$.

★*Note 2.* In the field of statistics, let (X, Y) denote a *two-dimensional random vector variable*, with the particular values (x, y). Let the range of (X, Y) be the region R in the xy-plane. Then, a continuous, nonnegative function $\delta(x, y)$ is called the *probability density function* for (X, Y) in case

$$\iint_R \delta(x, y)dA = 1 \quad and \quad pr[(X, Y) \ in \ T] = \iint_T \delta(x, y)dA, \tag{12}$$

for every subregion T of R. Then, we refer to $\bar{x}$ and $\bar{y}$ of (6) as the *means*, or *expected values* of X and Y, respectively, and write $\bar{x} = E(X)$ and $\bar{y} = E(Y)$. From the item at the left in (12), and from (6) with $m = 1$,

$$\bar{x} = E(X) = \iint_R x\delta\, dA \quad and \quad \bar{y} = E(Y) = \iint_R y\delta\, dA. \tag{13}$$

EXERCISE 121

Find the centroid of the region with the specified boundary. Use symmetry. Do not integrate for any familiar area.

1. Bounded by the lines $x = 0$, $y = 0$, and $x + 3y = 6$.
2. Bounded by the lines $y = 0$, $y = x$, and $x + y = 4$.
3. Bounded by the lines $x = 0$, $x + 2y = 4$, and $x - 2y = 4$.
4. Bounded by the parabola $y^2 = 4 + x$ and the lines $y = 0$ and $x = 5$. with $y \geq 0$.
5. Bounded by the parabola $x^2 = 9y$ and the line $y = 1$, with $x \geq 0$.
6. Bounded by the x-axis and the curve $y = 2x - x^2$.
7. Bounded by the y-axis and the curve $x = 4y - y^2$.

8. Bounded by the y-axis and the curve $x = y^2 - 4y + 3$.

9. Bounded by the lines $x = 0$, $x = 4$, $x + 2y = 4$, and $4y - 3x = 12$.

10. Bounded by the curves $y^2 = 4 + 4x$ and $y^2 = 4 - 8x$.

11. Bounded by the ellipse $b^2x^2 + a^2y^2 = a^2b^2$, with $y \geq 0$.

12. Bounded by the lines $x = 0$, $y = 1$, and $y = 3$, and the curve $xy = 4$.

13. Bounded by the curves $y = x^3$ and $x = y^3$ in quadrant I.

14. Bounded by the x-axis and the circle $x^2 + y^2 = a^2$ where $y \geq 0$.

15. Bounded by the x-axis, y-axis, and the ellipse $4x^2 + 25y^2 = 100$ where $x \geq 0$ and $y \geq 0$.

16. Bounded by the lines $x = 0$, $y = 0$, and $bx + ay = ab$.

17. Bounded by the x-axis and the curve $y = \sin x$ where $0 \leq x \leq \pi$.

18. Bounded by the x-axis, the line $x = \frac{1}{2}\pi$, and $y = \sin x$, for $0 \leq x \leq \frac{1}{2}\pi$.

Find the center of mass of the region having the given boundary and density.

19. Bounded by the lines $x = 0$, $y = 0$, $x = 2$, and $y = 3$; $\delta = x^2y$.

20. In Problem 1; $\delta = 4x$.   **21.** In Problem 2; $\delta = 3y$.

22. In Problem 2; $\delta = 2x$.   **23.** In Problem 6; $\delta = 2x^2$.

24. In Problem 10; $\delta = ky^2$.

25. Bounded by the curve $4y^3 = x^2$ and the line $y = 1$; $\delta = 5y$.

26. Bounded on the left by the circle $x^2 - 4x + y^2 = 0$ and on the right by the circle $x^2 + y^2 = 4$; $\delta = 2|y|$.

27. Bounded by the parabola $y^2 = 9x$ and the line $x = 4$, with the density at any point (x, y) proportional to its distance from the line $x = 4$.

28. Bounded by the curve $x^2 = 2y + 1$ and the line $y = 4$; $\delta = 3|x|$.

Find the centroid of the region with the specified boundary.

29. Bounded by the curve $y = \sec x$ and the line $y = 2$, within the range $-\frac{1}{2}\pi < x < \frac{1}{2}\pi$.

30. Bounded by the triangle with the vertices $(-2, 0)$, $(0, 1)$ and $(4, 0)$.

31. Bounded by the triangle with vertices $(0, 0)$, $(a, 0)$, and (b, c). Then, specify the point $(\bar{x}, \bar{y})$ in language not involving coordinates. Apply the result to write $(\bar{x}, \bar{y})$ for the region bounded by the triangle with vertices (a_1, a_2), (b_1, b_2), and (c_1, c_2). Notice that the result is the same as the center of mass of three unit masses located at the vertices.

32. Bounded by the curves $y = x^3 + x^2 - 2x$ and $y = 4x$, where $x \leq 0$.

33. By starting with double integrals, find expressions involving simple integrals for the coordinates of the centroid of the region bounded by the lines $y = 0$, $x = a$, and $x = b$, and the curve $y = f(x)$, where $f(x) \geq 0$.

34. Bounded above by the ellipse whose parametric equations are $x = a \cos t$ and $y = b \sin t$, with $a > 0$ and $b > 0$, and below by the x-axis.

35. Bounded by the x-axis and the cycloid whose parametric equations are

$$x = t - \sin t \quad and \quad y = 1 - \cos t, \quad with \quad 0 \leq t \leq 2\pi.$$

★196. Center of mass for two or more regions

In an xy-plane, consider distributions of mass over two regions R_1 and R_2, which do not overlap except possibly at boundaries. In R_1 and R_2, suppose that the densities of mass are $\delta_1(x, y)$ and $\delta_2(x, y)$, the centers of mass are $(\bar{x}_1, \bar{y}_1)$ and $(\bar{x}_2, \bar{y}_2)$, the masses are m_1 and m_2, and the moments with respect to the y-axis are $M_{y,1}$ and $M_{y,2}$, respectively. Let R be the region consisting of the component regions R_1 and R_2, with R having the mass m, center of mass $(\bar{x}, \bar{y})$, and M_y as the moment with respect to the y-axis. We define the double integral of any function of x and y over R as the sum of the double integrals of the function over R_1 and R_2. Hence, since mass and moments are defined as integrals, we have

$$m = m_1 + m_2; \quad M_y = M_{y,1} + M_{y,2} = m_1\bar{x}_1 + m_2\bar{x}_2.$$

Since $M_y = m\bar{x}$, $\qquad\qquad m\bar{x} = m_1\bar{x}_1 + m_2\bar{x}_2,$ or

$$\bar{x} = \frac{m_1\bar{x}_1 + m_2\bar{x}_2}{m}; \quad similarly, \quad \bar{y} = \frac{m_1\bar{y}_1 + m_2\bar{y}_2}{m}. \tag{1}$$

Similarly, if n regions $\{R_i\}$ are involved, there is obtained

$$\bar{x} = \frac{\sum_{i=1}^{n} m_i\bar{x}_i}{\sum_{i=1}^{n} m_i}; \quad \bar{y} = \frac{\sum_{i=1}^{n} m_i\bar{y}_i}{\sum_{i=1}^{n} m_i}. \tag{2}$$

Comparison of (2) with (5) on page 286 justifies the following conclusion: *The center of mass of a set of regions $\{R_i\}$, with masses $\{m_i\}$, is that point $(\bar{x}, \bar{y})$ which would be the center of mass for a set of mass points $\{m_i\}$, concentrated at the centers of mass $(\bar{x}_i, \bar{y}_i)$ for the regions R_i.* If the density of mass is a constant δ, then $m_i = \delta A_i$, where A_i is the area of R_i, and (2) gives the centroid of R, where δ divides out:

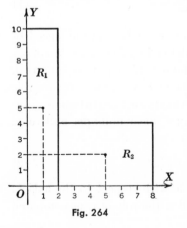

Fig. 264

$$\bar{x} = \frac{\sum_{i=1}^{n} A_i\bar{x}_i}{\sum_{i=1}^{n} A_i} \quad and \quad \bar{y} = \frac{\sum_{i=1}^{n} A_i\bar{y}_i}{\sum_{i=1}^{n} A_i}. \tag{3}$$

Sometimes, we may use (3) to find the centroid without integration.

ILLUSTRATION 1. Suppose that mass is spread uniformly over the L-shaped region R in quadrant I of Figure 264. To find the centroid of R without integration, divide R into the two rectangular regions R_1 and R_2, whose areas A_1 and A_2, and centroids (x_1, y_1) and (x_2, y_2) are, respectively,

$$A_1 = 20, \ (x_1 = 1, y_1 = 5) \quad and \quad A_2 = 24, \ (x_2 = 5, y_2 = 2).$$

Hence, by (3), $\qquad\qquad \bar{x} = \tfrac{140}{44} = \tfrac{35}{11} \quad and \quad \bar{y} = \tfrac{148}{44} = \tfrac{37}{11}.$

EXERCISE 122

By use of a coordinate system locate and mark the centroid of the region in the problem. Numbers indicate dimensions. Any curved boundary arc is a circle or a semicircle. Use Problems 14 and 31 of Exercise 121.

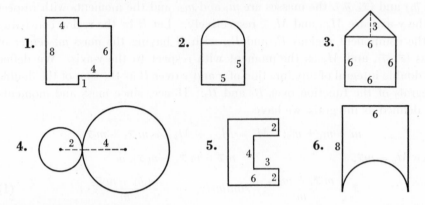

197. Moment of inertia

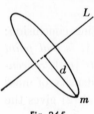

Fig. 265

In three-dimensional space, let a mass particle m be at a distance d from a line L, which is an axis about which m might revolve, as in Figure 265. Then, the **moment of inertia** of m about the axis L is defined as md^2. If mass particles $\{m_i\}$ are situated at distances $\{d_i\}$, from L, the moment of inertia, I, of the system about L is defined as the sum of the moments of inertia of the particles:

$$I = \sum_{i=1}^{n} m_i d_i^2. \tag{1}$$

Note 1. If a mass particle of m units is moving with a linear speed of v units, the kinetic energy, E, of the particle is defined by $E = \frac{1}{2}mv^2$, in energy units. Suppose, now, that the particle is revolving in a circle of radius d, as in Figure 265, and let the line L be perpendicular to the plane of the circle at its center. At any instant, if the angular velocity of the particle is ω radians per unit time, the speed of the particle is ωd linear units per unit time. Then, the kinetic energy in energy units is

$$E = \frac{1}{2}m(\omega d)^2 = \frac{1}{2}(md^2)\omega^2 = \frac{1}{2}I\omega^2, \tag{2}$$

where I is the moment of inertia of the particle with respect to the axis L. Thus, in (2), I plays the role of the *mass* m and ω the role of v, as compared to the formula $E = \frac{1}{2}mv^2$.

Suppose that a total mass m is distributed over a region R in the xy-plane, as in Figure 266 on page 407, with $\delta(x, y)$ as the density of mass at any point

(x, y), where δ is continuous in R. Let P be a partition of R into subregions $\{T\}$, and let d_P be the maximum of their diameters. Let ΔA be the area and Δm be the mass of the typical subregion T. Then, as on page 382, there exists a point (x', y') in T such that

$$\Delta m = \delta(x', y')\Delta A. \tag{3}$$

If Δm is considered as concentrated at an arbitrary point (x'', y'') in T, the moment of inertia of Δm about the y-axis is

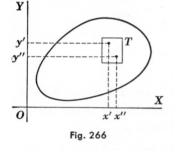

Fig. 266

$$x''^2\Delta m, \quad or \quad x''^2\delta(x', y')\Delta A. \tag{4}$$

The **moment of inertia**, I_y, of the mass in R *about the y-axis* is defined as the limit of the sum, S_P, of all elements (4) for the subregions of P, as $d_P \to 0$. By familiar reasoning, as applied in (3) on page 401, we decide that the preceding limit may be evaluated with x'' replaced by x' in (4), to give the element

$$\Delta I_y = x'^2\delta(x', y')\Delta A, \quad and\ then \quad I_y = \lim_{d_p \to 0} \sum \Delta I_y. \tag{5}$$

In (5), the sum extends over the moment elements ΔI_y corresponding to all subregions of P. From (5) on page 375, we recognize ΔI_y in (5) as the typical element of an approximating sum S_P for the double integral of the function $x^2\delta(x, y)$ over R. Thus,

$$I_y = \iint_R x^2\delta(x, y)dA; \quad similarly \quad I_x = \iint_R y^2\delta(x, y)dA. \tag{6}$$

Consider an axis L perpendicular to the xy-plane at the origin, as in Figure 267. Let a mass particle m be located at (x_0, y_0) in the plane. Then, the moment of inertia of m with respect to L is called the **polar moment of inertia** of m. The distance, d, of m from L is given by $d^2 = x_0^2 + y_0^2$, and thus the polar moment of inertia of m is

$$md^2 \quad or \quad m(x_0^2 + y_0^2), \quad or \quad (mx_0^2 + my_0^2), \tag{7}$$

which is the sum of the moments of inertia of m with respect to the x-axis and the y-axis. Similarly, if there is a *continuous* distribution of mass over a region R in the xy-plane, the moment of inertia, I_O, of this mass with respect to a line perpendicular to the plane at the origin is called the **polar moment of inertia of the mass.** When (7) is used for Δm from (3), and details similar to (5) are discussed, we obtain

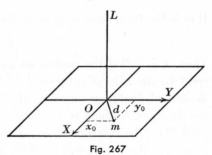

Fig. 267

$$I_O = \int\int_R (x^2 + y^2)\delta(x, y)dA. \tag{8}$$

From (6) and (8),
$$I_O = I_x + I_y. \tag{9}$$

EXAMPLE 1. For the lamina of Example 1 on page 402, find I_x, I_y, and I_O.

SOLUTION. From page 402 and (6),

$$I_x = \int\int_R 2xy^2 \, dA \quad and \quad I_y = \int\int_R 2x^3 \, dA;$$

$$I_x = \int_0^4 \int_0^{2x^{\frac{1}{2}}} 2xy^2 \, dy \, dx = \frac{4096}{21}; \quad I_y = \frac{4096}{9}.$$

Hence,
$$I_O = \frac{4096}{21} + \frac{4096}{9} = \frac{40,960}{63}.$$

EXAMPLE 2. A homogeneous plane lamina is bounded by an isosceles right triangle. Find the moment of inertia of the lamina about an axis perpendicular to its plane at the vertex of the 90° angle.

SOLUTION. 1. Let the constant density of mass be δ, and each leg of the triangle be a units long. Place the triangle on an xy-coordinate system with the 90° vertex at the origin, and the legs on the positive halves of the axes, as in Figure 268. With this setting, the problem requests I_O.

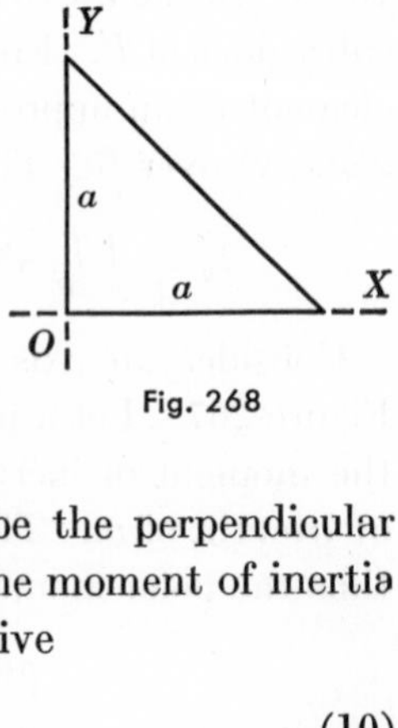

2. Let R be the region bounded by the right triangle in Figure 268. The hypotenuse has the equation $x + y = a$. Hence,

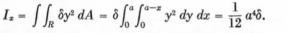

$$I_x = \int\int_R \delta y^2 \, dA = \delta \int_0^a \int_0^{a-x} y^2 \, dy \, dx = \frac{1}{12} a^4\delta.$$

Fig. 268

By symmetry, $I_y = I_x$. Hence, $I_O = \frac{1}{6}a^4\delta.$

Let L be any line in the xy-plane, and let $h(x, y)$ be the perpendicular distance (positive) from a point (x, y) to L. Let I be the moment of inertia about L for the mass over region R. Then, we could derive

$$I = \int\int_R [h(x, y)]^2 \, \delta(x, y)dA. \tag{10}$$

If m is the total mass over R, define a positive constant k by

$$I = mk^2. \tag{11}$$

Then, k is called the **radius of gyration** of the mass distribution with respect to the axis of rotation L. That is, by (11), if all of the mass were located at the perpendicular distance k from L, the resulting moment of inertia about L would be the same as in (10). If I_x, I_y, or I_O is written in the form (11), the corresponding constant is called the radius of gyration with respect to the x-axis, y-axis, or the origin, respectively.

On account of the notion of a radius of gyration, frequently we give the final expression for any moment of inertia in the form $I = mk^2$, so that k^2 is immediately in evidence.

ILLUSTRATION 1.   In Example 2, the total mass m is given by $m = A\delta$ where $A = \frac{1}{2}a^2$, and thus we have $I_O = \frac{1}{6}a^4\delta = \frac{1}{3}a^2m$.   Hence, $k^2 = \frac{1}{3}a^2$, or the radius of gyration is $\frac{1}{3}a\sqrt{3}$.

EXAMPLE 3.   Find the radius of gyration, k, about the x-axis for the mass described in Example 2 on page 403.

SOLUTION.   From page 403, $m = 27$.   By use of (6),

$$I_x = \int\int_R 3y^2|\,x\,|y\,dA = 6\int\int_{R_1} xy^3\,dA, \tag{12}$$

where R_1 is described on page 403.   From (12), with limits of integration found from Figure 263 on page 403, we obtain

$$I_x = 6\int_0^2 \int_0^{\frac{3}{2}\sqrt{4-y^2}} xy^3\,dx\,dy = 27\left(\frac{4}{3}\right) = \frac{4}{3}\,m.$$

Hence, $k^2 = \frac{4}{3}$ or $k = 1.155$.

★*Note 2.*   With the background in Note 2 on page 403, I_y and I_x of (6) on page 407 are called the *second* * *moments* of X and of Y, respectively, with respect to the x-origin and y-origin, and are represented by

$$E(X^2) = \int\int_R x^2\delta(x, y)dA \quad and \quad E(Y^2) = \int\int_R y^2\delta(x, y)dA.$$

Similarly, we define $E(X - c)^2$ and $E(Y - d)^2$, for any numbers c and d.   In particular, we let

$$\sigma_X^2 = E(X - \bar{x})^2 = \int\int_R (x - \bar{x})^2\delta(x, y)dA\,;$$

$$\sigma_Y^2 = E(Y - \bar{y})^2 = \int\int_R (y - \bar{y})^2\delta(x, y)dA,$$

and call σ_X^2 and σ_Y^2 the **variances** of X and of Y, respectively.   The positive numbers σ_X and σ_Y are called the *standard deviations* of the variables.

EXERCISE 123

1. Find the moment of inertia and the radius of gyration of a homogeneous square lamina of side h and constant density, (a) about one side; (b) about the center.

2. A homogeneous lamina is bounded by an isosceles triangle with base 4 altitude 6.   Find the moment of inertia and radius of gyration of the lamina about the perpendicular bisector of the base.

* Moments of higher order are used in statistics.   Thus, the moment of orders h and k in X and Y, respectively, with respect to the points $x = 0$ and $y = 0$, is defined as

$$E(X^hY^k) = \int\int_R x^hy^k\delta(x, y)dA.$$

If mass is distributed over the specified region with the indicated density δ, *obtain* I_x, I_y, *and* I_O. *In Problems 3–5, obtain the radius of gyration about an axis perpendicular to the xy-plane at the origin. Pertinent results from previous problems may be used without integration.*

3–10. The region of Problems 1–7 and 15, respectively, of Exercise 121, with δ as a constant.

11–16. The mass in Problems 19–23 and 25, respectively, of Exercise 121.

17. The region bounded below by the x-axis and above by the ellipse whose parametric equations are $x = a \cos t$ and $y = b \sin t$, where $a > 0$ and $b > 0$; δ is a constant.

HINT. $$I_x = \delta \int_{-a}^{a} \int_{0}^{y} y^2 \, dy \, dx = \frac{1}{3} \delta \int_{-a}^{a} y^3 \, dx.$$

Then, use the parametric equations.

18. The region bounded by the circle defined parametrically by $x = a \cos^2 t$ and $y = a \sin t \cos t$, where $a > 0$; δ is a constant.

19. Find the polar moment of inertia for the region bounded by the ellipse $x = a \cos t$ and $y = b \sin t$ if δ is a constant.

20. Find the polar moment of inertia for a homogeneous circular lamina with radius a, by use of the result of Problem 19.

21. A region is bounded by the coordinate axes and the curve $x^{\frac{1}{2}} + y^{\frac{1}{2}} = a^{\frac{1}{2}}$, between $x = 0$ and $x = a$; δ is a constant. Find I_x, I_y, and I_O.

22. Use the method employed in arriving at formulas for I_x and I_y to develop formulas for the moments of inertia with respect to lines $x = h$ and $y = k$, for the mass over a region R in an xy-plane.

By use of the results of Problem 22, obtain the moment of inertia of the specified mass about the given line. In each case, δ *is a constant.*

23. The mass in Problem 1, page 403, about the line $x = 4$.

24. The mass in Problem 7, page 403, about the line $y = 4$.

25. The mass in Problem 5, page 403, about the line $x = -2$.

Note 1. Suppose that a region R_1 is included in a region R_2. Let R_3 be that part of R_2 remaining if all points inside the boundary of R_1 are removed. Then, any moment of inertia for R_3 is the difference of the corresponding moments of inertia for R_2 and R_1, because any double integral over R_2 is the sum of double integrals over R_1 and R_3.

By use of Note 1 and preceding problems, find the polar moment of inertia of the homogeneous mass distributed over the region whose outer and inner boundaries are the given curves.

26. The ellipse $4x^2 + 9y^2 = 36$ and circle $x^2 + y^2 = 4$.

27. The circle $x^2 + y^2 = 16$ and the square formed by the lines $x = \pm 2$ and $y = \pm 2$.

28. The ellipses $9x^2 + 25y^2 = 225$ and $x^2 + 4y^2 = 4$.

198. Centers of mass and moments of inertia, in polar coordinates

Suppose that the boundary of a region R in an xy-plane can be described conveniently in the associated $r\theta$-system of polar coordinates. Then, it may be desirable to find some of the quantities M_x, M_y, $\bar{x}$, $\bar{y}$, and various moments of inertia by evaluating double integrals by use of iterated integrals in polar coordinates.

EXAMPLE 1. Mass is distributed uniformly over the region R bounded above by the cardioid $r = 2(1 - \cos\theta)$ and below by the x-axis. Find the center of mass, and the moment of inertia with respect to the x-axis.

SOLUTION. 1. R is shown in Figure 269. The density of mass is a constant, δ. Let A be the area of R. Then, from (7) on page 401,

$$A\bar{x} = \iint_R x\, dA; \quad A\bar{y} = \iint_R y\, dA. \tag{1}$$

In (1), use $x = r\cos\theta$ and $y = r\sin\theta$. From a previous example in this text, $A = 3\pi$. Recall the element of area "$r\, dr\, d\theta$" in polar coordinates. Hence, from (1), with the inner limits of integration indicated by the arrow in Figure 269,

$$3\pi\bar{x} = \int_0^\pi \int_0^{2(1-\cos\theta)} (r\cos\theta)r\, dr\, d\theta = \frac{8}{3}\int_0^\pi (1-\cos\theta)^3 \cos\theta\, d\theta = -5\pi;$$

$$3\pi\bar{y} = \int_0^\pi \int_0^{2(1-\cos\theta)} r^2 \sin\theta\, dr\, d\theta = \frac{8}{3}\int_0^\pi (1-\cos\theta)^3 \sin\theta\, d\theta = \frac{32}{3}.$$

Thus, $\bar{x} = -\frac{5}{3}$ and $\bar{y} = 32/9\pi$.

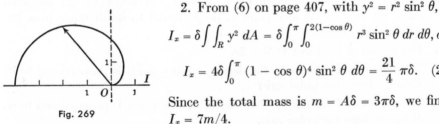

Fig. 269

2. From (6) on page 407, with $y^2 = r^2 \sin^2\theta$,

$$I_x = \delta\iint_R y^2\, dA = \delta\int_0^\pi \int_0^{2(1-\cos\theta)} r^3 \sin^2\theta\, dr\, d\theta, \text{ or}$$

$$I_x = 4\delta\int_0^\pi (1-\cos\theta)^4 \sin^2\theta\, d\theta = \frac{21}{4}\pi\delta. \tag{2}$$

Since the total mass is $m = A\delta = 3\pi\delta$, we find $I_x = 7m/4$.

When polar coordinates are employed, a convenient expression arises for the polar moment of inertia. Since $x^2 + y^2 = r^2$,

$$I_O = I_x + I_y = \iint_R y^2\delta\, dA + \iint_R x^2\delta\, dA = \iint_R (x^2 + y^2)\delta\, dA, \text{ or}$$

$$I_O = \iint_R r^2\delta\, dA. \tag{3}$$

EXAMPLE 2. If the density of mass at any point is proportional to its distance from the origin, obtain the polar moment of inertia of the mass over the region R bounded by the cardioid $r = a(1 - \cos\theta)$.

INCOMPLETE SOLUTION. Inspect Figure 269, showing one half of a cardioid, for limits of integration. By symmetry, I_0 is equal to twice the result obtained on integrating over the upper half, R_1, of the region R. Let $\delta = kr$, where k is a constant of proportionality. Then,

$$I_O = 2k \int \int_{R_1} r^2(r)dA = 2k \int_0^\pi \int_0^{a(1-\cos\theta)} r^4 \, dr \, d\theta.$$

EXERCISE 124

Use polar coordinates in evaluating integrals. Any familiar area may be taken as known without integration. Use symmetry where available.

Find the rectangular coordinates of the centroid if mass is distributed uniformly over the region with the specified boundary.

1. Bounded by the upper semicircle of the curve $r = a \cos\theta$, where $a > 0$, and the polar axis.

2. Bounded by the x-axis, the y-axis, and the circle $x^2 + y^2 = a^2$ in quadrant I. Notice symmetry.

3. Bounded by the lines $\theta = \frac{1}{3}\pi$, $r \cos\theta = 4$, and the polar axis.

4. The smaller segment bounded by the circle $r = 2a$ and the line $r \cos\theta = a$, where $a > 0$.

5. The smaller segment bounded by the circle $r = 4 \sin\theta$ and $\theta = \frac{1}{3}\pi$.

6. Bounded on the left by the cardioid $r = 3(1 - \cos\theta)$ and on the right by the line $\theta = \frac{1}{2}\pi$.

Find the center of mass for the region having the specified boundary, with the given density of mass, δ.

7. Bounded above by the circle $r = a$ where $a > 0$, and below by the polar axis; the density at any point is proportional to its distance from the center of the circle.

8. The region of Problem 1; $\delta = 2r$.

9. The region of Problem 3; the density at any point is proportional to its distance from the polar axis.

10. The region of Problem 4; the density at any point is proportional to its distance from the polar axis.

11. Mass is distributed over the region bounded by the circle $r = h$, where $h > 0$. Find the polar moment of inertia and the corresponding radius of gyration, (a) if the density is a constant; (b) if the density at any point is proportional to its distance from the pole.

12. Repeat Problem 11 for the region bounded by the circle $r = h \sin\theta$. That is, find the moment of inertia and radius of gyration about an axis perpendicular to the plane of the circle at a point on its circumference.

13. Mass is distributed over the region of Problem 1 with the density at any point proportional to its distance from the polar axis. Find the moment of inertia and radius of gyration with respect to this axis.

14. Mass is distributed uniformly over the region bounded by the lemniscate $r^2 = 4 \cos 2\theta$. Find the moment of inertia with respect to the line $\theta = \frac{1}{2}\pi$. Use symmetry to simplify the limits of integration.

15. Find the polar moment of inertia and the corresponding radius of gyration for the mass in Problem 14.

16. Find the polar moment of inertia, and the corresponding radius of gyration, for a homogeneous distribution of mass over the region bounded by the curve $r = \cos 2\theta$.

Find the centroid of the region with the specified boundary.

17. Bounded by the lines $r \cos \theta = 1$ and $\theta = 0$, and the curve $r = 2 \tan \theta$.

18. Bounded by that leaf of the curve $r = \cos 2\theta$ obtained if $- \frac{1}{4}\pi \leq \theta \leq \frac{1}{4}\pi$.

★199. Center of mass on a curve in a plane

Let W be a *regular* curve (see page 316) in an xy-plane, with s as arc distance on W measured from some fixed point. Let an arc C of W be defined by the parametric equations

$$x = \Phi(s) \quad and \quad y = \Psi(s); \quad a \leq s \leq b. \tag{1}$$

Suppose that mass is distributed on C with $\delta(s)$ as the density at any point given by (1). We may visualize C as a material wire of negligible diameter. Then, if m is the mass on C,

$$m = \int_a^b \delta(s)ds. \tag{2}$$

If τ is an arc of C where $\alpha \leq s \leq \alpha + \Delta s$, with mass Δm, then

$$\Delta m = \int_\alpha^{\alpha + \Delta s} \delta(s)ds = \delta(s')\Delta s, \tag{3}$$

where $\alpha \leq s' \leq \alpha + \Delta s$. By a discussion similar to that for mass on an x-axis, on page 287, we obtain elements of moments of the forms

$$\Delta M_x = y\delta(s)\Delta s \quad and \quad \Delta M_y = x\delta(s)\Delta s.$$

Then,
$$M_x = \int_a^b y\delta(s)ds; \quad M_y = \int_a^b x\delta(s)ds. \tag{4}$$

In (4), $x = \Phi(s)$ and $y = \Psi(s)$. By use of $m\bar{x} = M_y$ and $m\bar{y} = M_x$,

$$\begin{Bmatrix} center\ of \\ mass \end{Bmatrix} \qquad \bar{x} = \frac{\int_a^b x\delta(s)ds}{m} \quad and \quad \bar{y} = \frac{\int_a^b y\delta(s)ds}{m}. \tag{5}$$

If δ is a constant in (5), we call $(\bar{x}, \bar{y})$ the *centroid* of C. In this case, from (2), $m = \delta L$ where L is the length of C, and (5) gives

$$(centroid) \qquad \bar{x} = \frac{\int_a^b x\ ds}{L} \quad and \quad \bar{y} = \frac{\int_a^b y\ ds}{L}. \tag{6}$$

The analog of Theorem I on page 402 is true for mass on a curve C. Thus, if C has an axis of symmetry, the centroid of C is on this axis.

In (2), (4), (5), and (6), we may express ds in terms of dx, dy, or dt, where t is another parameter for C.

EXAMPLE 1. Let C be the arc of the circle $x = a \cos t$ and $y = a \sin t$ in quadrant I. Mass is distributed on C with the density $\delta = 2y$. Find the center of mass of C.

SOLUTION. We find $ds = a\, dt$. Then,

$$m = \int_{t=0}^{t=\frac{1}{2}\pi} 2y\, ds = 2a^2 \int_0^{\frac{1}{2}\pi} \sin t\, dt = 2a^2.$$

$$M_x = 2a^3 \int_0^{\frac{1}{2}\pi} \sin^2 t\, dt = \frac{1}{2}\pi a^3; \quad M_y = 2a^3 \int_0^{\frac{1}{2}\pi} \sin t \cos t\, dt = a^3.$$

Hence, from $m\bar{x} = M_y$ and $m\bar{y} = M_x$, we obtain $\bar{x} = \frac{1}{2}a$ and $\bar{y} = \frac{1}{4}\pi a$.

EXAMPLE 2. Find the centroid of the arc C of the parabola $8y = x^2$ on the range $-4 \leq x \leq 4$.

SOLUTION. 1. By symmetry, as seen in Figure 270, $\bar{x} = 0$.

2. From $8y = x^2$, $\qquad ds = \sqrt{\dfrac{2+y}{y}}\, dy; \qquad ds = \dfrac{\sqrt{16 + x^2}}{4}\, dx.$

Then, $\qquad L = 2\int_{x=0}^{x=4} ds = 2\int_0^4 \frac{1}{4}\sqrt{16 + x^2}\, dx = 9.18.$

From (6), $\qquad L\bar{y} = \int_{y=0}^{y=2} y\, ds$

$$= 2\int_0^2 y \sqrt{\frac{2+y}{y}}\, dy = 6.72.$$

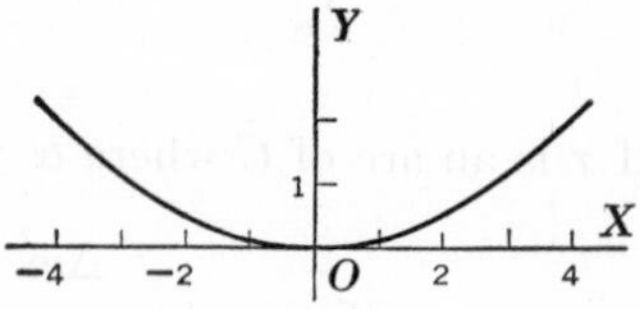

Thus, $\bar{y} = 6.72/9.18 = .73.$

Fig. 270

★EXERCISE 125

An arc of a curve in an xy-plane is defined by the given xy-equation or parametric equations. Find the center of mass if mass is distributed on the arc with the assigned density, δ, at any point (x, y). A request for a centroid implies that δ is a constant.

1. The semicircle of $x = a \cos t$ and $y = a \sin t$ where $0 \leq t \leq \pi$; $\delta = 3y$.

2. Find the centroid of the arc in Problem 1.

3. The arch of the cycloid $x = a(t - \sin t)$ and $y = a(1 - \cos t)$, for $0 \leq t \leq 2\pi$, with $\delta = 2y$.

4. Find the centroid of the arc of the hypocycloid $x = a \cos^3 t$ and $y = a \sin^3 t$ in quadrant I.

5. Find the centroid of the cardioid $r = a(1 - \cos \theta)$.

6. Find the centroid of the arc of $y^3 = x^2$ where $-8 \leq x \leq 8$.

21

TRIPLE INTEGRALS

200. The three-dimensional definite integral

Suppose that the function $F(x, y, z)$ is defined at all points of a region W in an xyz-system of rectangular coordinates, where W is bounded by some closed surface T. We shall define the integral of $F(x, y, z)$ over the region W illustrated in Figure 271. Let the ranges for x, y, and z in W be

$$a \leqq x \leqq b, \quad c \leqq y \leqq d, \quad g \leqq z \leqq q, \tag{1}$$

so that all of W is included in the parallelepiped U with faces in the planes $x = a$, $x = b$, $y = c$, etc. Form partitions of the x-interval, the y-interval, and the z-interval in (1), with the following typical subintervals:

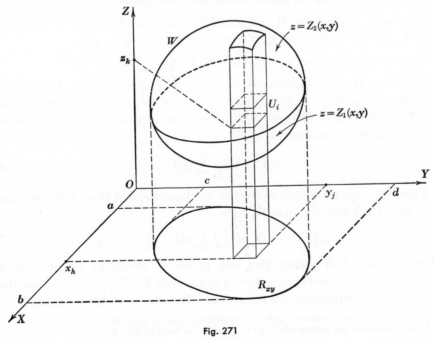

Fig. 271

$$x_{h-1} \leqq x \leqq x_h, \quad y_{j-1} \leqq y \leqq y_j, \quad z_{k-1} \leqq z \leqq z_k. \qquad (2)$$

Construct planes perpendicular to the x-axis at x_h, to the y-axis at y_j, and to the z-axis at z_k, as in Figure 271, for all values of h, j, and k. These planes superimpose a grid of parallelepipeds on W, and divide it into subregions, to create a partition P of W. We define the norm, d_P, of P as the maximum of the diameters of the subregions of the grid for P. In Figure 271, the points of W project into the region R_{xy} in the xy-plane. Suppose that just n of the subregions in P consist of entire parallelepipeds,

$$(\textit{parallelepipeds in P}) \qquad U_1, \ U_2, \cdots, \ U_i, \cdots, \ U_n. \qquad (3)$$

Then, we define the three dimensional integral of $F(x, y, z)$ over W as follows.

DEFINITION I. *Let P be any partition of W. In each whole parallelepiped U_i in P, select a point (ξ_i, η_i, ζ_i) arbitrarily, and let*

$$S_P = \sum_{i=1}^{n} F(\xi_i, \eta_i, \zeta_i)\Delta_i V, \qquad (4)$$

where $\Delta_i V$ is the volume * *of U_i. Then, if S_P approaches a limit as $d_P \to 0$, we call this limit the* "**triple integral** *of $F(x, y, z)$ over W," denoted by the following symbol at the left:*

$$\iiint_W F(x, \ y, \ z)dV = \lim_{d_P \to 0} \sum_{i=1}^{n} F(\xi_i, \eta_i, \zeta_i)\Delta_i V. \qquad (5)$$

The following result is proved at an advanced mathematical level.

THEOREM I. *If the region W is of a suitable type,† and $F(x, y, z)$ is continuous in W, then the triple integral of $F(x, y, z)$ over W exists.*

The volume of a general region can be defined by use of (4).

DEFINITION II. *For a region W in space, let P be a partition created by a rectangular grid, as in Definition I. Then, if the sum of the volumes of all of the whole parallelepipeds in P approaches a limit as $d_P \to 0$, we define this limit as the* **volume,** *V, of W:*

$$V = \lim_{d_P \to 0} \sum_{i=1}^{n} \Delta_i V. \qquad (6)$$

From (5), equation (6) is equivalent to the statement that, if the function $F(x, y) = 1$ is integrable over W, then

$$V = \iiint_W dV. \qquad (7)$$

Hereafter, we shall assume that any region W which we use with triple integrals will be of the type mentioned in Theorem I. Then, since the function $F(x, y) = 1$ is continuous, the integral in (7) exists, or W *has a volume.*

---

* At present, we use "*volume*" only for rectangular parallelepipeds.
† A description of the admissible type is beyond the level of this text.

With the aid of Definition II, by use of volumes of *irregular* subregions, we may obtain a new interpretation for the right-hand side of (5).

THEOREM II. *Let P be a partition of the region W into subregions {U_i} of* **any shape** *such that each U_i has a volume $\Delta_i V$, and let d_P be the maximum of the diameters of the subregions {U_i}. Let (ξ_i, η_i, ζ_i) be an arbitrary point in U_i. Then, if F(x, y, z) is continuous in R, (5) is valid with the new meaning for a partition P.*

We accept Theorem II on an intuitional basis. Also, without verification, we note that triple integrals possess properties analogous to those considered for double integrals on page 377.

201. Computation of triple integrals by iterated integrals

In the following discussion, we shall assume that any integrand is continuous. Also, any region of integration, W, will be of one of the following types, or W will consist of two or more component regions of these types. The boundary functions Z_1, Z_2, Y_1, etc. in the descriptions are assumed to be single-valued and continuous, so that iterated integrals in later formulas will exist.

$$(W \text{ of type I}) \qquad \left\{ \begin{array}{l} (x, y) \text{ in region } R_{xy} \text{ in } xy\text{-plane;} \\ \quad Z_1(x, y) \leq z \leq Z_2(x, y). \end{array} \right\} \qquad (1)$$

$$(W \text{ of type II}) \qquad \left\{ \begin{array}{l} (y, z) \text{ in region } R_{yz} \text{ in } yz\text{-plane;} \\ \quad X_1(y, z) \leq x \leq X_2(y, z). \end{array} \right\} \qquad (2)$$

$$(W \text{ of type III}) \qquad \left\{ \begin{array}{l} (x, z) \text{ in region } R_{xz} \text{ in } xz\text{-plane;} \\ \quad Y_1(x, z) \leq y \leq Y_2(x, z). \end{array} \right\} \qquad (3)$$

The region W in Figure 271 on page 415 is of type I. In (1), R_{xy} is the projection on the xy-plane of all points in W, as seen in Figure 271. The equations $z = Z_1(x, y)$ and $z = Z_2(x, y)$ define lower and upper boundary surfaces, respectively, as in Figure 271. All of W is inside or on the cylinder formed by moving a line parallel to OZ around the boundary of R_{xy}. The following results can be proved, expressing a triple integral as a double integral of a simple integral.

$$(W \text{ of type I}) \quad \int\int\int_W F(x, y, z)dV = \int\int_{R_{xy}} \left[\int_{Z_1(x,y)}^{Z_2(x,y)} F(x, y, z)dz \right] dA_{xy}; \quad (4)$$

$$(W \text{ of type II}) \qquad = \int\int_{R_{yz}} \left[\int_{X_1(y,z)}^{X_2(y,z)} F(x, y, z)dx \right] dA_{yz}; \quad (5)$$

$$(W \text{ of type III}) \qquad = \int\int_{R_{xz}} \left[\int_{Y_1(x,z)}^{Y_2(x,z)} F(x, y, z)dy \right] dA_{zz}. \quad (6)$$

In evaluating a triple integral, we start with (4), (5), or (6), and then apply the normal procedure for double integrals. Thus, if R_{xy} in (1) is of type I as in (1) on page 379, from (4) we obtain

$$\int\int\int_W F(x, y, z)dV = \int_b^a \int_{Y_1(x)}^{Y_2(x)} \int_{Z_1(x,y)}^{Z_2(x,y)} F(x, y, z)dz\, dy\, dx. \quad (7)$$

Suppose that mass is distributed over a region W in space. Let the function $\delta(x, y, z)$ be defined, continuous, and nonnegative when (x, y, z) is in W. Then, if the mass of any subregion, U, of W is equal to the triple integral of δ over U, we call $\delta(x, y, z)$ the density of mass over W. This definition is the space analog of Definition III on page 382. Then, for the case of $\delta(x, y, z)$, we could parallel the discussion given on page 382 for a two-dimensional density, with *volume* replacing *area*, and *triple integrals* replacing *double integrals*. In particular, if m is the total mass over W,

$$m = \iiint_W \delta(x, y, z)\,dV. \tag{8}$$

EXAMPLE 1. If the density function is $\delta(x, y, z) = 2|x|$, find the mass, m, of the region W bounded by the surfaces

$$z = 8 - 3x^2 - y^2 \quad and \quad z = x^2 + 3y^2. \tag{9}$$

SOLUTION. 1. The values of $\delta(x, y, z)$, and the surfaces in (9), are symmetric with respect to the xz-plane and yz-plane. Hence, m is four times the mass of the part of W in the 1st octant, in Figure 272.

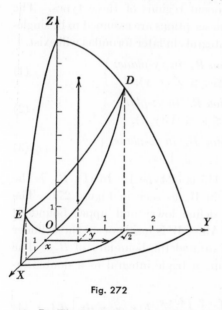

Fig. 272

2. We project W onto the xy-plane. The cylinder (see page 353), which projects the intersection of surfaces (9) onto the xy-plane, has an equation found on eliminating z by use of (9):

$$8 = 4x^2 + 4y^2, \quad or \quad x^2 + y^2 = 2. \tag{10}$$

All of W is in the cylinder (10). Surfaces (9) intersect along curve ED on cylinder (10), in Figure 272. Thus, we use (4) with * R_{xy} as the region bounded by the x-axis, the y-axis, and the circle $x^2 + y^2 = 2$.

3. In Figure 272, the vertical arrow indicates the inner limits of integration for use in (4), the arrow in the xy-plane shows the limits for integration with respect to y. From (8) and (4), by use of (7),

$$m = 4 \iiint_W 2x\,dV = 4 \iint_R \left[\int_{x^2+3y^2}^{8-3x^2-y^2} 2x\,dz \right] dA$$

$$= 32 \int_0^{\sqrt{2}} \int_0^{\sqrt{2-x^2}} x(2 - x^2 - y^2)dy\,dx = \frac{256}{15}\sqrt{2},$$

where we evaluated $\int x^3\sqrt{2 - x^2}\,dx$ by substituting $u = \sqrt{2 - x^2}$.

* Later, we drop the subscripts "xy" of (4).

*Background * for* (4).   Let W be of type I, as in Figure 273.   Recall the rectangular grid used on page 416 to create a partition P of W.   The vertical planes of the grid superimpose a grid of rectangles on R_{xy}, and thus create a partition P_{xy} of R_{xy}.   In P_{xy}, let $\gamma_{h,j}$ be the rectangle with sides $\Delta_h x$ and $\Delta_j y$, as shown in Figure 273.   Above $\gamma_{h,j}$, there is a column of parallelepipeds of the partition P, of type $U_{h,j,k}$ with height $\Delta_k z$ and volume $(\Delta_h x)(\Delta_j y)(\Delta_k z)$. In $U_{h,j,k}$, select (x_h, y_j, z_k) as the arbitrary point for use on the right in (4) on page 416.   Then, the contribution of $U_{h,j,k}$ to S_P in (4) on page 416 is

$$[F(x_h, y_j, z_k)\Delta_k z](\Delta_h x)(\Delta_j y). \tag{11}$$

If we first add terms (11) for all parallelepipeds of P over $\gamma_{h,j}$, by summing with respect to k, then

$$S_P = \sum_{(h,j)} \left[\sum_{(k)} F(x_h, y_j, z_k)\Delta_k z \right] \Delta_h x \Delta_j y. \tag{12}$$

From page 416, S_P in (12) is in the form of an approximating sum for a double integral over R_{xy}, where *the sum with respect to k* in (12) takes the place of a value of the *integrand* for the double integral.   Now, suppose that all $\Delta_h x \to 0$, $\Delta_j y \to 0$, and $\Delta_k z \to 0$.   Then, it is plausible that the sum within brackets in (12) will lead to the integral of $F(x, y, z)$ with respect to z, and the sum for (h, j) in (12) will lead to a double integral over R_{xy}, as in (4).

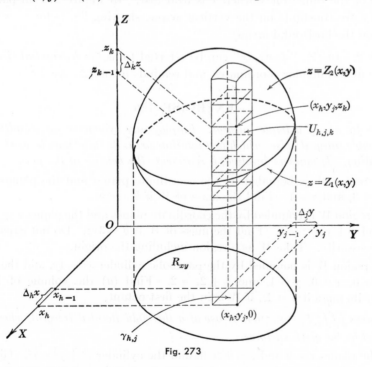

Fig. 273

* A proof of (4)–(6) is beyond the level of this text.

EXAMPLE 2. Obtain the volume of the region bounded above by the paraboloid

$$z = 6 - x^2 - 3y^2$$

and below by the xy-plane.

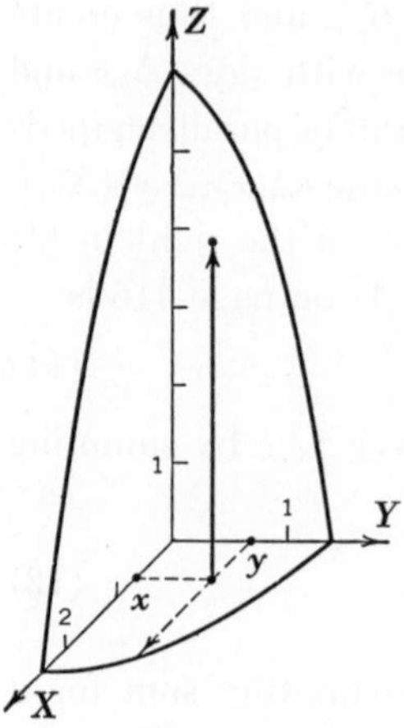

PARTIAL SOLUTION. Figure 274 shows that part, W, of the specified region which is in the 1st octant. Because of symmetry, the desired volume, V, is four times the volume of W. The xy-trace of the paraboloid is the ellipse $x^2 + 3y^2 = 6$. Hence, we use (4) with R_{xy} as the region in the xy-plane bounded by the axes and the ellipse, in quadrant I:

Fig. 274

$$V = 4 \int\int\int_W dV = 4 \int\int_R \left[\int_0^{6-x^2-3y^2} dz \right] dA; \quad (13)$$

$$V = 4 \int\int_R (6 - x^2 - 3y^2) dA$$

$$= 4 \int_0^{\sqrt{2}} \int_0^{\sqrt{6-3y^2}} (6 - x^2 - 3y^2) dx\, dy. \quad (14)$$

Note 1. In (7), $Z_1(x, y)$ and $Z_2(x, y)$ can be described as the end-points of the range for z in W when x and y are fixed; $Y_1(x)$ and $Y_2(x)$ are the end-points of the range for y when x is held fast. In Figure 272 on page 418, x and y are constants on the vertical arrow, showing limits for z; x is constant on the horizontal arrow.

Note 2. In (7), "$dz\, dy\, dx$" can be referred to as *the differential element of volume* in rectangular coordinates, and reminds us of "$\Delta z\, \Delta y\, \Delta x$."

EXERCISE 126

Solve by use of a triple integral. Employ any symmetry for simplification. If a double integral arises which is a familiar area, its value may be used without integrating. If mass is involved, δ represents the density at the point (x, y, z).

1. A region W is bounded by the coordinate planes and the planes $x = 2$, $y = 3$, and $z = 1$. Find the mass of W if $\delta = x^2 yz$.

2. A region W is bounded by the coordinate planes and the planes $x + 2y = 4$ and $x + y + z = 6$. Find the mass of W if $\delta = 3yz$. Do not expand unnecessarily. Take W as a region including the origin.

3. A region W is bounded by the parabolic cylinder $x^2 = 4y$, and the planes $z = 0$, $x = 0$, $y = 1$, and $x + 2z = 2$. Find (a) the volume of W and (b) its mass if $\delta = 2z$, if W is in the first octant.

Express $\int\int\int_W F(x, y, z) dV$ by use of a threefold iterated integral, where W is bounded by the given surfaces.

4. The planes $z = 0$ and $z = h > 0$, and the cylinder $x^2 + y^2 = c^2$. Give two forms for the result.

5. Inside the cylinder $x^2 + y^2 = 9$ and the sphere $x^2 + y^2 + z^2 = 25$.

6. W is the smaller segment of the sphere $x^2 + y^2 + z^2 = 4$ cut off by the plane $z = 1$. Give two forms for the result.

7. The cylinder $z = 6 - 3x^2$ and paraboloid $z = 2 + x^2 + 2y^2$, and the planes $x = 0$ and $y = 0$, where $x \geqq 0$ and $y \geqq 0$.

8. Inside the surfaces $z = 6 - x^2 - y^2$ and $z^2 = x^2 + y^2$, where $z \geqq 0$.

First formulate the result as a triple integral for the region W bounded by the given surfaces. Find the volume, V, of W or its mass, m, for the given density δ, as requested.

9. For W in Problem 4, compute V, and m if $\delta = 2|x|$.

10. The coordinate planes and the plane $2x + 3y + z = 6$. Compute V, and m if $\delta = 2 + z$.

11. The planes $x = 0$, $y = 0$, $z + 3x + 2y = 6$, and $z = 3x + y$. Compute V, and m if $\delta = (xy + 1)$.

12. Surfaces $x^2 + y^2 = 8y$, $4z = x^2 + y^2$, and $z = 0$. Find m if $\delta = 2|x|$.

13. Surfaces $z = 4 - x^2$ and $x^2 + y^2 = 4$, and $z = 0$. Find m if $\delta = z|yx|$.

14. Surfaces $z = 4 - x^2 - 4y^2$ and $z = 0$. Find m if $\delta = 3z|y|$.

15. Surfaces $z = 8 - y^2$ and $z = 2x^2 + y^2$. Find m if $\delta = 2|zy|$.

16. Surfaces $z = 2x$ and $z = x^2 + y^2$. Find m if $\delta = 2|y|$.

17. Find the volume of the sphere $x^2 + y^2 + z^2 = a^2$.

18. Find the volume of the region W in Problem 6. Integrate first with respect to x. Also, try integration first with respect to z.

202. Triple integrals in cylindrical coordinates

In connection with an xyz-system of coordinates, let us also use the related $r\theta z$-system of cylindrical coordinates, as on page 394. Then, any function $F(x, y, z)$ is transformed into a function $f(r, \theta, z)$. Let W be a region of points $[r, \theta, z]$ such that

$$\left\{\begin{matrix} [r, \theta] \text{ is in a region } R \text{ in the } r\theta\text{-plane, and} \\ Z_1(r, \theta) \leqq z \leqq Z_2(r, \theta), \end{matrix}\right\} \tag{1}$$

where the functions Z_1 and Z_2 are continuous and single-valued in R. Then, if $f(r, \theta, z)$ is continuous in W, from (4) on page 417 we obtain

$$\int\int\int_W f(r, \theta, z)dV = \int\int_R \left[\int_{Z_1(r, \theta)}^{Z_2(r, \theta)} f(r, \theta, z)dz\right]dA, \tag{2}$$

where we omit the subscripts xy as used on page 417. When the boundary for R can be defined conveniently in the $r\theta$-system of polar coordinates, we may compute (2) by use of polar coordinates in R. For instance, if R is of type I as in (4) on page 389, we introduce "$r\ dr\ d\theta$" and obtain

$$\int\int\int_W f(r, \theta, z)dV = \int_\alpha^\beta \int_{h_1(\theta)}^{h_2(\theta)} \int_{Z_1(r, \theta)}^{Z_2(r, \theta)} rf(r, \theta, z)dz\ dr\ d\theta. \tag{3}$$

EXAMPLE 1. Find the volume, V, of the region W bounded above by the paraboloid $z = 8 - \frac{1}{4}(x^2 + y^2)$ and below by the cone $z^2 = x^2 + y^2$.

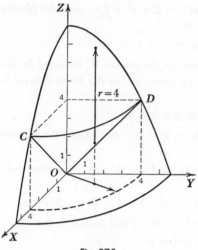

Fig. 275

SOLUTION. 1. Change the equations to cylindrical coordinates:

$$z = 8 - \tfrac{1}{4}r^2 \quad and \quad z = r. \qquad (4)$$

On solving (4) simultaneously, with $r > 0$, we obtain $(r = 4, z = 4)$. The curve of intersection of (4) is CD in Figure 275. Thus, the cylinder projecting the curve of intersection of (4) onto the $r\theta$-plane has the equation $r = 4$; the region R for use in (3) is bounded by the circle $r = 4$ in the $r\theta$-plane, as seen in Figure 275. Part of the projecting cylinder is shown by broken lines in the figure.

2. We use (3) with $f(r, \theta, z) = 1$:

$$V = \iiint_W dV = \iint_R \left[\int_r^{8-\frac{1}{4}r^2} dz \right] dA = \iint_R (8 - \tfrac{1}{4}r^2 - r)\,dA \qquad (5)$$

$$= \int_0^{\frac{1}{2}\pi} \int_0^4 r(32 - r^2 - 4r)\,dr\,d\theta = \frac{160}{3}\,\pi. \qquad (6)$$

Comment. In (3), $Z_1(r, \theta)$ and $Z_2(r, \theta)$ are the end-points of the range for z in W when r and θ are held fast, as indicated for (5) by the vertical arrow in Figure 275. Then, $h_1(\theta)$ and $h_2(\theta)$ of (3) are, respectively, the least and the greatest values of r when θ is held fast, as indicated for (6) by the horizontal arrow in Figure 275.

Note 1. We derived (3) from (2) on the basis of knowledge of double integrals. Instead, we could have proceeded directly from (5) on page 416, by use of a partition P of W formed by a set of cylinders $r = r_h$, on the range for r, and a set of planes $\theta = \theta_j$ and $z = z_k$ on the ranges for θ and z. In P, a regular subregion, to replace the typical parallelepiped in Definition I, would have the appearance of the subregion CE in Figure 276; the height of CE is Δz. The base CD of CE, or the pro-

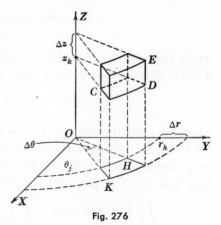

Fig. 276

jection KH of CD on the xy-plane, has the same shape as region $BCDE$ of Note 1 and Figure 250 on page 391. Thus, the area of CD is of the form $r'\Delta r \Delta \theta$. Hence, the volume ΔV of CE is given by

$$\Delta V = r'\Delta r \Delta \theta \Delta z, \quad where \quad r' = r_h + \tfrac{1}{2}\Delta r. \tag{7}$$

Then, details similar to those involved for (11) on page 419 would lead to (3). We refer to "$r\,dz\,dr\,d\theta$" in (3) as the differential *element of volume in cylindrical coordinates;* this element recalls the volume $r'\Delta r \Delta \theta \Delta z$ of region CE in Figure 276.

ILLUSTRATION 1. Suppose that mass is distributed over the region of Example 1 with the density of mass $\delta = 3(x^2 + y^2)$ at any point (x, y, z). Then, the total mass is

$$m = 4\int\int\int_W 3(x^2 + y^2)dV.$$

To compute m by use of (2), we first use

$$x = r \cos \theta \quad and \quad y = r \sin \theta, \quad or \quad x^2 + y^2 = r^2,$$

and obtain limits of integration as in (5) and (6):

$$m = 4\int\int\int_W 3r^2\,dV = 4\int_0^{\frac{1}{2}\pi}\int_0^4\int_r^{8-\frac{1}{4}r^2} 3r^3\,dz\,dr\,d\theta.$$

EXERCISE 127

A region W is bounded by the given surfaces. Formulate the requested volume, V, or mass, m, for W as a triple integral. Then compute by use of an iterated integral in cylindrical coordinates. Where mass is involved, the density at any point is represented by δ. We shall always take $r \geq 0$ in cylindrical coordinates. Any literal constant is assumed to be positive.

1. Surfaces $x^2 + y^2 = 16$, $z = 0$, and $z = 5$. Find m if $\delta = 4z$.

2. Surfaces $z = 0$ and $x^2 + y^2 + z^2 = a^2$ where $z \geq 0$. Find m if $\delta = 4z$.

3. By $z = a$ and $x^2 + y^2 + z^2 = 5a^2$, with $z > 0$, inside $x^2 + y^2 = a^2$; find V.

4. Compute the volume of a sphere of radius a.

5. The cylinder $r = a$, the $r\theta$-plane, and the cylinder $z = a^2 - x^2$. Find V, and m if $\delta = 2r$.

6. Compute the volume for the region in Problem 8, page 421.

7. Surfaces $z = 12 - x^2 - y^2$ and $z = 8$. Find V.

8. W is the smaller segment of the sphere $x^2 + y^2 + z^2 = 4$ cut off by the plane $z = 1$. Find V.

9. Surfaces $r = 4 \sin \theta$, $z = 0$, and $2z = x^2 + y^2$. Find m if $\delta = 2r$.

10. Surfaces $z = 8 - y^2$ and $z = 2x^2 + y^2$. Compute V.

11. The planes $z = 1$, $z + y = 2$, and the cylinder $r = \sin \theta$. Find V, and m if $\delta = 2y$.

12. Surfaces $z = 0$, $z = 4 - x^2$, and $z = 4 - y^2$, with $z \geq 0$. Find m if $\delta = 2r$.

13. W is bounded by the half-cone $z = 4 - \sqrt{x^2 + y^2}$ and the xy-plane, inside the cylinder $r = 2 \cos \theta$. Find V, and m if $\delta = 3x$.

203. Moments, and centers of mass in space

Assume that a mass particle m is at a point (x, y, z) in an xyz-system of coordinates, as in Figure 277. Then, the *moment* of m with respect to any coordinate plane is defined as the product of m and the directed distance of

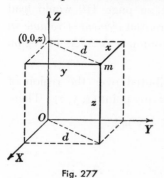

Fig. 277

m from the plane. Let the moments of m with respect to the yz-plane, xz-plane, and xy-plane, respectively, be M_{yz}, M_{xz}, and M_{xy}:

$$M_{yz} = mx; \quad M_{xz} = my; \quad M_{xy} = mz. \quad (1)$$

Then, as in the case of moments about coordinate axes in a plane, first we could discuss the moments M_{yz}, M_{xz}, and M_{xy} for a discrete distribution of n masses $\{m_i\}$ at points (x_i, y_i, z_i) and define the corresponding center of mass. We shall omit such details.

Suppose, now, that mass is distributed over a region W in the xyz-system of coordinates, with $\delta(x, y, z)$ as the density of mass at the point (x, y, z), where δ is continuous in W. Let U be any subregion of W with volume ΔV and mass Δm. By the definition of a density function, from the three-dimensional analog of (2) on page 382, there exists a point (x', y', z') in U such that

$$\Delta m = \delta(x', y', z')\Delta V. \quad (2)$$

If Δm is considered as concentrated at an arbitrary point (x'', y'', z'') in U, the resulting moment, ΔM_{yz}, of Δm about the yz-plane becomes

$$\Delta M_{yz} = x''\delta(x', y', z')\Delta V. \quad (3)$$

With (3) as a basis, we could present details which would parallel those on page 401 for moments in a plane, with triple integrals now replacing double integrals. Finally, with δ meaning $\delta(x, y, z)$, we obtain

$$M_{yz} = \iiint_W x\delta\, dV; \quad M_{xz} = \iiint_W y\delta\, dV; \quad M_{xy} = \iiint_W z\delta\, dV. \quad (4)$$

The *center of mass* for the mass distribution over W is defined as that point $(\bar{x}, \bar{y}, \bar{z})$ where the total mass, m, in W should be concentrated in order for m to have the same moments as in (4). Thus, $m\bar{x} = M_{yz}$, etc., and

$$\bar{x} = \frac{\iiint_W x\delta\, dV}{m}; \quad \bar{y} = \frac{\iiint_W y\delta\, dV}{m}; \quad \bar{z} = \frac{\iiint_W z\delta\, dV}{m}. \quad (5)$$

In (5),
$$m = \iiint_W \delta\, dV. \quad (6)$$

If δ is a constant, $(\bar{x}, \bar{y}, \bar{z})$ is called the **centroid** of W; in this case, δ divides out from each numerator and denominator in (5). For instance, the

x-coordinate of the centroid is found to be

$$\bar{x} = \frac{\iiint_W x \, dV}{V}, \quad \text{where} \quad V = \iiint_W dV. \tag{7}$$

Note 1. The perpendicular from a point (x, y, z) to the z-axis meets it at the point $(0, 0, z)$, as in Figure 277. Hence, the perpendicular distance, d, between (x, y, z) and the z-axis is the distance between this point and $(0, 0, z)$, or $d = \sqrt{x^2 + y^2}$. Similarly, the perpendicular distance from (x, y, z) to the x-axis is $\sqrt{y^2 + z^2}$, and to the y-axis is $\sqrt{x^2 + z^2}$.

Let I_x, I_y, and I_z be the moments of inertia of the mass over W with respect to the corresponding coordinate axes. Then, with the aid of Note 1, a discussion similar to that involved for (6) on page 407 leads to

$$\left. \begin{array}{c} I_x = \iiint_W (y^2 + z^2) \delta \, dV; \quad I_y = \iiint_W (x^2 + z^2) \delta \, dV; \\[2mm] I_z = \iiint_W (x^2 + y^2) \delta \, dV. \end{array} \right\} \tag{8}$$

Note 2. If mass is spread over a region W in the xyz-system of coordinates, with a given density function $\delta(x, y, z)$, let us refer to W as a *solid*. It can be proved that the location of the center of mass for a solid W is independent of the positions of the coordinate planes. Also, if W is subject to the attraction of gravity, in physics it is found that the center of mass of W coincides with its center of gravity. If W could be supported at its center of gravity, then W would remain in equilibrium under the attraction of gravity. The center of mass of a solid does not necessarily lie in the solid.

Note 3. By reasoning similar to that involved in proving Theorem I on page 402, the following fact can be established: *If a region W in three-dimensional space has a plane of symmetry, then the centroid of W lies in this plane.*

EXAMPLE 1. If the density is a constant, find the center of mass of the solid W bounded by the xy-plane and the upper hemisphere of the sphere $x^2 + y^2 + z^2 = a^2$, shown in Figure 278 for the 1st octant.

SOLUTION. 1. The center of mass (or, the *centroid*, since δ is a constant) lies in both the xz-plane and the yz-plane, because W is symmetric to each of these planes. Hence, $(\bar{x}, \bar{y}, \bar{z})$ lies on the z-axis; or, $\bar{x} = \bar{y} = 0$. From (5) with δ as a constant, or from the $\bar{z}$-form for (7),

$$\bar{z} = \frac{\iiint_W z \, dV}{V}, \quad \text{where} \quad V = \frac{2}{3} \pi a^3.$$

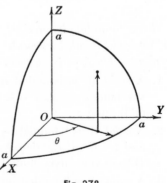

Fig. 278

2. We decide to use cylindrical coordinates. The hemisphere has the equation $z = \sqrt{a^2 - (x^2 + y^2)}$, or $z = \sqrt{a^2 - r^2}$. Hence,

$$\iiint_W z \, dV = \int_0^{2\pi} \int_0^a \int_0^{\sqrt{a^2-r^2}} rz \, dz \, dr \, d\theta = \frac{1}{4}\pi a^4. \qquad (9)$$

Thus, $\bar{z} = (\frac{1}{4}\pi a^4)/(\frac{2}{3}\pi a^3) = \frac{3}{8}a$. The center of mass is $(0, 0, \frac{3}{8}a)$. Arrows in Figure 278 indicate limits of integration for (9).

EXAMPLE 2. The altitude of a right circular cone (in the elementary sense) is 8 units, and the radius of its base is 6 units. If the density of mass in the cone is a constant, δ, find the moment of inertia of the cone about its axis.

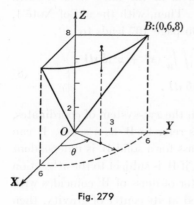

Fig. 279

SOLUTION. Place the cone with the vertex at the origin and the axis of the cone along the positive part of the z-axis in an yxz-system, as in Figure 279. The surface of the cone is generated by revolving OB about the z-axis, where the equation of OB is $z = \frac{4}{3}y$. Hence, as on page 352, the cone has the equation $z^2 = \frac{16}{9}(x^2 + y^2)$, or $z = \frac{4}{3}r$ in cylindrical coordinates. From (8), the desired result is

$$I_z = \iiint_W (x^2 + y^2)\delta \, dV,$$

where W is the region bounded by the cone. The points in W project vertically into the region R in the xy-plane bounded by the circle $x^2 + y^2 = 36$, or $r = 6$ in polar coordinates. Then, with dA replaced by $r \, dr \, d\theta$,

$$I_z = \delta \iint_R \left(\int_{\frac{4}{3}r}^8 r^2 \, dz \right) dA = \delta \int_0^{2\pi} \int_0^6 \int_{\frac{4}{3}r}^8 r^3 \, dz \, dr \, d\theta = \frac{5184}{5}\pi\delta.$$

Note 4. In finding a centroid by use of (7) and similar formulas for y and z, V may be evaluated without integration if possible.

EXERCISE 128

First formulate the desired result by use of triple integrals. Compute by use of threefold iterated integrals in rectangular or cylindrical coordinates, as convenient. The density of mass at any point is δ.

1. A solid W is bounded by the coordinate planes of the xyz-system and the planes $x = 2$, $y = 3$, and $z = 5$. If $\delta = 2xy$, find the center of mass of W, and I_x.

2. A solid W is bounded by the cylinder $x^2 + y^2 = 16$, and the planes $z = 0$ and $z = 6$. If the density of mass at any point P is twice the distance of P from the z-axis, find the mass of W, its center of mass, and I_z.

3. A solid W is bounded by $x^2 + y^2 + z^2 = a^2$; $\delta = 2\sqrt{x^2 + y^2}$. Find I_z.

4. A solid W is bounded by the $r\theta$-plane in cylindrical coordinates, the cylinder $r = 2 \sin \theta$, and the plane $z = y$. With $\delta = 3r$, find the rectangular coordinates of the center of mass for W.

5. A solid W of uniform density is bounded by the coordinate planes and the plane $x + y + z = 4$. Find the centroid of W. Notice symmetry.

6. A solid W of uniform density is bounded below by the xy-plane and above by the cylinders $x^2 + z^2 = a^2$ and $y^2 + z^2 = a^2$. Find (a) the center of mass for W, and (b) I_z.

7. Mass is distributed with uniform density over the region W of Problem 8 on page 421. Find the centroid of W.

8. A solid W with uniform density is bounded by the cone $y^2 = 4x^2 + 4z^2$ and the plane $y = 2$. Find (a) the centroid of W, and (b) I_y.

   HINT. It is useful to introduce cylindrical coordinates, with the xz-plane becoming the $r\theta$-plane, and the y-coordinate unaltered.

9. A solid W is bounded by the paraboloid $x^2 + z^2 = 4y$ and the plane $y = 4$. Find (a) the centroid of W, and (b) I_y.

10. Find the center of mass of the solid W described in Problem 14, page 421. Use the result of that problem.

    HINT. For experience, the student may desire to give reasoning about sums S_P as in Theorem I on page 402, to prove that $(\bar{x}, \bar{y}, \bar{z})$ lies in the yz-plane and the xz-plane.

11. Find the center of mass of the solid W of Problem 16 on page 421. Use the result of that problem.

12. A solid W is bounded below by the xy-plane and above by the ellipsoid $4x^2 + 2y^2 + z^2 = 8$. If $\delta = 2|xy|$, find the center of mass of W.

★13. Consider an xyz-system of rectangular coordinates. Let $y = f(z)$ define a curve C in the yz-plane. Then, revolution of C about the z-axis generates a surface S whose equation in an $r\theta z$-system of cylindrical coordinates is verified to be $r = f(z)$. Let W be the region in three-dimensional space bounded by S and the planes $z = a$ and $z = b$, where $a < b$. Let mass be distributed uniformly over W, with the density δ. Then, by starting with a triple integral, obtain the following expression for the moment of inertia I_z (by integrating with the order $dr\, d\theta\, dz$):
$\frac{1}{2}\pi\delta \int_a^b [f(z)]^4 dz.$

★*Apply Problem 13 to obtain the moment of inertia about the z-axis for the homogeneous solid bounded by the given surface of revolution.*

14. The sphere $x^2 + y^2 + z^2 = a^2$.

15. The cone $z^2 = 4x^2 + 4y^2$, between $z = 0$ and $z = h$, where $h > 0$.

16. The cylinder $x^2 + y^2 = a^2$, between $z = 0$ and $z = h$, where $h > 0$.

★17. Find I_x for the homogeneous solid bounded by the surface obtained on revolving the curve $y = 2x - x^2$ about the x-axis, and the planes $x = 0$ and $x = 2$.

204. Spherical coordinates

Consider an xyz-system of rectangular coordinates, as in Figure 280. Then, we define corresponding *spherical* (or, *geographical*) *coordinates* $\{r, \theta, \phi\}$ for a point P as follows: r *is the distance* OP; θ *is the angle from* OX *to* OP' *where* P' *is the projection of* P *on the* xy-*plane*; ϕ *is the angle from* OZ *to* OP. For any point P,

$$r \geqq 0; \quad 0° \leqq \theta < 360°; \quad 0° \leqq \phi \leqq 180°.$$

We call r the *radius vector* of P. With a geographical background, we may call θ the *longitude* of P and ϕ its *colatitude*. From Figure 280, if (x, y, z) and $\{r, \theta, \phi\}$ are the corresponding coordinates for a point P, we obtain $r \sin \phi = OP'$, and

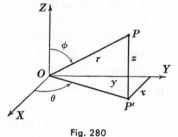

Fig. 280

$$r^2 = x^2 + y^2 + z^2; \quad x = r \sin \phi \cos \theta; \tag{1}$$

$$y = r \sin \phi \sin \theta; \quad z = r \cos \phi. \tag{2}$$

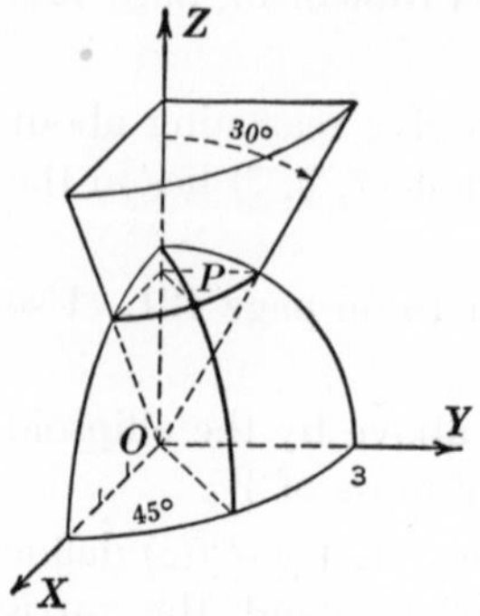

Note 1. If R, α, β are given constants, the locus of the equation

$$\left.\begin{array}{l} r = R \text{ is a sphere of radius } R, \text{ center } O; \\ \theta = \alpha \text{ is a half-plane through } OZ; \\ \phi = \beta \text{ is a half-cone with axis } OZ. \end{array}\right\} \tag{3}$$

Point $P:\{r = R, \theta = \alpha, \phi = \beta\}$ is the intersection of the surfaces (3).

ILLUSTRATION 1. $P:\{3, 45°, 30°\}$ is shown in Figure 281 as the intersection of the sphere $r = 3$, the half-plane $\theta = 45°$, and the half-cone $\phi = 30°$.

Fig. 281

205. Triple integrals in spherical coordinates

Let W be a region in an $r\theta\phi$-system of spherical coordinates, and assume that the function $f(r, \theta, \phi)$ is continuous in W, where

$$a \leqq r \leqq b, \quad \alpha \leqq \theta \leqq \beta, \quad \text{and} \quad \gamma \leqq \phi \leqq \eta. \tag{1}$$

We propose expressing the value of $\iiint_W f(r, \theta, \phi)dV$ as an iterated integral with respect to r, θ, and ϕ. A complete demonstration of the results is beyond the scope of this text.

Consider an elementary subregion, U, of W bounded by

1. *two spheres* $r = r_0$ *and* $r = r_0 + \Delta r$,
2. *two half planes* $\theta = \theta_0$ *and* $\theta = \theta_0 + \Delta\theta$, *and*
3. *two half cones* $\phi = \phi_0$ *and* $\phi = \phi_0 + \Delta\phi$.

In Figure 282, page 429, C is the point $\{r_0, \theta_0, \phi_0\}$, and U is the region CH, with six faces, like a parallelepiped. At any corner of U, the three edges (two curves and a line) are mutually orthogonal. In Figure 282, $KC = r_0 \sin \phi_0$,

$$\angle CKD = \Delta\theta \quad and \ hence \quad \widehat{CD} = r_0 \sin \phi_0 \, \Delta\theta;$$
$$\angle DOE = \Delta\phi \quad and \ hence \quad \widehat{DE} = r_0 \Delta\phi.$$

Also, $EH = \Delta r$. Then, as an approximation to the volume ΔV of U, take

$$\Delta V = (\widehat{CD})(\widehat{DE})(EH), \quad or \quad \Delta V = r_0^2 \sin \phi_0 \, \Delta r \Delta\theta \Delta\phi. \tag{2}$$

We shall call U, of Figure 282, a *regular subregion* of W.

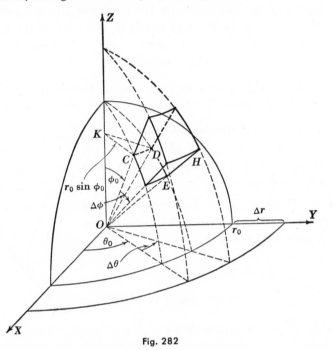

Fig. 282

Now, construct a set of h concentric spheres of type $r = r_0$ where r_0 ranges from $r_0 = a$ to $r_0 = b$, a set of k half planes of type $\theta = \theta_0$ where θ_0 ranges from $\theta_0 = \alpha$ to $\theta_0 = \beta$, and s half cones of type $\phi = \phi_0$ where ϕ_0 ranges from $\phi_0 = \gamma$ to $\phi_0 = \eta$. These surfaces create a partition, P, of W where the regular subregions of W form a set $\{U\}$, with the typical U shown in Figure 282. We shall assume that all nonregular subregions of W which are in P can be *neglected* as we proceed. Let d_P be the maximum of the diameters of the regular subregions formed by the mesh of surfaces which created P. Let $\{r, \theta, \phi\}$ represent the coordinates at a corner, C, of the subregion U. Then, from (2), by use of (5) and Theorem II of Section 200 on page 417, we obtain

$$\iiint_W f(r, \theta, \phi)dV = \lim_{d_P \to 0} \sum_{(all, \, for \, P)} f(r, \theta, \phi)\Delta V$$

$$= \lim_{(\Delta r \to 0, \ \Delta\theta \to 0, \ \Delta\phi \to 0)} \sum_{(all, \, for \, P)} f(r, \theta, \phi)r^2 \sin \phi \, \Delta r \Delta\theta \Delta\phi. \tag{3}$$

On applying the usual procedure, we may express (3) as an iterated integral, with the possibility of six different orders for the integrations, when W has a convenient boundary. For instance, we may obtain

$$\iiint_W f(r,\,\theta,\,\phi)dV = \int_\gamma^\eta \int_{\theta_1(\phi)}^{\theta_2(\phi)} \int_{r_1(\theta,\,\phi)}^{r_2(\theta,\,\phi)} r^2 \sin\phi\,dr\,d\theta\,d\phi. \tag{4}$$

In (4), W has the following nature: for points $\{r,\,\theta,\,\phi\}$ in W with θ and ϕ fixed temporarily, $r_1(\theta,\,\phi)$ and $r_2(\theta,\,\phi)$ are the least and greatest values of r; then, for fixed ϕ, $\theta_1(\phi)$ and $\theta_2(\phi)$ are the least and greatest values of θ for points in W; γ and η are the end-points of the interval for ϕ in W. In (4), with (2) as a background, we refer to "$r^2 \sin\phi\,dr\,d\theta\,d\phi$" as the *differential element of volume in spherical coordinates*.

Note 1. With an $r\theta\phi$-system, we may also use the related xyz-system. In such a case, x, y, and z must be expressed in terms of r, θ, and ϕ.

EXAMPLE 1. A region W is bounded below by the cone $\phi = \frac{1}{6}\pi$ and above by the plane $z = a > 0$. Find the mass, m, of W if the density at any point $\{r,\,\theta,\,\phi\}$ is $\delta = r \cos\phi$.

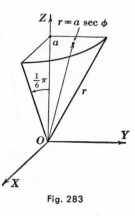

SOLUTION. From $z = a$, we find $r \cos\phi = a$, or $r = a \sec\phi$. The arrow in Figure 283 indicates the range for r, with fixed θ and ϕ.

$$m = \iiint_W \delta(r,\,\theta,\,\phi)dV$$

$$= \int_0^{\frac{1}{6}\pi} \int_0^{2\pi} \int_0^{a\sec\phi} (r\cos\phi)r^2 \sin\phi\,dr\,d\theta\,d\phi$$

$$= \frac{1}{4}a^4 \int_0^{\frac{1}{6}\pi} \int_0^{2\pi} \cos^{-3}\phi \sin\phi\,d\theta\,d\phi = \frac{1}{12}\pi a^4.$$

Fig. 283

EXAMPLE 2. A region W is bounded below by the plane $z = 4$ and above by the sphere $x^2 + y^2 + z^2 = 25$. Mass is distributed over W with the density δ at the point (x, y, z) inversely proportional to the distance from the origin. Find the center of mass.

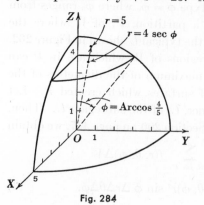

Fig. 284

SOLUTION. 1. The given surfaces have the $r\theta\phi$-equations $r = 4 \sec\phi$ and $r = 5$; also $\delta = kr^{-1}$. By symmetry, the center of mass $(\bar{x},\,\bar{y},\,\bar{z})$ is on the z-axis, so that only $\bar{z}$ is unknown. With $m = \iiint_W \delta\,dV$,

$$\bar{z} = \frac{\iiint_W \delta z\,dV}{m}. \tag{5}$$

2. For fixed ϕ and θ, the range for r is $4 \sec \phi \leq r \leq 5$, as shown by an arrow in Figure 284. For fixed θ, the range for ϕ is $0 \leq \phi \leq \text{Arccos } \frac{4}{5}$.

$$\iiint_W \delta z \, dV = \int_0^{2\pi} \int_0^{\text{Arccos } \frac{4}{5}} \int_{4 \sec \phi}^5 kr^{-1}(r \cos \phi) r^2 \sin \phi \, dr \, d\phi \, d\theta = \frac{13}{3} k\pi.$$

Similarly, we find $m = k\pi$. Hence, from (5), $\bar{z} = 4\frac{1}{3}$.

EXERCISE 129

Formulate by use of triple integrals. Compute by use of spherical coordinates.

1. Find the volume of a sphere of radius a, and the mass if $\delta = |xy|$.

2. W is the region whose outer boundary is the sphere $r = 2a$ and whose inner boundary is the sphere $r = a$. If $\delta = 3r^2$, find the mass of W.

3. Find the volume of a right circular cone (elementary sense) with a as the radius of the base and α as the half-angle at the vertex.

4. W is the region bounded above by the sphere $x^2 + y^2 + z^2 = 4h^2$ and below by the plane $z = h$, where $h > 0$. Find (a) the volume of W, and (b) its mass and center of mass if $\delta = 2r$.

5. W is the region in the 1st octant bounded by the coordinate planes of the xyz-system and the sphere $x^2 + y^2 + z^2 = a^2$. If δ is a constant, find the center of mass of W. Notice its symmetry.

6. W is the region bounded by the sphere $r = a$ and the half-cone $\phi = \alpha$, where $0 < \alpha < \frac{1}{2}\pi$. Find (a) the volume of W, and (b) its center of mass, if mass is spread over W with uniform density.

7. Find the center of mass of the upper half of W in Problem 2.

8. W is the region bounded by the sphere $r = a$ and the half-cones $\phi = \frac{1}{3}\pi$ and $\phi = \frac{1}{4}\pi$. Mass is spread over W with the density $\delta = 2z$. Find (a) the mass of W, and (b) its center of mass.

9. Find the moment of inertia I_z for W in Problem 8.

10. In a solid sphere of radius a, the density of mass at any point is proportional to its distance from the center. Find the moment of inertia of the sphere and its radius of gyration about any diameter.

11. A homogeneous solid W is bounded below by the cone $x^2 + y^2 = 3z^2$ and above by the plane $z = 4$. Find the centroid of W.

12. A homogeneous solid spherical shell has the inner radius h and outer radius a. Find the moment of inertia of the shell about a diameter.

13. A homogeneous solid W is bounded, inside and outside, respectively, by the spheres $x^2 + y^2 + (z - a)^2 = a^2$ and $x^2 + y^2 + (z - 2a)^2 = 4a^2$. Find the centroid of W first by integration, and second on the basis of an extension of Section 196 to space of three dimensions. (Find the $r\theta\phi$-equations of the spheres.) Also, find I_z for W.

14. W is the region bounded above by the sphere $r = 2$ and below by the sphere $r = 4 \cos \phi$. Find the volume of W.

15. In Problem 14, find the center of mass of W if $\delta = 3r$.

C H A P T E R

22

INFINITE SERIES

206. Convergent and divergent sequences

Recall the introduction to sequences and their limits, on pages 62–63. Thus, S_n represents a function of the positive integer n, and a *sequence* $\{S_n\}$ consists of the set of numbers $S_1, S_2, S_3, \cdots$, with S_n referred to as the *general term*, or the nth *term* of the sequence. The sequence is said to have a *limit*, or to be *convergent*, in case there exists a finite number L such that $S_n \to L$ as $n \to \infty$. Then, we say that the sequence $\{S_n\}$ *converges to L*. If the sequence is *not convergent*, it is said to be *divergent*.

ILLUSTRATION 1. If $S_n = \dfrac{3n^2 + 2n - 3}{7n^2 + 5n - 4}$, we obtain the limit of S_n as $n \to \infty$ by first dividing the numerator and denominator of S_n by the *highest power of n in the denominator*:

$$\lim_{n \to \infty} S_n = \lim_{n \to \infty} \frac{3 + \dfrac{2}{n} - \dfrac{3}{n^2}}{7 + \dfrac{5}{n} - \dfrac{4}{n^2}} = \frac{3 + 0 + 0}{7 + 0 + 0} = \frac{3}{7}.$$

Suppose that S_n assumes an indeterminate form as $n \to \infty$. Then, to obtain $\lim_{n \to \infty} S_n$, first we may allow n to be a *continuous* variable with $1 \leqq n < \infty$, and apply the methods of Chapter 10 for indeterminate forms. If $S_n \to L$ as $n \to \infty$ when n is a continuous variable, then $S_n \to L$ as $n \to \infty$ with n assuming only positive integral values.

ILLUSTRATION 2. $\qquad \lim_{n \to \infty} \dfrac{3n^2 + 5}{2n + 7} = \lim_{n \to \infty} \dfrac{6n}{2} = +\infty.$

ILLUSTRATION 3. If $S_n = (\ln n)/n$, we observe that S_n assumes the indeterminate form ∞/∞ as $n \to \infty$. Then, by the method of page 180, using the derivatives of the numerator and denominator,

$$\lim_{n \to \infty} \frac{\ln n}{n} = \lim_{n \to \infty} \frac{\dfrac{1}{n}}{1} = \lim_{n \to \infty} \frac{1}{n} = 0.$$

207. Increasing and decreasing sequences

To say that a sequence $\{S_n\}$ is *nondecreasing* will mean that S_n *does not decrease when n increases*. Similarly, to say that a sequence $\{S_n\}$ is *nonincreasing* will mean that S_n *does not increase when n increases*. The following result, which we accept intuitively,* is useful frequently.

THEOREM I. *If a sequence $\{S_n\}$ is* **bounded and nondecreasing,** *then the sequence has a limit. That is, if there exists a constant B such that, for all values of n,*

$$S_n \leqq B \quad and \quad S_n \leqq S_{n+1}, \tag{1}$$

then there exists a number $S \leqq B$ such that $\lim_{n \to \infty} S_n = S$.

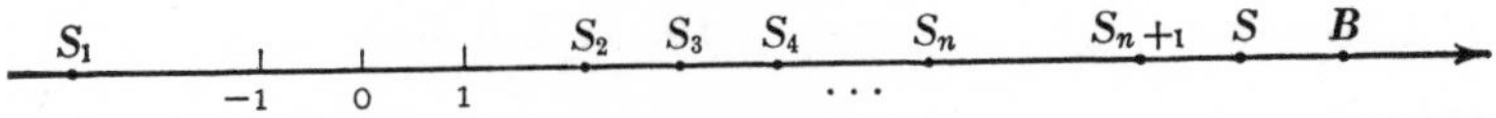

Fig. 285

In Figure 285, conditions (1) are interpreted geometrically, with S_n represented on a number scale; as n increases, the point S_n may move to the right, but not to the left, on the scale. Since $S_n \leqq B$ and $\lim_{n \to \infty} S_n = S$, we conclude that $S \leqq B$, because points of the sequence $\{S_n\}$ cannot cluster about any number $S > B$ in Figure 285. Moreover, we cannot have any value $S_n > S$, because then S_n would not *decrease toward S* as n increases; hence, $S_n \leqq S$ for all values of n.

ILLUSTRATION 1. If $S_n = 3 - \dfrac{1}{2^n}$, then $S_n < 3$. We verify that

$$S_1 = 3 - \tfrac{1}{2} = \tfrac{5}{2}, \quad S_2 = \tfrac{11}{4}, \quad S_3 = \tfrac{23}{8}, \cdots,$$

where S_n increases as n increases, because $1/2^n$ decreases. Or, $S_n < S_{n+1}$ for all values of n. Hence, Theorem I states that S_n has a limit as $n \to \infty$. By direct evaluation, $\lim_{n \to \infty} S_n = 3$.

If a *nondecreasing sequence* $\{S_n\}$ *is* **not bounded,** *then $S_n \to +\infty$ as $n \to \infty$.* Hence, Theorem I justifies the following result.

THEOREM II. *A nondecreasing sequence $\{S_n\}$ converges if and only if the sequence is bounded; otherwise, $S_n \to \infty$ as $n \to \infty$.*

By use of Theorem I, we could prove a similar result for a *nonincreasing* sequence: *if there exists a number B such that, for all values of n,*

$$B \leqq S_n \quad and \quad S_{n+1} \leqq S_n, \tag{2}$$

then there exists a number S such that $S_n \to S$ as $n \to \infty$, where $B \leqq S$. We accept the preceding fact, as well as Theorem I, without proof.

---

* At an advanced mathematical level, Theorem I is proved on the basis of a previous foundation for the system of real numbers.

EXERCISE 130

Evaluate the limit. Use differentiation if desirable.

1. $\lim\limits_{n\to\infty} \dfrac{3n+2}{2-5n}$.

2. $\lim\limits_{n\to\infty} \dfrac{2n+n^3}{3n^3+n^2}$.

3. $\lim\limits_{n\to\infty} \dfrac{n-2n^2}{2+5n}$.

4. $\lim\limits_{n\to\infty} \dfrac{\ln n}{n^3}$.

5. $\lim\limits_{n\to\infty} \dfrac{e^n}{\ln 2n}$.

6. $\lim\limits_{n\to\infty} \dfrac{\ln n}{3n+5}$.

7. $\lim\limits_{n\to\infty} \dfrac{n^2}{\ln n}$.

8. $\lim\limits_{n\to\infty} \dfrac{10^n}{e^n+4}$.

9. $\lim\limits_{n\to\infty} \dfrac{3^n+3^2}{2(3^n)+5}$.

10. $\lim\limits_{n\to\infty} \cos n\pi$.

11. $\lim\limits_{n\to\infty} 2+5(-1)^n$.

12. $\lim\limits_{n\to\infty} (\sin n\pi)/n$.

Is the sequence convergent or divergent? If convergent, find its limit.

13. $\frac{1}{2},\ \frac{2}{3},\ \frac{3}{4},\ \frac{4}{5},\ \cdots$.

14. $\frac{2}{1},\ -\frac{3}{2},\ \frac{4}{3},\ -\frac{5}{4},\ \cdots$.

15. $1,\ -\frac{1}{2},\ \frac{1}{4},\ -\frac{1}{8},\ \cdots$.

16. $2,\ 4,\ 6,\ 8,\ \cdots$.

208. Infinite series

If $u_1, u_2, \cdots, u_n, \cdots$ is an infinite sequence, then the symbol

$$u_1 + u_2 + u_3 + \cdots + u_n + \cdots \tag{1}$$

is referred to as an *infinite series.** We abbreviate (1) by writing $\sum_{n=1}^{\infty} u_n$, which is read *"the sum of u_n from $n = 1$ to infinity."* However, this phraseology does not assign a *value* to the series, because no meaning has been given to the sum of infinitely many numbers. We shall introduce the concept of a *value* for an infinite series. For this purpose, in $\sum_{n=1}^{\infty} u_n$, let

$$S_1 = u_1, \quad S_2 = u_1 + u_2, \cdots,$$

$$S_n = u_1 + u_2 + \cdots + u_n = \sum_{k=1}^{n} u_k, \tag{2}$$

where we call S_n the nth **partial sum.**

DEFINITION I. *To say that an infinite series* **converges,** *or that* **it is convergent,** *means that the sum of the first n terms has a limit as $n \to \infty$, and then this limit is called the* **sum** *of the series.*

That is, to say that a series $\sum_{n=1}^{\infty} u_n$ converges, means that *the sequence of partial sums $\{S_n\}$ converges.* If $S = \lim_{n\to\infty} S_n$, then S is the sum of the series, or its *value,* and we say that the series *converges to S.* Sometimes we use "$\sum_{n=1}^{\infty} u_n$" not only as a symbol for the series, but also for its sum, when the series converges, and write

$$\sum_{n=1}^{\infty} u_n = S = \lim_{n\to\infty} S_n. \tag{3}$$

Notice that the sum of an infinite series is *not a sum in the ordinary sense,* but is *the limit of an ordinary sum of n terms as $n \to \infty$.*

---

* A sum $u_1 + u_2 + \cdots + u_k$ is called a *finite series.* Unless otherwise stated, any reference to a *series* will mean an *infinite series.*

DEFINITION II. *If an infinite series does not converge, it is said to* **diverge,** *or to be* **divergent.**

Note 1. Let S_n be the sum of the first n terms of an arithmetic progression with first term a and common difference d:

$$S_n = a + (a + d) + (a + 2d) + \cdots + [a + (n - 1)d].$$

We recall that $\qquad S_n = \tfrac{1}{2}n[2a + (n - 1)d].$ \hfill (4)

Note 2. Let S_n be the sum of the first n terms of a geometric series with first term a and common ratio r:

$$S_n = a + ar + ar^2 + \cdots + ar^{n-1}.$$

We recall that $\qquad S_n = \dfrac{a - ar^n}{1 - r} = \dfrac{a}{1 - r} - \dfrac{ar^n}{1 - r}.$ \hfill (5)

ILLUSTRATION 1. We call the following series an *infinite geometric series,* because the terms form a geometric progression:

$$1 + \frac{1}{2} + \frac{1}{4} + \cdots + \frac{1}{2^{n-1}} + \cdots. \tag{6}$$

In (6), we use (5) with $a = 1$ and $r = \tfrac{1}{2}$. Then,

$$S_n = \frac{1 - 2^{-n}}{1 - \frac{1}{2}} = 2 - \frac{1}{2^{n-1}}; \quad \lim_{n \to \infty} S_n = 2 - 0 = 2.$$

Thus, series (6) *converges* to the sum 2.

ILLUSTRATION 2. In the infinite geometric series

$$1 + 2 + 4 + \cdots + 2^{n-1} + \cdots, \tag{7}$$

we obtain $\qquad S_n = \dfrac{1 - 2^n}{1 - 2} = 2^n - 1.$ \hfill (8)

From (8), $S_n \to +\infty$ as $n \to \infty$. Hence, (7) *diverges.*

ILLUSTRATION 3. We call $2 + 4 + 6 + \cdots + 2n + \cdots$ an *infinite arithmetic series.* From (4) with $a = 2$ and $d = 2$,

$$S_n = \tfrac{1}{2}n(2 + 2n) = n(n + 1). \tag{9}$$

From (9), $S_n \to +\infty$ as $n \to \infty$. Hence, the given series is *divergent.*

ILLUSTRATION 4. With the series $1 - 1 + 1 - 1 + \cdots$, we obtain $S_1 = 1$, $S_2 = 0$, $S_3 = 1, \cdots$, where S_n is alternately 1 and 0. Hence, S_n does *not* have a limit as $n \to \infty$, and the given series is *divergent.*

EXAMPLE 1. The following series is called the **harmonic series** because the reciprocals of the terms form an arithmetic progression. Prove that the series diverges.

$$1 + \frac{1}{2} + \frac{1}{3} + \cdots + \frac{1}{n} + \cdots. \tag{10}$$

SOLUTION. 1. Consider the following inequalities, where all terms of the series (10) occur in turn on the left:

$$1 + \frac{1}{2} > \frac{1}{2}; \tag{11}$$

$$\frac{1}{3} + \frac{1}{4} > \frac{1}{4} + \frac{1}{4} = \frac{1}{2}; \tag{12}$$

$$\frac{1}{5} + \frac{1}{6} + \frac{1}{7} + \frac{1}{8} > \frac{1}{8} + \frac{1}{8} + \frac{1}{8} + \frac{1}{8} = \frac{1}{2}; \tag{13}$$

$$\frac{1}{9} + \frac{1}{10} + \cdots + \frac{1}{16} > \frac{1}{16} + \frac{1}{16} + \cdots + \frac{1}{16} = \frac{1}{2}; \tag{14}$$

$$\cdots \cdots \cdots \ etc. \ \cdots \cdots \cdots,$$

where the sum of the terms in each line exceeds $\frac{1}{2}$.

2. Let S_n be the sum of the first n terms in (10). Then, if $n > 2$,

$$S_n = 1 + \frac{1}{2} + \cdots + \frac{1}{n} > \frac{1}{2} + \frac{1}{2} + \cdots + \frac{1}{2}, \tag{15}$$

where we include $\frac{1}{2}$ from each right-hand side in those inequalities (11), (12), $\cdots$ *preceding* the line where $1/n$ occurs on the left. If n is large enough, the right-hand side in (15) will be as large as we please. Hence, $S_n \to \infty$ as $n \to \infty$, and the harmonic series diverges.

209. A necessary condition for convergence

THEOREM III. *If* $\sum_{n=1}^{\infty} u_n$ *converges, then the nth term,* u_n, *approaches zero as* $n \to \infty$. *Or, a necessary condition for convergence is that* $u_n \to 0$ *as* $n \to \infty$.

Proof. 1. For the *u*-series, we have

$$S_{n-1} = u_1 + u_2 + \cdots + u_{n-1} \quad and \quad S_n = u_1 + u_2 + \cdots + u_{n-1} + u_n;$$

$$u_n = S_n - S_{n-1}. \tag{1}$$

2. By hypothesis, the *u*-series converges, with a certain sum S. Thus, $S_n \to S$ and $S_{n-1} \to S$ as $n \to \infty$. Therefore, from (1),

$$\lim_{n \to \infty} u_n = \lim_{n \to \infty} S_n - \lim_{n \to \infty} S_{n-1} = S - S = 0$$

ILLUSTRATION 1. In Illustration 1 on page 435, $\sum_{n=1}^{\infty} 1/2^{n-1}$ converges. Also, the *n*th term approaches zero as $n \to \infty$.

THEOREM IV. *In a series* $\sum_{n=1}^{\infty} u_n$, **if the nth term does not approach zero as** $n \to \infty$, **then the series diverges.**

Proof (indirect). Assume that the conclusion of the theorem is *false*, or that the series *converges*. Then, we should have $u_n \to 0$ as $n \to \infty$. But, by hypothesis, this is *not true*. Hence, we have a *contradiction*, which eliminates the assumption that the series *converges*. Therefore, it *diverges*.

EXAMPLE 1. Prove that the series $\sum_{n=1}^{\infty} \frac{2n+1}{3n+2}$ diverges.

SOLUTION. $\lim\limits_{n\to\infty} \frac{2n+1}{3n+2} = \frac{2}{3} \neq 0$. Hence, the series diverges.

ILLUSTRATION 2. The harmonic series $\sum_{n=1}^{\infty} 1/n$ diverges, although $(1/n) \to 0$ as $n \to \infty$. This proves that the condition "$u_n \to 0$ as $n \to \infty$" is *not sufficient* to imply convergence in a series $\sum_{n=1}^{\infty} u_n$.

210. Infinite geometric series

Suppose that $a \neq 0$ and $r \neq 1$ in the infinite geometric series

$$a + ar + ar^2 + \cdots + ar^{n-1} + \cdots. \tag{1}$$

Then, if $r \neq 1$, $\qquad S_n = \dfrac{a - ar^n}{1 - r} = \dfrac{a}{1 - r} - \dfrac{ar^n}{1 - r}. \tag{2}$

If $|r| < 1$, we notice that $ar^n \to 0$ as $n \to \infty$, and hence

$$\lim_{n\to\infty} S_n = \frac{a}{1 - r}, \tag{3}$$

so that (1) converges, with the sum $a/(1 - r)$. If $|r| \geq 1$,

$$|ar^{n-1}| \geq |a| > 0,$$

and thus does *not* approach zero as $n \to \infty$. Hence, by Theorem IV, series (1) diverges if $|r| \geq 1$.

SUMMARY. $\sum_{n=1}^{\infty} ar^{n-1}$ *converges if* $|r| < 1$ *and diverges if* $|r| \geq 1$.

ILLUSTRATION 1. The repeating decimal $3.272727 \cdots$ is defined as
$$3 + .27 + .0027 + .000027 + \cdots. \tag{4}$$
In (4), after the term 3, the terms form an infinite geometric series with first term $a = .27$ and common ratio $r = .01$. Then, by use of (3),

$$3.272727 \cdots = 3 + \frac{.27}{1 - .01} = 3 + \frac{.27}{.99} = 3 + \frac{3}{11} = \frac{36}{11}.$$

Similarly, *any endless repeating decimal is a symbol for a rational number.*

EXERCISE 131

Find S_n *if possible. If* S_n *is obtained, investigate* $\lim_{n\to\infty} S_n$. *In any case, decide whether the series converges or diverges. Give reasons.*

1. $1 + \dfrac{1}{3} + \dfrac{1}{3^2} + \cdots$.

2. $5 - \dfrac{5}{2} + \dfrac{5}{2^2} - \dfrac{5}{2^3} + \cdots$.

3. $2 + 2(3) + 2(3^2) + \cdots$.

4. $1 - 4 + 4^2 - 4^3 + \cdots$.

5. $1 + 3 + 5 + \cdots$.

6. $2 - 4 + 6 - 8 + \cdots$.

7. $3 - 2 + 3 - 2 + \cdots$.

8. $4 + 7 + 11 + \cdots$.

9. $40 + 4 + .4 + .04 + \cdots$.

10. $.22 + .0022 + .000022 + \cdots$.

11. $.838383 \cdots$.

12. $.2111 \cdots$.

13. $.345345345 \cdots$.

14. $\frac{2}{3} + \frac{3}{4} + \frac{4}{5} + \cdots.$ **15.** $3 + 5 + 7 + \cdots.$

16. $1 - 2 + 3 - 4 + \cdots.$ **17.** $1 + 6 + 6^2 + \cdots.$

18. $\displaystyle\sum_{n=1}^{\infty} \frac{3n+5}{n+1}.$ **19.** $\displaystyle\sum_{n=1}^{\infty} \frac{2^n(3n)}{4n+1}.$ **20.** $\displaystyle\sum_{n=1}^{\infty} \sin\left(n \cdot \frac{\pi}{2}\right).$

21. $\ln\frac{1}{2} + \ln\frac{1}{3} + \ln\frac{1}{4} + \cdots.$ **22.** $\ln\frac{2}{1} + \ln\frac{3}{2} + \ln\frac{4}{3} + \cdots.$

211. Miscellaneous theorems on convergence and divergence

In the following results, we meet a u-series and a v-series with partial sums S_n and T_n, respectively.

THEOREM V. *If* $\displaystyle\sum_{n=1}^{\infty} u_n$ *and* $\displaystyle\sum_{n=1}^{\infty} v_n$ *converge, with sums S and T, respectively, then* $\displaystyle\sum_{n=1}^{\infty} (u_n + v_n)$ *converges, with sum* $(S + T)$.

Proof. Let W_n be the nth partial sum for $\displaystyle\sum_{n=1}^{\infty} (u_n + v_n)$. Then, we have $W_n = S_n + T_n$. Since $S_n \to S$ and $T_n \to T$, then $W_n \to (S + T)$ as $n \to \infty$, which proves the theorem.

Note 1. From Theorem V, we may write

$$\sum_{n=1}^{\infty} u_n + \sum_{n=1}^{\infty} v_n = \sum_{n=1}^{\infty} (u_n + v_n), \tag{1}$$

when the u-series and v-series converge. Thus, because of (1), we say that *two (or more) convergent series may be added term by term.*

The following Theorems VI and VII show that the convergence or divergence of a series is not altered if the series is multiplied term by term by a fixed constant (not zero in the case of divergence).

THEOREM VI.* *If* $\displaystyle\sum_{n=1}^{\infty} u_n$ *converges, with sum S, and if k is any constant, then* $\displaystyle\sum_{n=1}^{\infty} ku_n$ *converges, with sum kS.*

THEOREM VII.* *If* $\displaystyle\sum_{n=1}^{\infty} v_n$ *diverges and k is any constant, not zero, then* $\displaystyle\sum_{n=1}^{\infty} kv_n$ *diverges.*

ILLUSTRATION 1. To investigate the convergence or divergence of

$$\frac{1}{2} + \frac{1}{4} + \frac{1}{6} + \cdots + \frac{1}{2n} + \cdots, \tag{2}$$

we notice that

$$\frac{1}{2n} = \frac{1}{2}\left(\frac{1}{n}\right), \tag{3}$$

and recall that $\displaystyle\sum_{n=1}^{\infty} (1/n)$ diverges. Hence, by Theorem VII with $k = \frac{1}{2}$, it follows that (2) diverges.

THEOREM VIII. *The convergence or divergence of a series is not altered by deleting, or inserting, a finite number of terms.*

---

* To be proved in the next exercise.

Proof. 1. In $\sum_{n=1}^{\infty} u_n$, *delete* a finite number of terms, say k terms with sum A, to obtain a new series $\sum_{m=1}^{\infty} v_m$. We also look on the u-series as obtained by *inserting* k terms in the v-series.

2. Let the partial sums be $\{S_n\}$ for the u-series, and $\{T_m\}$ for the v-series. Suppose that m is so large that the original location of v_m in the u-series is beyond all deleted terms, whose sum is A. Then, T_m can be obtained by subtracting A from a corresponding partial sum, S_n, where $n = m + k$ because k terms were deleted:

$$T_m = S_n - A, \quad or \quad S_n = T_m + A. \tag{4}$$

3. From (4), if the sequence $\{T_m\}$ converges to a limit T, then $\{S_n\}$ converges to a limit S where $S = T + A$, because

$$\lim_{n \to \infty} S_n = \lim_{m \to \infty} T_m + A = T + A. \tag{5}$$

Similarly, if $S_n \to S$ as $n \to \infty$, then the sequence $\{T_m\}$ has a limit T where $T = S - A$. Thus, the u-series and the v-series *both converge if either one converges*. Hence, also, they *both diverge if either one diverges*, because we cannot have one divergent and one convergent.

ILLUSTRATION 2. If we delete the first three terms in

$$1 + \frac{1}{2} + \frac{1}{3} + \cdots + \frac{1}{n} + \cdots, \tag{6}$$

we obtain

$$\frac{1}{4} + \frac{1}{5} + \cdots + \frac{1}{m+3} + \cdots. \tag{7}$$

Then, Theorem VIII shows that (7) diverges because (6) diverges.

212. Remainder after k terms in a series

Consider a convergent series $\qquad u_1 + u_2 + \cdots + u_n + \cdots, \tag{1}$

with partial sums $\{S_n\}$, and let S be the sum of (1). From Theorem VIII, if k is any positive integer, the series

$$u_{k+1} + u_{k+2} + \cdots + u_n + \cdots \tag{2}$$

converges because (1) converges. Let R_k be the sum of (2). Then, for any value of k, we refer to R_k as the *remainder after k terms* in (1). From (5) on this page, with R_k playing the role of T in (5), and $A = S_k = u_1 + \cdots + u_k$,

$$S = S_k + R_k, \quad or \quad R_k = S - S_k. \tag{3}$$

From (3), $\qquad \lim_{k \to \infty} R_k = S - \lim_{k \to \infty} S_k = S - S = 0.$

Thus, we have proved the following result.

THEOREM IX. *In a convergent series, the remainder after k terms approaches zero as $k \to \infty$.*

EXERCISE 132

We have shown that the harmonic series diverges. Then, quote a theorem or theorems to prove that the series in the problem diverges.

1. $\frac{1}{6} + \frac{1}{7} + \frac{1}{8} + \cdots$.

2. $3 + 2 + 1 + \frac{1}{2} + \frac{1}{3} + \cdots$.

3. $\frac{1}{3} + \frac{1}{6} + \frac{1}{9} + \cdots$.

4. $\frac{1}{6} + \frac{1}{8} + \frac{1}{10} + \cdots$.

5. Prove Theorem VI of page 438. Then, prove Theorem VII of page 438.

213. Basic characteristics of series of nonnegative terms

In a series $\sum_{n=1}^{\infty} u_n$ where $u_n \geq 0$, the sequence of partial sums $\{S_n\}$ for the series is *nondecreasing*, because

$$S_{n+1} = S_n + u_{n+1} \geq S_n.$$

Hence, from Theorem II on page 433, S_n has a limit as $n \to \infty$, or the u-series converges, *if and only if the sequence $\{S_n\}$ is bounded.* These remarks prove the following result.

THEOREM X. *A series of nonnegative terms, with partial sums $\{S_n\}$, converges if and only if there exists a number B such that $S_n \leq B$ for all values of n. Then, if S is the sum of the series,*

$$S_n \leq S \leq B. \tag{1}$$

EXAMPLE 1. Prove that the following series is convergent if $p > 1$:

$$1 + \frac{1}{2^p} + \frac{1}{3^p} + \cdots + \frac{1}{n^p} + \cdots. \tag{2}$$

SOLUTION. 1. The following inequalities involve all terms from (2) in the expressions at the left:

$$1 \leq 1.$$

$$\frac{1}{2^p} + \frac{1}{3^p} \leq \frac{1}{2^p} + \frac{1}{2^p} = \frac{2}{2^p} = \frac{1}{2^{p-1}},$$

$$\frac{1}{4^p} + \frac{1}{5^p} + \frac{1}{6^p} + \frac{1}{7^p} \leq \frac{1}{4^p} + \frac{1}{4^p} + \frac{1}{4^p} + \frac{1}{4^p} = \frac{4}{4^p} = \frac{1}{4^{p-1}} = \left(\frac{1}{2^{p-1}}\right)^2,$$

$$\frac{1}{8^p} + \frac{1}{9^p} + \cdots + \frac{1}{15^p} \leq \frac{8}{8^p} = \frac{1}{8^{p-1}} = \left(\frac{1}{2^3}\right)^{p-1} = \left(\frac{1}{2^{p-1}}\right)^3.$$

$$\cdots \cdots \cdots \text{etc.} \cdots \cdots \cdots \tag{3}$$

2. The terms on the right in (3) form the geometric series

$$1 + \frac{1}{2^{p-1}} + \frac{1}{(2^{p-1})^2} + \cdots, \tag{4}$$

whose ratio is $r = 1/2^{p-1}$, where $r < 1$ because $p > 1$. Hence, (4) converges. If its sum is A, the sum of any number of terms from (2) in the inequalities (3) will be at most A. Thus, if S_n is the nth partial sum of (2), $S_n \leq A$ for all values of n. Therefore, by Theorem X, (2) converges.

214. Comparison tests, with nonnegative terms

To test a series for *convergence* will mean to determine whether the series *converges* or *diverges*. We refer to the following Theorems XI and XII as *comparison tests* for convergence and divergence, respectively.

THEOREM XI. *If $\sum_{n=1}^{\infty} u_n$ and $\sum_{n=1}^{\infty} v_n$ are series of positive * terms, where the u-series is known to converge, and where*

$$v_n \leqq u_n, \tag{1}$$

for all values of n, then the v-series also converges.

Proof. 1. Let $T_n = v_1 + v_2 + \cdots + v_n$, and
$$S_n = u_1 + u_2 + \cdots + u_n.$$

Then, from (1), $T_n \leqq S_n$ for all values of n. Also, the sequences $\{T_n\}$ and $\{S_n\}$ are increasing sequences.

2. By hypothesis, the sequence $\{S_n\}$ converges to a limit S, the sum of the u-series. Hence, $S_n \leqq S$ for all values of n, because $\{S_n\}$ is an increasing sequence. Then $T_n \leqq S_n \leqq S$, for all values of n, or the partial sums of the v-series are *bounded*. Hence, by Theorem X, the v-series converges.

THEOREM XII. *If $\sum_{n=1}^{\infty} u_n$ and $\sum_{n=1}^{\infty} v_n$ are series of positive terms, where the v-series is known to diverge, and where*

$$v_n \leqq u_n, \tag{2}$$

for all values of n, then the u-series also diverges.

Proof. Suppose that (2) is true, but assume that the u-series *converges*. Then, by Theorem XI, the v-series also *converges*. This is a *contradiction*. Hence, the u-series cannot converge.

EXAMPLE 1. Test for convergence:

$$\frac{1}{1\cdot2\cdot3} + \frac{1}{2\cdot3\cdot4} + \frac{1}{3\cdot4\cdot5} + \cdots + \frac{1}{n(n+1)(n+2)} + \cdots \tag{3}$$

SOLUTION. Since $n(n+1)(n+2)$, when expanded, is of degree 3 in n, we shall compare with $\sum_{n=1}^{\infty} 1/n^3$, and we suspect that (3) converges. In (3),

$$\frac{1}{1\cdot2\cdot3} < \frac{1}{1\cdot1\cdot1} = \frac{1}{1^3}; \quad \frac{1}{2\cdot3\cdot4} < \frac{1}{2\cdot2\cdot2} = \frac{1}{2^3}; \quad \cdots \tag{4}$$

$$\frac{1}{n(n+1)(n+2)} < \frac{1}{n\cdot n\cdot n} = \frac{1}{n^3}. \tag{5}$$

We know that $\sum_{n=1}^{\infty} 1/n^3$ converges $[p = 3$ in (2) on page 440]. Hence, by Theorem XI, series (3) converges. The verification of the *general* inequality in (5) was essential.

---

* In Theorems XI and XII, we may allow the terms to be *nonnegative* (positive or zero). Then, only slight changes would be necessary in the proofs.

EXAMPLE 2. Prove divergent:

$$\frac{1}{\sqrt{4}} + \frac{1}{\sqrt{5}} + \frac{1}{\sqrt{6}} + \cdots + \frac{1}{\sqrt{n+3}} + \cdots. \tag{6}$$

SOLUTION. For a comparison series, we use

$$\frac{1}{4} + \frac{1}{5} + \frac{1}{6} + \cdots + \frac{1}{n+3} + \cdots. \tag{7}$$

By Theorem VIII of page 438, (7) diverges because it is obtained on omitting three terms of the harmonic series, which diverges. Observe that

$$\frac{1}{\sqrt{4}} > \frac{1}{4}, \quad \frac{1}{\sqrt{5}} > \frac{1}{5}, \cdots, \frac{1}{\sqrt{n+3}} > \frac{1}{n+3}, \tag{8}$$

because $\sqrt{n+3} < n+3$. Hence, (6) diverges because (7) diverges.

EXAMPLE 3. Prove convergent:

$$\frac{5}{2 \cdot 3 \cdot 4} + \frac{7}{3 \cdot 4 \cdot 5} + \frac{9}{4 \cdot 5 \cdot 6} + \cdots + \frac{2n+3}{(n+1)(n+2)(n+3)} + \cdots. \tag{9}$$

SOLUTION. The degree of the numerator in n is 1, and of the denominator is 3. Since $(3 - 1) = 2$, we work toward comparison with the series $\sum_{n=1}^{\infty} 1/n^2$, or some series related simply to it, and suspect that (9) converges. Consideration of the first two terms from (9) leads us to (10) for the nth term:

$$\frac{5}{2 \cdot 3 \cdot 4} < \frac{1}{2 \cdot 2} \cdot \frac{5}{4} < \frac{1}{1^2} \cdot 2; \qquad \frac{7}{3 \cdot 4 \cdot 5} < \frac{1}{3 \cdot 3} \cdot \frac{7}{5} < \frac{1}{2^2} \cdot 2;$$

$$\frac{2n+3}{(n+1)(n+2)(n+3)} < \frac{1}{n \cdot n} \cdot \frac{2n+3}{n+3} < \frac{1}{n^2} \cdot 2, \tag{10}$$

because $2n + 3 < 2(n + 3) = 2n + 6$. Hence, each term in (9) is less than the corresponding term in $\sum_{n=1}^{\infty} 2/n^2$, which converges because $\sum_{n=1}^{\infty} 1/n^2$ converges [$p = 2$ in (2) on page 440]. Therefore, (9) converges.

Note 1. If (1) in Theorem XI, or (2) in Theorem XII, is true only for all values of *n greater than some fixed integer K*, then the conclusion of the theorem remains true. This is seen by applying the theorem as originally stated to the new series obtained by *omitting the first K terms* in each given series, and recalling that this omission does not alter convergence or divergence. Also, we observe that the comparison tests apply indirectly to series where all terms are negative or zero. In such a case, first we could multiply each term by -1, which does not affect convergence or divergence, and then apply a comparison test, if possible.

Any series of positive terms which is known to converge, or to diverge, is eligible as a comparison series for proving the convergence or divergence, respectively, of other series. The following series are particularly useful. Sometimes, (12) is called the **hyperharmonic series.**

Convergent series for comparison

$$a + ar + ar^2 + \cdots + ar^{n-1} + \cdots; \quad (a > 0; \ 0 \leqq r < 1). \tag{11}$$

$$1 + \frac{1}{2^p} + \frac{1}{3^p} + \cdots + \frac{1}{n^p} + \cdots; \quad (p > 1). \tag{12}$$

$$1 + \frac{1}{2^2} + \frac{1}{3^3} + \cdots + \frac{1}{n^n} + \cdots. \tag{13}$$

Divergent series for comparison

$$1 + \frac{1}{2} + \frac{1}{3} + \cdots + \frac{1}{n} + \cdots. \tag{14}$$

$$a + ar + ar^2 + \cdots + ar^{n-1} + \cdots; \quad (a > 0; \ r \geqq 1). \tag{15}$$

Note 2. To test a series $\sum_{n=1}^{\infty} u_n$ for convergence by use of a comparison test, first it is desirable to make a guess as to the convergence or divergence of the series. For this purpose, the following result may be useful.

Suppose that $u_n > 0$ and $u_n = P(n)/Q(n)$, where $P(n)$ and $Q(n)$ are polynomials in n of fixed degrees h and k, respectively. Let $k - h = \alpha$. Then, the u-series is convergent if $\alpha > 1$ and divergent if $\alpha \leqq 1$.

We shall not prove this result, or use it to establish convergence or divergence. However, the student may desire to use the result, where it applies, in deciding whether a proof of convergence or of divergence is to be attempted.

EXERCISE 133

Prove convergent; use Theorem VIII, *page* 438, *or the comparison test.*

1. Series (13) above, by comparison with (11) where $a = 1$ and $r = \frac{1}{2}$.

2. $\dfrac{1}{1 \cdot 2 \cdot 3 \cdot 4} + \dfrac{1}{2 \cdot 3 \cdot 4 \cdot 5} + \cdots + \dfrac{1}{n(n+1)(n+2)(n+3)} + \cdots.$

3. $\dfrac{1}{1 \cdot 3} + \dfrac{1}{2 \cdot 3^2} + \dfrac{1}{3 \cdot 3^3} + \cdots.$ **4.** $\dfrac{1}{2^2} + \dfrac{1}{4^2} + \dfrac{1}{6^2} + \cdots.$

5. $\dfrac{1}{3^3} + \dfrac{1}{5^3} + \dfrac{1}{7^3} + \cdots.$ **6.** $\dfrac{1}{1 \cdot 2} + \dfrac{1}{2 \cdot 3} + \dfrac{1}{3 \cdot 4} + \cdots.$

7. $\dfrac{1}{1!} + \dfrac{1}{2!} + \dfrac{1}{3!} + \cdots.$ **8.** $\dfrac{1}{2!} + \dfrac{1}{4!} + \dfrac{1}{6!} + \cdots.$

9. $\dfrac{1}{k + 1^2} + \dfrac{1}{k + 2^2} + \dfrac{1}{k + 3^2} + \cdots, k > 0.$

10. $\dfrac{1}{2^p} + \dfrac{1}{4^p} + \dfrac{1}{6^p} + \cdots, p > 1.$

Prove divergent by the comparison test or by other means.

11. $3 + 5 + 7 + \cdots.$ **12.** $\dfrac{3}{1} + \dfrac{4}{2} + \dfrac{5}{3} + \cdots.$

13. $\dfrac{1}{\sqrt{1}} + \dfrac{1}{\sqrt{2}} + \dfrac{1}{\sqrt{3}} + \cdots.$ **14.** $\dfrac{2}{1} + \dfrac{2^2}{2} + \dfrac{2^3}{3} + \cdots.$

15. $\dfrac{1}{1-.1} + \dfrac{1}{1-.01} + \dfrac{1}{1-.001} + \cdots$

16. $\dfrac{1}{1} + \dfrac{1}{3} + \dfrac{1}{5} + \cdots$.

17. $\dfrac{1}{1^p} + \dfrac{1}{2^p} + \dfrac{1}{3^p} + \cdots, \; p < 1.$

Test for convergence by use of available theorems.

18. $\dfrac{1}{1\cdot4} + \dfrac{1}{2\cdot5} + \dfrac{1}{3\cdot6} + \cdots$.

19. $\dfrac{1}{2\cdot4} + \dfrac{1}{4\cdot6} + \dfrac{1}{6\cdot8} + \cdots$.

20. $-\dfrac{1}{2\cdot3} - \dfrac{3}{4\cdot3^2} - \dfrac{5}{6\cdot3^3} - \cdots$.

21. $-\dfrac{1}{\sqrt{2}} - \dfrac{1}{\sqrt{4}} - \dfrac{1}{\sqrt{6}} - \cdots$.

22. $\displaystyle\sum_{n=1}^{\infty} \dfrac{1}{(2n)^3}$.

23. $\displaystyle\sum_{n=1}^{\infty} \dfrac{1}{n+1-\sqrt{n}}$.

24. $\displaystyle\sum_{n=1}^{\infty} \dfrac{1}{n(2n+1)}$.

25. $\dfrac{3}{1\cdot4} + \dfrac{4}{2\cdot5} + \dfrac{5}{3\cdot6} + \cdots$.

26. $\dfrac{1}{1\cdot2\cdot3} + \dfrac{3}{2\cdot3\cdot4} + \dfrac{5}{3\cdot4\cdot5} + \cdots$.

27. $\displaystyle\sum_{n=1}^{\infty} \dfrac{1}{n^n} \cdot \dfrac{n-1}{n+1}$.

28. $\displaystyle\sum_{n=1}^{\infty} \dfrac{1}{(2n-1)!}$.

29. $\displaystyle\sum_{n=1}^{\infty} \dfrac{6}{n^2+1}$.

30. $\displaystyle\sum_{n=1}^{\infty} \dfrac{3n+2}{2n^3+n}$.

31. $\displaystyle\sum_{n=1}^{\infty} \dfrac{2n^2+n}{n^3+3}$.

32. $\displaystyle\sum_{n=1}^{\infty} \dfrac{n+1}{n^2+5}$.

HINT for Problem 30. Show that the nth term is at most $\frac{5}{2}(1/n^2)$.

33. $\dfrac{2}{1\cdot3} + \dfrac{2\cdot4}{1\cdot3\cdot5} + \dfrac{2\cdot4\cdot6}{1\cdot3\cdot5\cdot7} + \cdots$.

34. $\dfrac{2}{5} + \dfrac{2\cdot3}{5\cdot7} + \dfrac{2\cdot3\cdot4}{5\cdot7\cdot9} + \cdots$.

★35. By definition, a *rearrangement* of a series $\sum_{n=1}^{\infty} u_n$ is a new series $\sum_{n=1}^{\infty} v_n$ where each term v_k is *some term* u_h, and where *each term* u_h *occurs just once in the v-series*. Prove that, if $u_n \geq 0$, then the u-series and the v-series both diverge or both converge, and then have the same sum. (Recall Theorem X, page 440.)

★36. Prove the following generalized comparison tests relating to two series of positive terms, $\sum_{n=1}^{\infty} u_n$ and $\sum_{n=1}^{\infty} v_n$.

A. *If the u-series converges, and if v_n/u_n approaches a finite limit H as $n \to \infty$, then the v-series converges.*

B. *If the u-series diverges, and if v_n/u_n approaches a limit $K \neq 0$ as $n \to \infty$, where K may be finite or $+\infty$, then the u-series diverges.*

HINT. For (A), if we choose $H_1 > H$, then $(v_n/u_n) < H_1$ for large n.

215. Alternating series

An alternating series is one whose terms alternate in sign,

$$u_1 - u_2 + u_3 - \cdots + (-1)^{n+1}u_n + \cdots, \tag{1}$$

where $u_1, u_2, \cdots, u_n, \cdots$ are all positive or all negative.

ILLUSTRATION 1. We call $1 - \frac{1}{2} + \frac{1}{3} - \frac{1}{4} + \cdots$ the **alternating harmonic series**. The following theorem proves it convergent.

THEOREM XIII. *An alternating series* (1) *converges if the terms decrease in absolute value,*

$$|u_n| > |u_{n+1}|,\tag{2}$$

and if the nth term approaches zero as $n \to \infty$,

$$\lim_{n\to\infty} u_n = 0.\tag{3}$$

Proof. 1. For convenience, suppose that $u_1 > 0$. Then, (2) gives

$$u_n > u_{n+1} \quad or \quad u_n - u_{n+1} > 0.\tag{4}$$

2. The partial sum, S_{2k}, of any *even* number of terms in (1) may be written in the following two forms:

$$S_{2k} = (u_1 - u_2) + (u_3 - u_4) + \cdots + (u_{2k-1} - u_{2k});\tag{5}$$
$$S_{2k} = u_1 - (u_2 - u_3) - \cdots - (u_{2k-2} - u_{2k-1}) - u_{2k}.\tag{6}$$

In (5) and (6), each difference within parentheses is positive, because of (4). Hence, (5) shows that $S_{2k} > 0$ and S_{2k} *increases as* k *increases*, while (6) shows that $S_{2k} < u_1$:

$$0 < S_2 < S_4 < S_6 < \cdots < S_{2k} < \cdots < u_1.$$

That is, S_{2k} is a *bounded, increasing sequence*. Therefore, by Theorem I on page 433, S_{2k} approaches a limit, S, as $k \to \infty$ where $S \leq u_1$, and where $S > 0$ because $S_{2k} > 0$. That is, $S_{2k} \to S$ as $k \to \infty$ and

$$0 < S \leq u_1.\tag{7}$$

3. In (1), let S_{2k+1} be the sum of any *odd number* of terms. Then,

$$S_{2k+1} = S_{2k} + u_{2k+1};$$
$$\lim_{k\to\infty} S_{2k+1} = \lim_{k\to\infty} S_{2k} + \lim_{k\to\infty} u_{2k+1} = S + 0 = S,$$

because $u_n \to 0$ as $n \to \infty$. Therefore, S_n is as near S as we please for all values of n, *odd or even*, which are sufficiently large. That is, $S_n \to S$ as $n \to \infty$, or (1) converges, with the sum S.

4. If $u_1 < 0$ in (1), we may first multiply all terms by -1. Then, the new series converges, by our result as just proved with $u_1 > 0$. Hence, (1) converges when $u_1 < 0$, and, in place of (7), we obtain

$$u_1 \leq S < 0.\tag{8}$$

From (7) and (8) we reach the following conclusion.

COROLLARY 1. *Under hypotheses* (2) *and* (3),

$$|S| \leq |u_1|.$$

Let R_n be the *remainder* after n terms in (1). Then, R_n is the sum of an alternating series:

$$R_n = \pm u_{n+1} \mp u_{n+2} \pm u_{n+3} \mp \cdots,\tag{9}$$

with the upper signs if n is *even*, and the lower signs if n is *odd*. On applying Corollary 1 in (9), we obtain the following result.

COROLLARY 2. *Under hypotheses* (2) *and* (3), *the error of any partial sum* S_n, *as an approximation to the sum* S, *is at most equal to the absolute value of the first neglected term:*

$$|S - S_n| = |R_n| \leq |u_{n+1}|. \tag{10}$$

Note 1. From (7) and (8), we see that the sum of an alternating series, satisfying (2) and (3), has *the same sign as the first term,* u_1.

ILLUSTRATION 2. In the series $\quad 1 - \dfrac{1}{2!} + \dfrac{1}{3!} - \cdots,$

$$u_n = \frac{1}{n!}; \quad u_{n+1} = \frac{1}{(n+1)!}; \quad \frac{1}{n!} > \frac{1}{(n+1)!}; \quad \lim_{n \to \infty} u_n = 0.$$

Thus, (2) and (3) are satisfied, and hence the series converges.

EXAMPLE 1. Test the alternating series for convergence:

$$\frac{1}{2 \cdot 3} - \frac{2}{3 \cdot 4} + \frac{3}{4 \cdot 5} - \cdots. \tag{11}$$

SOLUTION. 1. $\qquad u_n = \dfrac{n}{(n+1)(n+2)}; \quad u_{n+1} = \dfrac{n+1}{(n+2)(n+3)}.$

$$\lim_{n \to \infty} u_n = \lim_{n \to \infty} \frac{n}{n^2 + 3n + 2} = \lim_{n \to \infty} \frac{1}{2n + 3} = 0.$$

2. To verify (2), we wish to prove that

$$\frac{n}{(n+1)(n+2)} > \frac{n+1}{(n+2)(n+3)}, \tag{12}$$

which is true if $\qquad n(n+3) > (n+1)^2,$

or if $\qquad n^2 + 3n > n^2 + 2n + 1, \quad$ or if $\quad n > 1.$

Hence, (2) and (3) are true if $n > 1$. Therefore, with the first term omitted in (11), Theorem XIII shows that the new series converges. But, this omission does not alter convergence. Hence, (11) converges.

In Example 1, we illustrated the fact that Theorem XIII remains true if (2) and (3) are assumed *only for n sufficiently large.*

EXERCISE 134

Test for convergence by use of Sections 209 and 215.

1. $\dfrac{1}{3} - \dfrac{1}{6} + \dfrac{1}{9} - \cdots.$ $\qquad\qquad$ 2. $-\dfrac{1}{\sqrt{2}} + \dfrac{1}{\sqrt{4}} - \dfrac{1}{\sqrt{6}} + \cdots.$

3. $\dfrac{1}{\ln 2} - \dfrac{1}{\ln 3} + \dfrac{1}{\ln 4} - \cdots.$ $\qquad\qquad$ 4. $\dfrac{1}{1 \cdot 2} - \dfrac{1}{2 \cdot 3} + \dfrac{1}{3 \cdot 4} - \cdots.$

5. $\dfrac{2}{2} - \dfrac{3}{4} + \dfrac{4}{6} - \dfrac{5}{8} + \cdots.$ 6. $-\dfrac{1}{5} + \dfrac{1}{7} - \dfrac{1}{9} + \cdots.$

7. $\dfrac{2}{1} - \dfrac{3}{2} + \dfrac{4}{3} - \cdots.$ 8. $\dfrac{1}{2\cdot3} - \dfrac{1}{3\cdot3^2} + \dfrac{1}{4\cdot3^3} - \cdots.$

9. $\displaystyle\sum_{n=1}^{\infty} \dfrac{(-1)^{n+1}}{1+\sqrt{n}}.$ 10. $\displaystyle\sum_{n=1}^{\infty} \dfrac{(-1)^{n+1}}{2^n+1}.$ 11. $\displaystyle\sum_{n=1}^{\infty} (-1)^n \ln\dfrac{1}{n}.$

12. $\dfrac{3}{1\cdot2} - \dfrac{4}{2\cdot3} + \dfrac{5}{3\cdot4} - \cdots.$ 13. $\dfrac{1}{1^p} - \dfrac{1}{2^p} + \dfrac{1}{3^p} - \cdots, \; (p>0).$

Verify that the series converges. Then, compute the sum S_4, and find a bound for the absolute value of its error as an approximation to the sum of the series.

14. $1 - \dfrac{1}{2^3} + \dfrac{1}{3^3} - \cdots.$ 15. $-1 + \dfrac{1}{\sqrt{3}} - \dfrac{1}{\sqrt{5}} + \cdots.$

216. Absolute convergence

The following theorem is of importance when we investigate the convergence of a series whose terms are not all of one sign.

THEOREM XIV. *A series converges if the series of the absolute values of its terms converges. That is, $\sum_{n=1}^{\infty} u_n$ converges if $\sum_{n=1}^{\infty} |u_n|$ converges.*

Proof. 1. Let the sum of the first n terms in $\sum_{n=1}^{\infty} u_n$ be S_n, and in $\sum_{n=1}^{\infty} |u_n|$ be T_n, and let $T = \lim_{n\to\infty} T_n$. Then, since the sequence $\{T_n\}$ is nondecreasing, we have $T_n \leq T$ for all values of n. In S_n, let P_n be the sum of the positive terms and let $-Q_n$ be the sum of the negative terms. Then,

$$S_n = P_n - Q_n \quad and \quad T_n = P_n + Q_n. \tag{1}$$

2. Since $P_n \geqq 0$, $Q_n \geqq 0$, and $T_n \leqq T$, from (1) we find

$$P_n \leqq T; \quad Q_n \leqq T. \tag{2}$$

As n increases, P_n and Q_n never decrease. By (2), each of the sequences $\{P_n\}$ and $\{Q_n\}$ is bounded. Therefore, by Theorem I on page 433, these sequences have limits P and Q, or $P_n \to P$ and $Q_n \to Q$ as $n \to \infty$.

3. Since $S_n = P_n - Q_n$, we obtain

$$\lim_{n\to\infty} S_n = \lim_{n\to\infty} P_n - \lim_{n\to\infty} Q_n = P - Q. \tag{3}$$

That is, $\sum_{n=1}^{\infty} u_n$ converges to the sum $(P-Q)$.

COROLLARY 1. *Suppose that $\sum_{n=1}^{\infty} |u_n|$ converges. Then, in $\sum_{n=1}^{\infty} u_n$, the series formed by the positive terms and the series formed by the negative terms are convergent, with sums P and $-Q$, respectively, and $\sum_{n=1}^{\infty} u_n$ converges to $(P-Q)$.*

DEFINITION III. *A series $\sum_{n=1}^{\infty} u_n$ is said to* **converge absolutely,** *or to be* **absolutely convergent,** *if and only if the series of absolute values $\sum_{n=1}^{\infty} |u_n|$ converges.*

DEFINITION IV. *If a series converges, but does not converge absolutely, the series is said to be* **conditionally convergent.**

We may restate Theorem XIV by saying that, if a series *converges absolutely*, then the series *converges in the ordinary sense.*

ILLUSTRATION 1.   The series $1 - \frac{1}{2} + \frac{1}{3} - \cdots$ is known to be convergent. The series of absolute values is $1 + \frac{1}{2} + \frac{1}{3} + \cdots$, which is divergent. Hence, the alternating harmonic series is conditionally convergent.

ILLUSTRATION 2.   The series $1 - \frac{1}{2} + \frac{1}{4} - \cdots$ is absolutely convergent, because $1 + \frac{1}{2} + \frac{1}{4} \cdots$ is a convergent geometric series.

★*Note 1.*   If $\sum_{n=1}^{\infty} u_n$ converges *conditionally*, it can be proved that, separately, the series of positive terms and the series of negative terms in $\sum_{n=1}^{\infty} u_n$ *diverge.* Also, it can be shown that, by rearrangement of the order of terms, a conditionally convergent series may be changed into a divergent series, or into a new convergent series with *any desired sum.* On the other hand, if the terms of an absolutely convergent series are rearranged, the new series also converges absolutely, to the same sum as the given series.

EXERCISE 135

State whether the series converges; diverges; converges absolutely; converges conditionally.   Give justification for your conclusions.

1. $1 - \frac{1}{3} + \frac{1}{5} - \cdots$.

2. $\frac{1}{2} - \frac{1}{4} + \frac{1}{6} - \cdots$.

3. $2 - \frac{2}{5} + \frac{2}{5^2} - \cdots$.

4. $1 - 2 + 4 - \cdots$.

5. $1 - \frac{1}{2^2} + \frac{1}{3^2} - \cdots$.

6. $3 - \frac{3}{2} + \frac{3}{2^2} - \cdots$.

7. $1 - \frac{1}{\sqrt{2}} + \frac{1}{\sqrt{3}} - \cdots$.

8. $\frac{1}{2 \cdot 3} - \frac{1}{3 \cdot 4} + \frac{1}{4 \cdot 5} - \cdots$.

★**9.** If we are given that $\sum_{n=1}^{\infty} |u_n|$ diverges, we cannot state that $\sum_{n=1}^{\infty} u_n$ diverges.   Give an example to justify this statement.   Thus, there is no utility for any concept of "*absolute divergence.*"

217. Ratio test

In a series $\sum_{n=1}^{\infty} u_n$, *form the ratio of the* $(n + 1)$th *term to the* nth *term. Suppose that, as* $n \to \infty$, *the absolute value of this ratio has a limit* R, *finite or possibly infinite* $(R = \infty)$:

$$\lim_{n \to \infty} \left| \frac{u_{n+1}}{u_n} \right| = R. \tag{1}$$

Then,   *if* $R < 1$, *the series converges absolutely;*   (A)

if $R > 1$ *or if* $R = \infty$, *the series diverges;*   (B)

if $R = 1$, *no conclusion can be drawn.*   (C)

Proof of (*A*). 1. Let $v_n = |u_n|$, and consider $\sum_{n=1}^{\infty} v_n$. If $R < 1$, we shall prove that the v-series converges.

2. Let $r_n = v_{n+1}/v_n$. Then,

$$r_n = \frac{v_{n+1}}{v_n} = \left|\frac{u_{n+1}}{u_n}\right| \quad and \quad \lim_{n\to\infty} r_n = R < 1. \tag{2}$$

3. Since $R < 1$, we may select ρ so that $R < \rho < 1$. Since $r_n \to R$ as $n \to \infty$, then, for all values of n which are sufficiently large, r_n will be so close to R, as in the diagram, that

$$r_n < \rho \quad or \quad \frac{v_{n+1}}{v_n} < \rho. \tag{3}$$

That is, there exists an integer k, sufficiently large, so that

$$v_{n+1} < \rho v_n \quad when \quad n \geqq k. \tag{4}$$

4. From (4),

when $n = k$, $\qquad\qquad v_{k+1} < \rho v_k$;

when $n = k + 1$, $\qquad\quad v_{k+2} < \rho v_{k+1} < \rho(\rho v_k), \quad or \quad v_{k+2} < \rho^2 v_k$;

when $n = k + 2$, $\qquad\quad v_{k+3} < \rho v_{k+2} < \rho(\rho^2 v_k), \quad or \quad v_{k+3} < \rho^3 v_k.$

Thus, below, each term in (5) is less than the corresponding term in (6):

$$v_{k+1} + v_{k+2} + v_{k+3} \cdots; \tag{5}$$
$$\rho v_k + \rho^2 v_k + \rho^3 v_k + \cdots. \tag{6}$$

Series (6) converges, because it is a geometric series whose ratio is $\rho < 1$. Therefore, by comparison, (5) converges. Hence, $\sum_{n=1}^{\infty} v_k$ converges, because it is obtained by adding $v_1 + \cdots + v_k$ at the beginning in (5), which does not alter its convergence. Thus, $\sum_{n=1}^{\infty} |u_n|$ converges, or $\sum_{n=1}^{\infty} u_n$ is *absolutely convergent*.

Proof of (*B*). Suppose that $r_n \to R > 1$ as $n \to \infty$. Then, if n is sufficiently large, r_n will be so close to R that $r_n > 1$, as in the diagram. If $r_n \to \infty$ as $n \to \infty$, then likewise $r_n > 1$ if n is sufficiently large. Hence, if $r_n \to R > 1$ or if $r_n \to \infty$ as $n \to \infty$, there exists an integer k, sufficiently large, so that

$$r_n = \frac{v_{n+1}}{v_n} > 1, \quad or \quad v_{n+1} > v_n \quad if \quad n \geqq k.$$

That is, if $n \geqq k$, v_n increases as n increases, and hence we do not have $v_n \to 0$ as $n \to \infty$. Since $v_n = |u_n|$, we do not have $u_n \to 0$ as $n \to \infty$. Hence, by Theorem IV on page 436, the u-series diverges.

Proof of (*C*). In the following Illustration 2, we shall exhibit a *convergent* series where $R = 1$ and also a *divergent* series where $R = 1$. Hence, knowledge that $R = 1$ for a series gives no evidence about its convergence or divergence. That is, the ratio test *fails if $R = 1$.*

ILLUSTRATION 1. In the series $\qquad \dfrac{1}{2} + \dfrac{2^2}{2^2} + \dfrac{3^2}{2^3} + \cdots,$

$$u_n = \frac{n^2}{2^n}; \quad u_{n+1} = \frac{(n+1)^2}{2^{n+1}}; \quad \frac{u_{n+1}}{u_n} = \frac{1}{2}\left(\frac{n+1}{n}\right)^2;$$

$$R = \lim_{n\to\infty} \frac{1}{2}\left(1 + \frac{1}{n}\right)^2 = \frac{1}{2}(1+0)^2 = \frac{1}{2}. \tag{7}$$

Since $\frac{1}{2} < 1$, the given series converges.

Note 1. If we apply the ratio test to a series $\sum_{n=1}^{\infty} u_n$ where all terms are of one sign, then no mention of absolute values in the test is necessary.

ILLUSTRATION 2. For the divergent series $\qquad 1 + \frac{1}{2} + \frac{1}{3} + \cdots,$

$$u_n = \frac{1}{n}; \quad u_{n+1} = \frac{1}{n+1}; \quad R = \lim_{n\to\infty} \frac{n}{n+1} = 1.$$

For the convergent series $\qquad \dfrac{1}{1^2} + \dfrac{1}{2^2} + \dfrac{1}{3^2} + \cdots,$

$$u_n = \frac{1}{n^2}; \quad u_{n+1} = \frac{1}{(n+1)^2}; \quad R = \lim_{n\to\infty} \left(\frac{n}{n+1}\right)^2 = 1.$$

These examples justify (C) in the ratio test.

ILLUSTRATION 3. In the series $\qquad \dfrac{2!}{3} - \dfrac{4!}{3^2} + \dfrac{6!}{3^3} - \cdots,$

$$|u_n| = \frac{(2n)!}{3^n}; \quad |u_{n+1}| = \frac{(2n+2)!}{3^{n+1}}; \quad \left|\frac{u_{n+1}}{u_n}\right| = \frac{(2n+1)(2n+2)}{3},$$

because $\qquad (2n+2)! = 1\cdot2\cdot3 \cdots (2n)\cdot(2n+1)(2n+2).$

$$R = \lim_{n\to\infty} \frac{1}{3}(2n+1)(2n+2) = +\infty. \tag{8}$$

Hence, the series diverges.

EXAMPLE 1. Test for convergence and absolute convergence:

$$\frac{3}{1\cdot2} - \frac{4}{2\cdot3} + \frac{5}{3\cdot4} - \cdots + \frac{(-1)^{n+1}(n+2)}{n(n+1)} + \cdots. \tag{9}$$

SOLUTION. 1. $\qquad \left|\dfrac{u_{n+1}}{u_n}\right| = \dfrac{n(n+3)}{(n+2)^2}; \qquad R = \lim_{n\to\infty} \dfrac{n^2+3n}{n^2+4n+4} = 1.$

Hence, the ratio test fails. We proceed to use other tests.

2. The series of absolute values for (9) is

$$\frac{3}{1\cdot2} + \frac{4}{2\cdot3} + \frac{5}{3\cdot4} + \cdots + \frac{n+2}{n(n+1)} + \cdots. \tag{10}$$

where $\qquad \dfrac{n+2}{n(n+1)} = \dfrac{1}{n}\dfrac{n+2}{n+1} > \dfrac{1}{n},$

because $n + 2 > n + 1$. Hence, each term in (10) is greater than the corresponding term in the divergent series $\sum_{n=1}^{\infty} 1/n$. Thus, by the comparison test, (10) diverges; therefore, (9) does *not converge absolutely*. Then, we must test (9) itself for convergence.

3. By the test applicable to alternating series, we find that (9) converges. Hence, (9) is *conditionally convergent*, because it *does not converge absolutely*.

Note 2. In (1), if desired, we may use u_{n+2}/u_{n+1}, or u_n/u_{n-1}, in place of u_{n+1}/u_n. In any case, we use a general pair of successive terms in the series.

EXERCISE 136

Test the series for convergence by the ratio test. If it fails, test otherwise. If any alternating series converges, determine whether the convergence is conditional.

1. $\dfrac{1}{3} + \dfrac{2}{3^2} + \dfrac{3}{3^3} + \cdots.$

2. $\dfrac{4}{1} + \dfrac{4^2}{2} + \dfrac{4^3}{3} + \cdots.$

3. $\dfrac{1!}{5} + \dfrac{2!}{5^2} + \dfrac{3!}{5^3} + \cdots.$

4. $\dfrac{2}{4} - \dfrac{3}{4^2} + \dfrac{4}{4^3} - \cdots.$

5. $\dfrac{1}{2!} + \dfrac{1}{3!} + \dfrac{1}{4!} + \cdots.$

6. $\dfrac{3}{1} - \dfrac{3^2}{2^2} + \dfrac{3^3}{3^2} - \cdots.$

7. $\dfrac{4}{1!} - \dfrac{4^2}{2!} + \dfrac{4^3}{3!} - \cdots.$

8. $\dfrac{3}{2!} - \dfrac{5}{4!} + \dfrac{7}{6!} - \cdots.$

9. $\dfrac{1}{3} - \dfrac{2}{4} + \dfrac{3}{5} - \cdots.$

10. $\dfrac{1}{\sqrt[3]{1}} - \dfrac{1}{\sqrt[3]{2}} + \dfrac{1}{\sqrt[3]{3}} - \cdots.$

11. $\dfrac{1 \cdot 2}{3} - \dfrac{2 \cdot 3}{3^2} + \dfrac{3 \cdot 4}{3^3} - \cdots.$

12. $\dfrac{1}{1 \cdot 2} - \dfrac{1}{2 \cdot 3} + \dfrac{1}{3 \cdot 4} - \cdots.$

13. $\dfrac{1}{1} - \dfrac{1}{4} + \dfrac{1}{7} - \cdots.$

14. $\dfrac{2!}{\sqrt{1}} + \dfrac{4!}{\sqrt{2}} + \dfrac{6!}{\sqrt{3}} + \cdots.$

15. $\dfrac{4}{1 \cdot 2 \cdot 3} - \dfrac{5}{2 \cdot 3 \cdot 4} + \dfrac{6}{3 \cdot 4 \cdot 5} - \cdots.$

16. $\dfrac{1!}{10^2} + \dfrac{3!}{10^3} + \dfrac{5!}{10^4} + \cdots.$

17. $\displaystyle\sum_{n=1}^{\infty} (-1)^{n+1} \dfrac{n^3}{2^n}.$

18. $\displaystyle\sum_{n=1}^{\infty} \dfrac{n^n}{n!}.$

19. $\displaystyle\sum_{n=1}^{\infty} \dfrac{n}{\sqrt{n^2 + 2}}.$

20. $\displaystyle\sum_{n=1}^{\infty} (-1)^{n+1} \dfrac{1 \cdot 3 \cdot 5 \cdots (2n - 1)}{4 \cdot 8 \cdot 12 \cdots (4n)}.$

21. $\displaystyle\sum_{n=1}^{\infty} \dfrac{(-1)^{n+1}}{\sqrt{n + 2} - 1}.$

22. $\displaystyle\sum_{n=1}^{\infty} (-1)^{n+1} \dfrac{n + \sqrt{n}}{n!}.$

23. $\displaystyle\sum_{n=1}^{\infty} \dfrac{3 \cdot 6 \cdot 9 \cdots (3n)}{1 \cdot 3 \cdot 5 \cdots (2n - 1)}.$

218. Power series

If the terms of a series are functions of one or more variables, it is desirable to find the values of the variables for which the series converges, or diverges. We proceed to study an important type of series of variable terms, called *power series*.

If c_0, c_1, c_2, $\cdots$ are constants and x is a variable, then

$$c_0 + c_1 x + c_2 x^2 + \cdots + c_n x^n + \cdots \tag{1}$$

is called a *power series in* x. Similarly, if a is a constant, then

$$c_0 + c_1(x - a) + c_2(x - a)^2 + \cdots + c_n(x - a)^n + \cdots \tag{2}$$

is called a power series in $(x - a)$. Any series (1) converges if $x = 0$. In any case, it can be proved * that the values of x for which (1) converges form a single interval, possibly of length 0, about $x = 0$ as a center, called the **interval of convergence** of the series. This interval may be the whole x-axis. If the interval of convergence is of finite length, the series may converge at just one of the end-points of the interval, at both end-points, or at neither end-point. Also, a series *converges absolutely at all values of x interior to the interval of convergence* of the series. Similar remarks apply to (2), with the center of the interval of convergence at $x = a$.

Suppose that the absolute value of the quotient of successive coefficients, c_{n+1}/c_n, in (1) or (2), has a limit as $n \to \infty$, and that we are able to evaluate this limit. Then, we may find the interval of convergence of the series by the ratio test. If the interval is finite, *the ratio test always fails at the end-points of the interval.* Then, the values of x at these end-points must be substituted in the series, and the resulting series of constants must be examined for convergence by some test other than the ratio test.

EXAMPLE 1. Test for convergence:

$$1 - \frac{x^2}{2 \cdot 2^2} + \frac{x^4}{3 \cdot 2^4} - \cdots + \frac{(-1)^n x^{2n}}{(n+1)2^{2n}} + \cdots . \tag{3}$$

SOLUTION. 1. *Application of the ratio test.* In (3), let the terms be labeled $u_0 + u_1 + u_2 + \cdots + u_n + \cdots$, where u_n is the term involving x^{2n}. Then,

$$|u_n| = \frac{x^{2n}}{(n+1)2^{2n}}; \quad |u_{n+1}| = \frac{x^{2n+2}}{(n+2)2^{2n+2}};$$

$$R = \lim_{n \to \infty} \left| \frac{u_{n+1}}{u_n} \right| = \frac{x^2}{4} \left(\lim_{n \to \infty} \frac{n+1}{n+2} \right) = \frac{x^2}{4} \cdot 1 = \frac{x^2}{4}. \tag{4}$$

Hence, by the ratio test, (3) *converges absolutely* if

$$\frac{x^2}{4} < 1 \quad or \quad x^2 < 4, \quad or \quad |x| < 2;$$

also, (3) diverges if $\dfrac{x^2}{4} > 1, \quad or \quad |x| > 2.$

The ratio test fails if $x^2 = 4, \quad or \quad |x| = 2, \quad or \quad x = \pm 2.$

2. *Test of the end-points.* When $x = \pm 2$ in (3), we obtain the series $1 - \frac{1}{2} + \frac{1}{3} - \cdots$, which we know is conditionally convergent.

* See texts on the theory of functions of real and complex variables.

3. *Summary.* The series converges absolutely interior to the interval of convergence from $x = -2$ to $x = 2$, converges conditionally at $x = \pm 2$, and diverges if $x < -2$ and if $x > 2$, as illustrated in Figure 286.

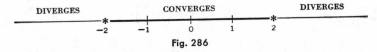

Fig. 286

ILLUSTRATION 1. On investigating $1 - \dfrac{x}{1!} + \dfrac{x^2}{2!} - \cdots$ by the ratio test, we find that, if x has any assigned value,

$$R = \lim_{n \to \infty} \left| \frac{x^{n+1}}{(n+1)!} \div \frac{x^n}{n!} \right| = \lim_{n \to \infty} \left| \frac{x}{n+1} \right| = 0.$$

Hence, the series converges absolutely for all values of x.

EXERCISE 137

Find the interval of convergence of the series. Give a summary specifying convergence or divergence for all values of x, with absolute convergence mentioned.

1. $1 + \dfrac{x}{2} + \dfrac{x^2}{3} + \cdots$,

2. $1 + \dfrac{x}{1!} + \dfrac{x^2}{2!} + \cdots$.

3. $x + 2x^2 + 3x^3 + \cdots$,

4. $1 + 2x + 2^2 x^2 + \cdots$,

5. $1 - \dfrac{x}{2 \cdot 4} + \dfrac{x^2}{3 \cdot 4^2} - \cdots$.

6. $1 - \dfrac{3x}{\sqrt{2}} + \dfrac{3^2 x^2}{\sqrt{3}} - \cdots$.

7. $\dfrac{x}{2^2 \cdot 3} + \dfrac{x^2}{3^2 \cdot 3^2} + \dfrac{x^3}{4^2 \cdot 3^3} + \cdots$.

8. $1 - \dfrac{x^2}{2!} + \dfrac{x^4}{4!} - \cdots$,

9. $\dfrac{x}{1!} - \dfrac{x^3}{3!} + \dfrac{x^5}{5!} - \cdots$.

10. $\dfrac{x(1!)}{2} + \dfrac{x^2(2!)}{3} + \dfrac{x^3(3!)}{4} + \cdots$.

11. $\dfrac{1}{\sqrt{1}} - \dfrac{x^2}{\sqrt{2}} + \dfrac{x^4}{\sqrt{3}} - \cdots$

12. $\dfrac{1}{1^3} - \dfrac{2^2 x^2}{3^3} + \dfrac{2^4 x^4}{5^3} - \cdots$.

13. $1 - 3^2 x^2 + 3^4 x^4 - \cdots$.

14. $1 + x\sqrt{2} + x^2\sqrt{3} + \cdots$,

15. $1 - \dfrac{x-4}{3\sqrt{2}} + \dfrac{(x-4)^2}{3^2\sqrt{3}} - \dfrac{(x-4)^3}{3^3\sqrt{4}} + \cdots$,

16. $\dfrac{1}{1 \cdot 2} - \dfrac{x+2}{2 \cdot 3} + \dfrac{(x+2)^2}{3 \cdot 4} - \dfrac{(x+2)^3}{4 \cdot 5} + \cdots$.

17. $\dfrac{2}{1} + \dfrac{3}{2} \cdot \dfrac{x+1}{3} + \dfrac{4}{3} \cdot \dfrac{(x+1)^2}{3^2} + \dfrac{5}{4} \cdot \dfrac{(x+1)^3}{3^3} + \cdots$.

18. $\dfrac{2}{1} \cdot \dfrac{(x-1)^2}{3} + \dfrac{2 \cdot 4}{1 \cdot 3} \cdot \dfrac{(x-1)^4}{5} + \dfrac{2 \cdot 4 \cdot 6}{1 \cdot 3 \cdot 5} \cdot \dfrac{(x-1)^6}{7} + \cdots$.

19. $1 - \dfrac{1}{2} \cdot \dfrac{2}{x} + \dfrac{1}{3} \cdot \dfrac{2^2}{x^2} - \cdots$.

20. $-\dfrac{2}{1} + \dfrac{3}{2} \cdot \dfrac{1}{3x} - \dfrac{4}{3} \cdot \dfrac{1}{3^2 x^2} + \cdots$.

21. $\dfrac{3}{1 \cdot 2} - \dfrac{4}{2 \cdot 3} \cdot \dfrac{x}{2} + \dfrac{5}{3 \cdot 4} \cdot \dfrac{x^2}{2^2} - \dfrac{6}{4 \cdot 5} \cdot \dfrac{x^3}{2^3} + \cdots$.

MISCELLANEOUS EXERCISE 138

Investigate for convergence and divergence. For each power series, specify convergence or divergence for all values of x.

1. $\displaystyle\sum_{n=1}^{\infty} \frac{n+2}{2n+3}.$

2. $\displaystyle\sum_{n=1}^{\infty} \cos\left(n\cdot\frac{\pi}{4}\right).$

3. $\displaystyle\sum_{n=1}^{\infty} \frac{(-1)^n n}{n+2}.$

4. $\dfrac{1}{1\cdot 4}+\dfrac{1}{2\cdot 5}+\dfrac{1}{3\cdot 6}+\cdots.$

5. $\dfrac{2}{1\cdot 2}+\dfrac{2^2}{2\cdot 3}+\dfrac{2^3}{3\cdot 4}+\cdots.$

6. $\dfrac{1}{1\cdot 2\cdot 3}-\dfrac{1}{2\cdot 3\cdot 4}+\dfrac{1}{3\cdot 4\cdot 5}-\cdots.$

7. $\dfrac{3}{1\cdot 4}+\dfrac{4}{2\cdot 5}+\dfrac{5}{3\cdot 6}+\cdots.$

8. $\dfrac{1!}{2}+\dfrac{2!}{3}+\dfrac{3!}{4}+\cdots.$

9. $\dfrac{1}{1}-\dfrac{1}{5}+\dfrac{1}{9}-\cdots.$

10. $\ln\dfrac{1}{2}+\ln\dfrac{2}{3}+\ln\dfrac{3}{4}+\cdots.$

11. $\dfrac{2}{1!}-\dfrac{3}{2!}+\dfrac{4}{3!}-\cdots.$

12. $\dfrac{2}{4}-\dfrac{3}{4^2}+\dfrac{4}{4^3}-\cdots.$

13. $\dfrac{3}{\sqrt{2}}+\dfrac{3^2}{\sqrt{3}}+\dfrac{3^3}{\sqrt{4}}+\cdots.$

14. $\displaystyle\sum_{n=1}^{\infty} \frac{n+1}{\sqrt{n^2+1}}.$

15. $\displaystyle\sum_{n=1}^{\infty} \frac{1\cdot 3\cdot 5\,\cdots\,(2n-1)}{3\cdot 6\cdot 9\,\cdots\,(3n)}.$

16. $1+\dfrac{x}{3}+\dfrac{x^2}{5}+\cdots.$

17. $\dfrac{1}{2!}+\dfrac{x}{4!}+\dfrac{x^2}{6!}+\cdots.$

18. $1+\dfrac{1}{2^2}\cdot\dfrac{x}{4}+\dfrac{1}{3^2}\cdot\dfrac{x^2}{4^2}+\cdots.$

19. $\dfrac{1}{1\cdot 2}+\dfrac{2x}{2\cdot 3}+\dfrac{2^2 x^2}{3\cdot 4}+\cdots.$

20. $\dfrac{1}{2}+\dfrac{2}{3}\cdot 3(x-2)+\dfrac{3}{4}\cdot 3^2(x-2)^2+\dfrac{4}{5}\cdot 3^3(x-2)^3+\cdots.$

21. $1+\dfrac{2(x+1)}{2!}+\dfrac{2^2(x+1)^2}{3!}+\dfrac{2^3(x+1)^3}{4!}+\cdots.$

22. $\displaystyle\sum_{n=1}^{\infty} \frac{\sqrt{n}}{\sqrt{n+1}-1}.$

23. $\displaystyle\sum_{n=1}^{\infty} \frac{(n+1)^2}{n^n}.$

24. $\dfrac{1}{\ln 2}+\dfrac{3}{\ln 3}+\dfrac{5}{\ln 4}+\cdots.$

25. $\dfrac{e}{1^3}+\dfrac{e^2}{2^3}+\dfrac{e^3}{3^3}+\cdots.$

★26. $\dfrac{1\cdot 3}{2\cdot 4}\cdot\dfrac{x^2}{1}+\dfrac{3\cdot 5}{4\cdot 6}\cdot\dfrac{x^4}{2}+\dfrac{5\cdot 7}{6\cdot 8}\cdot\dfrac{x^6}{3}+\cdots.$

★27. $\dfrac{1}{4}\cdot\dfrac{x^2}{3}+\dfrac{1\cdot 3}{4\cdot 6}\cdot\dfrac{x^4}{5}+\dfrac{1\cdot 3\cdot 5}{4\cdot 6\cdot 8}\cdot\dfrac{x^6}{7}+\cdots.$

★28. Prove that $\displaystyle\sum_{n=1}^{\infty} \frac{(\cos nx)}{n^2}$ converges absolutely for all values of x.

★29. If m has any value, prove that the following series converges if $|x|<1$ and diverges if $|x|>1$. Consideration of $x=\pm 1$ is not possible at the level of this course. The series is called the **binomial series,** and its relation to $(1+x)^m$ is discussed later.

$$1+mx+\frac{m(m-1)x^2}{2!}+\cdots+\frac{m(m-1)(m-2)\,\cdots\,(m-n+1)}{n!}x^n+\cdots$$

219. Integral test for convergence or divergence

The following result sometimes enables us to prove the convergence or divergence of a series of positive terms by establishing the convergence or divergence of a corresponding improper integral.

THEOREM XV.   *Let* $\sum_{k=1}^{\infty} u_k$ *be a series of positive terms where* $u_k \geqq u_{k+1}$ *for all values of* k. *Suppose that there exists a function* $f(x)$, *which is defined, continuous, and decreasing* * *when* $x \geqq 1$, *and such that* $f(k) = u_k$. *Then, the u-series converges or diverges according as* $\int_1^{\infty} f(x)dx$ *converges or diverges.*

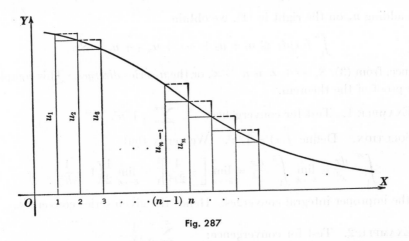

Fig. 287

Proof.   1. A graph of $f(x)$ is shown in Figure 287.   With the interval $1 \leqq x \leqq 2$ as a base, the rectangle with a broken line at the top has the altitude u_1 and area $(u_1) \cdot (1)$ or u_1; the smaller rectangle has the altitude u_2 and area u_2.   The area of the region bounded by the lines $x = 1$ and $x = 2$, the x-axis, and the curve $y = f(x)$, lies between the values u_1 and u_2.   Similar remarks apply over each unit interval, with the larger and smaller rectangles over the interval from $x = n - 1$ to $x = n$ having the areas u_{n-1} and u_n, respectively.   The area of the whole region bounded by the x-axis, the curve $y = f(x)$, and the lines $x = 1$ and $x = n$ is the integral below.   Hence,

$$u_2 + u_3 + \cdots + u_n \leqq \int_1^n f(x)dx \leqq u_1 + u_2 + \cdots + u_{n-1}, \qquad (1)$$

where the expressions at the left and the right are the sums of the areas of the rectangles *under* the curve $y = f(x)$, and *above* the curve, respectively.

2. Now, assume that $\int_1^{\infty} f(x)dx$ converges, to a value V.   That is,

$$\lim_{n \to \infty} \int_1^n f(x)dx = V: \quad also, \quad \int_1^n f(x)dx \leqq V, \qquad (2)$$

* Theorem XV remains true if "*decreasing*" is changed to "*nonincreasing*," and "$x \geqq 1$" is changed to "$x \geqq c$," where c is sufficiently large.

because $f(x) \geqq 0$ and thus $\int_1^n f(x)dx$ increases as n increases. From (1),

$$u_1 + u_2 + \cdots + u_n \leqq \int_1^n f(x)dx + u_1, \quad or \quad S_n \leqq V + u_1,$$

where S_n is the nth partial sum of the u-series. Thus, S_n is *bounded*, and then Theorem X of page 440 shows that the u-series *converges*.

3. Assume, next, that $\int_1^\infty f(x)dx$ diverges. Then,

$$\int_1^n f(x)dx \to +\infty \quad as \quad n \to \infty. \tag{3}$$

On adding u_n on the right in (1), we obtain

$$\int_1^n f(x)dx \leqq u_1 + u_2 + \cdots + u_{n-1} + u_n = S_n. \tag{4}$$

Hence, from (3), $S_n \to +\infty$ as $n \to \infty$, or the u-series *diverges*. This completes the proof of the theorem.

EXAMPLE 1.   Test for convergence: $\sum_{n=1}^\infty 1/n^3$.

SOLUTION.   Define $f(x) = 1/x^3$.   We verify that

$$\int_1^\infty \frac{dx}{x^3} = \lim_{h \to \infty} \int_1^h \frac{dx}{x^3} = \lim_{h \to \infty} \left[-\frac{1}{2x^2} \right]_1^h = \lim_{h \to \infty} \frac{1}{2}\left(1 - \frac{1}{h^2}\right) = \frac{1}{2},$$

or the improper integral converges. Hence the given series converges.

EXAMPLE 2.   Test for convergence: $\displaystyle\sum_{n=2}^\infty \frac{1}{2n \ln n}$.

SOLUTION.   Let $f(x) = 1/(x \ln x)$.   Then, $f(x)$ decreases as x increases.

$$\int_2^\infty \frac{1}{x} \cdot \frac{1}{\ln x}\, dx = \lim_{h \to \infty} \int_2^h \frac{d(\ln x)}{\ln x} = \lim_{h \to \infty} \Big[\ln\,(\ln x) \Big]_{x=2}^{x=h} = +\infty,$$

because $\ln\,(\ln h) \to \infty$ as $h \to \infty$. Hence, $\int_2^\infty f(x)dx$ diverges, and therefore the given series diverges.

EXERCISE 139

Apply an integral test to prove convergence, or divergence.

1. $\displaystyle\sum_{n=1}^\infty \frac{1}{n^4}$.

2. $\displaystyle\sum_{n=1}^\infty \frac{1}{n}$.

3. $\displaystyle\sum_{n=1}^\infty \frac{1}{\sqrt[3]{n}}$.

4. $\displaystyle\sum_{n=2}^\infty \frac{1}{n(\ln n)^3}$.

5. $\displaystyle\sum_{n=1}^\infty \frac{1}{n^p}$, $p < 1$; $p > 1$.

6. $\displaystyle\sum_{n=1}^\infty \frac{n}{n^2 + 1}$.

7. $\displaystyle\sum_{n=1}^\infty \frac{1}{3n + 2}$.

8. $\displaystyle\sum_{n=1}^\infty \frac{1}{n^2 + 4}$.

9. $\displaystyle\sum_{n=1}^\infty \frac{1}{\sqrt{n^2 + 9}}$.

10. $\displaystyle\sum_{n=1}^\infty \frac{1}{n(n + 1)}$.

11. $\displaystyle\sum_{n=4}^\infty \frac{1}{n(\ln n)[\ln\,(\ln n)]^p}$, $p = 2$; $p > 1$; $p \leqq 1$.

CHAPTER

23

EXPANSION OF FUNCTIONS

220. Taylor series

Suppose that a series $\sum_{n=0}^{\infty} b_n(x - a)^n$ has the interval of convergence $|x - a| < R$, and let $f(x)$ represent the sum of the series. Then, by advanced methods, it can be proved that (1) $f(x)$ possesses continuous derivatives of all orders if $|x - a| < R$; (2) for every positive integer k, the series obtained by differentiating the given series term by term, k times in succession, also has the interval of convergence $|x - a| < R$; (3) the sum of the series in (2) is equal to $f^{(k)}(x)$ when $|x - a| < R$. We shall use these facts in discussing the expansion of functions into power series.

EXAMPLE 1. IF the series on the right below converges and has $\sin x$ as its sum at all values of x on some interval $|x| < R$, find the coefficients:

$$\sin x = b_0 + b_1 x + b_2 x^2 + \cdots + b_n x^n + \cdots. \tag{1}$$

SOLUTION. 1. From (1), on differentiating both sides, we obtain

$$\frac{d \sin x}{dx} = \cos x = b_1 + 2b_2 x + 3b_3 x^2 + \cdots + n b_n x^{n-1} + \cdots; \tag{2}$$

$$\frac{d^2 \sin x}{dx^2} = -\sin x = (2!)b_2 + 3 \cdot 2b_3 x + \cdots + n(n-1)b_n x^{n-2} + \cdots; \tag{3}$$

$$\frac{d^3 \sin x}{dx^3} = -\cos x = (3!)b_3 + \cdots + n(n-1)(n-2)b_n x^{n-3} + \cdots. \tag{4}$$

2. On placing $x = 0$ in (1)–(4), we obtain $b_0 = 0$ and

$$\cos 0 = 1 = b_1; \quad 0 = b_2; \quad -1 = (3!)b_3 \quad or \quad b_3 = -\frac{1}{3!}. \tag{5}$$

Since $D_x^4 \sin x = \sin x$, the successive derivatives of $\sin x$ *repeat in groups of four.* Hence, as in (5), we find that $b_n = 0$ if n is *even.* Since $D_x^n x^n = n!$, we find $\pm 1 = (n!)b_n$ when n is *odd*, or $b_n = \pm 1/n!$. Thus, we obtain

$$\sin x = x - \frac{x^3}{3!} + \frac{x^5}{5!} - \cdots + (-1)^{k+1} \frac{x^{2k-1}}{(2k-1)!} + \cdots. \tag{6}$$

457

THEOREM I. *Let $f(x)$ be a function which possesses derivatives of all orders at all values of x on some interval with $x = a$ as an interior point. Suppose that there exists an infinite series in powers of $(x - a)$ which converges, and has $f(x)$ as the sum, at all values of x on some interval $|x - a| < R$. Then, when $|x - a| < R$,*

$$\left.\begin{aligned} f(x) = f(a) + f'(a)(x - a) + \frac{f''(a)}{2!}(x - a)^2 + \cdots \\ + \frac{f^{(n)}(a)}{n!}(x - a)^n + \cdots. \end{aligned}\right\} \qquad (7)$$

Proof. 1. Suppose that coefficients $\{b_n\}$ exist such that the series on the right below converges to the sum $f(x)$ when $|x - a| < R$:

$$f(x) = b_0 + b_1(x - a) + b_2(x - a)^2 + \cdots + b_n(x - a)^n + \cdots. \qquad (8)$$

Then, on recalling that $d^n(x - a)^n/dx^n = n!$, we obtain

$$f'(x) = b_1 + 2b_2(x - a) + 3b_3(x - a)^2 + \cdots + nb_n(x - a)^{n-1} + \cdots;$$

$$f''(x) = (2!)b_2 + 3 \cdot 2b_3(x - a) + \cdots + n(n - 1)b_n(x - a)^{n-2} + \cdots;$$

$$\vdots$$

$$f^{(n)}(x) = (n!)b_n + (n + 1)(n)(n - 1) \cdots 2b_{n+1}(x - a) + \cdots.$$

2. On placing $x = a$ above, we find

$$b_0 = f(a); \quad b_1 = f'(a); \quad b_2 = f''(a)/2!; \quad \cdots; \quad b_n = f^{(n)}(a)/n!.$$

Hence, the series in (8) is identical with (7), which proves Theorem I.

The right-hand side of (7) is called the **Taylor series** for $f(x)$ in powers of $(x - a)$, or *Taylor's expansion* of $f(x)$ about the point $x = a$. Before (7) is of any use, we must ask, first, "*does the Taylor series in* (7) *converge on some interval* $|x - a| < R$?" If the answer to this question is "*yes,*" then we shall ask, "*is $f(x)$ the sum of the series?*" Such questions will be considered later. At present, we shall assume that, *if we obtain a Taylor series for a function $f(x)$, then the sum of the series is $f(x)$ wherever the series converges.*

If $a = 0$ in (7), the resulting Taylor series sometimes is called the **Maclaurin series** for $f(x)$, and has the form

$$f(x) = f(0) + f'(0)x + \frac{f''(0)}{2!}x^2 + \cdots + \frac{f^{(n)}(0)}{n!}x^n + \cdots. \qquad (9)$$

Note 1. Taylor series are named in honor of the English mathematician BROOK TAYLOR (1685–1731). Maclaurin series are named after the Scottish mathematician COLIN MACLAURIN (1698–1746).

EXAMPLE 2. Expand $\cos x$ in powers of $(x - \frac{1}{4}\pi)$.

SOLUTION. We calculate the derivatives of $\cos x$, and then substitute $x = \frac{1}{4}\pi$, to use (7) with $f(x) = \cos x$ and $a = \frac{1}{4}\pi$:

$f(x) = \cos x;$ $\qquad f(\tfrac{1}{4}\pi) = \tfrac{1}{2}\sqrt{2}.$ $\qquad\qquad f'(x) = -\sin x;$ $\quad f'(\tfrac{1}{4}\pi) = -\tfrac{1}{2}\sqrt{2}.$

$f''(x) = -\cos x;$ $\quad f''(\tfrac{1}{4}\pi) = -\tfrac{1}{2}\sqrt{2}.$ $\quad f'''(x) = \sin x;$ $\qquad f'''(\tfrac{1}{4}\pi) = \tfrac{1}{2}\sqrt{2}.$

$$f^{(\mathrm{IV})}(x) = \cos x; \qquad f^{(\mathrm{IV})}(\tfrac{1}{4}\pi) = \tfrac{1}{2}\sqrt{2}. \quad Etc.$$

Since $f^{(\mathrm{IV})}(x) = \cos x = f(x)$, the successive derivatives at $x = \tfrac{1}{4}\pi$ repeat in groups of four each. Each coefficient in the expansion will have $\tfrac{1}{2}\sqrt{2}$ as a factor. Thus, from (7), with signs of terms alternating in pairs,

$$\cos x = \frac{\sqrt{2}}{2}\left[1 - \left(x - \frac{\pi}{4}\right) - \frac{1}{2!}\left(x - \frac{\pi}{4}\right)^2 + \frac{1}{3!}\left(x - \frac{\pi}{4}\right)^3 + \cdots\right].$$

On substituting $x = a + h$ in (7), we obtain the following form for the Taylor expansion about $x = a$:

$$f(a + h) = f(a) + hf'(a) + \frac{1}{2!}h^2 f''(a) + \cdots + \frac{1}{n!}h^n f^{(n)}(a) + \cdots. \quad (10)$$

That is, by (10), the value of $f(x)$ at $x = a + h$ is expressed in terms of $f(a)$, the derivatives of $f(x)$ at $x = a$, and the increment h by which the value $x = a + h$ differs from $x = a$.

EXAMPLE 3. Obtain the Maclaurin expansion of $(1 - x)^{-\frac{1}{3}}$.

SOLUTION. We use (9) with $f(x) = (1 - x)^{-\frac{1}{3}}$, or (7) with $a = 0$.

$f'(x) \quad = +\dfrac{1}{3}(1 - x)^{-\frac{4}{3}}$ $\qquad\qquad$ and $\quad f'(0) \quad = \dfrac{1}{3};$

$f''(x) \quad = \dfrac{1 \cdot 4}{3^2}(1 - x)^{-\frac{7}{3}}$ $\qquad$ and $\quad f''(0) \quad = \dfrac{1 \cdot 4}{3^2},$

$f'''(x) \quad = \dfrac{1 \cdot 4 \cdot 7}{3^3}(1 - x)^{-\frac{10}{3}}$ $\qquad$ and $\quad f'''(0) \quad = \dfrac{1 \cdot 4 \cdot 7}{3^3};$

$$f^{(n)}(x) \quad = \frac{1 \cdot 4 \cdot 7 \cdots (3n - 2)}{3^n}(1 - x)^{-\frac{1+3n}{3}} \quad and \quad f^{(n)}(0) \quad = \frac{1 \cdot 4 \cdot 7 \cdots (3n - 2)}{3^n}.$$

$$(1 - x)^{-\frac{1}{3}} = 1 + \frac{1}{3}x + \frac{1 \cdot 4}{2 \cdot 3^2}x^2 + \frac{1 \cdot 4 \cdot 7}{3^3(3!)}x^3 + \cdots + \frac{1 \cdot 4 \cdots (3n - 2)}{3^n(n!)}x^n + \cdots.$$

EXAMPLE 4. How many terms in the Maclaurin series for $\sin x$ would be sufficient to obtain $\sin x$ with accuracy to six decimal places, if $|x| < .5$?

SOLUTION. 1. By Corollary 2 on page 446, if $S_k(x)$ in (6) is used as an approximation to $\sin x$ when $|x| < .5$,

$$|error| = |\sin x - S_k(x)| < \frac{|x^{2k+1}|}{(2k + 1)!} < \frac{.5^{2k+1}}{(2k + 1)!}. \quad (11)$$

2. On the right in (11), we obtain .000002 when $k = 3$, and $5.4(10^{-9})$ when $k = 4$. Since $5.4(10^{-9}) < 5(10^{-8})$, then $S_4(x)$ gives $\sin x$ with accuracy to seven decimal places, or 4 terms are sufficient for the desired accuracy.

EXERCISE 140

Obtain the Taylor expansion of $f(x)$ about the given point as specified. In the following problems, obtain the general term of the series.

1. $f(x) = \cos x$; about $x = 0$.   **2.** $f(x) = \sin x$; about $x = \frac{1}{4}\pi$.

3. $f(x) = e^x$; the Maclaurin series.   **4.** $f(x) = e^x$; about $x = 2$.

5. $f(x) = e^{-2x}$; about $x = 0$.   **6.** $f(x) = \sin 2x$; about $x = 0$.

7. $f(x) = e^x$; about $x = a$.   **8.** $f(x) = (1 - x)^{-1}$; about $x = 0$.

9. $f(x) = 3x^4 + 2x^2 - x + 5$; (a) about $x = 0$; (b) about $x = -2$.

10. $f(x) = (2x - 1)^5$; (a) about $x = 1$; (b) about $x = 2$.

11. $f(x) = (1 - x)^{-2}$; about $x = 0$.   **12.** $f(x) = a^x$; about $x = 0$.

13. $f(x) = \ln x$; (a) about $x = 2$; (b) about $x = a$, where $a > 0$.

14. $f(x) = \ln (1 + x)$; about $x = 0$.   **15.** $f(x) = \ln (1 - x)$, about $x = 0$.

Obtain the first three nonzero terms of the Taylor series for the function.

16. $\tan x$; about $x = \frac{3}{4}\pi$.   **17.** $\tan x$; about $x = 0$.

18. $\ln \sin x$; about $x = \frac{1}{2}\pi$.   **19.** $\ln \cos x$; about $x = 0$.

20. $\ln (2 - e^x)$; about $x = 0$.   **21.** $e^{\sin x}$; about $x = \frac{1}{2}\pi$.

22. $(1 + x)^{\frac{3}{2}}$; about $x = 0$.   **23.** $(1 - x)^{-\frac{5}{3}}$; about $x = 0$.

24. Arctan x; about $x = 0$. Make an inference as to the general term.

25. Arcsin x; about $x = 0$.   **26.** $\sec x$; about $x = 0$.

27. $e^x \sin x$; about $x = \frac{1}{2}\pi$.   **28.** $xe^{\sin x}$; about $x = 0$.

29. $\sin (\frac{1}{6}\pi + x)$; about $x = 0$.   **30.** $\cos (\frac{1}{3}\pi + x)$; about $x = 0$.

Obtain the Maclaurin series for the function by substituting some expression for x in a Maclaurin series previously obtained.

31. $\cos 2x$.   **32.** $\cos (-\frac{1}{2}x)$.   **33.** e^{5x}.   **34.** $\ln (1 + 2x)$.

35. $\ln (1 - 3x)$.   **36.** $\tan 3x$.   **37.** $\sin 4x$.   **38.** $(1 - x^2)^{-1}$.

39. Obtain the Maclaurin expansion of $(1 + x)^m$, where m may be any real number, and include the general term. Prove that the series converges if $|x| < 1$, and diverges if $|x| > 1$.

Note 1. The series in Problem 39 is called the **binomial series**. It can be proved to converge to $(1 + x)^m$ if $|x| < 1$, for all values of m, and at $x = +1$ and $x = -1$ for certain corresponding ranges of values of m.

Obtain the first four nonzero terms in the Maclaurin series for each function by substituting in the binomial series.

40. $(1 - x)^{\frac{1}{3}}$.   **41.** $(1 + x^2)^{-\frac{1}{2}}$.   **42.** $(1 + x)^{-3}$.   **43.** $(4 + x^3)^{\frac{1}{2}}$.

Compute with accuracy to four decimal places by use of a Maclaurin series, and check the degree of accuracy by use of Corollary 2 on page 446, if possible.

44. $\cos .2$.   **45.** $\sin .3$.   **46.** $e^{-.4}$.   **47.** $e^{.5}$.   **48.** $\sin 4°$.

49. $.98^{-1}$, from $(1 + x)^{-1}$.   **50.** $\sin 32°$, from $\sin (\frac{1}{6}\pi + x)$.   **51.** $\cos 63°$.

52. $\ln 1.1$.   **53.** Arctan $.2$.   **54.** $1.03^{\frac{1}{2}}$.   **55.** $130^{\frac{1}{3}}$.

56. If $0 \leq x \leq .3$, how many terms in the Maclaurin expansion of $\ln (1 + x)$ would be sufficient to give $\ln (1 + x)$ accurate to 5 decimal places?

57. Obtain the Taylor series about $x = a$ for (1) $\sin x$; (2) $\cos x$.

221. Taylor's formula

THEOREM II. *Let n represent a positive integer, and assume that a function $f(x)$ is differentiable n times, with $f^{(n)}(x)$ continuous, at all values of x on some interval T including $x = a$. Then, for each point x on T, there exists a point ξ_n between* * *a and x such that*

$$\left. \begin{aligned} f(x) = f(a) + f'(a)(x - a) + \frac{f''(a)}{2!} (x - a)^2 + \cdots \\ + \frac{f^{(n-1)}(a)}{(n-1)!} (x - a)^{n-1} + R_n(x), \end{aligned} \right\} \tag{1}$$

where $$R_n(x) = \frac{f^{(n)}(\xi_n)}{n!} (x - a)^n. \tag{2}$$

Note 1. In (1), the first n terms on the right are the first n terms in the Taylor series for $f(x)$ in powers of $(x - a)$. Hence, in (1), even if the corresponding Taylor series should not converge, we call $R_n(x)$ *the remainder after n terms* in the Taylor series. We refer to (1) as **Taylor's formula with a remainder,** for $f(x)$ in powers of $(x - a)$, and Theorem II is called **Taylor's theorem.** Also, we call $R_n(x)$ the *error term,* when we consider the sum of the other terms on the right in (1) as an approximation to $f(x)$. The expression for $R_n(x)$ in (2) is known as *Lagrange's form* for the remainder term, in honor of the French mathematician COUNT JOSEPH LOUIS LAGRANGE (1736–1813). Other forms for $R_n(x)$ are available. We observe that the mean value theorem of page 176 is the special case of Taylor's theorem when $n = 1$, because then (1) becomes $f(x) = f(a) + f'(\xi_1)(x - a)$.

When $a = 0$ in (1), we obtain the Maclaurin form of Taylor's formula, and the result sometimes is referred to as **Maclaurin's formula:**

$$f(x) = f(0) + f'(0)x + \frac{f''(0)}{2!} x^2 + \cdots + \frac{f^{(n-1)}(0)}{(n-1)!} x^n + R_n(x), \tag{3}$$

where $$R_n(x) = \frac{f^{(n)}(\xi_n)}{n!} x^n. \tag{4}$$

and ξ_n is some number between 0 and x.

EXAMPLE 1. Find an approximating polynomial for e^x by taking the sum of the first four terms in the Maclaurin series for e^x. Then, if $|x| < .3$, by use of Taylor's formula obtain an upper bound for the error made if the value of this polynomial is taken as an approximation to e^x.

---

* For a proof not involving integration, and assuming only that $f^{(n)}(x)$ *exists,* see page 568. The possibilities $\xi = a$ and $\xi = x$ in (2) are excluded by the proof on page 568.

SOLUTION. 1. Since $d^n e^x/dx^n = e^x$, Maclaurin's series and Taylor's formula with a remainder after four terms, in powers of x, are as follows:

$$\left\{ \begin{array}{c} Taylor's \\ series \end{array} \right\} \qquad e^x = 1 + x + \frac{x^2}{2} + \frac{x^3}{6} + \cdots ; \qquad (5)$$

$$\left\{ \begin{array}{c} Taylor's \\ formula \end{array} \right\} \qquad e^x = S_4(x) + R_4(x), \quad with \quad R_4(x) = \frac{e^\xi x^4}{4!}, \qquad (6)$$

where $S_4(x)$ is the sum of the four terms explicitly written in (5), and ξ is between 0 and x. The desired approximating polynomial is $S_4(x)$.

2. Since $e^x - S_4(x) = R_4(x)$, then $|R_4(x)|$ is the error made if $S_4(x)$ is taken as an approximate value for e^x. From (6), if $|x| < .3$,

$$|R_4(x)| < \frac{e^\xi (.3)^4}{24}, \quad where \quad |\xi| < .3.$$

Hence, $-.3 < \xi < .3$. Then $e^\xi < e^{.3}$, and thus

$$error = |R_4(x)| < \frac{e^{.3}(.3^4)}{24} = .0005 \quad (by\ logarithms).$$

To prove Theorem II, we shall need the following result.

LEMMA I. *(First Mean Value Theorem for an Integral). Assume that $g(t)$ and $h(t)$ are continuous, with $h(t)$ of one sign or zero on the interval $W:(a \leq t \leq x)$. Then, there exists a point ξ on W such that*

$$\int_a^x g(t)h(t)dt = g(\xi)\int_a^x h(t)dt. \qquad (7)$$

Proof [when $h(t) \geq 0$]. Let m and M, respectively, be the absolute minimum and absolute maximum of $g(t)$ on W. Then, $m \leq g(t) \leq M$ and (since $h(t) \geq 0$)

$$mh(t) \leq g(t)h(t) \leq Mh(t). \qquad (8)$$

Hence, $\qquad m\int_a^x h(t)dt \leq \int_a^x g(t)h(t)dt \leq M\int_a^x h(t)dt. \qquad (9)$

Therefore, there exists a number μ, where $m \leq \mu \leq M$, such that

$$\int_a^x g(t)h(t)dt = \mu\int_a^x h(t)dt. \qquad (10)$$

Since $g(t)$ is continuous, there exists a point ξ on W such that $\mu = g(\xi)$. With this expression for μ, then (10) gives (7).

Comment. To prove (7) with $h(t) \leq 0$, on the basis of the preceding proof, we first write (7) with $h(t)$ replaced by $-h(t)$, and then multiply both sides of the resulting equation by -1 to obtain (7) for $h(t) \leq 0$. If $a > x$, we prove (7) by first writing it with x and a interchanged in the limits, and then multiply both sides by -1 to obtain (7) in the desired form. Hence, (7) remains true if the lower limit of integration is greater than the upper limit.

Proof of Theorem II. 1. Since $f^{(n)}(x)$ exists, all derivatives of lower order, as well as $f^{(n)}(x)$, are continuous. Hence, all of the following manipulations of integrals are justified. Let x have a fixed value. Then, by the fundamental theorem of integral calculus,

$$f(x) - f(a) = \int_a^x f'(t)dt. \tag{11}$$

2. In (11), integrate by parts, in the form $\int u\, dv$ with $u = f'(t)$, $dv = dt$, and $v = t - x$; then again with $dv = (x - t)dt$ and $v = -\tfrac{1}{2}(x - t)^2$; etc., to obtain

$$f(x) - f(a) = \left\{ (t - x)f'(t) \Big]_{t=a}^{t=x} \right\} - \int_a^x (t - x)f''(t)dt$$

$$= 0 + (x - a)f'(a) + \int_a^x (x - t)f''(t)dt \tag{12}$$

$$= (x - a)f'(a) + \frac{1}{2!}(x - a)^2 f''(a) + \frac{1}{2!}\int_a^x (x - t)^2 f'''(t)dt; \ etc. \tag{13}$$

After $(n - 1)$ successive integrations, we obtain (1) with

$$R_n(x) = \frac{1}{(n - 1)!} \int_a^x (x - t)^{n-1} f^{(n)}(t)dt. \tag{14}$$

3. In (14), apply (7) with $g(t)$ as $f^{(n)}(t)$, $h(t)$ as $(x - t)^{n-1}$, and

$$\int_a^x (x - t)^{n-1}\, dt = -\frac{1}{n}(x - t)^n \Big]_{t=a}^{t=x} = \frac{(x - a)^n}{n}.$$

From (7), a point ξ_n exists on the interval from a to x, inclusive, such that

$$R_n = \frac{1}{(n - 1)!} \cdot \frac{1}{n}(x - a)^n f^{(n)}(\xi_n) = \frac{f^{(n)}(\xi_n)}{n!}(x - a)^n, \tag{15}$$

which proves Theorem II. Attention is called also to (14), which gives a useful integral formula for the remainder.

222. Applications of Taylor's formula

We now have available two distinct but related expressions:

$$\left\{ \begin{array}{c} Taylor's \\ series \end{array} \right\} f(x) = f(a) + f'(a)(x - a) + \cdots + \frac{f^{n-1}(a)}{(n - 1)!}(x - a)^{n-1} + \cdots. \tag{1}$$

$$\left\{ \begin{array}{c} Taylor's \\ formula \end{array} \right\} f(x) = S_n(x) + R_n(x), \quad where \quad R_n(x) = \frac{f^{(n)}(\xi_n)}{n!}(x - a)^n, \tag{2}$$

in which $S_n(x)$ is the sum of the first n terms in (1), and ξ_n is somewhere between a and x. Without questioning the equality in (1), by use of $R_n(x)$ in (2) we frequently can solve the following problem:

For any particular values of n and x, what upper bound can we specify for the error if we use $S_n(x)$ as an approximation to $f(x)$?

EXAMPLE 1. Compute ln .9 with accuracy to 5 decimal places.

SOLUTION. 1. Let $f(x) = \ln(1 - x)$; we wish $f(.1)$.

$\left\{ \begin{array}{c} Maclaurin's \\ series \end{array} \right\}$ $\qquad \ln(1-x) = 0 - x - \dfrac{x^2}{2} - \dfrac{x^3}{3} - \cdots - \dfrac{x^n}{n} - \cdots.$ $\qquad$ (3)

In (3), $\qquad S_5(.1) = 0 - .1 - .005 - .000333 - .000025 = -.105358.$ $\qquad$ (4)

2. To prove that $S_5(.1)$ is sufficiently close to $\ln .9$, write Maclaurin's formula with a remainder after five terms. From (2),

$$\ln(1-x) = 0 - x - \frac{x^2}{2} - \frac{x^3}{3} - \frac{x^4}{4} + R_5(x) = S_5(x) + R_5(x), \qquad (5)$$

where $\qquad \dfrac{d^5 \ln(1-x)}{dx^5} = -\dfrac{4!}{(1-x)^5}$ $\quad and \quad$ $R_5(x) = -\dfrac{x^5}{5(1-\xi)^5}.$ $\qquad$ (6)

With $x = .1$ in (6), we know that ξ is between 0 and .1. Hence,

$$1 - \xi > 1 - .1 = .9, \quad and \quad |R_5(.1)| < \frac{.1^5}{5(.9)^5} = .000003. \qquad (7)$$

Thus, by (5), the value $\ln .9 = S_5(.1) = -.10536$ is correct to five decimal places, because the error, in (7), is less than .000003.

Comment. We kept the term 0 explicitly in (3), (4), and (5) in order to maintain the notation of (1) and (2).

EXAMPLE 2. Obtain a polynomial of degree 2 in $(x - \frac{1}{4}\pi)$ as an approximation to $\tan x$. Then, find an upper bound for the error made if this polynomial is used to compute $\tan 48°$.

SOLUTION. 1. Let $f(x) = \tan x$. We expand $f(x)$ about $x = \frac{1}{4}\pi$.

$$f'(x) = \sec^2 x; \quad f''(x) = 2 \sec^2 x \tan x; \quad f'''(x) = 2 \sec^2 x(\sec^2 x + 2 \tan^2 x);$$

$$f(\tfrac{1}{4}\pi) = 1; \quad f'(\tfrac{1}{4}\pi) = 2; \quad f''(\tfrac{1}{4}\pi) = 4.$$

Taylor's series: $\qquad \tan x = 1 + 2(x - \tfrac{1}{4}\pi) + 2(x - \tfrac{1}{4}\pi)^2 + \cdots.$ $\qquad$ (8)

Taylor's formula: $\qquad \tan x = 1 + 2(x - \tfrac{1}{4}\pi) + 2(x - \tfrac{1}{4}\pi)^2 + R_3(x),$

where $\qquad R_3(x) = \dfrac{2(1 + \tan^2 \xi)(3 \tan^2 \xi + 1)}{3!}(x - \tfrac{1}{4}\pi)^3.$ $\qquad$ (9)

2. The desired polynomial is the sum, $S_3(x)$, of the terms given explicitly in (8). With x as the radian measure of 48°,

$$x - \tfrac{1}{4}\pi = (48 - 45)\frac{\pi}{180} = \frac{\pi}{60},$$

and ξ in (9) is the radian measure of an angle between 45° and 48°. Since $\tan \theta$ increases as θ increases from 45° to 48°, $\tan \xi < \tan 48°$ and

$$R_3(x) < \frac{2(1 + \tan^2 48°)(3 \tan^2 48° + 1)\pi^3}{6(60^3)} = .00050, \qquad (10)$$

where logarithms were used to compute the fraction. That is, $\tan 48°$ is given by $S_3(x)$ with an error less than .00051.

EXERCISE 141

Solve by use of Taylor's formula.

Find an approximating polynomial for the given function by taking the sum of the indicated nonzero terms of the Taylor series in the specified powers. Then, for the given range of values of x, obtain an upper bound for the error (to just one significant digit) if the value of this polynomial is taken as an approximation to the value of the function. Use logarithms where convenient.

1. $(1 - x)^{-1}$; in powers of x; three terms; when $| x | < .4$.

2. e^x; in powers of x; four terms; when $| x | < .2$.

3. $\ln (1 + x)$; in powers of x; four terms; when $| x | < .2$.

4. $\sin x$; the Maclaurin series; two terms; when $| x | < .1$.

5. $\cos x$; the Maclaurin series; two terms; when $| x | < .2$.

6. e^x; in powers of $(x - 3)$; three terms; when $| x - 3 | < .4$.

7. $\ln x$; in powers of $(x - 2)$; three terms; when $| x - 2 | < .5$.

8. $\sin x$; in powers of $(x - \frac{1}{2}\pi)$; two terms; if $| x - \frac{1}{2}\pi | < .2$.

9. $\cos x$; in powers of $(x - \frac{1}{4}\pi)$; two terms; if $| x - \frac{1}{4}\pi | < .1$.

10. $(1 + x)^{\frac{1}{2}}$; Maclaurin series; three terms; when $| x | < .5$.

11. Prove that the sum of the first ten terms in the Maclaurin series for e^x gives e^x correct to six decimal places if $| x | < .9$. Assume that $e < 3$.

12. Find a value for h so that, if $| x | < h$, the sum of the first two nonzero terms in the Maclaurin series for $\sin x$ will give the value of $\sin x$ with accuracy to four decimal places.

13. In (1) and (2) on page 463, let $x = a + h$, with ξ_n written $(a + \theta_n h)$, where $0 < \theta_n < 1$. Rewrite (1) and (2) in this notation.

★14. Apply (7) of page 462 to $R_n(x)$ in (14) on page 463, with $h(t) = 1$ and $g(t) = (x - t)^{n-1}f^{(n)}(t)$; then let $\xi = a + \theta(x - a)$, with $0 \leqq \theta \leqq 1$. The result, below, is called *Cauchy's form* for the remainder, in honor of the French mathematician Augustin Louis Cauchy (1789–1857):

$$R_n = (1 - \theta)^{n-1}(x - a)^n f^{(n)}[a + \theta(x - a)]/(n - 1)!.$$

223. Equality of a function and the sum of its Taylor series

Theorem III. *At any value of x, a necessary and sufficient condition for the Taylor series for $f(x)$ in powers of $(x - a)$ to converge to $f(x)$ is that, in Taylor's formula for $f(x)$ in powers of $(x - a)$, $R_n(x) \to 0$ as $n \to \infty$.*

Proof. 1. With $0!$ defined as 1 and $f^{(0)}(a)$ defined as $f(a)$, we have

(*Taylor's series*)
$$\sum_{n=0}^{\infty} \frac{f^{(n)}(a)}{n!} (x - a)^n ;$$
(1)

(*Taylor's formula*)
$$f(x) = S_n(x) + R_n(x),$$
(2)

where $S_n(x)$ is the sum of the first n terms in (1).

2. Proof of the necessity. At some value of x, assume that the series in (1) converges, with $f(x)$ as the sum. Then $S_n(x) \to f(x)$ as $n \to \infty$. Hence, from (2), since $f(x)$ is a constant as n varies,

$$\lim_{n \to \infty} f(x) = f(x) = \lim_{n \to \infty} S_n(x) + \lim_{n \to \infty} R_n(x), \ or$$

$$f(x) = f(x) + \lim_{n \to \infty} R_n(x), \quad or \quad 0 = \lim_{n \to \infty} R_n(x).$$

Thus, if (1) converges to $f(x)$, it is necessary that $R_n(x) \to 0$ as $n \to \infty$.

3. Proof of sufficiency. Assume that $R_n(x) \to 0$ as $n \to \infty$. Then, from (2),

$$S_n(x) = f(x) - R_n(x); \quad \lim_{n \to \infty} S_n(x) = f(x) - 0,$$

which shows that (1) converges to $f(x)$ if "$R_n(x) \to 0$ *as* $n \to \infty$."

EXAMPLE 1. Prove that e^x is the sum of its Maclaurin series, for all x.

SOLUTION. 1. Let $f(x) = e^x$. Then, $f^{(n)}(x) = e^x$. We have

$$\left\{ \begin{matrix} Maclaurin's \\ series\ for\ e^x \end{matrix} \right\} \qquad 1 + x + \frac{x^2}{2!} + \cdots + \frac{x^{n-1}}{(n-1)!} + \frac{x^n}{n!} + \cdots; \qquad (3)$$

$$\left\{ \begin{matrix} Taylor's \\ formula \end{matrix} \right\} \qquad e^x = S_n(x) + R_n(x), \quad with \quad R_n(x) = \frac{e^{\xi_n}}{n!} x^n, \qquad (4)$$

where $S_n(x)$ is the sum of the first n-terms in (3), and ξ_n is between 0 and x.

2. Discussion of convergence for (3). We apply the ratio test:

$$\lim_{n \to \infty} \left| \frac{x^n}{n!} \div \frac{x^{n-1}}{(n-1)!} \right| = \lim_{n \to \infty} \left| \frac{x}{n} \right| = 0, \ at\ all\ values\ of\ x.$$

Hence, (3) converges absolutely; thus, there exists a sum $S(x)$ such that $\lim_{n \to \infty} S_n(x) = S(x)$, *at all values of* x.

3. Let x have any fixed value. Then, in (4),

$$|\xi_n| < |x|, \quad or \quad -|x| < \xi_n < |x|.$$

Hence, $\qquad e^{\xi_n} < e^{|x|} \quad and \quad |R_n(x)| < e^{|x|} \left(\left| \frac{x^n}{n!} \right| \right). \qquad (5)$

From Step 1 of the solution, $x^n/n!$ is the general term of a convergent series, and thus approaches zero as $n \to \infty$. Since $|x|$ is fixed,

$$\lim_{n \to \infty} e^{|x|} \cdot \left| \frac{x^n}{n!} \right| = e^{|x|} \lim_{n \to \infty} \left| \frac{x^n}{n!} \right| = e^{|x|} \cdot 0 = 0,$$

and thus, also, $R_n(x) \to 0$ as $n \to \infty$. Hence, by Theorem III, $e^x = S(x)$, which justifies writing

$$e^x = 1 + x + \frac{x^2}{2!} + \frac{x^3}{3!} + \cdots + \frac{x^n}{n!} + \cdots. \qquad (6)$$

EXAMPLE 2. Prove that $\sin x$ is the sum of its Maclaurin series.

SOLUTION. 1. Let $f(x) = \sin x$. Then, $f^{(n)}(x) = \sin(x + n\pi/2)$. We have

(*Maclaurin's series*) $\qquad a_0 + a_1 x + \cdots + a_{n-1} x^{n-1} + \cdots;$ $\qquad$ (7)

$\left\{\begin{array}{l}\textit{Taylor's} \\ \textit{formula}\end{array}\right\}$ $\quad \sin x = S_n(x) + R_n(x), \quad \text{with} \quad R_n(x) = \dfrac{\sin\,(\xi_n + n\pi/2)}{n!}\, x^n,$

where ξ_n is between 0 and x. Let x have any fixed value. Then,

$$\left| \sin\left(\xi_n + n\,\frac{\pi}{2}\right) \right| \le 1 \quad and \quad |R_n(x)| \le \left|\frac{x^n}{n!}\right|. \qquad (8)$$

2. Since $x^n/n!$ is the general term of a convergent series (the Maclaurin

series for e^x), we have $\qquad \lim\limits_{n\to\infty} \dfrac{x^n}{n!} = 0 \quad and\ hence \quad \lim\limits_{n\to\infty} R_n(x) = 0.$

Therefore, (7) converges and has $\sin x$ as its sum at all values of x, or

$$\sin x = x - \frac{x^3}{3!} + \frac{x^5}{5!} - \cdots + \frac{(-1)^{k+1}}{(2k-1)!}\, x^{2k-1} + \cdots.$$

Note 1. The method of Examples 1 and 2 applies only to a very restricted set of functions, but is of fundamental importance. At advanced levels, it is proved that any one of the elementary functions of a real variable x is represented by the Taylor series for the function in powers of $(x - a)$, on some interval $|x - a| < R$, if the function and its derivatives of all orders exist at $x = a$. Hereafter in this text, except as specified otherwise, we assume the preceding fact, with x on the interval of convergence of the Taylor series.

★*Note 2.* It is possible that a function $f(x)$, even of simple form, may not be represented by its Taylor series about $x = a$ even though all derivatives $f^{(n)}(x)$ are continuous at $x = a$. Thus, let

$$f(x) = e^{-1/x^2} \text{ if } x \ne 0 \quad and \quad f(0) = \lim_{x\to 0} f(x) = 0.$$

Then, $f^{(n)}(x)$ is continuous at $x = 0$. However, all terms in the Maclaurin series for $f(x)$ are 0, and $f(x)$ is not represented by the series if $x \ne 0$.

EXERCISE 142

Prove the specified result.

1. Taylor's series for e^x in powers of $(x - a)$ converges to e^x at all values of x.
2. $\cos x$ is represented by its Maclaurin series at all values of x.
3. Taylor's series for e^{2x} in powers of $(x - 1)$ represents e^{2x} at all values of x.
4. At all values of x, $\sin x$ is represented by its Taylor series in powers of $(x - \frac{1}{4}\pi)$.
★5. $\ln(1 + x)$ is represented by its Maclaurin series if $-1 < x \le 1$.

   HINT. Consider separately (a) $0 < x \le 1$ and (b) $-1 < x < 0$. For Case (b), use the Cauchy form for $R_n(x)$ from Problem 14 on page 465, and show that $|R_n(x)| < |x|^n/(1 + x)$. A similar method applies to the function $(1 + x)^m$, with $|x| < 1$.

6. Suppose that $f(x)$ possesses derivatives $f'(x)$ and $f''(x)$, and $f''(x) \geq 0$ when x is on the interval $V:(c \leq x \leq d)$. Let L be the tangent to the curve $y = f(x)$ at any point $x = a$ on V. Prove that the curve does not fall below L if x is on V. Use Taylor's formula as proved on page 568.

224. Applications of Taylor's series

To obtain the Taylor expansion of a function $f(x)$ in powers of $(x - a)$, we are not limited to computation of the coefficients by the usual formula. We may employ any available method for representing $f(x)$ as a power series in $(x - a)$, because Theorem I of page 458 states that *any* series which we obtain *must be the Taylor series.*

Note 1. We shall use the following properties of power series without proof. Demonstrations of the facts are met in more advanced texts.

I. A power series may be differentiated term by term (as described in remarks on page 457), and similarly may be integrated term by term.

II. Suppose that $\sum_{n=0}^{\infty} a_n x^n$ and $\sum_{n=0}^{\infty} b_n x^n$ converge when $|x| < R$. Then, if $|x| < R$, the series may be multiplied term by term, with like powers of x combined, to yield a convergent power series in x whose sum is the product of the sums of the given series.

III. *Suppose that* $f(z) = \sum_{n=0}^{\infty} a_n z^n$, *which converges if* $|z| < R_1$, *and that* $z = \sum_{k=0}^{\infty} b_k x^k$, *which converges and yields* $|z| < R_1$ *when* $|x| < R$. *Then, we may substitute for z in terms of x in* $f(z)$, *and rearrange into a power series in x converging to* $f(z)$ *when* $|x| < R$.

ILLUSTRATION 1. We may obtain the Maclaurin series through the term of degree 3 for $e^x \sin x$ by termwise multiplication of the Maclaurin series for e^x and $\sin x$. Thus, we use (1) below to prove (2):

$$\sin x = x - \frac{x^3}{6} + \cdots; \quad e^x = 1 + x + \frac{x^2}{2} + \cdots; \tag{1}$$

$$e^x \sin x = x - \frac{x^3}{6} + x^2 + \frac{x^3}{2} + \cdots = x + x^2 + \frac{x^3}{3} + \cdots. \tag{2}$$

ILLUSTRATION 2. To obtain the Maclaurin series for $\cos x$, we may write

$$\int_0^x \sin x \, dx = -\cos x \Big]_0^x = 1 - \cos x.$$

Hence,

$$1 - \cos x = \int_0^x \left[x - \frac{x^3}{3!} + \cdots + \frac{(-1)^{k-1} x^{2k-1}}{(2k-1)!} + \cdots \right] dx$$

$$= \left[\frac{x^2}{2!} - \frac{x^4}{4!} + \cdots + \frac{(-1)^{k-1} x^{2k}}{(2k-1)!(2k)} + \cdots \right] \Big]_{x=0}^{x=x}, \text{ or} \tag{3}$$

$$\cos x = 1 - \frac{x^2}{2!} + \frac{x^4}{4!} - \cdots + \frac{(-1)^k x^{2k}}{(2k)!} + \cdots. \tag{4}$$

ILLUSTRATION 3.   From $\qquad$ $\dfrac{1}{1+z} = 1 - z + z^2 + \cdots,$ $\qquad$ (5)

with $z = x^2$, we obtain the Maclaurin series for Arctan x as follows:

$$\int_0^x \frac{dx}{1+x^2} = \text{Arctan } x = \int_0^x [1 - x^2 + x^4 - \cdots + (-1)^{n+1}x^{2n} + \cdots]dx$$

$$= x - \frac{x^3}{3} + \frac{x^5}{5} - \cdots + \frac{(-1)^{n+1}x^{2n+1}}{2n+1} + \cdots,$$

which converges when $-1 < x < 1$, because (5) converges if $-1 < z < 1$.

EXAMPLE 1.   Obtain the Maclaurin series for sec x.

SOLUTION.   1. We shall calculate sec $x = 1/\cos x$, by use of (III):

$$\sec x = \frac{1}{\cos x} = \frac{1}{1 - \dfrac{x^2}{2!} + \dfrac{x^4}{4!} - \dfrac{x^6}{6!} + \cdots} \qquad (6)$$

2. Let $z = \left(\dfrac{x^2}{2!} - \dfrac{x^4}{4!} + \dfrac{x^6}{6!} - \cdots\right)$.   Then,

$$\sec x = \frac{1}{1 - z} = 1 + z + z^2 + z^3 + \cdots. \qquad (7)$$

To obtain powers of z, multiply the series for z by itself repeatedly:

$$z^2 = \frac{x^4}{4} - 2\frac{x^2}{2!}\cdot\frac{x^4}{4!} + \cdots; \quad z^3 = \frac{x^6}{8} + \cdots.$$

Hence, from (7), $\qquad$ $\sec x = 1 + \dfrac{x^2}{2!} - \dfrac{x^4}{4!} + \dfrac{x^6}{6!} + \dfrac{x^4}{4} - \dfrac{x^6}{4!} + \dfrac{x^6}{8} + \cdots.$

Thus, $\qquad$ $\sec x = 1 + \dfrac{x^2}{2} + \dfrac{5x^4}{24} + \dfrac{61x^6}{720} + \cdots. \qquad (8)$

In (7), the series converges if $|z| < 1$. Since $\cos x = 1 - z$, then $|z| < 1$ if $|x| < \frac{1}{2}\pi$. Hence, by (III), series (8) converges to sec x if $|x| < \frac{1}{2}\pi$.

ILLUSTRATION 4.   The following integral cannot be expressed in terms of elementary functions. We expand by use of the binomial series, and then integrate term by term. The series involved converges if $|x| < 1$.

$$\int_0^{\frac{1}{2}} \frac{dx}{\sqrt{1+x^3}} = \int_0^{\frac{1}{2}} (1+x^3)^{-\frac{1}{2}}\, dx = \int_0^{\frac{1}{2}} \left(1 - \frac{x^3}{2} + \frac{1\cdot3}{2\cdot4}x^6 - \frac{1\cdot3\cdot5}{2\cdot4\cdot6}x^9 + \cdots\right)dx$$

$$= \left(x - \frac{x^4}{8} + \frac{1\cdot3x^7}{2\cdot4\cdot7} - \frac{1\cdot3\cdot5x^{10}}{2\cdot4\cdot6\cdot10} + \cdots\right)\Big]_0^{\frac{1}{2}}. \qquad (9)$$

With $x = \frac{1}{2}$, in (9) we have a convergent alternating series with terms decreasing in absolute value, and the 4th term is approximately .00003. Hence, with an error less than .00005, from (9) we obtain .4926.

Note 2. Let $g(x) = \sum_{n=0}^{\infty} b_n x^n$, where the series converges if $|x| < R$. Then, since $g(x)$ possesses derivatives of all orders, $g(x)$ is continuous when $|x| < R$, and thus is continuous at $x = 0$. Hence, $\lim_{x \to 0} g(x) = g(0) = b_0$.

ILLUSTRATION 5. We evaluate the following limit by use of Maclaurin series:

$$\lim_{x \to 0} \frac{e^x - e^{-x}}{\sin x} = \lim_{x \to 0} \frac{\left(1 + x + \frac{x^2}{2!} + \cdots\right) - \left(1 - x + \frac{x^2}{2!} - \cdots\right)}{x - \frac{x^3}{3!} + \frac{x^5}{5!} - \cdots}$$

$$= \lim_{x \to 0} 2 \frac{x + \frac{x^3}{3!} + \frac{x^5}{5!} + \cdots}{x - \frac{x^3}{3!} + \frac{x^5}{5!} + \cdots} = \lim_{x \to 0} 2 \frac{1 + \frac{x^2}{3!} + \frac{x^4}{5!} + \cdots}{1 - \frac{x^2}{3!} + \frac{x^4}{5!} + \cdots} = 2. \quad \text{[By Note 2.]}$$

EXERCISE 143

Solve by use of Maclaurin or Taylor series by the methods of Section 224.
Find the first three nonzero terms in the Maclaurin series for the function. In simple cases, obtain the general term of the expansion.

1. The **hyperbolic sine** of x, or $\sinh x = \dfrac{e^x - e^{-x}}{2}$.

2. The **hyperbolic cosine** of x, or $\cosh x = \dfrac{e^x + e^{-x}}{2}$.

3. $\sin^2 x$, by use of the series (a) for $\cos 2x$; (b) for $\sin x$.

4. $\sec^2 x$, by differentiation in Problem 17 on page 460.

5. $\ln \cos x$, from $\int_0^x \tan x \, dx$.   6. $\ln (1 + x)$, from $\int_0^x (1 + x)^{-1} \, dx$.

7. Arcsin x, by integration.

8. $e^x \sec x$.   9. $(1 + x^2) \sin x$.   10. $\tan x \cosh x$.

11. $\sqrt{1 - \sin x}$, first using the binomial series.

12. $\dfrac{e^{-x}}{1 + x}$.   13. $\dfrac{\sin x}{1 + \cos x}$.   14. $\dfrac{\sin x}{e^x}$.

Evaluate the limit by use of Maclaurin series appearing earlier.

15. $\lim\limits_{x \to 0} \dfrac{\sin x}{x}$.   16. $\lim\limits_{x \to 0} \dfrac{\ln (1 + x)}{x}$.   17. $\lim\limits_{x \to 0} \dfrac{\tan x - x}{x^3}$.

18. $\lim\limits_{x \to 0} \dfrac{\sin x - x}{\tan x - x}$.   19. $\lim\limits_{x \to 0} \dfrac{\text{Arctan } x - x}{e^x - e^{-x} - 2x}$.

Compute the integral to three decimal places by use of a series in x, with the accuracy estimated on the basis of the sizes of the terms involved.

20. $\int_0^{.5} \sqrt[3]{1 + x^2} \, dx$.   21. $\int_0^{.4} e^{-x^2} \, dx$.   22. $\int_0^1 \sqrt{4 - x^3} \, dx$.

23. $\int_0^{.2} \dfrac{e^x \, dx}{2 - x}$.   24. $\int_0^{.4} \dfrac{dx}{\sqrt{1 - \sin x}}$.   25. $\int_0^{.3} \dfrac{\cos x \, dx}{1 + x}$.

26. $\int_0^{.2} \ln (1 - x) \, dx$.

★225. Calculus for complex-valued functions of a real variable

Let $u(x)$ and $v(x)$ be real-valued functions of x when $a \leq x \leq b$, let i represent the imaginary unit,* $\sqrt{-1}$, and let $f(x) = u(x) + iv(x)$. We may define the notions of a *limit*, a *derivative*, and an *integral* for $f(x)$.

ILLUSTRATION 1. To say that $f(x) \to L$ *as* $x \to c$ means that, when $x \neq c$, $|f(x) - L|$ will be as small as we please if $|x - c|$ is sufficiently small. The theorems on limits on page 19 can be proved to apply to the preceding type of limit. In particular, $f(x)$ has a limit as $x \to c$ if and only if $u(x)$ and $v(x)$ have limits as $x \to c$, and then

$$\lim_{x \to c} f(x) = \lim_{x \to c} u(x) + i \lim_{x \to c} v(x). \tag{1}$$

Continuity is defined as in (1) on page 21. Then, by use of (1), $f(x)$ is continuous at $x = c$ if and only if $u(x)$ and $v(x)$ are continuous at $x = c$.

ILLUSTRATION 2. Let $S_n = \alpha_n + i\beta_n$, where α_n and β_n are real, and n is a positive integer. To say that $S_n \to L$ means that $|S_n - L| \to 0$ as $n \to \infty$. We find, as in (1), that $\lim_{n \to \infty} S_n$ exists if and only if the real sequences $\{\alpha_n\}$ and $\{\beta_n\}$ converge; then

$$\lim_{n \to \infty} S_n = \lim_{n \to \infty} \alpha_n + i\left(\lim_{n \to \infty} \beta_n\right). \tag{2}$$

Now, suppose that $w_n = u_n + iv_n$ where u_n and v_n are real, and consider $\sum_{n=1}^{\infty} w_n$. By use of (2), applied to partial sums of $\sum u_n$, $\sum v_n$, and $\sum w_n$, the w-series converges if and only if the u-series and v-series converge; then

$$\sum_{n=1}^{\infty} w_n = \sum_{n=1}^{\infty} u_n + i \sum_{n=1}^{\infty} v_n. \tag{3}$$

We define *absolute convergence* and *conditional convergence* for the w-series in the same words as on page 447, and then arrive at Theorem XIV of page 447 for the w-series. Also, the ratio test for convergence of the w-series applies with no change in wording as compared with the discussion in Chapter 22.

ILLUSTRATION 3. Let $z = x + yi$, and plot values of z in the complex plane, as in Figure 288 on page 472. Consider $\sum_{n=0}^{\infty} a_n z^n$ where a_n is a complex number. Suppose that

$$\lim_{n \to \infty} \left| \frac{a_{n+1}}{a_n} \right| = \eta; \quad then \quad \lim_{n \to \infty} \left| \frac{a_{n+1} z^{n+1}}{a_n z^n} \right| = \eta |z|.$$

By the ratio test, the z-series converges absolutely if

$$\eta |z| < 1, \quad or \quad |z| < \frac{1}{\eta} \ when \ \eta \neq 0.$$

---

* Recall that, if a and b are real numbers, the absolute value of $(a + bi)$ is defined by $|a + bi| = \sqrt{a^2 + b^2}$.

Thus, if we let $r = 1/\eta$, the z-series converges if $|z| < r$, that is, if z is any point interior to the *circle of convergence* $|z| = r$ in the complex plane, as in Figure 288, and diverges if z is outside this circle. For points z_0 on the circle, the ratio test fails; then, advanced theory must be employed in any discussion of convergence for the z-series at $z = z_0$.

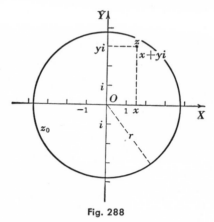

Fig. 288

ILLUSTRATION 4. Let $f(x) = u(x) + iv(x)$. At any value of x, define

$$f'(x) = \lim_{\Delta x \to 0} \frac{f(x + \Delta x) - f(x)}{\Delta x}$$

$$= \lim_{\Delta x \to 0} \left(\frac{\Delta u}{\Delta x} + i\,\frac{\Delta v}{\Delta x} \right).$$

From (1), $f(x)$ has a derivative $f'(x)$ if and only if the real-valued functions $u(x)$ and $v(x)$ have derivatives, and then $f'(x) = u'(x) + iv'(x)$. We define $\int_a^b f(x)dx$ by the same symbolism as on page 190; $\int_a^b f(x)dx$ exists if and only if $\int_a^b u(x)dx$ and $\int_a^b v(x)dx$ exist, and then

$$\int_a^b f(x)dx = \int_a^b u(x)dx + i\int_a^b v(x)dx. \tag{4}$$

In particular, $\int_a^b f(x)dx$ exists if $f(x)$ is continuous. Similarly, we introduce the concept of an antiderivative, or an indefinite integral for $f(x)$, and obtain

$$\int f(x)dx = \int u(x)dx + i\int v(x)dx.$$

In (4), if $F(x)$ is such that $F'(x) = f(x)$, then $\int_a^b f(x)dx = F(b) - F(a)$.

★226. The exponential function with an imaginary exponent

The function e^u has been considered only where u is real; then

$$e^u = 1 + u + \frac{u^2}{2!} + \cdots + \frac{u^n}{n!} + \cdots. \tag{1}$$

By the ratio test, we showed that (1) converges absolutely for all real values of u. We accept the fact that the preceding application of the ratio test could be repeated to show that the series on the right in (1) converges absolutely for *all complex numbers u*. Then, for every complex number u, *we define e^u as the sum of the series at the right in* (1). By multiplication of infinite series, it can be verified that, for any complex numbers u_1 and u_2,

$$e^{u_1} \cdot e^{u_2} = \left(\sum_{n=0}^{\infty} \frac{u_1^n}{n!} \right)\left(\sum_{m=0}^{\infty} \frac{u_2^m}{m!} \right) = \sum_{k=0}^{\infty} \frac{(u_1 + u_2)^k}{k!}, \text{ or}$$

$$e^{u_1}e^{u_2} = e^{u_1+u_2}. \tag{2}$$

As a special case of (2), if a and b are real, $e^{a+bi} = e^a e^{bi}$.

THEOREM IV. *If x is any real number, then*

$$e^{ix} = \cos x + i \sin x. \tag{3}$$

Proof. Substitute $u = ix$ in (1), to obtain

$$e^{ix} = 1 + ix + \frac{i^2 x^2}{2!} + \cdots + \frac{i^n x^n}{n!} + \cdots. \tag{4}$$

The series of the terms in even powers of x in (4) is

$$\left(1 - \frac{x^2}{2!} + \frac{x^4}{4!} - \cdots\right), \quad \text{or} \quad \cos x. \tag{5}$$

The series of the terms in odd powers of x in (4) is

$$i\left(x - \frac{x^3}{3!} + \frac{x^3}{5!} - \cdots\right), \quad \text{or} \quad i \sin x. \tag{6}$$

Let E_k, C_k, and S_k represent the sums of the first k terms in (4), (5), and (6), respectively. Then, for each value of n, there are corresponding values of h and k so that $E_n = C_h + S_k$. Since (4), (5), and (6) converge for all values of x, we have

$$e^{ix} = \lim_{n \to \infty} E_n = \lim_{h \to \infty} C_h + \lim_{k \to \infty} S_k = \cos x + i \sin x.$$

ILLUSTRATION 1. From (3),

$$e^{\pi i} = \cos \pi + i \sin \pi = -1; \quad e^{\frac{1}{2}\pi i} = \cos \tfrac{1}{2}\pi + i \sin \tfrac{1}{2}\pi = i.$$

ILLUSTRATION 2. If a and b are real numbers,

$$e^{a+bi} = e^a e^{bi} = e^a(\cos b + i \sin b).$$

THEOREM V. *If a and b are real, and $k = a + bi$, then*

$$\frac{de^{kx}}{dx} = ke^{kx}. \tag{7}$$

Proof. $e^{kx} = e^{ax+ibx} = e^{ax}(\cos bx + i \sin bx);$

$$\frac{de^{kx}}{dx} = ae^{ax}(\cos bx + i \sin bx) + e^{ax}(-b \sin bx + bi \cos bx)$$

$$= e^{ax}(a + bi)(\cos bx + i \sin bx)$$

$$= (a + bi)e^{ax}e^{ibx} = (a + bi)e^{ax+ibx} = ke^{kx}.$$

Note 1. The preceding results concerning the exponential function are very useful in connection with differential equations. Sometimes (3) is referred to as *Euler's formula* for e^{ix}.

24

ADVANCED TOPICS IN PARTIAL DIFFERENTIATION

227. A fundamental increment formula

The following result deals with a function $u = f(x, y)$, a given point (x_1, y_1), and increments Δx and Δy. We let

$$\Delta u = f(x_1 + \Delta x, y_1 + \Delta y) - f(x_1, y_1). \tag{1}$$

THEOREM I. *Suppose that the function $u = f(x, y)$ has continuous partial derivatives $f_x(x, y)$ and $f_y(x, y)$, and let (x_1, y_1) be any given point. Then, there exist quantities ϵ_1 and ϵ_2, which are functions of Δx and Δy, such that*

$$\Delta u = \frac{\partial u}{\partial x} \Delta x + \frac{\partial u}{\partial y} \Delta y + \epsilon_1 \Delta x + \epsilon_2 \Delta y, \tag{2}$$

where the derivatives are evaluated at (x_1, y_1), and

$$\epsilon_1 \to 0 \quad and \quad \epsilon_2 \to 0 \quad when \quad \Delta x \to 0 \quad and \quad \Delta y \to 0.$$

Proof. 1. In (1), subtract and then add $f(x_1, y_1 + \Delta y)$:

$$\left.\begin{aligned} \Delta u = &[f(x_1 + \Delta x, y_1 + \Delta y) - f(x_1, y_1 + \Delta y)] \\ &+ [f(x_1, y_1 + \Delta y) - f(x_1, y_1)]. \end{aligned}\right\} \tag{3}$$

2. The first difference in (3) is the increment of $f(x, y_1 + \Delta y)$ as x changes from x_1 to $(x_1 + \Delta x)$. Then, by the mean-value theorem of page 176, as applied to $f(x, y_1 + \Delta y)$, which is a function of x alone,

$$f(x_1 + \Delta x, y_1 + \Delta y) - f(x_1, y_1 + \Delta y) = f_x(\xi, y_1 + \Delta y)\Delta x, \tag{4}$$

where ξ is between x_1 and $(x_1 + \Delta x)$. We observe the location of $Q:(\xi, y_1 + \Delta y)$ in Figure 289. Similarly, the second difference in (3) is the increment of $f(x_1, y)$ as y changes from y_1 to $(y_1 + \Delta y)$. Hence,

$$f(x_1, y_1 + \Delta y) - f(x_1, y_1) = f_y(x_1, \eta)\Delta y, \tag{5}$$

where η is between y_1 and $(y_1 + \Delta y)$. We observe $R:(x_1, \eta)$ in Figure 289.

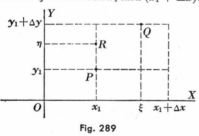

Fig. 289

474

3. If $\Delta x \to 0$ and $\Delta y \to 0$, then $Q \to P$ and $R \to P$ in Figure 289. Thus, since $f_x(x, y)$ and $f_y(x, y)$ are continuous at (x_1, y_1),

$$[f_x(\xi, y_1 + \Delta y) - f_x(x_1, y_1)] \to 0; \quad [f_y(x_1, \eta) - f_y(x_1, y_1)] \to 0. \tag{6}$$

Or, if we let ϵ_1 and ϵ_2 represent the differences in (6), then

$$f_x(\xi, y_1 + \Delta y) = f_x(x_1, y_1) + \epsilon_1 \quad and \quad f_y(x_1, \eta) = f_y(x_1, y_1) + \epsilon_2, \tag{7}$$

where $\epsilon_1 \to 0$ and $\epsilon_2 \to 0$ when $\Delta x \to 0$ and $\Delta y \to 0$. After using (7) in (4) and (5), and then placing the results in (3), we obtain (2).

There is a formula similar to (2) for a function of any number of variables. Thus, if $u = f(x, y, z)$, we obtain

$$\Delta u = \frac{\partial u}{\partial x} \Delta x + \frac{\partial u}{\partial y} \Delta y + \frac{\partial u}{\partial z} \Delta z + \epsilon_1 \Delta x + \epsilon_2 \Delta y + \epsilon_3 \Delta z. \tag{8}$$

228. A notational agreement

Sometimes, when dealing with general functional notations, we may restrict the values of an original set of independent variables, such as $x, y, s, \cdots$, so that they no longer will be independent. In such a case, the symbol for a partial derivative involving "∂" may become ambiguous (see page 366). To avoid such a complication, we shall adhere to the following agreement.

Suppose that a function is represented by a single letter, and is defined as a function of certain variables, say $x, y, s, \cdots$. Then, the subscript notation for any partial derivative with respect to $x, y, s, \cdots$ will mean a partial derivative evaluated when all of $x, y, s, \cdots$ are taken as independent, even though, later, they may cease to be independent.

ILLUSTRATION 1. With a function $f(x, y, s, t)$,

$$\left. \frac{\partial f(x, y, s, t)}{\partial s} \right|_{(x, y, t\ held\ fast)} \quad is\ represented\ by \quad f_s(x, y, s, t). \tag{1}$$

If x and y are differentiable functions of s and t, we may also consider $f(x, y, s, t)$ as a function of s and t, and then use

$$\left. \frac{\partial f(x, y, s, t)}{\partial s} \right|_{(t\ held\ fast)}, \tag{2}$$

and this is *not necessarily equal to f_s of (1).*

229. Change of variables

We shall assume that any derivative mentioned later in this chapter exists and is continuous. Then, consider a differentiable function $u = f(x, y)$, and suppose that $x = g(t)$ and $y = h(t)$, where $g(t)$ and $h(t)$ are differentiable functions. The result which we shall obtain for $f(x, y)$ is a generalization of the formula on page 46 for the derivative of a composite function. Under the given conditions, u becomes a function of t, and we shall prove that

$$\frac{du}{dt} = u_x \frac{dx}{dt} + u_y \frac{dy}{dt}; \ or \tag{1}$$

$$\frac{df(x, y)}{dt} = f_x(x, y) \frac{dx}{dt} + f_y(x, y) \frac{dy}{dt}. \tag{2}$$

Proof of (2). 1. Let t have any fixed value, with x and y representing the corresponding fixed values $x = g(t)$ and $y = h(t)$. Let Δt be any nonzero increment of t, with Δx, Δy, and Δu as the corresponding increments of x, y, and u. From (2) on page 474,

$$\Delta u = f_x(x, y)\Delta x + f_y(x, y)\Delta y + \epsilon_1 \Delta x + \epsilon_2 \Delta y; \tag{3}$$

$$\frac{\Delta u}{\Delta t} = f_x(x, y)\frac{\Delta x}{\Delta t} + f_y(x, y)\frac{\Delta y}{\Delta t} + \epsilon_1 \frac{\Delta x}{\Delta t} + \epsilon_2 \frac{\Delta y}{\Delta t}. \tag{4}$$

2. If $\Delta t \rightarrow 0$, then $\Delta x \rightarrow 0$ and $\Delta y \rightarrow 0$, because the functions $x = g(t)$ and $y = h(t)$ are differentiable and hence are continuous. Thus, if $\Delta t \rightarrow 0$ in (4), we obtain

$$\epsilon_1 \rightarrow 0, \quad \epsilon_2 \rightarrow 0, \quad \frac{\Delta x}{\Delta t} \rightarrow \frac{dx}{dt}, \quad \frac{\Delta y}{\Delta t} \rightarrow \frac{dy}{dt}, \tag{5}$$

because of the nature of ϵ_1 and ϵ_2 on page 474, and because the functions $x = g(t)$ and $y = h(t)$ possess derivatives. Hence, from (4) and (5), $\Delta u/\Delta t$ has a limit as $\Delta t \rightarrow 0$, and thus u has a derivative given by

$$\frac{du}{dt} = \lim_{\Delta t \rightarrow 0} \frac{\Delta u}{\Delta t} = f_x(x, y)\frac{dx}{dt} + f_y(x, y)\frac{dy}{dt} + 0 \cdot \frac{dx}{dt} + 0 \cdot \frac{dy}{dt},$$

which proves (2).

ILLUSTRATION 1. If $u = \sin x \cos y$, $x = 3t^2$, and $y = 5t^3 + 3t$,

$$u_x = \cos x \cos y; \quad u_y = - \sin x \sin y;$$

by (1), $\quad \frac{du}{dt} = (\cos x \cos y)(6t) - (\sin x \sin y)(15t^2 + 3).$

We could have found the result without (1), as in Problems 29–32 on page 97. However, (1) often is indispensable in theoretical discussions.

A special case of (1) arises if $u = f(x, y)$ where y is a function of x, say $y = h(x)$. Then, with x in place of t in (1), and $dx/dx = 1$,

$$\frac{du}{dx} = u_x + u_y \frac{dy}{dx}, \ or \tag{6}$$

$$\frac{du}{dx} = \left(\frac{\partial u}{\partial x}\right)_y + \left(\frac{\partial u}{\partial y}\right)_x \frac{dy}{dx}. \tag{7}$$

On the right in (7), $\frac{\partial u}{\partial x}$ is the partial derivative of u with respect to x when y is considered independent of x; the second term occurs on the right because y

actually is a function of x. The two terms thus account for the *total* dependence of u on x. Accordingly, we sometimes call du/dt in (1) the **total derivative** of u with respect to t, and du/dx in (6) the total derivative of u with respect to x.

ILLUSTRATION 2. If $u = e^{xy} \sin x$, and $y = \ln x$, then

$$u_x = e^{xy} \cos x + ye^{xy} \sin x, \quad and \quad u_y = xe^{xy} \sin x.$$

Hence, from (6), the total derivative with respect to x is

$$\frac{du}{dx} = e^{xy} \cos x + ye^{xy} \sin x + (xe^{xy} \sin x)\frac{1}{x}.$$

Similarly, as in (1), if $u = f(x, y, z)$ and x, y, and z are functions of t,

$$\frac{du}{dt} = u_x\frac{dx}{dt} + u_y\frac{dy}{dt} + u_z\frac{dz}{dt}. \tag{8}$$

If y and z are functions of x, then

$$\frac{du}{dx} = u_x + u_y\frac{dy}{dx} + u_z\frac{dz}{dx}. \tag{9}$$

Suppose, now, that $u = f(x, y)$, where

$$x = g(s, t) \quad and \quad y = h(s, t), \tag{10}$$

and s and t are independent variables. Then, with s temporarily considered as a constant, we may apply (1). Since x, y, and u are functions of two independent variables s and t, the derivatives with respect to t in (1) become partial derivatives, with s held fast, and we obtain

$$\frac{\partial u}{\partial t} = u_x\frac{\partial x}{\partial t} + u_y\frac{\partial y}{\partial t}; \quad \frac{\partial u}{\partial s} = u_x\frac{\partial x}{\partial s} + u_y\frac{\partial y}{\partial s}. \tag{11}$$

Similarly, let u be a differentiable function of any number of independent variables, say x, y, and z. If x, y, and z are placed equal to differentiable functions of any number of independent variables, say r, s, and t, then u has a partial derivative with respect to each of these variables. Thus,

$$\frac{\partial u}{\partial t} = u_x\frac{\partial x}{\partial t} + u_y\frac{\partial y}{\partial t} + u_z\frac{\partial z}{\partial t}. \tag{12}$$

ILLUSTRATION 3. If $u = f(x, y)$, and if we transform variables by use of $x = r \sin \theta$ and $y = r \cos \theta$, then

$$\frac{\partial x}{\partial r} = \sin \theta; \quad \frac{\partial x}{\partial \theta} = r \cos \theta; \quad \frac{\partial y}{\partial r} = \cos \theta; \quad \frac{\partial y}{\partial \theta} = -r \sin \theta. \tag{13}$$

From (11), with t as r, and then t as θ,

$$\frac{\partial u}{\partial r} = u_x \sin \theta + u_y \cos \theta; \quad \frac{\partial u}{\partial \theta} = ru_x \cos \theta - ru_y \sin \theta.$$

Note 1. In formulas like (11), we may refer to (x, y) as variables of the *first class*, and to (s, t) as variables of the *second class*. Variables of the first class play two roles. First, in the evaluation of u_x and u_y, we consider x and y as independent variables. Later, x and y become dependent variables. The variables of the second class are the final independent variables.

ILLUSTRATION 4. Suppose that $u = f(x, y, s, t)$, and that x and y are differentiable functions of s and t. With x, y, s, and t as the variables of the 1st class, and s and t as the variables of the 2d class, from (12) we obtain

$$\left(\frac{\partial u}{\partial t}\right)_s = f_x \frac{\partial x}{\partial t} + f_y \frac{\partial y}{\partial t} + f_t, \tag{14}$$

because s is considered as a constant in obtaining $\dfrac{\partial u}{\partial t}$, and $\dfrac{\partial t}{\partial t} = 1$; or

$$\left(\frac{\partial u}{\partial t}\right)_s = u_x \frac{\partial x}{\partial t} + u_y \frac{\partial y}{\partial t} + u_t. \tag{15}$$

Notice the confusion if we use an ambiguous $\dfrac{\partial u}{\partial t}$ instead of u_t in (15):

$$\frac{\partial u}{\partial t} = \frac{\partial u}{\partial x}\frac{\partial x}{\partial t} + \frac{\partial u}{\partial y}\frac{\partial y}{\partial t} + \frac{\partial u}{\partial t}, \tag{16}$$

where $\dfrac{\partial u}{\partial t}$ appears to cancel out. In (16), $\dfrac{\partial u}{\partial t}$ on the left and on the right have different meanings, and (16) becomes intelligible only when the other independent variables are shown by subscripts:

$$\left(\frac{\partial u}{\partial t}\right)_s = \left(\frac{\partial u}{\partial x}\right)_{(y, s, t)}\left(\frac{\partial x}{\partial t}\right)_s + \left(\frac{\partial u}{\partial y}\right)_{(x, s, t)}\left(\frac{\partial y}{\partial t}\right)_s + \left(\frac{\partial u}{\partial t}\right)_{(x, y, s)}. \tag{17}$$

230. Derivatives of implicit functions by general formulas

I. *If x and y are related by an equation $F(x, y) = 0$, then*

$$\frac{dy}{dx} = -\frac{F_x(x, y)}{F_y(x, y)}. \tag{1}$$

Proof. Let $u = F(x, y)$, where y represents the function of x defined implicitly by $F(x, y) = 0$. Then, $u = 0$ and hence $du/dx = 0$ for all values of x. We obtain du/dx by use of (6) on page 476:

$$\frac{du}{dx} = F_x + F_y \frac{dy}{dx} = 0, \quad or \quad \frac{dy}{dx} = -\frac{F_x(x, y)}{F_y(x, y)}.$$

II. *If the variable z is defined implicitly as a function of x and y by an equation $F(x, y, z) = 0$, then*

$$\frac{\partial z}{\partial x} = -\frac{F_x(x, y, z)}{F_z(x, y, z)}; \quad \frac{\partial z}{\partial y} = -\frac{F_y(x, y, z)}{F_z(x, y, z)}. \tag{2}$$

Proof. To obtain $\dfrac{\partial z}{\partial x}$ in (2), we consider y as a constant temporarily and use (1), with y replaced by z; we find a partial derivative from (1) because z is a function of *two* variables. Similarly, we obtain $\dfrac{\partial z}{\partial y}$ in (2) by use of (1) with y replaced by z and x replaced by y.

Formulas (1) and (2) have important theoretical applications. Also, for experience, the formulas may be used to obtain the derivatives of implicit functions in explicit equations as met on pages 50 and 365. However, the student should *continue to use the earlier methods when* (1) *and* (2) *are not specified for use.*

EXAMPLE 1. Obtain $\dfrac{\partial z}{\partial x}$ if $z^3 + 3xz^2 - yz + xy^2 = 8x.$

SOLUTION. Let $F(x, y, z) = z^3 + 3xz^2 - yz - 8x + xy^2.$ Then, by (2),

$$\frac{\partial z}{\partial x} = -\frac{3z^2 - 8 + y^2}{3z^2 + 6xz - y}.$$

EXERCISE 144

Solve each problem by use of a formula from Sections 229 *and* 230.

Find $\dfrac{du}{dt}$, *without eliminating* x, y, *or* z.

1. $u = x^2 + 3xy + 5y^2$, when $x = 3t^3 + t$ and $y = 2t - t^2.$
2. $u = x^3 - xy^2$, when $x = 4 \sin t$ and $y = 3 \cos 2t.$
3. $u = x - y^2 - z^2$, when $x = e^t$, $y = 3 \ln t$, and $z = 4t^2.$
4. $u = \sqrt{x^2 + y^2 + z^2}$, when $x = \sin 2t$, $y = 3 \cos 2t$, and $z = 4t^3.$

HINT. Let $v = x^2 + y^2 + z^2$. Then, $u = v^{\frac{1}{2}}$ and $\dfrac{du}{dt} = \dfrac{1}{2} v^{-\frac{1}{2}} \dfrac{dv}{dt}.$

5. $u = e^z \cos y$, when $y = t \ln t$ and $z = \text{Arctan } t.$
6. $u = \ln (x - 2y + 3z)$, when $x = 3t^3$, $y = e^{2t}$, and $z = \tan t.$
7. $u = \text{Arcsin } xyz$, when $x = \sin 2t$, $y = \cos 2t$, and $z = \sec t.$
8. $u = e^{3x+4y} \ln z$, when $x = t^2 + t$, $y = t^3$, and $z = \cos t.$

Find the total derivative of u *with respect to* x, *without eliminating* y *or* $z.$

9. $u = x^3 + xy - y^3$, when $y = e^x \ln x + x.$
10. $u = \sin x + \cos y^{\frac{3}{2}}$, when $y = x^2 + 5x.$
11. $u = \sin x^2 + x \cos y^2$, when $y = \sin 2x.$
12. $u = x^3 + 4xy^3$, when $y = xe^{2x} - \ln x.$
13. $u = x^2 - xz + yz$, when $y = \cos x$ and $z = e^{-3x}.$
14. $u = \sqrt{x^2 + y^2 + z^2}$, when $y = (3x - 5)^2$ and $z = \sec x.$
15. $u = \dfrac{x + e^y}{z - e^z}$, when $y = 3 \sin x$ and $z = \ln x.$

Find $\dfrac{\partial u}{\partial s}$ and $\dfrac{\partial u}{\partial t}$, without eliminating x and y.

16. $u = x^3 + 3x^2 y$, where $x = te^s$ and $y = se^t$.

17. $u = x^2 - xy + y^3$, where $x = s \cos t$ and $y = st^2$.

18. $u = \text{Arcsin} (2x + y)$, where $x = t^2 \ln s$ and $y = se^t$.

19. $u = \sin 2x + \cos 3y$, where $x = 2s + t^2$ and $y = 3t - s^3$.

20. If $z = \sin xy$, $x = \ln \sqrt{u+v}$, and $y = \text{Arcsin } uv$, find $\dfrac{\partial z}{\partial u}$.

21. If $u = x^2 y - yz^2$, $x = 2r + 3s$, $y = 4r + s$, and $z = 4 \sin rs$, find $\dfrac{\partial u}{\partial r}$.

22. If $z = \cos uvw$, $u = s + e^t$, $v = \ln t + e^s$, and $w = e^s + e^{2t}$, find $\dfrac{\partial z}{\partial t}$.

Solve by use of Section 229.

23–26. Problems 29–32 on page 97.

27. If $u = x^2 + y^2 + z^2$, find $\dfrac{\partial u}{\partial r}$, $\dfrac{\partial u}{\partial \theta}$, and $\dfrac{\partial u}{\partial \phi}$ if

$$x = r \sin \phi \cos \theta, \quad y = r \sin \phi \sin \theta, \quad z = r \cos \phi.$$

28. If $u = e^{x^2 y}$, $x = \text{Arcsin} \sqrt{s^2 + t^2}$, and $y = \ln st$, find $\dfrac{\partial u}{\partial s}$ and $\dfrac{\partial u}{\partial t}$.

29. If $z = \dfrac{\sin x}{1 + \cos y}$, $x = e^t + \ln t$, and $y = 5t^2$, find dz/dt.

All functions mentioned in the following problems are differentiable.

30. If $u = f(x, y, z)$, where x and z are functions of y, write an expression for du/dy.

31. If $v = g(x, y, u, t)$, where u and t are functions of x and y, write expressions for $\left(\dfrac{\partial v}{\partial x}\right)_y$ and $\left(\dfrac{\partial v}{\partial y}\right)_x$.

32. If u and y are functions of x, write an expression for $df(u, x, y)/dx$.

33. If w is defined as a function of y, z, r, and t, and if r and t are functions of y and z, write expressions for $\left(\dfrac{\partial w}{\partial y}\right)_z$ and $\left(\dfrac{\partial w}{\partial z}\right)_y$.

34. Assume that the function $f(x, y)$ has derivatives f_x and f_y which are continuous near $(x = x_0, y = y_0)$. Prove that $f(x, y)$ is continuous at (x_0, y_0).

★231. Implicit differentiation in general systems

Note 1. In dealing with a function such as $F(x, y, z, w)$, occasionally we may use $F_1(x, y, z, w)$, instead of $F_x(x, y, z, w)$, for the partial derivative with respect to the variable in the *first* place, F_2 instead of F_y, etc. In the following result, we assume that $F(x, y, z, w)$ and $G(x, y, z, w)$ possess continuous partial derivatives of the first order with respect to x, y, z, and w. Also, we assume that the denominator appearing in (2) on page 481 is not zero.

If w and s are defined implicitly as functions of x and y by

$$F(x, y, w, s) = 0 \quad \text{and} \quad G(x, y, w, s) = 0, \tag{1}$$

then

$$\frac{\partial w}{\partial x} = - \frac{\begin{vmatrix} F_1 & F_4 \\ G_1 & G_4 \end{vmatrix}}{\begin{vmatrix} F_3 & F_4 \\ G_3 & G_4 \end{vmatrix}}, \quad \frac{\partial s}{\partial x} = - \frac{\begin{vmatrix} F_3 & F_1 \\ G_3 & G_1 \end{vmatrix}}{\begin{vmatrix} F_3 & F_4 \\ G_3 & G_4 \end{vmatrix}}. \tag{2}$$

Proof of (2). On both sides of each equation in (1), differentiate with respect to x, with w and s considered as functions of x and y, and with y held fast. In this differentiation use (12) of page 477 with $u = F(x, y, w, s)$ and t replaced by x, and then with $u = G(x, y, w, s)$:

$$\left. \begin{aligned} F_1 + F_3 \frac{\partial w}{\partial x} + F_4 \frac{\partial s}{\partial x} &= 0, \\ G_1 + G_3 \frac{\partial w}{\partial x} + G_4 \frac{\partial s}{\partial x} &= 0. \end{aligned} \right\} \tag{3}$$

On solving (3) for the derivatives by determinants, we obtain (2). Similarly, we obtain $\dfrac{\partial w}{\partial y}$ and $\dfrac{\partial s}{\partial y}$ from (1) on replacing the subscript "1" by "2" in (2).

Note 2. As a rule, special cases of (1) should be treated by the elementary method on page 365, without using (2) or similar formulas. Results such as (2) are useful in advanced discussions.

EXAMPLE 1. Find $\dfrac{\partial w}{\partial x}$ if x and y are the independent variables, and if (x, y, w, s) are related by

$$\left. \begin{aligned} 3w^2 - 2swx + y^2 &= 2s^2, \\ 2x^2 - s^3w + w^2y &= 2x. \end{aligned} \right\} \tag{4}$$

SOLUTION. From (2) with

$$F = 3w^2 - 2swx + y^2 - 2s^2 = 0, \quad \text{and} \quad G = 2x^2 - s^3w + w^2y - 2x = 0,$$

$$\frac{\partial w}{\partial x} = - \frac{\begin{vmatrix} -2sw & -2wx - 4s \\ 4x - 2 & -3s^2w \\ 6w - 2sx & -2wx - 4s \\ -s^3 + 2wy & -3s^2w \end{vmatrix}}{} = \frac{3s^3w^2 + 4wx^2 + 8sx - 2wx - 4s}{9s^2w^2 - 2s^3wx + 2s^4 - 2w^2xy - 4swy}.$$

Note 3. If (1) does not involve y, then the unknown partial derivatives in (3) become ordinary derivatives dw/dx and ds/dx, respectively.

DEFINITION I. *The **Jacobian** of two differentiable functions $F(x, y)$ and $G(x, y)$ with respect to x and y is the function defined as follows:*

$$\left\{ \begin{aligned} &\text{Jacobian of } F(x, y) \text{ and } G(x, y) \\ &\quad \text{with respect to } x \text{ and } y \end{aligned} \right\} = \begin{vmatrix} F_x & F_y \\ G_x & G_y \end{vmatrix}. \tag{5}$$

Frequently, we use the symbol $\dfrac{\partial(F,\,G)}{\partial(x,\,y)}$ to denote the Jacobian in (5). This symbol is read as given at the left in (5). The use of "∂" in the symbol merely is a reminder that partial derivatives are present in (5). In Definition I, if F and G are functions of other variables besides x and y, the determinant in (5) is unchanged in form.

ILLUSTRATION 1. If $F(x,\,y) = x^2 + 3xy$ and $G(x,\,y) = \sin xy$,

$$\frac{\partial(F,\,G)}{\partial(x,\,y)} = \begin{vmatrix} 2x + 3y & 3x \\ y\cos xy & x\cos xy \end{vmatrix} = 2x^2\cos xy.$$

In (1) and (2), we implicitly assumed that (1) defines a unique solution for w and s as functions of x and y, near all points (x, y) which are to be considered. The theorem * justifying this assumption demands, as a hypothesis, that *the Jacobian of F and G with respect to w and s is not zero on the ranges considered for* (x, y, w, s), or

$$\frac{\partial(F,\,G)}{\partial(w,\,s)} = \begin{vmatrix} F_w & F_s \\ G_w & G_s \end{vmatrix} \neq 0. \tag{6}$$

We note that (6) is the denominator in (2). Thus, hypothesis (6), which justifies dealing with (1), also is necessary for arrival at (2).

Note 4. As an extension of Definition I, if $F^{(1)}, \cdots, F^{(n)}$ are n functions of the independent variables $(x_1, \cdots, x_n)$, the Jacobian of the functions with respect to these variables is defined as the determinant of the nth order having $F_{x_j}^{(i)}$ as the element in the ith row and jth column.

EXAMPLE 2. If u is a function of x and y, where they occur only in the combination xy, prove that

$$x\,\frac{\partial u}{\partial x} - y\,\frac{\partial u}{\partial y} = 0.$$

SOLUTION. Let $w = xy$. Then, there exists a function $f(w)$ such that

$$w = xy \quad and \quad u = f(w). \tag{7}$$

Consider (7) as simultaneous equations defining u and w as functions of x and y. From $u = f(w)$, by use of (VII) on page 46,

$$\frac{\partial u}{\partial x} = \frac{df(w)}{dw}\frac{\partial w}{\partial x} = f'(w)\frac{\partial w}{\partial x}; \quad \frac{\partial u}{\partial y} = f'(w)\frac{\partial w}{\partial y}, \ or$$

$$\frac{\partial u}{\partial x} = yf'(w); \quad \frac{\partial u}{\partial y} = xf'(w). \tag{8}$$

From (8), $\quad x\,\dfrac{\partial u}{\partial x} = y\,\dfrac{\partial u}{\partial y}, \quad or \quad x\,\dfrac{\partial u}{\partial x} - y\,\dfrac{\partial u}{\partial y} = 0.$

* See the *fundamental theorem on implicit functions*, in advanced texts.

★232. General definition of homogeneity

The following definition extends the notion of a homogeneous function beyond the elementary stage arrived at previously in algebra.

DEFINITION II.   *A function $f(x, y, z)$ is said to be homogeneous and of degree n in x, y, and z if and only if*

$$f(\lambda x, \lambda y, \lambda z) = \lambda^n f(x, y, z), \tag{1}$$

for all permissible values of x, y, z, and λ.

The degree n in (1) may be any real number.   Definition II applies with appropriate alterations to a function of any number of variables.

ILLUSTRATION 1.   The function $f(x, y, z) = 3x^3 + 4xy^2 + z^3$ is homogeneous and of degree 3 because

$$f(\lambda x, \lambda y, \lambda z) = 3\lambda^3 x^3 + 4\lambda^3 xy^2 + \lambda^3 z^3 = \lambda^3(3x^3 + 4xy^2 + z^3) = \lambda^3 f(x, y, z).$$

ILLUSTRATION 2.   The function $f(x, y, z) = \sqrt{x + y - z}$ is homogeneous and of degree $\frac{1}{2}$ because

$$f(\lambda x, \lambda y, \lambda z) = \sqrt{\lambda x + \lambda y - \lambda z} = \sqrt{\lambda}\sqrt{x + y - z} = \lambda^{\frac{1}{2}} f(x, y, z).$$

THEOREM II.   *(Euler's theorem.)   If $f(x, y, z)$ is homogeneous of degree n, then*

$$xf_x(x, y, z) + yf_y(x, y, z) + zf_z(x, y, z) = nf(x, y, z). \tag{2}$$

Outline of proof.   We can obtain (2) by differentiating both sides of (1) with respect to λ, and then placing $\lambda = 1$.   (The converse can be proved.)

★EXERCISE 145

1–14. Solve Problem 1–14, respectively, of page 366 by use of (2) on page 481.

Prove that the function is homogeneous and find its degree, by substituting λx, λy, λz for x, y, and z.   Then, verify identity (2) for the function.

15. $f(x, y, z) = x^3 + 3xy^2 - y^3$.   **16.** $f(x, y, z) = \sqrt[3]{x^2 + y^2 + z^2}$.

17. $\sin (y/x)$.   **18.** Arcsin $[x/(x + y)]$.   **19.** $z\sqrt{x^2 + y^2}$.

20. If u is a function of x and y, where they occur only in the combination $(x - y)$, prove that $u_x + u_y = 0$.

21. If $u = f(x, y, z)$, where $x = a + gt, y = b + ht, z = c + kt$, and a, b, c, g, h, k are constants, find du/dt.

22. If $u = f(x, y)$ and if we change to polar coordinates by use of $x = r \cos \theta$ and $y = r \sin \theta$, obtain $\dfrac{\partial u}{\partial r}$ and $\dfrac{\partial u}{\partial \theta}$.

23. If u is a function of $(2x + 3y)$, prove that $3u_x = 2u_y$.

24. If u is a function of x/y, prove that $xu_x = - yu_y$.

25. If u is a function of $(x^2 + y^2)$, prove that $yu_x = xu_y$.

★233. Results about differentials

If u is a function of the variables x and y, the differential of u with respect to x and y as independent variables has been defined as

$$du = \frac{\partial u}{\partial x}\, dx + \frac{\partial u}{\partial y}\, dy. \tag{1}$$

We proceed to establish the important result that (1) remains true even when x and y no longer are the independent variables, but are specified as functions of certain other underlying independent variables.

THEOREM III. *Suppose that $u = f(x, y)$, where x and y are functions of s and t. Then, the differential of u with respect to s and t as independent variables is given by $du = u_x\, dx + u_y\, dy$, where dx and dy also are computed with respect to s and t.*

Proof. 1. With respect to s and t as independent variables,

$$du = \frac{\partial u}{\partial s}\, ds + \frac{\partial u}{\partial t}\, dt; \quad dx = \frac{\partial x}{\partial s}\, ds + \frac{\partial x}{\partial t}\, dt; \quad dy = \frac{\partial y}{\partial s}\, ds + \frac{\partial y}{\partial t}\, dt. \tag{2}$$

2. Since $u = f(x, y)$, from (11) on page 477 we obtain

$$\frac{\partial u}{\partial s} = \frac{\partial u}{\partial x}\frac{\partial x}{\partial s} + \frac{\partial u}{\partial y}\frac{\partial y}{\partial s}; \quad \frac{\partial u}{\partial t} = \frac{\partial u}{\partial x}\frac{\partial x}{\partial t} + \frac{\partial u}{\partial y}\frac{\partial y}{\partial t}. \tag{3}$$

On using (3) in du in (2), and reordering terms, we find

$$du = \frac{\partial u}{\partial x}\left(\frac{\partial x}{\partial s}\, ds + \frac{\partial x}{\partial t}\, dt\right) + \frac{\partial u}{\partial y}\left(\frac{\partial y}{\partial s}\, ds + \frac{\partial y}{\partial t}\, dt\right). \tag{4}$$

From (2), equation (4) can be rewritten $du = u_x\, dx + u_y\, dy$.

EXAMPLE 1. Obtain du if $u = \sin x + \cos y$, where $x = \sqrt{s^2 + t^2}$ and $y = e^{st}$, if s and t are the independent variables.

SOLUTION. By Theorem III, $du = \cos x\, dx - \sin y\, dy$, where

$$dx = \tfrac{1}{2}(s^2 + t^2)^{-\frac{1}{2}}(2s\, ds + 2t\, dt) \quad and \quad dy = e^{st}(s\, dt + t\, ds).$$

Thus, $\quad du = \left(\dfrac{s\cos x}{\sqrt{s^2 + t^2}} - te^{st}\sin y\right) ds - \left(se^{st}\sin y - \dfrac{t\cos x}{\sqrt{s^2 + t^2}}\right) dt. \tag{5}$

Note 1. Theorem I on page 370 is a special case of Theorem III, with w as a function of just one variable u, instead of two, x and y. Theorem III extends to the case of any number of variables.

EXAMPLE 2. Obtain dz in terms of x, y, dx, and dy if

$$z^3 + 4xyz = 5xy + 8. \tag{6}$$

SOLUTION. Equation (6) is considered as defining z as a function of x and y. Then, the differentials of the two sides with respect to x and y as independent variables are equal. By Theorem III, we obtain the differential of the left-hand side with respect to x and y by writing the differential with respect to x, y, and z:

$$d(z^3 + 4xyz) = d(5xy + 8), \text{ or}$$

$$(3z^2 + 4xy)dz + 4xz\, dy + 4yz\, dx = 5y\, dx + 5x\, dy, \text{ or}$$

$$dz = \frac{5y\, dx + 5x\, dy - 4xz\, dy - 4yz\, dx}{3z^2 + 4xy}. \tag{7}$$

The preceding method would apply in finding the differentials of functions defined implicitly by a system of equations.

★EXERCISE 146

Obtain du with s and t as independent variables; do not eliminate x and y.

1. $u = x^3y + x^5y^2$, where $x = 3st^3$ and $y = \sin(s + 3t)$.

2. $u = y \sin 3x + x \cos 4y$, where $x = (s + 3t)^3$ and $y = e^s \ln t$.

3. $u = \text{Arcsin}(x + 3y)$, where $x = \sin st$ and $y = s^2 e^t$.

4. $u = \dfrac{x + 3y}{2x - y}$, where $x = t + e^s$ and $y = s \ln(\ln t)$.

Find dz in terms of x, y, z, dx, and dy.

5. $3x^2 + 2yz + xz^2 = 4$. 6. $xy + \sin z = 7$.

7. $\tan z = x/y$. 8. $e^z = x^2 + y^2$.

Obtain the result without solving for z in terms of x and y.

9. If $z^2 = x^2 + y^2$, find dz when $x = 5$, $y = -12$, $dx = .1$, and $dy = -.2$.

10. If $z^2 = 3x/(2y + 1)$, find dz when $x = 3$, $y = 12$, $dx = .2$, and $dy = .3$.

11. If $e^z + xy - e^{xz} = a$, find dz when $x = 2$, $z = 1$, $y = 4$, $dx = .2$, and $dy = .3$.

The system of simultaneous equations defines x and y as functions t. Obtain dx and dy in terms of dt.

12. $xy - tx = 5$; $x^2y^2 - ty = 4$.

13. $t^3 + tx^3 - y^3 = 0$; $t^2 + x^2 - ty^2 = 0$.

14. $3x + t^2y + x^2 = 4$; $4y - t^2x + t^2 = 3$.

15. If $u = g(x + kt)$, where k is a constant, prove that $\dfrac{\partial^2 u}{\partial t^2} = k^2 \dfrac{\partial^2 u}{\partial x^2}$.

HINT. Let $z = x + kt$; then $u = g(z)$. Obtain derivatives of u in terms of $g'(z)$ and $g''(z)$.

16. Obtain expressions for dy/dx and dz/dx if (x, y, z) satisfy the simultaneous equations $F(x, y, z) = 0$ and $K(x, y, z) = 0$.

★17. Assume that the function $u = f(x, y)$ has continuous derivatives u_x and u_y, and that $u_x = u_y = 0$ at all points (x, y). Prove that u is a constant. In other words, if $du = 0$ for all points (x, y), and all values of dx and dy, prove that u is a constant. Use (3), (4), and (5) on page 474.

18. If x and y satisfy $y = f(x, y)$, obtain dy/dx.

25

ENVELOPES, SPACE CURVES, AND SURFACES

234. Envelope of a family of curves

Let a family of curves be defined by

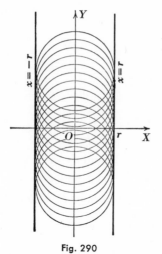

Fig. 290

$$f(x, y, t) = 0, \tag{1}$$

where t is a parameter. For each value of t, a curve of the family is determined as the graph of (1) in the xy-plane. For any family (1), suppose that $f(x, y, t)$ possesses continuous partial derivatives f_x, f_y, f_t.

ILLUSTRATION 1. If β is a parameter, the following equation

$$x^2 + (y - \beta)^2 = r^2, \tag{2}$$

where r is a constant, defines a family of circles with radius r. Curves of this family are shown in Figure 290.

We define *an* **envelope** of a family (1) as a curve E such that

I. *each curve C of the family is tangent to E at some point;*

II. *through each point P of E, there passes a curve of the family tangent to E.*

For a given family (1), the set of all curves E (if any exist) satisfying (I) and (II) will be called THE envelope of the family.

ILLUSTRATION 2. In Figure 290, each of the lines $x = r$ and $x = -r$ is an envelope for family (2). THE envelope consists of these lines.

ILLUSTRATION 3. Suppose that, in an xy-plane, a projectile is shot from the origin with an initial speed of v_0 feet per second, at an angle of elevation t. Under idealized conditions, the trajectory of the projectile has the equation

$$y = -\frac{gx^2}{2v_0^2 \cos^2 t} + x \tan t, \tag{3}$$

where $g = 32$, approximately. If v_0 is a constant and t varies, the family of parabolas (3) has an envelope, whose equation is

$$y = \frac{v_0^2}{2g} - \frac{gx^2}{2v_0^2},$$

which the student will obtain later. Figure 291 shows the envelope and curves of family (3).

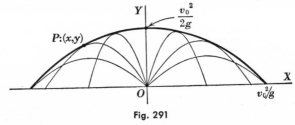

Fig. 291

Let E be an envelope for (1), as in Figure 291. Then, for each value of t, there is a corresponding point $P:(x, y)$ on E at which E is tangent to the curve C given by (1), and each point of E is obtained in this way. Thus, if $P:(x, y)$ is on E, the coordinates x and y are functions of t, or E can be considered in parametric form with t as the parameter,

$$x = g(t) \quad and \quad y = h(t). \tag{4}$$

Theorem I. **IF** *a family of curves* $f(x, y, t) = 0$ *has an envelope* E, *then the parametric equations for* E *in terms of* t *satisfy*

$$f(x, y, t) = 0 \quad and \quad f_t(x, y, t) = 0. \tag{5}$$

Proof. 1. Suppose that an envelope E exists, and has the equations (4). For each value of t, equations (4) give a point (x, y) on the graph of (1), or (1) is satisfied by $x = g(t)$, $y = h(t)$:

$$f[g(t), h(t), t] = 0. \tag{6}$$

2. Let $u = f(x, y, t)$ with $x = g(t), y = h(t)$. Then, by (6), $u = 0$ for all values of t and thus $du/dt = 0$. From (9) on page 477,

$$\frac{du}{dt} = f_x \frac{dx}{dt} + f_y \frac{dy}{dt} + f_t = 0, \quad or \quad f_x g'(t) + f_y h'(t) + f_t = 0. \tag{7}$$

3. With t fixed, the slope at $P:(x, y)$ on curve C of family (1) is equal to dy/dx, obtained on differentiating with respect to x in (1):

$$f_x + f_y \frac{dy}{dx} = 0, \quad or \quad \frac{dy}{dx} = -\frac{f_x}{f_y}. \tag{8}$$

At $P:(x, y)$ on E, from (4),

$$\frac{dy}{dx} = \frac{h'(t)\, dt}{g'(t)\, dt} = \frac{h'(t)}{g'(t)}. \tag{9}$$

Since C and E have the same slope at P, from (8) and (9) we obtain

$$-\frac{f_x}{f_y} = \frac{h'(t)}{g'(t)}, \quad or \quad f_x g'(t) + f_y h'(t) = 0. \tag{10}$$

When (10) is used, (7) becomes simply $f_t = 0$. Thus, from (6) and (7), $x = g(t)$ and $y = h(t)$ satisfy the equations in (5).

Note 1. In (8) of the proof, we assumed that the tangent at P on the envelope is not vertical, so that dy/dx exists. In case this is not true, we could use dx/dy in (8). Also, we assumed that, in (4), g and h possess continuous derivatives.

Note 2. For a particular case, equations (5) might be inconsistent; then, no envelope exists. Or, (5) might have a solution for x and y which does not give an envelope. Hence, after solving (5), it is advisable to check graphically.

SUMMARY. *To obtain the envelope E of a family $f(x, y, t) = 0$.*

1. *To obtain parametric equations for E, solve the system consisting of $f(x, y, t) = 0$ and $f_t(x, y, t) = 0$ for x and y in terms of t.*

2. *To derive an equation in x and y for the envelope, eliminate t between $f(x, y, t) = 0$ and $f_t(x, y, t) = 0$.*

ILLUSTRATION 4. It is evident geometrically that any curve is the envelope of its tangent lines.

ILLUSTRATION 5. For (2), where β is the parameter, (5) becomes

$$x^2 + (y - \beta)^2 = r^2 \quad and \quad - 2(y - \beta) = 0. \tag{11}$$

On using $y - \beta = 0$, equations (11) give $x^2 = r^2$. Thus, the envelope consists of the lines $x = r$ and $x = -r$, verified in Figure 290, page 486.

EXAMPLE 1. Obtain the envelope of the family of all lines at a fixed distance p from the origin in an xy-plane.

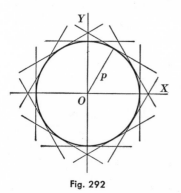

Fig. 292

SOLUTION. 1. For any line of the family, let ω be the angle made by the positive direction of the x-axis and a ray from the origin perpendicular to the line. Then, by use of the normal form for the equation of a line, from analytic geometry, with ω as a parameter, the equation of the family is

$$x \cos \omega + y \sin \omega - p = 0. \tag{12}$$

Differentiate partially with respect to the parameter ω in (12):

$$- x \sin \omega + y \cos \omega = 0. \tag{13}$$

2. To derive parametric equations for the envelope, solve (12) and (13) for x and y in terms of ω, and obtain $x = p \cos \omega$ and $y = p \sin \omega$. To find an xy-equation for the envelope, eliminate ω by squaring and adding; this gives $x^2 + y^2 = p^2$. In Figure 292, we verify that this circle is the envelope.

On page 324, we saw that the *normal* at any point on a given curve C, as in Figure 196 on page 325, is *tangent to the evolute of C.* Then, since *the evolute is the envelope of its own tangents*, we reach the following conclusion.

The evolute of a curve C is the envelope of the normals of C. (14)

EXAMPLE 2. By use of (14), find the evolute of the curve

$$x^2 = 4y. \tag{15}$$

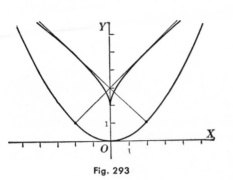

Fig. 293

SOLUTION. 1. From (15), $y' = \frac{1}{2}x$. Hence, at (x_1, y_1) on (15), the normal has the slope $-2/x_1$ and the equation

$$(y - y_1) = -\frac{2}{x_1}(x - x_1), \quad or$$

$$x_1 y - x_1 y_1 = -2x + 2x_1. \tag{16}$$

From (15) at (x_1, y_1), $x_1^2 = 4y_1$ or $y_1 = \frac{1}{4}x_1^2$. Then, with x_1 as a parameter, equation (16) for the **family of normals** becomes

$$8x + 4x_1 y - x_1^3 - 8x_1 = 0. \tag{17}$$

2. *To obtain the envelope of* (17). For (17), equations (5) become

$$4y - 3x_1^2 - 8 = 0 \quad and \quad 8x + 4x_1 y - x_1^3 - 8x_1 = 0. \tag{18}$$

From (18), $\qquad\qquad y = \frac{3}{4}x_1^2 + 2 \quad and \quad x = -\frac{1}{4}x_1^3. \tag{19}$

Thus, (19) gives the parametric equations of the evolute of (15) in terms of x_1 as the parameter. From (19),

$$x_1^6 = \frac{64}{27}(y - 2)^3 \quad and \quad x_1^6 = 16x^2. \tag{20}$$

Hence, on eliminating x_1 by use of (20), we obtain $4(y - 2)^3 = 27x^2$ as the xy-equation of the evolute. Graphs of (15) and (20) are shown in Figure 293, with three normals for (15).

EXERCISE 147

All curves are in the xy-plane. Any letter other than x or y is a variable parameter, except where the letter is stated to be a constant.

Find an xy-equation for the envelope of the family.

1. $(x - t)^2 + y^2 = r^2$; r is a constant.

2. $x^2 + (y - 2t)^2 = t^2$.

3. $(x - \alpha)^2 + (y + \alpha)^2 = \alpha^2$.

4. $ky = k^2 x + p$; p is a constant.

5. $y = 5x + t$.

6. $3m^2 x - 3y = 2m^3$.

7. $x^2 = 4t(y - t)$.

8. $8x + m^2 y = 16m$.

9. $4(x - t)^2 + (2y - t)^2 = t^2$.

10. $x^2 = t^2(y - t)$.

11. $ty = x + t^3$.

12. The envelope of (3), page 486.

13. $3x \sin t + 2y \cos t = 3$.

14. $x - y \sin \theta = k \cos \theta$, where k is a constant.

Obtain an equation for the tangent to the curve at any point. From this equation, find the envelope of the family of tangents.

15. $y^2 = 8x - 16$.

16. $x^2 = 2y + 6$.

17. $y = x^3$.

18. The ellipse with the parametric equations $x = a \cos \theta$, $y = b \sin \theta$.

19. Find an equation for the curve whose family of tangents is

$$bx - ay \sin \theta = ab \sec \theta - ab \sin \theta \tan \theta.$$

Find an xy-equation, or parametric equations, for the evolute of the curve by obtaining the envelope of its normals.

20–22. The given curves in Problems 15, 16, and 18, respectively.

23. Find the envelope of the family of lines where, on any line, the length of the segment between the coordinate axes is a constant, k (and is defined as equal to k at quadrantal positions).

★24. Find the envelope of the family of ellipses $b^2x^2 + a^2y^2 = a^2b^2$ where the sum of the semi-axes is equal to a constant, k.

★25. Find the envelope of the family of circles through the origin which have their centers on $y^2 - x^2 = k^2$, where k is a constant. Finally, show that the envelope is a lemniscate.

235. Length of a space curve

In an *xyz*-system of coordinates, consider a path C defined by

$$x = f(t), \quad y = g(t), \quad z = h(t), \tag{1}$$

where the range for t is an interval, finite or infinite. An arc of C is defined as the set of points obtained for the values of t on some interval $a \leq t \leq b$. The definition of arc length for a plane path, on page 307, applies with no essential alteration to a space path (1). We continue under the assumption that f, g, and h have continuous derivatives. Then, pertinent parts of the discussion for plane paths in Chapter 16 could be repeated with negligible changes to give the following results.

Every arc of (1) has length. If distance s is measured positive on C in the direction in which t increases, with $s = 0$ at $t = a$, then the distance s to the point P given by (1) is

$$s = \int_{t=a}^{t} ds = \int_{a}^{t} \sqrt{\left(\frac{dx}{dt}\right)^2 + \left(\frac{dy}{dt}\right)^2 + \left(\frac{dz}{dt}\right)^2}\, dt; \tag{2}$$

$$\frac{ds}{dt} = \sqrt{\left(\frac{dx}{dt}\right)^2 + \left(\frac{dy}{dt}\right)^2 + \left(\frac{dz}{dt}\right)^2}; \tag{3}$$

$$(ds)^2 = (dx)^2 + (dy)^2 + (dz)^2. \tag{4}$$

A path C will be called a *regular path* in case it has a parametric representation (1) where $f'(t)$, $g'(t)$, and $h'(t)$ are continuous and

$$[f'(t)]^2 + [g'(t)]^2 + [h'(t)]^2 \neq 0 \tag{5}$$

at all values of t. On a regular path, with s as the parameter,

$$\left(\frac{dx}{ds}\right)^2 + \left(\frac{dy}{ds}\right)^2 + \left(\frac{dz}{ds}\right)^2 = 1. \tag{6}$$

EXAMPLE 1. Find the length of arc, L, from $t = 0$ to $t = \frac{1}{2}\sqrt{3}$ on the curve $x = 2t^2 + t$, $y = 2t^2 - 2t$, and $z = t^2 + 2t$.

SOLUTION. $dx = (4t + 1)dt$; $dy = (4t - 2)dt$; $dz = (2t + 2)dt$.

$$(ds)^2 = [(4t + 1)^2 + (4t - 2)^2 + (2t + 2)^2](dt)^2 = (36t^2 + 9)(dt)^2.$$

$$L = \int_0^{t=\frac{1}{2}\sqrt{3}} ds = 3\int_0^{\frac{1}{2}\sqrt{3}} \sqrt{4t^2 + 1}\, dt = \frac{3}{2}\int_0^{\frac{1}{2}\sqrt{3}} \sqrt{(2t)^2 + 1}(2\, dt) = 3.59.$$

EXERCISE 148

Find the length of the curve between the specified points.

1. $x = 3t + 2$, $y = 1 - 2t$, $z = 4t + 3$; from $t = 1$ to $t = 5$.
2. $x = 3t + 1$, $y = 4t - 2$, $z = t^2 + 3$; from $t = 0$ to $t = 3$.
3. $x = t + 3$, $y = 3t^2 + 4$, $z = t - 2$; from $t = -1$ to $t = 2$.
4. The helix: $x = 3 \cos t$, $y = 3 \sin t$, $z = 4t$; from $t = 0$ to $t = 4\pi$.
5. $x = 2 \cos t$, $y = 2 \sin t$, $z = 3t$; from $t = 0$ to $t = 3$.
6. $x = 4 \cos^2 t$, $y = 4 \sin^2 t$, $z = 2 \cos 2t$; from $t = 0$ to $t = \pi/2$.
7. Find the length of the curve of intersection, C, of the surfaces $x + z = 6$ and $x^2 = 4y$ between $(0, 0, 6)$ and $(4, 4, 2)$. Use (3) on page 490, with $t = x$.
8. A coil spring forms a cylindrical helix $x = a \cos t$, $y = a \sin t$, $z = kt$, where the radius of the cylinder is $4''$. The coil makes 3 turns per inch along the axis of the coil. The length of the axis is $10''$. Find the length of the spring.
9. Prove that the "*conical helix*" with the parametric equations $x = 2t \sin t$, $y = 2t \cos t$, $z = 3t$ lies on a cone. Find the arc length from $(0, 0, 0)$ to the point where $t = \sqrt{3}$.

236. Tangent line and normal plane, for a space curve

Let C be a regular curve defined by

$$x = f(t), \quad y = g(t), \quad z = h(t). \tag{1}$$

In (1), let $P:(x_0, y_0, z_0)$ and $Q:(x_0 + \Delta x, y_0 + \Delta y, z_0 + \Delta z)$ be obtained when $t = t_0$ and $t = t_0 + \Delta t$, respectively, as in Figure 294 on page 492. Then, we shall prove that, at P, there is a tangent line PT, which has the direction numbers

$$\left\{ \begin{array}{l} \textit{tangent at } P, \\ \textit{direction numbers} \end{array} \right\} \qquad \left(\frac{dx}{dt}\right)_P : \left(\frac{dy}{dt}\right)_P : \left(\frac{dz}{dt}\right)_P. \tag{2}$$

Proof of (2). From Theorem IV on page 335, PQ has the direction numbers $\Delta x : \Delta y : \Delta z$. With $\Delta t \neq 0$, we may divide by Δt and obtain

$$(\textit{direction numbers for } PQ) \qquad \frac{\Delta x}{\Delta t} : \frac{\Delta y}{\Delta t} : \frac{\Delta z}{\Delta t}. \tag{3}$$

As $\Delta t \rightarrow 0$, the quotients in (3) have as limits the corresponding numbers in (2), where the subscript indicates that the derivatives are evaluated at P. In (2), not all derivatives can be zero, because of (5) on page 490, which holds for a regular curve. Hence, we may define a line PT having (2) as direction numbers. Since the direction numbers of PQ have as limits the corresponding direction numbers of PT, we accept the fact that any chosen set of direction cosines for PQ would approach the corresponding cosines for PT. Hence, the angle between PT and PQ approaches zero, or PT is the limiting position of PQ as $\Delta t \to 0$. That is, C has PT as the tangent at P.

DEFINITION I. *At any point P on a space curve, the plane perpendicular to the tangent line at P is called the* **normal plane** *for C at P.*

A normal plane for a curve is illustrated in Figure 295.

To write equations for the tangent line and an equation for the normal plane for a regular curve (1) at P, use (2) as the direction of the line and as the normal direction for the plane. Also, recall pages 340 and 345.

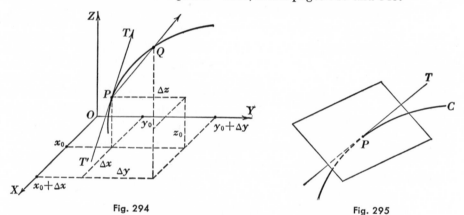

Fig. 294   Fig. 295

SUMMARY. *At $P:(x_0, y_0, z_0)$ on a regular curve, with the parameter t:*

1. *The tangent line has the equations*

$$\frac{x - x_0}{\left(\dfrac{dx}{dt}\right)_P} = \frac{y - y_0}{\left(\dfrac{dy}{dt}\right)_P} = \frac{z - z_0}{\left(\dfrac{dz}{dt}\right)_P}. \tag{4}$$

2. *The normal plane has the equation*

$$\left(\frac{dx}{dt}\right)_P (x - x_0) + \left(\frac{dy}{dt}\right)_P (y - y_0) + \left(\frac{dz}{dt}\right)_P (z - z_0) = 0. \tag{5}$$

EXAMPLE 1. Obtain the tangent line and normal plane where $\theta = \frac{1}{4}\pi$ on the helix $\qquad\qquad x = 3 \cos \theta, \quad y = 3 \sin \theta, \quad z = 2\theta.$

SOLUTION. With $\theta = \frac{1}{4}\pi$, we find $x = \frac{3}{2}\sqrt{2}$, $y = \frac{3}{2}\sqrt{2}$, and $z = \frac{1}{2}\pi$.

$$\frac{dx}{d\theta} = -3 \sin \theta; \quad \frac{dy}{d\theta} = 3 \cos \theta; \quad \frac{dz}{d\theta} = 2. \tag{6}$$

From (2), direction numbers for the tangent line where $\theta = \frac{1}{4}\pi$ are

$$-\tfrac{3}{2}\sqrt{2} : \tfrac{3}{2}\sqrt{2} : 2, \quad or \quad -3\sqrt{2} : 3\sqrt{2} : 4.$$

Then, by (4), equations for the tangent line are

$$\frac{x - \tfrac{3}{2}\sqrt{2}}{-3\sqrt{2}} = \frac{y - \tfrac{3}{2}\sqrt{2}}{3\sqrt{2}} = \frac{z - \tfrac{1}{2}\pi}{4}.$$

From (5), the normal plane at $\theta = \frac{1}{4}\pi$ is

$$-3\sqrt{2}(x - \tfrac{3}{2}\sqrt{2}) + 3\sqrt{2}(y - \tfrac{3}{2}\sqrt{2}) + 4(z - \tfrac{1}{2}\pi) = 0.$$

Let α, β, γ be the direction angles for a direction along the tangent line at P determined by (2). All derivatives will be evaluated at P. Then, from (2) and page 334, one value for $\cos \alpha$ is

$$\cos \alpha = \frac{\dfrac{dx}{dt}}{+\sqrt{\left(\dfrac{dx}{dt}\right)^2 + \left(\dfrac{dy}{dt}\right)^2 + \left(\dfrac{dz}{dt}\right)^2}} = \frac{\dfrac{dx}{dt}}{\dfrac{ds}{dt}} = \frac{dx}{ds}, \tag{7}$$

and similarly for $\cos \beta$ and $\cos \gamma$. Thus, we arrive at

$$\cos \alpha = \left(\frac{dx}{ds}\right)_P, \qquad \cos \beta = \left(\frac{dy}{ds}\right)_P, \qquad \cos \gamma = \left(\frac{dz}{ds}\right)_P, \tag{8}$$

as the direction cosines for one of the directions on the tangent line.

On any regular curve C, the direction in which the parameter t and arc distance s increase will be called the *positive* or *forward* direction on C. In Figure 294, page 492, assume that $\Delta t > 0$, and consider the *forward* chord PQ as a directed ray. As $\Delta t \to 0+$, the ray PQ has a limiting position, which is a ray along the tangent to C at P; let PT be this ray, as in Figure 294. Then, we call PT the **forward tangent** at P. Let $\alpha_1, \beta_1, \gamma_1$ be the direction angles of ray PQ. From (1) on page 332,

$$\cos \alpha_1 = \frac{\Delta x}{\sqrt{(\Delta x)^2 + (\Delta y)^2 + (\Delta z)^2}}. \tag{9}$$

Since $\Delta t > 0$, we have $\Delta t = \sqrt{(\Delta t)^2}$. Hence, on the right in (9), we may divide the numerator and the denominator by Δt, with $\sqrt{(\Delta t)^2}$ used in the denominator:

$$\cos \alpha_1 = \frac{\Delta x / \Delta t}{\sqrt{(\Delta x/\Delta t)^2 + (\Delta y/\Delta t)^2 + (\Delta z/\Delta t)^2}}. \tag{10}$$

Thus, $\qquad \displaystyle \lim_{\Delta t \to 0} \cos \alpha_1 = \frac{dx/dt}{\sqrt{\left(\dfrac{dx}{dt}\right)^2 + \left(\dfrac{dy}{dt}\right)^2 + \left(\dfrac{dz}{dt}\right)^2}} = \frac{dx}{ds} = \cos \alpha,$

where α is a direction angle of the forward ray on the tangent at P. Similar remarks apply to $\cos \beta$ and $\cos \gamma$ for the forward tangent. Hence, we have shown that the direction (8) applies to the *forward tangent*.

Note 1. In (8), it can be remembered that *the direction cosines of the forward tangent are obtained on dividing the direction numbers* (2) *by a positive radical.*

EXAMPLE 2. Find the direction cosines of the forward tangent at the point where $t = 2$ on the curve

$$x = 3t - 2, \quad y = t^2 + t^3, \quad z = 4t - 3t^2. \tag{11}$$

SOLUTION. From (11): $\dfrac{dx}{dt} = 3, \dfrac{dy}{dt} = 2t + 3t^2, \dfrac{dz}{dt} = 4 - 6t.$ From (2) at $t = 2$, direction numbers for the tangent line are $3 : (4 + 12) : (4 - 12)$, or $3 : 16 : -8$. By Note 1, the cosines for the forward tangent are $\cos \alpha = 3/\sqrt{329}$, etc.

EXERCISE 149

Find equations for the tangent line and an equation for the normal plane for the curve. Also, find the direction cosines of the forward tangent at the point.

1. $x = 3t - 2, y = 2t^2 + t, z = 1 - 4t^3$; when $t = 2$.

2. $x = t^2 - t, y = t - t^{\frac{1}{2}}, z = 2t^2 - t$; when $t = 4$.

3. $x = 3t + t^2, y = 3t + 4t^3, z = 3t - t^2$; when $t = -1$.

4. $x = 3t + t^2, y = e^{2t}, z = 2e^{-t}$; when $t = 0$.

5. $x = 2 \cos t, y = 2 \sin t, z = 4t$; when $t = \frac{1}{4}\pi$.

6. $x = \sin 2t, y = \cos 2t$; $z = \tan t$; when $t = \frac{1}{6}\pi$.

7. $x = t^2 - 2, y = 3t + 4, z = 3t^3 - t^2$; at the point $(-1, 7, 2)$.

Note 1. Any regular curve C given by $x = f(t), y = g(t)$ in the *xy-plane* can be thought of as a curve *in space* as given by (1) on page 490 with $h(t) \equiv 0$. Then, with $dz/dt = 0$ and $\cos \gamma = 0$ throughout Section 236, we obtain facts about C in terms of direction angles, their cosines, and direction numbers in the *xy*-plane, where *we do not have to mention a third coordinate.* In particular, (5) of page 492 becomes the equation of the normal line for C in the *xy*-plane, because this line is the *xy*-trace of the normal plane for C when it is thought of as a *space curve.* *The student should review Note 1 on page 348.*

By Note 1, find equations for the tangent and normal to the plane curve.

8. $x = 4(t - \sin t), y = 4(1 - \cos t)$; at $t = \frac{5}{3}\pi$.

9. $x = t^2(3 + 2t), y = -t^3(3 + 2t)$; at $t = -3$.

10. $x = 3 \cos^3 t, y = 3 \sin^3 t$; at $t = \frac{2}{3}\pi$.

11. Show that the following curves (A) and (B) intersect at right angles at the point $(3, 2, 1)$:

  (A) $x = 3 - 2t, \quad y = 2e^t - 2 \sin t, \quad z = e^{2t}$;

  (B) $x = 2\tau + 5, \quad y = \tau^3 + \tau + 4, \quad z = 2 - \tau^2.$

12. Find the cosine of the angle made by the normal to the plane $x + y + z = 0$ and the tangent to the curve $(x = -2t, y = -t^2, z = t^3)$ at each point where the plane and curve intersect.

237. Motion of a particle in space

Let the position of a moving particle at any time t be specified by

$$x = f(t), \quad y = g(t), \quad z = h(t), \tag{1}$$

where (1) defines a regular path C. Let the positive direction for arc distance s on (1) be the direction in which t increases. For the motion (1), the time rates of change of the coordinates, v_x, v_y, and v_z, and the time rates of change of these quantities, a_x, a_y, and a_z, are

$$v_x = \frac{dx}{dt}, \quad v_y = \frac{dy}{dt}, \quad v_z = \frac{dz}{dt}; \tag{2}$$

$$a_x = \frac{d^2x}{dt^2}, \quad a_y = \frac{d^2y}{dt^2}, \quad a_z = \frac{d^2z}{dt^2}. \tag{3}$$

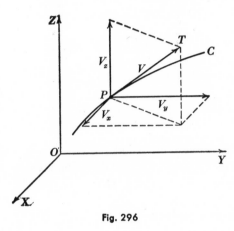

Fig. 296

Then, we define *vector velocities* V_x, V_y, and V_z in the directions of the axes with the corresponding scalar components (2). The *velocity* of the particle at any instant t is defined as the vector V which is the resultant of V_x, V_y, and V_z, as in Figure 296. Let v, or $|V|$, represent the magnitude of V, or the length of PT in Figure 296, and let α, β, γ be the direction angles of V. Then,

$$v = |V| = \sqrt{v_x^2 + v_y^2 + v_z^2}$$
$$= \sqrt{\left(\frac{dx}{dt}\right)^2 + \left(\frac{dy}{dt}\right)^2 + \left(\frac{dz}{dt}\right)^2} = \frac{ds}{dt}; \tag{4}$$

$$\cos \alpha = \frac{v_x}{v}; \quad \cos \beta = \frac{v_y}{v}; \quad \cos \gamma = \frac{v_z}{v}. \tag{5}$$

$$v_x = v \cos \alpha; \quad v_y = v \cos \beta; \quad v_z = v \cos \gamma. \tag{6}$$

At any point P in the motion of the particle, the magnitude of V is called the *speed* of the particle, and is given by (4). From (4) and (5),

$$\cos \alpha = \left(\frac{dx}{dt} \div \frac{ds}{dt}\right) = \frac{dx}{ds}, \quad \cos \beta = \frac{dy}{ds}, \quad \cos \gamma = \frac{dz}{ds}, \tag{7}$$

which are seen to be the direction cosines of the forward tangent at P. Thus, the instantaneous direction of the motion of the particle is the direction of the forward tangent, and the instantaneous speed in this direction is ds/dt.

Corresponding to (3), we introduce vectors A_x, A_y, and A_z, called the *accelerations* of the particle in the directions of the axes, with the scalar components in (3). Then, the acceleration of the particle is defined as the vector A which is the resultant of A_x, A_y, and A_z.

EXERCISE 150

The velocity V of a moving particle has the given scalar components. Find the speed, and the direction cosines of V. Also, in a coordinate system, draw a vector from any convenient point to represent V to scale.

1. $v_x = 3$; $v_y = 6$; $v_z = -2$.   **2.** $v_x = -6$; $v_y = 2$; $v_z = 9$.

The motion of a particle is determined by the equations, where t is the time. Find the speed, and the direction cosines of the velocity.

3. $x = 3t + 2$, $y = 2t + 4$, $z = -3t + 1$; when $t = 2$.

4. $x = e^{-t}$, $y = e^{-t} \cos t$, $z = 3t$; when $t = 0$.

5. $x = 3t^2 - 2$, $y = 3t + 5$, $z = t - t^3$; when $t = 3$.

6. $x = 2 \sin 2t$, $y = 3 \cos 2t$; $z = \sin t$; when $t = \frac{7}{4}\pi$.

7. $x = 2t \sin t$, $y = 2t \cos t$, $z = 4t$; when $t = 2\pi$.

8–9. Find the scalar components of the acceleration in the x-, y-, z-directions in Problems 4 and 5, respectively.

10. A particle moves on the curve with the equations $x = 4y^2$ and $z = 2y^2$. The y-component of the velocity is 2 units per second. Find the speed of the particle when $y = 2$, and the direction cosines of the instantaneous direction of motion.

11. A particle moves downward on the curve with the equations

$$4 - z = y^2 - x^2 \quad and \quad x + z = 2.$$

The speed in the z-direction is 3 units per second. Find the x-, y-, z-components of the velocity of the particle, its speed, and the direction cosines of the direction of the motion when $(x = 1, y = 2, z = 1)$.

238. Normal line and tangent plane to a surface

Let $F(x, y, z)$ have continuous derivatives F_x, F_y, and F_z, where

$$[F_x(x, y, z)]^2 + [F_y(x, y, z)]^2 + [F_z(x, y, z)]^2 \neq 0 \qquad (1)$$

at any point (x, y, z) which we consider. Let P:(x_0, y_0, z_0) be any point on the surface S with the equation $F(x, y, z) = 0$. Let C be any regular curve on S through P, as in Figure 297, where C has the parametric equations

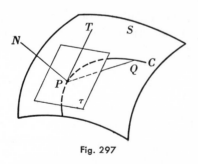

$$x = f(t), \quad y = g(t), \quad z = h(t), \qquad (2)$$

with $(x = x_0, y = y_0, z = z_0)$ at $t = t_0$. From page 491, the tangent line PT to C at P has the direction numbers

Fig. 297

$$f'(t_0) : g'(t_0) : h'(t_0). \qquad (3)$$

DEFINITION II. *A line l is a tangent line to a surface S at a point P if and only if l is tangent at P to a curve C on S.*

In Figure 297, secant PQ of the surface S is drawn through P and Q on the curve C through P. Then, as $Q \to P$ along C, PQ tends to the limiting position PT, which is a tangent to S at P.

THEOREM II. *All tangent lines at $P:(x_0, y_0, z_0)$ on a surface with the equation $F(x, y, z) = 0$ are perpendicular to the direction*

$$F_x(x_0, y_0, z_0) : F_y(x_0, y_0, z_0) : F_z(x_0, y_0, z_0). \tag{4}$$

Proof. 1. Let PT be the tangent at P to a curve C on S. By use of (2), along the curve C, the function $u = F(x, y, z)$ becomes a function of t which is equal to zero for all values of t, because C lies on the surface $F(x, y, z) = 0$. Hence, $du/dt = 0$. From (8) on page 477,

$$\frac{du}{dt} = F_x(x, y, z) \frac{dx}{dt} + F_y(x, y, z) \frac{dy}{dt} + F_z(x, y, z) \frac{dz}{dt} = 0. \tag{5}$$

2. In (5), place $t = t_0$. Then, $x = x_0, y = y_0, z = z_0$,

$$\frac{dx}{dt} = f'(t_0), \quad \frac{dy}{dt} = g'(t_0), \quad \frac{dz}{dt} = h'(t_0), \quad and$$

$$F_x(x_0, y_0, z_0)f'(t_0) + F_y(x_0, y_0, z_0)g'(t_0) + F_z(x_0, y_0, z_0)h'(t_0) = 0. \tag{6}$$

By (6) of page 336, equation (6) states that the tangent line PT, with direction numbers (3), is *perpendicular to the direction* (4).

DEFINITION III. *The line PN which is perpendicular to all tangent lines for a surface S at P is called the **normal line**, and the direction (4) of PN is called the **normal direction**, for S at P.*

DEFINITION IV. *The **tangent plane** for a surface $F(x, y, z) = 0$ at a point P is the plane τ through P perpendicular to the normal PN.*

From Theorem II, all tangent lines for the surface S at P lie in the tangent plane τ at P. Conversely, it can be shown, by details which we shall omit, that any line l through P in the plane τ is tangent to some curve C on S. Thus, the tangent plane at P may be described as *the locus of all lines tangent to the surface at P.* In the following summary, we use (4) as the direction of the normal line, and as the normal direction for the tangent plane.

SUMMARY. *At $P:(x_0, y_0, z_0)$ on a surface $F(x, y, z) = 0$:*

1. *The normal line has the equations*

$$\frac{x - x_0}{\left(\dfrac{\partial F}{\partial x}\right)_P} = \frac{y - y_0}{\left(\dfrac{\partial F}{\partial y}\right)_P} = \frac{z - z_0}{\left(\dfrac{\partial F}{\partial z}\right)_P}. \tag{7}$$

2. *The tangent plane has the equation*

$$\left(\frac{\partial F}{\partial x}\right)_P (x - x_0) + \left(\frac{\partial F}{\partial y}\right)_P (y - y_0) + \left(\frac{\partial F}{\partial z}\right)_P (z - z_0) = 0. \tag{8}$$

If a surface S has the equation $z = f(x, y)$, we may rewrite the equation in the standard form

$$F(x, y, z) = 0, \quad where \quad F(x, y, z) = f(x, y) - z.$$

Then, $F_x = f_x$, $F_y = f_y$, $F_z = -1$, and the normal direction (4) becomes

$$f_x(x_0, y_0) : f_y(x_0, y_0) : -1. \tag{9}$$

Equations (7) and (8) could be written by use of (9) instead of (4). However, it is unnecessary to introduce (9) because any particular case $z = f(x, y)$ can be written easily in the standard form $F(x, y, z) = 0$.

EXAMPLE 1. Obtain equations for the normal line, and an equation for the tangent plane at $(2, -3, 5)$ on the surface

$$z = 4x^2 + y^2 - 20. \tag{10}$$

SOLUTION. Write (10) in the standard form $F(x, y, z) = 0$, or

$$4x^2 + y^2 - 20 - z = 0, \quad with \quad F(x, y, z) = 4x^2 + y^2 - 20 - z.$$

Then, $F_x = 8x$, $F_y = 2y$, $F_z = -1$. At $(2, -3, 5)$, we have $F_x = 16$, $F_y = -6$, and $F_z = -1$. Hence, from (7) and (8),

the normal line is
$$\frac{x-2}{16} = \frac{y+3}{-6} = \frac{z-5}{-1};$$

the tangent plane is
$$16(x-2) - 6(y+3) - (z-5) = 0.$$

Let a curve C in the xy-plane be defined by the equation $f(x, y) = 0$, where $f_x^2 + f_y^2 \neq 0$. Then, C may be thought of as *the xy-trace of the cylinder S with the equation $f(x, y) = 0$*, as in Figure 298. The tangent line PT to C at a point $P:(x_0, y_0, 0)$ is the xy-trace of the tangent plane τ for S at P, and τ is perpendicular to the xy-plane. *The normal direction PN for the plane τ also is the direction of the normal to the curve C at P.* Then, with $F_z = 0$ and $z_0 = 0$ in (4), (7), and (8), we obtain the following results, where there is no need to mention a z-coordinate. The student should review Note 1, page 348.

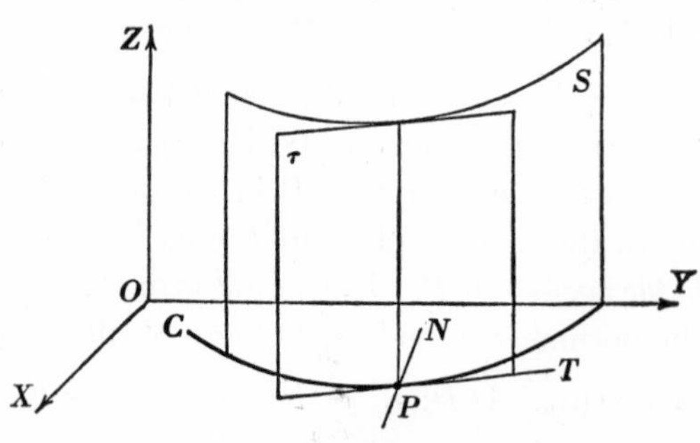

Fig. 298

THEOREM III. *At $P:(x_0, y_0)$ on a curve $f(x, y) = 0$ in the xy-plane, the normal has the direction numbers*

$$f_x(x_0, y_0) : f_y(x_0, y_0); \tag{11}$$

the normal line is
$$\frac{x - x_0}{f_x(x_0, y_0)} = \frac{y - y_0}{f_y(x_0, y_0)}; \tag{12}$$

the tangent line is
$$f_x(x_0, y_0)(x - x_0) + f_y(x_0, y_0)(y - y_0) = 0. \tag{13}$$

EXAMPLE 2. Obtain direction cosines for the normal, and equations for the tangent and the normal, at $P:(2, -3)$ on the curve in the xy-plane given by

$$x^2 + 4xy + 3y^2 - 6x + 5 = 0. \tag{14}$$

SOLUTION. 1. With $f(x, y) = x^2 + 4xy + 3y^2 - 6x + 5$,

$$f_x = 2x + 4y - 6; \quad f_y = 4x + 6y. \tag{15}$$

At $P:(2, -3)$, from Theorem III, the normal has the direction numbers $-14 : -10$, or $7 : 5$. Hence, direction cosines for the normal are

$$\cos \alpha = \frac{7}{\sqrt{74}} \quad and \quad \cos \beta = \frac{5}{\sqrt{74}}; \quad or \quad \cos \alpha = -\frac{7}{\sqrt{74}} \quad and \quad \cos \beta = -\frac{5}{\sqrt{74}}.$$

2. From (12), (13), and (15), we obtain

(the normal) $\qquad \dfrac{x - 2}{-14} = \dfrac{y + 3}{-10}, \quad or \quad 5x - 7y = 31;$

(the tangent) $\qquad 7(x - 2) + 5(y + 3) = 0, \quad or \quad 7x + 5y = -1.$

EXERCISE 151

Find equations for the normal line, and an equation for the tangent plane for the surface at the given point.

1. $x^2 + y^2 + z^2 = 121$, at $(2, -6, 9)$; at $(0, 0, 11)$.
2. $3x^2 + y^2 + 4z^2 = 20$, at $(0, -2, 2)$.
3. $x^2 - 3y^2 + 4z^2 = 28$, at $(2, -2, 3)$.   4. $4y^2 - x^2 = 20$, at $(4, -3, 5)$.
5. $z = 4x^2 - y^2$ at $(2, -3, 7)$.   6. $z = x^2 - xy - y^2$, at $(3, 2, -1)$.
7. $xz^2 + xy^3 - y^2z = 19$, at $(2, -1, -3)$.
8. $x^{\frac{2}{3}} + y^{\frac{2}{3}} + z^{\frac{2}{3}} = 9$, at $(8, -8, 1)$.   9. $z = 3x/(2y - x)$, at $(2, 3, \frac{3}{2})$.
10. $z = \sin xy + \tan(x + 2y)$, at $(0, \frac{1}{8}\pi, 1)$.
11. Prove that the normal to the sphere $x^2 + y^2 + z^2 = a^2$ at any point passes through the center of the sphere.

Obtain direction cosines for the normal at each given point on the curve in the xy-plane having the given equation. Write equations for the tangent and normal at the point.

12. $x^2 + 2xy - y^2 = -1$; at $(2, -1)$.   13. $x^2 - ye^x + y^2 = 2$; at $(0, 2)$.
14. $4x^2 + 9y^2 - 36 = 0$; at $(0, 2)$ and at $(3, 0)$.
15. $2 \cos x \sin y - 4 \sin x \cos y = 3$; at $(\frac{1}{4}\pi, \frac{3}{4}\pi)$.

Obtain an equation for the tangent plane for the surface at the point (x_1, y_1, z_1), and simplify by use of the given equation.

16. $x^2 + y^2 + z^2 = a^2$.   17. $2z = x^2 + 4y^2$.
18. $\dfrac{x^2}{a^2} + \dfrac{y^2}{b^2} + \dfrac{z^2}{c^2} = 1$.   19. $2az = \dfrac{x^2}{a^2} - \dfrac{y^2}{b^2}$.

Note 1. Two surfaces S and T are said to be tangent at a point of intersection P if they have the same tangent plane (or, normal direction) at P. S and T are said to intersect orthogonally at P if the normals (or, tangent planes) of S and T at P are perpendicular. The angle of intersection, θ, of a curve C and a surface S at any point of intersection P is defined as the acute angle made by the tangent to C and the tangent plane of S, at P. Or, θ is the *complement* of the angle between the normal of S and the tangent to C, at P.

Determine whether the surfaces intersect orthogonally, or are tangent.

20. $x^2 + z^2 = a^2$ and $y^2 + z^2 = a^2$, at $(a, a, 0)$.

21. $x^2 - 2y^2 + z^2 = 6$ and $4x - 2y^2 + z^2 = 10$, at $(2, 1, -2)$.

22. $4x^2 + 9y^2 + 2z^2 = 33$ and $4x^2 - 8y^2 + z^2 = 12$, at $(2, -1, 2)$.

23. Find the sine of the angle of intersection at $(2, -1, 1)$ of the surface with the equation $x^2 + 4y^2 + z^2 = 9$ and the curve given by

$$x = 2 - 3t, \quad y = -1 + 4t, \quad z = 1 - 2t.$$

★24. Let $P:(x_0, y_0, z_0)$ be a point on the surface $z = f(x, y)$. Then, at $(x = x_0, y = y_0)$, with arbitrary increments $dx = \Delta x$ and $dy = \Delta y$, we have $dz = f_x(x_0, y_0)\, \Delta x + f_y(x_0, y_0)\, \Delta y$. Prove that dz is equal to the increment of the value of z on the tangent plane to the surface at P corresponding to a change from $(x = x_0, y = y_0)$ to $(x = x_0 + \Delta x, y = y_0 + \Delta y)$.

239. Another form for the tangent to a space curve

Suppose that the functions $F(x, y, z)$ and $G(x, y, z)$ possess continuous derivatives $F_x, F_y, F_z, G_x, G_y, G_z$. Let C be the curve * defined as the intersection of the surfaces

$$F(x, y, z) = 0 \quad and \quad G(x, y, z) = 0. \tag{1}$$

At $P:(x_0, y_0, z_0)$ on C, the tangent line PT for C will lie in the tangent plane at P for each of the surfaces in (1). Hence, PT is *the intersection of the tangent planes*. Direction numbers for PT can be found from the fact that PT is perpendicular to the normals at P for the two surfaces. An exception to the preceding remarks arises when the surfaces have the same normal direction at P, and hence are tangent at P.

EXAMPLE 1. Obtain equations for the tangent line and an equation for the normal plane at $P:(1, 3, 2)$ on the intersection C of the surfaces

$$x^2 + y^2 + z^2 = 14 \quad and \quad 4x^2 + y^2 = 13. \tag{2}$$

SOLUTION. 1. Direction numbers for the normals of the surfaces at any point of intersection (x, y, z) are $\qquad 2x : 2y : 2z \quad and \quad 8x : 2y : 0.$ $\qquad(3)$

Hence, at P, the normal directions are $\qquad 1 : 3 : 2 \quad and \quad 4 : 3 : 0.$ $\qquad(4)$

---

* We assume that hypotheses are satisfied which make C a regular curve.

2. The tangent line PT for C at P is perpendicular to both directions in (4). Thus, from (5) on page 337, direction numbers for PT are $-6:8:-9$,

and PT has the equations $\qquad \dfrac{x-1}{-6} = \dfrac{y-3}{8} = \dfrac{z-2}{-9}.$ (5)

The normal plane for C at P has the normal direction $-6:8:-9$, and hence the equation $-6(x-1) + 8(y-3) - 9(z-2) = 0$.

EXERCISE 152

Find equations for the tangent line, and an equation for the normal plane at the point P on the curve of intersection of the surfaces having the given equations, or prove that the surfaces are tangent at P.

1. $x^2 + y^2 + z^2 = 81$, $x^2 + z^2 = 17$; at P:(4, 8, 1).
2. $x^2 + 2y^2 - z^2 = 21$, $2x^2 - y^2 = -1$; at P:(2, -3, 1).
3. $2z = 1 + x^2 + y^2$, $z^2 = x^2 + y^2$; at P:(0, 1, 1).
4. $x^2 + 3y^2 + 2z^2 = 49$, $y^2 - 2x^2 + z^2 = 10$; at P:(-2, 3, -3).
5. $x^2 + 3z^2 - 4y = 25$, $3x - 2y + z = 13$; at P:(3, -1, 2).
6. $z^2 = x^2 + y^2$, $y^2 = x^2 + z^2$; at P:(0, 1, 1).

240. A relation between areas on two intersecting planes

Let L_1 be a first plane BCE, visualized as horizontal, and L_2 be a second plane ACE intersecting L_1, to form a dihedral angle whose measure is an acute angle θ. In Figure 299, AC and BC are perpendicular to CE, so that $\angle BCA = \theta$; CN_1 and CN_2 are normals to L_1 and L_2, so that also $\angle N_1CN_2 = \theta$. Let T_2 be a rectangle with area K_2 in L_2, where one side is parallel to CE, and let T_1 with area K_1 be the vertical projection of T_2 on L_1. To obtain a relation between K_1 and K_2, we may think of moving T_2 in L_2 to a position where one side of T_2 is on CE so that T_2 is $ACEH$ and T_1 is $MCED$ in Figure 299. From right triangle MCA, where $\angle MCA = \theta$, we have $\overline{CM} = \overline{CA} \cos \theta$. Hence,

$$K_1 = \overline{CM} \cdot \overline{CE} = \overline{CA} \cdot \overline{CE} \cos \theta, \quad or \quad K_1 = K_2 \cos \theta. \tag{1}$$

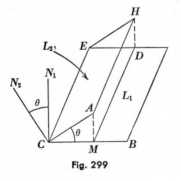

Fig. 299

Now, let R_2 be any region in L_2, with area A_2, and let R_1, with area A_1, be the perpendicular projection of R_2 on L_1. Then, by Definition II on page 375, A_2 can be expressed as the limit of a sum of areas of rectangles, which we may take of type T_2 as met above. Also, we may express A_1 as the limit of the sum of the areas of the corresponding rectangles T_1. Since (1) holds for each pair, T_1 and T_2, a similar relation holds for A_1 and A_2, or

$$A_1 = A_2 \cos \theta. \tag{2}$$

241. Area of a curved surface

We propose defining the notion of *area* for a curved surface S in an xyz-system of rectangular coordinates, where S is the locus of an equation $z = f(x, y)$ corresponding to points (x, y) in a region R of the xy-plane. We assume that $f_x(x, y)$ and $f_y(x, y)$ are continuous if (x, y) is in R.

Let P be any partition of R into subregions $\{T\}$, where the representative region T has the area ΔA, as in Figure 300. Construct a cylinder formed by moving a vertical line through all boundary points of T; this cylinder cuts out a piece T' of S. Now, choose arbitrarily a point $C:(x', y', 0)$ in T, and erect a vertical line at C to meet S at $Q:(x', y', z')$, where $z' = f(x', y')$. At Q,

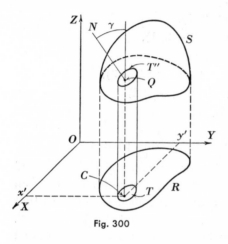

Fig. 300

construct the tangent plane τ for S. The cylinder with T as a base cuts a plane region T'' from τ. Let $\Delta\sigma$ be the area of T''; we visualize T'' as a desirable approximation to T', which is on S. Let γ be the *acute angle* between the normal QN to S and a vertical line at Q. Then, γ also is the measure of the acute angle between the xy-plane and the tangent plane τ. We observe that T'' projects into T on the xy-plane. Hence, by (2) on page 501, $\Delta\sigma \cos \gamma = \Delta A$. Or, on dividing by $\cos \gamma$, we obtain

$$\Delta\sigma = \sec \gamma \, \Delta A. \qquad (1)$$

Let d_P be the maximum of the diameters of all subregions $\{T\}$ of the partition P. Then, we *define* the area, σ, of S to be the limit, as $d_P \to 0$, of the sum of the areas $\{\Delta\sigma\}$ of all regions * $\{T''\}$ cut from the tangent planes to S at points corresponding to the subregions $\{T\}$. We recognize $\Delta\sigma$ in (1) as the general element of an approximating sum for a double integral over R, where $\sec \gamma$ is known as a function of x and y. Hence, from (1),

$$\sigma = \int\int_R \sec \gamma \, dA. \qquad (2)$$

From (9) on page 498, direction numbers for the normal to S at any point (x, y, z) are $f_x : f_y : -1$. Direction cosines of the normal then are obtained by dividing the direction numbers by $\pm \sqrt{1 + f_x^2 + f_y^2}$. Since the direction angle γ (with the z-axis) for the normal is to be acute, we use the negative sign for the radical, and obtain

$$\cos \gamma = \frac{1}{\sqrt{1 + f_x^2 + f_y^2}}, \quad or \quad \sec \gamma = \sqrt{1 + f_x^2 + f_y^2}. \qquad (3)$$

---

* It might seem more natural to take areas of elementary quadrilaterals inscribed in S. However such a method leads to insurmountable difficulties.

From (2) and (3), with f_x and f_y expressed in terms of x and y,

$$\sigma = \int\int_R \sqrt{1 + \left(\frac{\partial z}{\partial x}\right)^2 + \left(\frac{\partial z}{\partial y}\right)^2}\, dA. \tag{4}$$

Note 1. In obtaining (4), S was projected orthogonally (perpendicularly) on the xy-plane to obtain R. Similarly, if it is desirable to project S into a region R on the xz-plane, or on the yz-plane, we obtain, respectively,

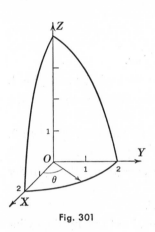

Fig. 301

$$\sigma = \int\int_R \sqrt{1 + \left(\frac{\partial y}{\partial x}\right)^2 + \left(\frac{\partial y}{\partial z}\right)^2}\, dA \quad and$$

$$\sigma = \int\int_R \sqrt{1 + \left(\frac{\partial x}{\partial y}\right)^2 + \left(\frac{\partial x}{\partial z}\right)^2}\, dA.$$

EXAMPLE 1. Obtain the area of that part, S, of the paraboloid $z = 4 - x^2 - y^2$ which is above the xy-plane.

SOLUTION. 1. In Figure 301, S projects into the region R bounded by the circle $x^2 + y^2 = 4$ in the xy-plane. From (4),

$$\sigma = \int\int_R \sqrt{1 + 4x^2 + 4y^2}\, dA. \tag{5}$$

2. We decide to compute (5) by use of an iterated integral in polar coordinates, because of the presence of $(x^2 + y^2)$. Then, with $x^2 + y^2 = r^2$, and $r\, dr\, d\theta$ as the element of area,

$$\sigma = \int_0^{2\pi}\int_0^2 r\sqrt{1 + 4r^2}\, dr\, d\theta = 2\pi\left(\frac{1}{12}\right)(1 + 4r^2)^{\frac{3}{2}}\Big]_0^2 = \frac{1}{6}\pi(17\sqrt{17} - 1).$$

EXAMPLE 2. Find the area of that part of the sphere $x^2 + y^2 + z^2 = a^2$ which is cut out by the cylinder $x^2 + y^2 = ax$.

SOLUTION. 1. The desired area σ is four times the area of that part, S, of the sphere cut out by the cylinder in the first octant, as in Figure 302. S projects into the region R in the xy-plane bounded by the x-axis and $x^2 + y^2 = ax$.

2. On differentiating with respect to x, and then with respect to y in the equation of the sphere, we obtain

$$2x + 2z\frac{\partial z}{\partial x} = 0 \quad or \quad \frac{\partial z}{\partial x} = -\frac{x}{z};\quad \frac{\partial z}{\partial y} = -\frac{y}{z};$$

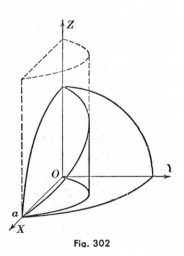

Fig. 302

$$1 + \left(\frac{\partial z}{\partial x}\right)^2 + \left(\frac{\partial z}{\partial y}\right)^2 = 1 + \frac{x^2}{z^2} + \frac{y^2}{z^2} = \frac{x^2 + y^2 + z^2}{z^2}. \tag{6}$$

From (4), by use of $x^2 + y^2 + z^2 = a^2$ twice in (6),

$$\sigma = 4a \int_0^a \int_0^{\sqrt{ax-x^2}} \frac{dy\, dx}{\sqrt{a^2 - x^2 - y^2}} = 4a \int_0^a \text{Arcsin}\, \sqrt{\frac{x}{a+x}}\, dx = 2a^2(\pi - 2).$$

In solving, we used integration by parts and substituted $u = \sqrt{x}$. Simpler details arise if cylindrical coordinates are used.

EXERCISE 153

Find the area of the specified region on the given surface.

1. The region cut from the plane $2x + 2y + 3z = 6$ by the cylinder $x^2 + y^2 = 4$.
2. The region on the plane $3x - 2y + 3z = 6$ above the rectangle on the xy-plane bounded by the lines $x = 0$, $x = 3$, $y = 0$, and $y = 2$.
3. The region on the cone $z^2 = 4x^2 + 4y^2$ above the rectangle of Problem 2.
4. Solve by use of polar coordinates in Example 2 on page 503.
5. The region cut from the paraboloid $z = 4a^2 - x^2 - y^2$ by the cylinder $x^2 + y^2 = a^2$.
6. The whole surface of the sphere $x^2 + y^2 + z^2 = a^2$.
7. The region on the hyperbolic paraboloid $z = y^2 - x^2$ cut out by the cylinder $x^2 + y^2 = 2$.
8. The region on the cylinder $x^2 + y^2 = 16$ cut out by the column bounded by the planes $y = 0$, $y = 2$, $z = 0$, and $z = 2$. (See Note 1 on page 503.)
9. The region cut from one of the cylinders $x^2 + y^2 = a^2$ and $x^2 + z^2 = a^2$ by the other cylinder.
10. The region cut from the sphere $x^2 + y^2 + z^2 = 8a^2$ by the cone $x^2 + y^2 = z^2$.
11. The region on the paraboloid $4z = 4 - x^2 - y^2$ cut out by the cylinder (in cylindrical coordinates) $r^2 = 4 \cos 2\theta$.
12. The region on the cylinder $x^2 + y^2 = 4$ included between the xy-plane and the plane $z = 3y$.
13. The region on the cylinder $z^2 = y$ cut out by the cylinder $x^2 = 3y$ and the plane $y = \frac{15}{4}$.
14. Refer to Example 2 on page 503. Find the area of that part of the cylinder which is cut out by the sphere.
15. The region on the sphere $x^2 + y^2 + z^2 = 2ay$ cut out by the cone $y^2 = x^2 + z^2$, by integration.
16. The region on the paraboloid $x^2 + z^2 = 8y$ cut out by the cylinder $x^2 = 2y$ and the plane $y = 6$.
17. In Problem 16, the region on the cylinder cut out by the paraboloid and the plane $y = 6$.

26

ADVANCED APPLICATIONS OF PARTIAL DERIVATIVES

242. Level curves and level surfaces

Consider a function $u = f(x, y)$, defined for some range of points (x, y) in the xy-plane. If u_0 is a value on the range for u, the locus of points (x, y) where $u_0 = f(x, y)$ is called a *level curve* for the function $f(x, y)$. Through any point (x_0, y_0) where $f(x, y)$ is defined, there passes just one level curve $u_0 = f(x, y)$, with $u_0 = f(x_0, y_0)$. Thus, the function $f(x, y)$ defines a family of level curves with the equation $u = f(x, y)$, where u is a parameter whose range is all values of $f(x, y)$. A chart showing a collection of these level curves, as in Figure 303, gives impressions about how u varies when the point (x, y) moves in the xy-plane. Also, such a chart gives indications about the surface with the equation $u = f(x, y)$, in xyu-space, just as a contour map gives information about elevations on the earth. A level curve $u_0 = f(x, y)$ is *the vertical projection on the xy-plane of the curve of intersection of the surface $u = f(x, y)$ and the plane $u = u_0$.*

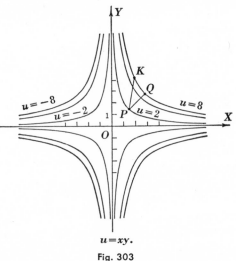

Fig. 303

ILLUSTRATION 1. Consider the function $u = xy$. If $u = 0$, we have $0 = xy$, whose graph in the xy-plane consists of the coordinate axes. If $u_0 \neq 0$, the level curve $u_0 = xy$ is a hyperbola. Various level curves are shown in Figure 303. With $x = 2$ and $y = 3$, we obtain $u = 6$. Hence, the level curve $xy = 6$ passes through the point $(2, 3)$.

Similarly, we may interpret a function $u = f(x, y, z)$ geometrically as defining a family of *level surfaces* in xyz-space.

505

ILLUSTRATION 2. For the function $u = x^2 + y^2 + z^2$, the level surfaces are the spheres whose centers are at the origin.

ILLUSTRATION 3. In physics, the notion of a *potential function* $f(x, y, z)$ in space proves important in the investigation of forces. Then, the level surfaces for $u = f(x, y, z)$ are the associated *equipotential surfaces*. Many other physical illustrations of level curves and level surfaces are met.

EXERCISE 154

Plot a collection of level curves for u. Also, by use of Theorem III, *page* 498, *find direction cosines in the xy-plane for the normal to the level curve through P.*

1. $u = x^2 + y^2$; normal at P:(4, 3); P:(0, 5); P:(5, $-$ 12).
2. $u = x^2 - y^2$; normal at P:(2, 1).   3. $u = ye^x$; normal at P:(0, 3).

For the given function u, find the equation of the level surface S through P. Find direction cosines for the normal to S at P.

4. $u = 4x^2 - y^2 + 3z^2$; at P:($-$ 1, 2, 1).
5. $u = x^2 + 4y^2 - z$; at P:(1, $-\frac{1}{2}$, $-$ 3).   6. $u = xyz$; at P:(2, $-$ 3, 1).

243. Directional derivatives in an xy-plane

In the xy-plane, let P:(x_0, y_0) be a particular point where the function $f(x, y)$ is defined. At P, let a direction PM be specified, with the direction angles α and β, as in Figure 304, and refer to this direction as "*direction* α, β." If R:(x, y) is on the directed line PM, let $s = PR$, where $s > 0$ in the direction α, β. Then, from (1) on page 345 with $z_0 = 0$ and $\cos \gamma = 0$, PM has the parametric equations, with s as the parameter,

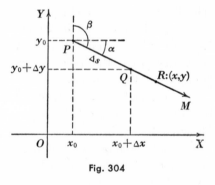

Fig. 304

$$x = x_0 + s \cos \alpha, \qquad y = y_0 + s \cos \beta. \qquad (1)$$

By use of (1), the function $u = f(x, y)$ becomes a function of s. If we move a distance Δs from P along PM to Q:($x_0 + \Delta x$, $y_y + \Delta y$), as in Figure 304, then $\Delta s = PQ$, and u takes on an increment Δu, where

$$\Delta u = f(x_0 + \Delta x, y_0 + \Delta y) - f(x_0, y_0).$$

Let us assume that $\Delta u / \Delta s$ has a limit as $\Delta s \to 0$. Then, this instantaneous rate of change, or du/ds at $s = 0$, is given a name as follows.

DEFINITION I. *The* **directional derivative** *of a function* $u = f(x, y)$ *at* P:(x_0, y_0) *in a direction* α, β *is the rate of change of u with respect to the distance s in the direction* α, β.

We shall denote the derivative in Definition I by

$$D_{\alpha,\beta}\, u\,|_P \quad or \quad D_{\alpha,\beta}\, f(x,y)\,|_P, \tag{2}$$

or simply by du/ds when the context makes the meaning clear. Then

$$D_{\alpha,\beta}\, u\,|_P = \lim_{\Delta s \to 0} \frac{\Delta u}{\Delta s} = \lim_{\Delta s \to 0} \frac{f(x_0 + \Delta x,\, y_0 + \Delta y) - f(x_0,\, y_0)}{\Delta s}. \tag{3}$$

If the direction α, β is the positive direction on the x-axis, Δs becomes Δx, the numerator in (3) becomes $f(x_0 + \Delta x,\, y_0) - f(x_0,\, y_0)$, and $D_{\alpha,\beta}\, u$ becomes $\dfrac{\partial u}{\partial x}$. Similarly, the directional derivative in the positive y-direction is $\dfrac{\partial u}{\partial y}$. Thus, a directional derivative is a generalization of a partial derivative.

THEOREM I. *Suppose that the function $u = f(x, y)$ has continuous derivatives f_x and f_y. Then, at $P:(x_0, y_0)$,*

$$\boldsymbol{D_{\alpha,\beta}\, u\,|_P = f_x(x_0,\, y_0)\, \cos\alpha + f_y(x_0,\, y_0)\, \cos\beta,\ or} \tag{4}$$

$$\boldsymbol{D_{\alpha,\beta}\, u\,|_P = \frac{\partial u}{\partial x}\cos\alpha + \frac{\partial u}{\partial y}\cos\beta.} \tag{5}$$

Proof. If $R:(x, y)$ is on PM, in Figure 304 on page 506, then x and y are given by (1) with $s = PR$, and $f(x, y)$ is a function of s. From (2), page 476,

$$\frac{du}{ds} = \frac{\partial f(x, y)}{\partial x}\frac{dx}{ds} + \frac{\partial f(x, y)}{\partial y}\frac{dy}{ds}. \tag{6}$$

From (1), $dx/ds = \cos\alpha$ and $dy/ds = \cos\beta$. Hence, (3) and (6) give

$$D_{\alpha,\beta}\, u\,\bigg|_P = \frac{du}{ds}\bigg|_{(s=0)} = f_x(x_0,\, y_0)\, \cos\alpha + f_y(x_0,\, y_0)\, \cos\beta.$$

Note 1. From page 498, recall that, at a point (x_0, y_0), the normal to a curve $f(x, y) = u$ has the direction numbers $f_x(x_0, y_0) : f_y(x_0, y_0)$.

EXAMPLE 1. Find the directional derivative of $u = x^2 + y^2$ at the point $P:(2, 3)$, (*a*) in the direction of $M:(5, 4)$; (*b*) in the direction opposite to PM; (*c*) in each of the directions on the normal PN at P to the level curve for $u = x^2 + y^2$ through P.

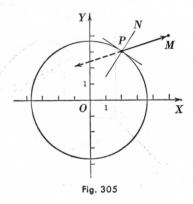

Fig. 305

SOLUTION. 1. From page 335 and Figure 305, direction numbers for PM are $3 : 1$, and the direction cosines of PM are seen to be $\cos\alpha = 3/\sqrt{10}$ and $\cos\beta = 1/\sqrt{10}$. Also, $u_x = 2x$ and $u_y = 2y$. Then, from (5),

$$D_{\alpha,\beta}\, u\,\Big|_{(2,\,3)} = \frac{(2x)(3) + (2y)(1)}{\sqrt{10}}\,\Big|_{(2,\,3)} = \frac{9}{5}\sqrt{10}. \tag{7}$$

2. The direction cosines of the direction opposite to PM are the *negatives* of the cosines for PM. Hence, from (5), the directional derivative in the opposite direction is the *negative* of (7), or $-\frac{9}{5}\sqrt{10}$.

3. Let the level curve C (a circle) through P be $u_0 = x^2 + y^2$, shown in Figure 305, where it is not necessary to obtain u_0. From Note 1, direction numbers for the normal PN to C are $2x : 2y$, or $2 : 3$ at $P:(2, 3)$. Hence, direction cosines for PN, in the two possible directions, are

$$\cos\alpha = \frac{2}{\pm\sqrt{13}} \quad and \quad \cos\beta = \frac{3}{\pm\sqrt{13}}.$$

From (5), $\qquad D_{\alpha,\beta}\, u\,\Big|_{(2,\,3)} = \pm\,\dfrac{2(2x) + 3(2y)}{\sqrt{13}}\,\Big|_{(2,\,3)} = \pm\,2\sqrt{13}.$

A useful interpretation of $D_{\alpha,\beta}\, u$ is associated with the surface K which is the graph of the function $u = f(x, y)$ in an xyu-system of rectangular coordinates, as in Figure 306. Let $P':(x_0, y_0, u_0)$ be a fixed point on K; the projection of P on the xy-plane is $P:(x_0, y_0, 0)$. In the xy-plane, let PM be the directed line through P with the direction angles α, β. Let C be the curve of intersection of K and the plane T perpendicular to the xy-plane along PM. In T, set up an su-system of rectangular coordinates, with PM as the s-axis and PP' as the u-axis. Then, the su-equation of C is $u = f(x, y)$, where x and y are given in (1). Recall that $D_{\alpha,\beta}\, u$ at P is equal to du/ds at $s = 0$. Hence, $D_{\alpha,\beta}\, u$ at P is equal to *the slope of the curve C at P* (compare page 360), or $D_{\alpha,\beta}\, u$ is the slope of the tangent $P'M$ to C at P'.

At this point, assume that the function $u = f(x, y)$ satisfies the condition $f_x^2(x, y) + f_y^2(x, y) \neq 0$ at all points (x, y). At $P:(x_0, y_0)$, let θ be the angle between direction α, β of PM and one direction on the normal PN to the level curve $u_0 = f(x, y)$ through P, as in Figure 307. Then, it can be proved that, at P,

$$\boldsymbol{D_{\alpha,\beta}\, u = \sqrt{f_x^2(x_0,\, y_0) + f_y^2(x_0,\, y_0)}\ \cos\theta.} \tag{8}$$

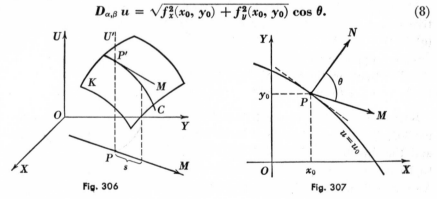

Fig. 306   Fig. 307

Proof. 1. Let α_1 and β_1 be the direction angles of PN in the xy-plane. From Note 1, PN has the direction numbers $f_x(x_0, y_0) : f_y(x_0, y_0)$. Then, from (5) on page 334 with just two cosines involved, and with derivatives evaluated at (x_0, y_0), we may take

$$\cos \alpha_1 = \frac{f_x}{\sqrt{f_x^2 + f_y^2}} \quad and \quad \cos \beta_1 = \frac{f_y}{\sqrt{f_x^2 + f_y^2}}. \tag{9}$$

2. In (4), divide and multiply on the right by $\sqrt{f_x^2 + f_y^2}$:

$$D_{\alpha,\beta} u = \left(\frac{f_x}{\sqrt{f_x^2 + f_y^2}} \cdot \cos \alpha + \frac{f_y}{\sqrt{f_x^2 + f_y^2}} \cdot \cos \beta \right) \sqrt{f_x^2 + f_y^2} \tag{10}$$

$$= (\cos \alpha_1 \cos \alpha + \cos \beta_1 \cos \beta) \sqrt{f_x^2 + f_y^2}. \tag{11}$$

From (1) on page 336, with γ_1 and γ_2 as 90°, and hence $\cos \gamma_1 = 0$ and $\cos \gamma_2 = 0$, note that (11) becomes $\sqrt{f_x^2 + f_y^2} \cos \theta$, where θ is the angle between the directions PM and PN. Hence, (8) has been proved.

From (8), $D_{\alpha,\beta} u$ attains its maximum absolute value if $\cos \theta = \pm 1$, or when $\theta = 0$ and $\theta = \pi$. Thus, the maximum occurs when the direction α, β falls along the normal PN, and then

$$(\textbf{maximum}\,|\,\boldsymbol{D}_{\alpha,\beta}\,\boldsymbol{u}\,|) = \sqrt{f_x^2(x_0, y_0) + f_y^2(x_0, y_0)}. \tag{12}$$

From (12), the maximum of $D_{\alpha,\beta} u$ at P is attained in that direction α, β on the normal PN which makes $D_{\alpha,\beta} u$ equal to the right-hand side of (12). From (4), this occurs when $\alpha = \alpha_1$ and $\beta = \beta_1$, as defined in (9).

Note 2. The maximum property of the derivative in the normal direction corresponds to intuitions associated with a chart like Figure 303 on page 505. In that figure, a displacement Δs from P to Q along the normal causes a change $\Delta u = 8 - 2 = 6$, whereas a larger displacement Δs from P to K is necessary to cause the same change $\Delta u = 6$.

ILLUSTRATION 1. In Example 1, the maximum directional derivative at $(2, 3)$ is $2\sqrt{13}$, in the direction with $\cos \alpha = 2/\sqrt{13}$ and $\cos \beta = 3/\sqrt{13}$.

Note 3. In applied mathematics, the **gradient** of a function $u = f(x, y)$ at $P:(x_0, y_0)$ is defined as a *vector* whose magnitude is *the maximum of* $D_{\alpha,\beta} u$, and whose direction is the direction of this derivative.

244. Directional derivatives and level surfaces in space

Space analogs for a function $u = f(x, y, z)$ are available concerning the principal items in Section 243. The directional derivative $D_{\alpha,\beta,\gamma} u$ at $P:(x_0, y_0, z_0)$ is defined as the instantaneous rate of change of u with respect to distance in the direction having direction angles α, β, γ. It is found that, with all derivatives calculated at P,

$$D_{\alpha,\beta,\gamma} u = f_x \cos \alpha + f_y \cos \beta + f_z \cos \gamma, \text{ or} \tag{1}$$

$$D_{\alpha,\beta,\gamma}\, u \;=\; \frac{\partial u}{\partial x}\cos\alpha + \frac{\partial u}{\partial y}\cos\beta + \frac{\partial u}{\partial z}\cos\gamma; \tag{2}$$

$$(with\ f_x^2 + f_y^2 + f_z^2 \neq 0) \qquad D_{\alpha,\beta,\gamma}\, u \;=\; \sqrt{f_x^2 + f_y^2 + f_z^2}\,\cos\theta, \tag{3}$$

where θ is the angle between the direction α, β, γ and that direction on the normal PN to the level surface for u through P with the direction cosines

$$\cos\alpha_1 = \frac{f_x}{\sqrt{f_x^2+f_y^2+f_z^2}}, \quad \cos\beta_1 = \frac{f_y}{\sqrt{f_x^2+f_y^2+f_z^2}}, \quad \cos\gamma_1 = \frac{f_z}{\sqrt{f_x^2+f_y^2+f_z^2}}. \tag{4}$$

The maximum of $D_{\alpha,\beta,\gamma}\, u\,|_P$ is $\sqrt{f_x^2+f_y^2+f_z^2}$, and occurs when α, β, γ is the direction (4) on the normal PN.

EXERCISE 155

Direction angles are represented as usual by α, β in the xy-plane, and by α, β, γ in an xyz-system of coordinates. Draw figures. Each problem refers wholly to the xy-plane if z is not involved.

Find the derivative of u at P in the specified direction.

1. $u = x^2 + y^2$, at P:(4, 3); (a) with $\alpha = 30°$ and $\beta = 60°$; (b) with $\alpha = 150°$ and β acute; (c) with $\beta = 135°$ and α obtuse; (d) in the positive direction of the x-axis, and in its negative direction; (e) in the direction from P to M:(9, 15); (f) in each direction along the normal to the level curve for $u = x^2 + y^2$ through P.

2. Repeat Problem 1 for $u = x^2 - y^2$ at P:(2, 1), with M:(5, 5).

3. Find the derivative of $u = x^2 + 2xy - y^2$ at P:(2, -3) in a direction (a) with direction numbers $3 : -4$; (b) with $\alpha = 45°$ and $\beta = 135°$; (c) upward, along a line whose inclination is 120°; (d) downward, along the preceding line; (e) toward the point (7, 9). (f) Find the maximum and minimum values of $D_{\alpha,\beta}\, u$ at P, and $\cos\alpha$ and $\cos\beta$ in each case.

4. Find the derivative of $u = (\ln y)\sin x$ at $(\frac{1}{6}\pi, e)$ in a downward direction which makes an angle of 30° with the positive direction on the x-axis; in an upward direction on a line whose inclination is 135°.

Find the maximum directional derivative of u and its direction.

5. $u = 4x^2 + y^2$, at $(-2, 3)$.   6. $u = e^{xy}$, at $(-3, 2)$.

Find the derivative of u at P in the specified directions.

7. $u = x^2 + y^2 + z^2$, at P:(3, -1, 2); (a) in a direction having the direction numbers $4 : 4 : 7$; (b) in the direction of M:(11, 3, 3); (c) in each direction normal to the level surface for u through P.

8. $u = x^2 - 2y + z$, at P:(-2, 1, 3); (a) in the direction of (4, 7, 10); (b) in each direction normal to the level surface for u through P.

9. $u = xyz$, at (4, -2, 3); in the direction of (10, 4, 10).

10. If $u = x^2 - 4yz + z^2$, (a) find the rate of change of u at the point P:(1, -2, 3) in the direction of M:(3, 4, -6); (b) find the maximum directional derivative of u at P, and the corresponding direction cosines.

★*The point Q is on the surface K with the given equation, and P is the pro-jection of Q on the xy-plane. Recall the geometrical interpretation of $D_{\alpha,\beta}\, u$ on page 508. (a) Find the rate of change of z with respect to horizontal distance, or $D_{\alpha,\beta}\, z$, in the direction PM. (b) Find the maximum absolute value of the slope at Q for vertical sections through Q on the surface.*

11. $z = x^2 + 2y^2$, at $Q:(1, 2, 9)$; from $P:(1, 2, 0)$ to $M:(13, -3, 0)$.

12. $z = x^2 - y^2$, at $Q:(4, 2, 12)$; from $P:(4, 2, 0)$ to $M:(1, 6, 0)$.

13. $x^2 + 4y^2 - z = 8$, at $Q:(1, -2, 9)$; from $P:(1, -2, 0)$ to $M:(6, 10, 0)$.

★**14.** The surface $z = xy - y^2$ is cut by the plane $4x = 3y$ in a curve C. At $(3, 4, -4)$ on C, find the absolute value of the rate of change of z on C with respect to horizontal distance.

245. Maxima and minima for functions of two variables

To say that a function $f(x, y)$ has a *maximum* * value, or a *minimum* * value, at (x_0, y_0) means that the corresponding following condition is satisfied at all points (x, y) sufficiently near (x_0, y_0) in the xy-plane.

For a maximum: $\qquad\qquad\qquad f(x, y) \leqq f(x_0, y_0).$ $\qquad\qquad\qquad$ (1)

For a minimum: $\qquad\qquad\qquad f(x, y) \geqq f(x_0, y_0).$ $\qquad\qquad\qquad$ (2)

Hereafter, assume that $f(x, y)$ possesses derivatives $f_x(x, y)$ and $f_y(x, y)$.

THEOREM II. *If $f(x, y)$ has a maximum or a minimum at (x_0, y_0), it is necessary that $x = x_0$ and $y = y_0$ satisfy the system of equations*

$$f_x(x_0, y_0) = 0, \quad f_y(x_0, y_0) = 0. \qquad\qquad (3)$$

Proof. Suppose that $f(x, y)$ has a maximum at (x_0, y_0). From (1) with $y = y_0$, we obtain $f(x, y_0) \leqq f(x_0, y_0)$, which shows that the function $f(x, y_0)$, *a function of x alone*, has a maximum value when $x = x_0$. Hence, from page 69, when $y = y_0$ the partial derivative of $f(x, y)$ with respect to x is equal to zero at $x = x_0$. That is, $f_x(x_0, y_0) = 0$. Similarly, from (1) with $x = x_0$, the function $f(x_0, y)$, *a function of y alone*, has a maximum at $y = y_0$. Hence, $f_y(x_0, y_0) = 0$. Thus, both of (3) must be satisfied. Similarly, (3) is true at a minimum.

In an xyz-system of coordinates, let T be the surface given by $z = f(x, y)$, as in Figure 308 on page 512. Then, if $f(x, y)$ has a maximum at (x_0, y_0), the corresponding point $P:(x_0, y_0, z_0)$ on T is *as high as*, or *higher than* all points on T near P. Similarly, a minimum for $f(x, y)$ corresponds to a *low point* on the surface T. From page 497, the equation of the tangent plane at any point $P:(x_0, y_0, z_0)$ on T is

$$f_x(x_0, y_0)(x - x_0) + f_y(x_0, y_0)(y - y_0) - (z - z_0) = 0. \qquad (4)$$

---

* Unless otherwise specified, *maximum* or *minimum* will refer to a *relative maximum* and *relative minimum*, respectively, at a point (x_0, y_0) such that $f(x, y)$ is defined in some circle in the xy-plane with (x_0, y_0) as the center.

Hence, from (3) and (4), if $f(x, y)$ has a maximum or a minimum at (x_0, y_0), the tangent plane τ at $P:(x_0, y_0, z_0)$ on the surface $z = f(x, y)$ is the horizontal plane $z = z_0$, as in Figure 308.

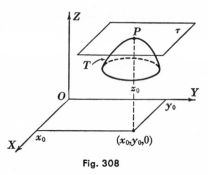

Fig. 308

Note 1. A result corresponding to Theorem II can be proved for functions of more than two independent variables. Thus, if $f(x, y, z)$ has a maximum or a minimum at (x_0, y_0, z_0), it is necessary that

$$f_x(x_0, y_0, z_0) = 0, \quad f_y(x_0, y_0, z_0) = 0, \quad f_z(x_0, y_0, z_0) = 0.$$

Problem 10 on page 514 will show that equations (3) are *not sufficient conditions* to imply a maximum or a minimum. The following tests present one set of sufficient conditions. They assume that $f(x, y)$ has continuous derivatives f_x, f_y, f_{xx}, f_{xy}, and f_{yy}. A proof of the tests is beyond the scope of this text.

SUMMARY. *Test for a maximum or a minimum of $f(x, y)$.*

I. *Solve the necessary conditions $f_x(x, y) = 0$ and $f_y(x, y) = 0$ to find all critical pairs $(x = x_0, y = y_0)$.*

II. *The function $f(x, y)$ has a relative maximum or a relative minimum at (x_0, y_0) in case*

$$[f_{xy}(x_0, y_0)]^2 - f_{xx}(x_0, y_0)f_{yy}(x_0, y_0) < 0. \tag{5}$$

Then,   *a maximum occurs if* $f_{xx}(x_0, y_0) < 0;$ (6)

        a minimum occurs if $f_{xx}(x_0, y_0) > 0.$ (7)

III. *No extremum occurs if "< 0" is changed to "> 0" in (5).*

Note 2. If "< 0" is replaced by "$= 0$" in (5), it can be shown that $f(x, y)$ may have a maximum, or a minimum, or neither at (x_0, y_0). The student should compare (6) with (2) on page 78. If we let $z = f(x, y)$, (5) becomes

$$\left(\frac{\partial^2 z}{\partial x\, \partial y}\right)^2 - \frac{\partial^2 z}{\partial x^2} \cdot \frac{\partial^2 z}{\partial y^2} < 0. \tag{8}$$

Note 3. From (5), $(f_{xy})^2 < f_{xx}f_{yy}$. Hence, f_{xx} and f_{yy} are of the same sign, and thus f_{yy} could be used where f_{xx} is found in (6) and (7).

EXAMPLE 1. Test the function $f(x, y)$ for maxima and minima:

$$f(x, y) = x^3 + y^3 - 3xy + 15. \tag{9}$$

SOLUTION 1. *Necessary conditions.* We find

$$f_x = 3x^2 - 3y = 0 \quad and \quad f_y = 3y^2 - 3x = 0. \tag{10}$$

From (10), $y = x^2$ and $x = y^2$. Hence, $x = x^4$, which gives $x = 0$ and $x = 1$. Then, (10) has the solutions $(x = 0, y = 0)$ and $(x = 1, y = 1)$.

2. From (9), $f_{xx} = 6x$; $f_{yy} = 6y$; $f_{xy} = -3$.

3. *Sufficiency test at* $(x = 0, y = 0)$: In (5),

$$[f_{xy}(0, 0)]^2 - f_{xx}(0, 0) f_{yy}(0, 0) = 9 - 0 > 0.$$

Hence, $(0, 0)$ gives neither a maximum nor a minimum.

4. *Sufficiency test at* $(x = 1, y = 1)$: In (5),

$$[f_{xy}(1, 1)]^2 - f_{xx}(1, 1) f_{yy}(1, 1) = 9 - (6)(6) = -27 < 0.$$

Hence, there is a maximum or a minimum at $(1, 1)$. Since $f_{xx}(1, 1) = 6 > 0$, a *minimum* exists. The corresponding minimum value of $f(x, y)$ is $f(1, 1) = 14$.

EXAMPLE 2. A rectangular box is inscribed in the sphere

$$x^2 + y^2 + z^2 = 49. \tag{11}$$

Find the dimensions for maximum volume.

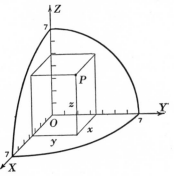

Fig. 309

SOLUTION. 1. Let V be the volume of that eighth of the box represented in Figure 309, where the corner $P:(x, y, z)$ is on the sphere. We have

$$V = xyz \quad and \quad x^2 + y^2 + z^2 = 49. \tag{12}$$

2. In (12), consider z as a function of x and y. Then, V is a function of x and y, and necessary conditions for a maximum are

$$\frac{\partial V}{\partial x} = 0 \quad and \quad \frac{\partial V}{\partial y} = 0, \tag{13}$$

where

$$\frac{\partial V}{\partial x} = yz + xy \frac{\partial z}{\partial x} \quad and \quad \frac{\partial V}{\partial y} = xz + xy \frac{\partial z}{\partial y}.$$

From (12),

$$2x + 2z \frac{\partial z}{\partial x} = 0 \quad or \quad \frac{\partial z}{\partial x} = -\frac{x}{z}; \quad \frac{\partial z}{\partial y} = -\frac{y}{z}. \tag{14}$$

After simplification, (13) becomes

$$yz - \frac{x^2y}{z} = 0 \quad and \quad xz - \frac{xy^2}{z} = 0, \text{ or}$$

$$y(z^2 - x^2) = 0 \quad and \quad x(z^2 - y^2) = 0. \tag{15}$$

From (15), since $x \neq 0$ and $y \neq 0$ for maximum volume, $z^2 = x^2$ and $z^2 = y^2$, or $x^2 = y^2 = z^2$. Hence, if there is a maximum for V, we have $x = y = z$.

3. The preceding details show that there is *just one* possible set of dimensions for a maximum volume. The geometrical setting convinces us that a maximum exists. Hence, without applying the sufficient conditions (5) and (6), we conclude that V has a maximum when $x = y = z$, and the box is a cube. From (11), $3x^2 = 49$ or $x = \frac{7}{3}\sqrt{3}$; the side of the maximum cube is $\frac{14}{3}\sqrt{3}$.

EXERCISE 156

Test the function for maxima and minima.

1. $2xy - x^2 - 2y^2 + 3x + 4.$ 2. $8x^3 + y^3 - 12xy + 8.$

3. $2x^2 + y^2 - 2xy - 4x + 3.$ 4. $x^4 - 4xy + 2y^2 - 5.$

5. $13x^2 + 16xy + 7y^2 + 10x + 2y - 5.$

6. $4x^2 - 16x - 3y^2 - 6y + 8.$ 7. $3xy + 4x^2 - 2y^2 - 5x - 7y + 3.$

8. $\cos(x + y) - 2x^2 - 2y^2 + 8x - 8y + 4xy$, if $0 < x < \frac{1}{2}\pi$ and $0 < y < \frac{1}{2}\pi.$

9. $z = \frac{1}{4}xy - \frac{1}{2x} - \frac{1}{y} + 7.$ 10. $z = \frac{x^2}{25} - \frac{y^2}{9}.$

Note 1. In Problem 10, consider the xz-trace and yz-trace of the hyperbolic paraboloid $z = f(x, y)$, as in Figure 223 on page 355. The saddle point of the surface, with $z = 0$, is obtained when $x = y = 0$. The traces show that z is less than zero, and also greater than zero in every neighborhood of $(x = 0, y = 0)$ in the xy-plane, however small this neighborhood may be. Hence, conditions (3) on page 511 are not sufficient conditions for a maximum or a minimum.

11. A rectangular bin with a capacity of 4000 cubic feet is to have an open top. Find the dimensions to minimize the material used for the bin.

12. Find the volume of the rectangular parallelepiped of maximum volume which can be inscribed in the ellipsoid $4x^2 + y^2 + 4z^2 = 12.$

13. By calculus, find the shortest distance between the point $(3, -3, 1)$ and the plane $2x - 6y + 3z = -22.$

14. By calculus, find the shortest distance between the lines

$$\frac{x-1}{2} = \frac{y-3}{1} = \frac{z+7}{2} \quad and \quad \frac{x+3}{3} = \frac{y+4}{-1} = \frac{z-5}{1}.$$

★15. By use of calculus, find the shortest distance between the point (x_0, y_0, z_0) and the plane $x \cos \alpha + y \cos \beta + z \cos \gamma = p$, where $\cos \alpha, \cos \beta, \cos \gamma$ are direction cosines for one of the directions normal to the plane.

★16. Let n sets of corresponding values of (x, y, z) be denoted by (x_i, y_i, z_i), with $i = 1, 2, \cdots, n$, where

$$\bar{x} = \frac{\sum_{i=1}^{n} x_i}{n} = 0, \quad \bar{y} = \frac{\sum_{i=1}^{n} y_i}{n} = 0, \quad \bar{z} = \frac{\sum_{i=1}^{n} z_i}{n} = 0.$$

We seek a_2, a_3, and b so that the function $z = a_2 x + a_3 y + b$ will give the best approximation *in the sense of least squares* for the values $(z_1, z_2, \cdots, z_n)$ when they are estimated by use of the pairs (x_i, y_i). That is, we desire a_2, a_3, and b so that the function

$$f(a_2, a_3, b) = \sum_{i=1}^{n} (z_i - a_2 x_i - a_3 y_i + b)^2$$

will have its minimum value. Obtain equations specifying necessary conditions on a_2, a_3, and b, and solve for them. The preceding results are fundamental in the theory of multiple regression in statistics.

246. Taylor's theorem for a function of two variables

Let the function $f(x, y)$ be defined and have continuous partial derivatives of all orders involved, at all points inside some circle in the xy-plane. Let (x_0, y_0) and $(x_0 + h, y_0 + k)$ be fixed points inside this circle. Define a function $G(t)$, where $0 \le t \le 1$, by the equation $G(t) = f(x, y)$, with *

$$x = x_0 + ht \quad and \quad y = y_0 + kt. \quad (1)$$

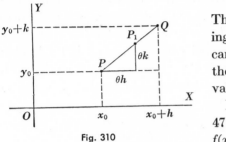

Fig. 310

Then, the results of Chapter 23, concerning Taylor's formula and Taylor series, can be extended to $f(x, y)$ by applying the previous results to $G(t)$ for particular values of t.

From (1), by application of (2) on page 476, with $x = x_0 + ht$ and $y = y_0 + kt$ in $f(x, y)$ and all of its partial derivatives,

$$\frac{dG}{dt} = \frac{df(x, y)}{dt} = \frac{\partial f}{\partial x}\frac{dx}{dt} + \frac{\partial f}{\partial y}\frac{dy}{dt} = hf_x + kf_y; \quad (2)$$

$$\frac{d^2 G}{dt^2} = h\left(\frac{\partial f_x}{\partial x}\frac{dx}{dt} + \frac{\partial f_x}{\partial y}\frac{dy}{dt}\right) + k\left(\frac{\partial f_y}{\partial x}\frac{dx}{dt} + \frac{\partial f_y}{\partial y}\frac{dy}{dt}\right), \text{ or} \quad (3)$$

$$G''(t) = h^2 f_{xx} + 2hk f_{xy} + k^2 f_{yy}. \quad (4)$$

Similarly, we may obtain

$$G^{(n)}(t) = \left(h\frac{\partial}{\partial x} + k\frac{\partial}{\partial y}\right)^n f(x, y)\Bigg|_{(x_0+ht,\, y_0+kt)}, \quad (5)$$

where we read the right-hand side as "h *times the partial derivative with respect to x, plus k times the partial derivative with respect to y, operating n times on* $f(x, y)$, *at* $(x_0 + ht, y_0 + kt)$."

ILLUSTRATION 1. Equation (5), with $n = 2$, checks with (4) because

$$\left(h\frac{\partial}{\partial x} + k\frac{\partial}{\partial y}\right)^2 = h^2\frac{\partial^2}{\partial x^2} + 2hk\frac{\partial^2}{\partial x\,\partial y} + k^2\frac{\partial^2}{\partial y^2}.$$

If $t = 0$ in (1), we find $x = x_0$ and $y = y_0$. Hence, from (2) and (5),

$$G'(0) = hf_x(x_0, y_0) + kf_y(x_0, y_0); \quad (6)$$

$$G^{(n)}(0) = \left(h\frac{\partial}{\partial x} + k\frac{\partial}{\partial y}\right)^n f(x_0, y_0), \quad (7)$$

where the expression for $G^{(n)}(0)$ means that the differentiation operator acts on $f(x, y)$, and then (x, y) is replaced by (x_0, y_0). We may apply Maclaurin's formula (3) of page 461 to $G(t)$. Then, for fixed t and n, there exists a number θ such that $0 < \theta < t$, and $G(t)$ is represented as follows:

* The point (x, y) varies on the line segment joining the points $P:(x_0, y_0)$ and $Q:(x_0+h, y_0+k)$, as in Figure 310.

$$G(t) = G(0) + tG'(0) + \frac{t^2}{2!} G''(0) + \cdots + \frac{t^{n-1}}{(n-1)!} G^{(n-1)}(0) + R_n, \quad (8)$$

where
$$R_n = \frac{t^n}{n!} G^{(n)}(\theta). \tag{9}$$

When $t = \theta$, equations (1) give $(x = x_0 + \theta h, y = y_0 + \theta k)$. This point is indicated as P_1 in Figure 310, and hereafter will be described simply as *a properly chosen point* $P_1:(x_1, y_1)$ *between* (x_0, y_0) *and* $(x_0 + th, y_0 + tk)$, where *"between" means "on the line segment between the given points."*

In (1), if $t = 0$, then $x = x_0, y = y_0$, and $G(0) = f(x_0, y_0)$. If $t = 1$, then $x = x_0 + h, y = y_0 + k$, and $G(1) = f(x_0 + h, y_0 + k)$. Hence, from (8) with $t = 1$ and $n = 1$, there exists a point (x_1, y_1) between (x_0, y_0) and $(x_0 + h, y_0 + k)$ such that

$$f(x_0 + h, y_0 + k) = f(x_0, y_0) + hf_x(x_1, y_1) + kf_y(x_1, y_1),$$

which is referred to as the *mean value theorem* for $f(x, y)$. If n is any positive integer, when $t = 1$ in (8) we obtain Taylor's formula for $f(x, y)$ with a remainder after n terms. In particular, when $n = 2$, there exists a point (x_1, y_1) between (x_0, y_0) and $(x_0 + h, y_0 + k)$ such that

$$f(x_0 + h, y_0 + k) = f(x_0, y_0) + hf_x(x_0, y_0) + kf_y(x_0, y_0) + R_2,$$

where
$$R_2 = \frac{1}{2!} [h^2 f_{xx}(x, y) + 2hk f_{xy}(x, y) + k^2 f_{yy}(x, y)]_{(x=x_1, y=y_1)}.$$

The Maclaurin series for $G(t)$ is

$$G(t) = G(0) + tG'(0) + \frac{t^2}{2!} G''(0) + \cdots + \frac{t^n}{n!} G^{(n)}(0) + \cdots. \tag{10}$$

When $t = 1$, equation (10) becomes

$$\left. \begin{aligned} f(x_0 + h, y_0 + k) = f(x_0, y_0) + [hf_x(x_0, y_0) + kf_y(x_0, y_0)] + \cdots \\ + \frac{1}{n!} \left(h \frac{\partial}{\partial x} + k \frac{\partial}{\partial y} \right)^n f(x_0, y_0) + \cdots. \end{aligned} \right\} \quad (11)$$

In (11), we may change the notation by using $x = x_0 + h$ and $y = y_0 + k$; $h = x - x_0$ and $k = y - y_0$. Then, (11) becomes

$$f(x, y) = f(x_0, y_0) + \sum_{n=1}^{\infty} \frac{1}{n!} \left[(x - x_0) \frac{\partial}{\partial x} + (y - y_0) \frac{\partial}{\partial y} \right]^n f(x_0, y_0), \quad (12)$$

which is referred to as the **Taylor series** *for $f(x, y)$ in powers of $(x - x_0)$ and $(y - y_0)$.* The series on the right in (12) converges, with $f(x, y)$ as the sum of the series, if and only if $R_n \to 0$ as $n \to \infty$, where R_n is given by (9) with $t = 1, h = x - x_0$, and $k = y - y_0$. In any application of (12) in this text, no discussion of R_n will be expected. If $x_0 = y_0 = 0$ in (12), the result is called the **Maclaurin series** for $f(x, y)$.

Note 1. Results similar to those just exhibited for $f(x, y)$ are available for a function of any number of variables, $f(x, y, z, w, \cdots)$.

EXAMPLE 1. If $f(x, y) = \sin xy + \sin x$, obtain the Taylor series for $f(x, y)$ in powers of $(x - \frac{1}{2}\pi)$ and y, through terms of degree 2.

SOLUTION. We shall use (12) with $(x_0 = \frac{1}{2}\pi, y_0 = 0)$. We have

$$f_x = y \cos xy + \cos x; \quad f_y = x \cos xy; \quad f_{xx} = -y^2 \sin xy - \sin x;$$

$$f_{xy} = \cos xy - xy \sin xy; \quad f_{yy} = -x^2 \sin xy.$$

At $(x = \frac{1}{2}\pi, y = 0)$, $f(x, y)$ and the derivatives become

$$f(\tfrac{1}{2}\pi, 0) = 1; \quad f_x = 0; \quad f_y = \tfrac{1}{2}\pi; \quad f_{xx} = -1; \quad f_{xy} = 1; \quad f_{yy} = 0.$$

Hence, from (12) with $(x_0 = \frac{1}{2}\pi, y_0 = 0)$,

$$f(x, y) = 1 + \frac{1}{2}\pi y + \frac{1}{2!}\left[-\left(x - \frac{1}{2}\pi\right)^2 + 2y\left(x - \frac{1}{2}\pi\right)\right] + \cdots. \qquad (13)$$

Comment. Series (13) could be used to compute approximate values for $f(x, y)$ if x is near $\frac{1}{2}\pi$ and y is near 0. The explicit terms on the right in (13) give a polynomial of degree 2 as an approximation to $f(x, y)$.

EXERCISE 157

Find the specified Taylor series by use of Section 246.

1. Expand $f(x, y) = \sin x + \cos xy$, (a) through the terms of the second degree in powers of $(x - \frac{1}{2}\pi)$ and $(y - 1)$; (b) through the terms of the fourth degree in powers of x and y.

2. Expand $(e^{xy} + \sin y)$ in powers of x and y through the terms of the third degree.

3. Expand $e^x \sin y$ in powers of x and y through the terms of the third degree, (a) by use of (12) on page 516; (b) by use of the Maclaurin series for e^x and $\sin y$, and then by multiplication of these series.

4. Expand $\sin (x + y)$ in powers of x and y through the terms of the third degree, (a) by use of (12) on page 516; (b) by use of the series for $\sin z$.

5. Expand $x^4 + 3x^3y + y^4$ in powers of $(x - 2)$ and $(y + 1)$.

By use of the first few terms in the Maclaurin series for the function on the left, show that it is approximately equal to the given expression if x and y are small. This assumes that the sum of any neglected terms of the series would be negligible when x and y are small.

6. $e^{-x} \sin y = y - xy$, approximately.

7. $e^y \ln (1 + x) = x + xy - \dfrac{x^2}{2}$, approximately.

8. Expand $e^{\frac{\ln y}{x}}$ in powers of $(x + 2)$ and $(y - 1)$, through the terms of the second degree.

9. Write out explicitly all terms for which $n = 3$ in (12) on page 516.

27

HYPERBOLIC FUNCTIONS

247. Definition of the hyperbolic functions *

Certain combinations of exponential functions arise so frequently that it proves convenient to introduce a related group of new functions, called the *hyperbolic functions* of a variable x. Their names are as follows, with the usual abbreviations in bold type:

hyperbolic sine of x,	**sinh x**;	*hyperbolic cosine of x,*	**cosh x;**
hyperbolic tangent of x,	**tanh x**;	*hyperbolic cotangent of x,*	**coth x;**
hyperbolic secant of x,	**sech x**;	*hyperbolic cosecant of x,*	**csch x.**

$$(1)$$

The functions $\cosh x$ and $\sinh x$ are defined by

$$\sinh x = \frac{e^x - e^{-x}}{2}; \quad \cosh x = \frac{e^x + e^{-x}}{2}. \tag{2}$$

The other hyperbolic functions are defined in terms of $\sinh x$ and $\cosh x$:

$$\tanh x = \frac{\sinh x}{\cosh x}; \quad \coth x = \frac{1}{\tanh x} = \frac{\cosh x}{\sinh x}, \tag{3}$$

$$\text{sech } x = \frac{1}{\cosh x}; \quad \text{csch } x = \frac{1}{\sinh x}. \tag{4}$$

We note a formal similarity between (3) and (4) and fundamental identities for trigonometric functions. Thus, it is not surprising that, in analogy with formulas of trigonometry, a long list of identities for hyperbolic functions can be established. First, the following identity (5) can be proved by inserting (2) on the left. Identities (6) are established by dividing on both sides of (5) by $\sinh x$, and $\cosh x$, in turn.

$$\cosh^2 x - \sinh^2 x = 1. \tag{5}$$

$$1 - \tanh^2 x = \text{sech}^2 x; \quad \coth^2 x - 1 = \text{csch}^2 x. \tag{6}$$

Then, various identities paralleling formulas from trigonometry, with certain

* Except where otherwise specified, all variables in this chapter will have just real values.

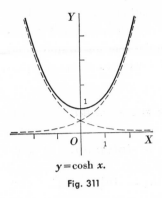

$y = \cosh x.$

Fig. 311

changes in signs, can be established for hyperbolic functions on the basis of (2)–(6). Consideration of these identities will be restricted to later exercises.

ILLUSTRATION 1. The full-line curve in Figure 311 is a graph of $y = \cosh x$, and the curve is called a **catenary.** We find

$$\cosh x - \tfrac{1}{2}e^x = \tfrac{1}{2}e^{-x}; \quad hence$$

$$\lim_{x \to \infty} (\cosh x - \tfrac{1}{2}e^x) = 0. \tag{7}$$

Similarly, $\quad \lim_{x \to -\infty} (\cosh x - \tfrac{1}{2}e^{-x}) = 0. \tag{8}$

The graphs of $y = \tfrac{1}{2}e^{-x}$ and $y = \tfrac{1}{2}e^x$ are shown by broken-line curves in Figure 311. From (7) and (8), the graph of $y = \cosh x$ has the graphs of $y = \tfrac{1}{2}e^x$ and $y = \tfrac{1}{2}e^{-x}$ as *asymptotic curves.* Similarly, the graph of $y = \sinh x$, in Figure 312, has the asymptotic curves $y = \tfrac{1}{2}e^x$ and $y = -\tfrac{1}{2}e^{-x}$.

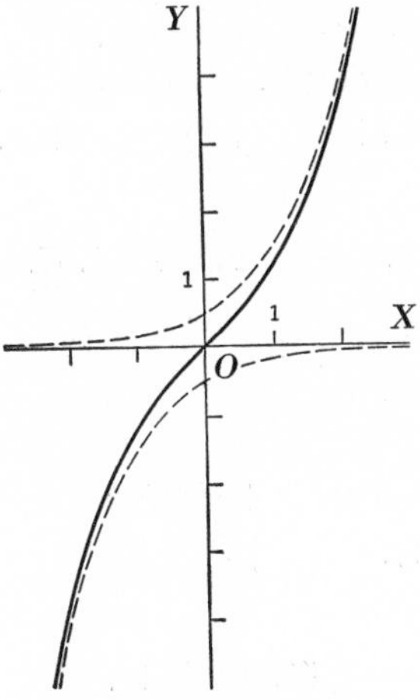

ILLUSTRATION 2. From (2) and (3),

$$\tanh x = \frac{e^x - e^{-x}}{e^x + e^{-x}}.$$

A graph of $y = \tanh x$ is shown in Figure 313. We verify that $\tanh x \to 1$ as $x \to \infty$, and $\tanh x \to -1$ when $x \to -\infty$.

ILLUSTRATION 3. From (2), $\sinh(-x) = -\sinh x$ and $\cosh(-x) = \cosh x$. Thus, $\cosh x$ is an *even* function of x, while $\sinh x$ changes sign if x is replaced by $-x$. From Table V,

$$\sinh .6 = .6367; \quad hence \quad \sinh(-.6) = -.6367.$$

$y = \sinh x.$

Fig. 312

ILLUSTRATION 4. If $a > 0$, the graph of

$$y = a \cosh \frac{x}{a}, \quad or \quad y = \frac{a}{2}\left(e^{\frac{x}{a}} + e^{-\frac{x}{a}}\right)$$

is called a catenary (see page 595).

ILLUSTRATION 5. From (2),

$$\frac{d \sinh x}{dx} = \frac{e^x + e^{-x}}{2} = \cosh x;$$

$$\frac{d \cosh x}{dx} = \frac{e^x - e^{-x}}{2} = \sinh x.$$

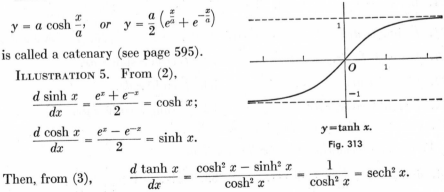

$y = \tanh x.$

Fig. 313

Then, from (3), $\quad \dfrac{d \tanh x}{dx} = \dfrac{\cosh^2 x - \sinh^2 x}{\cosh^2 x} = \dfrac{1}{\cosh^2 x} = \operatorname{sech}^2 x.$

Similarly, derivatives of the other hyperbolic functions can be found by use of (3)–(6). Then, from these derivatives, we obtain corresponding differentials and indefinite integrals. Only those formulas relating to sinh x and cosh x will be of importance for us later. In the following formulas, u represents any differentiable function of x.

$$\frac{d \sinh u}{dx} = \cosh u \frac{du}{dx}, \quad or \quad d \sinh u = \cosh u \, du. \tag{9}$$

$$\frac{d \cosh u}{dx} = \sinh u \frac{du}{dx}, \quad or \quad d \cosh u = \sinh u \, du. \tag{10}$$

$$\int \sinh u \, du = \cosh u + C; \quad \int \cosh u \, du = \sinh u + C. \tag{11}$$

EXERCISE 158

1. Obtain expressions in terms of e^x and e^{-x} for coth x, sech x, and csch x.

Investigate the graph of the function, determining the ranges for x and y, any horizontal or vertical asymptotes, extrema, and inflection points. Use Table V.

2. $y = \sinh x$.   **3.** $y = \cosh x$.   **4.** $y = \tanh x$.   **5.** $y = \coth x$.

Find the quantity by interpolation in Table V.

6. sinh .273.   **7.** cosh .784.   **8.** cosh 2.13.   **9.** sinh 1.67.

Prove the identity.

10. $\sinh (x + y) = \sinh x \cosh y + \cosh x \sinh y$.

11. $\cosh (x + y) = \cosh x \cosh y + \sinh x \sinh y$.

12. $\sinh 2x = 2 \sinh x \cosh x$.   **13.** $\cosh 2x = \cosh^2 x + \sinh^2 x$.

14. $\sinh^2 x = \frac{1}{2}(\cosh 2x - 1)$; $\cosh^2 x = \frac{1}{2}(\cosh 2x + 1)$.

Find the derivative of the function.

15. $\sinh 3x$.   **16.** $\cosh x^3$.   **17.** $\tanh 4x$.

18. $\coth x$.   **19.** $\tanh \frac{1}{3}x$.   **20.** $\cosh^2 2x$.

Evaluate the limit or integral.

21. $\lim\limits_{x \to 0} \dfrac{\sinh x}{x}$.   **22.** $\lim\limits_{x \to 0} \dfrac{\cosh x - 1}{x}$.   **23.** $\lim\limits_{x \to 0} \dfrac{x}{\tanh x}$.

24. $\int \sinh 4x \, dx$.   **25.** $\int \cosh 2x \, dx$.   **26.** $\int x \sinh x \, dx$.

27. $\int x \cosh 3x \, dx$.   **28.** $\int \cosh x \sinh x \, dx$.

29. $\int \cosh^2 x \, dx$.   **30.** $\int \cosh^3 x \, dx$.

31. $\int \sinh^2 x \cosh^3 x \, dx$.   **32.** $\int \sinh^2 x \cosh^2 x \, dx$.

33. Find the derivatives of sech x and csch x.

Verify the Maclaurin series for the function.

34. $\sinh x = x + \dfrac{x^3}{3!} + \dfrac{x^5}{5!} + \cdots$.   **35.** $\cosh x = 1 + \dfrac{x^2}{2!} + \dfrac{x^4}{4!} + \cdots$.

248. Inverse hyperbolic functions

If $x = \sinh y$, we say that "*y is the inverse hyperbolic sine of x*," and write $y = \sinh^{-1} x$. Similarly we introduce inverses for each of the hyperbolic functions. Thus, by definition,

$$y = \sinh^{-1} x \quad means\ that \quad x = \sinh y; \tag{1}$$

$$y = \cosh^{-1} x \quad means\ that \quad x = \cosh y; \tag{2}$$

$$y = \tanh^{-1} x \quad means\ that \quad x = \tanh y. \tag{3}$$

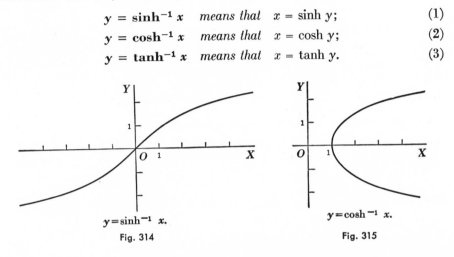

$y = \sinh^{-1} x.$

Fig. 314

$y = \cosh^{-1} x.$

Fig. 315

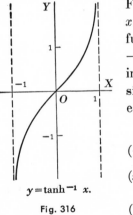

$y = \tanh^{-1} x.$

Fig. 316

From Figures 311–313, on interchanging the roles of x and y, we obtain the graphs of the preceding inverse functions in Figures 314–316. The range for x is $-\infty < x < \infty$ in (1); $x \geqq 1$ in (2); $-1 < x < 1$ in (3). Notice that $\sinh^{-1} x$ and $\tanh^{-1} x$ are **single-valued**, while $\cosh^{-1} x$ **has two values** for each value on the range for x.

It can be proved that

$$(-\infty < x < \infty) \quad \sinh^{-1} x = \ln (x + \sqrt{x^2 + 1}); \tag{4}$$

$$(x \geqq 1) \quad \cosh^{-1} x = \pm \ln (x + \sqrt{x^2 - 1}); \tag{5}$$

$$(-1 < x < 1) \quad \tanh^{-1} x = \frac{1}{2} \ln \frac{1 + x}{1 - x}. \tag{6}$$

Proof of (4). From (1), $\quad x = \frac{1}{2}(e^y - e^{-y}), \quad or \quad e^{2y} - 2xe^y - 1 = 0. \tag{7}$

In (7), let $u = e^y$. Then, $\qquad\qquad u^2 - 2xu - 1 = 0.$

Hence, on solving for u by the quadratic formula, we obtain

$$e^y = x \pm \sqrt{x^2 + 1}. \tag{8}$$

In (8), we must use $+ \sqrt{x^2 + 1}$ because $e^y > 0$. Thus,

$$e^y = x + \sqrt{x^2 + 1} \quad and \quad y = \ln (x + \sqrt{x^2 + 1}).$$

ILLUSTRATION 1. To obtain $v = \cosh^{-1} 1.1945$, write $\cosh v = 1.1945$. In Table V, $\cosh .61 = 1.1919$ and $\cosh .62 = 1.1984$. By interpolation,

$$v = \cosh^{-1} 1.1945 = .61 + \tfrac{2}{5}(.01) = .614.$$

Proof of (5). Similarly as in (8), from (2) with $x \geqq 1$,

$$y = \cosh^{-1} x = \ln (x \pm \sqrt{x^2 - 1}). \tag{9}$$

Since $\quad x - \sqrt{x^2 - 1} = \dfrac{(x - \sqrt{x^2 - 1})(x + \sqrt{x^2 - 1})}{x + \sqrt{x^2 - 1}} = \dfrac{1}{x + \sqrt{x^2 - 1}},$

we obtain $\ln (x - \sqrt{x^2 - 1}) = - \ln (x + \sqrt{x^2 - 1})$, and (9) gives (5).

Hereafter, unless otherwise specified, let "**Cosh**$^{-1}$ **x**" denote the *non-negative value* on the right in (5), and call the resulting function the **principal value**, Cosh^{-1} x. Thus, Cosh^{-1} $x = \ln (x + \sqrt{x^2 - 1})$.

By differentiation on the right in (4)–(6), we obtain

$$\frac{d \sinh^{-1} x}{dx} = \frac{1}{\sqrt{1 + x^2}}; \qquad \frac{d \, \text{Cosh}^{-1} x}{dx} = \frac{1}{\sqrt{x^2 - 1}}; \tag{10}$$

$$\frac{d \tanh^{-1} x}{dx} = \frac{1}{1 - x^2}. \tag{11}$$

From (10) and (11), corresponding forms are obtained for derivatives, differentials, and indefinite integrals by familiar methods:

$$\frac{d \sinh^{-1} u}{dx} = \frac{1}{\sqrt{1 + u^2}} \frac{du}{dx}, \quad or \quad d \sinh^{-1} u = \frac{du}{\sqrt{1 + u^2}}. \tag{12}$$

$$\frac{d \, \text{Cosh}^{-1} u}{dx} = \frac{1}{\sqrt{u^2 - 1}} \frac{du}{dx}, \quad or \quad d \, \text{Cosh}^{-1} u = \frac{du}{\sqrt{u^2 - 1}}. \tag{13}$$

$$\frac{d \tanh^{-1} u}{du} = \frac{1}{1 - u^2} \frac{du}{dx}, \quad or \quad d \tanh^{-1} u = \frac{du}{1 - u^2}. \tag{14}$$

$$\int \frac{du}{\sqrt{a^2 + u^2}} = \sinh^{-1} \frac{u}{a} + C. \tag{15}$$

$(u > a)$ $\qquad\qquad \displaystyle\int \frac{du}{\sqrt{u^2 - a^2}} = \text{Cosh}^{-1} \frac{u}{a} + C. \tag{16}$

$(u < -a)$ $\qquad\qquad\qquad\qquad = - \text{Cosh}^{-1} \left| \frac{u}{a} \right| + C. \tag{17}$

ILLUSTRATION 2. From (10), $\qquad \displaystyle\int \frac{dw}{\sqrt{1 + w^2}} = \sinh^{-1} w + C.$

Then, with $w = \dfrac{u}{a}$, $\quad \displaystyle\int \frac{du}{\sqrt{a^2 + u^2}} = \frac{1}{a} \int \frac{du}{\sqrt{1 + \left(\dfrac{u}{a}\right)^2}} = \sinh^{-1} \frac{u}{a} + C.$

By use of (15), and (46) on page 586 with $(u^2 + a^2)$, we justify the remark about $\sinh^{-1}(u/a)$ in Note 6 on page 585.

ILLUSTRATION 3. By use of (15),

$$\int_{.4}^{.6} \frac{dx}{\sqrt{4+9x^2}} = \frac{1}{3}\int_{.4}^{.6} \frac{3\,dx}{\sqrt{4+(3x)^2}} = \frac{1}{3}\sinh^{-1}\frac{3x}{2}\Big]_{.4}^{.6}$$

$$= \tfrac{1}{3}(\sinh^{-1}.9 - \sinh^{-1}.6) = .079. \qquad \text{(interpolation in Table V)}$$

ILLUSTRATION 4. From (10),

$$(\textit{when } w > 1) \qquad\qquad \int \frac{dw}{\sqrt{w^2-1}} = \text{Cosh}^{-1}\,w + C. \qquad (18)$$

The left-hand side of (18) is well defined when $w < -1$ as well as when $w > 1$, but $\text{Cosh}^{-1}w$ is defined only when $w \geq 1$. Now, suppose that $w < -1$. Then, with $z = -w$, we have $z > 1$ and (18) applies to give

$$\int \frac{dw}{\sqrt{w^2-1}} = -\int \frac{dz}{\sqrt{z^2-1}} = -\text{Cosh}^{-1}\,z + C. \qquad (19)$$

Since $z = |w|$, in (19) we have proved that

$$(\textit{when } w < -1) \qquad\qquad \int \frac{dw}{\sqrt{w^2-1}} = -\text{Cosh}^{-1}|w| + C. \qquad (20)$$

From (18) and (20), we may prove (16) and (17).

ILLUSTRATION 5. $\qquad \int_5^6 \frac{dx}{\sqrt{x^2-9}} = \text{Cosh}^{-1}\frac{x}{3}\Big]_5^6 = .22. \qquad \text{(Table V)}$

ILLUSTRATION 6. To evaluate the following integral, use (17):

$$I = \int_{-6}^{-5} \frac{dx}{\sqrt{x^2-9}} = -\text{Cosh}^{-1}\Big|\frac{x}{3}\Big|\Big]_{-6}^{-5} = -(\text{Cosh}^{-1}1.6667 - \text{Cosh}^{-1}2) = .22.$$

When an extensive table of values of the hyperbolic functions is available, (15)–(17) sometimes are more convenient than the corresponding logarithmic formula (46) in Table VII, for computing definite integrals. Also, observe (25_1) and (25_2) in Table VII, involving the inverse hyperbolic tangent and cotangent.

EXAMPLE 1. Prove that, if $a > 0$,

$$(\textit{when } u \geq a) \qquad \ln|u + \sqrt{u^2-a^2}| = \text{Cosh}^{-1}\Big|\frac{u}{a}\Big| + \ln a; \qquad (21)$$

$$(\textit{when } u \leq -a) \qquad\qquad = -\text{Cosh}^{-1}\Big|\frac{u}{a}\Big| + \ln a. \qquad (22)$$

SOLUTION. 1. We verify that $(u + \sqrt{u^2-a^2})$ is positive or negative according as $u > a$ or $u < -a$. Hence, the absolute value signs are redundant if $u \geq a$, in (21), but are essential in (22).

2. Assume that $u \geqq a$. Then, from (5) with "+" on the right,

$$\ln (u + \sqrt{u^2 - a^2}) = \ln a \left(\frac{u}{a} + \sqrt{\left(\frac{u}{a}\right)^2 - 1} \right) = \ln a + \text{Cosh}^{-1} \frac{u}{a}. \tag{23}$$

3. Assume that $u \leqq -a$, and let $w = -u = |u|$. Then,

$$\ln |u + \sqrt{u^2 - a^2}| = \ln |-w + \sqrt{w^2 - a^2}|.$$

Since $\quad -w + \sqrt{w^2 - a^2} = \dfrac{(\sqrt{w^2 - a^2} - w)(\sqrt{w^2 - a^2} + w)}{\sqrt{w^2 - a^2} + w} = \dfrac{-a^2}{\sqrt{w^2 - a^2} + w},$

$$\ln |-w + \sqrt{w^2 - a^2}| = \ln \frac{a^2}{\sqrt{w^2 - a^2} + w}$$

$$= 2 \ln a - \ln (\sqrt{w^2 - a^2} + w)$$

[from (23)] $\qquad = 2 \ln a - \text{Cosh}^{-1} \dfrac{w}{a} - \ln a = \ln a - \text{Cosh}^{-1} \left| \dfrac{u}{a} \right|.$

Notice that the right-hand side in (21) or (22) is a hyperbolic term *plus a constant*. Thus, the hyperbolic term may be used in place of the left-hand side, in the formula for any indefinite integral mentioned in Note 6 on page 585.

<h3 style="text-align:center">EXERCISE 159</h3>

1–20. Solve Problems 1–20 of Exercise 64 on page 231 by use of hyperbolic forms for the integrals.

21. Prove (6) on page 521, and a corresponding formula for coth⁻¹ x.

★22. Prove (25_1) and (25_2) in Table VII.

★Evaluate the integral by use of (25_1) and (25_2) in Table VII.

23–36. Solve problems 1–14 on page 226.

249. Geometric interpretation of hyperbolic functions

ILLUSTRATION 1. Let α be any angle and let $x = \cos \alpha$. For simplicity, assume that $0 < \alpha < \frac{1}{2}\pi$. The circle in Figure 317 is a graph of $x^2 + y^2 = 1$. In Figure 317, construct $\angle XOP = \alpha$ and $\angle QOX = \alpha$, and let P have the coordinates (x, y). Then $OM = \cos \alpha = x$. The area, A, of the sector QOP of the circle is given by $\frac{1}{2}r^2(2\alpha)$, with $r = 1$, or

$$A = \alpha = \text{Cos}^{-1} x, \tag{1}$$

where we use $\text{Cos}^{-1} x$ in place of Arccos x.

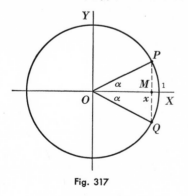

Fig. 317

ILLUSTRATION 2. Figure 318 on page 525 shows a branch of the equilateral hyperbola $x^2 - y^2 = 1$. For any value of $x \geqq 1$, locate the corresponding points $P:(x, y)$ and $Q:(x, -y)$ on the hyperbola; let A be the area of the ruled sector OPQ. Then, by subtracting the area of the region bounded by the hyperbola and PQ, from the area of $\triangle OPQ$, we obtain

$$A = (OM)(MP) - 2\int_1^x y \, dx = x\sqrt{x^2 - 1} - 2\int_1^x \sqrt{x^2 - 1} \, dx.$$

By use of the hyperbolic form for (41) in Table VII,

$$2\int_0^x \sqrt{x^2 - 1} \, dx = x\sqrt{x^2 - 1} - \text{Cosh}^{-1} x, \text{ and hence}$$

$$A = \text{Cosh}^{-1} x. \tag{2}$$

Let A be any number, to be interpreted as *the measure of an angle*, or *area* in Figure 317, and as the measure of *an area* in Figure 318. In either case, let x be the abscissa of the corresponding point P determined by A. Then, from (1), we may define $\text{Cos}^{-1} x$ by the relation $A = \text{Cos}^{-1} x$, or define $\cos A$ by the relation $x = \cos A$. From (2), similarly, we may define $\text{Cosh}^{-1} x$, or $\cosh A$, by the relation $A = \text{Cosh}^{-1} x$, or $x = \cosh A$. Although these definitions would be inconvenient, the similarity of the geometric backgrounds in Figures 317 and 318 justifies the similarities of the notations for trigonometric and hyperbolic functions. Also, we are led to anticipate the analogies which we have observed between properties of the two types of functions. Moreover, the preceding geometric backgrounds justify the names *circular functions* and *hyperbolic functions*, as previously applied.

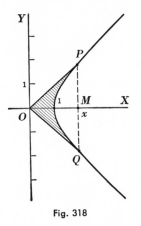

Fig. 318

Note 1. From Euler's formula, (3) on page 473, since $\cos(-x) = \cos x$ and $\sin(-x) = -\sin x$, we obtain the useful expression

$$e^{-ix} = \cos(-x) + i \sin(-x), \text{ or}$$

$$e^{-ix} = \cos x - i \sin x. \tag{3}$$

Also, $\qquad\qquad e^{ix} = \cos x + i \sin x. \tag{4}$

Hence, on adding and then subtracting, we find

$$\cos x = \frac{1}{2}(e^{ix} + e^{-ix}); \qquad \sin x = \frac{1}{2i}(e^{ix} - e^{-ix}).$$

Thus, as another feature of similarity between circular and hyperbolic functions, $\cos x$ and $\sin x$ are expressible in terms of the exponentials e^{ix} and e^{-ix} by formulas which resemble (2) of page 518 for $\cosh x$ and $\sinh x$.

Note 2. Parametric equations for the circle $x^2 + y^2 = a^2$ are $x = a \cos t$ and $y = a \sin t$. The student may show that, analogously, parametric equations for the equilateral hyperbola $x^2 - y^2 = a^2$ are $x = a \cosh t$ and $y = a \sinh t$.

28

DIFFERENTIAL EQUATIONS

250. Review of terminology

Suppose that certain dependent variables are known to be functions of a specified set of independent variables. Then, a *differential equation* in the variables is an equation involving at least one of the derivatives of the dependent variables and, as a rule, although not necessarily, one or more of the independent and dependent variables. If there is just one independent variable, any derivative is an *ordinary derivative*, and the equation is called an *ordinary differential equation.* Otherwise, the derivatives are partial derivatives and the equation is called a *partial differential equation.**

ILLUSTRATION 1. The first equation below is an ordinary differential equation. The second equation is a partial differential equation.

$$x \frac{d^2y}{dx^2} - 3 \frac{dy}{dx} - \cos x \sin y = 8x; \quad \frac{\partial^2 u}{\partial x^2} + \frac{\partial^2 u}{\partial y^2} = u \sin (x + y).$$

Hereafter, we shall consider only ordinary differential equations. Then, a single differential equation in x and an unknown function y, of x, usually determines a family of functions y. Similarly, n simultaneous differential equations in x and n unknown functions of x usually determine a family of *sets of n functions*. We shall treat only the case of a single differential equation in two variables.

EXAMPLE 1. Prove that, for all values of c_1 and c_2, the following equation is satisfied by $y = c_1 e^{2x} + c_2 e^{-3x}$:

$$\frac{d^2y}{dx^2} + \frac{dy}{dx} - 6y = 0. \tag{1}$$

SOLUTION. We obtain $y' = 2c_1 e^{2x} - 3c_2 e^{-3x}$ and $y'' = 4c_1 e^{2x} + 9c_2 e^{-3x}$. On substituting for y, y', and y'' in (1), we obtain $0 = 0$, which verifies the solution:

$$4c_1 e^{2x} + 9c_2 e^{-3x} + 2c_1 e^{2x} - 3c_2 e^{-3x} - 6c_1 e^{2x} - 6c_2 e^{-3x} = 0.$$

* It is desirable to review Sections 113–115 of Chapter 12 at this point.

In a differential equation for y as a function of x, suppose that each side of the equation is an integral rational polynomial in the derivatives of y. Then, the **degree** of the equation is defined as the exponent of the *highest power* of the derivative of *highest order* which occurs in the equation.

ILLUSTRATION 2. The following equation of the 3d order is of degree 4:

$$\left(\frac{d^3y}{dx^3}\right)^4 + 3y^5\left(\frac{d^2y}{dx^2}\right)^6 - 2x\left(\frac{dy}{dx}\right)^5 = 8x.$$

251. The type form $y^{(n)} = f(x)$

Consider a differential equation which specifies the nth derivative of a variable y as a given continuous function of the independent variable x. Then, the equation can be solved by n successive integrations.

EXAMPLE 1. Solve: $\qquad\qquad\qquad \dfrac{d^3s}{dt^3} = e^t - t^2.$ $\qquad\qquad$ (1)

SOLUTION. 1. Let $\quad u = \dfrac{d^2s}{dt^2}.\quad$ Then, $\quad \dfrac{du}{dt} = \dfrac{d^3s}{dt^3},\quad$ or

$$\frac{du}{dt} = e^t - t^2; \quad du = (e^t - t^2)dt;$$

$$u = \int (e^t - t^2)dt, \quad or \quad \frac{d^2s}{dt^2} = e^t - \frac{1}{3}t^3 + C_1.$$

2. Let $v = \dfrac{ds}{dt}.\quad$ Then, $\quad \dfrac{dv}{dt} = \dfrac{d^2s}{dt^2}\quad$ or $\quad \dfrac{dv}{dt} = e^t - \dfrac{1}{3}t^3 + C_1;$

$$v = \int \left(e^t - \frac{1}{3}t^3 + C_1\right)dt, \quad or \quad v = e^t - \frac{1}{12}t^4 + C_1t + C_2 = \frac{ds}{dt};$$

$$s = \int \left(e^t - \frac{1}{12}t^4 + C_1t + C_2\right)dt, \quad or \quad s = e^t - \frac{1}{60}t^5 + \frac{1}{2}C_1t^2 + C_2t + C_3.$$

The final expression is the general solution of (1).

Note 1. The integration of a known function frequently is called a **quadrature.** Thus, we solved (1) by performing three successive quadratures. Similarly, we could solve $y^{(n)} = f(x)$ by n successive quadratures.

252. Extension of the treatment of separable equations

Any differential equation of the first order and first degree in x and y can be written in the following form:

$$P(x, y)dx + Q(x, y)dy = 0.\qquad\qquad (1)$$

When each of the functions P and Q is a product of a function of x and a function of y, we can change (1) to the following equivalent form on dividing both sides by appropriate functions:

$$f(x)dx = g(y)dy.\qquad\qquad (2)$$

Then, we call (1) an equation of *separable type*, and say that, in (2), *the variables are separated*. We consider (2) where $f(x)$ and $g(y)$ are continuous, and at least one of these functions is not equal to zero on the ranges involved for x and y. On page 241, we saw that the general solution of (2) is

$$\int f(x)dx = \int g(y)dy + C. \tag{3}$$

Frequently it is convenient to use the following result, rather than (3):

THEOREM I. *The solution of (2) satisfying the initial conditions $y = \alpha$ when $x = a$ is the function $y = \phi(x)$, or $x = \psi(y)$, defined implicitly by the equation*

$$\int_a^x f(t)dt = \int_\alpha^y g(u)du. \tag{4}$$

Proof. The integrals on the left and right in (4) are particular indefinite integrals of $f(x)$ and $g(y)$, respectively, because

$$\frac{d}{dx}\int_a^x f(t)dt = f(x); \quad \frac{d}{dy}\int_\alpha^y g(u)du = g(y).$$

Hence, (4) is a special case of (3) with $C = 0$. Also, (4) is satisfied when $x = a$ and $y = \alpha$, because then each side of (4) is equal to zero. Thus, (4) defines a solution $y = \phi(x)$, or $x = \psi(y)$, of (2) satisfying the initial conditions.

EXAMPLE 1. Find the particular solution of the following equation to satisfy the conditions $x = 4$ at $t = 2$:

$$\frac{dx}{dt} = 3(x - 2). \tag{5}$$

SOLUTION. From (5), $\qquad\qquad \dfrac{dx}{x - 2} = 3\,dt.$

Hence, from (4), $\qquad\qquad \displaystyle\int_4^x \frac{du}{u - 2} = \int_2^t 3\,dv; \quad or,$

$$\ln|u - 2|\Big]_{u=4}^{u=x} = 3v\Big]_{v=2}^{v=t}, \quad or \quad \ln(x - 2) = 3(t - 2) + \ln 2. \tag{6}$$

Hence, $\qquad\qquad x - 2 = 2e^{3(t-2)}, \quad or \quad x = 2 + 2e^{3(t-2)}. \tag{7}$

Comment. Notice that $x = 2$ is not admissible in the preceding details. Since $x = 4$ is included in the range for x, we are restricted to $x > 2$; thus $u > 2$ or $u - 2 > 0$. Hence, in (6), $|u - 2| = u - 2$.

Note 1. In (7), we illustrated how to obtain an exponential form, or possibly an algebraic form, in place of a relation involving logarithms. Thus, if $A = B + C$, we may write

$$e^A = e^{B+C}, \quad or \quad e^A = e^B e^C.$$

We recall that $e^{\ln k} = k$. Hence, from (6) we obtained

$$e^{\ln(x-2)} = e^{3(t-2)}e^{\ln 2}, \quad or \quad x - 2 = 2e^{3(t-2)}.$$

253. Geometrical interpretation of solutions

Let the equation $f(x, y, c) = 0$ be the general solution of

$$P \, dx + Q \, dy = 0. \tag{1}$$

With c as a parameter, $f(x, y, c) = 0$ defines a family of curves in the xy-plane, and (1) is called the differential equation of this family. As a rule, just one of the curves will pass through any given point.

ILLUSTRATION 1. The general solution of $x \, dx + y \, dy = 0$ is found to be $x^2 + y^2 = c^2$, which defines a family of circles. To obtain the solution through $H:(3, 4)$, we use the initial conditions $(x = 3, y = 4)$, which give $c^2 = 25$; the circle is $x^2 + y^2 = 25$.

For a given equation (1), we can find the slope of the tangent to the solution through any point $H:(x_0, y_0)$ by substituting $x = x_0$ and $y = y_0$ in (1).

ILLUSTRATION 2. At $H:(3, 4)$, the solution of $x \, dx + y \, dy = 0$ through P has the slope dy/dx obtained by substituting $x = 3$ and $y = 4$:

$$3 \, dx + 4 \, dy = 0, \quad or \quad y' = -.75.$$

EXERCISE 160

Verify the given solution of the differential equation.

1. $y'' - 4y = 0$; solution, $y = c_1 e^{2x} + c_2 e^{-2x}$, where c_1 and c_2 are constants.

2. $xy' - y = x^2 + 4$; solution, $y = x^2 - 4$.

3. $y'(x + y) + y - x = 0$; solution, $y^2 + 2xy - x^2 = c$, where c is a constant.

Find the general solution of the equation, or the particular solution satisfying the initial conditions. Obtain a result not involving logarithms where convenient.

4. $\dfrac{dy}{dx} = x \cos 3x.$

5. $\dfrac{d^2u}{dx^2} = 2 \sin x + 3 \cos x.$

6. $\dfrac{d^3s}{dt^3} = 2t + e^{3t}.$

7. $\dfrac{d^3y}{dx^3} = \cos 2x + 3e^{-x}.$

8. $y \, dx + x \, dy = 0$; find the general solution in a form not involving logarithms; obtain the particular solutions passing through the points $(-2, 3)$ and $(2, 4)$, and sketch the graphs of these solutions.

9. $2y \, dx + x \, dy + 6 \, dx = 0.$

10. $x^3 \, dy + y^3 \, dx = 0.$

11. $\dfrac{dy}{dx} = \dfrac{\cos y}{\cos x}.$

12. $\dfrac{dy}{dx} + \dfrac{e^x(xy + 2x)}{3y + 10} = 0.$

13. $\sqrt{y} \, dx + \sqrt{1 + x} \, dy = 0$; $y = 4$ when $x = 8$.

14. $(1 + y^2)dx = (1 + x^2)dy$; $y = -1$ when $x = 1$.

15. $\sqrt{4 - x^2} \, dy = \sqrt{1 - y^2} \, dx$; $y = \frac{1}{2}$ when $x = 1$.

16. $3y + xy' + 9 = 0$; $y = 6$ when $x = 2$.

17. $x^2 \, dy - y^3 \, dx = 0$; $x = 2$ when $y = -1$.

18. (*a*) Without solving the equation $x \, dx + 4y \, dy = 0$, find the slope at $(-3, 2)$ on the graph of the particular solution which passes through $(-3, 2)$. (*b*) Find the specified particular solution.

19. In the motion of a particle on an *s*-axis, the acceleration at any time *t* seconds is given by $a = 2t - 5$. If $s = 2$ and $v = 4$ at $t = 1$, find the equation of motion.

20. Solve Problem 19 if $a = -4 \sin 2t$, with $s = 4$ and $v = 2$ at $t = 0$.

21. In a cylindrical tank, let *h* be the height of the surface of the fluid above the center of an orifice through which the fluid is being discharged. Then, $dh/dt = -K\sqrt{h}$, where *K* is a positive constant depending on the physical situation and the units for *t* and *h*. (*a*) If $h = h_1$ when $t = t_1$, solve for *h* as a function of *t* by use of (4) on page 528. (*b*) If, besides, $h = h_2$ when $t = t_2$, express $(t_2 - t_1)$ in terms of h_1 and h_2.

254. Homogeneous equations

We say that the equation $\qquad P(x, y)dx + Q(x, y)dy = 0 \qquad\qquad (1)$

is of the *homogeneous type* if $P(x, y)$ and $Q(x, y)$ are homogeneous * functions of *x* and *y* and of the same degree. Then, we find that, if the variables are changed to *x* and *v* by the substitution $y = vx$, the new equation is of the *separable type*. Thus, we arrive at the following method.

1. *Substitute $y = vx$, to obtain a new equation, which always is of the separable type, in x and v.*

2. *Solve the equation in x and v, and then substitute $v = y/x$.*

In substituting $y = vx$ in (1), we replace *dy* by use of

$$dy = v \, dx + x \, dv. \qquad\qquad (2)$$

Before solving (1) under present circumstances, we may prefer to write

$$\frac{dy}{dx} = -\frac{P(x, y)}{Q(x, y)}. \qquad\qquad (3)$$

Then, in substituting $y = vx$ in (3), we use

$$\frac{dy}{dx} = v + x \frac{dv}{dx}. \qquad\qquad (4)$$

EXAMPLE 1. Solve: $\qquad (2xy + y^2)dx - x^2 \, dy = 0. \qquad\qquad (5)$

SOLUTION. 1. The coefficients of *dx* and *dy* are homogeneous functions of the same degree, 2. Hence, substitute $y = vx$ and use (2):

$$(2vx^2 + v^2x^2)dx - x^2(v \, dx + x \, dv) = 0. \qquad\qquad (6)$$

Divide both sides by x^2, to obtain an equation of separable type:

$$(v^2 + v)dx - x \, dv = 0, \quad or \quad \frac{dx}{x} - \frac{dv}{v(v + 1)} = 0. \qquad\qquad (7)$$

* As defined on page 483. The degree is not necessarily an integer.

2. With $C > 0$, the general solution of (7) is

$$\int \frac{dx}{x} - \int \frac{dv}{v(v+1)} = \ln C; \text{ or} \tag{8}$$

$$\ln |x| - \ln |v| + \ln |v+1| = \ln C; \text{ or}$$

$$\ln \left| \frac{x(v+1)}{v} \right| = \ln C; \text{ or} \quad \left| \frac{x(v+1)}{v} \right| = C; \text{ or} \tag{9}$$

$$\frac{x(v+1)}{v} = K, \tag{10}$$

where K is an arbitrary constant, which may be positive or negative. On substituting $v = y/x$ in (10), we obtain the general solution of (5):

$$x(x+y) = Ky.$$

Comment. We could solve (5) by using (4), after writing

$$\frac{dy}{dx} = \frac{2xy+y^2}{x^2}.$$

EXERCISE 161

Solve the equation by the method of Section 254, if applicable.

1. $2y\, dx - x\, dy = 0.$ **2.** $2xy\, dy = (3y^2 - x^2)dx.$ **3.** $x\, dy = -(4x+y)dx.$

4. $\dfrac{dy}{dx} = \dfrac{x^3 y}{x^4 - y^4}.$ **5.** $\dfrac{ds}{dt} = \dfrac{s+4t}{4s+t}.$ **6.** $w\dfrac{du}{dw} = u + w.$

7. $(x^2 + 3xy + y^2)dx - x^2\, dy = 0.$ **8.** $(2x + 3y)dx + (2y - 3x)dy = 0.$

9. $(y + 4x)dx + (x + y)dy = 0.$ **10.** $(4x + 3y)dx + (3x - y)dy = 0.$

11. $(6x + 5y)dx + (3y + 5x)dy = 0.$ **12.** $x\, dy + \left(x \cos \dfrac{y}{x} \right) dx = y\, dx.$

13. $(4y + 3x)dy - (3y + 4x)dx = 0.$

Find the particular solution of the equation satisfying the initial conditions.

14. $2x\, dy = (3y - 2x)dx;\ \ y = 0$ when $x = 1.$

15. $(2x - y)dx + (4y - x)dy = 0;\ \ y = 2$ when $x = -1.$

255. Exact differentials

An expression $P(x, y)dx + Q(x, y)dy$ is called an *exact differential* * if and only if there exists a function $u(x, y)$ such that

$$du = P\, dx + Q\, dy. \tag{1}$$

ILLUSTRATION 1. The expression $x\, dy + y\, dx$ is an exact differential because $d(xy) = x\, dy + y\, dx.$

Hereafter, we shall assume that P and Q have continuous first partial derivatives with respect to x and y.

---

* Also called a *perfect differential*, or simply a *differential*.

THEOREM II. *A necessary and sufficient condition for $(P\,dx + Q\,dy)$ to be an exact differential is that $P_y = Q_x$.*

Proof of the necessity. We assume that $P\,dx + Q\,dy$ is exact. Then, there exists a function $u(x, y)$ such that $du = P\,dx + Q\,dy$. We recall that,

$$du = \frac{\partial u}{\partial x}\,dx + \frac{\partial u}{\partial y}\,dy. \tag{2}$$

Then, from (2),

$$\frac{\partial u}{\partial x} = P \quad and \quad \frac{\partial u}{\partial y} = Q. \tag{3}$$

Hence,

$$\frac{\partial^2 u}{\partial y\,\partial x} = \frac{\partial}{\partial y}\left(\frac{\partial u}{\partial x}\right) = \frac{\partial P}{\partial y}; \quad \frac{\partial^2 u}{\partial x\,\partial y} = \frac{\partial}{\partial x}\left(\frac{\partial u}{\partial y}\right) = \frac{\partial Q}{\partial x}. \tag{4}$$

Since $u_{xy} = u_{yx}$, we have proved that $P_y = Q_x$.

Note 1. To establish the *sufficiency* in Theorem II, we would take the hypothesis $P_y = Q_x$ and then prove that $u(x, y)$ exists so that $du = P\,dx + Q\,dy$. The proof is found in Note 11 of the Appendix.

ILLUSTRATION 2. We find $(6x + 5y - y\cos xy)dx + (5x - x\cos xy)dy$ to be an exact differential because

$$\frac{\partial(6x + 5y - y\cos xy)}{\partial y} = 5 - \cos xy + xy\sin xy = \frac{\partial(5x - x\cos xy)}{\partial x}.$$

256. Exact differential equations

A differential equation of the first order and first degree,

$$P(x, y)dx + Q(x, y)dy = 0, \tag{1}$$

is called *exact* if and only if $(P\,dx + Q\,dy)$ is an exact differential. Hence, *a necessary and sufficient condition for (1) to be exact is that $P_y = Q_x$.*

THEOREM III. *If the equation $P\,dx + Q\,dy = 0$ is exact, its solution is $u(x, y) = C$, where $u(x, y)$ is any function such that $du = P\,dx + Q\,dy$, and C is an arbitrary constant.*

Proof. 1. Let $u(x, y)$ be such that $du = P\,dx + Q\,dy$. Then, (1) becomes $du = 0$. Consider (1) as defining y to be a function of x.

2. Let $\phi(x)$ be any function with a continuous derivative $\phi'(x)$. If $y = \phi(x)$ in $u(x, y)$, then $u(x, y)$ becomes a function of x alone, say $u(x, y) = \Phi(x)$, and $du = \Phi'(x)dx$.

3. We have $du \equiv 0$ if and only if $\Phi'(x) \equiv 0$, or $\Phi(x) \equiv C$, where C is some constant. Thus, $y = \phi(x)$ satisfies (1), or $du = 0$, if and only if $y = \phi(x)$ satisfies $u(x, y) = C$, where C is a constant whose value depends on the choice of $\phi(x)$. That is, the family of solutions of (1) is defined by $u(x, y) = C$, where C may have any value for which the equation defines y as a function of x with a continuous derivative, y'.

EXAMPLE 1. Solve $(9x^2 + 2y^2)dx + (4xy + 15y^2)dy = 0.$ (2)

SOLUTION. 1. The equation is exact because

$$\frac{\partial(9x^2 + 2y^2)}{\partial y} = 4y = \frac{\partial(4xy + 15y^2)}{\partial x}.$$

2. To apply Theorem III, we seek $u(x, y)$ so that (2) becomes $du = 0$, or

$$\frac{\partial u}{\partial x}\, dx + \frac{\partial u}{\partial y}\, dy = (9x^2 + 2y^2)dx + (4xy + 15y^2)dy.$$ (3)

3. From (3), $\dfrac{\partial u(x, y)}{\partial x}\, dx = (9x^2 + 2y^2)dx.$ (4)

Integrate both sides in (4) with y considered as a constant:

$$\int \frac{\partial u(x, y)}{\partial x}\, dx = \int (9x^2 + 2y^2)dx + \phi(y), \text{ or}$$

$$u(x, y) = 3x^3 + 2xy^2 + \phi(y),$$ (5)

where the constant of integration $\phi(y)$ depends on the value of y.

4. For u in (5), $u_x = 9x^2 + 2y^2$ and $u_y = 4xy + \phi'(y)$. Hence, we shall have $u_y = 4xy + 15y^2$, and (3) will be true if

$$4xy + \phi'(y) = 4xy + 15y^2; \quad \phi'(y) = 15y^2; \quad \phi(y) = \int 15y^2\, dy = 5y^3.$$

Thus, from (5), equation (3) is true if $u = 3x^3 + 2xy^2 + 5y^3$. Then, by Theorem III, the general solution of (2) is $3x^3 + 2xy^2 + 5y^3 = C.$

SUMMARY. *Solution of an exact equation $P\, dx + Q\, dy = 0$.*

1. *Search for $u(x, y)$ so that $u_x\, dx + u_y\, dy = P\, dx + Q\, dy.$*

2. *Let $\int P(x, y)dx = H(x, y)$. Then, from $u_x\, dx = P\, dx$, obtain*

$$u(x, y) = \int P(x, y)dx + \phi(y) = H(x, y) + \phi(y).$$

3. *From $u_y = Q = H_y + \phi'(y)$, obtain $\phi'(y)$; then*

$$\phi(y) = \int \phi'(y)dy \quad and \quad u(x, y) = H(x, y) + \phi(y).$$

4. *The general solution is $u(x, y) = C.$*

Note 1. In the Summary, $\int P(x,y)\, dx$ and $\int \phi'(y)dy$ represent any particular functions denoted by the symbols, without arbitrary constants. *The solution $u = C$ always should be checked by calculating du.*

Without using the routine test for exactness, it may be convenient to show that a differential equation is exact, and then obtain its solution, *by recognizing combinations of terms which form exact differentials.* For this purpose, recall exact differentials from page 157, and note that *a sum of exact differentials is an exact differential.*

ILLUSTRATION 1. Any term of the form $f(x)dx$ or $g(y)dy$ is an exact differential, because

$$f(x)dx = d\left[\int f(x)dx\right] \quad and \quad g(y)dy = d\left[\int g(y)dy\right].$$

Thus, any equation $f(x)dx + g(y)dy = 0$, where the variables are separated, is exact and is of the form $du = 0$ where

$$u = \int f(x)dx + \int g(y)dy;$$

the general solution is $\int f(x)dx + \int g(y)dy = C$, as on page 528.

ILLUSTRATION 2. We decide that the equation

$$(y + 2e^{2x+y})dx + (x + e^{2x+y})dy = x\ dx \tag{6}$$

is exact, because we may group terms to obtain

$$(y\ dx + x\ dy) + e^{2x+y}(2\ dx + dy) = x\ dx; \quad or \quad du + dv = dw,$$

where $\qquad u = xy, \quad v = e^{2x+y}, \quad and \quad w = \int x\ dx = \tfrac{1}{2}x^2.$

Hence, the general solution of (6) is $u + v = w + C$, or $xy + e^{2x+y} = \tfrac{1}{2}x^2 + C$.

A function $g(x, y)$ is called an **integrating factor** for (1) if it becomes exact after both sides are multiplied by $g(x, y)$. It can be proved * that any equation (1) has an unlimited number of integrating factors. Except with special types of equations, it is impractical to search for these factors. Occasionally, integrating factors are very useful.

ILLUSTRATION 3. By the usual test, the equation $x\ dy - y\ dx = 0$ is not exact. If both sides are multiplied by $1/x^2$, we obtain

$$\frac{x\ dy - y\ dx}{x^2} = 0, \quad or \quad d\left(\frac{y}{x}\right) = 0, \tag{7}$$

which is exact. Hence, $1/x^2$ is an integrating factor for $x\ dy - y\ dx = 0$; its solution, as obtained from (7), is $x^{-1}y = C$, or $y = Cx$. Another integrating factor is $1/xy$, which separates the variables.

EXERCISE 162

Test for exactness. Then, solve the equation if it is exact.

1. $(9x^2 + 8xy^2 + y)dx + (8x^2y + x + 4y)dy = 0.$

2. $(x - y)dx + (6y^2 - x)dy = 0.$ $\qquad$ 3. $3x\ dx + 2x\ dy = 5y\ dy - 2y\ dx.$

4. $(6x + 5y)dx + (3y^2 - 5x)dy = 0.$

5. $(2e^{2x+3y} + y)dx + (3e^{2x+3y} + x)dy = 0.$

6. $(6x^2 + \ln y)dx + xy^{-1}\ dy = 12y^2\ dy.$

7. $(\cos y \cos x + x^{-1})dx + (y^{-1} + \sin x \sin y)dy = 0.$

* See page 14, *A First Course in Differential Equations,* by *Rudolph E. Langer;* John Wiley & Sons, publishers.

8. $3 \sin x \cos x \, dx + 5 \sin y \cos y \, dy = 0$.

9. $e^{3x} \, dy + 3ye^{3x} \, dx = 0$.   **10.** $3xe^x \, dx = \cos y \, dy$.

11. $x^{-1}e^{2y} \, dx + 2(\ln x)e^{2y} \, dy = 0$.

12. $ye^x \, dx + xye^x \, dx + y^{-1} \, dy + x^{-1} \, dx + xe^x \, dy = 0$.

13. Find the equation of a curve in the xy-plane passing through the point $(3, -1)$, if the slope of the curve at any point (x, y) is equal to $(3x + 3y)/(y - 3x)$.

Group terms into one or more exact differentials, in order to see that the equation is exact. Then, solve the equation.

14. $x^2 \, dy + 2xy \, dx + xe^{xy} \, dy + ye^{xy} \, dx = 0$.

15. $\dfrac{2x \, dx}{x^2 + y^2} + \dfrac{2y \, dy}{x^2 + y^2} = x^3 \, dx + y^2 \, dy$.

16. $2 \cos (2x + 3y) \, dx + 3 \cos (2x + 3y) \, dy = x \, dy + y \, dx$.

Prove that the specified integrating factor makes the equation exact; then, find the general solution of the equation.

17. $x \, dy - y \, dx = 0$; integrating factor, $1/xy$.

18. $x \, dy - 2y \, dx = x^4 \, dx$; integrating factor, $1/x^3$.

19. $y \, dx + dy = e^x \, dx$; integrating factor, e^x.

20. $dy + y \sec^2 x \, dx = \sec^2 x \, dx$; integrating factor, $e^{\tan x}$.

257. Linear differential equations of the first order

A differential equation of the first order, defining y as a function of x, is said to be linear with respect to y if the equation is of the first degree in y and y' jointly. Hence, the coefficients of y and of y' in the equation are functions of x alone. If both sides of the equation are divided by the co-efficient of y', the equation can be written in the standard form

$$\frac{dy}{dx} + p(x)y = q(x), \text{ or} \tag{1}$$

$$dy + p(x)y \, dx = q(x)dx, \tag{2}$$

where we assume that $p(x)$ and $q(x)$ are continuous on the range for x. When a differential equation of the first order is written in differential form, we recognize linearity with respect to y by observing that the equation is *linear in y and dy jointly*.

ILLUSTRATION 1. The following equations are linear in y:

$$x^3 \frac{dy}{dx} + y \sin x = e^x; \quad x^2 \, dy + (\ln x)y \, dx = \cos x \, dx.$$

The following equation is linear in x, with y as the independent variable:

$$y^2 \frac{dx}{dy} + x \tan y = \cos y, \quad or \quad y^2 \, dx + x \tan y \, dy = \cos y \, dy.$$

Theorem IV. *An integrating factor for* (2) *is* $e^{\int p(x)dx}$, *where* $\int p(x)dx$ *is any particular indefinite integral of* $p(x)$.

Proof. Let $\sigma(x)$ be a function such that (2) becomes exact after each side is multiplied by $\sigma(x)$, to give

$$\sigma(x)dy + p(x)y\sigma(x)dx = q(x)\sigma(x)dx. \tag{3}$$

The right-hand side of (3) creates no limitation on $\sigma(x)$ because $q(x)\sigma(x)dx$ is exact if $\sigma(x)$ is *any* continuous function of x. Hence, (3) will be exact if the left-hand side is exact. From Theorem II on page 532, the condition for exactness is

$$\frac{d\sigma}{dx} = \frac{\partial}{\partial y}[p(x)y\sigma(x)], \quad or \quad \frac{d\sigma}{dx} = p(x)\sigma(x). \tag{4}$$

From (4), $\dfrac{d\sigma}{\sigma} = p(x)dx$, or $\ln \sigma = \int p(x)dx$, or $\sigma = e^{\int p(x)dx}$.

Theorem V. *The general solution of* $y' + p(x)y = q(x)$ *is*

$$ye^{\int p(x)dx} = \int q(x)e^{\int p(x)dx}\, dx + C, \tag{5}$$

where C is an arbitrary constant.

Proof. Multiply in (2) by the integrating factor $e^{\int p(x)dx}$:

$$e^{\int p(x)dx}\, dy + p(x)e^{\int p(x)dx}\, y\, dx = q(x)e^{\int p(x)dx}\, dx. \tag{6}$$

We verify that

$$d\big[ye^{\int p(x)dx}\big] = e^{\int p(x)dx}\, dy + y\, d\big[e^{\int p(x)dx}\big] = e^{\int p(x)dx}\, dy + ye^{\int p(x)dx}\, p(x)dx,$$

because $d\big[\int p(x)dx\big] = p(x)dx$. Hence, (6) becomes

$$d\big[ye^{\int p(x)dx}\big] = d\big[\int q(x)e^{\int p(x)dx}\, dx\big]. \tag{7}$$

On integrating in (7) we obtain (5).

Example 1. Solve: $\qquad\qquad\qquad xy' - 2y = x^5. \tag{8}$

Solution. 1. To change (8) to the form (1), divide by x:

$$\frac{dy}{dx} - \frac{2}{x}y = x^4, \tag{9}$$

where $p = -2/x$ and $q = x^4$. For use in (5), we obtain

$$\int p\, dx = -2\int \frac{dx}{x} = -2\ln|x| = -\ln x^2 = \ln\frac{1}{x^2}; \quad e^{\int p(x)dx} = \frac{1}{x^2}.$$

2. From (5), the solution of (9) is

$$y\cdot\frac{1}{x^2} = \int x^4\cdot\frac{1}{x^2}\, dx + C, \quad or \quad \frac{y}{x^2} = \frac{x^3}{3} + C,$$

which gives $y = \frac{1}{3}x^5 + Cx^2$.

EXERCISE 163

Solve the equation by the preceding method.

1. $x \dfrac{dy}{dx} + y = x^4.$

2. $x \dfrac{dy}{dx} + 2y = -x^{-3}.$

3. $y' + y \cot x = 2 \cos x.$

4. $y' - y \tan x = 3 \cos^3 x.$

5. $\dfrac{ds}{dt} = 3s + 5.$

6. $\dfrac{dx}{dy} + 4x = e^{3y}.$

7. $x \, dy + y \, dx = e^x \, dx.$

8. $t \, ds - 2s \, dt = (t^5 + t^2)dt.$

9. $dx + x \tan y \, dy = \sec y \, dy.$

10. $dy - my \, dx = 0.$

11. $2uv \, du - 2u \, du + dv = 0.$

12. $xy' - 2y + x^3 e^{2x} - x^4 = 0.$

13. $dy + y \, dx = \cos x \, dx + \sin x \, dx.$

14. $\dfrac{ds}{dt} = \dfrac{\cos^3 t - s \sin t}{\cos t}.$

15. $\dfrac{du}{dv} = \dfrac{(v+2)^3 - 3u}{v+2}.$

16. $s \dfrac{dt}{ds} + t = s \cos 3s.$

17. $x \dfrac{dy}{dx} - 2y = x^4 \sin 2x.$

18. $\dfrac{dy}{dx} = (1 - y)\cos x.$

19. $\dfrac{dx}{dy} = e^y - 2x \cot 2y.$

20. $3y \, dx - x \, dy + 5x^5(\ln x) \, dx = 0.$

21. $3xy \, dx + x^2 \, dy - \text{Arctan } x \, dx = 0.$

Find the particular solution satisfying the initial conditions.

22. $y' + 2y \cot 2x = \cos 2x + 1; \ y = 2$ when $x = \frac{1}{4}\pi.$

23. $x(2x + 1)dy = 2x(2x + 1)dx - y \, dx; \ y = 3$ when $x = 2.$

24. The differential equation specifying the current i in an electric circuit involving a constant resistance R and inductance L, due to an impressed electromotive force E, at any instant of time t, is

$$E = Ri + L \frac{di}{dt}.$$

Solve the preceding equation (*a*) if E is a constant; (*b*) if $E = k \sin \omega t$ where k and ω are constants.

258. Certain types of equations of the second order

If a differential equation of the second order defines y as a function of x, and if y is not involved explicitly in the equation, it can be written in the following form:

Type I: $\qquad\qquad F(x, y', y'') = 0,$ $\qquad\qquad\qquad$ (1)

where F is some function of x, y', y''. It is sometimes possible to solve (1) by commencing with the substitution $p = y'$, which changes (1) into $F(x, p, p') = 0$, a differential equation of the first order in x and p. After p, or y', is obtained as a function of x, the resulting equation of the first order is solved to obtain y as a function of x.

EXAMPLE 1. Solve: $x^2y'' + 2xy' = 3.$ (2)

SOLUTION. 1. Let $p = y'$. Then, $y'' = dp/dx$ and (2) becomes

$$x^2 \frac{dp}{dx} + 2xp = 3, \quad or \quad \frac{dp}{dx} + \frac{2}{x} p = \frac{3}{x^2},$$ (3)

which is linear in p. By the method of Section 257, we solve (3):

$$px^2 = 3x + C_1, \quad or \quad x^2y' = 3x + C_1.$$ (4)

2. From (4), $dy = 3x^{-1}\, dx + C_1 x^{-2}\, dx.$ (5)

On solving (5), we obtain the general solution of (2):

$$y = \ln |x|^3 + K_1 x^{-1} + C_2,$$ (6)

where $K_1 = -C_1$, and K_1 and C_2 are arbitrary constants.

If a differential equation of the second order defines y as a function of x, and involves just y'' and y, the equation can be written as follows:

Type II: $y'' = f(y),$ (7)

where $f(y)$, as indicated, is a function of y alone. To solve (7), we use $y'' = dy'/dx$, and also multiply both sides of (7) by $y'\, dx$. Then, since $y'\, dx = dy$, (7) becomes

$$y'\, dy' = f(y)y'\, dx, \quad or \quad y'\, dy' = f(y)dy,$$ (8)

which is of the first order, of separable type, in y and y'. By solving (8) for y' in terms of y, we obtain an equation of the first order defining y as a function of x.

EXAMPLE 2. Solve: $y'' = -y^{-3}.$ (9)

SOLUTION. 1. Use $y'' = dy'/dx$, and multiply by $2y'$ in (9):

$$2y' \frac{dy'}{dx} = -\frac{2y'}{y^3}, \quad or \quad 2y'\, dy' = -\frac{2\, dy}{y^3},$$ (10)

because $y'\, dx = dy$. On integrating in (10), we obtain

$$\int 2y'\, dy' = -\int \frac{2\, dy}{y^3} + c_1, \quad or \quad y'^2 = \frac{1}{y^2} + c_1.$$

2. Hence, $y'y = \pm \sqrt{1 + c_1 y^2}$, or

$$\pm \frac{y\, dy}{\sqrt{1 + c_1 y^2}} = dx; \quad \pm \int \frac{y\, dy}{\sqrt{1 + c_1 y^2}} = \int dx + c_2.$$

Thus, $$\pm \frac{\sqrt{1 + c_1 y^2}}{c_1} = x + c_2.$$ (11)

On squaring both sides in (11), we find a single equation equivalent to the two equations implied by " $\pm$ " in (11). Then, with $c_1 c_2 = k_1$,

$$1 + c_1 y^2 = (c_1 x + k_1)^2$$

is the general solution of (10), where c_1 and k_1 are arbitrary constants.

EXERCISE 164

Find the general solution of the equation.

1. $y'' + y' - 3e^x = 0.$ 2. $xy'' + 2y' = 8.$

3. $y''(x + 1) + y' = 0.$ 4. $y'' = y' + xe^{-x}.$

5. $x \dfrac{d^2y}{dx^2} + \dfrac{dy}{dx} = x^3.$ 6. $\dfrac{d^2s}{dt^2} = \dfrac{1}{s^3}.$ 7. $\dfrac{d^2y}{dx^2} = -\dfrac{4}{y^3}.$

8. $\dfrac{d^2s}{dt^2} = -(s - 1).$ 9. $\dfrac{d^2u}{dv^2} = -4u.$ 10. $\dfrac{d^2y}{dx^2} = -9y.$

11. $\dfrac{d^2y}{dx^2} + x = \sin 2x.$ 12. $x \dfrac{d^2y}{dx^2} + x^3 = 4.$ 13. $\dfrac{d^2y}{dx^2} e^x - x = 1.$

Find the solution of the differential equation satisfying the initial conditions.

14. $x \dfrac{d^2y}{dx^2} - 3\dfrac{dy}{dx} = 3x^4;$ $y = 1$ and $\dfrac{dy}{dx} = 5$ when $x = 1.$

15. $\dfrac{d^2s}{dt^2} = 2s^3;$ $s = 2$ and $s' = 4$ when $t = 2.$

16. A particle P moves on an s-axis with the acceleration, a, at any time t given by $a = -2s^{-2}.$ If P is at $s = 4$ with the velocity $v = 1$ when $t = 0$, obtain the coordinate s of P at any time t.

259. The differential equation of a given family of curves

We have seen that a differential equation of the first order may have a general solution $f(x, y, c) = 0$, giving a family of solution curves in the xy-plane. Conversely, if we are given a family of curves $f(x, y, c) = 0$, with c as the parameter, we may be able to construct a differential equation with the general solution $f(x, y, c) = 0$, as follows. Then, we call $f(x, y, c) = 0$ a **primitive** of the differential equation. To obtain a differential equation for a family of curves $f(x, y, c) = 0$, *differentiate with respect to x in $f(x, y, c) = 0$, to derive a relation between x, y, y', and c; use the preceding relation, and the equation $f(x, y, c) = 0$, to eliminate c and obtain a relation between x, y, and y'.*

EXAMPLE 1. Find the differential equation of the family of curves

$$x^2 + y^2 - 2cy = c^2. \tag{1}$$

SOLUTION. 1. Differentiate with respect to x in (1):

$$2x + 2yy' - 2cy' = 0. \tag{2}$$

2. Eliminate c between (1) and (2), by solving (2) for c and using (1):

$$c = \frac{x + yy'}{y'}; \quad x^2 + y^2 - 2y\frac{x + yy'}{y'} = \frac{(x + yy')^2}{y'^2}, \text{ or}$$

$$(x^2 - 2y^2)\left(\frac{dy}{dx}\right)^2 - 4xy\frac{dy}{dx} - x^2 = 0. \tag{3}$$

Thus, (3) is the differential equation of the family (1).

260. Orthogonal trajectories

A curve U is called an *orthogonal trajectory* of a family F of smooth curves if U cuts each curve of F orthogonally (at right angles). Two families F and G of smooth curves are said to be *mutually orthogonal* if each curve of G is an orthogonal trajectory of F. Then, also, each curve of F is an orthogonal trajectory of G. Suppose that F is defined by

$$f(x, y, c) = 0, \tag{1}$$

where c is a parameter, and that a curve U of F passes through each point $P:(x_0, y_0)$ in a corresponding region. Then, as a rule, there exists just one family G of orthogonal trajectories for F with the property that a curve V of G passes through each point $P:(x_0, y_0)$.

Note 1. Mutually orthogonal families of curves are of interest in applied mathematics. Thus, the curves of one family may be lines of force, lines of flow, or streamlines, while the curves of the other family are equipotential curves, level lines, or isothermal lines, respectively.

ILLUSTRATION 1. The family of circles $x^2 + y^2 = c^2$ is cut orthogonally by the straight lines $y = kx$, where c and k are parameters.

The following method for finding orthogonal trajectories is based on the fact that lines with slopes m and $-1/m$ are perpendicular.

SUMMARY. *To find the family orthogonal to a family $f(x, y, c) = 0$.*

1. *From (1), derive a differential equation for the given family F.*

2. *In the differential equation for F, replace y' by $-1/y'$ to obtain a differential equation for the orthogonal family G. Then, find the general solution of this equation, to obtain an equation for G.*

EXAMPLE 1. Obtain the family G of orthogonal trajectories for the family F defined by the following equation, where c is a parameter:

$$x^2 = 4cy. \tag{2}$$

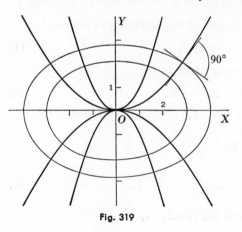

Fig. 319

SOLUTION. 1. Parabolas of the family are seen in Figure 319. Obtain a differential equation for F by differentiating with respect to x in (2), and eliminating c by use of $c = x^2/4y$:

$$2x = 4c\frac{dy}{dx}, \quad or \quad 2x = \frac{x^2}{y}y', \ or$$

$$2y = xy'. \tag{3}$$

2. In (3), replace y' by $-1/y'$, where y' now is the slope for an orthogonal trajectory, to obtain a differential equation for G:

$$2yy' = -x, \quad \text{or} \quad 2y\,dy + x\,dx = 0. \tag{4}$$

The general solution of (4) is $2y^2 + x^2 = k^2$, where k^2 is an arbitrary constant. Thus, G is a family of ellipses, illustrated in Figure 319.

EXERCISE 165

If c is an arbitrary constant, (a) find the differential equation of the given family of curves; (b) find the equation of the family of orthogonal trajectories.

1. $y^2 = 4(x - c)$.

2. $x^2 = 2(c - y)$.

3. $x^2 + y^2 = c^2$.

4. $x^2 + 4y^2 = c^2$.

5. $y^2 = 4cx$.

6. $cx^2 + y^2 = 4$.

7. $x^2 - y^2 = c$.

8. $xy = c$.

9. $y = ce^x$.

If c and k represent arbitrary constants, find the differential equation of the given family of curves. Differentiate twice if necessary.

10. $cx^2 + 2y + c^2 = 0$.

11. $y = ce^x + ke^{2x}$.

12. $y = c \cos x + k \sin x$.

13. $y = ce^{-x} + kxe^{-x}$.

261. Compound interest law and other applications

If y is a function of x, and if the rate of change of y with respect to x is proportional to the value of y, it is said that y obeys the *compound interest law*, also called the law of *exponential growth* $(k > 0)$, or *decay* $(k < 0)$. Then, with k as a fixed constant of proportionality,

$$\frac{dy}{dx} = ky. \tag{1}$$

Illustration 1. If a principal of P dollars is invested now at compound interest at the rate of interest i, compounded m times per year, then the compound amount y_m dollars at the end of x years is given by

$$y_m = P\left(1 + \frac{i}{m}\right)^{mx}, \quad \text{or} \quad y_m = P\left[\left(1 + \frac{i}{m}\right)^{\frac{m}{i}}\right]^{ix}. \tag{2}$$

The limit of y_m as $m \to \infty$ is called the compound amount on P with interest at the rate i, *compounded continuously*. From (1) on page 146, if we let $y = \lim_{m\to\infty} y_m$ then $y = Pe^{ix}$, because the quantity in square brackets in (2) has the limit e as $m \to \infty$. With i fixed in $y = Pe^{ix}$, let P be an arbitrary constant. Then, by the method of page 539, the differential equation with the general solution $y = Pe^{ix}$ is found to be $y' = iy$, which is of the form (1), and thus justifies the name *compound interest law*. Continuously compounded interest is of importance in the theory of life insurance.

From (1), $dy = ky\,dx$, or

$$\frac{dy}{y} = k\,dx. \tag{3}$$

By the method which uses (3) on page 528, from (3) we obtain

$$\ln |y| + \ln |c| = kx, \quad or \quad cy = e^{kx}, \tag{4}$$

where c is an arbitrary constant, with $c > 0$ or $c < 0$ according as $y > 0$ or $y < 0$ on the range to be used for y. Or, by use of (4) on page 528, the solution of (3) satisfying the initial conditions $y = y_0$ when $x = x_0$ is defined by the equation

$$\int_{y_0}^{y} \frac{dy}{y} = \int_{x_0}^{x} k \, dx, \quad or \quad \ln |y| - \ln |y_0| = k(x - x_0), \ or \tag{5}$$

$$(yy_0 > 0) \qquad\qquad\qquad y = y_0 e^{k(x-x_0)}. \tag{6}$$

EXAMPLE 1. The rate of decomposition of a radioactive substance is proportional to the amount which remains. (a) If there are x_0 atoms at the beginning of decomposition, and if the half-life of the substance is 2 days, find the number of atoms remaining at the end of t days. (b) When will only one fourth of the original atoms remain?

SOLUTION. 1. Let x be the number of atoms remaining t days after decomposition starts. Then, we desire to solve

$$\frac{dx}{dt} = -kx, \quad or \quad \frac{dx}{x} = -k \, dt, \tag{7}$$

with the initial conditions $x = x_0$ at $t = 0$, and then find k. The use of $-k$ instead of merely k in (7) is for later convenience. By the method of (5),

$$\int_{x_0}^{x} \frac{dx}{x} = -\int_{0}^{t} k \, dt, \quad or \quad \ln \frac{x}{x_0} = -kt; \tag{8}$$

$$x = x_0 e^{-kt}. \tag{9}$$

From (8), with $x = \frac{1}{2}x_0$ when $t = 2$,

$$\ln \tfrac{1}{2} = -2k; \quad -\ln 2 = -2k; \quad k = \tfrac{1}{2} \ln 2 = .3466.$$

Hence, from (9), $x = x_0 e^{-.3466t}. \tag{10}$

2. To find t when $x = \frac{1}{4}x_0$, substitute $x = \frac{1}{4}x_0$ in (8): $\ t = \dfrac{\ln 4}{.3466} = 4.000.$

EXERCISE 166

1. A certain radioactive substance decomposes, with a half-life of 3 years. (a) If x_0 units of the substance are on hand, how many will remain at the end of t years? (b) When will only 30% remain?

2. The population of a colony of bacteria is increasing at a time-rate proportional to the number in the population. An initial population of 2000 grew to 2,000,000 at the end of 6 days. (a) Express the population x as a function of the time t, measured in days from the instant when $x = 2000$. (b) When will $x = 10,000,000$?

3. Let τ be the temperature of a body which is cooling in a medium with constant temperature τ_0. Then, Newton's law of cooling states that the time-rate of decrease of τ is proportional to the difference $(\tau - \tau_0)$:

$$\frac{d\tau}{dt} = -k(\tau - \tau_0), \quad or \quad \frac{du}{dt} = -ku, \tag{1}$$

where $u = \tau - \tau_0$ and $k > 0$. If an object cools from 50° above to 20° above the temperature of the medium in 3 hours, when will $u = 10°$?

4. The distance-rate of decrease of the intensity I of a beam of light passing through an absorbing medium is proportional to the intensity, at any point. If the intensity is reduced from I_0 to $.75I_0$ by 10 centimeters of a glass, how many centimeters of it are needed for reduction by 75%?

5. In an electric circuit, if the impressed electromotive force is removed, the time-rate of decrease of the current i is proportional to i. (a) If i changes from 30 amperes to 2 amperes in .05 seconds after removal of the electromotive force, express i in terms of the time t, measured in seconds from the instant when $i = 30$. (b) When will $i = .1$?

6. The important radioactive element uranium 235, employed in atomic research, has a half-life of $7.0(10^8)$ years. How long does it take for 90% of a given quantity of this element to decompose?

7. Assume that, if we ascend vertically from the earth, the rate of change of the atmospheric pressure with respect to the altitude h above sea level is proportional to p. If the pressure p, in millimeters of mercury, is 760 at sea level and is 675 at 1000 meters above sea level, express p as a function of h, and find h where $p = 600$.

8. Let α be the amount of a substance at the beginning of a unimolecular chemical reaction and let x be the amount which will react in t time-units. Then, at any time, the speed of the reaction, or dx/dt, is proportional to the remaining amount of the substance, or $dx/dt = k(\alpha - x)$, where k depends on the reaction. Find k if $x = .75\alpha$ when $t = 3$.

9. In a bimolecular chemical reaction, let α and β be the original amounts of the two reacting substances, and let x be the amount of each which will react in t time-units. Then, $dx/dt = k(\alpha - x)(\beta - x)$, where $k > 0$. Find t in terms of x if $k = 4$, $\alpha = 3$, and $\beta = 2$.

10. A tank contains v gallons of a solution in which there are α pounds of salt. A solution containing β pounds of salt per gallon is run into the tank at the rate of k gallons per minute, and the contents of the tank flow out at the same rate. Let x be the amount of salt in the tank t minutes after the process starts. Then, if the solution is kept uniform by being stirred, salt is added at the rate of βk pounds, and flows out at the rate of $k \cdot (x/v)$ pounds, per minute, so that $\dfrac{dx}{dt} = \beta k - \dfrac{k}{v} x$.

Solve for x in terms of t if $v = 2000$, $\alpha = 30$, $\beta = .5$, and $k = 4$. Also, show that $x \to 1000$ as $t \to \infty$.

262. Linear differential equations and the operator D

A linear differential equation of order n, defining y as a function of x, can be written in the form

$$\frac{d^n y}{dx^n} + a_1 \frac{d^{n-1} y}{dx^{n-1}} + a_2 \frac{d^{n-2} y}{dx^{n-2}} + \cdots + a_{n-1} \frac{dy}{dx} + a_n y = Q, \tag{1}$$

where $a_1, a_2, \cdots, a_n, Q$ are functions of x alone. If $Q = 0$, then (1) is said to be *homogeneous*. Hereafter, in our limited discussion of (1), we shall assume that the coefficients $a_1, a_2, \cdots, a_n$ are constants.

In dealing with (1), it is convenient to use "D," as on page 26, for differentiation with respect to x, and D^k for k successive differentiations with respect to x. If c is a constant, $(cD^k)y$ is defined by

$$(cD^k)y = cD^k y = c \frac{d^k y}{dx^k}, \tag{2}$$

with the added agreement that $(cD^0)y = cy$. Then, any polynomial in D with constant coefficients is taken as an *operator* which is applicable term by term to any function of x possessing enough derivatives. We read the polynomial as if D were a number of algebra.

ILLUSTRATION 1. $3 \dfrac{d^2 y}{dx^2} + 2 \dfrac{dy}{dx} - 5y = (3D^2 + 2D - 5)y,$

which we read "$(3D^2 + 2D - 5)$ *operating on y.*"

$$(D^2 - 2D)\sin x = \frac{d^2(\sin x)}{dx^2} - 2 \frac{d(\sin x)}{dx} = -\sin x - 2 \cos x.$$

We use functional notation for polynomials in D. Thus, (1) becomes

$$(D^n + a_1 D^{n-1} + a_2 D^{n-2} + \cdots + a_{n-1} D + a_n)y = Q, \text{ or} \tag{3}$$

$$f(D)y = Q, \quad \text{where} \quad f(D) = D^n + a_1 D^{n-1} + \cdots + a_{n-1}D + a_n. \tag{4}$$

Any solution $y = y_1(x)$ of (1) satisfies $f(D)y_1 = Q$.

ILLUSTRATION 2. The equation $(D^2 - 5D + 6)y = e^{4x}$ has the solution $y = \frac{1}{2}e^{4x}$ because $D(\frac{1}{2}e^{4x}) = 2e^{4x}$, $D^2(\frac{1}{2}e^{4x}) = 8e^{4x}$, and thus

$$(D^2 - 5D + 6)(\tfrac{1}{2}e^{4x}) = 8e^{4x} - 10e^{4x} + 3e^{4x} = e^{4x}. \tag{5}$$

To indicate successive operations by polynomials in D, we write the polynomials side by side, and we call the result an *operational product*. By the properties of differentiation with respect to x,

$$D^m(D^n y) = D^n(D^m y) = D^{n+m} y. \tag{6}$$

Thus, powers of D are commutative and obey the law of exponents for multiplication. We conclude finally that, in an operational product of polynomials in D, we may act as if D is a number of algebra in formal multiplication, or factoring, before operating on any function of x.

ILLUSTRATION 3. $(D-2)(D-3)y = (D^2 - 5D + 6)y = y'' - 5y' + 6y.$

Since the derivative of a sum of functions is equal to the sum of their derivatives, $f(D)$ is a *linear operator* as applied to linear combinations of functions with constant coefficients. Thus, if c_1 and c_2 are constants and y_1 and y_2 are functions of x,

$$f(D)(c_1 y_1 + c_2 y_2) = c_1 f(D)y_1 + c_2 f(D)y_2. \tag{7}$$

EXERCISE 167

In the problems, D means d/dx. Carry out each indicated operation.

1. $D(xe^{2x}); \quad D^2(xe^{2x}); \quad D^3(xe^{2x}).$
2. $De^{4x}; \quad D^2 e^{4x}; \quad D^3 e^{4x}; \quad D^k e^{4x}.$
3. $De^{mx}; \quad D^3 e^{mx}; \quad D^k e^{mx}.$
4. $(D+2)(x^2 + \sin 3x).$
5. $(D-3)\sin x.$
6. $(D+5)\cos 2x.$
7. $(D^2 - 3)\sin 3x.$
8. $(D-2)(D+3)xe^{3x}.$
9. $(D+3)(D-1)e^{-2x}.$
10. $D(D-2)\sin 3x.$
11. $D^2(D+1)\cos 2x.$
12. Prove that $(D-a)[(D-b)y] = (D-b)[(D-a)y].$
13. Write the differential equation by use of D: $4y'' + 3y' + 2y = \sin x.$

Verify the statement by substitution in the differential equation.

14. $y = e^{3x}$ is a solution of $(D^2 - 2D - 3)y = 0.$
15. $y = e^{-x}\sin 2x$ and $y = e^{-x}\cos 2x$ are solutions of $(D^2 + 2D + 5)y = 0.$
16. $y = \frac{1}{3}e^x$ is a solution of $(D^2 + 5D - 3)y = -e^x.$

263. Theorems on homogeneous linear differential equations

The following theorems are useful in solving the homogeneous equation

$$f(D)y = 0, \tag{1}$$

where $\qquad f(D) = D^n + a_1 D^{n-1} + a_2 D^{n-2} + \cdots + a_{n-1}D + a_n. \tag{2}$

Although we assume that the coefficients in (2) are constants, the results to be obtained extend to (1) when the coefficients involve x.

THEOREM VI. *If $y = y_1(x)$ is a solution of a homogeneous equation $f(D)y = 0$, and c is any constant, then $y = cy_1(x)$ is a solution.*

Proof. By hypothesis, $f(D)y_1(x) = 0.$ Hence,

$$f(D)[cy_1(x)] = cf(D)y_1(x) = 0,$$

which proves that $y = cy_1(x)$ is a solution of $f(D)y = 0.$

THEOREM VII. *If $y = y_1(x)$ and $y = y_2(x)$ are solutions of a homogeneous equation $f(D)y = 0$, then $y = y_1(x) + y_2(x)$ is a solution.*

Proof. By hypothesis, $f(D)y_1(x) = f(D)y_2(x) = 0.$ Hence,

$$f(D)[y_1(x) + y_2(x)] = f(D)y_1(x) + f(D)y_2(x) = 0 + 0 = 0, \tag{3}$$

which states that $y = y_1(x) + y_2(x)$ satisfies $f(D)y = 0.$

Note 1. To say that certain functions are **linearly independent,** means that it is *impossible* to express any one of them as a linear combination of the others, with constant coefficients. If the functions are *not* linearly independent, they are said to be **linearly dependent.** Then, at least one of them can be expressed as a linear combination of the others.

THEOREM VIII. *If $y = y_1(x), y = y_2(x), \cdots, y = y_n(x)$ are n linearly independent * solutions of a homogeneous linear differential equation of order n, then the general solution of the equation is*

$$y = c_1y_1 + c_2y_2 + \cdots + c_ny_n, \tag{4}$$

where $c_1, c_2, \cdots, c_n$ are arbitrary constants.

Proof. (*Written for the case $n = 2$.*) We have the solutions $y = y_1(x)$ and $y = y_2(x)$. Then, by Theorem VI, $y = c_1y_1(x)$ and $y = c_2y_2(x)$ are solutions. Hence, by Theorem VII, the equation $f(D)y = 0$ has the solution

$$y = c_1y_1(x) + c_2y_2(x), \tag{5}$$

where c_1 and c_2 are arbitrary constants.

★*Note 2.* It is interesting to observe why (5) is *not* the general solution of $f(D)y = 0$ if $y_1(x)$ and $y_2(x)$ are *linearly dependent.* In this case, we may suppose that $y_2(x) = hy_1(x)$, where h is a fixed constant, and (5) becomes

$$y = c_1y_1(x) + c_2hy_1(x) = (c_1 + hc_2)y_1(x). \tag{6}$$

Hence, (5) yields only those solutions where y is a multiple of $y_1(x)$, and (5) is not the general solution of $f(D)y = 0$.

264. Homogeneous case, where the characteristic equation has real roots

Consider $$\frac{d^2y}{dx^2} + a_1\frac{dy}{dx} + a_2y = 0, \quad or \quad f(D)y = 0, \tag{1}$$

where $$f(D) = D^2 + a_1D + a_2, \tag{2}$$

in which a_1 and a_2 are constants. In Problem 10, page 537, we found that the linear equation of the first order $y' - my = 0$ has the solution $y = ce^{mx}$, which suggests seeking similar solutions for (1).

THEOREM IX. *A function $y = e^{mx}$ satisfies $f(D)y = 0$ if and only if*

$$f(m) = 0, \quad or \quad m^2 + a_1m + a_2 = 0. \tag{3}$$

Proof. To obtain m so that $y = e^{mx}$ satisfies (1), we substitute $y = e^{mx}$, $y' = me^{mx}$, and $y'' = m^2e^{mx}$ in (1), and find

$$m^2e^{mx} + a_1me^{mx} + a_2e^{mx} = 0, \quad or \quad e^{mx}(m^2 + a_1m + a_2) = 0. \tag{4}$$

Since $e^{mx} \neq 0$ for any values of m and x, from (4) we obtain (3).

---

* It is beyond our level to discuss why linear independence is essential.

We shall call (3) the *characteristic equation*, or the *auxiliary equation*, for (1). The roots of (3) may be real and distinct, real and equal, or imaginary. Theorem VIII proves the following result.

COROLLARY 1. *If the characteristic equation has distinct real roots* $m = m_1$ *and* $m = m_2$, *then* (1) *has the linearly independent solutions* $y = e^{m_1 x}$ *and* $y = e^{m_2 x}$, *and the general solution*

$$y = c_1 e^{m_1 x} + c_2 e^{m_2 x}. \tag{5}$$

ILLUSTRATION 1. The characteristic equation for

$$y'' - 3y' - 4y = 0, \quad or \quad (D^2 - 3D - 4)y = 0, \tag{6}$$

is $m^2 - 3m - 4 = 0$, whose roots are $m = 4$ and $m = -1$. Hence, the general solution of (6) is $y = c_1 e^{4x} + c_2 e^{-x}$.

THEOREM X. *If the characteristic equation has a double root* $m = m_1$, *then* (1) *has the solutions* $e^{m_1 x}$ *and* $x e^{m_1 x}$, *and the general solution*

$$y = e^{m_1 x}(c_1 + c_2 x). \tag{7}$$

Proof. 1. By hypothesis, (3) can be written $f(m) = (m - m_1)^2 = 0$. Then, $f(D) = (D - m_1)^2$, and (1) becomes

$$(D - m_1)(D - m_1)y = 0. \tag{8}$$

2. Let $v = (D - m_1)y$. Then (8) becomes $\quad (D - m_1)v = 0. \tag{9}$

The solution of (9) is $v = c_1 e^{m_1 x}$. Hence, from $v = (D - m_1)y$,

$$(D - m_1)y = c_1 e^{m_1 x}, \quad or \quad \frac{dy}{dx} - m_1 y = c_1 e^{m_1 x}. \tag{10}$$

By use of (5) on page 536, with $p = -m_1$, the solution of (10) is

$$y e^{-m_1 x} = c_1 \int e^{-m_1 x} e^{m_1 x} \, dx + c_2 = c_1 x + c_2. \tag{11}$$

On multiplying by $e^{m_1 x}$ in (11), we obtain the general solution of (1):

$$y = (c_1 x + c_2) e^{m_1 x}. \tag{12}$$

3. We obtain the particular solutions $y = x e^{m_1 x}$ and $y = e^{m_1 x}$ from (12) by using $(c_1 = 1, c_2 = 0)$ and $(c_1 = 0, c_2 = 1)$, respectively.

EXAMPLE 1. Find the particular solution of $y'' - 6y' + 9y = 0$ which satisfies the conditions $y = 2$ and $y' = -1$ when $x = 0$.

SOLUTION. 1. The characteristic equation is $m^2 - 6m + 9 = 0$, which has the double root $m = 3$. Hence, the general solution is

$$y = e^{3x}(c_1 + c_2 x). \tag{13}$$

2. From (13), $\qquad\qquad y' = e^{3x}(3c_1 + c_2 + 3c_2 x). \tag{14}$

With $x = 0$ in (13) and (14), the initial conditions give $c_1 = 2$ and $c_2 = -7$. Thus, the particular solution is $y = e^{3x}(2 - 7x)$.

EXERCISE 168

Solve the equation. If no independent variable is visible, assume that it is x. Find any specified particular solution.

1. $\dfrac{d^2y}{dx^2} + \dfrac{dy}{dx} - 2y = 0.$
2. $\dfrac{d^2s}{dt^2} + 5\dfrac{ds}{dt} + 4s = 0.$

3. $3\dfrac{d^2u}{dv^2} + 5\dfrac{du}{dv} - 2u = 0.$
4. $\dfrac{d^2y}{dt^2} + 4\dfrac{dy}{dt} + 4y = 0.$

5. $y'' - 10y' + 25y = 0.$
6. $2y'' - 5y' + 3y = 0.$

7. $\dfrac{d^2y}{dt^2} - 9y = 0.$
8. $\dfrac{d^2s}{dt^2} = 25s.$
9. $4\dfrac{d^2u}{dv^2} = 9u.$

10. $y'' - y = 0.$
11. $y'' = 3y'.$
12. $4y'' = 9y'.$

13. $6y'' + 7y' + 2y = 0.$
14. $3y'' + 2y' - y = 0.$

15. $4s'' + s = 4s'.$
16. $y'' = a^2y.$
17. $49y'' - 4y = 0.$

18. $4y'' + 24y' + 9y = 0.$
19. $a^2y'' - 2aby' + b^2y = 0.$

20. $y'' + y' - 6y = 0;\ y = 5$ and $y' = -5$ when $x = 0.$

21. $9y'' - 12y' + 4y = 0;\ y = -2$ and $y' = 3$ when $x = 0.$

265. The characteristic equation with imaginary roots *

Consider the equation of the second order

$$(D^2 + a_1D + a_2)y = 0, \quad \text{or} \quad f(D)y = 0, \tag{1}$$

when the characteristic equation $f(m) = 0$ has imaginary roots $m = \alpha \pm \beta i$, where α and β are real and $\beta \neq 0$. Then, the general solution of (1) is

$$y = c_1 e^{(\alpha+i\beta)x} + c_2 e^{(\alpha-i\beta)x} = e^{\alpha x}(c_1 e^{i\beta x} + c_2 e^{-i\beta x}). \tag{2}$$

In (2), use the Euler formula (3) of page 473 to obtain

$$e^{\pm i\beta x} = \cos\beta x \pm i\sin\beta x.$$

Then, $\qquad y = e^{\alpha x}[(c_1 + c_2)\cos\beta x + (c_1 i - c_2 i)\sin\beta x]. \tag{3}$

If c_1 and c_2 are unequal real numbers in (3), then y has imaginary values. However, y is real-valued if we choose c_1 and c_2 so that

$$\left.\begin{array}{c} ic_1 - ic_2 = A, \\ c_1 + c_2 = B, \end{array}\right\} \tag{4}$$

where A and B are real. Observe that (4) has a unique solution for c_1 and c_2 if A and B are assigned arbitrarily. Then, (3) becomes

$$y = e^{\alpha x}(A\sin\beta x + B\cos\beta x). \tag{5}$$

From (5), we obtain the linearly independent solutions $e^{\alpha x}\sin\beta x$ and $e^{\alpha x}\cos\beta x$, by use of $(A = 1,\ B = 0)$ and $(A = 0,\ B = 1)$, respectively.

---

* Recall the discussion on page 471 concerning calculus for complex-valued functions. Thus, Theorem IX on page 546 is valid when m is an imaginary number.

SUMMARY. *If the characteristic equation* $f(m) = 0$ *has imaginary roots* $m = \alpha \pm i\beta$, *then* $f(D)y = 0$ *has the solutions* $y = e^{\alpha x} \sin \beta x$ *and* $y = e^{\alpha x} \cos \beta x$, *and the general solution* (5).

Note 1. If A and B are not both zero, define $H > 0$ and ω by

$$A^2 + B^2 = H^2; \quad H \cos \omega = A; \quad H \sin \omega = B. \tag{6}$$

Then, (5) becomes $y = H(\sin \beta x \cos \omega + \cos \beta x \sin \omega)e^{\alpha x}$, or

$$y = He^{\alpha x} \sin (\beta x + \omega). \tag{7}$$

Similarly, define γ and $H > 0$ by the equations

$$A^2 + B^2 = H^2; \quad -H \sin \gamma = A; \quad H \cos \gamma = B. \tag{8}$$

Then, the general solution (5) becomes

$$y = He^{\alpha x} \cos (\beta x + \gamma). \tag{9}$$

Without reference to A and B, let us allow $H = 0$ in (7) and (9) in order to obtain the solution $y = 0$ for (1). Then, either (7) or (9), as well as (5), can be taken as the general solution of (1).

EXAMPLE 1. Find the particular solution of

$$\frac{d^2y}{dx^2} - 4\frac{dy}{dx} + 13y = 0 \tag{10}$$

satisfying the conditions $y = 5$ and $y' = -5$ when $x = 0$.

SOLUTION. 1. The characteristic equation $m^2 - 4m + 13 = 0$ has the solutions $m = 2 \pm 3i$. Hence, the general solution of (10) is

$$y = e^{2x}(c_1 \sin 3x + c_2 \cos 3x). \tag{11}$$

Then, $\qquad y' = e^{2x}[(2c_1 - 3c_2)\sin 3x + (2c_2 + 3c_1)\cos 3x].$ $\qquad$ (12)

2. With $x = 0$, $y = 5$, and $y' = -5$ in (11) and (12), we obtain

$$c_2 = 5; \quad 2c_2 + 3c_1 = -5.$$

Thus, $c_1 = -5$ and $c_2 = 5$. The solution is $y = e^{2x}(-5 \sin 3x + 5 \cos 3x)$.

Comment. The general solution of (10) also can be written

$$y = He^{2x} \sin (3x + \omega) \quad or \quad y = He^{2x} \cos (2x + \gamma).$$

Whenever the characteristic equation for (1) has imaginary roots, we agree to use a *real form* (5), (7), or (9), for the general solution.

EXERCISE 169

Solve the equation. If no independent variable is visible, assume that it is x. Give three trigonometric forms, if they apply.

1. $\dfrac{d^2y}{dx^2} + 2\dfrac{dy}{dx} + 5y = 0.$ $\qquad$ 2. $\dfrac{d^2s}{dt^2} - 4\dfrac{ds}{dt} + 8s = 0.$

3. $(D^2 + 6D + 25)y = 0.$ $\qquad$ 4. $(4D^2 - 12D + 25)u = 0.$

5. $2y'' - 2y' + 5y = 0.$　　　　　　**6.** $9y'' - 6y' + 10y = 0.$

7. $\dfrac{d^2s}{dt^2} + s = 0.$　　　　　**8.** $\dfrac{d^2u}{dv^2} + 9u = 0.$　　　　　**9.** $9\,\dfrac{d^2u}{dx^2} + 4u = 0.$

10. $6y'' - 7y' - 3y = 0.$　　　　　　**11.** $y'' - 3y' + 3y = 0.$

12. $(D^2 + 4)y = 0.$　　　　**13.** $s'' + k^2s = 0.$　　　　　**14.** $y'' = 49y.$

15. $2\,\dfrac{d^2s}{dt^2} + 5\,\dfrac{ds}{dt} - 12s = 0.$　　　　**16.** $4\,\dfrac{d^2u}{dv^2} - 12\,\dfrac{du}{dv} + 13u = 0.$

17. $4y'' - 8y' + 5y = 0.$　　　　　　**18.** $4y'' - 25y = 0.$

Find the desired particular solution of the differential equation.

19. $\dfrac{d^2y}{dx^2} + y = 0;\ y = 2$ and $y' = -3$ when $x = 0.$

20. $(D^2 + 6D + 13)y = 0;\ y = -1$ and $y' = 2$ when $x = 0.$

21. $\dfrac{d^2s}{dt^2} + 16s = 0;\ s = 3$ and $\dfrac{ds}{dt} = 4$ when $t = \frac{1}{4}\pi.$

22. $y'' + 4y = 0;\ y = 3$ and $y' = -2$ when $x = \frac{3}{4}\pi.$

23. $u'' - 4u' + 20u = 0;\ u = 3e^{\frac{1}{2}\pi}$ and $u' = -3e^{\frac{1}{2}\pi}$ when $x = \frac{1}{4}\pi.$

266. Nonhomogeneous linear differential equations

Consider the nonhomogeneous linear differential equation

$$f(D)y = Q(x), \tag{1}$$

of order n, defining y as a function of x, where

$$f(D) = D^n + a_1D^{n-1} + a_2D^{n-2} + \cdots + a_{n-1}D + a_n, \tag{2}$$

in which $a_1, a_2, \cdots, a_n$ are constants. The method of solution for (1) is based on the following result, stated for the case $n = 2$.

Theorem XI. *Suppose that $y = P(x)$ is a particular solution of a nonhomogeneous equation $f(D)y = Q(x)$. Let $y = H(x, c_1, c_2)$ be the general solution of the corresponding homogeneous equation $f(D)y = 0$. Then, the general solution of the nonhomogeneous equation is*

$$y = H(x, c_1, c_2) + P(x). \tag{3}$$

Proof. 1. Let $y = g(x)$ be *any* solution of (1), where $n = 2$. On substituting the solutions $y = P(x)$ and $y = g(x)$ in (1), we obtain

$$f(D)g(x) = Q(x) \quad and \quad f(D)P(x) = Q(x). \tag{4}$$

Hence, $\quad f(D)[g(x) - P(x)] = f(D)g(x) - f(D)P(x) = Q(x) - Q(x) = 0. \tag{5}$

Thus, (5) states that $y = [g(x) - P(x)]$ satisfies the homogeneous equation $f(D)y = 0$. Therefore, by use of proper values of the constants c_1 and c_2 in the general solution $H(x, c_1, c_2)$, we would obtain

$$g(x) - P(x) = H(x, c_1, c_2), \quad or \quad g(x) = H(x, c_1, c_2) + P(x). \tag{6}$$

2. To prove, conversely, that *any function $g(x)$ of the form (6) is a solution of (1)*, we substitute $y = g(x)$ in $f(D)y$ on the left in (1):

$$f(D)[H(x, c_1, c_2) + P(x)] = f(D)H(x, c_1, c_2) + f(D)P(x)$$

$$= 0 + Q(x) = Q(x), \tag{7}$$

because $y = H(x, c_1, c_2)$ satisfies $f(D)y = 0$, and $y = P(x)$ satisfies (1). From (7), $y = g(x)$ satisfies (1), and thus is its general solution.

ILLUSTRATION 1. We verify that the equation $y'' - 4y = e^{3x}$ has the particular solution $y = \frac{1}{5}e^{3x}$. By Section 264, we find that the homogeneous equation $y'' - 4y = 0$ has the general solution $y = c_1e^{2x} + c_2e^{-2x}$. Hence, the general solution of the nonhomogeneous equation is $y = c_1e^{2x} + c_2e^{-2x} + \frac{1}{5}e^{3x}$.

In (3), the general solution $H(x, c_1, c_2)$ of the homogeneous equation is called the **complementary function.** To obtain the general solution for a given nonhomogeneous equation $f(D)y = Q(x)$,

1. *obtain a particular solution $y = P(x)$ by any device;*

2. *find the general solution $y = H(x, c_1, c_2)$ of the homogeneous equation $f(D)y = 0$, and then use (3).*

In the absence of advanced theory, we shall proceed as follows to obtain a particular solution $y = P(x)$ for (1). The suggestions will be stated in such a way as to apply later to equations of *any order n*.

Write $P(x)$ with undetermined coefficients in accordance with later suggestions. Then, obtain these coefficients by substituting $y = P(x)$ in (1).

Forms for $y = P(x)$ to satisfy $f(D)y = Q(x)$.

A. *When $Q(x)$ is a polynomial of degree k:*

1. If $m = 0$ is not a solution of $f(m) = 0$, use

$$P(x) = b_0 + b_1x + b_2x^2 + \cdots + b_kx^k. \tag{8}$$

2. If $m = 0$ is a simple root of $f(m) = 0$, use

$$P(x) = x(b_0 + b_1x + b_2x^2 + \cdots + b_kx^k). \tag{9}$$

B. *When $Q(x) = he^{kx}$, where h and k are constants:*

1. Use $P(x) = be^{kx}$ if $m = k$ is not a solution of $f(m) = 0$.

2. If $m = k$ is a simple root of $f(m) = 0$, use $\qquad P(x) = bxe^{kx}.$ $\tag{10}$

C. *When $Q(x) = h \cos rx + k \sin rx$, where h, k, and r are constants:*

1. Use * $P(x) = b_1 \cos rx + b_2 \sin rx$, if $m = ri$ is not a solution of $f(m) = 0$.

2. If $m = ri$ is a simple root of $f(m) = 0$, use

$$P(x) = x(b_1 \cos rx + b_2 \sin rx). \tag{11}$$

* Even if h or k is equal to zero in (C), we use both sin rx and cos rx in (C, 1).

D. *When $Q(x)$ is a sum of terms of preceding types, use $P(x)$ as a corresponding sum of terms as suggested.*

Note 1. In (A, 2), (B, 2), (C, 2), if the value of m is a double root of $f(m) = 0$, use x^2 instead of x as a factor in (9), (10), (11); use x^s as a factor if the value of m is a root of multiplicity s.

EXAMPLE 1. Solve:
$$\frac{d^2y}{dx^2} + \frac{dy}{dx} - 2y = 25 - 4x - 6x^2. \tag{12}$$

SOLUTION. 1. *The complementary function:* The corresponding homogeneous equation is $(D^2 + D - 2)y = 0$, whose solution is $y = c_1e^x + c_2e^{-2x}$.

2. *The particular solution:* By (A, 1), we substitute the function
$$y = b_0 + b_1x + b_2x^2$$
in (12), and equate coefficients of corresponding powers of x on the two sides:
$$2b_2 + (2b_2x + b_1) - 2(b_0 + b_1x + b_2x^2) = 25 - 4x - 6x^2, \text{ or} \tag{13}$$
$$(2b_2 + b_1 - 2b_0) + x(2b_2 - 2b_1) - 2b_2x^2 = 25 - 4x - 6x^2.$$

Thus, $\quad -2b_2 = -6; \quad 2b_2 - 2b_1 = -4; \quad 2b_2 + b_1 - 2b_0 = 25. \tag{14}$

From (14), $b_2 = 3$, $b_1 = 5$, and $b_0 = -7$. Hence, a particular solution of (12) is $y = 3x^2 + 5x - 7$. From (3), the general solution of (12) is
$$y = c_1e^x + c_2e^{-2x} + 3x^2 + 5x - 7.$$

EXAMPLE 2. Solve: $\qquad\qquad y'' - 4y = 2e^{3x}. \tag{15}$

SOLUTION. 1. The complementary function is the solution of $(D^2 - 4)y = 0$:
$$y = c_1e^{2x} + c_2e^{-2x}. \tag{16}$$

2. We substitute $y = be^{3x}$ in (15) to find a particular solution, and obtain
$$9be^{3x} - 4(be^{3x}) = 2e^{3x}, \quad \text{or} \quad 5be^{3x} = 2e^{3x}.$$

Hence, $b = \frac{2}{5}$ and a particular solution of (15) is $y = \frac{2}{5}e^{3x}$. From (3) and (16), the general solution of (15) is $y = c_1e^{2x} + c_2e^{-2x} + \frac{2}{5}e^{3x}$.

EXAMPLE 3. Solve: $\qquad\qquad y'' - 4y = 4e^{2x}. \tag{17}$

SOLUTION. 1. The complementary function is in (16).

2. We recall from (16) that $y = e^{2x}$ is a particular solution of the homogeneous equation corresponding to (17), or $m = 2$ is a simple root of the characteristic equation $m^2 - 4 = 0$. Then, by (B, 2), we use $y = bxe^{2x}$ for a particular solution of (17). It is found that
$$D(bxe^{2x}) = 2bxe^{2x} + be^{2x}; \quad D^2(bxe^{2x}) = 4be^{2x} + 4bxe^{2x}.$$

Hence, from (17), with $y = bxe^{2x}$,
$$4bxe^{2x} + 4be^{2x} - 4bxe^{2x} = 4e^{2x}, \quad \text{or} \quad be^{2x} = e^{2x}.$$

Thus, $b = 1$ and a particular solution of (17) is $y = xe^{2x}$. Then, from (3) and (16), the general solution of (17) is $y = c_1e^{2x} + c_2e^{-2x} + xe^{2x}$.

EXAMPLE 4. Solve: $\qquad y'' + 3y' = 8 \cos 2x - 14 \sin 2x.$ $\qquad$ (18)

SOLUTION. 1. The complementary function is $y = c_1 + c_2 e^{-3x}$.

2. For a particular solution of (18), by (C, 1), we use the form

$$y = h \sin 2x + k \cos 2x. \qquad (19)$$

On substituting (19) in (18), we obtain

$$(6h - 4k)\cos 2x - (4h + 6k)\sin 2x = 8 \cos 2x - 14 \sin 2x.$$

Thus, $\qquad\qquad 6h - 4k = 8 \quad and \quad 4h + 6k = 14.$ $\qquad$ (20)

We solve (20) simultaneously, and obtain $h = 2$ and $k = 1$. A particular solution is $y = 2 \sin 2x + \cos 2x$, and the general solution of (18) is

$$y = c_1 + c_2 e^{-3x} + 2 \sin 2x + \cos 2x.$$

EXERCISE 170

Solve the equation. If no independent variable is visible, assume that it is x.

1. $\dfrac{d^2y}{dx^2} + \dfrac{dy}{dx} - 6y = 12x.$

2. $\dfrac{d^2s}{dt^2} - \dfrac{ds}{dt} - 2s = 16.$

3. $y'' - 9y = 18x - 27.$

4. $y'' + 4y = 12x^2 - 2.$

5. $y'' + 2y' + 5y = 25.$

6. $9y'' + 6y' + y = 2x + 7.$

7. $4\dfrac{d^2u}{dx^2} - 9u = 8 + 18x - 9x^2.$

8. $\dfrac{d^2z}{dy^2} + z = 6y + y^3.$

9. $2y'' + 3y' - 2y = 4e^{3x}.$

10. $s'' + 3s' + 2s = 3e^{2x}.$

11. $y'' - 6y' = -8e^{4x}.$

12. $3y'' - 2y' = -6e^{3x}.$

13. $y'' + 4y' + 5y = 29e^{\frac{1}{2}x}.$

14. $y'' - y = -8 \sin x.$

15. $y'' + y = 9 \cos 2x.$

16. $2y'' + y = 2 \sin \frac{1}{2}x.$

17. $2y'' - y' = 20 \sin 3x.$

18. $y'' - 6y' + 10y = 30.$

19. $y'' + 9y = 5 \sin 2x + 5 \cos 2x.$

20. $y'' - 4y' + 3y = 6 \sin 3x + 12 \cos 3x.$

21. $z'' + 3z' + 2z = 2x^2 + 14x + 14.$

22. $2y'' + y' = 6 + 2x.$

23. $3y'' - 2y' = 10 - 8x.$

24. $(D^2 - 25)y = 20e^{5x}.$

25. $(D^2 - 1)y = 4e^x.$

26. $(D^2 - 16)y = e^{4x}.$

27. $(D^2 + 9)y = 6 \cos 3x.$

28. $(D^2 + 4)y = 16 \sin 2x.$

29. $y'' - y' - 2y = -\frac{9}{2}e^{-x}.$

30. $y'' + 2y' = 6x^2 + 6x + 6.$

31. $y'' + 25y = 10 \sin 5x - 5 \cos 5x.$

32. $y'' - y = 8e^{3x} - x.$

33. $4y'' + y = 5e^x - 6 \sin x.$

HINT. Recall (D), page 552. In Problem 32, use $P(x) = ae^{3x} + bx + c$.

34. $9y'' - y = 10e^{\frac{1}{2}x} + 8.$

35. $y'' - 2y' + y = 5e^{2x} - 4.$

36. $3y'' + y' - 2y = 4e^x - 6x + 3.$

37. $2y'' + y' - y = -10 \sin x + 6.$

38. $\dfrac{d^2s}{dt^2} - 4\dfrac{ds}{dt} + 4s = 6e^{2t}.$ **39.** $(D^2 + 10D + 25)\,y = 3e^{-5x}.$

40. $y'' - 6y' + 9y = 27x + 27.$

Find the particular solution of the equation satisfying the conditions.

41. $3\dfrac{d^2u}{dv^2} - \dfrac{du}{dv} - 2u = 6v - 11;\ \ u = 5$ and $u' = -3$ when $v = 0.$

42. $\dfrac{d^2z}{dw^2} + 49z = -25\sin 2w;\ \ z = 4$ and $z' = -2$ when $w = \pi.$

267. Applications of linear differential equations

In this section, when dealing with the motion of a particle on an s-axis, we shall use t, v, and a to represent the time, velocity, and acceleration, respectively. Suppose that a particle P has the acceleration

$$\frac{d^2s}{dt^2} = -k^2s, \tag{1}$$

where k^2 is a positive constant, and we take $k > 0$. From Problem 13 on page 550, the general solution of (1) can be written as

$$s = H \sin (kt - \omega), \tag{2}$$

where H and ω are arbitrary constants, with $H \geqq 0$. With any initial conditions $s = s_0$ and $v = v_0$ at $t = t_0$, where s_0 and v_0 are not both zero, we may obtain corresponding values of H and ω so that (2) is the equation of motion for the particle. Motion governed by (1), with the equivalent relation (2), is called **simple harmonic motion.** We met this type of motion on page 154. From the characteristics of the sine function in (2), the motion is periodic with the period $2\pi/k$ seconds. The particle P oscillates between $s = -H$ and $s = H$ on the s-axis, with an interval of π/k seconds between extreme positions, as shown by the graph of (2) in Figure 320. From physics, if P has mass m, then P is acted on by a force f where

$$f = ma = m\frac{d^2s}{dt^2} = -k^2ms,$$

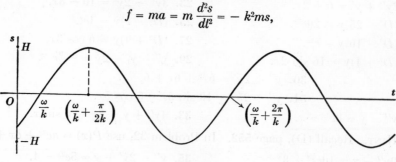

Fig. 320

whose magnitude is $k^2m\,|\,s\,|$. The direction of f on the s-axis is to the left

($f < 0$) if $s > 0$, and to the right ($f > 0$) if $s < 0$, as in Figure 321. Thus, simple harmonic motion occurs if a particle of mass m moves on a line subject to a force *proportional to the displacement of the particle from some fixed point on the line, and directed at this point.*

Note 1. We shall not use (2) as a formula. Any special case of (1) should be solved as in Section 265.

EXAMPLE 1. Study the motion determined by (1) with $k^2 = 4$, if the initial conditions are $s = \frac{5}{2}\sqrt{2}$ and $v = 5\sqrt{2}$ at $t = 0$.

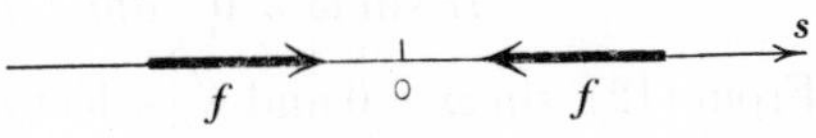

Fig. 321

SOLUTION. 1.
$$\frac{d^2s}{dt^2} = -4s, \quad or \quad s'' + 4s = 0, \tag{3}$$

whose general solution is
$$s = c_1 \cos (2t + c_2). \tag{4}$$

2. From (4),
$$v = \frac{ds}{dt} = -2c_1 \sin (2t + c_2). \tag{5}$$

From (3) and (4), with $s = \frac{5}{2}\sqrt{2}$ and $v = 5\sqrt{2}$ at $t = 0$, we obtain
$$\tfrac{5}{2}\sqrt{2} = c_1 \cos c_2; \quad 5\sqrt{2} = -2c_1 \sin c_2. \tag{6}$$

Hence,
$$\frac{\sin c_2}{\cos c_2} = \tan c_2 = -1.$$

We select $c_2 = -\frac{1}{4}\pi$. Then, (6) gives $c_1 = 5$, and (4) becomes
$$s = 5 \cos (2t - \tfrac{1}{4}\pi). \tag{7}$$

3. From (7), s is a periodic function of t with the period $2\pi/2$ or π seconds. The maximum $s = 5$ occurs when
$$\cos (2t - \tfrac{1}{4}\pi) = 1, \quad or \quad 2t - \tfrac{1}{4}\pi = 2h\pi, \quad or \quad t = \tfrac{1}{8}\pi + h\pi,$$

where h is any integer; $s = -5$ when $t = (\tfrac{1}{8}\pi + \tfrac{1}{2}\pi) + h\pi$. The particle P oscillates between 5 and -5 on the s-axis.

EXAMPLE 2. A particle P moves on an s-axis with the acceleration $a = -\frac{17}{4}s - v$. Find s in terms of t if $s = 0$ and $v = 2$ at $t = 0$.

Comment. If P has mass m, the force f acting on P is
$$f = ma = -\tfrac{17}{4}ms - mv. \tag{8}$$

The component $-mv$ resists the motion if $v \neq 0$, because $-mv$ and v have opposite signs. The force $-\frac{17}{4}ms$ alone would cause simple harmonic motion. Thus, the motion of P is the result of disturbing simple harmonic motion by a resistance proportional to the velocity, and is called a **damped harmonic motion,** or a **damped vibration.**

SOLUTION. 1. We have
$$4\frac{d^2s}{dt^2} + 4\frac{ds}{dt} + 17s = 0, \tag{9}$$

whose characteristic equation is $4m^2 + 4m + 17 = 0$, with the solutions $m = -\frac{1}{2} \pm 2i$. Hence, with $H \geq 0$, the general solution of (9) is

$$s = He^{-\frac{1}{2}t} \sin (2t + \omega). \tag{10}$$

Then, $\qquad v = \dfrac{ds}{dt} = He^{-\frac{1}{2}t}[-\tfrac{1}{2} \sin (2t + \omega) + 2 \cos (2t + \omega)]. \tag{11}$

2. On using $(s = 0, v = 2, t = 0)$ in (10) and (11), we obtain

$$H \sin \omega = 0 \quad and \quad H(-\tfrac{1}{2} \sin \omega + 2 \cos \omega) = 2. \tag{12}$$

From (12), $\sin \omega = 0$ and we select $\omega = 0$; then $2H = 2$ or $H = 1$. Hence,

$$s = e^{-\frac{1}{2}t} \sin 2t. \tag{13}$$

From (13), $\qquad v = \dfrac{ds}{dt} = \tfrac{1}{2}e^{-\frac{1}{2}t}(4 \cos 2t - \sin 2t). \tag{14}$

3. From (14), $v = 0$ when $\sin 2t = 4 \cos 2t$, or $\tan 2t = 4$. Then, from Table IV, $2t = 1.326 + n\pi$ or $t = .663 + n(\frac{1}{2}\pi)$, where $n = 0, 1, 2, \cdots$. These values of t locate the successive maxima and minima of the graph of (13) in Figure 100 on page 156.

4. *The motion of P when $t \geq 0$.* In (13), $\sin 2t$ is periodic with the period $2\pi/2$ or π, but the motion is not periodic because of the factor $e^{-\frac{1}{2}t}$. However, the motion exhibits certain features periodically. Thus, from (13), $s = 0$ when $\sin 2t = 0$ or $t = 0 + n(\frac{1}{2}\pi)$, where $n = 0, 1, 2, \cdots$, so that P oscillates through the origin on the s-axis at intervals of $\frac{1}{2}\pi$ seconds. Also, from (14), P is instantaneously at rest at intervals of $\frac{1}{2}\pi$ seconds, when s attains a maximum or a minimum, or P arrives at an extreme point of an oscillation. The amplitudes of these oscillations approach zero as $t \to \infty$, on account of $e^{-\frac{1}{2}t}$ in (13). This fact causes $e^{-\frac{1}{2}t}$ to be called the **damping factor.**

Comment. If the term $-mv$ were omitted in (8), the motion would become simple harmonic and we would obtain an expression of the form $s = M \sin (kt - \gamma)$, where $k = \frac{1}{2}\sqrt{17}$. This motion is periodic with the period $2\pi/k$ or 3.048 seconds. Thus, the particle P oscillates through the origin $s = 0$, between extreme positions $s = \pm M$, at intervals of $\frac{1}{2}(3.048)$ or 1.524 seconds. In Example 2, the corresponding interval was $\frac{1}{2}\pi$ or 1.571 seconds. Thus, as compared to this simple harmonic motion, the resistance $-mv$ in (8) increases the period of the oscillations and damps their amplitudes.

If a particle P of mass m is moving with simple harmonic motion, or with a damped vibration, and if an oscillatory force is added to the force acting on P, then "**forced vibration**" occurs.

ILLUSTRATION 1. If a particle P with mass m has the acceleration

$$\frac{d^2s}{dt^2} = -k^2s + h \sin (\mu t + \gamma), \tag{15}$$

where $\mu > 0$, $k > 0$, and $h \neq 0$, then the force f acting on P is

$$f = -mk^2s + mh \sin(\mu t + \gamma). \qquad (16)$$

By the method of Section 266, if $\mu \neq k$, the solution of (15) is found to be

$$s = c_1 \sin(kt + c_2) + \frac{h}{k^2 - \mu^2} \sin(\mu t + \gamma), \qquad (17)$$

where c_1 and c_2 are arbitrary constants. We refer to the term involving $\sin(\mu t + \gamma)$ in (17) as a *forced vibration*, due to $mh \sin(\mu t + \gamma)$ in (16). If $c_1 \neq 0$ in (17), the motion of P is the result of superimposing the effects of two simple harmonic motions, given by the terms in (17). If $\mu = k$ in (15), its solution is found to be

$$s = c_1 \sin(kt + c_2) - \frac{h}{2k} t \cos(kt + \gamma).$$

Then, as $t \to \infty$, no upper bound exists for $|s|$. In this case, the resulting phenomenon is referred to as *resonance*.

★ILLUSTRATION 2. If a particle P with mass m has the acceleration

$(h \neq 0)$ $$\frac{d^2s}{dt^2} = -6\frac{ds}{dt} - 10s + h \sin 3t, \qquad (18)$$

where $h \neq 0$, then the force f acting on P is

$$f = ma = -6mv - 10ms + hm \sin 3t. \qquad (19)$$

The motion of P is the result of disturbing a damped vibration, as in Example 2, by the periodic force $hm \sin 3t$ in (19). The solution of (18) is

$$s = c_1e^{-3t} \sin(t + c_2) + k \sin(3t + \alpha). \qquad (20)$$

In (20), k and α are fixed constants, and c_1 and c_2 are arbitrary constants. In (20), we call $k \sin(3t + \alpha)$ the forced vibration, due to $hm \sin 3t$ in (19). As $t \to \infty$ in (20), the first term on the right tends to zero, and the forced vibration becomes the dominant term. That is, as t grows large, the oscillations of P tend to give up the natural period 2π of the term $\sin(t + c_2)$, and take on the period $2\pi/3$ of the disturbing periodic force in (19). In (20), the first term is called the **transient part** of the solution, and the second term the **steady state.**

EXERCISE 171

The units are one foot for distance and one second for time. Use $g = 32$.

A particle P with the coordinate s moves on the s-axis with the acceleration a. Find s in terms of t. If P oscillates, find its period.

1. $a = -4s$; $s = 3$ and $v = 6\sqrt{3}$ at $t = 0$.
2. $a = -9s$; $s = -4$ and $v = -12\sqrt{3}$ at $t = \pi/3$.
3. $a = -s + 12 \sin 2t$; $s = 6$ and $v = -2$ at $t = 0$.

4. $a = -4v - 5s$; $s = 0$ and $v = 4$ at $t = 0$.

5. $a = -2v - 5s$; $s = 0$ and $v = -6$ at $t = 0$.

6. $a = -6v - 5s$; $s = 12$ and $v = 0$ at $t = 0$.

7. $a = -4v - 13s + 40 \cos t$; $s = 0$ and $v = 13$ at $t = 0$.

8. $a = -9s + 18 \sin 3t$; $s = -8$ and $v = 6$ at $t = 0$.

9. The engines of a boat stop and it continues to move in a straight line with the water resistance proportional to the velocity. Then, $a = -kv$, where $k > 0$. If $v = 20'$ per second at $t = 0$, and $k = .1$, find the distance s traveled in the next t seconds. How far will the boat go?

10. A man and parachute fall from rest under the action of gravity, with air resistance proportional to the velocity. Then, the acceleration of the man is given by $a = g - kv$, where $k > 0$. (1) If $k = \frac{1}{2}$, find the distance fallen in t seconds. (2) Find $v_0 = \lim_{t \to \infty} v$, where v_0 is called the *limiting velocity*, and is approximately the velocity at which the man hits the ground if he falls from a considerable height.

11. A spring is extended to length l and hangs in equilibrium with a body of mass m attached to the free end. We set the spring into vertical vibration by pulling downward on the body and then releasing it. Let y be the length of the spring t seconds later. Then, if $s = y - l$, it is found that $s'' = -\lambda^2 s$, where $\lambda^2 = k/m$ and k is a measure of the stiffness of the spring. Find the period of the vibration.

12. A simple pendulum, with length l, swings in a vertical plane in a medium offering no resistance. Let θ be the angle of smallest absolute value made by the pendulum with the vertical, where θ is signed as in trigonometry. If $|\theta|$ is small, it is found that, approximately,

$$\frac{d^2\theta}{dt^2} = -k^2\theta,$$

where $k^2 = g/l$. If the pendulum is released from rest with $\theta = \alpha$ at $t = 0$, express θ as a function of t, and obtain the half-period of the pendulum.

★13. If the pendulum of Problem 11 is oscillating in a medium where the resistance is proportional to the velocity, then

$$\frac{d^2\theta}{dt^2} = -2\lambda \frac{d\theta}{dt} - k^2\theta, \tag{1}$$

where $\lambda > 0$ and $k^2 = g/l$. Find the general solution for this damped vibration if $\lambda < k$; $\lambda = k$; $\lambda > k$. If oscillatory motion occurs, what is its period? Investigate θ as $t \to \infty$ in each case.

★14. A particle of mass m falls from rest in a liquid under the action of gravity. If the resistance of the liquid is proportional to the square of the velocity, the acceleration of the particle is given by $a = g - hv^2$, or $a = h(k^2 - v^2)$, where $h > 0$ and $k^2 = g/h$. Find the distance s fallen in t seconds, and the limiting velocity, as $t \to \infty$.

MISCELLANEOUS EXERCISE 172

Find the general solution of the equation, or the specified particular solution.

1. $(2x - y)dx + (2y - x)dy = 0.$

2. $(3x^2 - 2xy)dx = (x^2 - 3y^2)dy.$

3. $(x + 2)(y - 1)dy = 3x(y + 3)dx.$

4. $\sqrt{9 + x^2}\, dy = \sqrt{1 - y^2}\, dx.$

5. $xy' + y = x^4$, by two methods.

6. $y' - 2y \tan 2x = \cos^3 2x.$

7. $\dfrac{d^2s}{dt^2} - \dfrac{ds}{dt} = 6s.$

8. $4\dfrac{d^2u}{dv^2} + 9u = 12\dfrac{du}{dv}.$

9. $(e^y \cos x + 2xy^3)dx + (e^y \sin x + 3x^2y^2)dy = 0.$

10. $2x(x + 1)yy' = (1 + 3x)(y^2 + 2).$

11. $xy\, dx + (y^2 - x^2)dy = 0.$

12. $(\cos x \cos y + \sec^2 x \sin y)dx + (\tan x \cos y - \sin x \sin y)dy = 0.$

13. $\dfrac{d^2y}{dx^2} + 6\dfrac{dy}{dx} + 14y = 0.$

14. $\dfrac{d^2s}{dt^2} + 9s = 3 \sin 4t.$

15. $\dfrac{d^3s}{dt^3} = \sin 2t.$

16. $3\dfrac{d^2y}{dx^2} + 2\dfrac{dy}{dx} = x^2 + 4.$

17. $\dfrac{d^2y}{dx^2} = e^x + \cos x$, with $y = 4$ and $y' = 2$ at $x = 0.$

18. $\dfrac{d^2x}{dt^2} = 25x$, with $x = 2$ and $\dfrac{dx}{dt} = -15$ when $t = 0.$

19. $2y'' + 5y' - 3y = e^{4x}.$

20. $y'' + 2y' + 10y = e^{2x}.$

21. $y'' - y' - 2y = 3e^{2x}.$

22. $y'' - 3y' = 13 \sin 2x.$

23. $\sin t\, dx + 2x \cos t\, dt - \sin t \cos t\, dt = 0.$

24. $\dfrac{d^2y}{dx^2} - 16y = 2 \sin 4x.$

25. $(x + 3)\dfrac{d^2y}{dx^2} - \dfrac{dy}{dx} = 0.$

26. $\dfrac{d^2y}{dx^2} = -\dfrac{1}{y^2}$, with $y = 1$ and $y' = 1$ at $x = 3.$

27. $\dfrac{d^2y}{dx^2} + 4y = 3 \sin 2x.$

28. $\dfrac{dy}{dx} = \dfrac{\sqrt{x^2 + 4xy + 3y^2}}{2x + 3y} + \dfrac{y}{x}.$

29. Find an equation for the orthogonal trajectories for the family of curves with the equation $(y - 3)^2 = 4k(x - 2)$, where k is the parameter.

30. The velocity dx/dt of a tri-molecular chemical reaction is given by

$$\frac{dx}{dt} = k(\alpha - x)(\beta - x)(\gamma - x),$$

where α, β, and γ are the original amounts of the three reacting substances, and x is the amount of each which has reacted in t units of time. Solve the equation for t in terms of x, if $\alpha = 3$, $\beta = 4$, and $\gamma = 1$.

★268. Linear differential equations of higher order

Let y be defined as a function of x by the equation

$$f(D)y = Q(x), \tag{1}$$

where

$$f(D) = D^n + a_1D^{n-1} + \cdots + a_{n-1}D + a_n \tag{2}$$

and n is any positive integer. We have solved instances of (1) only where $n = 2$. A few added details of proof, which we omit, would justify extensions of our methods for any value of n. The following results become available.

Corresponding to the n roots of the characteristic equation $f(m) = 0$, obtain n particular solutions of the homogeneous equation $f(D)y = 0$ as follows:

1. *If $f(m) = 0$ has a real root $m = m_1$, of multiplicity h, there are h solutions: $e^{m_1 x}, xe^{m_1 x}, \cdots, x^{h-1}e^{m_1 x}$.*

2. *A pair of imaginary roots $m = \alpha \pm \beta i$ gives two solutions:*

$$e^{\alpha x} \sin \beta x \quad and \quad e^{\alpha x} \cos \beta x. \tag{3}$$

If the roots $m = \alpha \pm \beta i$ are repeated h times, there are 2h solutions of $f(D)y = 0$ consisting of (3) and each of these multiplied in turn by $x, x^2, \cdots, x^{h-1}$.

EXAMPLE 1. Solve: $\qquad\qquad y''' + y'' + 3y' - 5y = 60e^{3x}. \tag{4}$

SOLUTION. 1. The characteristic equation for (4) is

$$m^3 + m^2 + 3m - 5 = 0,$$

whose roots are $m = 1$ and $m = -1 \pm 2i$. Hence, the complementary function for (4), or the general solution of $y''' + y'' + 3y' - 5y = 0$, is

$$y = c_1 e^x + e^{-x}(c_2 \sin 2x + c_3 \cos 2x).$$

2. To find a particular solution of (4), we try $y = ke^{3x}$ by substitution, and obtain $k = \frac{3}{2}$. Hence, the general solution of (4) is

$$y = c_1 e^x + e^{-x}(c_2 \sin 2x + c_3 \cos 2x) + \tfrac{3}{2}e^{3x}.$$

★ EXERCISE 173

Solve. If no independent variable is visible, assume that it is x.

1. $(D - 2)(D + 3)^2 y = 0.$ **2.** $(D - 1)(D^2 + 4D + 5)y = 0.$

3. $(D - 2)^3 y = 0.$ **4.** $(D - 3)(D^2 + 4)y = 0.$ **5.** $(D^2 + 9)^2 y = 0.$

6. $\dfrac{d^3s}{dt^3} - 2\dfrac{d^2s}{dt^2} - 3\dfrac{ds}{dt} = 0.$ **7.** $\dfrac{d^3u}{dv^3} - 2\dfrac{d^2u}{dv^2} + \dfrac{du}{dv} = 0.$

8. $\dfrac{d^3y}{dv^3} - 9\dfrac{dy}{dv} = 0.$ **9.** $\dfrac{d^3s}{dx^3} = \dfrac{d^2s}{dx^2}.$ **10.** $\dfrac{d^4y}{dx^4} = 16y.$

11. $y''' - 2y'' - 5y' + 6y = 0.$

12. $2y''' + y'' - 12y' + 9y = 0.$

13. $y''' - y = 0.$ **14.** $s''' = 8s.$ **15.** $16y^{IV} = 81y.$

16. $y''' + y = 365 \sin 3x.$ **17.** $y''' + 8y = 5e^{4x}.$

18. $y''' + y'' - 6y' = 4x + 8.$ **19.** $y^{IV} - 2y''' - 3y'' = x - 3.$

20. $y^{IV} - 81y = 2e^{3x}.$ **21.** $y''' - 2y'' - 3y' = 4 \sin 2x.$

APPENDIX

Note 1. The Greek Alphabet

Letters		Names	Letters		Names	Letters		Names
A	α	alpha	I	ι	iota	P	ρ	rho
B	β	beta	K	κ	kappa	Σ	σ	sigma
Γ	γ	gamma	Λ	λ	lambda	T	τ	tau
Δ	δ	delta	M	μ	mu	Υ	υ	upsilon
E	ϵ	epsilon	N	ν	nu	Φ	ϕ	phi
Z	ζ	zeta	Ξ	ξ	xi	X	χ	chi
H	η	eta	O	o	omicron	Ψ	ψ	psi
Θ	θ	theta	Π	π	pi	Ω	ω	omega

Note 2. Miscellaneous Formulas

1. *The binomial expansion $(x + y)^n$, where n is a positive integer.*

$$(x + y)^n = x^n + nx^{n-1}y + \frac{n(n-1)}{2!}x^{n-2}y^2 + \cdots$$
$$\left. + \frac{n(n-1)(n-2)\cdots(n-r+1)}{r!}x^{n-r}y^r + \cdots + nxy^{n-1} + y^n; \right\} \quad (1)$$

$$(x + y)^n = x^n + {}_nC_1x^{n-1}y + \cdots + {}_nC_rx^{n-r}y^r + \cdots + {}_nC_{n-1}xy^{n-1} + {}_nC_ny^n, \quad (2)$$

where ${}_nC_r = n!/[r!(n-r)!]$.

2. *Formulas from elementary geometry.*

Circle of radius r: Area $= \pi r^2$; circumference $= 2\pi r$.

Circular sector with central angle α radians: Area $= \frac{1}{2}r^2\alpha$.

Sphere of radius r: Volume $= \frac{4}{3}\pi r^3$; (surface area) $= 4\pi r^2$.

Right circular cylinder with radius r and altitude h:

$$\text{Volume} = \pi r^2 h; \quad (\text{lateral area}) = 2\pi rh.$$

Right circular cone with altitude h, slant height s, and r as the radius of the base:

$$\text{Volume} = \frac{1}{3}\pi r^2 h; \quad (\text{lateral area}) = \pi rs.$$

Pyramid with base area A and altitude h: Volume $= \frac{1}{3}Ah$.

3. *Quadratic formula for solution of $ax^2 + bx + c = 0$:*

$$x = \frac{-b \pm \sqrt{b^2 - 4ac}}{2a}.$$

Note 3. Facts from Trigonometry

An angle θ is said to be in its **standard position** on a coordinate system if the vertex of θ is at the origin and the initial side of θ lies on the positive part of the horizontal axis. An angle θ is said to *lie in a certain quadrant* if the terminal side of θ falls *inside* that quadrant when θ is in its standard position. Two or more angles are said to be **coterminal** if their terminal sides coincide after the angles are placed in their standard positions.

Let θ represent any angle, where θ may be positive, negative, or zero.

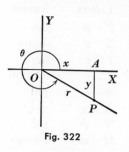

Fig. 322

Place θ in its standard position on a coordinate system, and let $P{:}(x, y)$ be any point other than the origin, O, on the terminal side of θ, as in Figure 322. Let r be the length of OP. Then, the fundamental trigonometric functions of θ are defined as follows:

$$\sin \theta = \frac{y}{r}; \quad \cos \theta = \frac{x}{r}; \quad \tan \theta = \frac{y}{x}; \tag{1}$$

$$\csc \theta = \frac{r}{y}; \quad \sec \theta = \frac{r}{x}; \quad \cot \theta = \frac{x}{y}. \tag{2}$$

If two angles are coterminal, they have the same trigonometric functions.

Let θ be an angle in standard position, in any quadrant. Then, we define the **reference angle** for θ as *the acute angle* α *between the terminal side of* θ *and the horizontal axis.* In Figure 322, $\alpha = \angle POA$.

THEOREM I. *Any function of an angle* θ, *in any quadrant, is numerically equal to the same function of the reference angle for* θ. *That is,*

(any function of θ) = $\pm$ (same function of reference angle α), (3)

with "$+$" or "$-$" used according as the function of θ *is positive or negative.*

Certain Trigonometric Identities

$$\tan \theta = \frac{\sin \theta}{\cos \theta}; \quad \cot \theta = \frac{\cos \theta}{\sin \theta}; \quad \csc \theta = \frac{1}{\sin \theta}; \quad \sec \theta = \frac{1}{\cos \theta}; \quad \cot \theta = \frac{1}{\tan \theta}. \tag{4}$$

$$\sin^2 \theta + \cos^2 \theta = 1; \quad \tan^2 \theta + 1 = \sec^2 \theta; \quad 1 + \cot^2 \theta = \csc^2 \theta. \tag{5}$$

[any function of $(\theta + 2\pi)$] = (same function of θ). (6)

$$\sin (-\theta) = -\sin \theta; \quad \cos (-\theta) = \cos \theta; \quad \tan (-\theta) = -\tan \theta. \tag{7}$$

$$\tan (\theta + \pi) = \tan \theta; \quad \cot (\theta + \pi) = \cot \theta. \tag{8}$$

$$\left\{ \begin{array}{l} [\textit{Any function of } (\tfrac{1}{2}\pi - \theta)] = (\textit{the } \mathbf{cofunction} \textit{ of } \theta), \\ \textit{for instance,} \qquad \sin (\tfrac{1}{2}\pi - \theta) = \cos \theta. \end{array} \right\} \tag{9}$$

$$\left\{ \begin{array}{c} \textit{Any function of an} \\ [(\textit{even multiple of } \tfrac{1}{2}\pi) \pm \theta] \end{array} \right\} = \pm (\textit{same function of } \theta). \tag{10}$$

$$\left\{ \begin{array}{c} \textit{Any function of an} \\ [(\textit{odd multiple of } \tfrac{1}{2}\pi) \pm \theta] \end{array} \right\} = \pm (\mathbf{cofunction} \textit{ of } \theta). \tag{11}$$

$$\sin (\alpha \pm \beta) = \sin \alpha \cos \beta \pm \cos \alpha \sin \beta. \tag{12}$$

$$\cos (\alpha \pm \beta) = \cos \alpha \cos \beta \mp \sin \alpha \sin \beta. \tag{13}$$

$$\tan (\alpha \pm \beta) = \frac{\tan \alpha \pm \tan \beta}{1 \mp \tan \alpha \tan \beta}. \tag{14}$$

$$\sin 2\alpha = 2 \sin \alpha \cos \alpha; \ \cos 2\alpha = \cos^2 \alpha - \sin^2 \alpha. \tag{15}$$

$$2 \sin \alpha \cos \beta = \sin (\alpha + \beta) + \sin (\alpha - \beta). \tag{16}$$

$$2 \cos \alpha \cos \beta = \cos (\alpha + \beta) + \cos (\alpha - \beta). \tag{17}$$

$$2 \sin \alpha \sin \beta = \cos (\alpha - \beta) - \cos (\alpha + \beta). \tag{18}$$

$$\sin x + \sin y = 2 \sin \tfrac{1}{2}(x + y)\cos \tfrac{1}{2}(x - y). \tag{19}$$

In any $\triangle ABC$, let α, β, and γ be the angles at A, B, and C, and let a, b, and c be the lengths of the opposite sides, respectively. Then, we have

(*the law of sines*) $$\frac{a}{\sin \alpha} = \frac{b}{\sin \beta} = \frac{c}{\sin \gamma}; \tag{20}$$

(*the law of cosines*) $$a^2 = b^2 + c^2 - 2bc \cos \alpha. \tag{21}$$

Note 4. Transformation of Coordinates in a Plane

Suppose that the original axes OX and OY, and the new axes $O'X'$ and $O'Y'$, respectively, have the same directions, with the new origin O' having the old coordinates $x = h$ and $y = k$, as in Figure 323. Then, transformation from the xy-system to the $x'y'$-system is referred to as a **translation of the axes** to the new origin O'. The equations for this transformation are

$$x = x' + h \quad and \quad y = y' + k, \ or \tag{1}$$

$$x' = x - h \quad and \quad y' = y - k. \tag{2}$$

Let the axes of the xy-system be rotated about the origin through an angle θ, to give an $x'y'$-system, as in Figure 324. Let P have the coordinates (x, y) and (x', y'). Then,

$$\begin{cases} x = x' \cos \theta - y' \sin \theta, \tag{3} \\ y = x' \sin \theta + y' \cos \theta; \tag{4} \end{cases}$$

$$\begin{cases} x' = x \cos \theta + y \sin \theta, \tag{5} \\ y' = - x \sin \theta + y \cos \theta. \tag{6} \end{cases}$$

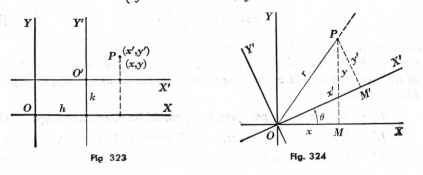

Fig 323   Fig. 324

Note 5. Results concerning Conic Sections

Parabola with vertex at origin:

When axis of parabola is x-axis: $\qquad\qquad\qquad y^2 = 2px.$ $\qquad\qquad$ (1)

When axis of parabola is y-axis: $\qquad\qquad\qquad x^2 = 2py.$ $\qquad\qquad$ (2)

Parabola with vertex at (x_0, y_0):

When axis of parabola is line $y = y_0$: $\qquad (y - y_0)^2 = 2p(x - x_0).$ $\qquad$ (3)

When axis of parabola is line $x = x_0$: $\qquad (x - x_0)^2 = 2p(y - y_0).$ $\qquad$ (4)

Ellipse with center at origin; axes along coordinate axes:

$$\frac{x^2}{a^2} + \frac{y^2}{b^2} = 1 \quad or \quad b^2x^2 + a^2y^2 = a^2b^2. \qquad\qquad (5)$$

Ellipse with center (x_0, y_0); axes parallel to coordinate axes:

$$\frac{(x - x_0)^2}{a^2} + \frac{(y - y_0)^2}{b^2} = 1. \qquad\qquad (6)$$

Hyperbola with center at origin; axes along coordinate axes:

$$\frac{x^2}{a^2} - \frac{y^2}{b^2} = 1 \quad or \quad b^2x^2 - a^2y^2 = a^2b^2. \qquad\qquad (7)$$

Hyperbola with center (x_0, y_0); axes parallel to coordinate axes:

$$\frac{(x - x_0)^2}{a^2} - \frac{(y - y_0)^2}{b^2} = 1. \qquad\qquad (8)$$

General equation for any conic in xy-plane:

$$Ax^2 + Bxy + Cy^2 + 2Dx + 2Ey + F = 0. \qquad\qquad (9)$$

We call $(B^2 - 4AC)$ the **discriminant** of (9). If $B \neq 0$, transformation of coordinates by rotation through an angle θ will change (9) to a form not involving the product xy,

$$A'x'^2 + C'y'^2 + 2D'x' + 2E'y' + F = 0,$$

if θ is any angle such that

$$\cot 2\theta = \frac{A - C}{B}. \qquad\qquad (10)$$

THEOREM I. *Any conic section (degenerate or not) in an xy-plane has an equation of the second degree in x and y. Conversely, the locus of any equation of the second degree in x and y is a conic section or imaginary, with possibilities as follows:*

$\qquad$ **$B^2 - 4AC = 0$:** *a parabola, two parallel lines, or imaginary.* $\qquad$ (11)

$\qquad$ **$B^2 - 4AC < 0$:** *an ellipse, a single point, or imaginary.* $\qquad\quad$ (12)

$\qquad$ **$B^2 - 4AC > 0$:** *a hyperbola or two intersecting lines.* $\qquad\qquad$ (13)

Note 6. The Derivative of a Composite Function

The following demonstration of Theorem I on page 46 eliminates the assumption of the previous proof that $\Delta u \neq 0$ when Δx is small.

Proof. 1. From page 46, $\qquad \lim_{\Delta u \to 0} \dfrac{\Delta y}{\Delta u} = \dfrac{dy}{du}; \quad \lim_{\Delta x \to 0} \dfrac{\Delta u}{\Delta x} = \dfrac{du}{dx}.$ (1)

2. Define a function $\eta(\Delta u)$ by the conditions $\eta(0) = 0$ and,

if $\Delta u \neq 0,$ $\qquad\qquad\qquad \eta(\Delta u) = \dfrac{\Delta y}{\Delta u} - \dfrac{dy}{du}.$ (2)

From the equality at the left in (1), $\eta(\Delta u) \to 0$ if $\Delta u \to 0$; also, by definition, $\eta(0) = 0$. Hence, $\eta(\Delta u)$ is a continuous function of Δu at $\Delta u = 0$. Since $\Delta u \to 0$ if $\Delta x \to 0$, it follows then that $\eta(\Delta u) \to 0$ as $\Delta x \to 0$.

3. From (2), if $\Delta u \neq 0,$ $\qquad\qquad \Delta y = \dfrac{dy}{du} \cdot \Delta u + (\Delta u)\eta(\Delta u).$ (3)

If $\Delta u = 0$, then $\Delta y = 0$, $\eta(\Delta u) = 0$, and hence (3) remains true because each term in (3) is zero. On dividing by Δx in (3), and letting $\Delta x \to 0$, we find

$$\lim_{\Delta x \to 0} \frac{\Delta y}{\Delta x} = \frac{dy}{du}\left(\lim_{\Delta x \to 0} \frac{\Delta u}{\Delta x}\right) + \left(\lim_{\Delta x \to 0} \frac{\Delta u}{\Delta x}\right)\left(\lim_{\Delta x \to 0} \eta(\Delta u)\right), \ or$$

$$\frac{dy}{dx} = \frac{dy}{du} \cdot \frac{du}{dx} + \frac{du}{dx}(0) = \frac{dy}{dx} \cdot \frac{du}{dx}.$$

Note 7. Concerning L'Hospital's Rule

THEOREM I. Extended law of the mean. *Assume that the functions $\phi(x)$ and $\psi(x)$ are continuous when $a \leq x \leq b$, and differentiable when $a < x < b$. Also, suppose that $\phi(b) \neq \phi(a)$ and that $\psi'(x)$ and $\phi'(x)$ are never zero simultaneously when $a < x < b$. Then, there exists a number ξ between a and b such that*

$$\frac{\psi(b) - \psi(a)}{\phi(b) - \phi(a)} = \frac{\psi'(\xi)}{\phi'(\xi)}.$$ (1)

Proof. Define a function $h(x)$ by the equation

$$h(x) = \psi(x)[\phi(b) - \phi(a)] - \phi(x)[\psi(b) - \psi(a)] - K,$$ (2)

where $\qquad\qquad\qquad K = \psi(a)\phi(b) - \psi(b)\phi(a).$ (3)

We find $h(a) = h(b) = K - K = 0$, and $h'(x)$ exists when $a < x < b$, with

$$h'(x) = \psi'(x)[\phi(b) - \phi(a)] - \phi'(x)[\psi(b) - \psi(a)].$$ (4)

Thus, $h(x)$ satisfies the hypotheses of Rolle's theorem on page 176. Hence, there exists a number ξ where $a < \xi < b$ and $h'(\xi) = 0$; or, from (4),

$$\psi'(\xi)[\phi(b) - \phi(a)] - \phi'(\xi)[\psi(b) - \psi(a)] = 0.$$ (5)

If $\phi'(\xi)$ were zero, then (5) would show that $\psi'(\xi) = 0$, which is contrary to the hypotheses of Theorem I. Hence, $\phi'(\xi) \neq 0$ and we obtain (1) on dividing by $\phi'(\xi)[\phi(b) - \phi(a)]$ in (5).

THEOREM II. *Assume that the functions $\phi(t)$ and $\psi(t)$ are differentiable when $a < t < c$ (or, $c < t < a$), with $\phi'(t) \neq 0$, $\phi(t) \neq 0$, and*

$$\phi(t) \to 0 \quad and \quad \psi(t) \to 0 \quad as \quad t \to a. \tag{6}$$

Suppose that $\psi'(t)/\phi'(t)$ has a limit λ, finite or infinite, as $t \to a$. Then

$$\lim_{t \to a} \frac{\psi(t)}{\phi(t)} = \lim_{t \to a} \frac{\psi'(t)}{\phi'(t)}. \tag{7}$$

Proof, Case 1: *a is finite.* 1. Extend the functions $\phi(t)$ and $\psi(t)$ by defining $\phi(a) = \psi(a) = 0$. Then, $\phi(t)$ and $\psi(t)$ are continuous on $a \leqq t < c$, and differentiable if $a < t < c$.

2. By Theorem I, there exists a point ξ with $a < \xi < t$, so that

$$\frac{\psi(t) - \psi(a)}{\phi(t) - \phi(a)} = \frac{\psi'(\xi)}{\phi'(\xi)}, \quad or \quad \frac{\psi(t)}{\phi(t)} = \frac{\psi'(\xi)}{\phi'(\xi)}. \tag{8}$$

Since $a < \xi < t$, then ξ will be as near a as we please if t is sufficiently near a.

Hence, (8) gives (7): $\qquad \lim_{t \to a} \dfrac{\psi(t)}{\phi(t)} = \lim_{\xi \to a} \dfrac{\psi'(\xi)}{\phi'(\xi)} = \lambda.$

Proof, Case 2: *$a = +\infty$, with $k < t < +\infty$ (or, similarly, for $a = -\infty$).*

1. Let $z = t^{-1}$, or $t = z^{-1}$, and introduce

$$\Phi(z) = \phi(t) = \phi(z^{-1}) \quad and \quad \Psi(z) = \psi(t) = \psi(z^{-1}). \tag{9}$$

From (9), $\qquad \Phi'(z) = \dfrac{d\phi(t)}{dz} = \dfrac{d\phi(t)}{dt}\dfrac{dt}{dz} = -\dfrac{1}{z^2}\phi'(t),$ or

$$\Phi'(z) = -\frac{1}{z^2}\phi'(z^{-1}); \quad \Psi'(z) = -\frac{1}{z^2}\psi'(z^{-1}). \tag{10}$$

Hence, $\qquad \lim_{z \to 0+} \dfrac{\Psi'(z)}{\Phi'(z)} = \lim_{z \to 0+} \dfrac{\psi'(z^{-1})}{\phi'(z^{-1})} = \lim_{t \to +\infty} \dfrac{\psi'(t)}{\phi'(t)} = \lambda.$

2. From (10), $\Phi'(z) \neq 0$ because $\phi'(t) \neq 0$. Also, $\Phi(z) \to 0$ and $\Psi(z) \to 0$ as $z \to 0+$. Hence, from Case 1 as applied to $\Psi(z)/\Phi(z)$,

$$\lim_{t \to +\infty} \frac{\psi(t)}{\phi(t)} = \lim_{z \to 0+} \frac{\Psi(z)}{\Phi(z)} = \lim_{z \to 0+} \frac{\Psi'(z)}{\Phi'(z)} = \lambda,$$

which proves Theorem II with $a = +\infty$.

THEOREM III. *Assume that $\phi(t)$ and $\psi(t)$ are differentiable when $c < t < a$, where a is finite, with $\phi'(t) \neq 0$, $\phi(t) \neq 0$, and $\phi(t) \to +\infty$ when $t \to a$. Also, assume that $\psi'(t)/\phi'(t)$ has a limit λ as $t \to a$. Then, (7) is true.*

Outline of proof. Let λ be finite. Since $\phi(t) \to \infty$ as $t \to a$, from Theorem I we obtain the following identities where s is appropriately large, $t > s$, and $s < \xi < t$. When $t \to a$, from (11) we obtain (7). Modified details, using (11), then prove (7) when $\lambda = \pm \infty$. A complete discussion would be somewhat complicated. A similar method applies if $a = \pm \infty$.

$$\frac{\psi(t) - \psi(s)}{\phi(t) - \phi(s)} = \frac{\psi'(\xi)}{\phi'(\xi)}, \quad or \quad \frac{\psi(t)}{\phi(t)} = \frac{\psi'(\xi)}{\phi'(\xi)}\left[1 - \frac{\phi(s)}{\phi(t)}\right] + \frac{\psi(s)}{\phi(t)}. \tag{11}$$

Note 8. Lateral Area of a Frustum of a Cone

Consider a right circular cone, thought of as a solid, and indicated partly by broken lines in Figure 325. If we remove the small cone above a plane parallel to and above the plane of the given cone's base, the remainder is called a **frustum** of a cone. In Figure 325, let r_1, r_2, k, and h be, respectively, the radius of the base of the cone, the radius of the top face of the frustum, the slant height of the cone, and the slant height of the frustum. The lateral area (or, the area of the curved surface) of a cone is equal to one half of the circumference of the base multiplied by the slant height. The lateral area, A, of the frustum is equal to the difference of the lateral areas of the given cone and the small cone which was cut off. Hence,

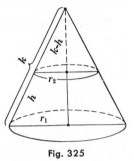

$$A = \pi r_1 k - \pi r_2(k - h) = \pi[k(r_1 - r_2) + r_2 h].$$

From similar triangles in Figure 325,

$$\frac{k - h}{r_2} = \frac{k}{r_1}, \quad or \quad k(r_1 - r_2) = r_1 h.$$

Hence, $A = \pi(r_1 h + r_2 h) = 2\pi h[\tfrac{1}{2}(r_1 + r_2)].$

Fig. 325

With $r_3 = \tfrac{1}{2}(r_1 + r_2)$, which is the radius of the midsection, $A = 2\pi r_3 h$. Or, A is equal to *the slant height times the circumference*, $2\pi r_3$, *of the midsection.*

Note 9. Effects of Parallel Projection in Figures

The traces of the sphere $x^2 + y^2 + z^2 = 9$ are correctly indicated in Figure 326. In contrast to Figure 208 on page 339, the xz-trace and xy-trace in Figure 326 are ellipses with axes rotated slightly from the coordinate axes. The resulting bulges over the circumference of the yz-trace could be verified by computing coordinates of points on the traces. The projecting lines of the system of parallel projection, for points in *front* of the yz-plane, map the actual points of space into positions *downward* and to the left on the yz-plane. The visible (full-line) parts and hidden (broken-line) parts of the traces in Figure 326 are drawn as if three diametral planes of a solid sphere are being represented, with the remainder of the sphere evaporated. Figure 326 could be augmented by drawing the elliptical border of the shadow of the sphere as it would appear on the yz-plane under a beam of light rays parallel to the system of lines of parallel projection. However, the complicated augmented figure would have no claim to presenting the sphere *as it is seen.* Hence, for simplicity, we adopt Figure 208 as a compromise.

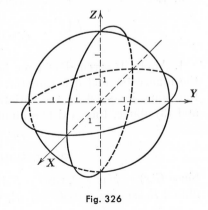

Fig. 326

Note 10. Taylor's Formula with Weakened Hypotheses

TAYLOR'S THEOREM. *Suppose that $f(s)$ has continuous derivatives of orders $1, 2, \cdots, (n-1)$ when $a \leqq s \leqq x$ (or, $x \leqq s \leqq a$), and that $f^{(n)}(s)$ exists when $a < s < x$. Then, there exists a number ξ between a and x such that*

$$f(x) = f(a) + f'(a)(x-a) + \cdots + \frac{f^{(n-1)}(a)}{(n-1)!}(x-a)^{n-1} + R_n(x), \qquad (1)$$

where
$$R_n(x) = \frac{(x-a)^n}{n!} f^{(n)}(\xi). \qquad (2)$$

Proof. 1. We define R_n by (1) and wish to prove (2). Let x have a fixed value. Let s be a variable with the range $a \leqq s \leqq x$. Define a function $G(s)$ by the following equation, whose terms are suggested by the right-hand side in (1) with $a = s$:

$$f(x) = f(s) + f'(s)(x-s) + \cdots + \frac{f^{(n-1)}(s)}{(n-1)!}(x-s)^{n-1} + G(s). \qquad (3)$$

We obtain $G'(s)$ by differentiating with respect to s on both sides of (3). Thus, for any integer $k > 1$,

$$\frac{d}{ds}\left[\frac{f^{(k)}(s)(x-s)^k}{k!}\right] = -\frac{f^{(k)}(s)(x-s)^{k-1}}{(k-1)!} + \frac{f^{(k+1)}(s)(x-s)^k}{k!}. \qquad (4)$$

When (4) is used for each corresponding term on the right in (3), cancellation termwise occurs, and we obtain

$$G'(s) + \frac{f^{(n)}(s)}{(n-1)!}(x-s)^{n-1} = 0, \; or$$

$$G'(s) = -\frac{f^{(n)}(s)(x-s)^{n-1}}{(n-1)!}. \qquad (5)$$

2. In (3), on placing $s = x$ and then $s = a$, we obtain $G(x) = 0$ and $G(a) = R_n(x)$, because of (1).

3. Let
$$\phi(s) = -\frac{(x-s)^n}{n!}; \; then$$

$$\phi'(s) = \frac{(x-s)^{n-1}}{(n-1)!}.$$

4. Apply Theorem I of page 565 with $G(s)$ and $\phi(s)$ as the functions of the numerator and denominator, respectively, and with $s = x$ and $s = a$ as the values involved for the variable. Then, from (1) of Note 7 on page 565 and (3) above, there exists a number ξ where $a < \xi < x$, such that

$$\frac{G(x) - G(a)}{\phi(x) - \phi(a)} = \frac{G'(\xi)}{\phi'(\xi)} = -f^{(n)}(\xi). \qquad (6)$$

Since $G(x) = \phi(x) = 0$, $G(a) = R_n(x)$, and $\phi(a) = -(x-a)^n/n!$, from (6) we obtain $R_n(x) = (x-a)^n f^{(n)}(\xi)/n!$, which we wish to prove.

Note 11. Sufficient Condition for an Exact Differential

$P(x, y)dx + Q(x, y)dy$ *is an exact differential if* $P_y = Q_x$.

Proof. 1. Assume that $P_y = Q_x$. Let (x_0, y_0) be any point on the range for (x, y). Define a function $u(x, y)$ as follows:

$$u = \int_{x_0}^{x} P(x, y)dx + \int_{y_0}^{y} Q(x_0, y)dy.$$

Then,* $\dfrac{\partial u}{\partial x} = P(x, y); \quad \dfrac{\partial u}{\partial y} = \int_{x_0}^{x} P_y(x, y)dx + Q(x_0, y).$

Since $P_y = Q_x$, $\dfrac{\partial u}{\partial y} = \int_{x_0}^{x} Q_x(x, y)dx + Q(x_0, y)$

$$= Q(x, y)\Big]_{x=x_0}^{x=x} + Q(x_0, y) = Q(x, y) - Q(x_0, y) + Q(x_0, y).$$

Thus, $u_x = P(x, y)$ and $u_y = Q(x, y)$, or $du = P\,dx + Q\,dy$, which shows that $P\,dx + Q\,dy$ is an exact differential.

Note 12. Newton's Method for Solving Equations

Let $f(x)$ be a function possessing first and second derivatives, $f'(x)$ and $f''(x)$, where $f''(x)$ is continuous, on an interval of values $a \leqq x \leqq b$. For reasons which we shall indicate later, assume that $f'(x) \neq 0$ and $f''(x) \neq 0$ at all values of x involved. We desire to solve the equation $f(x) = 0$. The roots (if any) of $f(x) = 0$ are the x-intercepts of the graph of $y = f(x)$. Since $f'(x)$ is continuous and $f'(x) \neq 0$, then $f(x)$ is either an increasing function $[f'(x) > 0]$ or a decreasing function $[f'(x) < 0]$ when $a \leqq x \leqq b$. Hence, there is just one root, or there are no roots, for $f(x) = 0$ on (a, b). We assume that there is an unknown root r for $f(x) = 0$ on (a, b), and propose finding r, to any specified degree of accuracy. If $f(x)$ is a polynomial of degree n, it might prove convenient to obtain r by Horner's method, as presented in any text on college algebra. If $f(x)$ is a very simple trigonometric expression, we might be able to solve $f(x) = 0$ conveniently by methods applying to trigonometric equations. However, as a rule, we should expect to use some other method, involving successive approximations, to obtain the root. One of the most popular means for solving a general equation $f(x) = 0$ is **Newton's method**, which we proceed to discuss.

Let the curve in Figure 327 be a graph of the equation $y = f(x)$. Assume that, by substitution, we have verified the fact that $f(a)$ and

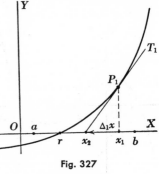

Fig. 327

* We use a result from advanced calculus: $\dfrac{\partial}{\partial y}\displaystyle\int_{x_0}^{x} P(x, y)dx = \int_{x_0}^{x} P_y(x, y)dx$

$f(b)$ have opposite signs, so that just one root $x = r$ of $f(x) = 0$ is known to exist between a and b. Since $f''(x) \neq 0$, then $f'(x)$ is a decreasing, or an increasing, function. Let x_1 be a number which we believe is close to the unknown root $x = r$, and assume that x_1 is on that side of r, as in Figure 327, where the absolute values of $f'(x)$ are largest. It can be verified that, in such a case, we take x_1 on the side where $f(x_1) > 0$ if $f''(x) > 0$, and where $f(x_1) < 0$ if $f''(x) < 0$.

Let $P_1:(x_1, y_1)$ be the corresponding point on the curve $y = f(x)$. At P_1, construct the tangent P_1T_1, intersecting the x-axis at $x = x_2$. Then, from Figure 327, it is evident intuitively that x_2 is closer than x_1 to the unknown root r. To obtain a formula for x_2 in terms of x_1, first we write the equation of P_1T_1:

$$y - y_1 = f'(x_1)(x - x_1). \tag{1}$$

When $y = 0$ in (1), then $x = x_2$. Hence $-y_1 = f'(x_1)(x_2 - x_1)$, or

$$x_2 = x_1 - \frac{y_1}{f'(x_1)}. \tag{2}$$

In Figure 327, the correction "$-y_1/f'(x_1)$," which is applied to x_1 in (2) to obtain x_2, is represented by $\Delta_1 x$. We summarize the preceding discussion, with $y_1 = f(x_1)$:

$$\left\{ \begin{array}{l} \textit{First approximation to root, } x_1; \quad \textit{correction, } \Delta_1 x = -\dfrac{f(x_1)}{f'(x_1)}; \\ \textit{second approximation to root, } x_2 = x_1 + \Delta_1 x. \end{array} \right\} \tag{3}$$

From Figure 327, it is evident intuitively that x_2 is nearer than x_1 to r. Then, we would obtain a correction $\Delta_2 x$, and a third approximation x_3,

$$\Delta_2 x = -\frac{f(x_2)}{f'(x_2)} \quad \textit{and} \quad x_3 = x_2 + \Delta_2 x; \textit{ etc.}$$

$$\Delta_n x = -\frac{f(x_n)}{f'(x_n)} \quad \textit{and} \quad x_{n+1} = x_n + \Delta_n x. \tag{4}$$

Thus, we define a sequence $\{x_n\}$. It can be proved that, with the hypotheses stated at the beginning of our discussion, $x_n \to r$ as $n \to \infty$. We accept this fact without proof.

EXAMPLE 1. Obtain the roots of

$$x^3 - 3x^2 - 2x + 5 = 0. \tag{5}$$

SOLUTION. 1. Let $f(x)$ represent the left-hand member of (5), and let $y = f(x)$. Then,

$$f'(x) = 3x^2 - 6x - 2. \tag{6}$$

2. *Crude approximations to the roots.* We compute a table of values of $f(x)$ and draw the graph of $y = f(x)$ in Figure 328. Thus, we

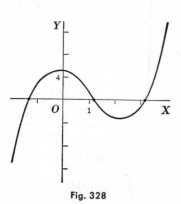

Fig. 328

bracket each root between integers, and show that there are roots near
− 1.3, 1.2, and 3.2.

3. *To obtain the root r near* 3.2. In Figure 328, we see that the slope of
the graph increases to the *right* of the unknown number r. Hence, as a first
approximation, certainly greater than r, we take $x_1 = 3.5$. From (3),

$$\Delta_1 x = -\frac{f(3.5)}{f'(3.5)} = -\frac{4.125}{13.75} = -.30; \quad x_2 = 3.5 - .30 = 3.20. \qquad (7)$$

From (5), $\Delta_2 x = -\dfrac{f(3.2)}{f'(3.2)} = -\dfrac{.648}{9.52} = -.07; \quad x_3 = 3.20 - .07 = 3.13.$ (8)

Similarly, $\Delta_3 x = -\dfrac{f(3.13)}{f'(3.13)} = -.0016; \quad x_4 = 3.13 - .0016 = 3.1284.$

We accept $x_4 = 3.128$ as our final approximation to the root. The other
roots could be obtained similarly.

Note 1. To check the accuracy of a result obtained by Newton's method,
such as $x_4 = 3.128$ in Example 1, we may proceed as follows.

Let x_n be the final approximation obtained, where x_n is expressed to the
$(k + 1)$th decimal place. Let $x = \xi$ be a point *in the direction of the unknown
root r from* x_n, where $|\, x_n - \xi \,|$ is less than 1 unit in the kth decimal place,
and compute $f(\xi)$ and $f(x_n)$. If $f(\xi)$ and $f(x_n)$ have opposite signs, then r is
between ξ and x_n, and hence the error of x_n is less than 1 unit in the kth
decimal place.

In Example 1, to apply the check, we would use $\xi = 3.128$. We know
that $f(3.129) > 0$. We compute $f(3.128) = -.004$. Hence, the root r is
between 3.128 and 3.129, and evidently very close to 3.128.

Note 2. Under preceding assumptions, suppose that the first approximation x_1 to a root r of $f(x) = 0$ is selected on that side of r where the values
of $|\, f'(x) \,|$ are *smallest*, as in Figure 329. Then, if the tangent construction
of Figure 327 is applied in the new situation, the second approximation x_2
is on the side of r opposite to x_1. From this point on, the successive approximations remain on the same side of r, as in the discussion leading to (3) and
(4). Hence, with $f'(x) \neq 0$ and $f''(x) \neq 0$, a first approximation x_1 may be
chosen somewhat recklessly,* if desirable, with assurance that the method
will yield a sequence $\{x_n\}$ having r as the limit when $n \to \infty$.

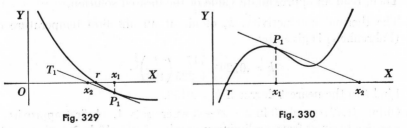

Fig. 329   Fig. 330

* Provided that, with x_1 as in Figure 329, the range of x where $f'(x) \neq 0$ and $f''(x) \neq 0$
is large enough so that x_2 is on the range.

ILLUSTRATION 1. Figure 330 on page 571 shows the tangent construction of Newton's method with a first approximation x_1 on a range where the condition $[f'(x) \neq 0, f''(x) \neq 0]$ is violated. In Figure 330, the second approximation x_2 is much less accurate than x_1.

Note 3. Newton's method can be motivated by Theorem II on page 176. Let x_1 be an approximation to a root r of the equation $f(x) = 0$. By the law of the mean, there exists a number ξ between x and x_1 so that

$$f(x) = f(x_1) + f'(\xi)(x - x_1). \tag{9}$$

As an approximation, let $\xi = x_1$; then, instead of considering $f(x) = 0$, solve

$$f(x_1) + f'(x_1)(x - x_1) = 0; \quad \textit{we obtain} \quad x = x_1 - \frac{f(x_1)}{f'(x_1)}. \tag{10}$$

We recognize x in (10) as the second approximation x_2 obtained from x_1 by Newton's method in (2), with $y_1 = f(x_1)$.

EXERCISE 174

Use Newton's method in solving each problem. Obtain the result correct to two decimal places except as otherwise specified.

Find the specified roots. The student may desire to use synthetic division in computing values of polynomials.

1. The two roots of $x^2 - 6x + 6 = 0$, without using the quadratic formula.

2. The root of $x^3 - 7x^2 + 15x + 89 = 0$ between -2 and -3.

3. The root of $x^3 + 3x - 5 = 0$ between 1 and 2.

4. All roots of $x^3 + 2x^2 - 7x + 1 = 0$.   5. All roots of $x^3 - 2x^2 = 5x - 4$.

Find the indicated root by use of Newton's method.

6. $\sqrt[4]{10}$.   7. $\sqrt[3]{185}$.   8. $\sqrt[3]{-62}$.   9. $\sqrt[5]{-148}$.

HINT for Problem 6. If x is the root, then $x^4 = 10$.

10. The relation $M = x - e \sin x$, called **Kepler's equation,** holds between the mean anomaly M and the eccentric anomaly x of a planet at any point in its path around the sun; e is the eccentricity of the ellipse which forms the path. If $e = .4$ and $M = 4$, find x.

HINT. Draw a rough graph of $y = x - .4 \sin x$, and draw the line $y = 4$. Then, read an approximate value of the desired solution.

11. The thermal conductivity, k, of air at an absolute temperature of $t°$ (Fahrenheit) is given by

$$k = .0129 \frac{717}{t + 225} \left(\frac{t}{492}\right)^{\frac{3}{2}}.$$

Find t to the nearest degree if $k = .0158$.

12. Obtain that root of $10 \ln x = x^2 - 3$ where $x > 1$. A first approximation can be obtained from preliminary graphs of $y_1 = 10 \ln x$ and $y_2 = x^2 - 3$ on the same coordinate system.

TABLES

I. POWERS AND ROOTS

No.	Sq.	Sq. Root	Cube	Cube Root	No.	Sq.	Sq. Root	Cube	Cube Root
1	1	1.000	1	1.000	51	2,601	7.141	132,651	3.708
2	4	1.414	8	1.260	52	2,704	7.211	140,608	3.732
3	9	1.732	27	1.442	53	2,809	7.280	148,877	3.756
4	16	2.000	64	1.587	54	2,916	7.348	157,464	3.780
5	25	2.236	125	1.710	55	3,025	7.416	166,375	3.803
6	36	2.449	216	1.817	56	3,136	7.483	175,616	3.826
7	49	2.646	343	1.913	57	3,249	7.550	185,193	3.848
8	64	2.828	512	2.000	58	3,364	7.616	195,112	3.871
9	81	3.000	729	2.080	59	3,481	7.681	205,379	3.893
10	100	3.162	1,000	2.154	60	3,600	7.746	216,000	3.915
11	121	3.317	1,331	2.224	61	3,721	7.810	226,981	3.936
12	144	3.464	1,728	2.289	62	3,844	7.874	238,328	3.958
13	169	3.606	2,197	2.351	63	3,969	7.937	250,047	3.979
14	196	3.742	2,744	2.410	64	4,096	8.000	262,144	4.000
15	225	3.873	3,375	2.466	65	4,225	8.062	274,625	4.021
16	256	4.000	4,096	2.520	66	4,356	8.124	287,496	4.041
17	289	4.123	4,913	2.571	67	4,489	8.185	300,763	4.062
18	324	4.243	5,832	2.621	68	4,624	8.246	314,432	4.082
19	361	4.359	6,859	2.668	69	4,761	8.307	328,509	4.102
20	400	4.472	8,000	2.714	70	4,900	8.367	343,000	4.121
21	441	4.583	9,261	2.759	71	5,041	8.426	357,911	4.141
22	484	4.690	10,648	2.802	72	5,184	8.485	373,248	4.160
23	529	4.796	12,167	2.844	73	5,329	8.544	389,017	4.179
24	576	4.899	13,824	2.884	74	5,476	8.602	405,224	4.198
25	625	5.000	15,625	2.924	75	5,625	8.660	421,875	4.217
26	676	5.099	17,576	2.962	76	5,776	8.718	438,976	4.236
27	729	5.196	19,683	3.000	77	5,929	8.775	456,533	4.254
28	784	5.291	21,952	3.037	78	6,084	8.832	474,552	4.273
29	841	5.385	24,389	3.072	79	6,241	8.888	493,039	4.291
30	900	5.477	27,000	3.107	80	6,400	8.944	512,000	4.309
31	961	5.568	29,791	3.141	81	6,561	9.000	531,441	4.327
32	1,024	5.657	32,768	3.175	82	6,724	9.055	551,368	4.344
33	1,089	5.745	35,937	3.208	83	6,889	9.110	571,787	4.362
34	1,156	5.831	39,304	3.240	84	7,056	9.165	592,704	4.380
35	1,225	5.916	42,875	3.271	85	7,225	9.220	614,125	4.397
36	1,296	6.000	46,656	3.302	86	7,396	9.274	636,056	4.414
37	1,369	6.083	50,653	3.332	87	7,569	9.327	658,503	4.431
38	1,444	6.164	54,872	3.362	88	7,744	9.381	681,472	4.448
39	1,521	6.245	59,319	3.391	89	7,921	9.434	704,969	4.465
40	1,600	6.325	64,000	3.420	90	8,100	9.487	729,000	4.481
41	1,681	6.403	68,921	3.448	91	8,281	9.539	753,571	4.498
42	1,764	6.481	74,088	3.476	92	8,464	9.592	778,688	4.514
43	1,849	6.557	79,507	3.503	93	8,649	9.644	804,357	4.531
44	1,936	6.633	85,184	3.530	94	8,836	9.695	830,584	4.547
45	2,025	6.708	91,125	3.557	95	9,025	9.747	857,375	4.563
46	2,116	6.782	97,336	3.583	96	9,216	9.798	884,736	4.579
47	2,209	6.856	103,823	3.609	97	9,409	9.849	912,673	4.595
48	2,304	6.928	110,592	3.634	98	9,604	9.899	941,192	4.610
49	2,401	7.000	117,649	3.659	99	9,801	9.950	970,299	4.626
50	2,500	7.071	125,000	3.684	100	10,000	10.000	1,000,000	4.642

N	0	1	2	3	4	5	6	7	8	9	Prop. Parts
10	.0000	0043	0086	0128	0170	0212	0253	0294	0334	0374	
11	.0414	0453	0492	0531	0569	0607	0645	0682	0719	0755	
12	.0792	0828	0864	0899	0934	0969	1004	1038	1072	1106	
13	.1139	1173	1206	1239	1271	1303	1335	1367	1399	1430	
14	.1461	1492	1523	1553	1584	1614	1644	1673	1703	1732	
15	.1761	1790	1818	1847	1875	1903	1931	1959	1987	2014	
16	.2041	2068	2095	2122	2148	2175	2201	2227	2253	2279	
17	.2304	2330	2355	2380	2405	2430	2455	2480	2504	2529	
18	.2553	2577	2601	2625	2648	2672	2695	2718	2742	2765	
19	.2788	2810	2833	2856	2878	2900	2923	2945	2967	2989	
20	.3010	3032	3054	3075	3096	3118	3139	3160	3181	3201	
21	.3222	3243	3263	3284	3304	3324	3345	3365	3385	3404	
22	.3424	3444	3464	3483	3502	3522	3541	3560	3579	3598	
23	.3617	3636	3655	3674	3692	3711	3729	3747	3766	3784	
24	.3802	3820	3838	3856	3874	3892	3909	3927	3945	3962	
25	.3979	3997	4014	4031	4048	4065	4082	4099	4116	4133	
26	.4150	4166	4183	4200	4216	4232	4249	4265	4281	4298	
27	.4314	4330	4346	4362	4378	4393	4409	4425	4440	4456	
28	.4472	4487	4502	4518	4533	4548	4564	4579	4594	4609	
29	.4624	4639	4654	4669	4683	4698	4713	4728	4742	4757	
30	.4771	4786	4800	4814	4829	4843	4857	4871	4886	4900	
31	.4914	4928	4942	4955	4969	4983	4997	5011	5024	5038	
32	.5051	5065	5079	5092	5105	5119	5132	5145	5159	5172	
33	.5185	5198	5211	5224	5237	5250	5263	5276	5289	5302	
34	.5315	5328	5340	5353	5366	5378	5391	5403	5416	5428	
35	.5441	5453	5465	5478	5490	5502	5514	5527	5539	5551	
36	.5563	5575	5587	5599	5611	5623	5635	5647	5658	5670	
37	.5682	5694	5705	5717	5729	5740	5752	5763	5775	5786	
38	.5798	5809	5821	5832	5843	5855	5866	5877	5888	5899	
39	.5911	5922	5933	5944	5955	5966	5977	5988	5999	6010	
40	.6021	6031	6042	6053	6064	6075	6085	6096	6107	6117	
41	.6128	6138	6149	6160	6170	6180	6191	6201	6212	6222	
42	.6232	6243	6253	6263	6274	6284	6294	6304	6314	6325	
43	.6335	6345	6355	6365	6375	6385	6395	6405	6415	6425	
44	.6435	6444	6454	6464	6474	6484	6493	6503	6513	6522	
45	.6532	6542	6551	6561	6571	6580	6590	6599	6609	6618	
46	.6628	6637	6646	6656	6665	6675	6684	6693	6702	6712	
47	.6721	6730	6739	6749	6758	6767	6776	6785	6794	6803	
48	.6812	6821	6830	6839	6848	6857	6866	6875	6884	6893	
49	.6902	6911	6920	6928	6937	6946	6955	6964	6972	6981	
50	.6990	6998	7007	7016	7024	7033	7042	7050	7059	7067	
N	0	1	2	3	4	5	6	7	8	9	

Prop. Parts

	28	27	26
1	2.8	2.7	2.6
2	5.6	5.4	5.2
3	8.4	8.1	7.8
4	11.2	10.8	10.4
5	14.0	13.5	13.0
6	16.8	16.2	15.6
7	19.6	18.9	18.2
8	22.4	21.6	20.8
9	25.2	24.3	23.4

	22	21	20
1	2.2	2.1	2.0
2	4.4	4.2	4.0
3	6.6	6.3	6.0
4	8.8	8.4	8.0
5	11.0	10.5	10.0
6	13.2	12.6	12.0
7	15.4	14.7	14.0
8	17.6	16.8	16.0
9	19.8	18.9	18.0

	16	15	14
1	1.6	1.5	1.4
2	3.2	3.0	2.8
3	4.8	4.5	4.2
4	6.4	6.0	5.6
5	8.0	7.5	7.0
6	9.6	9.0	8.4
7	11.2	10.5	9.8
8	12.8	12.0	11.2
9	14.4	13.5	12.6

	13	12	11
1	1.3	1.2	1.1
2	2.6	2.4	2.2
3	3.9	3.6	3.3
4	5.2	4.8	4.4
5	6.5	6.0	5.5
6	7.8	7.2	6.6
7	9.1	8.4	7.7
8	10.4	9.6	8.8
9	11.7	10.8	9.9

	43	42	41	40	39		38	37	36	35	34		33	32	31	30	29	
1	4.3	4.2	4.1	4.0	3.9	1	3.8	3.7	3.6	3.5	3.4	1	3.3	3.2	3.1	3.0	2.9	1
2	8.6	8.4	8.2	8.0	7.8	2	7.6	7.4	7.2	7.0	6.8	2	6.6	6.4	6.2	6.0	5.8	2
3	12.9	12.6	12.3	12.0	11.7	3	11.4	11.1	10.8	10.5	10.2	3	9.9	9.6	9.3	9.0	8.7	3
4	17.2	16.8	16.4	16.0	15.6	4	15.2	14.8	14.4	14.0	13.6	4	13.2	12.8	12.4	12.0	11.6	4
5	21.5	21.0	20.5	20.0	19.5	5	19.0	18.5	18.0	17.5	17.0	5	16.5	16.0	15.5	15.0	14.5	5
6	25.8	25.2	24.6	24.0	23.4	6	22.8	22.2	21.6	21.0	20.4	6	19.8	19.2	18.6	18.0	17.4	6
7	30.1	29.4	28.7	28.0	27.3	7	26.6	25.9	25.2	24.5	23.8	7	23.1	22.4	21.7	21.0	20.3	7
8	34.4	33.6	32.8	32.0	31.2	8	30.4	29.6	28.8	28.0	27.2	8	26.4	25.6	24.8	24.0	23.2	8
9	38.7	37.8	36.9	36.0	35.1	9	34.2	33.3	32.4	31.5	30.6	9	29.7	28.8	27.9	27.0	26.1	9

Prop. Parts			N	0	1	2	3	4	5	6	7	8	9
			50	.6990	6998	7007	7016	7024	7033	7042	7050	7059	7067
			51	.7076	7084	7093	7101	7110	7118	7126	7135	7143	7152
			52	.7160	7168	7177	7185	7193	7202	7210	7218	7226	7235
			53	.7243	7251	7259	7267	7275	7284	7292	7300	7308	7316

	25	24	23
1	2.5	2.4	2.3
2	5.0	4.8	4.6
3	7.5	7.2	6.9
4	10.0	9.6	9.2
5	12.5	12.0	11.5
6	15.0	14.4	13.8
7	17.5	16.8	16.1
8	20.0	19.2	18.4
9	22.5	21.6	20.7

N	0	1	2	3	4	5	6	7	8	9
54	.7324	7332	7340	7348	7356	7364	7372	7380	7388	7396
55	.7404	7412	7419	7427	7435	7443	7451	7459	7466	7474
56	.7482	7490	7497	7505	7513	7520	7528	7536	7543	7551
57	.7559	7566	7574	7582	7589	7597	7604	7612	7619	7627
58	.7634	7642	7649	7657	7664	7672	7679	7686	7694	7701
59	.7709	7716	7723	7731	7738	7745	7752	7760	7767	7774
60	.7782	7789	7796	7803	7810	7818	7825	7832	7839	7846

	19	18	17
1	1.9	1.8	1.7
2	3.8	3.6	3.4
3	5.7	5.4	5.1
4	7.6	7.2	6.8
5	9.5	9.0	8.5
6	11.4	10.8	10.2
7	13.3	12.6	11.9
8	15.2	14.4	13.6
9	17.1	16.2	15.3

N	0	1	2	3	4	5	6	7	8	9
61	.7853	7860	7868	7875	7882	7889	7896	7903	7910	7917
62	.7924	7931	7938	7945	7952	7959	7966	7973	7980	7987
63	.7993	8000	8007	8014	8021	8028	8035	8041	8048	8055
64	.8062	8069	8075	8082	8089	8096	8102	8109	8116	8122
65	.8129	8136	8142	8149	8156	8162	8169	8176	8182	8189
66	.8195	8202	8209	8215	8222	8228	8235	8241	8248	8254
67	.8261	8267	8274	8280	8287	8293	8299	8306	8312	8319
68	.8325	8331	8338	8344	8351	8357	8363	8370	8376	8382
69	.8388	8395	8401	8407	8414	8420	8426	8432	8439	8445
70	.8451	8457	8463	8470	8476	8482	8488	8494	8500	8506

	10	9
1	1.0	0.9
2	2.0	1.8
3	3.0	2.7
4	4.0	3.6
5	5.0	4.5
6	6.0	5.4
7	7.0	6.3
8	8.0	7.2
9	9.0	8.1

N	0	1	2	3	4	5	6	7	8	9
71	.8513	8519	8525	8531	8537	8543	8549	8555	8561	8567
72	.8573	8579	8585	8591	8597	8603	8609	8615	8621	8627
73	.8633	8639	8645	8651	8657	8663	8669	8675	8681	8686
74	.8692	8698	8704	8710	8716	8722	8727	8733	8739	8745
75	.8751	8756	8762	8768	8774	8779	8785	8791	8797	8802
76	.8808	8814	8820	8825	8831	8837	8842	8848	8854	8859
77	.8865	8871	8876	8882	8887	8893	8899	8904	8910	8915
78	.8921	8927	8932	8938	8943	8949	8954	8960	8965	8971
79	.8976	8982	8987	8993	8998	9004	9009	9015	9020	9025
80	.9031	9036	9042	9047	9053	9058	9063	9069	9074	9079

	8	7
1	0.8	0.7
2	1.6	1.4
3	2.4	2.1
4	3.2	2.8
5	4.0	3.5
6	4.8	4.2
7	5.6	4.9
8	6.4	5.6
9	7.2	6.3

N	0	1	2	3	4	5	6	7	8	9
81	.9085	9090	9096	9101	9106	9112	9117	9122	9128	9133
82	.9138	9143	9149	9154	9159	9165	9170	9175	9180	9186
83	.9191	9196	9201	9206	9212	9217	9222	9227	9232	9238
84	.9243	9248	9253	9258	9263	9269	9274	9279	9284	9289
85	.9294	9299	9304	9309	9315	9320	9325	9330	9335	9340
86	.9345	9350	9355	9360	9365	9370	9375	9380	9385	9390
87	.9395	9400	9405	9410	9415	9420	9425	9430	9435	9440
88	.9445	9450	9455	9460	9465	9469	9474	9479	9484	9489
89	.9494	9499	9504	9509	9513	9518	9523	9528	9533	9538
90	.9542	9547	9552	9557	9562	9566	9571	9576	9581	9586

	6	5	4
1	0.6	0.5	0.4
2	1.2	1.0	0.8
3	1.8	1.5	1.2
4	2.4	2.0	1.6
5	3.0	2.5	2.0
6	3.6	3.0	2 4
7	4.2	3.5	2.8
8	4.8	4.0	3.2
9	5.4	4.5	3.6

N	0	1	2	3	4	5	6	7	8	9
91	.9590	9595	9600	9605	9609	9614	9619	9624	9628	9633
92	.9638	9643	9647	9652	9657	9661	9666	9671	9675	9680
93	.9685	9689	9694	9699	9703	9708	9713	9717	9722	9727
94	.9731	9736	9741	9745	9750	9754	9759	9763	9768	9773
95	.9777	9782	9786	9791	9795	9800	9805	9809	9814	9818
96	.9823	9827	9832	9836	9841	9845	9850	9854	9859	9863
97	.9868	9872	9877	9881	9886	9890	9894	9899	9903	9908
98	.9912	9917	9921	9926	9930	9934	9939	9943	9948	9952
99	.9956	9961	9965	9969	9974	9978	9983	9987	9991	9996
N	0	1	2	3	4	5	6	7	8	9

N	0	1	2	3	4	5	6	7	8	9
1.0	0.0 0000	0995	1980	2956	3922	4879	5827	6766	7696	8618
1.1	0.0 9531	*0436	*1333	*2222	*3103	*3976	*4842	*5700	*6551	*7395
1.2	0.1 8232	9062	9885	*0701	*1511	*2314	*3111	*3902	*4686	*5464
1.3	0.2 6236	7003	7763	8518	9267	*0010	*0748	*1481	*2208	*2930
1.4	0.3 3647	4359	5066	5767	6464	7156	7844	8526	9204	9878
1.5	0.4 0547	1211	1871	2527	3178	3825	4469	5108	5742	6373
1.6	0.4 7000	7623	8243	8858	9470	*0078	*0682	*1282	*1879	*2473
1.7	0.5 3063	3649	4232	4812	5389	5962	6531	7098	7661	8222
1.8	0.5 8779	9333	9884	*0432	*0977	*1519	*2058	*2594	*3127	*3658
1.9	0.6 4185	4710	5233	5752	6269	6783	7294	7803	8310	8813
2.0	0.6 9315	9813	*0310	*0804	*1295	*1784	*2271	*2755	*3237	*3716
2.1	0.7 4194	4669	5142	5612	6081	6547	7011	7473	7932	8390
2.2	0.7 8846	9299	9751	*0200	*0648	*1093	*1536	*1978	*2418	*2855
2.3	0.8 3291	3725	4157	4587	5015	5442	5866	6289	6710	7129
2.4	0.8 7547	7963	8377	8789	9200	9609	*0016	*0422	*0826	*1228
2.5	0.9 1629	2028	2426	2822	3216	3609	4001	4391	4779	5166
2.6	5551	5935	6317	6698	7078	7456	7833	8208	8582	8954
2.7	0.9 9325	9695	*0063	*0430	*0796	*1160	*1523	*1885	*2245	*2604
2.8	1.0 2962	3318	3674	4028	4380	4732	5082	5431	5779	6126
2.9	6471	6815	7158	7500	7841	8181	8519	8856	9192	9527
3.0	1.0 9861	*0194	*0526	*0856	*1186	*1514	*1841	*2168	*2493	*2817
3.1	1.1 3140	3462	3783	4103	4422	4740	5057	5373	5688	6002
3.2	6315	6627	6938	7248	7557	7865	8173	8479	8784	9089
3.3	1.1 9392	9695	9996	*0297	*0597	*0896	*1194	*1491	*1788	*2083
3.4	1.2 2378	2671	2964	3256	3547	3837	4127	4415	4703	4990
3.5	5276	5562	5846	6130	6413	6695	6976	7257	7536	7815
3.6	1.2 8093	8371	8647	8923	9198	9473	9746	*0019	*0291	*0563
3.7	1.3 0833	1103	1372	1641	1909	2176	2442	2708	2972	3237
3.8	3500	3763	4025	4286	4547	4807	5067	5325	5584	5841
3.9	6098	6354	6609	6864	7118	7372	7624	7877	8128	8379
4.0	1.3 8629	8879	9128	9377	9624	9872	*0118	*0364	*0610	*0854
4.1	1.4 1099	1342	1585	1828	2070	2311	2552	2792	3031	3270
4.2	3508	3746	3984	4220	4456	4692	4927	5161	5395	5629
4.3	5862	6094	6326	6557	6787	7018	7247	7476	7705	7933
4.4	1.4 8160	8387	8614	8840	9065	9290	9515	9739	9962	*0185
4.5	1.5 0408	0630	0851	1072	1293	1513	1732	1951	2170	2388
4.6	2606	2823	3039	3256	3471	3687	3902	4116	4330	4543
4.7	4756	4969	5181	5393	5604	5814	6025	6235	6444	6653
4.8	6862	7070	7277	7485	7691	7898	8104	8309	8515	8719
4.9	1.5 8924	9127	9331	9534	9737	9939	*0141	*0342	*0543	*0744
5.0	1.6 0944	1144	1343	1542	1741	1939	2137	2334	2531	2728
5.1	2924	3120	3315	3511	3705	3900	4094	4287	4481	4673
5.2	4866	5058	5250	5441	5632	5823	6013	6203	6393	6582
5.3	6771	6959	7147	7335	7523	7710	7896	8083	8269	8455
5.4	1.6 8640	8825	9010	9194	9378	9562	9745	9928	*0111	*0293
5.5	1.7 0475	0656	0838	1019	1199	1380	1560	1740	1919	2098
5.6	2277	2455	2633	2811	2988	3166	3342	3519	3695	3871
5.7	4047	4222	4397	4572	4746	4920	5094	5267	5440	5613
5.8	5786	5958	6130	6302	6473	6644	6815	6985	7156	7326
5.9	7495	7665	7834	8002	8171	8339	8507	8675	8842	9009
6.0	1.7 9176	9342	9509	9675	9840	*0006	*0171	*0336	*0500	*0665
N	0	1	2	3	4	5	6	7	8	9

N	0	1	2	3	4	5	6	7	8	9
6.0	1.7 9176	9342	9509	9675	9840	*0006	*0171	*0336	*0500	*0665
6.1	1.8 0829	0993	1156	1319	1482	1645	1808	1970	2132	2294
6.2	2455	2616	2777	2938	3098	3258	3418	3578	3737	3896
6.3	4055	4214	4372	4530	4688	4845	5003	5160	5317	5473
6.4	5630	5786	5942	6097	6253	6408	6563	6718	6872	7026
6.5	7180	7334	7487	7641	7794	7947	8099	8251	8403	8555
6.6	1.8 8707	8858	9010	9160	9311	9462	9612	9762	9912	*0061
6.7	1.9 0211	0360	0509	0658	0806	0954	1102	1250	1398	1545
6.8	1692	1839	1986	2132	2279	2425	2571	2716	2862	3007
6.9	3152	3297	3442	3586	3730	3874	4018	4162	4305	4448
7.0	4591	4734	4876	5019	5161	5303	5445	5586	5727	5869
7.1	6009	6150	6291	6431	6571	6711	6851	6991	7130	7269
7.2	7408	7547	7685	7824	7962	8100	8238	8376	8513	8650
7.3	1.9 8787	8924	9061	9198	9334	9470	9606	9742	9877	*0013
7.4	2.0 0148	0283	0418	0553	0687	0821	0956	1089	1223	1357
7.5	1490	1624	1757	1890	2022	2155	2287	2419	2551	2683
7.6	2815	2946	3078	3209	3340	3471	3601	3732	3862	3992
7.7	4122	4252	4381	4511	4640	4769	4898	5027	5156	5284
7.8	5412	5540	5668	5796	5924	6051	6179	6306	6433	6560
7.9	6686	6813	6939	7065	7191	7317	7443	7568	7694	7819
8.0	7944	8069	8194	8318	8443	8567	8691	8815	8939	9063
8.1	2.0 9186	9310	9433	9556	9679	9802	9924	*0047	*0169	*0291
8.2	2.1 0413	0535	0657	0779	0900	1021	1142	1263	1384	1505
8.3	1626	1746	1866	1986	2106	2226	2346	2465	2585	2704
8.4	2823	2942	3061	3180	3298	3417	3535	3653	3771	3889
8.5	4007	4124	4242	4359	4476	4593	4710	4827	4943	5060
8.6	5176	5292	5409	5524	5640	5756	5871	5987	6102	6217
8.7	6332	6447	6562	6677	6791	6905	7020	7134	7248	7361
8.8	7475	7589	7702	7816	7929	8042	8155	8267	8380	8493
8.9	8605	8717	8830	8942	9054	9165	9277	9389	9500	9611
9.0	2.1 9722	9834	9944	*0055	*0166	*0276	*0387	*0497	*0607	*0717
9.1	2.2 0827	0937	1047	1157	1266	1375	1485	1594	1703	1812
9.2	1920	2029	2138	2246	2354	2462	2570	2678	2786	2894
9.3	3001	3109	3216	3324	3431	3538	3645	3751	3858	3965
9.4	4071	4177	4284	4390	4496	4601	4707	4813	4918	5024
9.5	5129	5234	5339	5444	5549	5654	5759	5863	5968	6072
9.6	6176	6280	6384	6488	6592	6696	6799	6903	7006	7109
9.7	7213	7316	7419	7521	7624	7727	7829	7932	8034	8136
9.8	8238	8340	8442	8544	8646	8747	8849	8950	9051	9152
9.9	2.2 9253	9354	9455	9556	9657	9757	9858	9958	*0058	*0158
10.0	2.3 0259	0358	0458	0558	0658	0757	0857	0956	1055	1154
N	0	1	2	3	4	5	6	7	8	9

NOTE 1: The base for natural logarithms is $e = 2.71828\ 18284\ 59045 \cdots$:

$$\log_e 10 = 2.3025\ 8509. \qquad \log_{10} e = 0.4342\ 9448. \tag{1}$$

NOTE 2. If $N > 10$ or $N < 1$, then we may write $N = P \cdot 10^k$ where k is an integer and $1 \leqq P < 10$. Then, to find $\log_e N$, use the following relation with $\log_e P$ obtained from the preceding table and $\log_e 10$ obtained from (1):

$$\log_e N = \log_e (P \cdot 10^k) = \log_e P + k \log_e 10.$$

α Rad.	Degrees in α	Sin α	Cos α	Tan α		α Rad.	Degrees in α	Sin α	Cos α	Tan α
.00	0° 00.0′	.00000	1.0000	.00000		.60	34° 22.6′	.56464	.82534	.68414
.01	0° 34.4′	.01000	.99995	.01000		.61	34° 57.0′	.57287	.81965	.69892
.02	1° 08.8′	.02000	.99980	.02000		.62	35° 31.4′	.58104	.81388	.71391
.03	1° 43.1′	.03000	.99955	.03001		.63	36° 05.8′	.58914	.80803	.72911
.04	2° 17.5′	.03999	.99920	.04002		.64	36° 40.2′	.59720	.80210	.74454
.05	2° 51.9′	.04998	.99875	.05004		.65	37° 14.5′	.60519	.79608	.76020
.06	3° 26.3′	.05996	.99820	.06007		.66	37° 48.9′	.61312	.78999	.77610
.07	4° 00.6′	.06994	.99755	.07011		.67	38° 23.3′	.62099	.78382	.79225
.08	4° 35.0′	.07991	.99680	.08017		.68	38° 57.7′	.62879	.77757	.80866
.09	5° 09.4′	.08988	.99595	.09024		.69	39° 32.0′	.63654	.77125	.82534
.10	5° 43.8′	.09983	.99500	.10033		.70	40° 06.4′	.64422	.76484	.84229
.11	6° 18.2′	.10978	.99396	.11045		.71	40° 40.8′	.65183	.75836	.85953
.12	6° 52.5′	.11971	.99281	.12058		.72	41° 15.2′	.65938	.75181	.87707
.13	7° 26.9′	.12963	.99156	.13074		.73	41° 49.6′	.66687	.74517	.89492
.14	8° 01.3′	.13954	.99022	.14092		.74	42° 23.9′	.67429	.73847	.91309
.15	8° 35.7′	.14944	.98877	.15114		.75	42° 58.3′	.68164	.73169	.93160
.16	9° 10.0′	.15932	.98723	.16138		.76	43° 32.7′	.68892	.72484	.95045
.17	9° 44.4′	.16918	.98558	.17166		.77	44° 07.1′	.69614	.71791	.96967
.18	10° 18.8′	.17903	.98384	.18197		.78	44° 41.4′	.70328	.71091	.98926
.19	10° 53.2′	.18886	.98200	.19232		.79	45° 15.8′	.71035	.70385	1.0092
.20	11° 27.5′	.19867	.98007	.20271		.80	45° 50.2′	.71736	.69671	1.0296
.21	12° 01.9′	.20846	.97803	.21314		.81	46° 24.6′	.72429	.68950	1.0505
.22	12° 36.3′	.21823	.97590	.22362		.82	46° 59.0′	.73115	.68222	1.0717
.23	13° 10.7′	.22798	.97367	.23414		.83	47° 33.3′	.73793	.67488	1.0934
.24	13° 45.1′	.23770	.97134	.24472		.84	48° 07.7′	.74464	.66746	1.1156
.25	14° 19.4′	.24740	.96891	.25534		.85	48° 42.1′	.75128	.65998	1.1383
.26	14° 53.8′	.25708	.96639	.26602		.86	49° 16.5′	.75784	.65244	1.1616
.27	15° 28.2′	.26673	.96377	.27676		.87	49° 50.8′	.76433	.64483	1.1853
.28	16° 02.6′	.27636	.96106	.28755		.88	50° 25.2′	.77074	.63715	1.2097
.29	16° 36.9′	.28595	.95824	.29841		.89	50° 59.6′	.77707	.62941	1.2346
.30	17° 11.3′	.29552	.95534	.30934		.90	51° 34.0′	.78333	.62161	1.2602
.31	17° 45.7′	.30506	.95233	.32033		.91	52° 08.3′	.78950	.61375	1.2864
.32	18° 20.1′	.31457	.94924	.33139		.92	52° 42.7′	.79560	.60582	1.3133
.33	18° 54.5′	.32404	.94604	.34252		.93	53° 17.1′	.80162	.59783	1.3409
.34	19° 28.8′	.33349	.94275	.35374		.94	53° 51.5′	.80756	.58979	1.3692
.35	20° 03.2′	.34290	.93937	.36503		.95	54° 25.9′	.81342	.58168	1.3984
.36	20° 37.6′	.35227	.93590	.37640		.96	55° 00.2′	.81919	.57352	1.4284
.37	21° 12.0′	.36162	.93233	.38786		.97	55° 34.6′	.82489	.56530	1.4592
.38	21° 46.3′	.37092	.92866	.39941		.98	56° 09.0′	.83050	.55702	1.4910
.39	22° 20.7′	.38019	.92491	.41105		.99	56° 43.4′	.83603	.54869	1.5237
.40	22° 55.1′	.38942	.92106	.42279		1.00	57° 17.7′	.84147	.54030	1.5574
.41	23° 29.5′	.39861	.91712	.43463		1.01	57° 52.1′	.84683	.53186	1.5922
.42	24° 03.9′	.40776	.91309	.44657		1.02	58° 26.5′	.85211	.52337	1.6281
.43	24° 38.2′	.41687	.90897	.45862		1.03	59° 00.9′	.85730	.51482	1.6652
.44	25° 12.6′	.42594	.90475	.47078		1.04	59° 35.3′	.86240	.50622	1.7036
.45	25° 47.0′	.43497	.90045	.48306		1.05	60° 09.6′	.86742	.49757	1.7433
.46	26° 21.4′	.44395	.89605	.49545		1.06	60° 44.0′	.87236	.48887	1.7844
.47	26° 55.7′	.45289	.89157	.50797		1.07	61° 18.4′	.87720	.48012	1.8270
.48	27° 30.1′	.46178	.88699	.52061		1.08	61° 52.8′	.88196	.47133	1.8712
.49	28° 04.5′	.47063	.88233	.53339		1.09	62° 27.1′	.88663	.46249	1.9171
.50	28° 38.9′	.47943	.87758	.54630		1.10	63° 01.5′	.89121	.45360	1.9648
.51	29° 13.3′	.48818	.87274	.55936		1.11	63° 35.9′	.89570	.44466	2.0143
.52	29° 47.6′	.49688	.86782	.57256		1.12	64° 10.3′	.90010	.43568	2.0660
.53	30° 22.0′	.50553	.86281	.58592		1.13	64° 44.7′	.90441	.42666	2.1198
.54	30° 56.4′	.51414	.85771	.59943		1.14	65° 19.0′	.90863	.41759	2.1759
.55	31° 30.8′	.52269	.85252	.61311		1.15	65° 53.4′	.91276	.40849	2.2345
.56	32° 05.1′	.53119	.84726	.62695		1.16	66° 27.8′	.91680	.39934	2.2958
.57	32° 39.5′	.53963	.84190	.64097		1.17	67° 02.2′	.92075	.39015	2.3600
.58	33° 13.9′	.54802	.83646	.65517		1.18	67° 36.5′	.92461	.38092	2.4273
.59	33° 48.3′	.55636	.83094	.66956		1.19	68° 10.9′	.92837	.37166	2.4979
.60	34° 22.6′	.56464	.82534	.68414		1.20	68° 45.3′	.93204	.36236	2.5722

α Rad.	Degrees in α	Sin α	Cos α	Tan α		α Rad.	Degrees in α	Sin α	Cos α	Tan α
1.20	68° 45.3'	.93204	.36236	2.5722		**1.40**	80° 12.8'	.98545	.16997	5.7979
1.21	69° 19.7'	.93562	.35302	2.6503		1.41	80° 47.2'	.98710	.16010	6.1654
1.22	69° 54.1'	93910	.34365	2.7328		1.42	81° 21.6'	.98865	.15023	6.5811
1.23	70° 28.4'	.94249	.33424	2.8198		1.43	81° 56.0'	.99010	.14033	7.0555
1.24	71° 02.8'	.94578	.32480	2.9119		1.44	82° 30.4'	.99146	.13042	7.6018
1.25	71° 37.2'	.94898	.31532	3.0096		**1.45**	83° 04.7'	.99271	.12050	8.2381
1.26	72° 11.6'	.95209	.30582	3.1133		1.46	83° 39.1'	.99387	.11057	8.9886
1.27	72° 45.9'	.95510	.29628	3.2236		1.47	84° 13.5'	.99492	.10063	9.8874
1.28	73° 20.3'	.95802	.28672	3.3413		1.48	84° 47.9'	.99588	.09067	10.983
1.29	73° 54.7'	.96084	.27712	3.4672		1.49	85° 22.2'	.99674	.08071	12.350
1.30	74° 29.1'	.96356	.26750	3.6021		**1.50**	85° 56.6'	.99749	.07074	14.101
1.31	75° 03.4'	.96618	.25785	3.7471		1.51	86° 31.0'	.99815	.06076	16.428
1.32	75° 37.8'	.96872	.24818	3.9033		1.52	87° 05.4'	.99871	.05077	19.670
1.33	76° 12.2'	.97115	.23848	4.0723		1.53	87° 39.8'	.99917	.04079	24.498
1.34	76° 46.6'	.97348	.22875	4.2556		1.54	88° 14.1'	.99953	.03079	32.461
1.35	77° 21.0'	.97572	.21901	4.4552		**1.55**	88° 48.5'	.99978	.02079	48.078
1.36	77° 55.3'	.97786	.20924	4.6734		1.56	89° 22.9'	.99994	.01080	92.620
1.37	78° 29.7'	.97991	.19945	4.9131		1.57	89° 57.3'	1.0000	.00080	1255.8
1.38	79° 04.1'	.98185	.18964	5.1774		1.58	90° 31.6'	.99996	−.00920	−108.65
1.39	79° 38.5'	.98370	.17981	5.4707		1.59	91° 06.0'	.99982	−.01920	−52.067
1.40	80° 12.8'	.98545	.16997	5.7979		**1.60**	91° 40.4'	.99957	−.02920	−34.233

DEGREES IN RADIANS

°	rad	°	rad	°	rad	°	rad	°	rad	°	rad
1°	0.01745	16°	0.27925	31°	0.54105	46°	0.80285	61°	1.06465	76°	1.32645
2	0.03491	17	0.29671	32	0.55851	47	0.82030	62	1.08210	77	1.34390
3	0.05236	18	0.31416	33	0.57596	48	0.83776	63	1.09956	78	1.36136
4	0.06981	19	0.33161	34	0.59341	49	0.85521	64	1.11701	79	1.37881
5	0.08727	**20**	0.34907	**35**	0.61087	**50**	0.87266	**65**	1.13446	**80**	1.39626
6	0.10472	21	0.36652	36	0.62832	51	0.89012	66	1.15192	81	1.41372
7	0.12217	22	0.38397	37	0.64577	52	0.90757	67	1.16937	82	1.43117
8	0.13963	23	0.40143	38	0.66323	53	0.92502	68	1.18682	83	1.44862
9	0.15708	24	0.41888	39	0.68068	54	0.94248	69	1.20428	84	1.46608
10	0.17453	**25**	0.43633	**40**	0.69813	**55**	0.95993	**70**	1.22173	**85**	1.48353
11	0.19199	26	0.45379	41	0.71558	56	0.97738	71	1.23918	86	1.50098
12	0.20944	27	0.47124	42	0.73304	57	0.99484	72	1.25664	87	1.51844
13	0.22689	28	0.48869	43	0.75049	58	1.01229	73	1.27409	88	1.53589
14	0.24435	29	0.50615	44	0.76794	59	1.02974	74	1.29154	89	1.55334
15	0.26180	**30**	0.52360	**45**	0.78540	**60**	1.04720	**75**	1.30900	**90**	1.57080

1° = .01745329 rad.   log .01745329 = 8.24187737 − 10.
1' = .0002908882 rad.   log .0002908882 = 6.46372612 − 10.
1″ = .0000048481368 rad.   log .0000048481368 = 4.68557487 − 10.

MINUTES IN RADIANS

′	rad	′	rad	′	rad	′	rad	′	rad	′	rad
1'	0.00029	11'	0.00320	21'	0.00611	31'	0.00902	41'	0.01193	51'	0.01484
2	0.00058	12	0.00349	22	0.00640	32	0.00931	42	0.01222	52	0.01513
3	0.00087	13	0.00378	23	0.00669	33	0.00960	43	0.01251	53	0.01542
4	0.00116	14	0.00407	24	0.00698	34	0.00989	44	0.01280	54	0.01571
5	0.00145	**15**	0.00436	**25**	0.00727	**35**	0.01018	**45**	0.01309	**55**	0.01600
6	0.00175	16	0.00465	26	0.00756	36	0.01047	46	0.01338	56	0.01629
7	0.00204	17	0.00495	27	0.00785	37	0.01076	47	0.01367	57	0.01658
8	0.00233	18	0.00524	28	0.00814	38	0.01105	48	0.01396	58	0.01687
9	0.00262	19	0.00553	29	0.00844	39	0.01134	49	0.01425	59	0.01716
10	0.00291	**20**	0.00582	**30**	0.00873	**40**	0.01164	**50**	0.01454	**60**	0.01745

V. EXPONENTIAL AND HYPERBOLIC FUNCTIONS

x	e^x	Sinh x	Cosh x	x	e^x	Sinh x	Cosh x
0.00	1.0000	0.0000	1.0000	0.45	1.5683	0.4653	1.1030
.01	1.0101	0.0100	1.0001	.46	1.5841	.4764	1.1077
.02	1.0202	0.0200	1.0002	.47	1.6000	.4875	1.1125
.03	1.0305	0.0300	1.0005	.48	1.6161	.4986	1.1174
.04	1.0408	0.0400	1.0008	.49	1.6323	.5098	1.1225
.05	1.0513	0.0500	1.0013	.50	1.6487	.5211	1.1276
.06	1.0618	0.0600	1.0018	.51	1.6653	.5324	1.1329
.07	1.0725	0.0701	1.0025	.52	1.6820	.5438	1.1383
.08	1.0833	0.0801	1.0032	.53	1.6989	.5552	1.1438
.09	1.0942	0.0901	1.0041	.54	1.7160	.5666	1.1494
.10	1.1052	0.1002	1.0050	.55	1.7333	.5782	1.1551
.11	1.1163	0.1102	1.0061	.56	1.7507	.5897	1.1609
.12	1.1275	0.1203	1.0072	.57	1.7683	.6014	1.1669
.13	1.1388	0.1304	1.0085	.58	1.7860	.6131	1.1730
.14	1.1503	0.1405	1.0098	.59	1.8040	.6248	1.1792
.15	1.1618	0.1506	1.0113	.60	1.8221	.6367	1.1855
.16	1.1735	0.1607	1.0128	.61	1.8404	.6485	1.1919
.17	1.1853	0.1708	1.0145	.62	1.8589	.6605	1.1984
.18	1.1972	0.1810	1.0162	.63	1.8776	.6725	1.2051
.19	1.2092	0.1911	1.0181	.64	1.8965	.6846	1.2119
.20	1.2214	0.2013	1.0201	.65	1.9155	.6967	1.2188
.21	1.2337	0.2115	1.0221	.66	1.9348	.7090	1.2258
.22	1.2461	0.2218	1.0243	.67	1.9542	.7213	1.2330
.23	1.2586	0.2320	1.0266	.68	1.9739	.7336	1.2402
.24	1.2712	0.2423	1.0289	.69	1.9937	.7461	1.2476
.25	1.2840	0.2526	1.0314	.70	2.0138	.7586	1.2552
.26	1.2969	0.2629	1.0340	.71	2.0340	.7712	1.2628
.27	1.3100	0.2733	1.0367	.72	2.0544	.7838	1.2706
.28	1.3231	0.2837	1.0395	.73	2.0751	.7966	1.2785
.29	1.3364	0.2941	1.0423	.74	2.0959	.8094	1.2865
.30	1.3499	.3045	1.0453	.75	2.1170	.8223	1.2947
.31	1.3634	.3150	1.0484	.76	2.1383	.8353	1.3030
.32	1.3771	.3255	1.0516	.77	2.1598	.8484	1.3114
.33	1.3910	.3360	1.0549	.78	2.1815	.8615	1.3199
.34	1.4049	.3466	1.0584	.79	2.2034	.8748	1.3286
.35	1.4191	.3572	1.0619	.80	2.2255	.8881	1.3374
.36	1.4333	.3678	1.0655	.81	2.2479	.9015	1.3464
.37	1.4477	.3785	1.0692	.82	2.2705	.9150	1.3555
.38	1.4623	.3892	1.0731	.83	2.2933	.9286	1.3647
.39	1.4770	.4000	1.0770	.84	2.3164	.9423	1.3740
.40	1.4918	.4108	1.0811	.85	2.3396	.9561	1.3835
.41	1.5068	.4216	1.0852	.86	2.3632	.9700	1.3932
.42	1.5220	.4325	1.0895	.87	2.3869	.9840	1.4029
.43	1.5373	.4434	1.0939	.88	2.4109	.9981	1.4128
.44	1.5527	.4543	1.0984	.89	2.4351	1.0122	1.4229

V. EXPONENTIAL AND HYPERBOLIC FUNCTIONS

x	e^x	Sinh x	Cosh x	x	e^x	Sinh x	Cosh x
.90	2.4596	1.0265	1.4331	2.75	15.643	7.7894	7.8533
.91	2.4843	1.0409	1.4434	2.80	16.445	8.1919	8.2527
.92	2.5093	1.0554	1.4539	2.85	17.288	8.6150	8.6728
.93	2.5345	1.0700	1.4645	2.90	18.174	9.0596	9.1146
.94	2.5600	1.0847	1.4753	2.95	19.106	9.5268	9.5791
.95	2.5857	1.0995	1.4862	3.00	20.086	10.018	10.068
.96	2.6117	1.1144	1.4973	3.05	21.115	10.534	10.581
.97	2.6379	1.1294	1.5085	3.10	22.198	11.076	11.122
.98	2.6645	1.1446	1.5199	3.15	23.336	11.647	11.689
.99	2.6912	1.1598	1.5314	3.20	24.533	12.246	12.287
1.00	2.7183	1.1752	1.5431	3.25	25.790	12.876	12.915
1.05	2.8577	1.2539	1.6038	3.30	27.113	13.538	13.575
1.10	3.0042	1.3356	1.6685	3.35	28.503	14.234	14.269
1.15	3.1582	1.4208	1.7374	3.40	29.964	14.965	14.999
1.20	3.3201	1.5095	1.8107	3.45	31.500	15.734	15.766
1.25	3.4903	1.6019	1.8884	3.50	33.115	16.543	16.573
1.30	3.6693	1.6984	1.9709	3.55	34.813	17.392	17.421
1.35	3.8574	1.7991	2.0583	3.60	36.598	18.286	18.313
1.40	4.0552	1.9043	2.1509	3.65	38.475	19.224	19.250
1.45	4.2631	2.0143	2.2488	3.70	40.447	20.211	20.236
1.50	4.4817	2.1293	2.3524	3.75	42.521	21.249	21.272
1.55	4.7115	2.2496	2.4619	3.80	44.701	22.339	22.362
1.60	4.9530	2.3756	2.5775	3.85	46.993	23.486	23.507
1.65	5.2070	2.5075	2.6995	3.90	49.402	24.691	24.711
1.70	5.4739	2.6456	2.8283	3.95	51.935	25.958	25.977
1.75	5.7546	2.7904	2.9642	4.00	54.598	27.290	27.308
1.80	6.0496	2.9422	3.1075	4.10	60.340	30.162	30.178
1.85	6.3598	3.1013	3.2585	4.20	66.686	33.336	33.351
1.90	6.6859	3.2682	3.4177	4.30	73.700	36.843	36.857
1.95	7.0287	3.4432	3.5855	4.40	81.451	40.719	40.732
2.00	7.3891	3.6269	3.7622	4.50	90.017	45.003	45.014
2.05	7.7679	3.8196	3.9483	4.60	99.484	49.737	49.747
2.10	8.1662	4.0219	4.1443	4.70	109.95	54.969	54.978
2.15	8.5849	4.2342	4.3507	4.80	121.51	60.751	60.759
2.20	9.0250	4.4571	4.5679	4.90	134.29	67.141	67.149
2.25	9.4877	4.6912	4.7966	5.00	148.41	74.203	74.210
2.30	9.9742	4.9370	5.0372	5.20	181.27	90.633	90.639
2.35	10.486	5.1951	5.2905	5.40	221.41	110.70	110.71
2.40	11.023	5.4662	5.5569	5.60	270.43	135.21	135.22
2.45	11.588	5.7510	5.8373	5.80	330.30	165.15	165.15
2.50	12.182	6.0502	6.1323	6.00	403.43	201.71	201.72
2.55	12.807	6.3645	6.4426	7.00	1096.6	548.32	548.32
2.60	13.464	6.6947	6.7690	8.00	2981.0	1490.5	1490.5
2.65	14.154	7.0417	7.1123	9.00	8103.1	4051.5	4051.5
2.70	14.880	7.4063	7.4735	10.00	22026.	11013.	11013.

VI. THREE-PLACE VALUES OF TRIGONOMETRIC FUNCTIONS
AND
DEGREES IN RADIAN MEASURE

Rad.	Deg.	Sin	Tan	Sec	Csc	Cot	Cos	Deg.	Rad.
.000	0°	.000	.000	1.000	——	——	1.000	90°	1.571
.017	1°	.017	.017	1.000	57.30	57.29	1.000	89°	1.553
.035	2°	.035	.035	1.001	28.65	28.64	0.999	88°	1.536
.052	3°	.052	.052	1.001	19.11	19.08	.999	87°	1.518
.070	4°	.070	.070	1.002	14.34	14.30	.998	86°	1.501
.087	5°	.087	.087	1.004	11.47	11.43	.996	85°	1.484
.105	6°	.105	.105	1.006	9.567	9.514	.995	84°	1.466
.122	7°	.122	.123	1.008	8.206	8.144	.993	83°	1.449
.140	8°	.139	.141	1.010	7.185	7.115	.990	82°	1.431
.157	9°	.156	.158	1.012	6.392	6.314	.988	81°	1.414
.175	10°	.174	.176	1.015	5.759	5.671	.985	80°	1.396
.192	11°	.191	.194	1.019	5.241	5.145	.982	79°	1.379
.209	12°	.208	.213	1.022	4.810	4.705	.978	78°	1.361
.227	13°	.225	.231	1.026	4.445	4.331	.974	77°	1.344
.244	14°	.242	.249	1.031	4.134	4.011	.970	76°	1.326
.262	15°	.259	.268	1.035	3.864	3.732	.966	75°	1.309
.279	16°	.276	.287	1.040	3.628	3.487	.961	74°	1.292
.297	17°	.292	.306	1.046	3.420	3.271	.956	73°	1.274
.314	18°	.309	.325	1.051	3.236	3.078	.951	72°	1.257
.332	19°	.326	.344	1.058	3.072	2.904	.946	71°	1.239
.349	20°	.342	.364	1.064	2.924	2.747	.940	70°	1.222
.367	21°	.358	.384	1.071	2.790	2.605	.934	69°	1.204
.384	22°	.375	.404	1.079	2.669	2.475	.927	68°	1.187
.401	23°	.391	.424	1.086	2.559	2.356	.921	67°	1.169
.419	24°	.407	.445	1.095	2.459	2.246	.914	66°	1.152
.436	25°	.423	.466	1.103	2.366	2.145	.906	65°	1.134
.454	26°	.438	.488	1.113	2.281	2.050	.899	64°	1.117
.471	27°	.454	.510	1.122	2.203	1.963	.891	63°	1.100
.489	28°	.469	.532	1.133	2.130	1.881	.883	62°	1.082
.506	29°	.485	.554	1.143	2.063	1.804	.875	61°	1.065
.524	30°	.500	.577	1.155	2.000	1.732	.866	60°	1.047
.541	31°	.515	.601	1.167	1.942	1.664	.857	59°	1.030
.559	32°	.530	.625	1.179	1.887	1.600	.848	58°	1.012
.576	33°	.545	.649	1.192	1.836	1.540	.839	57°	0.995
.593	34°	.559	.675	1.206	1.788	1.483	.829	56°	0.977
.611	35°	.574	.700	1.221	1.743	1.428	.819	55°	0.960
.628	36°	.588	.727	1.236	1.701	1.376	.809	54°	0.942
.646	37°	.602	.754	1.252	1.662	1.327	.799	53°	0.925
.663	38°	.616	.781	1.269	1.624	1.280	.788	52°	0.908
.681	39°	.629	.810	1.287	1.589	1.235	.777	51°	0.890
.698	40°	.643	.839	1.305	1.556	1.192	.766	50°	0.873
.716	41°	.656	.869	1.325	1.524	1.150	.755	49°	0.855
.733	42°	.669	.900	1.346	1.494	1.111	.743	48°	0.838
.750	43°	.682	.933	1.367	1.466	1.072	.731	47°	0.820
.768	44°	.695	0.966	1.390	1.440	1.036	.719	46°	0.803
.785	45°	.707	1.000	1.414	1.414	1.000	.707	45°	0.785
Rad.	Deg.	Cos	Cot	Csc	Sec	Tan	Sin	Deg.	Rad.

Note 1. An arbitrary constant may be added to any result.

Note 2. No formula in the table may be used with any value of the variable, or of any constant, for which the integrand on the left, or the result on the right, is imaginary or otherwise undefined.

Note 3. In each formula, u may be considered as the independent variable, or as a differentiable function of some independent variable.

Note 4. If ambiguous signs, $\pm$ or $\mp$, occur more than once in a formula, it is understood that the *upper* (*lower*) signs apply simultaneously throughout.

Note 5. Arctan u, Arcsin u, Arcsec u, and Cosh^{-1} u, in any formulas, represent *principal values*, and have the following ranges:

$$-\tfrac{1}{2}\pi \leq \text{Arcsin } u \leq \tfrac{1}{2}\pi; \qquad (\text{Arcsin } u < 0 \text{ if } u < 0)$$

$$-\tfrac{1}{2}\pi < \text{Arctan } u < \tfrac{1}{2}\pi; \qquad (\text{Arctan } u < 0 \text{ if } u < 0)$$

$$0 \leq \text{Arcsec } u < \tfrac{1}{2}\pi \text{ if } u > 0; \qquad -\pi \leq \text{Arcsec } u < -\tfrac{1}{2}\pi \text{ if } u < 0;$$

$$0 \leq \text{Cosh}^{-1} u. \qquad (u \geq 1 \text{ always})$$

Also, we remark that sinh^{-1} u, tanh^{-1} u, and coth^{-1} u are single-valued.

Integrals of Rational Functions of u and $(a + bu)$

1. $\displaystyle\int u^n \, du = \frac{u^{n+1}}{n+1}.$

2. $\displaystyle\int \frac{du}{u} = \ln |u|.$

3. $\displaystyle\int (a + bu)^n \, du = \frac{(a + bu)^{n+1}}{b(n+1)}.$

4. $\displaystyle\int \frac{du}{a + bu} = \frac{1}{b} \ln |a + bu|.$

5. $\displaystyle\int \frac{du}{u(a + bu)} = \frac{1}{a} \ln \left| \frac{u}{a + bu} \right|.$

6. $\displaystyle\int \frac{du}{u^2(a + bu)} = -\frac{1}{au} + \frac{b}{a^2} \ln \left| \frac{a + bu}{u} \right|.$

7. $\displaystyle\int \frac{du}{u(a + bu)^2} = \frac{1}{a(a + bu)} + \frac{1}{a^2} \ln \left| \frac{u}{a + bu} \right|.$

8. $\displaystyle\int \frac{du}{u^2(a + bu)^2} = -\frac{a + 2bu}{a^2 u(a + bu)} + \frac{2b}{a^3} \ln \left| \frac{a + bu}{u} \right|.$

9. $\displaystyle\int \frac{u \, du}{(a + bu)^2} = \frac{1}{b^2} \left(\ln |a + bu| + \frac{a}{a + bu} \right).$

10. $\displaystyle\int \frac{u \, du}{(a + bu)^3} = \frac{1}{b^2} \left[-\frac{1}{a + bu} + \frac{a}{2(a + bu)^2} \right].$

11. $\displaystyle\int \frac{u^2 \, du}{(a + bu)^3} = \frac{1}{b^3} \left[\ln |a + bu| + \frac{2a}{a + bu} - \frac{a^2}{2(a + bu)^2} \right].$

12. $\displaystyle\int \frac{du}{u^m(a + bu)^n} = \frac{-1}{a(m-1)u^{m-1}(a + bu)^{n-1}} - \frac{b(m + n - 2)}{a(m - 1)} \int \frac{du}{u^{m-1}(a + bu)^n}.$

13. $\displaystyle\int \frac{du}{u^m(a + bu)^n} = \frac{1}{a(n-1)u^{m-1}(a + bu)^{n-1}} + \frac{(m + n - 2)}{a(n - 1)} \int \frac{du}{u^m(a + bu)^{n-1}}.$

Irrational Integrands Involving $(a + bu)$

14. $\displaystyle\int u\sqrt{a + bu}\, du = -\frac{2(2a - 3bu)(a + bu)^{\frac{3}{2}}}{15b^2}.$

15. $\displaystyle\int u^m\sqrt{a + bu}\, du = \frac{2u^m(a + bu)^{\frac{3}{2}}}{b(2m + 3)} - \frac{2am}{b(2m + 3)}\int u^{m-1}\sqrt{a + bu}\, du.$

16. $\displaystyle\int \frac{u\, du}{\sqrt{a + bu}} = \frac{2(bu - 2a)\sqrt{a + bu}}{3b^2}.$

17. $\displaystyle\int \frac{u^2\, du}{\sqrt{a + bu}} = \frac{2(3b^2u^2 - 4abu + 8a^2)\sqrt{a + bu}}{15b^3}.$

18. $\displaystyle\int \frac{u^m\, du}{\sqrt{a + bu}} = \frac{2u^m\sqrt{a + bu}}{b(2m + 1)} - \frac{2am}{b(2m + 1)}\int \frac{u^{m-1}\, du}{\sqrt{a + bu}}.$

19. $\displaystyle\int \frac{du}{u\sqrt{a + bu}} = \frac{1}{\sqrt{a}}\ln\left|\frac{\sqrt{a + bu} - \sqrt{a}}{\sqrt{a + bu} + \sqrt{a}}\right|,$ if $a > 0.$

20. $\displaystyle\int \frac{du}{u\sqrt{a + bu}} = \frac{2}{\sqrt{-a}}\operatorname{Arctan}\sqrt{\frac{a + bu}{-a}},$ if $a < 0.$

21. $\displaystyle\int \frac{du}{u^m\sqrt{a + bu}} = -\frac{\sqrt{a + bu}}{a(m - 1)u^{m-1}} - \frac{b(2m - 3)}{2a(m - 1)}\int \frac{du}{u^{m-1}\sqrt{a + bu}}.$

22. $\displaystyle\int \frac{\sqrt{a + bu}}{u}\, du = 2\sqrt{a + bu} + a\int \frac{du}{u\sqrt{a + bu}}.$

23. $\displaystyle\int \frac{\sqrt{a + bu}}{u^m}\, du = -\frac{(a + bu)^{\frac{3}{2}}}{a(m - 1)u^{m-1}} - \frac{b(2m - 5)}{2a(m - 1)}\int \frac{\sqrt{a + bu}\, du}{u^{m-1}}.$

Rational Forms Involving $*$ $(a^2 \pm u^2)$

24. $\displaystyle\int \frac{du}{a^2 + u^2} = \frac{1}{a}\operatorname{Arctan}\frac{u}{a}.$ **25.** $\displaystyle\int \frac{du}{u^2 - a^2} = \frac{1}{2a}\ln\left|\frac{u - a}{u + a}\right|.$

25₁. $\displaystyle\int \frac{du}{a^2 - u^2} = \frac{1}{a}\tanh^{-1}\frac{u}{a}.$ $\quad (u^2 < a^2)$

25₂. $\displaystyle\int \frac{du}{u^2 - a^2} = -\frac{1}{a}\coth^{-1}\frac{u}{a}.$ $\quad (u^2 > a^2)$

26. $\displaystyle\int \frac{du}{(a^2 + u^2)^n} = \frac{u}{2(n - 1)a^2(a^2 + u^2)^{n-1}} + \frac{2n - 3}{(2n - 2)a^2}\int \frac{du}{(a^2 + u^2)^{n-1}}.$

Irrational Forms Involving $\sqrt{a^2 - u^2}$

27. $\displaystyle\int \sqrt{a^2 - u^2}\, du = \frac{u}{2}\sqrt{a^2 - u^2} + \frac{a^2}{2}\operatorname{Arcsin}\frac{u}{a}.$

28. $\displaystyle\int \frac{du}{\sqrt{a^2 - u^2}} = \operatorname{Arcsin}\frac{u}{a}.$ **29.** $\displaystyle\int \frac{du}{(a^2 - u^2)^{\frac{3}{2}}} = \frac{u}{a^2\sqrt{a^2 - u^2}}.$

30. $\displaystyle\int u^2\sqrt{a^2 - u^2}\, du = -\frac{1}{4}u(a^2 - u^2)^{\frac{3}{2}} + \frac{1}{4}a^2\int \sqrt{a^2 - u^2}\, du.$

* Wherever a constant a^2 enters, infer that $a > 0$.

31. $\displaystyle\int \frac{u^2\,du}{\sqrt{a^2-u^2}} = -\frac{u}{2}\sqrt{a^2-u^2} + \frac{a^2}{2}\operatorname{Arcsin}\frac{u}{a}.$

32. $\displaystyle\int \frac{u^2\,du}{(a^2-u^2)^{\frac{3}{2}}} = \frac{u}{\sqrt{a^2-u^2}} - \operatorname{Arcsin}\frac{u}{a}.$

33. $\displaystyle\int \frac{du}{u\sqrt{a^2-u^2}} = -\frac{1}{a}\ln\left|\frac{a+\sqrt{a^2-u^2}}{u}\right|; \qquad = -\frac{1}{a}\operatorname{Cosh}^{-1}\frac{a}{u}, \ \text{if } 0 < u < a.$

34. $\displaystyle\int \frac{du}{u^2\sqrt{a^2-u^2}} = -\frac{\sqrt{a^2-u^2}}{a^2 u}.$

35. $\displaystyle\int \frac{\sqrt{a^2-u^2}\,du}{u} = \sqrt{a^2-u^2} - a\ln\left|\frac{a+\sqrt{a^2-u^2}}{u}\right|;$

35′. $\displaystyle\qquad\qquad = \sqrt{a^2-u^2} - a\operatorname{Cosh}^{-1}\frac{a}{u}, \ \text{if } 0 < u < a.$

36. $\displaystyle\int \frac{\sqrt{a^2-u^2}}{u^2}\,du = -\frac{\sqrt{a^2-u^2}}{u} - \operatorname{Arcsin}\frac{u}{a}.$

37. $\displaystyle\int u^m(a^2-u^2)^{\frac{n}{2}}\,du \qquad (m \geqq 0 \quad\text{or}\quad m < 0)$

$$= \frac{u^{m+1}(a^2-u^2)^{\frac{n}{2}}}{n+m+1} + \frac{a^2 n}{n+m+1}\int u^m(a^2-u^2)^{\frac{n}{2}-1}\,du.$$

38. $\displaystyle\int u^m(a^2-u^2)^{\frac{n}{2}}\,du \qquad (n > 0 \quad\text{or}\quad n < 0)$

$$= -\frac{u^{m-1}(a^2-u^2)^{\frac{n}{2}+1}}{n+m+1} + \frac{a^2(m-1)}{n+m+1}\int u^{m-2}(a^2-u^2)^{\frac{n}{2}}\,du.$$

39. $\displaystyle\int \frac{(a^2-u^2)^{\frac{n}{2}}}{u^m}\,du \qquad (n > 0 \quad\text{or}\quad n < 0)$

$$= -\frac{(a^2-u^2)^{\frac{n}{2}+1}}{a^2(m-1)u^{m-1}} + \frac{m-n-3}{a^2(m-1)}\int \frac{(a^2-u^2)^{\frac{n}{2}}}{u^{m-2}}\,du.$$

40. $\displaystyle\int \frac{u^m\,du}{(a^2-u^2)^{\frac{n}{2}}} \qquad (m \geqq 0 \quad\text{or}\quad m < 0)$

$$= \frac{u^{m+1}}{a^2(n-2)(a^2-u^2)^{\frac{n}{2}-1}} - \frac{m-n+3}{a^2(n-2)}\int \frac{u^m\,du}{(a^2-u^2)^{\frac{n}{2}-1}}.$$

Irrational Forms Involving $\sqrt{u^2 \pm a^2}$

Note 6. In any formula of the present types, by the method of proof used in Example 1, page 523, it can be shown that we may replace

$$\ln(u+\sqrt{u^2+a^2}) \quad by \quad \sinh^{-1}\frac{u}{a}; \quad \ln\left|\frac{a+\sqrt{u^2+a^2}}{u}\right| \quad by \quad \sinh^{-1}\left|\frac{a}{u}\right|;$$

$$\ln|u+\sqrt{u^2-a^2}| \quad by \quad \begin{cases} \operatorname{Cosh}^{-1}\dfrac{u}{a} & \text{if } u \geqq a \\[2mm] -\operatorname{Cosh}^{-1}\left|\dfrac{u}{a}\right| & \text{if } u \leqq -a \end{cases}.$$

41. $\int \sqrt{u^2 \pm a^2}\, du = \frac{1}{2}[u\sqrt{u^2 \pm a^2} \pm a^2 \ln|u + \sqrt{u^2 \pm a^2}|].$

42. $\int u^2\sqrt{u^2 \pm a^2}\, du = \frac{1}{8}u(2u^2 \pm a^2)\sqrt{u^2 \pm a^2} - \frac{1}{8}a^4 \ln|u + \sqrt{u^2 \pm a^2}|.$

43. $\int \frac{\sqrt{u^2 + a^2}}{u}\, du = \sqrt{u^2 + a^2} - a \ln\left|\frac{a + \sqrt{u^2 + a^2}}{u}\right|.$

44. $\int \frac{\sqrt{u^2 - a^2}}{u}\, du = \sqrt{u^2 - a^2} - a \operatorname{Arcsec} \frac{u}{a}.$

45. $\int \frac{\sqrt{u^2 \pm a^2}}{u^2}\, du = - \frac{\sqrt{u^2 \pm a^2}}{u} + \ln|u + \sqrt{u^2 \pm a^2}|.$

46. $\int \frac{du}{\sqrt{u^2 \pm a^2}} = \ln|u + \sqrt{u^2 \pm a^2}|.$ **46₁.** $\int \frac{du}{\sqrt{u^2 + a^2}} = \sinh^{-1}\frac{u}{a}.$

46₂. $\int \frac{du}{\sqrt{u^2 - a^2}} = \operatorname{Cosh}^{-1}\frac{u}{a}, \; (u > a);$ $= -\operatorname{Cosh}^{-1}\left|\frac{u}{a}\right|, \; (u < -a).$

47. $\int \frac{du}{u\sqrt{u^2 - a^2}} = \frac{1}{a} \operatorname{Arcsec}\frac{u}{a}.$ **48.** $\int \frac{du}{u\sqrt{u^2 + a^2}} = \frac{1}{a} \ln\left|\frac{u}{a + \sqrt{u^2 + a^2}}\right|$

49. $\int \frac{u^2\, du}{\sqrt{u^2 \pm a^2}} = \frac{1}{2}\left(u\sqrt{u^2 \pm a^2} \mp a^2 \ln|u + \sqrt{u^2 \pm a^2}|\right).$

50. $\int \frac{du}{u^2\sqrt{u^2 \pm a^2}} = \mp \frac{\sqrt{u^2 \pm a^2}}{a^2 u}.$ **51.** $\int \frac{du}{(u^2 \pm a^2)^{\frac{3}{2}}} = \frac{\pm u}{a^2\sqrt{u^2 \pm a^2}}.$

52. $\int \frac{u^2\, du}{(u^2 \pm a^2)^{\frac{3}{2}}} = \frac{-u}{\sqrt{u^2 \pm a^2}} + \ln|u + \sqrt{u^2 \pm a^2}|.$

53. $\int u^m(u^2 \pm a^2)^{\frac{n}{2}}\, du$ $(n > 0 \;\; \text{or} \;\; n < 0)$

$$= \frac{u^{m-1}(u^2 \pm a^2)^{\frac{n}{2}+1}}{n + m + 1} \mp \frac{a^2(m - 1)}{n + m + 1} \int u^{m-2}(u^2 \pm a^2)^{\frac{n}{2}}\, du.$$

54. $\int \frac{(u^2 \pm a^2)^{\frac{n}{2}}\, du}{u^m}$ $(n > 0 \;\; \text{or} \;\; n < 0)$

$$= \frac{\mp (u^2 \pm a^2)^{\frac{n}{2}+1}}{a^2(m - 1)u^{m-1}} \mp \frac{m - n - 3}{a^2(m - 1)} \int \frac{(u^2 \pm a^2)^{\frac{n}{2}}}{u^{m-2}}\, du.$$

55. $\int \frac{u^m\, du}{(u^2 \pm a^2)^{\frac{n}{2}}}$ $(m \geqq 0 \;\; \text{or} \;\; m < 0)$

$$= \frac{\pm u^{m+1}}{a^2(n - 2)(u^2 \pm a^2)^{\frac{n}{2}-1}} \mp \frac{m - n + 3}{a^2(n - 2)} \int \frac{u^m\, du}{(u^2 \pm a^2)^{\frac{n}{2}-1}}.$$

56. $\int u^m(u^2 \pm a^2)^{\frac{n}{2}}\, du$ $(m \geqq 0 \;\; \text{or} \;\; m < 0)$

$$= \frac{(u^2 \pm a^2)^{\frac{n}{2}}u^{m+1}}{n + m + 1} \pm \frac{a^2 n}{n + m + 1} \int u^m(u^2 \pm a^2)^{\frac{n}{2}-1}\, du.$$

Irrational Forms Involving $\sqrt{2au \pm u^2}$

Note 7. $\sqrt{2au + u^2} = \sqrt{(u+a)^2 - a^2}$; $\sqrt{2au - u^2} = \sqrt{a^2 - (u-a)^2}$.

57. $\displaystyle\int (2au + u^2)^{\frac{n}{2}}\, du$. Use $\displaystyle\int (v^2 - a^2)^{\frac{n}{2}}\, dv$ with $v = u + a$.

58. $\displaystyle\int (2au - u^2)^{\frac{n}{2}}\, du$. Use $\displaystyle\int (a^2 - v^2)^{\frac{n}{2}}\, dv$ with $v = u - a$.

59. $\displaystyle\int \sqrt{2au - u^2}\, du = \frac{u-a}{2}\sqrt{2au - u^2} + \frac{a^2}{2}\, \text{Arcsin}\, \frac{u-a}{a}$.

60. $\displaystyle\int \sqrt{2au + u^2}\, du = \frac{u+a}{2}\sqrt{2au + u^2} - \frac{a^2}{2}\ln|u + a + \sqrt{2au + u^2}|$.

61. $\displaystyle\int u\sqrt{2au + u^2}\, du = \frac{2u^2 + au - 3a^2}{6}\sqrt{2au + u^2} + \frac{a^3}{2}\ln|u + a + \sqrt{2au + u^2}|$.

62. $\displaystyle\int u\sqrt{2au - u^2}\, du = \frac{2u^2 - au - 3a^2}{6}\sqrt{2au - u^2} + \frac{a^3}{2}\, \text{Arcsin}\, \frac{u-a}{a}$.

63. $\displaystyle\int \frac{du}{\sqrt{2au - u^2}} = \text{Arcsin}\, \frac{u-a}{a}$.

64. $\displaystyle\int \frac{du}{\sqrt{2au + u^2}} = \ln|u + a + \sqrt{u^2 + 2au}|$.

65. $\displaystyle\int \frac{u\, du}{\sqrt{2au - u^2}} = -\sqrt{2au - u^2} + a\, \text{Arcsin}\, \frac{u-a}{a}$.

66. $\displaystyle\int \frac{u\, du}{\sqrt{2au + u^2}} = \sqrt{2au + u^2} - a\ln|u + a + \sqrt{2au + u^2}|$.

67. $\displaystyle\int \frac{u^n\, du}{\sqrt{2au - u^2}} = -\frac{u^{n-1}\sqrt{2au - u^2}}{n} + \frac{a(2n-1)}{n}\int \frac{u^{n-1}\, du}{\sqrt{2au - u^2}}$.

68. $\displaystyle\int \frac{du}{u^n\sqrt{2au - u^2}} = \frac{\sqrt{2au - u^2}}{a(1 - 2n)u^n} + \frac{n-1}{(2n-1)a}\int \frac{du}{u^{n-1}\sqrt{2au - u^2}}$.

69. $\displaystyle\int u^n\sqrt{2au - u^2}\, du = -\frac{u^{n-1}(2au - u^2)^{\frac{3}{2}}}{n+2} + \frac{(2n+1)a}{n+2}\int u^{n-1}\sqrt{2au - u^2}\, du$.

70. $\displaystyle\int \frac{\sqrt{2au - u^2}}{u^n}\, du = \frac{(2au - u^2)^{\frac{3}{2}}}{a(3 - 2n)u^n} + \frac{n-3}{(2n-3)a}\int \frac{\sqrt{2au - u^2}}{u^{n-1}}\, du$.

Forms Involving $f(u) = a + bu \pm cu^2$, $c > 0$

Note 8. By completing a square with the terms in u, $f(u)$ assumes the form $\pm c(A^2 + v^2)$, $\pm c(v^2 - A^2)$, or $\pm cv^2$, with $v = u \pm \dfrac{b}{2c}$. Then, substitution of $v = (2cu \pm b)/2c$ gives an integrand $F(v)$ involving $(A^2 \pm v^2)$, $(v^2 - A^2)$, or v^2.

Note 9. Any radicand $(4ac + b^2)$ is assumed to be positive.

71. $\displaystyle\int \frac{du}{a + bu - cu^2} = \frac{1}{\sqrt{b^2 + 4ac}}\ln\left|\frac{\sqrt{b^2 + 4ac} - b + 2cu}{\sqrt{b^2 + 4ac} + b - 2cu}\right|$.

72. $\displaystyle\int \frac{du}{\sqrt{a + bu + cu^2}} = \frac{1}{\sqrt{c}}\ln|2cu + b + 2\sqrt{c}\sqrt{a + bu + cu^2}|$.

73. $\displaystyle\int \frac{du}{\sqrt{a + bu - cu^2}} = \frac{1}{\sqrt{c}} \, \text{Arcsin} \, \frac{2cu - b}{\sqrt{b^2 + 4ac}} \, .$

74. $\displaystyle\int \frac{du}{(a + bu \pm cu^2)^{\frac{3}{2}}} = \frac{2(\pm 2cu + b)}{(\pm 4ac - b^2)\sqrt{a + bu \pm cu^2}} \, .$

75. $\displaystyle\int \sqrt{a + bu + cu^2} \, du = \frac{2cu + b}{4c} \sqrt{a + bu + cu^2}$

$$- \frac{b^2 - 4ac}{8c^{\frac{3}{2}}} \ln | \, 2cu + b + 2\sqrt{c}\sqrt{a + bu + cu^2} \, | .$$

76. $\displaystyle\int \sqrt{a + bu - cu^2} \, du = \frac{2cu - b}{4c} \sqrt{a + bu - cu^2}$

$$+ \frac{b^2 + 4ac}{8c^{\frac{3}{2}}} \, \text{Arcsin} \, \frac{2cu - b}{\sqrt{b^2 + 4ac}} \, .$$

77. $\displaystyle\int \frac{u \, du}{\sqrt{a + bu + cu^2}} = \frac{\sqrt{a + bu + cu^2}}{c}$

$$- \frac{b}{2c^{\frac{3}{2}}} \ln | \, 2cu + b + 2\sqrt{c}\sqrt{a + bu + cu^2} \, | .$$

78. $\displaystyle\int \frac{u \, du}{\sqrt{a + bu - cu^2}} = - \frac{\sqrt{a + bu - cu^2}}{c} + \frac{b}{2c^{\frac{3}{2}}} \, \text{Arcsin} \, \frac{2cu - b}{\sqrt{b^2 + 4ac}} \, .$

79. $\displaystyle\int u \sqrt{a + bu \pm cu^2} \, du = \frac{(a + bu \pm cu^2)^{\frac{3}{2}}}{\pm 3c} \mp \frac{b}{2c} \int \sqrt{a + bu \pm cu^2} \, du .$

Binomial Reduction Formulas

$$\int u^m (a + bu^n)^p du : \qquad (m \text{ and } p, \text{ positive or negative})$$

80. $\displaystyle = \frac{u^{m-n+1}(a + bu^n)^{p+1}}{b(np + m + 1)} - \frac{a(m - n + 1)}{b(np + m + 1)} \int u^{m-n}(a + bu^n)^p \, du .$

81. $\displaystyle = \frac{u^{m+1}(a + bu^n)^p}{np + m + 1} + \frac{npa}{np + m + 1} \int u^m (a + bu^n)^{p-1} \, du .$

82. $\displaystyle = \frac{u^{m+1}(a + bu^n)^{p+1}}{a(m + 1)} - \frac{b(np + n + m + 1)}{a(m + 1)} \int u^{m+n}(a + bu^n)^p \, du .$

83. $\displaystyle = - \frac{u^{m+1}(a + bu^n)^{p+1}}{na(p + 1)} + \frac{np + n + m + 1}{na(p + 1)} \int u^m (a + bu^n)^{p+1} \, du .$

Trigonometric Forms

Note 10. Hereafter, any constant a, b, h, k may have any real value, subject to Note 2 and other specified conditions.

84. $\displaystyle\int \sin u \, du = \cos u .$ **85.** $\displaystyle\int \cos u \, du = - \sin u .$

86. $\displaystyle\int \tan u \, du = - \ln | \cos u | = \ln | \sec u | .$

87. $\displaystyle\int \cot u \, du = \ln | \sin u | .$ **88.** $\displaystyle\int \sec u \, du = \ln | \sec u + \tan u | .$

89. $\displaystyle\int \csc u \, du = \ln | \csc u - \cot u | = \ln \left| \tan \frac{u}{2} \right| .$

90. $\int \sec^2 u \; du = \tan u.$ **91.** $\int \csc^2 u \; du = -\cot u.$

92. $\int \sec u \tan u \; du = \sec u.$ **93.** $\int \csc u \cot u \; du = -\csc u.$

94. $\int \sin^2 au \; du = \dfrac{1}{2} u - \dfrac{1}{4a} \sin 2au.$ **95.** $\int \cos^2 au \; du = \dfrac{1}{2} u + \dfrac{1}{4a} \sin 2au.$

96. $\int \sin hu \sin ku \; du = -\dfrac{\sin (k+h)u}{2(k+h)} + \dfrac{\sin (k-h)u}{2(k-h)}.$

97. $\int \cos hu \cos ku \; du = \dfrac{\sin (k+h)u}{2(k+h)} + \dfrac{\sin (k-h)u}{2(k-h)}.$

98. $\int \sin hu \cos ku \; du = -\dfrac{\cos (k+h)u}{2(k+h)} - \dfrac{\cos (k-h)u}{2(k-h)}.$

99. $\int \dfrac{du}{a + b \cos u} = \dfrac{2}{\sqrt{a^2 - b^2}} \operatorname{Arctan} \dfrac{\sqrt{a^2 - b^2} \tan \frac{1}{2}u}{a + b};$ $\quad (0 < b,\; a^2 > b^2)$

$\qquad = \dfrac{1}{\sqrt{b^2 - a^2}} \ln \left| \dfrac{a + b + \sqrt{b^2 - a^2} \tan \frac{1}{2}u}{a + b - \sqrt{b^2 - a^2} \tan \frac{1}{2}u} \right|.$ $\quad (0 < a,\; b^2 > a^2)$

100. $\int \dfrac{du}{a + b \sin u} = \dfrac{2}{\sqrt{a^2 - b^2}} \operatorname{Arctan} \dfrac{a \tan \frac{1}{2}u + b}{\sqrt{a^2 - b^2}};$ $\quad (0 < a,\; a^2 > b^2)$

$\qquad = \dfrac{1}{\sqrt{b^2 - a^2}} \ln \left| \dfrac{a \tan \frac{1}{2}u + b - \sqrt{b^2 - a^2}}{a \tan \frac{1}{2}u + b + \sqrt{b^2 - a^2}} \right|.$ $\quad (0 < a,\; b^2 > a^2)$

101. $\int \dfrac{du}{a \sin u + b \cos u} = \dfrac{1}{\sqrt{a^2 + b^2}} \ln |\csc (u + \alpha) - \cot (u + \alpha)|.$ $\quad \left(\tan \alpha = \dfrac{b}{a} \right)$

102. $\int \sec^3 u \; du = \dfrac{1}{2} [\sec u \tan u + \ln | \sec u + \tan u |].$

103. $\int \csc^3 u \; du = -\dfrac{1}{2} [\cot u \csc u - \ln | \csc u - \cot u |].$

104. $\int \operatorname{Arcsin} u \; du = u \operatorname{Arcsin} u + \sqrt{1 - u^2}.$

105. $\int \operatorname{Arctan} u \; du = u \operatorname{Arctan} u - \ln \sqrt{1 + u^2}.$

Trigonometric Reduction Formulas

106. $\int \sin^n u \; du = -\dfrac{\sin^{n-1} u \cos u}{n} + \dfrac{n-1}{n} \int \sin^{n-2} u \; du.$

107. $\int \cos^n u \; du = \dfrac{\cos^{n-1} u \sin u}{n} + \dfrac{n-1}{n} \int \cos^{n-2} u \; du.$

108. $\int \sec^n u \; du = \dfrac{\tan u \sec^{n-2} u}{n-1} + \dfrac{n-2}{n-1} \int \sec^{n-2} u \; du.$

109. $\int \csc^n u \; du = -\dfrac{\cot u \csc^{n-2} u}{n-1} + \dfrac{n-2}{n-1} \int \csc^{n-2} u \; du.$

110. $\int \tan^n u \; du = \dfrac{\tan^{n-1} u}{n-1} - \int \tan^{n-2} u \; du.$

589

111. $\int \cot^n u \, du = - \dfrac{\cot^{n-1} u}{n-1} - \int \cot^{n-2} u \, du.$

$\int \cos^m u \sin^n u \, du:$ (m and n, positive or negative)

112. $= \dfrac{\cos^{m-1} u \sin^{n+1} u}{m+n} + \dfrac{m-1}{m+n} \int \cos^{m-2} u \sin^n u \, du.$

113. $= - \dfrac{\sin^{n-1} u \cos^{m+1} u}{m+n} + \dfrac{n-1}{m+n} \int \cos^m u \sin^{n-2} u \, du.$

114. $= - \dfrac{\sin^{n+1} u \cos^{m+1} u}{m+1} + \dfrac{m+n+2}{m+1} \int \cos^{m+2} u \sin^n u \, du.$

115. $= \dfrac{\sin^{n+1} u \cos^{m+1} u}{n+1} + \dfrac{m+n+2}{n+1} \int \cos^m u \sin^{n+2} u \, du.$

116. $\int u^n \sin au \, du = - \dfrac{u^n \cos au}{a} + \dfrac{n}{a} \int u^{n-1} \cos au \, du.$

117. $\int u^n \cos au \, du = \dfrac{u^n \sin au}{a} - \dfrac{n}{a} \int u^{n-1} \sin au \, du.$

Exponential and Logarithmic Forms

118. $\int e^u \, du = e^u.$ **119.** $\int a^u \, du = \dfrac{a^u}{\ln a}.$

120. $\int u^n e^{au} \, du = \dfrac{u^n e^{au}}{a} - \dfrac{n}{a} \int u^{n-1} e^{au} \, du.$

121. $\int \dfrac{e^{au}}{u^n} \, du = - \dfrac{e^{au}}{(n-1)u^{n-1}} + \dfrac{a}{n-1} \int \dfrac{e^{au} \, du}{u^{n-1}}.$

122. $\int \ln u \, du = u \ln u - u.$ **123.** $\int u^n \ln u \, du = \dfrac{u^{n+1} \ln u}{n+1} - \dfrac{u^{n+1}}{(n+1)^2}$

124. $\int u^m \ln^n u \, du = \dfrac{u^{m+1} \ln^n u}{m+1} - \dfrac{n}{m+1} \int u^m \ln^{n-1} u \, du.$

125. $\int e^{au} \sin nu \, du = \dfrac{e^{au}(a \sin nu - n \cos nu)}{a^2 + n^2}.$

126. $\int e^{au} \cos nu \, du = \dfrac{e^{au}(n \sin nu + a \cos nu)}{a^2 + n^2}.$

Forms Involving Hyperbolic Functions

127. $\int \sinh u \, du = \cosh u.$ **128.** $\int \cosh u \, du = \sinh u.$

129. $\int \tanh u \, du = \ln \cosh u.$ **130.** $\int \coth u \, du = \ln | \sinh u |.$

131. $\int \operatorname{sech} u \, du = \operatorname{Arctan} (\sinh u).$ **132.** $\int \operatorname{csch} u \, du = \ln \left| \tanh \dfrac{1}{2} u \right|.$

133. $\int \operatorname{sech}^2 u \, du = \tanh u.$ **134.** $\int \operatorname{csch}^2 u \, du = - \coth u.$

135. $\int \operatorname{sech} u \tanh u = - \operatorname{sech} u$ **136.** $\int \operatorname{csch} u \coth u = - \operatorname{csch} u.$

VIII. CURVES FOR REFERENCE

1. SINE FUNCTION

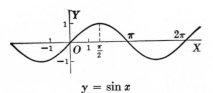

$$y = \sin x$$

2. COSINE FUNCTION

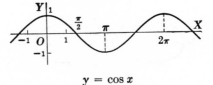

$$y = \cos x$$

3. TANGENT FUNCTION

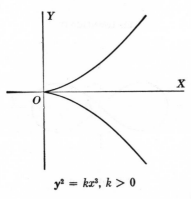

$$y = \tan x$$

4. SECANT FUNCTION

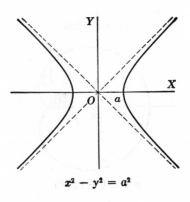

$$y = \sec x$$

INVERSE TRIGONOMETRIC FUNCTIONS

Note 1. See pages 136 and 138 for graphs of the following functions.

$$y = \arcsin x; \quad y = \arccos x; \quad y = \arctan x; \quad y = \operatorname{arccot} x.$$

5. SEMICUBICAL PARABOLA

6. EQUILATERAL HYPERBOLA

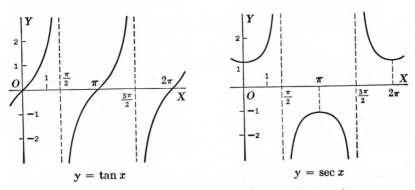

$$y^2 = kx^3, \; k > 0$$

$$x^2 - y^2 = a^2$$

7. FOUR-LEAVED ROSE

8. FOUR-LEAVED ROSE

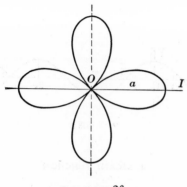

$r = a \cos 2\theta$

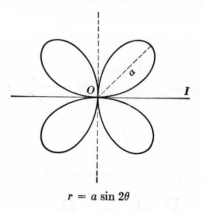

$r = a \sin 2\theta$

9. THREE-LEAVED ROSE

10. THREE-LEAVED ROSE

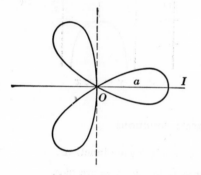

$r = a \cos 3\theta$

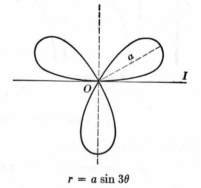

$r = a \sin 3\theta$

11. CARDIOID

12. LEMNISCATE

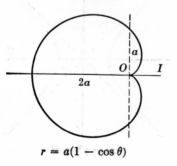

$r = a(1 - \cos \theta)$

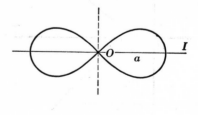

$r^2 = a^2 \cos 2\theta$

13. LIMAÇON

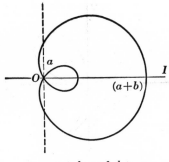

$$r = a + b \cos \theta, \; b > a$$

14. LIMAÇON

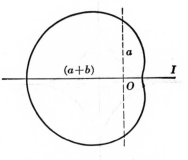

$$r = a - b \cos \theta, \; 0 < b < a$$

15. KAPPA CURVE

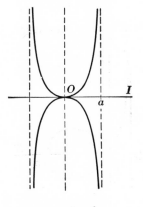

$$r = a \tan \theta$$

16. PARABOLA

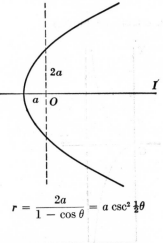

$$r = \frac{2a}{1 - \cos \theta} = a \csc^2 \tfrac{1}{2}\theta$$

17. EXPONENTIAL FUNCTION

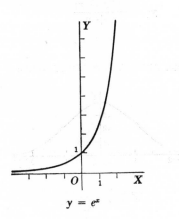

$$y = e^x$$

18. LOGARITHM FUNCTION

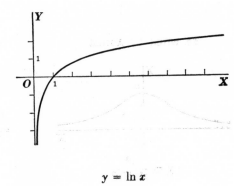

$$y = \ln x$$

19. HYPOCYCLOID OF FOUR CUSPS

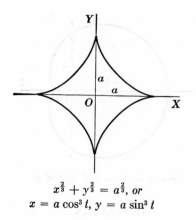

$$x^{\frac{2}{3}} + y^{\frac{2}{3}} = a^{\frac{2}{3}}, \text{ or}$$
$$x = a\cos^3 t, \ y = a\sin^3 t$$

20. FOLIUM OF DESCARTES

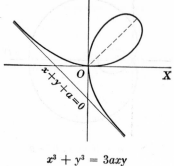

$$x^3 + y^3 = 3axy$$

21. CISSOID OF DIOCLES

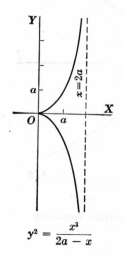

$$y^2 = \frac{x^3}{2a - x}$$

22. TRISECTRIX OF MACLAURIN

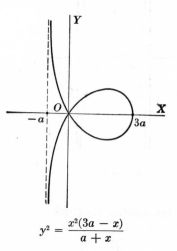

$$y^2 = \frac{x^2(3a - x)}{a + x}$$

23. WITCH OF AGNESI

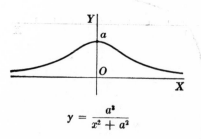

$$y = \frac{a^3}{x^2 + a^2}$$

24. NORMAL PROBABILITY CURVE

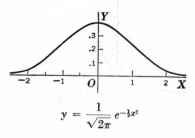

$$y = \frac{1}{\sqrt{2\pi}} \, e^{-\frac{1}{2}x^2}$$

594

25. CYCLOID

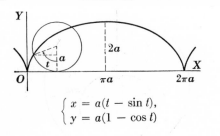

$$\begin{cases} x = a(t - \sin t), \\ y = a(1 - \cos t) \end{cases}$$

26. CONCHOID OF NICOMEDES

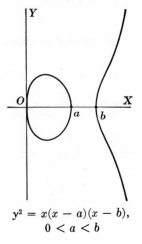

$r = h \csc \theta$

$$r = h \csc \theta + b,$$
$$b > h > 0$$

27. CATENARY

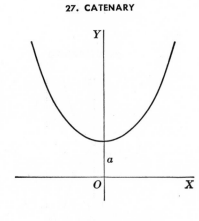

$$y = \frac{a}{2} \left(e^{\frac{x}{a}} + e^{-\frac{x}{a}} \right)$$

28. BIPARTITE CUBIC

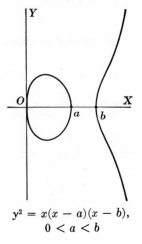

$$y^2 = x(x - a)(x - b),$$
$$0 < a < b$$

29. HYPERBOLA

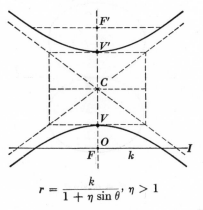

$$r = \frac{k}{1 + \eta \sin \theta}, \; \eta > 1$$

30. ELLIPSE

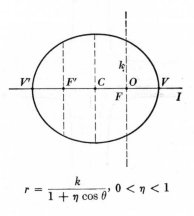

$$r = \frac{k}{1 + \eta \cos \theta}, \; 0 < \eta < 1$$

31. LOGARITHMIC SPIRAL

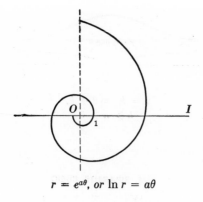

$$r = e^{a\theta}, \text{ or } \ln r = a\theta$$

32. SPIRAL OF ARCHIMEDES

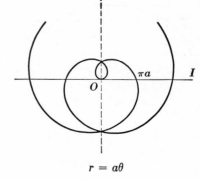

$$r = a\theta$$

33. HYPERBOLIC SPIRAL

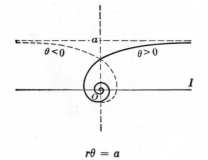

$$r\theta = a$$

34. STROPHOID

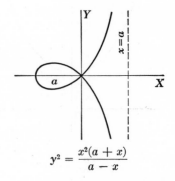

$$y^2 = \frac{x^2(a + x)}{a - x}$$

35. CRUCIFORM CURVE

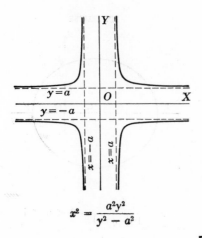

$$x^2 = \frac{a^2 y^2}{y^2 - a^2}$$

36. TWO–LEAVED ROSE

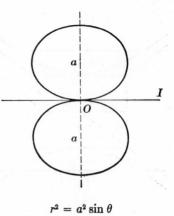

$$r^2 = a^2 \sin \theta$$

ANSWERS TO EXERCISES

Note. Answers to odd-numbered problems are given here. Answers to even-numbered problems are furnished in a separate pamphlet, when ordered by the instructor.

Exercise 1. Page 9

3. $x < -4$. **5.** $3 < x < 7$. **7.** $-8 < x < 5$. **9.** $x < -a$ or $x > a$.
11. $-3 < x < 9$; $-3 < x \leq 9$. **13.** 9; $(c^2 - cd + 3d^2)/d^2$; $(x^2 + 3x + 5)$.
15. $a^2 + 6a + 8$. **17.** $h^2 + 8h + 15$. **19.** $3\sin^2(x - 1) + 2$.
21. $y = \frac{4}{3}x^2 - \frac{7}{3}$; $x = \pm\frac{1}{2}\sqrt{7 + 3y}$. **29.** 23. **31.** $3a^2 - a + b^2$.

Exercise 2. Page 10

1. 8. **3.** $\frac{7}{3}$. **5.** $y = 3x - 2$. **7.** $y = 2x + 8$. **9.** $y = 2$. **11.** $y = 2x + 1$.

Exercise 3. Page 14

1. 2.5; 1.5; 2.2; 1.8; 2.1; 1.9; 2.01; 1.99; 2; $y = 2x - 12$. **3.** 12. **5.** 17. **7.** -14.

Exercise 4. Page 16

1. (a) $96'$, $80'$, $32'$, per sec.; (b) $(48', 80')$, $(56', 72')$, $(60.8', 67.2')$, $(62.4', 65.6')$, $(63.84', 64.16')$, all per sec.; (c) $64'$ per sec.
3. $23'$ and $17'$ per sec. **5.** $5'$ and $14'$ per sec.

Exercise 5. Page 20

1. 4. **3.** 2. **5.** 0. **7.** $\frac{11}{4}$. **9.** 6. **11.** $\frac{5}{2}$. **15.** $\frac{1}{3}$.

Exercise 6. Page 24

1. $\frac{7}{18}$. **3.** $1 - \sqrt{2}$. **5.** -3.

Exercise 7. Page 27

1. $(6x + 4)$; 22; -8. **3.** $(2x - 1)$; 5; $\frac{3}{2}$. **5.** 12. **7.** $-2 + 6x$.
9. $4z^3$. **11.** $9z^2 - 3$. **13.** $-3/z^2$. **15.** $-4/(2y + 3)^2$.
17. $(2x^2 + 2x)/(2x + 1)^2$. **19.** $\frac{1}{2}x^{-\frac{1}{2}}\sqrt{2}$. **21.** $-\frac{1}{6}x^{-\frac{3}{2}}\sqrt{3}$.

Exercise 8. Page 32

Note. Use the result of (a) in parts (b) and (c) in each problem.
1. $y' = 2x - 6$; $y' = 0$ at $x = 3$; $y = -2x - 1$; $y = 2x - 13$.
3. $y' = -4x + 4$; $y' = 0$ at $x = 1$; $y = -1$; $y + 12x = 29$; at $x = -\frac{1}{4}$.
5. $y' = 3x^2 - 3$; $y' = 0$ at $x = \pm 1$; $y = 9x - 14$; $y + 3x = 2$.

Exercise 9. Page 34

Note. All velocities are in feet per second.
1. $v = -32t + 64$; $32'$ and $-32'$; speed $= 32'$; $32'$ at $t = 1$, $t = 3$.
3. $v = -32t + 32$. **5.** $v = 16t + 4$; $52'$; $4'$.
7. $v = 3t^2 + 1$; $28'$; $29'$; $13'$ at $t = 2$; $49'$ at $t = 4$.

Exercise 10. Page 36

1. $\dfrac{dy}{dx} = 2$; $dy = 2\,dx$; $dy = .6$ and $dy = 12$.

3. $\dfrac{dy}{dx} = 3x^2 - 2$; $dy = (3x^2 - 2)dx$; $dy = 3$ and $dy = 60$.

597

Exercise 11. Page 42

1. $6x + 15x^2$.   **3.** $3 + 5z^4 - 8z^7$.   **5.** $-3 - 5x + \frac{7}{2}x^2 - \frac{1}{2}x^3$.

7. $28z^3 - 9z^2 + \frac{1}{3}z$.   **9.** $4t^2 - \frac{4}{3}t + 6$.   **11.** $-5 - \frac{3}{4}x + 9x^8$.

13. $6x^2 + 6x + 6$.   **15.** $4x^3 - 20x^4 + 4x - 24x^2$.   **17.** $-16z^3 + 3z^2 + 24z - 3$.

19. $8t^3 - 9t^2 - 28t + 15$.   **21.** $24t^3 + 3t^2 - 74t - 6$.   **23.** $y = 9x + 3$.

25. $y = \frac{22}{3} - x$.   **27.** At $x = -1$.   **29.** At $x = 2$.   **33.** $64'$, $64'$, per sec.; $t = 2$.

35. \$180 per unit.   **37.** 1.2 per unit output.

Exercise 12. Page 48

1. $\dfrac{9}{(2x + 5)^2}$.   **3.** $\dfrac{42x - 10 - 15x^2}{(5x - 7)^2}$.   **5.** $-\dfrac{6}{(2s + 4)^2}$.   **7.** $-21x^{-4}$.   **9.** $-24x^{-9}$.

11. $-8x^{-4}$.   **13.** $24(3x + 1)(3x^2 + 2x)^{11}$.   **15.** $5(3 + 8x^{-5})(3x - 2x^{-4})^4$.

17. $-3(t^{-2} + 8t^3)(t^{-1} - 2t^4)^2$.   **19.** $(x^2 + 3x)^2(x - x^3)^3(10x^2 + 21x - 45x^3 - 18x^4)$.

21. $(s^2 - 2s^{-3})^2(s - 5s^4)(8s^2 + 14s^{-3} - 70s^5 - 10)$.

23. $(x + 2x^2)^{-2}(24x^2 + x - 2)(2 - 3x)^{-3}$.

25. $\dfrac{4(x + 3)^3(5 - 24x - 4x^2)}{(4x^2 + 5)^5}$.   **27.** $\dfrac{2(y^4 - 2y^2)(20y^3 - 20y - 2y^4 - y^6)}{(5 - y^3)^3}$.

Exercise 13. Page 49

1. $\frac{8}{3}x^{\frac{1}{3}}$.   **3.** $\frac{1}{3}\sqrt[3]{4}\,y^{-\frac{2}{3}}$.   **5.** $-\frac{14}{3}t^{-\frac{5}{3}}$.   **7.** $-\frac{1}{2}x^{-\frac{3}{2}}$.

9. $-\frac{1}{3}ab^{-1}x^{-\frac{4}{3}}$.   **11.** $5x(2x^2 + 1)^{\frac{1}{4}}$.   **13.** $\frac{3}{2}(1 + 6u)(u + 3u^2)^{-\frac{2}{5}}$.

15. $\dfrac{3s}{\sqrt{3s^2 + 5}}$.   **17.** $\dfrac{3s - 1}{\sqrt{3s^2 - 2s + 5}}$.   **19.** $-9(2x + 5)^{-\frac{5}{2}}$.   **21.** $-(3t + 5)^{-\frac{4}{3}}$.

23. $-2(z - 1)^{-\frac{3}{2}}(3z + 1)^{-\frac{1}{2}}$.   **25.** $\frac{1}{6}s^{-\frac{1}{2}}(s^{\frac{1}{2}} - a^{\frac{1}{2}})^{-\frac{2}{3}}$.   **27.** $-x^{-\frac{1}{3}}(a^{\frac{2}{3}} - x^{\frac{2}{3}})^{\frac{1}{2}}$.

29. $\dfrac{2a^2z - z^3}{(a^2 - z^2)^{\frac{3}{2}}}$.   **31.** $\dfrac{18x^2 - 8 - 5x^4}{2\sqrt{x^3 - 2x}\sqrt{4 - x^2}}$.   **33.** $\dfrac{-1}{\sqrt{x^2 - 1}(x + \sqrt{x^2 - 1})}$.

35. $\dfrac{(2x - 3x^2)^2(30 - 106x + 60x^2)}{(5 - 4x)^2}$.   **37.** $\dfrac{(2y + 3)^4(9 - 76y - 8y^2)}{(4y^2 - y)^4}$.

Exercise 14. Page 52

1. $3x^2y + x^3y'$.   **3.** $y^3 + 3xy^2y'$.   **5.** $-(xy' + y)x^{-2}y^{-2}$.   **7.** $\dfrac{1 - 2yy'}{2\sqrt{x} - y^2}$.

9. $-\dfrac{x^2}{y^2} = y'$.   **11.** $-\dfrac{1 + y}{x} = y'$.   **13.** $\dfrac{4x}{9y}$.   **15.** $\dfrac{x + y}{y - x}$.   **17.** $\dfrac{-2xy}{x^2 + 3y^2}$.

19. $\dfrac{xy^2 - 4x}{4y - x^2y}$.   **21.** $-\dfrac{2\sqrt{y}}{3\sqrt{x}}$.   **23.** $\dfrac{5 - 6r^3t}{2r + 9r^2t^2}$.   **25.** $\dfrac{9y}{4x}$.   **27.** $\dfrac{y - x}{x + y}$.

29. $5y = 3x - 34$.   **31.** $3y = 2x + 2$.   **33.** $-\frac{7}{9}$ and $\frac{92}{48}$.

35. $[4(x + 3y^2) - 6(2x + 5y)^2]/[15(2x + 5y)^2 - 24y(x + 3y^2)]$.

Exercise 15. Page 55

1. $x = y^{\frac{1}{5}}$; $\dfrac{dy}{dx} = 5x^4$.   **3.** $y = \pm\sqrt{4 - x}$; $\dfrac{dx}{dy} = -2y$.

5. $\dfrac{dy}{dx} = \dfrac{6x - y}{x - 3y^2}$.   **7.** $\dfrac{dy}{dx} = \dfrac{2y - 3}{2y - 2x + 2}$.   **9.** $\dfrac{dy}{dx} = \dfrac{3x}{4y^2}$.

11. $\dfrac{dy}{dx} = -\dfrac{x}{4y}$.   **13.** $\dfrac{dy}{dx} = -\sqrt{\dfrac{y}{x}}$.   **15.** $\dfrac{dy}{dx} = \dfrac{3x^2 - 2y^2}{4xy - 3y^2}$.

Exercise 16. Page 57

1. $60x^3 - 12x$; $180x^2 - 12$; $360x$.

3. $30x^4 - 12x^2 - 6x$; $120x^3 - 24x - 6$; $360x^2 - 24$.   **5.** $y'' = \dfrac{-2}{(s - 1)^3}$.

EXERCISES

599

7. $g''(x) = \frac{35}{2}t^{\frac{3}{2}} + \frac{2}{3}t^{-\frac{5}{3}}$.

9. $120t^{-7} - 18t^{-4}$.

11. $168(2t - 3)^5$.

13. $\frac{4}{5}(2s^2 + 5)^{-\frac{3}{5}}(15 - 2s^2)$.

15. $1296(2t - 1)^2(5t - 1)$.

17. $\frac{3t^2 - 36t + 72}{8t^3(t - 3)^{\frac{3}{2}}}$.

19. $y'' = -a^2/y^3$.

21. $y'' = -a^2/y^3$.

23. $y'' = -6/25y^3$.

25. $y'' = -\frac{b^4}{a^2y^3}$.

27. $y'' = \frac{a^{\frac{1}{2}}}{2x^{\frac{3}{2}}}$.

29. $\frac{6[x(3y^2 - 1)^2 - y(3x^2 + 1)^2]}{(3y^2 - 1)^3}$.

31. At $(2, 1)$, $y' = -1$; $y'' = -\frac{12}{5}$. At $(2, -\frac{3}{7})$, $y' = \frac{9}{7}$; $y'' = \frac{84}{35}$.

33. $\frac{4xy^3 + 3y^5}{4x^4}$.

35. $\frac{d^2x}{dy^2} = -\frac{a^2}{x^3}$.

37. $\frac{d^2x}{dy^2} = \frac{a^2}{y^3}$.

39. $\frac{d^2x}{dy^2} = -\frac{15}{4x^3}$.

41. $\frac{d^2x}{dy^2} = -\frac{a^4}{b^2x^3}$.

Exercise 17. Page 60

1. 0; $+\infty$.   **3.** 0; $+\infty$; $-\infty$.   **5.** $\frac{4}{5}$.   **7.** $-\frac{1}{2}$.   **9.** $-\infty$.   **11.** 0.
13. $+\infty$.   **15.** $-\infty$; $+\infty$; no limit.   **17.** No limit.   **19.** Limit zero.   **21.** $-\infty$.

Exercise 18. Page 64

1. $4n - 2$.   **3.** $3(-2)^{n-1}$.   **5.** $5, 8, 11, 14$.   **7.** $9, -45, 189, -729$.
9. $(2n)!$.   **11.** $(-1)^{n+1}2^n/(2n - 1)$.   **13.** $\frac{1}{3}$.   **15.** $-\frac{2}{3}$.   **17.** $+\infty$.   **19.** $\frac{3}{2}$.

Exercise 19. Page 67

1. $y = 2x - 3$; $x + 2y = 9$.   **3.** $8y = x + 5$; $8x + y = 25$.
5. At $(2, 1)$, $x + 2y = 4$; $y = 2x - 3$. At $(2, -1)$, $2y = x - 4$; $y + 2x = 3$.
7. $25y = 12x + 17$; $60y + 125x = -113$.   **9.** $12y = x + 4$; $12x + y = 97$.
11. At $(0, 0)$, $90°$; at $(1, 1)$, $36.9°$.   **13.** $49.4°$.   **15.** $11.5°$.   **19.** $b^2xx_1 - a^2yy_1 = a^2b^2$.
21. $axx_1 + byy_1 + d(x + x_1) + e(y + y_1) + f = 0$.   **23.** $53.1°$; $17.1°$.
25. At $(0, 0)$, $71.6°$; $(-1, 2)$, $76.0°$; $(3, 18)$, $2.4°$.

Exercise 20. Page 72

1. Min., 0.   **3.** No extremum.   **5.** Min. -5 at $x = 3$.
7. Min. 16 at $x = 2$; max. 17 at $x = 1$.   **9.** No extremum.
11. Max. 0 at $x = 0$; min. $-\frac{4}{27}$ at $x = \frac{2}{3}$.
13. Min. 0 at $x = -1$; min. 0 at $x = 2$; max. $\frac{81}{16}$ at $x = \frac{1}{2}$.   **15.** Max. 10; min. -6.
17. Max. 182; min. -34.   **19.** M? 0 at $x = 0$; max. 256 at $x = -4$.
21. Max. 256 at $x = 1$; min. 0 at $x = -1$; min. 0 at $x = 3$.   **23.** Max. 6 at $x = 2$.

Exercise 21. Page 75

1. Hor. at $(0, 0)$.   **3.** Ver. at $(4, 0)$.   **5.** Ver. at $(-5, 2)$.
7. Hor. at $(2, 1)$, $(2, -7)$; ver. at $(-2, -3)$, $(6, -3)$.   **9.** Min. at $x = 0$, a cusp.
11. Min. at $x = 0$.   **13.** Min. at $x = -2$, a cusp.   **15.** Max. at $x = 1$.

Exercise 22. Page 80

25. Min. at $x = a$.   **27.** Max. at $x = a$; min. at $x = (ma + nb)/(m + n)$.

Exercise 24. Page 86

1. 75×50, in yd.   **3.** Side, $(5 - \frac{5}{3}\sqrt{3})$ in.   **5.** $2x + 3y = 12$.
7. In ft., 40 by 40 by 40.   **9.** On 67th day.   **11.** In ft., $8\sqrt{2}$ by $8\sqrt{2}$.
13. $\frac{1}{4}h$ by $\frac{1}{4}h$.   **15.** $\sqrt{3}$ ft.   **17.** $\frac{16}{3}$ by $\frac{16}{3}\sqrt{3}$.   **19.** $20'' \times 20'' \times 40''$.
21. Base rad. $\frac{1}{2}r\sqrt{2}$; alt. $r\sqrt{2}$.   **23.** $10'$ by $4'$.   **25.** h/n.   **27.** Alt. $4r$; base rad. $r\sqrt{2}$.
29. $\sqrt{c/b}$ yr.   **31.** Min. at $x = 3$.   **33.** 7.   **35.** $\$47,000$; increase $\frac{4}{5}\tau$, dollars.

Exercise 25. Page 90

1. $\frac{1}{2}r\sqrt{2}$ by $r\sqrt{2}$.   **3.** Box is a cube.   **5.** A square in both cases.   **7.** $\frac{1}{2}$.

9. Is a cube.   **11.** $2r/h$, where r is base rad. and h is alt. of cone.

13. Alt. is $\sqrt{2}$ times base rad.   **15.** Equal.   **17.** 1.

19. 1.   **21.** $\frac{1}{3}$ alt. of given cone.   **23.** 1.

Exercise 26. Page 95

1. 64.   **3.** $\pm\frac{37}{20}$.   **5.** Decr., $32\frac{1}{2}$ ft. per min.   **7.** 20 mi. p.h.   **9.** 1.9′ p.s.

11. 1.25′ p.s.   **13.** Decr., 2.77 mi. p.h.; at end 3.2 hr.   **15.** Incr., 483′ p.m.

17. .0442′ p.m.; 724 cu. ft. p.m.   **19.** Decr., .110 amp. p.s.   **21.** Incr., .1 lb. p.m.

23. Incr., $3.90 p.mo.   **25.** Incr., .0354′ p.s.

27. 2.87 mi. p.m.   **29.** $(\frac{1}{2}xt^{-\frac{1}{2}} + 2ty + 2z)/u$.   **31.** $7(4^8)$.

33. $.2\frac{2}{3}$ ohms p.s.   **35.** $T = 450°$; decr., $11.55°$ p.s.

Exercise 27. Page 100

Note. Velocity is in feet p.s.; acceleration is in feet per second per second.

1. $v = 138$, $a = 90$.   **3.** $v = 2$, $a = -4$; $v = 71$, $a = 50$.

5. Max. at $t = 8$; $v > 0$ if $t < 8$; $v < 0$ if $t > 8$; $a = -32$; at $s = 0$, $v = -256$.

7. Max. at $t = 0$; $v < 0$ at $t > 0$; $a = -32$; at $s = 0$, $v = -320$.

9. Max. at $t = 6$; $v > 0$ at $t < 6$; $v < 0$ at $t > 6$; at $s = 0$, $t = 12\frac{3}{4}$ and $v = -216$.

Exercise 28. Page 103

1. $dy = 1$; $\Delta y = 1.125$.   **3.** $(6x^2 + 10x)dx$.   **5.** $-20(3 - 5x)^3\,dx$.

7. $\dfrac{2x + 1}{2\sqrt{x^2 + x}}\,dx$.   **9.** $(3x + 2)(45x - 8)dx$.   **11.** $\frac{1}{2}\sqrt{3}x^{-\frac{1}{2}}\,dx$.

13. $-10(2x + 3)^{-2}\,dx$.   **15.** $\frac{2}{21}(2x + 4)^{-\frac{2}{3}}\,dx$.   **17.** $(16x^2 + 24x - 16)(4x + 3)^{-2}\,dx$.

19. $-24x(4x^2 + 7)^{-2}\,dx$.   **21.** $-4(2x + 5)^{-\frac{4}{3}}\,dx$.   **23.** $\dfrac{(1 - x)dx}{x^2\sqrt{2x - 1}}$.

25. $\dfrac{(3 - y - 3x^{\frac{1}{2}})}{x + 2y}\,dx$.   **27.** $dy = \dfrac{2x - 12(3x + 2y)^3}{8(3x + 2y)^3 + 3y^2}\,dx$.   **29.** $dy = -\dfrac{y^{\frac{1}{3}}}{x^{\frac{1}{3}}}\,dx$.

Exercise 29. Page 106

1. $.9\pi$ cu. in.   **3.** 60π cu. in.   **5.** (a) $50'$; (b) $2.5'$ p.s.   **7.** 6 sq. in.; 6%.

9. 2%.   **11.** .016″.   **13.** $7\frac{1}{14}$.   **15.** $5\frac{1}{15}$.   **19.** 6%.

21. 6%.   **25.** $1 + \frac{1}{2}y$.   **27.** $1 - y$.   **29.** .00188″.

Exercise 30. Page 112

1. $x = 2 + 3t$, $y = 5 + 2t$.   **3.** $x = -2 + 3t$, $y = -4 + 9t$.

5. $\dfrac{dy}{dx} = \dfrac{1 - 2t}{2t}$; $\dfrac{d^2y}{dx^2} = -\dfrac{1}{4t^3}$.   **7.** $y' = \dfrac{2t + 1}{1 + 9t^2}$; $y'' = \dfrac{2 - 18t - 18t^2}{(1 + 9t^2)^3}$.

9. $y' = \dfrac{2(2 - t)^2}{3(3 - t)^2}$; $y'' = -\dfrac{4}{9}\left(\dfrac{2 - t}{3 - t}\right)^3$.   **11.** $y' = \dfrac{2t - t^4}{1 - 2t^3}$; $y'' = \dfrac{2(1 + t^3)^4}{3(1 - 2t^3)^3}$.

13. $7x + 13y + 36 = 0$.   **15.** $4y^2 = x^2(x - 4)$.   **17.** $xy = 4$.   **19.** Tangents, $x = \pm 4y$.

Exercise 31. Page 119

1. $v = 3\sqrt{26}$; $a = 2\sqrt{37}$.   **3.** $v = \sqrt{85}$; $a = 2\sqrt{10}$.   **5.** $v = 1$; $a = 2\sqrt{2}$.

7. $v = 4\sqrt{241}$, $a = 32$; speed 100; min. at $t = \frac{5}{2}$.

9. At $(-4, 2)$, $(v_x = 10, v_y = -10)$; at $(4, 2)$, $(v_x = 10, v_y = 10)$.

11. (a) $v_x = -12$, $v_y = 18$; (b) at $15\sqrt{2}$ ft. p.s.

13. $(v_x = 8, v_y = 0)$; $(v_y = -8, v_x = 0)$.

15. $v_x = -9$, $a_x = -36$, $v = \sqrt{97}$, $a = 12\sqrt{10}$.   **17.** $\frac{5}{16}$ ft. p.s.

Exercise 32.   Page 120

1. $y = 15x + 45$, $x + 15y = 223$; $2y + 24x = 9$, $24y - 2x = 253$.

3. 71.6° at each.   **9.** Min. at $x = 1$; max. at $x = \frac{3}{5}$; infl. at $x = 0$ and $x = \frac{1}{10}(6 \pm \sqrt{6})$.

17. $16\sqrt{3}$.   **19.** $- .232''$ p.s.; 1.35 sq. in. p.s.   **21.** Incr. 24 mi. p.h.   **23.** 5''.

25. $[\frac{3}{2}x^{\frac{1}{2}} + 6(2x - 1)^2]dx$.   **27.** $\frac{3}{2}(2 + 3t)^{\frac{1}{2}} dt$.   **29.** $-\dfrac{(28t + 34)dt}{(2t - 5)^5\sqrt{3 + 4t}}$.

31. $\frac{200}{3}\pi$ cu. ft.   **33.** 3%.   **35.** 6%; 4%.

37. $x = 2 + 6t$; $y = 3 + t$.   **39.** $v = 3\sqrt{65}$; $a = 2\sqrt{65}$.

Exercise 33.   Page 128

1. $5 \cos 5x$.   **3.** $4 \sec^2 4t$.   **5.** $- \frac{3}{2} \csc \frac{3}{2}t \cot \frac{3}{2}t$.   **7.** $- 5 \cot^4 z \csc^2 z$.

9. $\dfrac{\cos x}{2\sqrt{\sin x}}$.   **11.** $-\dfrac{\sin 2x}{2\sqrt[4]{\cos^3 2x}}$.   **13.** $-\dfrac{12 \cos 4x}{\sin^4 4x}$.   **15.** $\dfrac{\sin \sqrt{x}}{2\sqrt{x} \cos^2 \sqrt{x}}$.

17. $(4x + 1)\cos (2x^2 + x)$.   **19.** $- 14 \csc^2 x \cot x$.   **21.** $\dfrac{(6 - 4x)\sin (2x - 3)^2}{\sqrt{\cos (2x - 3)^2}}$.

23. $x^2(3 \sin x + x \cos x)$.   **25.** $4 \cos^2 x \cos 4x - 2 \cos x \sin x \sin 4x$.

27. $(3 + 4x)[8 \sec^2 x + (6 + 8x) \sec^2 x \tan x]$.   **29.** $\dfrac{2 \sin x}{(1 + \cos x)^2}$.

31. $\dfrac{2 \tan^2 2x + 6 \cos 2x - 2}{(3 - \sec 2x)^2}$.   **33.** $\dfrac{3(t + \cos t)\cos (3t - 1) - (1 - \sin t)\sin (3t - 1)}{(t + \cos t)^2}$.

35. $\dfrac{- 6 \cos 2x}{(3 \sin 2x - 1)^2}$.   **37.** $- \dfrac{2(2x + \sec^2 x)}{(x^2 + \tan x)^2}$.

39. $\dfrac{2(\cos 2x + \sin 2x - \sin 2x \sec^2 2x)}{(1 + \tan 2x)^2}$.   **41.** 4.   **43.** $- \frac{1}{4}\pi\sqrt{2}$.   **45.** $\sqrt{3}$.

47. $- 9 \cos 3x$.   **49.** $2(1 + x^2 \sec^2 x)\tan x + 4x \sec^2 x$.

51. $6[(3z^2 \tan 3z - 2z)\sec^2 3z + \tan 3z]/z^4$.   **53.** $\dfrac{\cos x}{3 - \sin y}$.   **55.** $\dfrac{1 - \cos (x + 3y)}{3 \cos (x + 3y)}$.

57. $\dfrac{2x \sec^2 (x^2 - y)}{\sec^2 (x^2 - y) + \csc^2 y}$.   **59.** $\dfrac{x \sec^2 (x^2 - 2y) - \csc^2 (2x - y^2)}{\sec^2 (x^2 - 2y) - y \csc^2 (2x - y^2)}$.

Exercise 34.   Page 131

13. 70.5°.   **15.** No extremum at π; max. at $\frac{1}{3}\pi$; min. at $\frac{5}{3}\pi$.

17. No extremum at $\frac{1}{2}\pi$ and $\frac{3}{2}\pi$; max. at $\frac{1}{6}\pi$, $\frac{7}{6}\pi$; min. at $\frac{5}{6}\pi$, $\frac{11}{6}\pi$.

Exercise 35.   Page 133

1. $\frac{3}{2}\sqrt{3} - .5$.   **3.** $\frac{1525}{9}\pi$ yd. p.s.   **5.** $\frac{4}{9}\pi a^3\sqrt{3}$.

7. $\frac{9}{170}$ rad. p.s.   **9.** Alt. equal to base rad.   **11.** $10\sqrt{5}$.

13. Incr., .0088 rad. p.s.; incr., .0530 rad. p.s.   **15.** .604'' incr. p.m.

17. $\frac{1}{2}r\sqrt{2}$.   **19.** .1144'' p.m.   **21.** $\frac{1}{3}r^2\sqrt{3}$; 60°.   **23.** $24\sqrt{3}$ ft.

25. $\dfrac{du}{dt} = (3 - 2t)(2x + 8y) + 8x(2 \cos 2t - 1)$.

Exercise 36.   Page 139

Note. Only sample values are given in Problems 5–21.

5. $- 2\pi$.   **7.** $- \pi$.   **9.** $- \frac{3}{2}\pi$.   **11.** $- \frac{1}{2}\pi$.   **13.** $\frac{4}{3}\pi$; $- \frac{2}{3}\pi$.

15. $\frac{1}{4}\pi$; $- \frac{1}{4}\pi$.   **17.** $- \frac{2}{3}\pi$.   **19.** No value.   **21.** $\frac{2}{3}\pi$; $- \frac{1}{3}\pi$.

23. .221; 3.363.   **25.** $\frac{1}{2}\pi$.   **27.** $\frac{1}{3}\pi$.   **29.** π.   **31.** $- \frac{1}{3}\pi$.

33. $\frac{1}{2}\pi$.   **35.** $- \frac{1}{8}\pi$.   **37.** $\frac{3}{4}\pi$.   **39.** $- .42$.

Exercise 37. Page 142

1. $\dfrac{4}{\sqrt{1-16x^2}}$.

3. $\dfrac{-3x^2}{\sqrt{1-x^6}}$.

5. $\dfrac{3}{5+12x+9x^2}$.

7. $\dfrac{3}{\sqrt{24x-9x^2-15}}$.

9. Not defined on any open interval.

11. $\dfrac{1}{\sqrt{9-z^2}}$.

13. $\dfrac{1}{2x\sqrt{x-1}}$.

15.* $\dfrac{3}{|2-z|\sqrt{1-z-2z^2}}$.

17. $\dfrac{3(1+2x)}{|x+x^2|\sqrt{x^4+2x^3+x^2-9}}$.

19. $\dfrac{1}{a^2+x^2}$.

21. $\dfrac{-\sqrt{2}}{|1-x|\sqrt{x^2-2x-1}}$.

23. $-\dfrac{2}{t^3}\operatorname{Arcsin} t + \dfrac{1}{t^2\sqrt{1-t^2}}$.

25. $3\cos 3x \operatorname{Arcsin}\sqrt{x} + \dfrac{\sin 3x}{2\sqrt{x-x^2}}$.

27. $\sqrt{a^2-x^2}$.

29. $-\dfrac{\sqrt{a^2-x^2}}{x^2}$.

31. $\left(3x^2-\dfrac{1}{\sqrt{1-x^2}}\right)(1+y^2)$.

33. $-\dfrac{1+[1+(x+2y)^2]\cos x}{2+[1+(x+2y)^2]\sin y}$.

35. $\dfrac{-128x}{(1+16x^2)^2}$.

41. Incr., $\frac{1}{82}$ rad. p.s.

43. Incr., .04757 rad. p.m.

47. 12.25′.

49. $\dfrac{du}{dt} = \dfrac{2yz\cos 2t - 2xz\sin 2t + xy\sec t\tan t}{\sqrt{1-x^2y^2z^2}}$.

Exercise 38. Page 147

1. $\log_3 N = 5$.

3. $\log_{10} N = -2$.

5. 36.

7. 32.

9. 4; .01; 64.

11. $\sqrt{e}$.

Exercise 39. Page 149

1. $\dfrac{5}{3+5x}$.

3. $\dfrac{3}{3x-4}$.

5. $\dfrac{2z}{z^2-4}$.

7. $\dfrac{2x\log_a e}{1+x^2}$.

9. $2\cot 2x\log_{10} e$.

11. $-\frac{1}{2}\tan\frac{1}{2}x$.

13. $\dfrac{1}{x\ln x}$.

15. $\dfrac{\tan x}{\ln\sec x}$.

17. $\dfrac{3(\ln x)^2}{x}$.

19. $\dfrac{6}{2+3x}$.

21. $\dfrac{5}{3(4+5x)}$.

23. $3\cot x$.

25. $\frac{1}{2}\tan x$.

27. $\dfrac{\ln\sin x}{x} + (\cot x)\ln 2x$.

29. $\dfrac{4x-15x^2-5}{(1+x^2)(2-5x)}$.

31. $\dfrac{22z^3-6z^2+30}{(3+z^3)(2z-1)}$.

33. $\dfrac{14x^2-6x+6}{3(3+x^2)(2x-1)}$.

35. $3\sec^2 x\cot x + 4\cot 2x - 3\tan 3x$.

37. $\dfrac{\cot x}{2} + \dfrac{\sin x}{3(1-\cos x)}$.

39. $\dfrac{3(\sec^2 x)(\ln\tan x)^2}{\tan x}$.

41. $\dfrac{-5}{x(\ln x)^2}$.

43. $\dfrac{2\tan x}{(\ln\cos x)^2}$.

45. $\dfrac{17}{(2+3x)(5-x)}$.

47. $\dfrac{(\cot x)\ln\cos x + (\tan x)\ln\sin x}{(\ln\cos x)^2}$.

49. $\dfrac{4x}{3(1-x^4)}$.

51. $\dfrac{\cot x}{2} + \dfrac{\sin x}{2(\cos x-1)}$.

53. $\dfrac{9-18\ln(3x-1)}{(3x-1)^3}$.

55. .09658.

57. 1.608.

59. $6\cot 3x - 9x\csc^2 3x$.

61. $-y/x$.

63. $\dfrac{2(4x^3+6x^2y+6y+3x)}{3x}$.

65. $(22x+23)(2+x)^2(2x-3)^7$.

67. $\dfrac{(27+3x)(2+x)^2}{(1-3x)^5}$.

69. $\dfrac{7}{2\sqrt{2x-1}(3x+2)^{\frac{3}{2}}}$.

71. $\dfrac{\frac{1}{15}(24x-38)}{(1-3x)^{\frac{4}{5}}(2+4x)^{\frac{4}{3}}}$.

73. $\dfrac{1}{x(a+bx)^2}$.

75. $\sqrt{a^2+x^2}$.

77. $\dfrac{(-1)^{n+1}(n-1)!}{x^n}$.

79. $\dfrac{(-1)^{n-1}(n-1)!}{(1+x)^n}$.

81. 7.275 money units per unit of demand.

* Since $(2-z)$ may be negative, $\sqrt{(2-z)^2} = |2-z|$.

Exercise 40. Page 153

1. $4e^{4x}$.   **3.** $- e^{\cot x} \csc^2 x$.   **5.** $- 2e^{-2x}$.   **7.** $4a^{4t} \ln a$.

9. $e^{\sec z} \sec z \tan z$.   **11.** $- 3(4^{-3z})\ln 4$.   **13.** $(3 - 2x)e^{3x - x^2}$.   **15.** $(3x^2 - 3x^5)e^{-x^3}$.

17. $e^{x \ln x}(1 + \ln x)$.   **19.** $- a^t(\ln a)\sin a^t$.   **21.** $\dfrac{1 - 3x \ln x}{xe^{3x}}$.

23. $\dfrac{\sqrt{2x} \cos x - \sin x}{\sqrt{2x}e^{\sqrt{2x}}}$.   **25.** $\dfrac{e^{2x}(1 + 2x)}{1 + x^2e^{4x}}$.   **27.** $\dfrac{e^{-3x}(3x - 1)}{\sqrt{1 - x^2e^{-6x}}}$.

29. $- e^{-2t}(5 \sin 5t + 2 \cos 5t)$.   **31.** $\dfrac{\sec^2 x + (\sec x)(\tan x + 2) + 2 \tan x}{e^{-2x}}$.

33. $\dfrac{6e^{3x}}{(e^{3x} + 1)^2}$.   **35.** $3e^{-3t}(5 - 2e^{-3t})^{-\frac{1}{2}}$.   **37.** $\dfrac{4e^{2x}}{x} - \dfrac{e^{2x}}{x^2} + 4e^{2x} \ln x$.

39. $\dfrac{5e^x(x^2 - 2x + 2)}{x^3}$.   **41.** $\dfrac{y^2}{1 - ye^{-y} - xy}$.   **43.** $y = 5.36x + 2.48$.

45. $\frac{1}{2}x^{\frac{1}{2}x}(1 + \ln x)$.   **47.** $(\sin x)^{\cos x - 1}[\cos^2 x - (\sin^2 x)\ln \sin x]$.

49. $[(\ln x)\ln (\ln x) + 1](\ln x)^{x-1}$.   **51.** $x^{e^x - 1}e^x(1 + x \ln x)$.   **53.** $xe^x + ne^x$.

55. $- \infty$.   **57.** 0.   **73.** 2.12 money units.

Exercise 41. Page 156

1. v: 6, 0, $- 6$, 0, 6. a: 0, $- 12$, 0, 12, 0.   Period is π sec.

3. v: $4\sqrt{3}$, $- 4\sqrt{3}$, 0, $4\sqrt{3}$, 0. a: $- 8$, $- 8$, 16, $- 8$, 16.   Period is π sec.

5. v: 6, 6, $- 6$, $- 6$. a: 12, $- 12$, $- 12$, 12.   Period is π sec.

Exercise 42. Page 159

3. $- 5 \sin 5x \, dx$.   **5.** $\frac{1}{3} \cos \frac{1}{3}x \, dx$.   **7.** $\dfrac{5 \, dx}{x + 3}$.   **9.** $\dfrac{dx}{x \ln x}$.   **11.** $\dfrac{3 \, dt}{1 + 9t^2}$.

13. $- (2e^{2x} + 1)\sin (e^{2x} + x)dx$.   **15.** $[(\sec^2 x)\ln x + (\tan x)x^{-1}]dx$.

17. $e^{3\theta}(2 \sin \theta + 4 \cos \theta)d\theta$.   **19.** $\dfrac{2e^x \, dx}{(e^x + 1)^2}$.

21. $\dfrac{(x^2 + 1 - 2x^2 \ln x)dx}{x(1 + x^2)^2}$.   **23.** $a^z[(\ln a)\ln \sin z + \cot z]dz$.   **25.** $.52'$.   **27.** $.6\%$; $.9\%$.

29. $1\frac{1}{2}\%$.   **39.** $dy = \cos x \csc y \, dx$.   **41.** $dy = \dfrac{3e^{3x-2y} + \cos x}{2e^{3x-2y} - \sin y} dx$.

Exercise 43. Page 163

1. $- \frac{2}{3} \tan \theta$.   **3.** $\dfrac{1 - \sin t}{\cos t}$.   **5.** $\dfrac{dy}{dx} = \dfrac{2}{3t^3}$; $\dfrac{d^2y}{dx^2} = - \dfrac{2}{3t^6}$.

7. $x + y = \frac{3}{2}\pi$; $y = x - 2 + \frac{3}{2}\pi$.   **9.** $x + y = \frac{3}{4}\pi r\sqrt{2}$; $y - x = r\sqrt{2}$.

11. $x^{\frac{2}{3}} + y^{\frac{2}{3}} = 3^{\frac{2}{3}}$.   **17.** $v = \sqrt{31}$; $a = 2\sqrt{21}$.   **19.** $v = 1.03$; $a = 2.28$.

21. (a) $v = 2rh \sin \frac{1}{2}\theta$; $a = h^2r$.   (b) Min. at $\theta = 0$ and $\theta = 2\pi$; max. at $\theta = \pi$.

Exercise 44. Page 167

13. $(\sqrt{3}, 1)$.   **15.** $(\sqrt{3}, - 1)$.   **17.** $[2\sqrt{2}, \frac{3}{4}\pi]$, etc.

19. $[5, 216.9°]$ or $[5, 3.786 \text{ (rad.)}]$.   **21.** $x^2 + y^2 = 256$.   **23.** $y = 6$.

25. $y = \pm x\sqrt{3}$, or $y^2 = 3x^2$.   **27.** $r = 4 \cos \theta$.

Exercise 45. Page 170

1. $x = 6 \cos^2 \theta$, $y = 3 \sin 2\theta$; slope 0.

3. Slope $- \frac{1}{3}\sqrt{3}$.   **5.** Slope 0.   **7.** Slope $\frac{1}{2}\sqrt{3}$.

9. Slope $- 3$.   **21.** Arctan $2\sqrt{3}$.   **23.** $\frac{1}{2}\pi$.

Exercise 46. Page 172

1. $\dfrac{dr}{dt} = -2\sin\theta$; $v_x = -2\sin 2\theta$; $v_y = 2\cos 2\theta$; $a_x = -2\cos 2\theta$; $a_y = -2\sin 2\theta$.

3. $\dfrac{dr}{dt} = \tfrac{1}{2}\cos\theta$; $v_x = \tfrac{1}{2}(\cos 2\theta - \sin\theta)$; $v_y = \tfrac{1}{2}(\cos\theta + \sin 2\theta)$;

$a_x = -\tfrac{1}{8}(2\sin 2\theta + \cos\theta)$; $a_y = \tfrac{1}{8}(2\cos 2\theta - \sin\theta)$.

5. $\dfrac{dr}{dt} = -\tfrac{1}{10}\sin\theta$; $v_x = -\tfrac{1}{10}(3\sin\theta + \sin 2\theta)$; $v_y = \tfrac{1}{10}(3\cos\theta + \cos 2\theta)$;

$a_x = -\tfrac{1}{100}(3\cos\theta + 2\cos 2\theta)$; $a_y = -\tfrac{1}{100}(3\sin\theta + 2\sin 2\theta)$.

Exercise 47. Page 173

1. $(9x^2 - 1)\sin 2(3x^3 - x)$.

3. $\dfrac{2\cos 2x}{1 + \sin^2 2x}$.

5. $3e^{3x}\sec e^{3x}\tan e^{3x}$.

7. $\dfrac{2e^{2t}}{\sqrt{1 - e^{4t}}}$.

9. $e^{3x}(3\sin 4x + 4\cos 4x)$.

11. $-12e^{3\cos 4x}\sin 4x$.

13. $\sin\dfrac{3}{x} - \dfrac{3}{x}\cos\dfrac{3}{x}$.

15. $\dfrac{\sin t - 1 - t(\ln t)\cos t}{t(\sin t - 1)^2}$.

17. $-3\tan x + 2\cot x$.

19. $\dfrac{2}{(2z - 3)\sqrt{\ln(2z - 3)^2}}$.

21. $\dfrac{2}{x\sqrt{1 - 4(\ln x)^2}}$.

23. $y' = \dfrac{1}{x(2y - e^y)}$.

25. $\dfrac{e^x - e^{-x}}{3 + e^{2x} + e^{-2x}}$.

27. $4(\cos 4z)\text{Arcsin } 2z + \dfrac{2\sin 4z}{\sqrt{1 - 4z^2}}$.

29. $y' = \dfrac{\cos(x + y) - \sec^2(x + 2y)}{2\sec^2(x + 2y) - \cos(x + y)}$.

31. $(\ln x)^{\cos x - 1}\left\{\dfrac{\cos x}{x} - (\sin x)(\ln x)[\ln(\ln x)]\right\}$.

33. 6.

35. $\dfrac{12x}{2x^2 + 5} + \dfrac{10\cos 2x}{\sin 2x - 1}$.

37. $\dfrac{2\{1 - [\ln(\ln x)](\ln x + 1)\}}{x^2(\ln x)^2}$.

39. Max. at $x = 0$; min. at $x = \pi$.

41. Max. at $x = 2.747$; min. at $x = 5.888$.

43. Max. at $x = \tfrac{1}{4}\pi$ and $x = \tfrac{5}{4}\pi$.

45. Incr., $1.15°$ p.s.

47. $e^{-2x}\left[\dfrac{1}{x\ln x} - 2\ln(\ln x)\right]dx$.

49. $10^{2x}[2(\ln 10)\cot 3x - 3\csc^2 3x]dx$.

51. $\dfrac{3[\csc x + \csc x\sec x + (\sin x)\ln\tan x]}{(1 + \cos x)^3}$.

53. 1414 cu. ft.

55. $y = x + \tfrac{1}{2}\pi\sqrt{2}$; $x + y = 2\sqrt{2}$; downward.

57. Decr. $.0709h$ atom p.h.; $.0142h$ atom.

59. 1; at $(0, 3)$, tangent $\tfrac{1}{3}$; at $(-\tfrac{3}{2}, 0)$, tangent $\tfrac{1}{2}$.

61. Ver. at $0, \pi$; hor. at 1.911 and 4.373.

63. $\dfrac{h\sin\alpha}{\sin\alpha + \cos 2\alpha}$.

Exercise 48. Page 179

1. $\xi = 4$.

3. $\xi = 1$.

Exercise 49. Page 182

1. 0.　**3.** $+\infty$.　**5.** 0.　**7.** 0.　**9.** 1.　**11.** 0.

13. -1.　**15.** ∞.　**17.** $-\infty$.　**19.** $-\infty$.　**21.** $+\infty$.　**23.** 0.

25. -2.　**27.** $\tfrac{1}{2}$.　**29.** 1.　**31.** $\tfrac{1}{12}$.　**33.** $-\infty$.　**35.** $\tfrac{1}{2}$.

37. $\tfrac{1}{4}$.　**39.** 1.　**41.** 0.　**43.** -3.　**45.** 1.　**47.** $-\tfrac{1}{2}$.

49. $\tfrac{2}{3}$.　**51.** $-\infty$.　**53.** $\tfrac{1}{5}$.　**55.** 0.　**57.** -1.

Exercise 50. Page 186

1. 0. **3.** 1. **5.** 0. **7.** 2. **9.** 1. **11.** 0.
13. $\frac{3}{2}$. **15.** $-\infty$. **17.** e^{12}. **19.** 1. **21.** e^{-6}. **23.** e^2.
25. 0. **27.** 1. **29.** $e^{-2/\pi}$. **31.** $\frac{1}{2}$. **33.** 0. **35.** $-\infty$.
37. 2. **39.** ∞. **41.** $\sec^2\alpha$. **43.** $\frac{1}{3}$. **45.** $-\infty$. **47.** e^{-3}. **49.** $-\infty$. **51.** 0.

Exercise 51. Page 191

1. 3.3125. **3.** 7.35. **5.** 1.78.

Exercise 52. Page 193

1. 25. **3.** b^3. **5.** $e^b - e^a$.

Exercise 53. Page 195

1. 1.375; 1.344. **3.** 11; $10\frac{3}{4}$.

Exercise 54. Page 200

1. $\frac{2}{5}x^5$. **3.** $-\frac{5}{2}x^{-2}$. **5.** $\frac{1}{2}x^6 - \frac{2}{3}x^3 - \frac{4}{3}x^{\frac{3}{2}} + 6x$. **7.** 56. **9.** -80.
11. $8\frac{1}{4}$. **13.** 52. **15.** $\frac{9}{2}$. **17.** $10\frac{2}{3}$. **19.** 4; $5\frac{3}{4}$. **21.** $\frac{2}{3}$.

Exercise 55. Page 203

1. 18. **3.** $\frac{9}{2}$. **5.** 36. **7.** 3. **9.** $189\frac{1}{3}$. **11.** $21\frac{1}{12}$.
13. $\frac{8}{5}$. **15.** $2\frac{2}{3}$. **17.** $\frac{16}{3}\sqrt{6}$. **19.** 2. **21.** 16.

Exercise 56. Page 207

1. $\frac{4}{3}\pi r^3$. **3.** $\frac{128}{7}\pi$. **5.** $\frac{81}{10}\pi$. **7.** 32π.
9. $\frac{243}{5}\pi$. **11.** 12π. **13.** 13π. **15.** $\frac{1}{3}\pi a^2 h$.

Exercise 57. Page 213

Note. In this answer book, an arbitrary constant C should be added to each indefinite integral which is given.

7. $-\frac{1}{4}x^{-2}$. **9.** $-\frac{4}{3}x^{-\frac{1}{4}}$. **11.** $-u^{-2} - 3u^{-1}$. **13.** $-\frac{9}{2}u^{-2} - 4u^{-\frac{3}{2}} - u^{-1}$.
15. $-\frac{1}{4}(3 + t)^{-4}$. **17.** $-\frac{1}{16}(3 - 4x)^4$. **19.** $\frac{2}{15}(2 + 5x)^{\frac{3}{2}}$. **21.** $\frac{1}{24}(3x^2 + 1)^4$.
23. $-\frac{1}{12}(3u + 2)^{-4}$. **25.** $-\frac{2}{3}(3 - 5z)^{\frac{1}{2}}$. **27.** $\frac{1}{4}\sin 4x$. **29.** $\frac{1}{2}(1 - \sqrt{2})$.
31. $\frac{1}{3}\tan 3x$. **33.** $-4\cot\frac{1}{4}t$. **35.** $\frac{1}{16}(x^2 + 2x - 3)^8$. **37.** $\frac{1}{9}(3v^2 + 2)^{\frac{3}{2}}$.
39. $-\frac{1}{4}\cos^4 x$. **41.** $-\frac{1}{5}\cot^5 x$. **43.** $\frac{1}{9}\sin^3 3x$. **45.** $-\frac{1}{20}(2 + 5\cos x)^4$.
47. $\frac{1}{35}(3 + 5e^t)^7$. **49.** $\frac{1}{3}\tan y^3$. **51.** $\frac{1}{3}\sin x^3$. **53.** $(\sin mx)/m$.
55. $-(\cot au)/a$. **57.** $-3\cot x$. **59.** $-\frac{1}{6}\sin^{-3} 2x$. **61.** $-\frac{1}{6}\tan^{-3} 2t$.
63. $\frac{2}{3}(2 - 3\cos t)^{\frac{1}{2}}$. **65.** $-\cos(t^2 + t)$. **67.** $\frac{1}{3}(\text{Arctan } x)^3$. **69.** $\frac{3}{4}(\sin t)^{\frac{4}{3}}$.
71. $-\frac{1}{4}\tan^{-4} u$. **73.** $-(e^x + e^{-x})^{-1}$. **75.** $(2t^5 + \cos t)^8$.
77. $\dfrac{(\sec u)e^{u^2}\,du}{\ln u}$. **79.** $\sqrt{2} - 1$. **81.** $\frac{19}{3}$.

Exercise 58. Page 217

1. $\frac{1}{3}e^{3x}$. **3.** $(10^x)/\ln 10$. **5.** $\frac{1}{5}e^{2+5x}$. **7.** $a^x e^x/(1 + \ln a)$. **9.** $-\frac{1}{2}e^{-2x}$.
11. $-8e^{-\frac{1}{2}x}$. **13.** $-\frac{1}{3}e^{-x^3}$. **15.** $2e^{\sqrt{x}}$. **17.** $-\frac{1}{2}e^{-x^2}$. **19.** $\frac{2}{3}e^{x\sqrt{x}}$.
21. $10^{cx}/(c\ln 10)$. **23.** $-e^{1/x}$. **25.** $e^{\sin u}$. **27.** $\frac{1}{2}e^{2x} + 2e^{-x} - \frac{1}{4}e^{-4x}$.
29. e^{x^2-x+3}. **31.** $e^{-1} - 1$. **33.** $\frac{1}{6}(3 + 4e^x)^{\frac{3}{2}}$. **35.** $\frac{1}{6}(2 - 3e^u)^{-2}$.
37. $\frac{1}{2}e^{\text{Arctan } y}$. **39.** $e^2 - e^{-1}$. **41.** $\frac{1}{2}(1 - e^{-1})$. **43.** $\frac{1}{2}\pi(e^4 - e^{-2})$. **45.** $e^{\frac{3}{2}} - e^{\frac{1}{2}}$.

Exercise 59. Page 219

1. 1.25276. **3.** $\frac{1}{2}\ln|2t + 1|$. **5.** $\ln(1 + x^2)$. **7.** $-\frac{1}{2}\ln|1 - 2\tan x|$.
9. $\frac{1}{4}\ln|1 + 4\sec t|$. **11.** $\ln|\sin u|$. **13.** $-\frac{1}{2}\ln|\cos 2t|$.

15. $\frac{1}{3}t^3 + \frac{1}{2}t^2 - 3t + 9\ln|t+3|.$ **17.** $\ln|3x^2 + 2x + 5|.$ **19.** $\ln|e^x - e^{-x}|.$
21. $\frac{1}{8}\ln(3 + 4e^{2u}).$ **23.** $\frac{1}{3}\ln|2 + \tan 3t|.$ **25.** $\ln|2 + \ln y|.$
27. $-\frac{1}{2}\ln(1 + \cos^2 u).$ **29.** $\frac{1}{2}e^x - \frac{1}{4}\ln(1 + 2e^x).$ **31.** $\ln(5 + \sin^2 x).$
33. $\ln|\text{Arctan } x|.$ **35.** $6.438.$ **37.** $.432.$

Exercise 60.   Page 222

1. $\frac{1}{2}\ln|\sec 2x|.$ **3.** $4\ln|\sin \frac{1}{4}x|.$ **5.** $-\frac{1}{4}\cot 4t.$ **7.** $\ln|\csc v - \cot v|.$
9. $\frac{1}{3}\sin 3v.$ **11.** $2\sec \frac{1}{2}x.$ **13.** $a^{-1}\ln|\sec ax + \tan ax|.$
15. $\frac{1}{2}x + \frac{1}{4}\sin 2x.$ **17.** $\frac{1}{2}x + \frac{1}{12}\sin 6x.$ **19.** $-x - \cot x.$ **21.** $\frac{1}{2}x + \frac{1}{2}\sin x.$
23. $\frac{1}{4}\tan 4u - u.$ **25.** $2\tan y - 2\sec y - y.$ **27.** $\frac{1}{3}\ln|4 + 3\tan t|.$
29. $-.34658.$ **31.** $\frac{1}{2}\tan 2t - \ln|\sec 2t + \tan 2t| + t.$
33. $\frac{19}{2}x - \frac{1}{4}\sin 2x + 6\cos x.$ **35.** $-\frac{1}{2}\ln|\sec 2e^{-x} + \tan 2e^{-x}|.$
37. $\ln|\sin(\ln x)|.$ **39.** $\frac{1}{2}\ln|\sec e^{2x}|.$ **41.** $-\cos(3x + x^2).$
43. $\frac{1}{2}\pi\sqrt{2} - 2\ln(1 + \sqrt{2}).$ **45.** $\pi.$ **47.** $0.$ **49.** $2(\ln 2)/\pi.$

Exercise 61.   Page 224

1. $\frac{1}{2}\text{Arctan } \frac{1}{2}x.$ **3.** $\frac{1}{5}\text{Arcsin } \frac{5}{3}x.$ **5.** $\frac{1}{3}\text{Arcsin } \frac{3}{4}y.$ **7.** $\frac{1}{3}\pi.$ **9.** $\frac{5}{12}\pi.$ **11.** $-\frac{1}{4}\pi.$
13. $.237.$ **15.** $\frac{1}{14}\text{Arctan }(\frac{2}{7}\sin \theta).$ **17.** $\frac{1}{3}\text{Arctan } \frac{1}{3}x^3.$ **19.** $\frac{1}{4}\text{Arctan } \frac{1}{2}x^2.$
21. $2x - \frac{23}{5}\text{Arctan } \frac{2}{5}x.$ **23.** $\text{Arcsin}(\ln u).$ **25.** $\text{Arcsin } \frac{1}{2}(2 + x).$
27. $\frac{1}{30}\text{Arctan } \frac{5}{3}(2x + 3).$ **29.** $\frac{1}{3}\pi.$ **31.** $\frac{7}{72}\pi.$ **33.** $.785.$

Exercise 62.   Page 226

1. $\frac{1}{4}\ln\left|\dfrac{u-2}{u+2}\right|.$ **3.** $\frac{1}{24}\ln\left|\dfrac{4z-3}{4z+3}\right|.$ **5.** $-.20118.$ **7.** $.02939.$

9. $\frac{1}{30}\sqrt{5}\ln\left|\dfrac{3e^x - \sqrt{5}}{3e^x + \sqrt{5}}\right|.$ **11.** $\frac{1}{18}\ln\left|\dfrac{x^3 - 3}{x^3 + 3}\right|.$

13. $\frac{1}{12}\ln\left|\dfrac{1+3x}{3-3x}\right|.$ **15.** $\frac{1}{6}\ln\left|\dfrac{\tan x - 3}{\tan x + 3}\right|.$

Exercise 63.   Page 229

1. $\frac{2}{5}(2+x)^{\frac{5}{2}} - \frac{4}{3}(2+x)^{\frac{3}{2}}.$ **3.** $\frac{3}{28}(1+2x)^{\frac{7}{3}} - \frac{3}{16}(1+2x)^{\frac{4}{3}}.$
5. $-\frac{2}{3}(1-3x)^{\frac{1}{2}} + \frac{4}{9}(1-3x)^{\frac{3}{2}}.$ **7.** $\frac{1}{24}(3+4u)^{\frac{3}{2}} - \frac{3}{8}(3+4u)^{\frac{1}{2}}.$
9. $\frac{3}{20}(5+2x)^{\frac{5}{3}} - \frac{15}{8}(5+2x)^{\frac{2}{3}}.$ **11.** $-\frac{2}{5}(3-x)^{\frac{5}{3}} + \frac{9}{8}(3-x)^{\frac{8}{3}}.$
13. $\frac{1}{2}(1+4x)^{\frac{1}{2}} - (1+4x)^{-\frac{1}{2}}.$ **15.** $-\frac{644}{5}.$ **17.** $\frac{516}{5}.$ **19.** $\frac{2350}{9}\sqrt{5}.$

Exercise 64.   Page 231

1. $\ln(x + \sqrt{x^2 + 4}).$ **3.** $\ln(z + \sqrt{z^2 + 16}).$ **5.** $\frac{1}{3}\ln(3t + \sqrt{9t^2 + 25}).$
7. $\frac{1}{3}\ln|3t + \sqrt{9t^2 - 121}|.$ **9.** $\frac{1}{6}\ln(6y + \sqrt{36y^2 + 1}).$
11. $\ln(\tan t + \sqrt{\tan^2 t + 9}).$ **13.** $\frac{1}{2}\ln(\sin 2x + \sqrt{16 + \sin^2 2x}).$
15. $.874.$ **17.** $.218.$ **19.** $.303.$ **21.** $.188; .111.$

Exercise 65.   Page 233

1. $\frac{1}{2}\text{Arctan } \frac{1}{2}(x + 3).$ **3.** $\frac{1}{4}\ln\left|\dfrac{3+x}{1-x}\right|.$ **5.** $\text{Arcsin } \frac{1}{5}(x + 4).$

7. No real value for any x.   **9.** $\frac{1}{4}\text{Arctan } \frac{1}{2}(2t - 1).$

11. $\frac{1}{2}\ln|2x - 1 + \sqrt{4x^2 - 4x + 10}|.$ **13.** $\frac{1}{4}\ln\left|\dfrac{w}{4-w}\right|.$ **15.** $\text{Arcsin } \frac{1}{3}(x + 3).$

17. $\dfrac{\sqrt{2}}{12}\ln\left|\dfrac{3u+1-\sqrt{2}}{3u+1+\sqrt{2}}\right|.$ **19.** $\frac{1}{3}\text{Arcsin } \frac{1}{3}\sqrt{3}(3x + 2).$ **21.** $\text{Arctan }(2x - 3).$

23. $\frac{1}{2}\sqrt{2}\text{ Arcsin } \frac{1}{3}(4x - 1).$ **25.** $\frac{1}{2}\ln\left|\dfrac{\tan x + 1}{\tan x + 3}\right|.$

27. $4\sqrt{x^2 - 1} - 2 \ln | x + \sqrt{x^2 - 1} |$.

29. $\frac{1}{2} \text{Arctan } \frac{2}{3}x - \frac{5}{8} \ln (4x^2 + 9)$.

31. $\frac{3}{8} \ln \left| \dfrac{4 + z}{4 - z} \right| + 2 \ln | 16 - z^2 |$.

33. $\frac{1}{2}(1 - 16y^2)^{\frac{1}{2}} + \text{Arcsin } 4y$.

35. $-3 \ln | x^2 + 4x - 5 | + \frac{5}{2} \ln \left| \dfrac{x - 1}{x + 5} \right|$.

37. $\sqrt{4z^2 + 4z + 13} - \frac{7}{2} \ln | 2z + 1 + \sqrt{4z^2 + 4z + 13} |$.

39. $-8\sqrt{7 + 6x - x^2} + 29 \text{ Arcsin } \frac{1}{4}(x - 3)$.

41. $\frac{4}{3}\sqrt{24 + 6y - 9y^2} + \frac{7}{3} \text{ Arcsin } \frac{1}{5}(3y - 1)$.

Exercise 66. Page 236

5. $y = 2x^2 + 7x - 19$. **7.** $s = \cos t + 2 - \frac{1}{2}\sqrt{2}$. **9.** $y = \frac{1}{3}x^3 - x^2 - 18x + 60$.

11. $u = -\frac{1}{6}t^4 + \frac{5}{2}t^2 + \frac{7}{3}t + 4$. **13.** $s = \frac{3}{4}e^{2t} + c_1 t + c_2$. **15.** $y = -3x^2 - 12x - 7$.

17. $y = 4x^{-1}$. **19.** $y = 4\sqrt{x + 1} - 6$. **21.** $y = -\frac{1}{2}e^{-2x} + e^2 + \frac{1}{2}e^{-2}$.

23. $y = \frac{3}{2}x^2 - 3x + 3$. **25.** $y = x^3 - \frac{5}{2}x^2 + 7$.

Exercise 67. Page 239

1. $s = \frac{3}{2}t^2 + 4t + 2$. **3.** $s = -\frac{1}{6}t^3 + 3t + 2$. **5.** $s = \frac{1}{2}(t^3 + t^2 + t - 3)$.

7. $s = \frac{1}{4}t^4 + t^3 - 22t + 35$. **9.** $s = t^3 + \frac{3}{2}t^2 + 3t - 2$. **11.** 10 sec.; 400' p.s.

13. 20. **15.** At end 6 sec.; 72' upward. **17.** $\alpha = \frac{1}{4}\pi$.

Exercise 68. Page 242

1. $\ln | xy^2 | = c$, or $xy^2 = k$. **3.** $1 + x^2 = c(3 + y)^2$. **5.** $\sqrt{4 + x} + \sqrt{9 - y} = c$.

7. $\sqrt{1 + x^2} \sec y = c$. **9.** $\tan y - \cot x = c$. **11.** $3x^3 + cx^3y = y$.

13. $\csc y - \cot y = c(\csc x - \cot x)$. **15.** $\text{Arcsin } \frac{1}{2}y = \text{Arcsin } \frac{1}{3}x + c$.

17. $x^2 - 4y^2 = 9$. **19.** $x^2(y + 3) = 8$. **21.** $4x^2 + 9y^2 = 160$.

23. $(x - 3)(2y + 1) = 3$. **25.** $y^3 = x^2 + 60$.

27. $\ln | y | = c - \frac{1}{2}x^2$, or $y = ke^{-\frac{1}{2}x^2}$; then, $y = \dfrac{1}{\sqrt{2\pi}} e^{-\frac{1}{2}x^2}$.

Exercise 69. Page 243

1. $\frac{1}{56}(2x + 3)^{28}$. **3.** $\sqrt{2}$. **5.** $\frac{1}{3} \ln | \sec x^3 + \tan x^3 |$.

7. $\frac{1}{9}(1 - 3 \sin x)^{-3}$. **9.** $\frac{1}{3}(2 - 6z)^{-\frac{1}{2}}$. **11.** $\frac{1}{3} \ln | \sec 3v + \tan 3v |$.

13. $\frac{3}{2}\sqrt[3]{2}z^{\frac{1}{3}}$. **15.** $2x + \frac{3}{2} \ln (x^2 + 16) - 8 \text{ Arctan } \frac{1}{4}x$. **17.** $\frac{2}{5}$.

19. $-\frac{1}{2} \cot 2x - x$. **21.** $\frac{1}{4} \tan 4x - x$.

23. $\text{Arcsin } \frac{1}{3}(x + 2)$. **25.** $\dfrac{1}{2\sqrt{26}} \ln \left| \dfrac{2u + 4 - \sqrt{26}}{2u + 4 + \sqrt{26}} \right|$.

27. $\frac{1}{4} \ln | 7x - 3 - 2x^2 | + \frac{9}{4} \ln \left| \dfrac{2x - 1}{2x - 6} \right|$. **29.** $s = \frac{1}{2}t^3 + t^2 - \frac{11}{2}t + 7$.

Exercise 70. Page 247

1. $e^x(x - 1)$. **3.** $x \sin x + \cos x$. **5.** $-e^{-x}(x + 1)$.

7. $\frac{1}{24}\pi(3\sqrt{2} - 4) + \frac{1}{2}(\sqrt{3} - \sqrt{2})$. **9.** $\frac{1}{4}x^2(2 \ln x - 1)$.

11. $\frac{1}{3}x^3(3 \ln x - 1)$. **13.** $x^{n+1}[(n + 1)\ln x - 1]/(n + 1)^2$.

15. $\frac{1}{2}x^2 \sin 2x + \frac{1}{2}x \cos 2x - \frac{1}{4} \sin 2x$. **17.** $x \text{ Arcsin } 3x + \frac{1}{3}\sqrt{1 - 9x^2}$.

19. $2 \ln 2 - \pi$. **21.** $\frac{1}{2}x^2 \text{ Arccot } 2x + \frac{1}{4}x + \frac{1}{8} \text{ Arccot } 2x$.

23. $-x^3 \cos x + 3x^2 \sin x + 6x \cos x - 6 \sin x$.

25. $x \text{ Arcsin } 2x + \frac{1}{2}(1 - 4x^2)^{\frac{1}{2}}$. **27.** $-\dfrac{x \cos kx}{k} + \dfrac{\sin kx}{k^2}$.

29. $\dfrac{xa^x}{\ln a} - \dfrac{a^x}{(\ln a)^2}.$ **31.** $- e^{-2x}(\frac{1}{2}x^2 + \frac{1}{2}x + \frac{1}{4}).$ **33.** $x^2(4 + x^2)^{\frac{1}{2}} - \frac{2}{3}(4 + x^2)^{\frac{3}{2}}.$

35. $2x^{\frac{1}{2}} \text{ Arcsin } \sqrt{x} + 2(1 - x)^{\frac{1}{2}}.$ **37.** $- \dfrac{\ln x}{x + 2} + \frac{1}{2} \ln \left| \dfrac{x}{x + 2} \right|.$

39. $\sqrt{1 + x^2} \text{ Arctan } x - \ln | x + \sqrt{1 + x^2} |.$

41. $2\sqrt{x} \text{ Arccot } \sqrt{x} + \ln | 1 + x |.$ **43.** $\dfrac{e^x(\sin 3x - 3 \cos 3x)}{10}.$

45. $\dfrac{e^{-2x}(- 2 \sin x - \cos x)}{5}.$ **47.** $\dfrac{4e^{-2x}(- 2 \sin \frac{1}{2}x - \frac{1}{2} \cos \frac{1}{2}x)}{17}.$

49. $\dfrac{e^{ax}(a \sin bx - b \cos bx)}{a^2 + b^2}.$ **51.** $\dfrac{6e^{\frac{1}{2}x}(3 \cos \frac{1}{3}x + 2 \sin \frac{1}{3}x)}{13}.$

53. $(2e^{-1} - 4e^{-3}); \frac{1}{4}\pi(5e^{-2} - 25e^{-6}).$

57. $\frac{1}{4} \sin x \sec^4 x + \frac{3}{8} \sec x \tan x + \frac{3}{8} \ln | \sec x + \tan x |.$

Exercise 71. Page 250

1. $\frac{1}{4} \sin^4 x.$ **3.** $\frac{1}{2} \cos^{-2} x.$ **5.** $- \frac{1}{3} \cos^3 x + \frac{1}{5} \cos^5 x.$ **7.** $- \frac{3}{4} \cos \frac{2}{3}x.$

9. $\frac{1}{2}x - \frac{1}{12} \sin 6x.$ **11.** $\frac{1}{2}x - \frac{1}{2} \sin x.$ **13.** $- \cos x + \frac{2}{3} \cos^3 x - \frac{1}{5} \cos^5 x.$

15. $\cos x + \sec x.$ **17.** $\frac{1}{2} \ln | \sec 2x | + \frac{1}{8} \cos 4x.$ **19.** $\frac{3}{8}x - \frac{1}{4} \sin 2x + \frac{1}{32} \sin 4x.$

21. $\frac{3}{8}x - \frac{1}{32} \sin 4x.$ **23.** $\frac{1}{320} \sin^5 2x + \frac{3}{256}x - \frac{1}{256} \sin 4x + \frac{1}{2048} \sin 8x.$

25. $- \frac{1}{96} \sin^3 4x + \frac{1}{16}x - \frac{1}{128} \sin 8x.$ **27.** $\frac{3}{128}x - \frac{1}{384} \sin 12x + \frac{1}{3072} \sin 24x.$

29. $\frac{1}{4} \sin 2x - \frac{1}{12} \sin 6x.$ **31.** $- \dfrac{1}{2(h + k)} \cos (h + k)x - \dfrac{1}{2(h - k)} \cos (h - k)x.$

33. $- \frac{1}{2} \cot 2x - \frac{3}{2}x - \frac{1}{8} \sin 4x.$ **35.** $\frac{1}{8} \tan^4 2x.$

37. $\frac{1}{8} \sin^4 2x.$ **39.** $- \frac{1}{2} \cot x.$ **41.** $- \cot \frac{1}{2}z.$

43. $\pm \frac{1}{4}\sqrt{2} \ln | \csc 2x - \cot 2x |$, where "$+$" applies if $(\sin 2x) > 0.$

45. $4\sqrt{2}.$ **47.** $4\sqrt{2}.$

Exercise 72. Page 252

1. $\frac{1}{2} \tan 2x - x.$ **3.** $- \frac{1}{2} \cot^2 y - \ln | \sin y |.$

5. $\frac{1}{4} \tan^4 x - \frac{1}{2} \tan^2 x + \ln | \sec x |.$

7. $- \frac{1}{2} \cot^4 \frac{1}{2}x + \cot^2 \frac{1}{2}x + 2 \ln | \sin \frac{1}{2}x |.$ **9.** $- \cot x - \frac{2}{3} \cot^3 x - \frac{1}{5} \cot^5 x.$

11. $\frac{1}{3} \tan 3x + \frac{1}{9} \tan^3 3x.$ **13.** $\frac{1}{3} \tan^3 t + \frac{1}{5} \tan^5 t.$

15. $- \frac{1}{8} \cot^4 2t - \frac{1}{4} \cot^2 2t.$ **17.** $\frac{1}{5} \sec^5 \theta - \frac{1}{3} \sec^3 \theta.$ **19.** $\frac{1}{21} \sec^7 3l - \frac{1}{15} \sec^5 3l.$

21. $- \frac{1}{18} \cot^9 2x - \frac{1}{7} \cot^7 2x - \frac{1}{10} \cot^5 2x.$ **23.** $- \cot x + \tan x.$

25. $\frac{1}{8} \tan^4 2x + \frac{1}{4} \tan^2 2x.$ **27.** $- \frac{1}{4} \cot^4 y - \frac{1}{6} \cot^6 y.$ **29.** $\frac{1}{4} \tan^4 x.$

31. $\frac{1}{5} \tan^5 \theta - \frac{1}{3} \tan^3 \theta + \tan \theta - \theta.$ **33.** $- \frac{1}{11} \cot^{\frac{11}{2}} 2x - \frac{2}{7} \cot^{\frac{7}{2}} 2x - \frac{1}{3} \cot^{\frac{3}{2}} 2x.$

35. $- \frac{1}{3} \cot^3 x - \frac{1}{5} \cot^5 x.$ **37.** $\frac{1}{2} \tan^2 x + \ln | \tan x |.$

39. $- \frac{1}{6} \cot^3 2x - \frac{1}{2} \cot 2x.$ **41.** $- \cos x + \frac{1}{3} \cos^3 x.$ **43.** $\frac{2}{5} \sec^{\frac{5}{2}} x - 2 \sec^{\frac{1}{2}} x.$

45. $\frac{1}{4} \sec 2x \tan 2x + \frac{1}{4} \ln | \sec 2x + \tan 2x |.$ **47.** $2 \sin \frac{1}{2}x - \frac{2}{3} \sin^3 \frac{1}{2}x.$

49. $- \frac{1}{2}x \cot 2x - \frac{1}{6}x \cot^3 2x + \frac{1}{6} \ln | \sin 2x | - \frac{1}{24} \cot^2 2x.$

51. $\frac{1}{2}z \sec^3 z - \frac{1}{6} \sec z \tan z - \frac{1}{6} \ln | \sec z + \tan z |.$

Exercise 73. Page 255

1. $\dfrac{x}{9\sqrt{9 - x^2}}.$ **3.** $\sqrt{x^2 - 9} - 3 \text{ Arctan } \frac{1}{3}\sqrt{x^2 - 9}.$ **5.** $\frac{1}{3} \ln \left| \dfrac{\sqrt{9 + 4y^2} - 3}{2y} \right|.$

7. $\ln \left| \dfrac{1 - \sqrt{1 - 9y^2}}{3y} \right|.$ **9.** See (31), Table VII, to check.

11. $- \frac{1}{3}(4 + u^2)\sqrt{2 - u^2}.$ **13.** $\frac{1}{54} \text{ Arctan } \dfrac{x}{3} + \dfrac{x}{18(9 + x^2)}.$

15. See (50), Table VII.   **17.** $\frac{4}{3}\sqrt{3} - \frac{1}{2}\pi$.

19. $\frac{1}{2}x\sqrt{a^2 + 9x^2} + \frac{1}{6}a^2 \ln (3x + \sqrt{a^2 + 9x^2})$.   **21.** See (27), Table VII.

23. $(x + 2)/9\sqrt{5 - x^2 - 4x}$.   **25.** $\frac{1}{8}x\sqrt{4x^2 - 49} + \frac{49}{16} \ln | 2x + \sqrt{4x^2 - 49} |$.

27. $\dfrac{\tan t}{4\sqrt{4 - \tan^2 t}}$.   **29.** $-\dfrac{3}{8(9 + 4x^2)} + \dfrac{5}{108} \text{Arctan} \dfrac{2x}{3} + \dfrac{5x}{18(9 + 4x^2)}$.

31. $\dfrac{16x^3 + 150x + 625}{1250(4x^2 + 25)^{\frac{3}{2}}}$.   **33.** $\frac{1}{9}(3 - x)(4x^2 - 24x + 27)^{-\frac{1}{2}}$.

35. $-\dfrac{39x + 28}{9\sqrt{9x^2 + 12x + 5}}$.

37. $\frac{2}{3}(4x^2 - 4x)^{\frac{3}{2}} - \frac{1}{4}(2x - 1)(4x^2 - 4x)^{\frac{1}{2}} + \frac{1}{4} \ln | 2x - 1 + \sqrt{4x^2 - 4x} |$.   **41.** πab.

Exercise 74.   Page 258

1. 12.   **3.** 2.1589.   **5.** $\frac{937}{12}$.   **7.** $\frac{1}{2}$.   **9.** $\frac{32}{15}\sqrt{2}$.

11. 1.555.   **13.** $\frac{3}{8}\pi a^2$.   **15.** $2\pi a^2$.   **17.** $\frac{192}{5}\sqrt{3}$.

Exercise 75.   Page 260

1. $\frac{3}{2}\pi$.   **3.** π.   **5.** $\frac{3}{2}\pi a^2$.   **7.** $\frac{3}{8}\pi$.   **9.** 2.   **11.** 6.

13. $\frac{1}{6}\pi^3 k^2$.   **15.** $2a^2/3\pi$.   **17.** $\frac{4}{3}\pi - \sqrt{3}$.   **19.** $\frac{7}{24}\pi - \frac{1}{2}\sqrt{3}$.

21. $\sqrt{3} - \frac{1}{3}\pi$.   **23.** 11π.   **25.** $\frac{5}{24}\pi - \frac{1}{4}\sqrt{3}$.   **27.** $4\pi + 12\sqrt{3}$.

Exercise 76.   Page 263

1. $\frac{1}{3}$.   **3.** Div.   **5.** Div.   **7.** $\frac{1}{8}\pi$.   **9.** 2.   **11.** .463.   **13.** Div.

15. Div.   **17.** $\frac{1}{4}\pi$.   **19.** Div.   **21.** 1.   **23.** 1.   **25.** 1.

Exercise 77.   Page 266

1. $2\sqrt{2}$.   **3.** Div.   **5.** $3\sqrt[3]{5}$.   **7.** 2.   **9.** $\frac{1}{6}\pi$.   **11.** Div.   **13.** Div.

15. 1.09861.   **17.** $1/(1 - k)$.   **19.** Div.   **21.** $\frac{2}{3}\pi$.   **23.** $a^2(\frac{1}{6}\pi + \frac{1}{8}\sqrt{3})$.

25. Div.   **27.** $\frac{2}{9}\pi$.   **29.** $\frac{1}{4}\pi$.   **31.** Div.

Exercise 78.   Page 269

1. 96.   **3.** 144π; 2304; $288\sqrt{3}$.   **5.** $3\sqrt{3}$; $\frac{3}{2}\pi$; $\frac{3}{2}\pi$.   **7.** 288.

9. $\frac{2}{3}\pi$.   **11.** $5\pi r^2$.   **13.** 100π cu ft.   **15.** $\frac{16}{3}$; 8; does not exist.

Exercise 79.   Page 273

1. $\frac{256}{5}\pi$.   **3.** $\frac{16}{15}\pi$; $\frac{136}{15}\pi$.   **5.** $(259\frac{1}{5})\pi$.   **7.** $\frac{9}{2}\pi$; $\frac{48}{7}\pi$; $\frac{96}{35}\pi$.

9. $\frac{512}{5}\pi$; $\frac{2560}{7}\pi$; $\frac{128}{5}\pi$.   **11.** $\pi[\frac{8}{3}\pi + 8 \ln (2 - \sqrt{3}) + 2\sqrt{3}]$.

13. $\frac{32}{105}\pi a^3$.   **15.** $\frac{5}{12}\pi$.   **17.** $\frac{1}{5}\pi$.   **19.** $\frac{1}{2}\pi$.   **21.** 2π.

23. Does not exist.   **25.** $\frac{1}{8}\pi a^3$.   **27.** $\pi a^3(2 - \frac{5}{8}\pi)$.

Exercise 80.   Page 277

1. 120π; 140π.   **3.** 216π; 360π.   **5.** $6\pi e^4$.   **7.** $\frac{4}{3}\pi(125 - 10\sqrt{10})$.   **9.** $2\pi^2 a^3$.

13. $\frac{2}{3}\pi^2 a^3$.   **15.** 8π.   **17.** $8\pi \ln \frac{5}{2}$; $4\pi(\text{Arctan} 2 - \frac{1}{10} - \frac{1}{4}\pi)$.   **19.** $\frac{5}{12}\pi$.

Exercise 81.   Page 282

1. 50,000 ft.-lb.   **3.** 8250 ft.-lb.   **5.** 2.232(10^6) ft.-lb.

7. $3.6\pi(10^6)$ft.-lb.; $3.2\pi(10^6)$ft.-lb.   **9.** 67.5 ft.-lb.   **11.** $\dfrac{6,348,800}{9} \pi$ ft.-lb.

13. 2.24(10^6)π ft.-lb.   **15.** $ke_1 e_2 \left(\dfrac{1}{b} - \dfrac{1}{a}\right)$.   **17.** 15,000 ln 3 in.-lb.

Exercise 82.   Page 288

1. $\frac{67}{13}$.   **3.** $(\frac{19}{14}, \frac{25}{7})$.   **5.** $\frac{107}{21}$.   **7.** $7e^8/(e^8 - e)$.

9. $\frac{15}{2}$ units from the end where the density is greatest.   **11.** $\frac{1}{3}$.   **13.** $\frac{1}{2}\pi$.

Exercise 83. Page 294

1. $\ln (x - 4)^4 | 2x + 1 |^{-\frac{3}{2}}$.

3. 1.28093.

5. -1.46274.

7. $2x + \ln | (x - 2)^3(x + 2)^5 |$.

9. $\ln | x - 1 | - 2(x - 1)^{-1} - (x - 1)^{-2}$.

11. $-\frac{5}{3}(t + 2)^{-3}$.

13. $\ln | t + 2 |^3 + 2(t + 2)^{-1} - \frac{1}{2}(t + 2)^{-2}$.

15. $\ln | x^2(x - 1)^{-1} | - (x - 1)^{-1} + (x - 1)^{-2}$.

17. $\frac{1}{2}x^2 + 2x + 3 \ln | x | - (x - 3)^{-1}$.

19. $\ln | (x + 2)(3x - 1)^{\frac{1}{3}}(x - 1)^{-2} |$.

21. $\ln (x - 1)^{-2}(3x + 2)^{-\frac{2}{3}} - 3(x - 1)^{-1} - \frac{1}{3}(3x + 2)^{-1}$.

Exercise 84. Page 295

1. $\ln | (x + 1) (x^2 + 3) | + \sqrt{3} \text{ Arctan } \frac{1}{3}x\sqrt{3}$.

3. $\ln (2x - 5)^2(x^2 + 2)^{-\frac{1}{2}} + \frac{3}{2}\sqrt{2} \text{ Arctan } \frac{1}{2}x\sqrt{2}$.

5. $\ln | (x - 2)^3(x^2 + 2x + 4)^{\frac{1}{2}} | - \frac{2}{3}\sqrt{3} \text{ Arctan } \frac{1}{3}\sqrt{3}(x + 1)$.

7. $\ln (2x^2 + 3)^{\frac{1}{2}}(x^2 + 5)^{\frac{3}{2}} + \frac{1}{6}\sqrt{6} \text{ Arctan } \frac{1}{3}x\sqrt{6}$.

9. $\ln (x^2 + 1)(4x^2 + 7)^{-\frac{1}{8}} + \frac{1}{7}\sqrt{7} \text{ Arctan } \frac{2}{7}x\sqrt{7}$.

11. $y^2 + \ln (2y + 1)^{-\frac{1}{2}}(4y^2 - 2y + 1)^{\frac{1}{4}} + \frac{1}{2}\sqrt{3} \text{ Arctan } \frac{1}{3}\sqrt{3}(4y - 1)$.

13. $3.2189 - \frac{1}{4}\pi$.

15. $.2027$.

17. $- \text{ Arctan } \frac{1}{2}x + \frac{3\sqrt{5}}{10} \ln \left| \frac{x + \sqrt{5}}{x - \sqrt{5}} \right|$.

Exercise 85. Page 297

1. $\frac{5}{54} \text{ Arctan } \frac{x}{3} + \frac{5x - 36}{18(9 + x^2)}$.

3. $\frac{y}{18(4y^2 + 9)} + \frac{1}{108} \text{ Arctan } \frac{2y}{3}$.

5. $(x^2 + 2)^{-1} + \ln (2 + x^2)^{\frac{1}{2}} + \frac{1}{2}\sqrt{2} \text{ Arctan } \frac{1}{2}x\sqrt{2}$.

7. $3 \ln | x - 1 | + \frac{9x - 2}{2(x^2 + 3)} + \frac{3}{2} \sqrt{3} \text{ Arctan } \frac{x}{\sqrt{3}}$.

9. $- \frac{1}{2(x^2 + 3)^2} - \frac{x}{3(x^2 + 3)} + \frac{14}{9} \sqrt{3} \text{ Arctan } \frac{x}{\sqrt{3}}$.

Exercise 86. Page 299

1. $\frac{1}{4} \ln \left| \frac{2 + \tan \frac{1}{2}y}{2 - \tan \frac{1}{2}y} \right|$.

3. $\frac{2}{1 - \tan \frac{1}{2}x}$.

5. $\frac{2}{5} \text{ Arctan } \frac{1}{5}$.

7. $\frac{1}{6} \ln | \tan \frac{3}{2}x | - \frac{1}{12} \tan^2 \frac{3}{2}x$.

9. $\frac{2}{3}\sqrt{3} \ln (1 + \sqrt{3})$.

11. $\frac{1}{8}\sqrt{2} \ln \left| \frac{\tan x + \sqrt{2}}{\tan x - \sqrt{2}} \right|$.

13. $\ln 2$.

15. $- \frac{1}{4} \cot^2 \frac{1}{2}x - \frac{1}{2} \ln | \tan \frac{1}{2}x |$.

17. $\frac{1}{2(1 + \tan x)^2} - \frac{1}{2(1 + \tan x)} + \frac{1}{4} \ln \left| \frac{1 + \tan x}{1 - \tan x} \right|$.

19. $\frac{-4}{5 + \tan \frac{1}{4}x}$.

21. $- \frac{1}{2} \text{ Arctan } (\tan \frac{1}{2}z) + \frac{5}{6} \text{ Arctan } (3 \tan \frac{1}{2}z)$.

Exercise 87. Page 302

1. $2x^{\frac{1}{2}} - 6x^{\frac{1}{3}} + 24x^{\frac{1}{6}} - 48 \ln (x^{\frac{1}{6}} + 2)$.

3. $\frac{1}{3}(9 + x^2)^{\frac{3}{2}} - 9(9 + x^2)^{\frac{1}{2}}$.

5. $\frac{2}{3}x^{\frac{3}{2}} + 8x^{\frac{1}{2}} + 4 \ln \left| \frac{\sqrt{x} - 1}{\sqrt{x} + 1} \right|$.

7. $3 - 3 \ln \frac{4}{3}$.

9. $\frac{2}{9}(4 + x^3)^{\frac{3}{2}} - \frac{8}{3}(4 + x^3)^{\frac{1}{2}}$.

11. $- \frac{1}{7}(1 + x^4)^{\frac{7}{4}}x^{-7}$.

13. $2\sqrt{2x} + 2\sqrt{x + 4} + 4\sqrt{2} \ln \left| \frac{\sqrt{x} - 2(\sqrt{x + 4} - 2\sqrt{2})}{x - 4} \right|$.

15. $x + \sqrt{1 + e^{2x}} - \ln (1 + \sqrt{1 + e^{2x}})$.

17. $3 \text{ Arcsin } \frac{1}{3}(x - 1) + \sqrt{8 + 2x - x^2}$.

19. $\dfrac{4\sqrt{1+4x^2}}{x} - \dfrac{(1+4x^2)^{\frac{3}{2}}}{3x^3}.$ **37.** $-\dfrac{\sqrt{1+4x^4}}{2x^2} + \dfrac{1}{2}\ln\left|\dfrac{\sqrt{1+4x^4}+2x^2}{\sqrt{1+4x^4}-2x^2}\right|.$

Exercise 88. Page 306

1. 9.03; exactly 9, the true value, by Simpson's rule (why).
3. 3.69; 3.68.   **5.** 1.401; 1.402.

Exercise 89. Page 310

1. $20\sqrt{10}-2.$ **3.** $\frac{1}{4}[6\sqrt{37}+\ln(6+\sqrt{37})].$ **5.** $\frac{1}{27}(80\sqrt{10}-8).$ **7.** $a(e-e^{-1}).$
9. $6a.$ **11.** $12\sqrt{3}.$ **13.** $\frac{14}{3}.$ **15.** $\frac{1}{2}[\sqrt{2}+\ln(1+\sqrt{2})].$ **17.** $\sqrt{2}(e-e^{-1}).$

Exercise 90. Page 312

1. $2\pi a.$ **3.** $8a.$ **5.** $\pi a\sqrt{2}.$ **7.** $\sqrt{1+k^2}(e^k-1)/k.$

9. $2a(\sqrt{7}-2)+2a\sqrt{3}\ln\dfrac{4+2\sqrt{3}}{\sqrt{3}+\sqrt{7}}.$

Exercise 91. Page 315

1. $\frac{1}{27}\pi(145\sqrt{145}-1).$ **5.** $4\pi^2 ab.$ **7.** $4\pi a^2.$ **9.** $\frac{56}{3}\pi.$
11. $\frac{1}{6}\pi[12\sqrt{145}+\ln(12+\sqrt{145})].$ **13.** $\frac{12}{5}\pi a^2.$
15. $\frac{32}{5}\pi.$ **17.** $4\pi[\sqrt{2}+\ln(1+\sqrt{2})].$
19. $\pi[32\sqrt{17}-16-8\sqrt{2}\ln(4+\sqrt{14})+8\sqrt{2}\ln(2+\sqrt{2})].$ **21.** $\frac{7424}{1215}\pi.$
23. $4\pi^2 a^2.$ **25.** $\pi[\sqrt{2}+\ln(1+\sqrt{2})].$ **27.** $2\pi ak$, where a is radius.

Exercise 92. Page 320

1. $\frac{1}{2}, 2.$ **3.** $\frac{3}{100}\sqrt{10}; \frac{10}{3}\sqrt{10}.$ **5.** $1, 1.$ **7.** $\frac{1}{4}\sqrt{2}, 2\sqrt{2}.$
9. $\frac{4}{25}\sqrt{5}, \frac{5}{4}\sqrt{5}.$ **11.** $\frac{3}{4}, \frac{4}{3}; \frac{9}{2}, \frac{9}{2}.$ **13.** $\frac{5}{4}, \frac{4}{5}.$ **15.** $\frac{1}{2}, 2.$
17. $\frac{6}{169}\sqrt{13}, \frac{13}{6}\sqrt{13}.$ **19.** $\frac{1}{3}, 3.$ **21.** $\frac{1}{4}, 4.$ **23.** $(\frac{1}{2}\sqrt{2}, -\frac{1}{2}\ln 2).$

25. On range $-\frac{1}{2}\pi < x < \frac{5}{2}\pi$, max. at $\frac{1}{2}\pi$ and $\frac{3}{2}\pi.$ **27.** $\dfrac{|p|^{\frac{1}{2}}}{|p+2x_1|^{\frac{3}{2}}}.$

29. $\dfrac{1}{|3a\sin t_1\cos t_1|}.$ **31.** $\frac{1}{3}, 3.$ **33.** $\frac{3}{4}, \frac{4}{3}; \frac{3}{4}\sqrt{2}, \frac{2}{3}\sqrt{2}.$
35. $\frac{3}{2}, \frac{2}{3}; \frac{3}{4}\sqrt{2}, \frac{2}{3}\sqrt{2}.$ **37.** $1/h, h; \sqrt{2}/4h, 2h\sqrt{2}.$

Exercise 93. Page 325

Note. The values of K will be omitted. Just R is given.
1. $(2, 2), 2.$ **3.** $(\frac{28}{3}, 12), \frac{10}{3}\sqrt{10}.$ **5.** $(1, 1), 1.$ **7.** $(3, -2), 2\sqrt{2}.$
9. $[\frac{1}{4}\pi - \frac{5}{2}, \frac{9}{4}], \frac{5}{4}\sqrt{5}.$ **11.** $(\frac{5}{3}, 0), \frac{4}{3}; (0, -\frac{5}{2}), \frac{9}{2}.$ **13.** $(0, \frac{29}{5}), \frac{4}{5}.$
15. $(\frac{1}{3}\pi - \sqrt{3}, 1 + \ln 2), 2.$ **17.** $(-\frac{11}{2}, \frac{16}{3}), \frac{13}{6}\sqrt{13}.$ **19.** $(2\sqrt{2}, 2\sqrt{2}), 3.$
21. $(-2, \pi), 4.$ **23.** $8(\alpha - 3)^3 = 81\beta^2.$ **25.** $(3\alpha)^{\frac{2}{3}} + (2\beta)^{\frac{2}{3}} = 5^{\frac{2}{3}}.$
27. $\alpha = a(\cos t)(\cos^2 t + 3\sin^2 t), \beta = a(\sin t)(\sin^2 t + 3\cos^2 t).$
29. $(\alpha + \beta)^{\frac{2}{3}} - (\alpha - \beta)^{\frac{2}{3}} = 8.$ **31.** $(a\alpha)^{\frac{2}{3}} - (b\beta)^{\frac{2}{3}} = (a^2 + b^2)^{\frac{2}{3}}.$
33. $\alpha^2 + \beta^2 = a^2.$ **35.** $(a\alpha)^{\frac{2}{3}} + (b\beta)^{\frac{2}{3}} = (a^2 - b^2)^{\frac{2}{3}}.$
37. $(\alpha + \beta)^{\frac{2}{3}} + (\alpha - \beta)^{\frac{2}{3}} = 2a^{\frac{2}{3}}.$

Exercise 94. Page 328

3. At origin, where R is least; max. is 16.

Exercise 95. Page 331

1. $\sqrt{29}.$ **3.** $\sqrt{21}.$ **5.** $\sqrt{29}.$ **7.** 3.   **9.** $\sqrt{14}.$

Exercise 96. Page 333

1. $\frac{2}{3} : -\frac{2}{3} : \frac{1}{3}.$ **3.** $\frac{9}{11} : \frac{6}{11} : -\frac{2}{11}.$ **5.** $-1 : 0 : 0.$
7. $\frac{2}{3} : \frac{2}{3} : -\frac{1}{3}.$ **9.** $\frac{3}{7} : -\frac{2}{7} : -\frac{6}{7}.$ **11.** $\frac{8}{17} : -\frac{12}{17} : \frac{9}{17}.$

13. Angles are $\frac{1}{2}\pi$, 0, $\frac{1}{2}\pi$; cosines $0 : 1 : 0$, for y-axis.
For negative x-axis, π, $\frac{1}{2}\pi$, $\frac{1}{2}\pi$; $-1 : 0 : 0$.

15. $\beta = \frac{1}{3}\pi$ or $\frac{2}{3}\pi$; $\cos\beta = \pm\frac{1}{2}$.

Exercise 97.   Page 335

1. $\pm\frac{3}{7} : \pm\frac{2}{7} : \mp\frac{6}{7}$.   **3.** $\pm\frac{6}{11} : \mp\frac{9}{11} : \mp\frac{2}{11}$.   **5.** $\mp\frac{10}{15} : \pm\frac{11}{15} : \mp\frac{2}{15}$.

7. $-3 : 5 : -6$.   **9.** $3 : -2 : 4$.   **11.** $-2 : 3 : 9$.

Exercise 98.   Page 338

1. $112.4°$.   **3.** $0°$.   **11.** $-6 : 4 : 7$.   **13.** $6 : 19 : 4$.   **15.** $-10 : -6 : 7$.

Exercise 100.   Page 341

1. $3x - y + 4z = -3$.   **3.** $-y + 2z = -2$.   **5.** $4x - y = 5$.

7. $2x - 3y + z = -11$.   **9.** $y = -1$.   **13.** $2x - y + z = -1$.

Exercise 101.   Page 343

11. $79.1°$.   **13.** $-14 : 22 : 3$.   **15.** $-14x + 22y + 3z = 27$.

17. N is $(p\cos\alpha, p\cos\beta, p\cos\gamma)$.   **21.** $\frac{9}{7}$.

Exercise 102.   Page 345

5. $x - y = -1$; $2y + 3z = 6$; $2x + 3z = 4$.   **7.** $(\frac{3}{2}, 1, 0)$.

9. $(0, 4, 3)$; $(4, 0, -3)$; $(2, 2, 0)$.

Exercise 103.   Page 347

3. $4x + 3y = 12$; $y = 4z - 4$.   **5.** $x = 2$; $3y - 4z = 4$.

7. $x = -1 + 2t, y = 2 - 3t, z = 3 + t$; $\dfrac{x+1}{2} = \dfrac{y-2}{-3} = \dfrac{z-3}{1}$.

9. $x = -t, y = -1 - 2t, z = 3 + 2t$; $\dfrac{x}{-1} = \dfrac{y+1}{-2} = \dfrac{z-3}{2}$.

11. $x = -1, y = -t, z = -3 + 3t$; $\dfrac{x+1}{0} = \dfrac{y}{-1} = \dfrac{z+3}{3}$.

13. $x = -3 + 3t, y = 1, z = -3t$; $\dfrac{x+3}{3} = \dfrac{y-1}{0} = \dfrac{z}{-3}$.

15. $x = 2 + 3t, y = -1 + 2t, z = 3 + 5t$; etc.

17. $\dfrac{x-2}{3} = \dfrac{y+1}{2} = \dfrac{z-3}{-1}$, etc.   **19.** $x = 2 - 3t, y = -1 - 2t, z = 2 + 5t$, etc.

21. $(4, 7, -1)$.   **23.** $\dfrac{x-\frac{2}{3}}{\frac{4}{3}} = \dfrac{y+5}{3} = \dfrac{z-\frac{1}{2}}{-\frac{5}{2}}$; through $(\frac{2}{3}, -5, \frac{1}{2})$.

25. $\dfrac{x-\frac{2}{5}}{-\frac{3}{5}} = \dfrac{y+\frac{3}{4}}{0} = \dfrac{z-\frac{1}{2}}{2}$; through $(\frac{2}{5}, -\frac{3}{4}, \frac{1}{2})$.

27. $\dfrac{x-\frac{1}{2}}{-3} = \dfrac{y-3}{4} = \dfrac{z}{-2}$; through $(\frac{1}{2}, 3, 0)$, as one possibility.

29. $\dfrac{x-\frac{1}{2}}{0} = \dfrac{y-\frac{9}{4}}{3} = \dfrac{z}{4}$, through $(\frac{1}{2}, \frac{9}{4}, 0)$.   **31.** $y + 4x = 7$.

33. $3 : -11$; $\cos\alpha = \pm\dfrac{3}{\sqrt{130}}$, $\cos\beta = \mp\dfrac{11}{\sqrt{130}}$.

35. $5 : 11$; $\cos\alpha = \pm\dfrac{5}{\sqrt{146}}$, $\cos\beta = \pm\dfrac{11}{\sqrt{146}}$.   **37.** $\dfrac{x+1}{3} = \dfrac{y-5}{-11}$.

39. $\dfrac{x+2}{5} = \dfrac{y+4}{11}$.   **41.** $\dfrac{x+1}{11} = \dfrac{y-5}{3}$.   **43.** $\dfrac{x+2}{11} = \dfrac{y+4}{-5}$.

Exercise 104.   Page 350

1. $(x-2)^2 + (y-5)^2 + (z-7)^2 = 4$.   **3.** $(-1, 3, 0)$; $\sqrt{15}$.

Exercise 105. Page 352

1. $x^2 + z^2 = 4y$.
7. $4y^2 - 9x^2 - 9z^2 = 36$.

3. $9x^2 + 4y^2 + 4z^2 = 36$.
9. Axis is z-axis.

5. $z^2 = 16x^2 + 16y^2$.
11. Axis is z-axis.

Exercise 107. Page 357

1. $x^2 + y^2 = 9$.

3. $x + y = 3$.

Exercise 108. Page 361

1. $u_x = 6xy + 12x^2y$; $u_y = 3x^2 + 4x^3$.
3. $w_x = 3e^{3x+2y}$; $w_y = 2e^{3x+2y}$.
5. $w_x = (6x + 3y)(x^2 + xy)^2$; $w_y = 3x(x^2 + xy)^2$.
7. $f_x = 9x(3x^2 - 2y)^{\frac{1}{2}}$; $f_y = -3(3x^2 - 2y)^{\frac{1}{2}}$.
9. $f_x = 4y \cos 4xy$; $f_y = 4x \cos 4xy$.
11. $G_x = -2ze^{-2x} + e^{-3z}$; $G_z = e^{-2x} - 3xe^{-3z}$
13. $H_x = 8(4x - 5y)\sec^2 (4x - 5y)^2$; $H_y = 10(5y - 4x)\sec^2 (4x - 5y)^2$.
15. $g_x = \dfrac{2(4x + 3z)10^{2x} \ln 10 - 4(10^{2x})}{(4x + 3z)^2}$; $g_z = \dfrac{-3(10^{2x})}{(4x + 3z)^2}$.
17. With f as the function, $f_x = e^y x^{-1}$; $f_y = e^y \ln x + e^z y^{-1}$; $f_z = e^z \ln y$.
19. 25; 42.
21. -36.
23. 8; 4.

Exercise 109. Page 362

1. $u_{xx} = 6xy^4$; $u_{yy} = 12x^3y^2$; $u_{xy} = 12x^2y^3$.
3. $u_{xx} = -4x^2y^2 \sin x^2y + 2y \cos x^2y$; $u_{yy} = -x^4 \sin x^2y$; $u_{xy} = 2x \cos x^2y - 2x^3y \sin x^2y$.
5. $w_{xx} = e^x \ln y$; $w_{xy} = e^x y^{-1}$; $w_{yy} = -e^x y^{-2}$.
7. $f_{xx} = 6x + 8y$; $f_{yy} = -6y$; $f_{xy} = 8x$.
9. $g_{xx} = -\dfrac{y^2}{(x^2 - y^2)^{\frac{3}{2}}}$; $g_{xy} = \dfrac{xy}{(x^2 - y^2)^{\frac{3}{2}}}$; $g_{yy} = -\dfrac{x^2}{(x^2 - y^2)^{\frac{3}{2}}}$.
11. $g_{xx} = -y^2z^2 \cos xyz$; $g_{xz} = -y \sin xyz - xy^2z \cos xyz$; etc.

Note. We shall use F hereafter as the function symbol where no symbol is given in the problem.

13. $F_{xx} = \dfrac{-2xy}{(x^2 + y^2)^2}$; $F_{xy} = \dfrac{x^2 - y^2}{(x^2 + y^2)^2}$; $F_{yy} = \dfrac{2xy}{(x^2 + y^2)^2}$.
15. $F_{yy} = -4 \cos (x + 2y - 3z)$; $F_{yz} = 6 \cos (x + 2y - 3z)$; etc.
17. $z_{xxy} = 4(\cos x^2y^2)(y - 2x^4y^5) - 20x^2y^3 \sin x^2y^2$; etc.
19. $-e^x \sin y$.

Exercise 110. Page 364

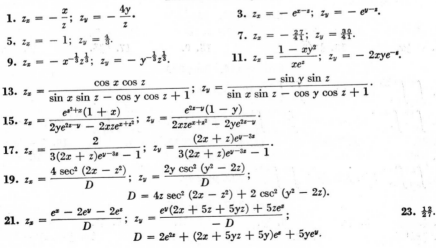

1. $z_x = -\dfrac{x}{z}$; $z_y = -\dfrac{4y}{z}$.

3. $z_x = -e^{x-z}$; $z_y = -e^{y-z}$.

5. $z_x = -1$; $z_y = \frac{4}{3}$.

7. $z_x = -\frac{27}{41}$; $z_y = \frac{30}{41}$.

9. $z_x = -x^{-\frac{1}{3}}z^{\frac{1}{3}}$; $z_y = -y^{-\frac{1}{3}}z^{\frac{1}{3}}$.

11. $z_x = \dfrac{1 - xy^2}{xe^z}$; $z_y = -2xye^{-z}$.

13. $z_x = \dfrac{\cos x \cos z}{\sin x \sin z - \cos y \cos z + 1}$; $z_y = \dfrac{-\sin y \sin z}{\sin x \sin z - \cos y \cos z + 1}$.

15. $z_x = \dfrac{e^{z^2+x}(1 + x)}{2ye^{2z-y} - 2xze^{x+z^2}}$; $z_y = \dfrac{e^{2z-y}(1 - y)}{2xze^{x+z^2} - 2ye^{2z-y}}$.

17. $z_x = \dfrac{2}{3(2x + z)e^{y-3z} - 1}$; $z_y = \dfrac{(2x + z)e^{y-3z}}{3(2x + z)e^{y-3z} - 1}$.

19. $z_x = \dfrac{4 \sec^2 (2x - z^2)}{D}$; $z_y = \dfrac{2y \csc^2 (y^2 - 2z)}{D}$;

$$D = 4z \sec^2 (2x - z^2) + 2 \csc^2 (y^2 - 2z).$$

21. $z_x = \dfrac{e^x - 2e^y - 2e^z}{D}$; $z_y = \dfrac{e^y(2x + 5z + 5yz) + 5ze^z}{-D}$;

$$D = 2e^{2z} + (2x + 5yz + 5y)e^z + 5ye^y.$$

23. $\frac{12}{27}$.

614

Exercise 111. Page 366

1. $y' = -\frac{9}{19}$; $z' = -\frac{13}{19}$.   **3.** $y' = \dfrac{x - 6z}{4z - y}$; $z' = \dfrac{2x - 3y}{4z - y}$.

5. $y' = \dfrac{6z - 2z^2 - xy - 2x^2}{4yz + x^2}$; $z' = \dfrac{4xy + 2y^2 + 3x - xz}{4yz + x^2}$.

7. $u_x = -11$; $v_y = -1$.   **9.** $u_x = \dfrac{1}{2u - 1}$; $v_y = \dfrac{u}{2uv - v}$.

11. $u_x = -\dfrac{u + 2u^2v}{x + 4uvx}$; $v_y = -\dfrac{v + 2uv^2}{y + 4uvy}$.

13. $u_x = \cos v$; $v_y = u^{-1}\cos v$.   **15.** $\dfrac{\partial x}{\partial u} = \frac{1}{3}$; $\dfrac{\partial y}{\partial v} = \frac{11}{3}$.

17. $\dfrac{\partial x}{\partial u} = 2u$; $\dfrac{\partial y}{\partial v} = 2v$.   **19.** $\dfrac{3\sin x - 2z\cos x}{4yz - 6}$.   **21.** $\left(\dfrac{\partial u}{\partial x}\right)_v = \dfrac{3 + 2xy}{y - 2u}$.

Exercise 112. Page 370

1. $du = 15x^2\,dx + 6xy^3\,dx + 9x^2y^2\,dy$.   **3.** $dv = \cos x \cos y\,dx - \sin x \sin y\,dy$.

5. $du = \dfrac{(\ln y)(\ln z)}{x}dx + \dfrac{(\ln x)(\ln z)}{y}dy + \dfrac{(\ln x)(\ln y)}{z}dz$.

7. $(2xy^4 + 9x^2)dx + 4x^2y^3\,dy$.   **9.** $e^{4x^2+y^2}(8x\,dx + 2y\,dy)$.

11. $4(x^2 + 3y + z^2)^3(2x\,dx + 3\,dy + 2z\,dz)$.

13. $\dfrac{x\,dx + y\,dy + z\,dz}{\sqrt{x^2 + y^2 + z^2}}$.   **15.** $e^y(z^2\,dx + xz^2\,dy + 2xz\,dz)$.

17. $\dfrac{2(\cos 2x)(1 + \cos y)dx + \sin 2x \sin y\,dy}{(1 + \cos y)^2}$.

19. $\dfrac{2x\,dx + 2y\,dy}{3(x^2 + y^2)}$.   **21.** $\dfrac{y^{-1}\,dx - xy^{-2}\,dy}{1 + x^2y^{-2}}$.

Exercise 113. Page 372

1. 45π cu. in.; 9%, or 45π cu. in.   **3.** 300π cu. in.; 1.8%.
5. $.434''$ and $.452''$.   **7.** Between 129.35 and 130.65.   **9.** 3%.   **11.** 4%.
13. 2%.   **15.** 2.685 sq. in.; .191 in.   **17.** p decr. by $\frac{1}{4}$ lb., or by $\frac{1}{2}\%$.

Exercise 114. Page 377

1. 69 square units.

Exercise 115. Page 379

1. $\frac{27}{2}$.   **3.** $\frac{1}{4}e^8 - \frac{5}{4}e^2$.   **5.** $\frac{38}{3}a^3 - 5a^2$.   **7.** $-\frac{8}{21}$.   **9.** $\frac{7}{96}\pi$.
11. $-\frac{1}{2}\pi$.   **13.** $\frac{1}{4}\sqrt{3} - \frac{1}{12}\pi$.   **15.** 0.   **17.** $\frac{397}{5}$.   **19.** $\frac{1}{2}\pi$.

Exercise 116. Page 383

1. $\displaystyle\int_0^3\int_{\frac{1}{3}x^2}^{\sqrt{3x}} F(x, y)dy\,dx$; $\displaystyle\int_0^3\int_{\frac{1}{3}y^2}^{\sqrt{3y}} F(x, y)dx\,dy$.

3. $\displaystyle\int_0^{\frac{1}{4}\pi}\int_{\sin x}^{\cos x} F(x, y)dy\,dx$; $\displaystyle\int_0^{\frac{1}{2}\sqrt{2}}\int_0^{\text{Arcsin } y} F(x, y)dx\,dy + \int_{\frac{1}{2}\sqrt{2}}^1\int_0^{\text{Arccos } y} F(x, y)dx\,dy$.

5. $\frac{16}{3}$.   **9.** $\frac{568}{3}$.   **11.** 4.   **13.** $e^3 - 1$.   **15.** $\frac{1}{2} - \frac{1}{2}e^{-1}$.
17. πa^2.   **19.** $\frac{1}{4}k$.   **21.** $\frac{1}{2}a^4$.   **23.** $\frac{1}{25}\ln 2$.   **25.** $\frac{211}{5}$.   **27.** πab.

31. $\displaystyle\int_{e^{-1}}^1\int_{-1}^{\ln y} F(x, y)dx\,dy + \int_1^e\int_{-1}^{-\ln y} F(x, y)dx\,dy$.

Exercise 117. Page 388

1. $\frac{1}{2}$.   **3.** $\frac{27}{2}$.   **5.** $\frac{22}{3}$.   **7.** $\frac{32}{21}$.   **9.** $\frac{26}{3}$.   **11.** 36.
13. $\frac{3}{4}\pi k^4$ **15.** 32.   **17.** $\frac{16}{3}a^3$.   **19.** $\frac{1}{3}\pi(3ah^2 - h^3)$.

Exercise 118. Page 393

1. $\int_{-\frac{1}{4}\pi}^{\frac{1}{4}\pi} \int_{3\sec\theta}^{4\cos\theta} rf(r,\theta)dr\,d\theta.$

3. $\int_0^{\frac{1}{4}\pi} \int_0^{2\sec\theta} rf(r,\theta)dr\,d\theta; \quad \int_0^2 \int_0^{\frac{1}{4}\pi} rf(r,\theta)d\theta\,dr + \int_2^{\frac{1}{4}\sqrt{3}} \int_{\text{Arccos }(2/r)}^{\frac{1}{4}\pi} rf(r,\theta)d\theta\,dr.$

7. $\frac{640}{3}\pi.$ **9.** $\frac{19}{2}.$ **11.** $(\pi+8);\ \frac{16}{3}k.$ **13.** $\frac{625}{384}k(20\pi+21\sqrt{3}).$

15. Area, $(\frac{1}{4}\sqrt{3}-\frac{1}{12}\pi);\ \frac{1}{48}k(2\pi+3\sqrt{3}).$ **17.** $\frac{1}{48}ku^3\sqrt{3}(4+3\ln 3).$ **19.** $\frac{32}{3}k.$

25. $\int_0^{\frac{1}{2}\sqrt{2}} \int_0^{\text{Arcsin }r} \cos^4\theta\,d\theta\,dr + \int_{\frac{1}{2}\sqrt{2}}^1 \int_0^{\text{Arccos }r} \cos^4\theta\,d\theta\,dr.$

Exercise 119. Page 396

1. $z=4r^2.$ **3.** $2r\cos\theta-r\sin\theta+z=5.$ **7.** $16\pi.$ **9.** $\frac{4}{3}.$

11. $96\pi.$ **13.** $\frac{3}{4}\pi a^4.$ **15.** $\frac{10}{3}.$ **17.** $\sqrt{2}+\ln(1+\sqrt{2}).$

Exercise 120. Page 398

Note. The weight of a cubic foot of liquid is represented by w.

1. $400w$ lb.   **3.** $(179\frac{2}{3})w$ lb.   **5.** $(1866\frac{2}{3})w$ lb.

7. $\frac{5000}{3}w$ lb.   **9.** $56\pi w$ lb.   **11.** 14,400 lb.; $(8100\sqrt{3}+7200\pi)$ lb.

Exercise 121. Page 403

1. $(2,\frac{2}{3}).$ **3.** $(\frac{4}{3},0).$ **5.** $(\frac{9}{8},\frac{3}{5}).$ **7.** $(\frac{8}{5},2).$ **9.** $(\frac{52}{21},\frac{59}{21}).$

11. $(0,4b/3\pi).$ **13.** $(\frac{16}{35},\frac{16}{35}).$ **15.** $(20/3\pi,8/3\pi).$ **17.** $(\frac{1}{2}\pi,\frac{1}{8}\pi).$

19. $(\frac{3}{2},2).$ **21.** $(2,1).$ **23.** $(\frac{4}{3},\frac{8}{21}).$ **25.** $(0,\frac{7}{9}).$ **27.** $(\frac{12}{7},0).$

29. $\left(0,\dfrac{4\pi-3\sqrt{3}}{4\pi-6\ln(2+\sqrt{3})}\right).$ **31.** $[\frac{1}{3}(a+b),\frac{1}{3}c];\ [\frac{1}{3}(a_1+a_2+a_3),\frac{1}{3}(b_1+b_2+b_3)].$

33. With $A=\int_a^b y\,dx$ and $y=f(x)$, $A\bar{x}=\frac{1}{2}\int_a^b xy\,dx;\ A\bar{y}=\frac{1}{2}\int_a^b y^2\,dx.$ **35.** $(\pi,\frac{5}{6}).$

Exercise 123. Page 409

1. (a) $I=\frac{1}{3}mh^2,\ k=\frac{1}{3}h\sqrt{3};$ (b) $I=\frac{1}{6}mh^2,\ k=\frac{1}{6}h\sqrt{6}.$

3. $I_x=4\delta;\ I_y=36\delta;\ I_0=\frac{20}{3}m;\ k=\frac{2}{3}\sqrt{15}.$

5. $I_x=\frac{16}{3}\delta;\ I_y=\frac{64}{3}\delta;\ I_0=\frac{10}{3}m;\ k=\frac{1}{3}\sqrt{30}.$

7. $I_x=\frac{6}{5}\delta;\ I_y=\frac{18}{5}\delta.$ **9.** $I_x=\frac{256}{5}\delta;\ I_y=\frac{4096}{105}\delta.$

11. $I_x=54;\ I_y=\frac{144}{5}.$ **13.** $I_x=\frac{48}{5};\ I_y=\frac{176}{5}.$

15. $I_x=\frac{128}{189};\ I_y=\frac{128}{21}.$ **17.** $I_x=\frac{1}{8}\pi ab^3\delta;\ I_y=\frac{1}{8}\pi a^3b\delta.$

19. $\frac{1}{4}\pi\delta(a^3b+ab^3).$ **21.** $I_x=I_y=\frac{1}{84}a^4\delta=\frac{1}{2}I_0.$

23. $36\delta.$ **25.** $\frac{1035}{5}\delta.$ **27.** $\frac{128}{3}(3\pi-1)\delta.$

Exercise 124. Page 412

1. $(\frac{1}{2}a,2a/3\pi).$ **3.** $(\frac{8}{3},\frac{4}{3}\sqrt{3}).$

5. $\left(\dfrac{9}{4\pi-3\sqrt{3}},\dfrac{8\pi-9\sqrt{3}}{4\pi-3\sqrt{3}}\right).$ **7.** $\left(0,\dfrac{3a}{2\pi}\right).$ **9.** $(3,2\sqrt{3}).$

11. (a) $I_0=\frac{1}{2}h^2m,\ k=\frac{1}{2}h\sqrt{2};$ (b) $I_0=\frac{3}{5}h^2m,\ k=\frac{1}{5}h\sqrt{15}.$

13. $I_x=\frac{1}{10}a^2m;\ k=\frac{1}{10}a\sqrt{10}.$ **15.** $I_0=\frac{1}{2}\pi m;\ k=\frac{1}{2}\sqrt{2\pi}.$

17. $\left(\bar{x}=\dfrac{2(16-9\sqrt{3})}{2\pi-3\sqrt{3}},\ \bar{y}=\dfrac{12\ln 3-13}{2\pi-3\sqrt{3}}\right).$

Exercise 125. Page 414

1. $(0,\frac{1}{4}\pi a).$ **3.** $(\pi a,\frac{8}{5}a).$ **5.** $(-\frac{4}{5}a,0).$

Exercise 126. Page 420

1. 6. **3.** $V = \frac{5}{6}$, $m = \frac{3}{5}$.

5. $\displaystyle\int_{-3}^{3}\int_{-\sqrt{9-x^2}}^{\sqrt{9-x^2}}\int_{-\sqrt{25-x^2-y^2}}^{\sqrt{25-x^2-y^2}} F(x, y, z)\,dz\,dy\,dx$.

7. $\displaystyle\int_{0}^{\sqrt{2}}\int_{0}^{\frac{1}{2}\sqrt{4-2y^2}}\int_{2+x^2+2y^2}^{6-3x^2} F(x, y, z)\,dz\,dx\,dy$.

9. $V = \pi c^2 h$, $m = \frac{8}{5}c^3 h$. **11.** $V = 2$, $m = \frac{11}{5}$. **13.** 32. **15.** $\frac{32,768}{105}$.

Exercise 127. Page 423

1. 800π. **3.** $\frac{1}{3}\pi a^3(10\sqrt{5} - 19)$. **5.** $\frac{3}{4}\pi a^4$, $m = \frac{14}{15}\pi a^5$. **7.** 8π.

9. $\frac{16,384}{75}$. **11.** $V = \frac{1}{8}\pi$, $m = \frac{3}{32}\pi$. **13.** $V = 4\pi - \frac{32}{9}$, $m = 12\pi - \frac{64}{5}$.

Exercise 128. Page 426

1. $(\frac{4}{3}, 2, \frac{5}{2})$; $I_x = 1155$. **3.** $\frac{1}{4}\pi^2 a^6$. **5.** $(1, 1, 1)$. **7.** $(0, 0, \frac{23}{8})$.

9. $(0, \frac{8}{3}, 0)$; $I_y = \frac{512}{3}\pi\delta$. **11.** $(1, 0, \frac{12}{7})$. **15.** $\frac{1}{160}\pi h^5\delta$. **17.** $2^7\pi\delta/315$.

Exercise 129. Page 431

1. $m = \frac{8}{15}a^5$. **3.** $\frac{1}{3}\pi a^2 h$, where $h = a\cot\alpha$. **5.** $(\frac{3}{8}a, \frac{3}{8}a, \frac{3}{8}a)$. **7.** $\bar{z} = \frac{315}{372}a$.

9. $\frac{5}{96}\pi a^6$. **11.** $\bar{z} = 3$. **13.** $\bar{z} = \frac{15}{7}a$; $I_z = \frac{248}{15}\pi a^5 = \frac{62}{35}a^2 m$. **15.** $\bar{z} = \frac{23}{21}$.

Exercise 130. Page 434

1. $-\frac{2}{5}$. **3.** $-\infty$. **5.** $+\infty$. **7.** $+\infty$. **9.** $\frac{1}{2}$.

11. No limit. **13.** Converges to 1. **15.** Converges to 0.

Exercise 131. Page 437

Note. Hereafter in this chapter, C and D abbreviate converges and diverges, respectively.

1. C to $\frac{3}{2}$. **3.** D. **5.** D. **7.** D. **9.** C to $\frac{400}{9}$. **11.** C to $\frac{83}{99}$.

13. C to $\frac{115}{333}$. **15.** D. **17.** D. **19.** D. **21.** D.

Exercise 133. Page 443

19. C. **21.** D. **23.** D. **25.** D. **27.** C. **29.** C. **31.** D. **33.** D.

Exercise 134. Page 446

1. C. **3.** C. **5.** D. **7.** D. **9.** C. **11.** D. **13.** C.

15. $S_4 = -.49190$; $|\text{error}| < \frac{1}{3}$.

Exercise 135. Page 148

1. C conditionally. **3.** C absolutely. **5.** C absolutely. **7.** C conditionally.

Exercise 136. Page 451

1. C. **3.** D. **5.** C. **7.** C. **9.** D. **11.** C absolutely. **13.** C conditionally.

15. C absolutely. **17.** C absolutely. **19.** D. **21.** C conditionally. **23.** D.

Exercise 137. Page 453

Note. The series diverges except where otherwise specified.

1. C absolutely, $|x| < 1$; C conditionally, $x = -1$. **3.** C absolutely, $|x| < 1$.

5. C absolutely, $|x| < 4$; C conditionally, $x = 4$. **7.** C absolutely, $|x| \leq 3$.

9. C absolutely, all values of x.

11. C absolutely, $|x| < 1$; C conditionally, $x = \pm 1$. **13.** C absolutely, $|x| < \frac{1}{3}$.

15. C absolutely, $1 < x < 7$; C conditionally, $x = 7$. **17.** C absolutely, $-4 < x < 2$.

19. C absolutely, $|x| > 2$; C conditionally, $x = 2$.

21. C absolutely, $|x| < 2$; C conditionally, $x = 2$.

Exercise 138. Page 454

1. D.   3. D.   5. D.   7. D.   9. C conditionally.

11. C absolutely.   13. D.   15. C.   17. C absolutely, all values of x.

19. C absolutely, $|x| \leqq \frac{1}{2}$.   21. C absolutely, all values of x.

23. C.   25. D.   27. C absolutely, $|x| \leqq 1$.

Exercise 139. Page 456

1. C.   3. D.   5. D if $p < 1$; C if $p > 1$.

7. D.   9. D.   11. C if $p > 1$; D if $p \leqq 1$.

Exercise 140. Page 460

Note. We define $0! = 1$.

1. $\sum_{n=0}^{\infty} \frac{(-1)^n x^{2n}}{(2n)!}$.

3. $\sum_{n=0}^{\infty} \frac{x^n}{n!}$.

5. $\sum_{n=0}^{\infty} (-1)^n \frac{2^n}{n!} x^n$.

7. $e^a \sum_{n=0}^{\infty} \frac{(x-a)^n}{n!}$.

9. $5 - x + 2x^2 + 3x^4$;
$63 - 105(x+2) + 74(x+2)^2 - 24(x+2)^3 + 3(x+2)^4$.

11. $\sum_{n=0}^{\infty} (n+1)x^n$.

13. $\ln a + \sum_{n=1}^{\infty} \frac{(-1)^{n-1}}{na^n} (x-a)^n$.

15. $\sum_{n=1}^{\infty} - \frac{x^n}{n}$.

17. $x + \frac{1}{3}x^3 + \frac{2}{15}x^5$.

19. $-\frac{1}{2}x^2 - \frac{1}{12}x^4 - \frac{1}{45}x^6$.

21. $e[1 - \frac{1}{2}(x - \frac{1}{2}\pi)^2 + \frac{1}{6}(x - \frac{1}{2}\pi)^4]$.

23. $1 + \frac{5}{3}x + \frac{20}{9}x^2$.

25. $x + \frac{1}{6}x^3 + \frac{3}{40}x^5$.

27. $e^{\frac{1}{2}\pi}[1 + (x - \frac{1}{2}\pi) - \frac{1}{3}(x - \frac{1}{2}\pi)^3]$.

29. $\frac{1}{2} + \frac{1}{2}\sqrt{3}x - \frac{1}{4}x^2$.

31. $\sum_{k=0}^{\infty} \frac{(-1)^k}{(2k)!} 2^{2k} x^{2k}$.

33. $\sum_{n=0}^{\infty} \frac{5^n x^n}{n!}$.

35. $-\sum_{n=1}^{\infty} \frac{3^n x^n}{n}$.

37. $\sum_{k=1}^{\infty} \frac{(-1)^{k+1}}{(2k-1)!} 4^{2k-1} x^{2k-1}$.

39. See Problem 29, page 454.

41. $1 - \frac{1}{2}x^2 + \frac{3}{8}x^4 - \frac{5}{16}x^6$.

43. $2(1 + \frac{1}{4}x^3)^{\frac{1}{2}} = 2 + \frac{1}{4}x^3 - \frac{1}{64}x^6 + \frac{1}{512}x^9 - \cdots$.

45. .2955.   47. 1.6487.   49. 1.0204.

51. .4540.   53. .1974.   55. 5.0658.

57. $\sin x = \sin a + (x-a)\cos a - \frac{1}{2}(x-a)^2 \sin a - \cdots$.
$\cos x = \cos a - (x-a)\sin a - \frac{1}{2}(x-a)^2 \cos a + \cdots$.

Exercise 141. Page 465

1. $1 + x + x^2$; $|\text{ error }| < .5$.   3. $x - \frac{1}{2}x^2 + \frac{1}{3}x^3 - \frac{1}{4}x^4$; .0002.   5. $1 - \frac{1}{2}x^2$; .0003.

7. $\ln 2 + \frac{1}{2}(x-2) - \frac{1}{8}(x-2)^2$; .01.   9. $\frac{1}{2}\sqrt{2} - \frac{1}{2}\sqrt{2}(x - \frac{1}{4}\pi)$; .004.

13. $f(a+h) = f(a) + hf'(a) + \frac{1}{2!} h^2 f''(a) + \cdots$; $R_n(x) = \frac{h^n f^{(n)}(a + \theta_n h)}{n!}$.

Exercise 143. Page 470

1. $\sum_{n=1}^{\infty} \frac{x^{2n-1}}{(2n-1)!}$.

3. $\sum_{k=1}^{\infty} (-1)^{k+1} \frac{2^{2k-1} x^{2k}}{(2k)!}$.

5. $-\frac{1}{2}x^2 - \frac{1}{12}x^4 - \frac{1}{45}x^6$.   7. $x + \frac{1}{6}x^3 + \frac{3}{40}x^5$.   9. $x + \frac{5}{6}x^3 - \frac{19}{120}x^5$.

11. $1 - \frac{1}{2}x - \frac{1}{8}x^2$.   13. $\frac{1}{2}x + \frac{1}{24}x^3 + \frac{1}{240}x^5$.   15. 1.   17. $\frac{1}{3}$.

19. -1.   21. .380.   23. .117.   25. .259.

Exercise 144. Page 479

1. $(2x + 3y)(9t^2 + 1) + (3x + 10y)(2 - 2t)$.

3. $e^t - 6yt^{-1} - 16tz$.

5. $e^z(\cos y)(1 + t^2)^{-1} - e^z(\sin y)(\ln t + 1)$.

7. $\dfrac{2yz \cos 2t - 2xz \sin 2t + xy(\sec t)\tan t}{\sqrt{1 - x^2y^2z^2}}$.

9. $3x^2 + y + (x - 3y^2)(e^x \ln x + e^x x^{-1} + 1)$.

11. $2x \cos x^2 + \cos y^2 - 4xy(\sin y^2) \cos 2x$.

13. $2x - z - 3(y - x)e^{-3x} - z \sin x$.

15. $\dfrac{(z - e^x)(1 + 3e^y \cos x) - (x + e^y)(x^{-1} - e^x)}{(z - e^x)^2}$.

17. $(2x - y)\cos t + (3y^2 - x)t^2$; $s(y - 2x)\sin t + 2st(3y^2 - x)$.

19. $4 \cos 2x + 9s^2 \sin 3y$; $4t \cos 2x - 9 \sin 3y$.   **21.** $4xy + 4(x^2 - z^2) - 8syz \cos rs$.

27. $\dfrac{\partial u}{\partial r} = 2x \sin \phi \cos \theta + 2y \sin \phi \sin \theta + 2z \cos \phi$;

$\dfrac{\partial u}{\partial \theta} = - 2rx \sin \phi \sin \theta + 2ry \sin \phi \cos \theta$; etc.

29. $\dfrac{(e^t + t^{-1})\cos x}{1 + \cos y} + \dfrac{10t \sin x \sin y}{(1 + \cos y)^2}$.   **33.** $\left(\dfrac{\partial w}{\partial y}\right)_z = w_y + w_r \dfrac{\partial r}{\partial y} + w_t \dfrac{\partial t}{\partial y}$, etc.

Exercise 145. Page 483

15. Degree 3.   **17.** Degree 0.   **19.** Degree 2.   **21.** $\dfrac{du}{dt} = gf_x + hf_y + kf_z$.

Exercise 146. Page 485

1. $(3x^2y + 5x^4y^2)(3t^3\,ds + 9st^2\,dt) + (x^3 + 2x^5y)[\cos(s + 3t)](ds + 3\,dt)$.

3. $\dfrac{(\cos st)(t\,ds + s\,dt) + 3e^t(s^2\,dt + 2s\,ds)}{\sqrt{1 - (x + 3y)^2}}$.   **5.** $-\dfrac{6x\,dx + 2z\,dy + z^2\,dx}{2y + 2xz}$.

7. $(\cos^2 z)(y\,dx - x\,dy)/y^2$.   **9.** $\pm \frac{29}{130}$.   **11.** $\dfrac{.2e^2 - 1.4}{e - 2e^2}$.

13. $dx = \dfrac{(3y^3 - 6ty + 6t^3 + 2tx^3)dt}{- 6t^2x^2 + 6xy}$; $dy = \dfrac{(3tx^2y^2 - 6t^2x^2 + 6t^2x + 2x^4)dt}{- 6t^2x^2y + 6xy^2}$.

Exercise 147. Page 489

1. $y = \pm r$, or $y^2 = r^2$.   **3.** $x = 0$ and $y = 0$, or $xy = 0$.

5. No envelope.   **7.** $x^2 = y^2$.   **9.** $3y^2 - 4xy = 0$.   **11.** $27x^2 = 4y^3$.

13. $9x^2 + 4y^2 = 9$.   **15.** $y^2 = 8x - 16$.   **17.** $y = x^3$.

19. $b^2x^2 - a^2y^2 = a^2b^2$.   **21.** $27x^2 = 8(y + 2)^3$.   **23.** $x^{\frac{2}{3}} + y^{\frac{2}{3}} = k^{\frac{2}{3}}$.

25. $(x^2 + y^2)^2 = 4k^2(y^2 - x^2)$, or $r^2 = - 4k^2 \cos 2\theta$.

Exercise 148. Page 491

1. $4\sqrt{29}$.   **3.** $\sqrt{146} + \frac{1}{2}\sqrt{38} + \frac{1}{6}\ln(12 + \sqrt{146}) - \frac{1}{6}\ln(\sqrt{38} - 6)$.   **5.** $3\sqrt{13}$.

7. $2\sqrt{6} + 2\ln(4 + 2\sqrt{6}) - \ln 8$.   **9.** $\frac{1}{4}[10\sqrt{3} + 13\ln(2\sqrt{3} + 5) - 13\ln\sqrt{3}]$.

Exercise 149. Page 494

1. $\dfrac{x - 4}{1} = \dfrac{y - 10}{3} = \dfrac{z + 31}{- 16}$; $x - 4 + 3(y - 10) - 16(z + 31) = 0$;

$\frac{1}{266}\sqrt{266} : \frac{3}{266}\sqrt{266} : - \frac{8}{133}\sqrt{266}$.

3. $x + 2 = \dfrac{y + 7}{15} = \dfrac{z + 4}{5}$; $x + 2 + 15(y + 7) + 5(z + 4) = 0$;

$\frac{1}{251}\sqrt{251} : \frac{15}{251}\sqrt{251} : \frac{5}{251}\sqrt{251}$.

5. $\dfrac{x - \sqrt{2}}{-\sqrt{2}} = \dfrac{y - \sqrt{2}}{\sqrt{2}} = \dfrac{z - \pi}{4}$; $-\sqrt{2}(x - \sqrt{2}) + \sqrt{2}(y - \sqrt{2}) + 4(z - \pi) = 0$;
$-\frac{1}{10}\sqrt{10} : \frac{1}{10}\sqrt{10} : \frac{2}{5}\sqrt{5}$.

7. $\dfrac{x + 1}{2} = \dfrac{y - 7}{3} = \dfrac{z - 2}{7}$; $2(x + 1) + 3(y - 7) + 7(z - 2) = 0$;
$\frac{1}{31}\sqrt{62} : \frac{3}{62}\sqrt{62} : \frac{7}{62}\sqrt{62}$.

9. Tangent, $\dfrac{x + 27}{4} = \dfrac{y + 81}{15}$; normal, $4(x + 27) + 15(y + 81) = 0$.

Exercise 150. Page 496

1. $v = 7$; $\frac{3}{7} : \frac{6}{7} : -\frac{2}{7}$. $\qquad\qquad$ **3.** $v = \sqrt{22}$; $\frac{3}{22}\sqrt{22} : \frac{1}{11}\sqrt{22} : -\frac{3}{22}\sqrt{22}$.
5. $v = \sqrt{1009}$; $\frac{18}{1009}\sqrt{1009} : \frac{3}{1009}\sqrt{1009} : -\frac{26}{1009}\sqrt{1009}$.

7. $v = 2\sqrt{4\pi^2 + 5}$; $\dfrac{2\pi}{\sqrt{4\pi^2 + 5}} : \dfrac{1}{\sqrt{4\pi^2 + 5}} : \dfrac{2}{\sqrt{4\pi^2 + 5}}$. $\qquad$ **9.** $6, 0, -18$.

11. $v_x = 3$, $v_y = \frac{9}{4}$, $v_z = -3$; $v = \frac{3}{4}\sqrt{41}$; $\frac{4}{41}\sqrt{41} : \frac{3}{41}\sqrt{41} : -\frac{4}{41}\sqrt{41}$.

Exercise 151. Page 499

1. $\dfrac{x - 2}{2} = \dfrac{y + 6}{-6} = \dfrac{z - 9}{9}$; $2(x - 2) - 6(y + 6) + 9(z - 9) = 0$.
$\dfrac{x}{0} = \dfrac{y}{0} = \dfrac{z - 11}{1}$; $z = 11$.

3. $\dfrac{x - 2}{1} = \dfrac{y + 2}{3} = \dfrac{z - 3}{6}$; $x - 2 + 3(y + 2) + 6(z - 3) = 0$.

5. $\dfrac{x - 2}{16} = \dfrac{y + 3}{6} = \dfrac{z - 7}{-1}$; $16(x - 2) + 6(y + 3) - (z - 7) = 0$.

7. $\dfrac{x - 2}{8} = \dfrac{y + 1}{0} = \dfrac{z + 3}{-13}$; $8(x - 2) - 13(z + 3) = 0$.

9. $\dfrac{x - 2}{-9} = \dfrac{y - 3}{6} = \dfrac{z - \frac{3}{2}}{8}$; $-9(x - 2) + 6(y - 3) + 8(z - \frac{3}{2}) = 0$.

13. $-\frac{2}{13}\sqrt{13} : \frac{3}{13}\sqrt{13}$. Normal, $\dfrac{x}{-2} = \dfrac{y - 2}{3}$; tangent, $-2x + 3(y - 2) = 0$.

15. $\frac{1}{2}\sqrt{2} : \frac{1}{2}\sqrt{2}$. Normal, $\dfrac{x - \frac{1}{4}\pi}{1} = \dfrac{y - \frac{3}{4}\pi}{1}$; tangent, $x - \frac{1}{4}\pi = \frac{3}{4}\pi - y$.

17. $z + z_1 = xx_1 + 4yy_1$. $\qquad$ **19.** $a(z + z_1) = \dfrac{xx_1}{a^2} - \dfrac{yy_1}{b^2}$. $\qquad$ **23.** $\frac{24}{609}\sqrt{609}$.

Exercise 152. Page 501

1. $\dfrac{x - 4}{1} = \dfrac{y - 8}{0} = \dfrac{z - 1}{-4}$; $x - 4 - 4(z - 1) = 0$. $\qquad$ **3.** Tangent.

5. $\dfrac{x - 3}{2} = \dfrac{y + 1}{3} = \dfrac{z - 2}{0}$; $2(x - 3) + 3(y + 1) = 0$.

Exercise 153. Page 504

1. $\frac{4}{3}\pi\sqrt{17}$. $\qquad\qquad$ **3.** $6\sqrt{5}$. $\qquad\qquad$ **5.** $\frac{1}{6}\pi[(1 + 4a^2)^{\frac{3}{2}} - 1]$.
7. $\frac{13}{3}\pi$. $\qquad\qquad$ **9.** $8a^2$. $\qquad\qquad$ **11.** $\frac{80}{9} - \frac{4}{3}\pi$.
13. $21\sqrt{3}$. $\qquad\qquad$ **15.** $2\pi a^2$. $\qquad\qquad$ **17.** $\frac{4}{3}\sqrt{3}(13\sqrt{13} - 1)$.

Exercise 154. Page 506

1. $\frac{4}{5} : \frac{3}{5}$; $0 : 1$; $\frac{5}{13} : -\frac{12}{13}$. $\qquad\qquad$ **3.** $\frac{3}{10}\sqrt{10} : \frac{1}{10}\sqrt{10}$.
5. $\frac{2}{21}\sqrt{21} : -\frac{4}{21}\sqrt{21} : -\frac{1}{21}\sqrt{21}$; $x^2 + 4y^2 - z = 5$.

Exercise 155. Page 510

1. $(3 + 4\sqrt{3})$; $(3 - 4\sqrt{3})$; $-7\sqrt{2}$; 8 and -8; $\frac{112}{13}$; ± 10.

3. $\pm \frac{46}{5}$; $-6\sqrt{2}$; $(5\sqrt{3} + 1)$; $(-1 - 5\sqrt{3})$; $\frac{110}{13}$; max. $2\sqrt{26}$, direction $-\dfrac{1}{\sqrt{26}} : \dfrac{5}{\sqrt{26}}$;

min. $-2\sqrt{26}$ in opposite direction.

5. $2\sqrt{73}$; $-\dfrac{8}{\sqrt{73}} : \dfrac{3}{\sqrt{73}}$ as direction cosines.   **7.** $\pm \frac{44}{9}$; $\frac{44}{9}$; $\pm 2\sqrt{14}$.

9. $-\frac{20}{11}$.   **11.** $-\frac{16}{13}$; $2\sqrt{17}$.   **13.** -14; $2\sqrt{65}$

Exercise 156. Page 514

1. Max. $(3, \frac{3}{2})$.   **3.** Min. $(2, 2)$.   **5.** Min. $(-1, 1)$.

7. None at $(1, -1)$.   **9.** Min. $(-1, -2)$.   **11.** Base $20' \times 20'$; height $10'$.

13. 7.   **15.** $|\, x_0 \cos \alpha + y_0 \cos \beta + z_0 \cos \gamma - p\,|$.

Exercise 157. Page 517

1. $1 - (x - \frac{1}{2}\pi) - \frac{1}{2}\pi(y - 1) - \frac{1}{2}(x - \frac{1}{2}\pi)^2 - (x - \frac{1}{2}\pi)(y - 1)$;
  $1 + x - \frac{1}{6}x^3 - \frac{1}{2}x^2y^2$.

3. $y + xy + \frac{1}{2}x^2y - \frac{1}{6}y^3$.

5. $-7 - 4(x - 2) + 20(y + 1) + 6(x - 2)^2 + 36(x - 2)(y + 1) + 6(y + 1)^2$
  $+ 5(x - 2)^3 + 18(x - 2)^2(y + 1) - 4(y + 1)^3$
  $+ (x - 2)^4 + 3(x - 2)^3(y + 1) + (y + 1)^4$.

Exercise 158. Page 520

1. $\coth x = \dfrac{e^x + e^{-x}}{e^x - e^{-x}}$; $\operatorname{sech} x = \dfrac{2}{e^x + e^{-x}}$; $\operatorname{csch} x = \dfrac{2}{e^x - e^{-x}}$.

7. 1.3234.   **9.** 2.563.   **15.** $3 \cosh 3x$.   **17.** $4 \operatorname{sech}^2 4x$.

19. $\frac{1}{3} \operatorname{sech}^2 \frac{1}{3}x$ **21.** 1.   **23.** 1.   **25.** $\frac{1}{2} \sinh 2x$.

27. $\frac{1}{3}x \sinh 3x - \frac{1}{9} \cosh 3x$.   **29.** $\frac{1}{4} \sinh 2x + \frac{1}{2}x$.   **31.** $\frac{1}{3} \sinh^3 x + \frac{1}{5} \sinh^5 x$.

33. $\dfrac{d \operatorname{sech} x}{dx} = -\operatorname{sech} x \tanh x$; $\dfrac{d \operatorname{csch} x}{dx} = -\operatorname{csch} x \coth x$.

Exercise 159. Page 524

1. $\sinh^{-1} \frac{1}{2}x$.   **3.** $\sinh^{-1} \frac{1}{4}z$.   **5.** $\frac{1}{3} \sinh^{-1} \frac{2}{5}t$.

7. $\frac{1}{3} \operatorname{Cosh}^{-1} \frac{3}{11}t$ if $t > \frac{11}{3}$; $-\frac{1}{3} \operatorname{Cosh}^{-1} \frac{3}{11} \,|\, t\,|$ if $t < -\frac{11}{3}$.

9. $\frac{1}{6} \sinh^{-1} 6y$.   **11.** $\sinh^{-1} (\frac{1}{3} \tan t)$.   **13.** $\frac{1}{2} \sinh^{-1} (\frac{1}{4} \sin 2x)$.

15. $\operatorname{Cosh}^{-1} \frac{5}{2} - \operatorname{Cosh}^{-1} \frac{5}{4}$. Obtain the decimal value by use of Table V and compare with
  the result in Exercise 64. Table V is too brief to give extended accuracy.

17. $\operatorname{Cosh}^{-1} 2 - \operatorname{Cosh}^{-1} \frac{5}{3}$.   **19.** $\operatorname{Cosh}^{-1} \frac{5}{3} - \operatorname{Cosh}^{-1} \frac{4}{3}$.

23. $-\frac{1}{2} \tanh^{-1} \frac{1}{2}u$ if $u^2 < 4$; $-\frac{1}{2} \coth^{-1} \frac{1}{2}u$ if $u^2 > 4$.   **25.** $-\frac{1}{12} \coth^{-1} \frac{4}{3}z$.

27. $-\frac{1}{4} \tanh^{-1} \frac{1}{2} - \frac{1}{4} \tanh^{-1} \frac{1}{4}$.   **29.** $\frac{1}{10}(\coth^{-1} 2 - \coth^{-1} 4)$.

31. $-\dfrac{1}{3\sqrt{5}} \coth^{-1} \dfrac{3e^x}{\sqrt{5}}$, if $3e^x > \sqrt{5}$.   **33.** $-\frac{1}{9} \coth^{-1} \frac{1}{3}x^3$, if $x^6 > 9$.

35. $\frac{1}{6} \tanh^{-1} \frac{1}{2}(3x - 1)$, if $(3x - 1)^2 < 4$.

Exercise 160. Page 529

5. $u = -2 \sin x - 3 \cos x + c_1 x + c_2$.

7. $y = -\frac{1}{8} \sin 2x - 3e^{-x} + c_1 x^2 + c_2 x + c_3$.   **9.** $x^2(2y + 6) = c$.

11. $\sec y + \tan y = c(\sec x + \tan x)$.   **13.** $\sqrt{1 + x} + \sqrt{y} = 5$.   **15.** $x = 2y$.

17. $2y^2 = x$.   **19.** $s = \frac{1}{3}t^3 - \frac{5}{2}t^2 + 8t - \frac{23}{6}$.

21. $\sqrt{h} = \sqrt{h_1} + \frac{1}{2}K(t_1 - t)$; $(t_2 - t_1) = 2K^{-1}(\sqrt{h_1} - \sqrt{h_2})$.

Exercise 161. Page 531

1. $x^2 = ky.$ **3.** $xy + 2x^2 = c.$ **5.** $(t - s)^5(s + t)^3 = c.$ **7.** $x = ce^{-x/(x+y)}.$
9. $y^2 + 2xy + 4x^2 = c.$ **11.** $6x^2 + 10xy + 3y^2 = c.$
13. $(y - x)^7(x + y) = c.$ **15.** $x^2 - xy + 2y^2 = 11.$

Exercise 162. Page 534

1. $3x^3 + 4x^2y^2 + xy + 2y^2 = c.$ **3.** $3x^2 + 4xy - 5y^2 = c.$ **5.** $e^{2x+3y} + xy = c.$
7. Not exact.   **9.** $ye^{3x} = c.$ **11.** $e^{2y} \ln x = c.$ **13.** $3x^2 + 6xy - y^2 = 8.$
15. $x^2 + y^2 = ke^{\frac{1}{4}x^4 + \frac{1}{3}x^3}.$ **17.** $y = cx.$ **19.** $2ye^x = e^{2x} + c.$

Exercise 163. Page 537

Note. For simplicity in the remaining answers, if a function enters as the argument of a logarithm, we shall assume that the function is positive, and omit inserting absolute value bars.

1. $5xy = x^5 + c.$ **3.** $y \sin x = \sin^2 x + c.$ **5.** $3s = -5 + ce^{3t}.$
7. $xy = e^x + c.$ **9.** $x = \sin y + c \cos y.$ **11.** $ve^{u^2} = e^{u^2} + c.$
13. $ye^x = e^x \sin x + c.$ **15.** $6u(v + 2)^3 = (v + 2)^6 + c.$
17. $4y = x^2 \sin 2x - 2x^3 \cos 2x + cx^2.$ **19.** $5x \sin 2y = e^y (\sin 2y - 2 \cos 2y) + c.$
21. $2x^3y = x^2 \operatorname{Arctan} x - x + \operatorname{Arctan} x + c.$
23. $2xy = 2x(2x + 1) - (2x + 1) \ln (2x + 1) + (\ln 5 - \frac{8}{5})(2x + 1).$

Exercise 164. Page 539

1. $y = c_1 e^{-x} + \frac{3}{2}e^x + c_2.$ **3.** $x = c_2 e^{y/c_1} - 1.$
5. $y = \frac{1}{16}x^4 + c_1 \ln x + c_2.$ **7.** $c_1 y^2 = (c_1 x + c_2)^2 - 4.$
9. $u = c \sin (2v + \alpha).$ **11.** $y = -\frac{1}{6}x^3 - \frac{1}{4} \sin 2x + c_1 x + c_2.$
13. $y = 3e^{-x} + xe^{-x} + c_1 x + c_2.$ **15.** $s^{-1} = \frac{5}{2} - t.$

Exercise 165. Page 541

1. $yy' = 2; \ y = ce^{-\frac{1}{2}x}.$ **3.** $x \, dx + y \, dy = 0; \ y = cx.$
5. $y = 2xy'; \ y^2 + 2x^2 = c.$ **7.** $yy' = x; \ xy = k.$
9. $y' = y; \ y^2 = c - 2x.$ **11.** $y'' - 3y' + 2y = 0.$ **13.** $y'' + 2y' + y = 0.$

Exercise 166. Page 542

1. $x_0 e^{-.23105t}; \ 5.21 \text{ yr.}$ **3.** 5.27 hr. **5.** $i = 30e^{-54.161t}; \ .1053 \text{ sec.}$
7. $p = 760e^{-.1186h}$, with h in kilometers; at $h = 1.99.$ **9.** $t = \frac{1}{4} \ln \frac{2(3 - x)}{3(2 - x)}.$

Exercise 167. Page 545

1. $2xe^{2x} + e^{2x}; \ 4e^{2x} + 4xe^{2x}; \ 12e^{2x} + 8xe^{2x}.$
3. $D^k e^{mx} = m^k e^{mx}.$ **5.** $\cos x - 3 \sin x.$
7. $-12 \sin 3x.$ **9.** $-3e^{-2x}.$ **11.** $8 \sin 2x - 4 \cos 2x.$

Exercise 168. Page 548

1. $y = c_1 e^x + c_2 e^{-2x}.$ **3.** $u = c_1 e^{-2v} + c_2 e^{\frac{1}{3}v}.$ **5.** $y = c_1 x e^{5x} + c_2 e^{5x}.$
7. $y = c_1 e^{3t} + c_2 e^{-3t}.$ **9.** $u = c_1 e^{\frac{3}{2}v} + c_2 e^{-\frac{3}{2}v}.$ **11.** $y = c_1 + c_2 e^{3x}.$
13. $y = c_1 e^{-\frac{1}{2}x} + c_2 e^{-\frac{2}{3}x}.$ **15.** $y = c_1 x e^{\frac{1}{2}x} + c_2 e^{\frac{1}{2}x}.$ **17.** $y = c_1 e^{\frac{2}{7}x} + c_2 e^{-\frac{2}{7}x}.$
19. $y = c_1 x e^{\frac{b}{a}x} + c_2 e^{\frac{b}{a}x}.$ **21.** $y = -2e^{\frac{2}{3}x} + \frac{13}{3}x e^{\frac{2}{3}x}.$

Exercise 169. Page 549

1. $y = e^{-x}(c_1 \cos 2x + c_2 \sin 2x),$ or $y = ke^{-x} \sin (2x + \alpha),$ etc.
3. $y = e^{-3x}(c_1 \cos 4x + c_2 \sin 4x),$ or $y = ke^{-3x} \cos (4x + \alpha),$ etc.

5. $y = e^{\frac{1}{2}x}(c_1 \cos \frac{3}{2}x + c_2 \sin \frac{3}{2}x)$.

7. $s = c_1 \cos t + c_2 \sin t$.

9. $u = c_1 \cos \frac{2}{3}x + c_2 \sin \frac{2}{3}x$.

11. $y = e^{\frac{3}{2}x}[c_1 \cos \frac{1}{2}x\sqrt{3} + c_2 \sin \frac{1}{2}x\sqrt{3}]$.

13. $s = c \cos (kt + \alpha)$, etc.

15. $s = c_1 e^{-4t} + c_2 e^{\frac{3}{2}t}$.

17. $y = ce^x \cos (\frac{1}{2}x + \alpha)$, etc.

19. $y = 2 \cos x - 3 \sin x$.

21. $y = -3 \cos 4t - \sin 4t$.

23. $u = e^{2x}(-3 \cos 4x + \frac{9}{4} \sin 4x)$.

Exercise 170. Page 553

1. $y = c_1 e^{2x} + c_2 e^{-3x} - \frac{1}{3} - 2x$.

3. $y = c_1 e^{3x} + c_2 e^{-3x} - 2x + 3$.

5. $y = e^{-x}(c_1 \cos 2x + c_2 \sin 2x) + 5$.

7. $u = c_1 e^{\frac{3}{2}x} + c_2 e^{-\frac{3}{2}x} - 2x + x^2$.

9. $y = c_1 e^{\frac{1}{2}x} + c_2 e^{-2x} + \frac{4}{25} e^{3x}$.

11. $y = c_1 + c_2 e^{6x} + e^{4x}$.

13. $y = e^{-2x}(c_1 \cos x + c_2 \sin x) + 4e^{\frac{1}{2}x}$.

15. $y = c_1 \sin x + c_2 \cos x - 3 \cos 2x$.

17. $y = c_1 + c_2 e^{\frac{1}{2}x} - \frac{120}{111} \sin 3x + \frac{20}{111} \cos 3x$.

19. $y = c_1 \cos 3x + c_2 \sin 3x + \sin 2x + \cos 2x$.

21. $y = c_1 e^{-x} + c_2 e^{-2x} + x^2 + 4x$.

23. $y = c_1 + c_2 e^{\frac{2}{3}x} + x + 2x^2$.

25. $y = c_1 e^x + c_2 e^{-x} + 2xe^x$.

27. $y = c_1 \cos 3x + c_2 \sin 3x + x \sin 3x$.

29. $y = c_1 e^{2x} + c_2 e^{-x} + \frac{3}{2} xe^{-x}$.

31. $y = c_1 \cos 5x + c_2 \sin 5x - x \cos 5x - \frac{1}{2} x \sin 5x$.

33. $y = c_1 \cos \frac{1}{2}x + c_2 \sin \frac{1}{2}x + e^x + 2 \sin x$.

35. $y = c_1 e^x + c_2 xe^x + 5e^{2x} - 4$.

37. $y = c_1 e^{-x} + c_2 e^{\frac{1}{2}x} - 6 + 3 \sin x + \cos x$.

39. $y = c_1 e^{-5x} + c_2 xe^{-5x} + \frac{3}{2} x^2 e^{-5x}$.

41. $u = -\frac{4}{5} e^v - \frac{6}{5} e^{-\frac{2}{3}v} - 3v + 7$.

Exercise 171. Page 557

1. $s = 6 \sin (2t + \frac{1}{6}\pi)$; period π.

3. $s = 6 \sin t + 6 \cos t - 4 \sin 2t$; period π.

5. $s = -3e^{-t} \sin 2t$.

7. $s = e^{-2t}(-3 \cos 3t + 2 \sin 3t) + \sin t + 3 \cos t$.

9. $s = 200 - 200e^{-.1t}$; will go 200′, or $s \to 200$ as $t \to \infty$.

11. $2\pi/\lambda$.

13. If $r_1 = -\lambda + \sqrt{\lambda^2 - k^2}$, $r_2 = -\lambda - \sqrt{\lambda^2 - k^2}$, and $\lambda > k$, then $\theta = c_1 e^{r_1 t} + c_2 e^{r_2 t}$, not periodic. If $\lambda = k$, then $\theta = (c_1 + c_2 t)e^{-\lambda t}$, not periodic. If $\lambda < k$, then

$$\theta = e^{-\lambda t}(c_1 \cos bt + c_2 \sin bt), \text{ where } \sqrt{\lambda^2 - k^2} = bi;$$

motion oscillatory, with half-period π/b. In all cases, $\theta \to 0$ as $t \to \infty$.

Exercise 172. Page 559

1. $x^2 - xy + y^2 = c$.

3. $\ln (x + 2)^6 - \ln (y + 3)^4 + y - 3x = c$.

5. $5xy = x^5 + c$.

7. $s = c_1 e^{3t} + c_2 e^{-2t}$.

9. $e^y \sin x + x^2 y^3 = c$.

11. $y = ce^{-\frac{x^2}{2y^2}}$.

13. $y = e^{-3x}(c_1 \cos x\sqrt{5} + c_2 \sin x\sqrt{5})$.

15. $s = \frac{1}{8} \cos 2t + c_1 t^2 + c_2 t + c_3$.

17. $y = e^x - \cos x + x + 4$.

19. $y = c_1 e^{-3x} + c_2 e^{\frac{1}{2}x} + \frac{1}{49} e^{4x}$.

21. $y = c_1 e^{2x} + c_2 e^{-x} + xe^{2x}$.

23. $3x \sin^2 t = \sin^3 t + c$.

25. $y = c_1 x^2 + 6c_1 x + c_2$.

27. $y = c_1 \cos 2x + c_2 \sin 2x - \frac{3}{4} x \cos 2x$.

29. $(y - 3)^2 + 2(x - 2)^2 = k$.

Exercise 173. Page 560

1. $y = c_1 e^{2x} + e^{-3x}(c_2 + c_3 x)$.

3. $y = e^{2x}(c_1 + c_2 x + c_3 x^2)$.

5. $y = (\cos 3x)(c_1 + c_2 x) + (\sin 3x)(c_3 + c_4 x)$.

7. $u = c_1 + e^v(c_2 + c_3 v)$.

9. $s = c_1 + c_2 x + c_3 e^x$.

11. $y = c_1 e^x + c_2 e^{3x} + c_3 e^{-2x}$.

13. $y = c_1 e^x + e^{-\frac{1}{2}x}(c_2 \cos \frac{1}{2}x\sqrt{3} + c_3 \sin \frac{1}{2}x\sqrt{3})$.

15. $y = c_1 e^{\frac{3}{2}x} + c_2 e^{-\frac{3}{2}x} + c_3 \cos \frac{3}{2}x + c_4 \sin \frac{3}{2}x$.

17. $y = c_1 e^{-2x} + e^x(c_2 \cos x\sqrt{3} + c_3 \sin x\sqrt{3}) + \frac{5}{72} e^{4x}$.

19. $y = c_1 + c_2 x + c_3 e^{3x} + c_4 e^{-x} - \frac{1}{18} x^3 + \frac{11}{18} x^2$.

21. $y = c_1 + c_2 e^{3x} + c_3 e^{-x} + \frac{8}{65} \sin 2x + \frac{14}{65} \cos 2x$.

Exercise 174. Page 572

1. 1.27; 4.73.

3. 1.15.

5. 3.18; -1.86; .68.

7. 5.70.

9. -2.72.

11. 636°.

INDEX

Numbers refer to pages.

9-12
-3

+4